WITHDRAWN

Higher Cerebral Functions
and their Clinical Disorders

I have no inclination at all to keep the domain of the psychological floating as it were in the air, without any organic foundation. . . . Let the biologists go as far as they can and let us go as far as we can. Some day the two will meet.

FREUD

Subjective concepts derived from introspection are among the essential tools for the study of life, and the only hope for a complete biology is to combine subjective and objective in the right proportion, using each approach with due circumspection and adequate safeguards, as is required.

THORPE

The coalescence of physiology and psychology is perhaps not so far off as it seems.

BABKIN

To recognize resemblences and relations within an evolutionary scheme is the very keynote of naturalistic science.

JASTROW

There is evidence of a very strong trend of psychiatry toward more physiology, physics, chemistry and medicine in general. It is no prophetic folly to predict that much which passes for modern psychiatry will turn out to be plain gibberish.

I. S. WECHSLER

If, on the one hand, every positive theory must necessarily be based on observation, it is equally sensible, on the other hand, that in order to carry out observations, our minds need some theory. If, in interpreting the phenomena, we did not attach them to some principles, it would not be possible to combine these isolated observations and to draw from them any conclusions. Moreover, we would not be able to fix them in our minds. Ordinarily, these facts would remain unnoticed beneath our eyes.

AUGUST COMTE

The subject matter of psychology is mental life and mental life is a function of the brain. Thus the physiology of the brain is the basis on which the science of psychology must of necessity rest. . . . There is a contradiction in American psychology between the highly developed experimental practice and the lack of scientific theory which could interpret the amassed but relatively isolated facts. . . . The pressure of facts . . . must lead sooner or later to a search for the scientific theory which can bring the facts into one integrated approach to the subject.

H. K. WELLS

Higher Cerebral Functions and their Clinical Disorders

The Organic Basis of Psychology and Psychiatry

BENNO SCHLESINGER, M.D.

Chief, Neurosurgical Division, Beth Israel Hospital; Associate Neurosurgeon, The Mount Sinai Hospital; Consulting Neuropsychiatrist, Elmhurst General Hospital, New York, N.Y.

Preface by I. S. Wechsler, M.D.
Professor of Neurology, Columbia University; Consulting Neurologist, The Mount Sinai Hospital, New York, N.Y.

GRUNE & STRATTON —————————————————— New York • London

Library of Congress Catalog Card No. 59–10265

Printed and Bound in the United States of America (M)

To the Memory of my Parents

PREFACE

A quaint notion partaking in some measure of a mild delusion is still current that to coin a phrase is to create a fact and that words alluringly put together somehow constitute knowledge. Uncritically viewed, such a notion gives rise to the assumption of new discoveries and great scientific contributions, which, on closer inquiry, are found to be neither new nor scientific. Some ideas thus put forth may contain a few kernels of truth but they are generally shrouded in so much fantasy that their meaning is obscured and their value entirely lost. What is more relevant to our subject is the perpetuation of the wholly fallacious view that there can be function without structure. It is quite clear that words, however appealing, unless they stand for verified facts, cannot bridge gaps which knowledge cannot fill and that notions spun out of fancy are ill-suited to replace experimental investigation.

At the present time, both psychiatry and psychology are, to a large extent, compelled to indulge in theoretical speculation and must rely on language, which is both a most unreliable tool and a very seductive one. The difficulty in explaining normal and abnormal mental or psychological processes derives from the lack of fundamental knowledge and the baffling complexity of brain structure and function. Undaunted by this complexity, the author bravely set out to study those structures and functions, to gather known facts, and, insofar as actual knowledge permitted, to build on solid anatomical-physiologic foundations. So he discusses in scholarly detail the higher cerebral functions and their clinical disorders, that is, the integration of normal functions and their dissolution in disease. The avowed purpose of the book is to present in a comprehensive fashion an organic background for psychology and psychiatry.

Mere perusal of the table of contents will reveal the wide field of cerebral functions over which the author has roamed and how deeply he has delved into the many problems which confront the neurologist, the psychiatrist and the psychologist. It was a heroic task which he set for himself. How well he has succeeded in the face of as yet limited knowledge the reader will judge for himself. The author's basic knowledge of the anatomy and physiology of the brain is wide and deep. The theories set forth are in large measure derived from scientific investigations and they attempt to correlate pertinent facts from highly diversified branches of knowledge. One may accept some and question others, but one cannot fail to be impressed by the profound scholarship that went into the making of this book and by the serious attempt to explain in terms of structure and function many normal and abnormal psychological processes. There is, indeed, food for thought in the book; Dr. Schlesinger has set a rich table for the neurologist, the psychologist and the psychiatrist.

I. S. Wechsler

It is a truism that the complexity of human behavior reflects the organization of the brain of man, a product of evolution. On the other hand, it is not generally appreciated that the more highly integrated functions of the organ of the mind are derivatives of the lower, or, as Hughlings Jackson expressed it, "the functions of the higher centers of the nervous system are those of the lower raised to a higher power." In the final analysis, the understanding of the higher functions of the brain, including mental functions, is dependent on the discovery of their radicals, literally, their roots. It may even be said that life processes are a unitary class of phenomena, and nervous system functions a special category of biological functions, nothing more.

It is one of the aims of this volume to demonstrate that the activities of the higher levels of the nervous systems are elaborations—elaborations of stupendous proportion of the activity of the cell —that the multifarious events involved in the function of the highest levels of the brain are primordially represented in primitive biological activity and that, accordingly, the most complex forms of behavior and the simplest biological processes can be expressed in unifying language.

Neuropsychology is that approach to the study of the mind which recognizes the uniqueness of psychic phenomena but stipulates that they are to be studied within the general framework of nervous system functions. The principle here followed should enable us to map out a natural history of normal mental phenomena and thereby to throw light upon their interrelations. In sharp contrast, psychological terms lacking an anchorage in general biology, have no referent and can hardly be regarded as useful tools of investigation. At the same time, it is also true that physiologic terms, such as reflex, facilitation, inhibition, threshold, summation, and the like are inadequate for our present purpose. Progress in this field is to

be expected only from an elucidation of the interrelationships of the phenomena concerned, including the common denominator of their extreme ranges. Not until the nature of normal mental functions is known will it be possible to define neurosis and psychosis (another major aim) in an intelligible fashion.

Purely descriptive or, for that matter, classificatory systems are not entirely free from theoretical concepts and, as such, especially if suspected of bias, they are open to challenge. On the other hand, the necessity of theorizing in science, although perhaps not in the direction here indicated, has been emphasized by many authorities. To quote, in the following order, Darwin, Jackson, Helmholtz, Pavlov and Claude Bernard: "Without hypothesis, there can be no useful observation. . . . He who does not go beyond facts never gets as far as facts. . . . Isolated facts and experiments have in themselves no value, however great their number may be. . . . Facts are the air of the scientist but theories give us the wings to fly. Ideas are the prime movers of science. An endless accumulation of facts leads nowhere."

In spite of the testimony of eminent men, we would hardly have ventured to present a system of knowledge unless convinced that it organized a large number of data, both normal and pathological, from what would otherwise be a mere accumulation of facts. It will become apparent that the natural history of higher central nervous system functions as we see it is not an empty construct. Just as developmental anatomy throws light on many otherwise incomprehensible conditions in the field of general medicine, the genetic approach to psychology and psychiatry followed here enables us to bring together seemingly unconnected data into a single scheme. It should counteract the trend toward inordinate specialization and bring together topics that have a powerful tendency to diverge.

Because of their close interrelation, any grouping of higher brain functions and their disorders is somewhat arbitrary. It was found convenient to divide the material into three main sections centering around the phenomena of affectivity, thought and skill. A clear-cut segregation of the subject matter was neither possible nor, indeed, desirable. Rather unconventionally, the phenomenon of art has been included in the present investigation. Although a function of the brain, artistic endeavor and realization have not thus far been studied in neuropsychological terms. However, since a theory covering higher central nervous system functions should prove its usefulness by its general applicability, I felt that some attempt in this direction might be warranted.

Science is a collective enterprise embodying the products of ideas of many individuals. Hence, in addition to my own experiences, I have had to lean heavily upon the work of others. I have sifted through the material and utilized such ideas as proved useful. Much had to be rejected which will account for the relative length of the critical comments included in the various chapters, but it was not at all uncommon that new and, perhaps, fruitful viewpoints emerged in the course of the evaluation of other opinions, as they may very likely emerge, at some future time, when my own points of view are critically examined.

Originally, the present volume concluded with a summarizing chapter in which the entire material was reviewed in a necessarily concentrated fashion. It proved difficult to digest without a thorough understanding of what had gone before and, hence, did not seem to add anything worthwhile to what had already been said. This chapter was therefore discarded in its original form and some of its essential passages were utilized in the individual sections. Due emphasis was thus achieved by repetition of salient points and since, in the original version of the text, the individual topics were treated from slightly different viewpoints, the reader, by combining them, may, like a surveyor, gain additional knowledge from the choice of a different route.

Not only are reiterations essential for the learning process but they convert the individual chapters into units which may be read more or less independently. The present volume can hardly be expected to be read from cover to cover. More likely than not, it will be used as a source book. On the other hand, the reader who does not follow the thesis here developed will not attain the comprehensive view the author wishes to convey. One cannot appreciate scenery by looking through a pinhole in a piece of paper at long intervals and in a haphazard fashion.

The reader will find mention of historical figures, of the works of physicists and inventors and, occasionally, of the writings of philosophers who were well ahead of their time. Without such references, a study on higher brain functions would be incomplete, for they reach their peak in the genius as "the highest representative of the human race."

The diagrams, designed by me in pencil and converted by Miss Ellen Ewald into India ink drawings, should help understand my conception of various problems of functional neuroanatomy and of pertinent psychological and psychopathological mechanisms. Reference to this point at the very beginning should make it unnecessary to add, to the legends of the diagrams or, for that matter, to the captions of the tables, that the visual data here offered represent the author's interpretation. Figs. 44 and 45 consist essentially of drawings by a patient who first aroused my interest in disorders of higher brain functions.

I am indebted to Drs. E. H. Feiring, I. S. Freiman, S. W. Gross, H. F. Harlow, O. Loewi and E. A. Spiegel who, in one way or another, have taken an interest in the present monograph. Lastly, I wish to express my sincerest thanks to Dr. I. S. Wechsler who has patiently read the manuscript and who, for the past several years, has spoken not only many encouraging but, more important, many critical words.

BENNO SCHLESINGER

Acknowledgments

Acknowledgement is made to the following organizations for permission to quote from copyrighted material:

AMERICAN INSTITUTE OF ELECTRICAL ENGINEERING, for W. Keister, The logic of relay circuits, 1949.

AMERICAN JOURNAL OF PSYCHIATRY, for D. M. MacKay, Ashby's design for a brain, 1954.

AMERICAN MEDICAL ASSOCIATION, for R. M. Brickner, Conscious inability to synthesize thought in a case of right frontal lobe tumor, Arch. Neurol. & Psychiat., June 1939; P. Gloor, Autonomic functions of the diencephalon, Arch. Neurol. & Psychiat., June, 1954; D. G. Hertz, K. H. Fellner, and M. Rosenblum, Psychosomatic approach to frontal lobe lesions, Arch. Neurol. & Psychiat., January, 1956; and N. A. Bercel, L. E. Travis, L. B. Olinger, and E. Dreikurs, Model psychoses induced by LSD-25 in normals, Arch. Neurol. & Psychiat., June, 1956.

ARCHIVES OF PSYCHOLOGY, for H. Wegrocky, Generalizing ability in schizophrenia, 1940.

BOLLINGEN FOUNDATION, for J. Maritain, Creative intuition in art and poetry, 1958.

CAMBRIDGE UNIVERSITY PRESS, for G. Tustin, Do modern machines help understand the mind? 1955.

COMPARATIVE PSYCHOLOGY MONOGRAPHS, for B. Katz and W. C. Halstead, Protein organization and mental function, 1950.

JOHN WILEY & SONS, INC., for W. R. Ashby, Design for a brain, 1952.

JOURNAL OF MENTAL SCIENCE, for B. Schlesinger, Grasp reflex and disturbances of attention, 1940; K. Zucker and L. Hubert, A study of the changes in function found in schizophrenic thought, 1935.

JOURNAL OF NEUROLOGY, Neurosurgery and Psychiatry, for F. Schiller, Aphasia studied in patients with missile wounds, 1947.

LIVERIGHT PUBLISHING CORPORATION, for W. Koehler, Gestaltpsychology, 1947.

M. D. PUBLICATIONS, INC., for E. Moniz, How I succeeded in performing the prefrontal lobotomy, 1954.

NEW YORK ACADEMY OF SCIENCES, for J. Masserman and C. Pechter, Neuroses in Monkeys, 1953.

PSYCHIATRY, for F. Fromm-Reichman, Notes on the development of treatment of schizophrenia by psychoanalysis, 1948.

QUARTERLY JOURNAL OF EXPERIMENTAL PSYCHOLOGY, for J. A. Deutsch, A machine with insight, 1954.

S. KARGER, for B. Schlesinger, Mental changes in intracranial tumors and related problems, Confinia neurol., 1950; B. Schlesinger, Time, neurologically considered, Monatsschr. Psychiat. u. Neurol., 1955.

SCIENCE, for Ch. J. Herrick, Evolution of cerebral localization patterns, 1933.

UNIVERSITY OF CHICAGO PRESS, for Ch. J. Herrick, The brain of the tiger salamander, 1948.

YALE UNIVERSITY PRESS, for E. Cassirer, The problem of knowledge, 1950.

CONTENTS

124-247
443-475

Skill

I

Basic Concepts

Living beings are pluralities rather than units. Even though they appear to us as individuals they are composed of autonomous entities that are basically similar or dissimilar as the case may be. The less perfect the individual, the more the parts resemble the whole; the more perfect the individual, the more diversified the parts. The more the parts resemble each other, the less subordination exists. Subordination of the parts means a more perfect individual.

GOETHE

I discovered the aforementioned sentence while leafing through F. A. Lange's *History of Materialism*. (*41*) I had scarcely opened this book since my college years, at which time I had read it at the expense, perhaps, of other subjects considered more important than a long and involved chapter of human thought. As we shall learn from what is to follow, Goethe's word applies not only to the organism but also to the nervous system. In this sense, he is one of the forerunners of Hughlings Jackson and, curiously enough, also of his—the amateur's—celebrated critic, Sir Charles Sherrington. (*67*)

The organism

Descriptive aspects of organization

As far as is known, the manifold which we call nature, reality, or the world issues from a primordial process, the *grouping activity of matter*. We thus follow the ancients, who thought in terms of chaos and cosmos. Both inanimate and animate forms are passing combinations of nature's building blocks. The former encompass the scale of objects ranging from unimaginably small subunits of the atom to equally incomprehensible cosmic systems, while animate objects are combinations of elements ranging from virus to man. While certain viruses combine properties of living beings with those of crystals, the world of plants and animals, which must have been preceded by the inanimate world, is nevertheless a realm in its own right, as is, indeed, its counterpart, the realm of the lifeless.

Inanimate matter assumes different shapes; it passes from an amorphous state to a formed state or is repatterned by the grouping activity of already organized matter, while living beings, ultimately, disintegrate into a non-organized state. Creation is followed by change, decay and destruction.

Reality is a stream of events although creation, change from one form to another and their final evanescence are more conspicious in the animate world. The inanimate world appears to be eternal by comparison. The flow of happenings may be hardly noticeable, whether it is the forms and shapes of nature coming into being or, inevitably, entering the phase of dissolution.

In the realm of the lifeless, events are by and large governed by chance factors; in the animate world, they follow their own trend, which, however, may be decisively influenced by fortuitous circumstances. It is truism that most plants fluorish where there happens to be sunshine, while they grow only slowly or wither where there happens to be shade. A seed falls to the ground where it happens to be carried by the wind. A man, forced to stop at a busy corner, may obtain vital information from someone he happens to see.

Although life processes are at all levels of organization influenced by chance factors, neither the structure nor the workings of the organism can be understood on the basis of chance alone. Biological phenomena are not fully determined by the specificity of atomic bonds, by electrical forces depending on the number of protons and electrons and by the order of their arrangement prevailing at a given time. For example, Bleuler (*9*) found that the probability of a fortuitous occurrence of the cornea, lens, vitreus humor and retina would amount to $1:10^{42}$ and, for the origin of the whole organ completely adapted to its purpose, this would have to be multiplied by thousands of fractions of the same order for every one part. Eddington (*22*) denied that a self-reproducing unit of the order of complexity of a nucleoprotein could have originated by the fortuitous synthesis of molecules. He maintained that such synthesis would be somewhat like $1:2,02^{321}$ and that the probability of a spontaneous synthesis of a virus molecule, even if it were composed of only 100,000 atoms, would be unimaginably low.

A discussion of the concepts of chance and probability is beyond the scope of this presentation. They were explained by Weaver (*75*), among others, in a popular article in which he mentioned that even chance and probability "which seem to be the very antithesis of all order and regularity" are subject to certain laws. Suffice it to add that, contrary to their dictionary meaning, the concepts in question are not coteriminous but that, nevertheless, the notions of certainty, probability and of uncertainty can be expressed in unifying language.

Events said to happen by chance are those which, under certain conditions (to the extent that they are known), are not expected to occur but which, were all determiners manifest, would be said to happen of necessity. Probable events are occurrences which, under similar conditions, would be expected to happen rather than not but which, were the entire concatenation of factors known or understood, would likewise be regarded as causally determined. However, since the presumption is that not all determiners are known, the events in question are said to be "uncertain." For example, one happens to see a friend by chance, against expectation, that is, at a crowded meeting. It is probable or reasonable to expect that one may see him at a meeting attended by some fifty persons. It is certain that one will see him at a dinner party attended by a few people only. These statements are valid regardless of whether the concepts of chance or, for that matter, of probability are developed on a naive, empirical basis or statistically, by involved computations. In any event, whatever happened in the first two eventualities, or even in the third, did not happen in the absence of certain conditions or causes. Needless to add, the terms "by chance" and "by design" are mutually exclusive.

To reiterate: In the inanimate world events are governed by fortuitous circumstances. (Exceptions to this rule will be mentioned below.) In sharp contrast, it appears from the figures quoted in one of the preceding paragraphs that biological events may be expressed by the very "inversion" of the laws of chance and probability. More specifically, the events in question are *integrative acts*. To quote Sherrington (66): "Integrative action ... is nervous reaction par excellence which welds the organism together from its component parts and constitutes from a mere collection of organs an animal individual." Integrative acts follow each other as, for example, ingestion and digestion or they materialize concurrently, like respiration and the circulation of the blood. In fact, it is tempting to express biological procesess by a combination of both propositions, i.e., *inversion* and *integration*, although not all concatenations of factors occurring "contrary" to the laws of probability involve living matter. Weaver tells us that at Monte Carlo "red" once came up 32 times in a row (obviously not by design), the probability having been about one in four billion. What's more, as an apparent exception, integrative acts are evident in machines. For a time at least, defying the laws of chance, the organism maintains its biological equilibrium

against the steep, adverse gradient inherent in the laws of probability. What is a singularity in the lifeless world (except in the realm of man-made "organisms" or machines—artificially created wholes, that is) is the rule in the animate world.

It has already been alluded to that the laws of chance and probability do not invalidate the *concept of causality*. It is a palpable fallacy that the abolishment of the law of cause and effect is a logical sequence of Heisenberg's (35) *law of indeterminacy*. As explained by Morris Cohen (16), "The basic law of quantum mechanics does not assert an invariant rule that determines the position and velocity of every individual particle but asserts, rather, a probability function so that, with respect to an electron or proton it can tell us only the relative frequency with which it will be found in a given position ... Heisenberg's principle does not mean a lawless world. It refers to the way multitudes are distributed rather than the way each particle behaves." (Other authorities, it is true, hold that the law of causality is valid in the world of macrophysics only, but this controversy does not concern us here.) By the same token, the route of an erythrocyte traveling through the vascular tree is *determinate* although not *determinable*. No doubt the course of an individual blood cell at a capillary bifurcation is dependent on certain factors but we are ignorant of the determiners of its course operating at the crucial moment. Convinced that the path of the cell is rigidly determined, we nevertheless say that it "happened" to turn to the left or to the right, as the case may be.

To return to the problem of organization, biological events are integrative acts regardless of whether every individual factor is known or their effects are predictable on a statistical basis only. If, through some miracle, integrative processes were endowed with self-awareness, they would experience themselves as purposive. Kant (40) expressed the matter with unsurpassed conciseness, although he qualified and, as may be appreciated from the following quotation, weakened his original thesis in a concluding remark: "One cannot banish the idea of purpose from biology," he wrote, "since the prime feature of the biological problem would thereby be overlooked. The concept of the organism cannot be grasped unless there is included in it the element of purposiveness. An organized product of nature is that in which all is reciprocally end and means. The causal laws alone cannot enable us to become even acquainted with that special realm of the phenomena confronting us in organic nature, to say nothing of completely explaining them. This principle is indispensable to the investigation of the phenomena of life. The concept of purpose can never be struck out of the whole of natural knowledge and absorbed in the idea of cause. For even if it is not an independent principle for the explanation of nature, still the approach to one of her most important domains would be barred without it, and the knowledge of the phenomenon would therefore be incomplete and defective* . . . *We can never adequately understand organized beings and their inner possibilities, and indeed we cannot even apprehend thereby that they exist, and how they exist, merely through the mechanical principles of nature.* (Emphasis added). The concept of purposive combinations and forms in nature is at least, then, one of the principles more for bringing the appearances under rules, where the laws of mechanic causality do not suffice. The principle of purposive functions, however, is not a mysterious power in the ground of things but, rather, a rule having regulatory significance for gaining knowledge of it."† On the one hand, Kant stressed the uniqueness of organization which is inseparably linked with the concept of purposiveness; on the other, he relegated, one might say, purposiveness to an ordering device as if suggesting that it be used as a heading in cross-filing biological phenomena according to one of their many aspects rather than that it be recognized as the crucial feature of life.

As regards the problem of purposiveness in biology, Darwin (17) was more outspoken than Kant, in spite of the fact that his reflections, as expressed in a letter to Graham, closed on a note of skepticism. Reminded of what he had once said "about the wonderful contrivances for certain purposes in nature," he confessed that it would come to him with overwhelming force that they are the effect and the expression of a mind but that, at other times, "that impression seems to go

* Lotzka,[47] a modern writer, neglects this crucial point entirely.

† We owe the above translation to W. H. Wogblom and Ch. W. Hendel. I found the original passages in "Immanuel Kant's "Sämtliche Werke," Ed. K. Rosenkranz, and F. W. Schubert, Leipzig, Voss, 1838, Part IV, p. 240, par. 60, and in "Kants Kritik der Urteilskraft," Ed. J. H. Kirchmann, Berlin, 1869, L. Heinemann Verlag, p. 287, par. 75; p. 290, par. 77, and p. 291, par. 78. See also Ungerer, "Die Teleologie Kants und ihre Bedeutung für die Logik der Biologie," Bornträger, Berlin, 1921.

away." He thus left open the question whether the expressions "purposive" and "by design" necessarily mean the same or, for that matter, whether the terms "by chance" and "purpose" are true antonyms. Considerations of space do not permit quotations either from Schopenhauer's (65) or from E. von Hartmann's (33) essays entitled, respectively, "Concerning Purposiveness" and "How Do We Arrive at the Idea of Purposiveness in Nature?". Suffice it to refer to the former's thesis of the "Will being blind," which happens to have a direct bearing on Darwin's meditations.

Significantly, the opinions of many, including contemporaneous scientists, conform to those of the above-quoted philosophers. "There is in the hypothalamus," Hess (36) writes, "a collective representation of a group of functions as purposive synergic functional unit to bring together different effectors. All single effects are parts of the global activation enabling the display of an extremely directed behavior; they all subserve well-defined autonomic needs of the organism. A certain part of the diencephalon coordinates various effectors in order to carry out a definite performance. Somatomotor and autonomic activities are integrated to a purposive act." Russel (61) asserts, in a similar vein, that "human directiveness inherent in life, and purposive activity issuing from purposive behavior, is to be regarded as a specialization of vital activity." Lillie (46) regards "protoplasm as a regulatory system of such kind that a disturbance of the normal structure or composition at once determines constructive and reparative processes that tend to restore the normal condition." According to Frédérique, (61) the living being is an agency of such sort that each disturbing influence induces by itself the calling forth of compensatory activity to neutralize or repair the disturbance. Pflüger, (52), making reference to the self-equilibrating capacity of the organism, writes that "the cause of every need of living beings is also the cause of the satisfaction of the need." Meyerhof, (49), following up an idea of Warburg's, advanced the general hypothesis that "in consequence of the fluid state of the protoplasm and the instability of cell stuffs, spontaneous events, chiefly of a chemical nature, are going on continuously, which aim at a balance of the existing potentials of energy." Considering that Meyerhof was opposed to a finalistic interpretation of life processes, (53), his use of tht term "aim" is worthy of note. It must be left to further considerations to demonstrate that the phenomena in question are related to the concept of *negative feedbacks,* which, however, are mere instrumentalities of the organism. (See Chapter III).

According to Heisenberg (*35*), "the living organism displays a degree of stability which general complicated structures consisting of many different types of molecules could certainly not have on the basis of physical and chemical laws alone." Richet, (*59*), too, emphasizes the stability of living beings: "The organism must be stable in order not to be destroyed, dissolved or disintegrated by the collossal, often adverse forces which surround it. By an apparent contradiction, it maintains its stability only if it is excitable and capable of modifying itself according to the existing stimuli and adjusting its response to stimulation. In a sense, it is stable because it is modifiable. The slight instability is the necessary condition for the true stability of the organism."

The modifiability of the organism raises an issue of prime importance as regards the subject of *higher cerebral functions.* Remote as this relationship may seem to be on the surface, the feature of modifiability brings to mind the *phenomena of productivity, of the initiation of events and the creation of forms that take shape through the medium of the organism as an already existing product of nature, or of the primordial grouping activity of matter.* In other words, the multifarious activities of the organism cannot be expressed in terms of a steady state alone. Like the tension of a bow "at rest," the state in question represents a dynamic equilibrium upon which there are superimposed various activities. On the whole, states of apparent rest at lower vital functional levels are merely the basis, or prerequisites, of action at higher levels.

With increasing integrational complexity of living beings, evaluative and overt responses occur in response to changing conditions, and they are goal-directed as seen from the vantage point of the organism. The attainment of goals involves the establishment of biological equilibrium in the face of extrinsic or intrinsic stimuli, including those stimuli which are represented by seemingly spontaneous states of disequilibrium. These stimuli, in turn, aim at reequilibration at higher levels than those at which they act upon the organism. We shall elaborate on this point later in a subsequent chapter. In any event, the functional equilibrium of the organism, at least of the higher organism, with which we shall chiefly concern ourselves, is a two-fold one. In

addition to the maintenance of vital functions, it involves the attainment of ever-new goals and, thereby, of gratification at ever-higher levels of experience and existence. The sum total of goals or strivings constitutes the *aspirational world* of the organism.

To summarize, with some additions, what has been said: Organisms are physicochemical systems which are stable, that is, in a state of adaptively modifiable equilibrium. On stimulation, they react with evaluative and overt responses which enable them to maintain both stability and functional competency. The concept of biological equilibrium, a simile introduced into the argument for want of deeper knowledge, is closely related to the concept of homeostasis. The expressions of homeostasis and biological equilibrium, however, are coterminous only if the concept of homeostasis is extended, as indicated in the preceding paragraphs, to include, to use a term coined by Kurt Goldstein (*29*), the "self-realization" of the organism beyond its elementary biological goals. It is granted that the expression "biological equilibrium" is metaphorical and, moreover, that the underlying notion is not entirely free from the circularity resulting from our ignorance of the nature of life, i.e., the "control" manifest in the activity of living matter which, without control, would be inanimate. The organism maintains its biological equilibrium by the institution of appropriate means at the appropriate time or the *timed actuation of synergies,* that is, of *coordinated integrative acts in various spheres of function.* An equally valid, if not preferable, version of the concept of biological organization is the statement that a system of appropriate means initiated at the appropriate time within a self-equilibrating and self-perpetuating whole *is* the organism. Contrary to materialistic concepts, such a fact as that urea and other organic substances can be produced in the laboratory does not support the mechanistic view of life, as, in the organism, urea is produced within a universal "end-means context." The maintenance of a steady state is not the essence of life but merely one of its prerequisites. The stabilization of a pendulum at its rest point, regarded by some as the symbol of homeostasis, excludes growth, change and development, which are crucial attributes of life.

In advance of what will be said later, it is pertinent to add that certain synergies actuated in response to stimuli are superimposed upon the performance patterns of already existing neural systems, that is to say, that they are creative, generated in response to the demands of the moment, while pre-existing structural provisions of the nervous system operate in the fashion of inbuilt mechanisms. The flow of life is thus maintained by the timed actuation of *predesigned* and *creative* synergies. It is needless to re-emphasize the ephemeral character of living beings. Neither creative performance patterns nor the blind foresight of the organism are infallible but, rather, are of limited scope, range and duration.

Organisms are visible manifestations of integrative acts. The crucial feature of organization is not the constancy of matter which constitutes the organism; matter is constantly replaced. It is the constancy, if only the "temporary constancy," of interconnected, interacting and, to a degree, self-perpetuating events which represent a harmonious "end-means system." Difficult as it may be to grasp the phenomenon of life even from a purely descriptive viewpoint, it is fair to say that life processes are maintained by the integrative properties of the parts which constitute the whole and that the parts, in their turn, express merely the integrative properties of the events which "constitute" the organism. The stability of living systems is maintained by *controlled lability*. The all-permeating factor of control sets apart, from the inanimate world, the world of the organism. We are thus left with Bichat's (7) cryptic yet illuminating words: *"La vie est l'ensemble des forces qui résistent á la mort."*

Genetic aspects of organization

The argument developed in the foregoing pages may be expressed from a somewhat different viewpoint as follows: The properties of the organism manifest themselves even in the most primitive living beings, which are believed by many authorities to have had the structure of genes or, perhaps, of viruses (37, 52, 55). However, in contrast to genes, the primitive living beings existed as independent biological units, and, in comparison to viruses, they did not live on hosts; they were autonomous, higher organisms not having existed at that time. It is a widely held belief that the primitive biological units maintained themselves by replacing their building blocks with suitable molecules taken from their environment (55). As far as can be known, the flow of life involved the perpetuation of a stereo-

chemical framework, which, in turn, was achieved by the continuous replacement of substance. In other words, at the lowest level of organization, life consisted in the *virtual synchrony of anabolic and catabolic processes*, or, if you wish, in the maintenance of a steady state at a relatively primitive chemical level. *Self-maintenance, homeostasis* and a *balanced metabolism* were basically identical autocatalytic processes. It is not known however, at what level of complexity life came into being.

At the above-outlined state of evolution of living beings, propagation was nothing other than an *excess anabolic phase*; the newly created biological units represented either *replicas* or *mutants* of the parent organism. Mutations, the replacement of certain molecular groups by others, were the earliest variety producing events in the realm of life. They were the earliest creations, or novel combinations of matter, *generated through the medium of already existing biological units*. Viable mutants were not only perpetuated but some of them must have increased the performance range of the biological systems from which they had sprung. Although Darwin's theory of evolution and natural selection through chance factors, both extrinsic and intrinsic, does not account for the existence of the organism as a unit fit for life, it appears inescapable to assume that the biopositive mutants survived as the fittest. Thus, the activity of somewhat more advanced units involved the *self-maintenance* of the whole, its *reproduction* and the *creation of new, more advanced patterns of organization*.

In the single celled organism, the maintenance of a steady state followed the same basic scheme; the genes, having become integrated into more complex units, continued to exert their influence over metabolic processes and the constancy of form (52). This constancy, however, was a relative one as the units of heredity controlled the creation of new forms through the mechanism of spontaneous and, indirectly, of induced mutations. However, since most mutations are lethal, the repertory of biopositive mutants, at the present stage of evolution at least, might have (perhaps temporarily) been exhausted.

Even at the early stages of the development of living beings, two, although not distinctly separable, principles of organization were at work, namely, a *technical principle* and a *thematic principle*. The former controlled the replacement of structural elements by other, identical elements;

the latter the production of new constituents in a variety of dimensions. As a result, the basic properties of the organism were preserved and, at the same time, new traits acquired.

As expressed in terms of self-maintenance and of the propagation of labile physicochemical systems, the general trend of life processes suggests the activity of a *teleological principle* in addition to the technical and the thematic principles inherent in the process of organization. In the absence of full knowledge, we consider legitimate the metaphorical expressions "controlled lability," ' biological equilibrium," etc. Although nonexplanatory, they drive home the point that, unlike events in the inanimate world, phenomena of organization cannot be regarded as effects of chance.

The appropriateness of the term "teleological," which is questioned by some, is upheld by others, at least by implication, e.g., (as we have already noted) by Russel, who asserted that purposive activity is merely a specialization of vital activity. In fact, reality may be regarded as a composite of two categories of events, namely, (a) processes which, although potentially pattern-forming, do not produce "end-means systems" but constitute the realm of the lifeless, and (b) integrative acts which, being the very reversal of the former, follow the peculiar design-like course involved in the formation of self-equilibrating wholes or biological units. The two categories of events have in common that no effect occurs without cause; they differ in that, in the second group, the causes interact in a concerted fashion.

We do not wish to continue the long-drawn-out argument between the vitalists and the mechanists, an account of which may be found in the writings of Cassirer (15) and of others. Our own viewpoint is one of "descriptive agnosticism" rather than vitalism as formulated, for example, by Driesch (18). However, since we have quoted numerous authorities who reject the mechanistic view (among them philosophers, physiologists and physicists), it is only fair to mention, however briefly, some of the arguments brought forward by the mechanistic school of thought. Reichenbach (58) admits that organismic activity represents a pattern that has the appearance of being controlled by a plan, and he denies that this fact can be a mere coincidence, that is, a product of chance. In his opinion, the arrangement of pebbles on a beach indicates neither the existence of a plan nor the operation of chance factors but

is a product of necessity. "Close to the ocean," he writes, "partly covered by the water, there lie the larger pebbles, followed a little further up by the smaller ones which, in turn, are followed by layers of sand, first consisting of coarse grains and, eventually, changing into finer grained sand of the upper parts of the beach. It looks as of someone has cleaned up the beach neatly assorting the pebbles to size . . . whereas, in actual fact, the water transports the pebbles and casts the lighter ones farther up the beach, thus automatically sorting them." Accordingly, the pattern of distribution, he goes on to say, is a product of chance (more accurately, it is the position of an individual pebble which is determined by chance factors) and, at the same time, a product of selection which determines why the smaller pebbles are carried a little farther. In a sweeping statement, Reichenbach claims that the apparent teleology of living beings can also be explained by a combination of chance and selection but makes no reference to the crucial point that selection cannot occur before organisms have come into being; neither does he invoke his own thesis, namely, that the organism cannot be the product of chance. (In his opinion, the conscience of the statistician revolts against such a contention.) In summary, then, since selection presupposes the existence of living beings which, in turn, are not the products of chance, the apparent teleology of biological units can hardly be explained by a combination of both propositions.

An apparently more serious attempt to challenge the vitalistic viewpoint was made by Needham (54) who, in his opus *Man a Machine* (fashioned after La Mettrie's famous work *L'Homme machine*), set out to answer Rignano's (60) book *Man Not a Machine*. Needham contends (a) that there is not as much teleology about the living organism as Rignano thinks there is, (b) that whatever teleology there is, is not a unique characteristic of life, and (c) that, if it were, it would have no scientific significance. (Points b and c are debatable issues which, perhaps, should have made it superfluous to take up point a at all.) Needham makes much of Francis Goth's statement that the nervous process which "rightly seems to us so recondite owes its physiological mystery to the circumstance that modes of energy displayed in the nonliving world occur in colloidal electrolytic structures of great complexity." Continuing in the same vein, he asserts that "the majority of current explanations of living processes have as part of their background the new knowledge of absorption of monomolecular films and that the part that surface plays in living cells can hardly be overestimated." (We mention these points as they epitomize his line of reasoning.) What he fails to explain is the pattern of interaction of those processes which do not fizzle out but which, on the contrary, behave in such fashion as to maintain, by producing self-equilibrating effects, the existence of the system in which they operate—this only in the presence of certain biochemical factors without which they could not occur. Rather than admit the purposive nature of biological phenomena, he claims that there is purposiveness in the inorganic universe no less than in the living organism; and rather than see that living organisms are adapted to their environment, he insists that the environment is adapted to the organism as well. As we have already alluded to, he is not impressed with the intelligence of the cell, which, incidentally, he hopes the biochemists will some day be able to create. That "there is not much teleology about living beings" is already demonstrated, e.g., by teratology, since, following experimentally produced lesions and also those occurring spontaneously, "everything goes wrong." Further, contrary to Rignano's statement (and here Needham seems to have a good point), "the cell does not select or admit certain substances and does not at the same time reject others. If this were otherwise, a cell could not be poisoned." However, it may be argued, by the same token, that the calvarium does not protect the brain against a bullet. The answer is, of course, that biological units function only within the limits of the integrational complexity they have attained. It is beyond the prospective potency of bone cells (as against their prospective destination) to function outside their natural response range of stimulation. On the other hand, it is not beyond the capacity of certain brain cells to act together in such fashion as to maintain, or help maintain, the existence of the whole of which they are a part, for example, by inventing the steel helmet. (See also the difference between clotting mechanisms and "ligating mechanisms," Chapter IV.) This is not to say that the organism is omnipotent or omniscient. We have already made reference to its imperfections, of which the choice of arguments brought forward by the mechanists is not a bad example. It is one of the perplexities in the history of human thought that such arguments could have been brought forward by Reichenbach, a positivistic philosopher, and by Needham, a biochemically oriented embryologist, both scientists of the highest standing.

To say that the organism *is* a machine is an overstatement (it is in this sense that we regard materialism as a thing of the past), as is the opposite view, namely, that it is *not* a machine. There are incorporated, in the organism, including the nervous system, machine-like features, activity patterns or principles which resemble man-made devices, examples of which will be given in the following chapters. What is more, not only is the existence of these features firmly established but they make possible the expression, in precise language, of certain crucial properties of the organism.

It remains to be added (although it is obvious by now) that, with the development of the higher forms of life, the maintenance of biological equilibrium became an increasingly complex process. The evolution of higher forms came to depend to an ever-increasing degree on the recording and the evaluation of events of different biological significance, as well as on appropriate responses to conditions emerging in the internal and the external environment of the organism. These functions became more and more concentrated in a specialized organ. In other words, recording of and reaction to stimuli came to depend on a *central nervous system* made up of a sensory and a motor division, including its peripheral auxiliaries, receptors and effectors. Recording, evaluative and reactive processes evolved to what is known as higher brain functions.

In spite of the astounding degree of complexity attained by the nervous system in the course of the evolution of living beings, the different types of neural arrangements constituting the central controlling agency in the diverse species are, as we have seen, merely variations on a theme as it were as are, indeed, the individual species themselves. No matter how complexly integrated, the system of neurons which constitute brain, spinal cord, etc., is in a certain sense a *basic mechanism which makes explicit the properties of the unicellular units of life, including the irritability of the protoplasm and its capacity to respond to stimuli in an appropriate fashion.*

What is the organizational framework of the nervous system in vertebrates? And, in broad outlines, the relationship between structure and function in man?

ORGANIZATIONAL ASPECTS OF NEURAL INTEGRATION

The concepts of stratification of the nervous system, and of higher cerebral functions

Jackson's (38) doctrine of the evolution of the nervous system (which should be read in conjunction with the sentences at the head of the current chapter) was epitomized by a contemporary reviewer (58) as follows: "Dr. Jackson regards the central nervous system as a hierarchy in which each grade controls the grade below and is controlled by the grade above; each grade represents over again and coordinates in more elaborate combination the parts represented and coordinated by the grade below; and every part or region or center of a grade represents a larger share of the organism than any corresponding part of the grade below, a more limited share of the corresponding part of the grade above. Thus, each center in the lowest grade represents but a limited portion of the organism; and at each center the highest grade represents the whole organism but in no two of the latter centers is the whole organism represented in quite the same way. The wholes of the grades are grouped in three main categories, the lowest, the middle and the highest. Of these, the lowest are the most completely organized; the highest, the least completely organized." Jackson himself wrote that the nervous system has grown to a hierarchy in which "there is a gradual transition from the lowest centers, which represent the *most rigidly organized, simplest* and *most automatic,* to the *highest, least organized* and *most voluntary.*" The lowest level comprises the entire region of the neuraxis from the conus terminalis to the tuber cinereum, the middle the basal ganglia and the rolandic area, and the highest the prefrontal and occipital lobes.

Like many other pioneers, Jackson had forerunners. One of them was Thomas Laycock (45) who considered the rostral part of the brain merely an elaboration of its lowest part, the medulla oblongata, and who dealt at length with its composition in lower animals where, lacking extraneous afferents and efferents, the bulb reveals its intrinsic segmental structure quite clearly. At the same time, Jackson's theory of evolution and dissolution of function is an application of Spencer's (70) ideas on the universal role of the two basic processes. According to Spencer, "evolution is the progress from an infinite incoherent homogeneity to a definite coherent heterogeneity."

For reasons which will become apparent later, we propose to regard as the three main levels of the neuraxis (rather than those suggested by Jackson) (a) the *spinal cord* and the *lower brain stem,* (b) the *upper brain stem* and (c) the *cerebral cortex.* The *lowest level* comprises that part of the neuraxis where segmentation has remained conspicuous, as in the spinal cord, or, because of the presence of cranial nerves, as in the medulla oblongata, pons and midbrain, more or less well-preserved. The *middle level* is the diencephalon and the basal ganglia complex. The highest level is the cerebral cortex or intellective level. It comprises three sublevels, namely, the *sensory-motor* properly so-called, the *psychoneural* and the *conceptual level.* As we ascend the scale of strata, new sources of sensory inflow appear which, although leaving the basic pattern unchanged, increase the complexity of the individual levels in the caudo-cranial direction.

As expressed in modern statistical language, the functions of the lowest levels of the nervous system, that is, of the most rigidly organized, simplest and most automatic, have the highest *confidence coefficient of integration;* the functions mediated by the highest levels (which are the least organized, most complex and most voluntary) have the lowest confidence coefficient. The term in question, we might add, designates the "numerical expression, computed on the basis of statistical inference, of the likelihood with which, given certain conditions, an event will occur" (75). From what has gone before, it follows that the "confidence coefficient of integration" is the opposite of the "confidence coefficient of happening," in other words, that *organismic probability** is the opposite of nonorganismic, or mechanistic, probability. In one of the foregoing paragraphs,

---

* The notion of biological or organismic probability is a key concept in studying certain pathological phenomena, including neurosis, psychosis and the dissociation of functions in the nervous system.

we expressed the phenomenon of life in terms of integrative acts, that is, causally connected events which by their peculiar arrangement in space and sequence in time maintain a self-equilibrating system by the very reversal of the law of mechanistic probability or, for that matter, of the law of chance. Thus, one may regard higher cerebral functions as activities mediated by the highest anatomic levels of the nervous system but having a confidence coefficient which is low by comparison, or, to put it in another way, activities that are integrated with a relatively wide margin of error. Lower cerebral functions, on the other hand, including homeostatic functions, have, by contrast, a high confidence coefficient. At lower strata of the nervous system, given a combination of certain stimuli and an appropriate reactivity on the parts of the centers concerned, appropriate physiologic effects will materialize almost with certainty, the probability of success being practically 1.0. At spinal reflex levels, for example, the complexity of response determination is of a low order and, accordingly, the degree of stereotypy high. In the autonomic sphere, the probability of occurrence of integrative acts increases in proportion to their homeostatic priority value. It is virtually certain that, in the healthy individual, one contraction of the heart muscle is followed by another heart beat, and the latter, in a regular, undisturbed sequence, by other beats. It is equally certain that, in response to muscular exercise, the heart action will become accelerated and the pulmonary ventilation increased. In the sphere of the least highly organized functions, on the other hand, the correlation between stimulus and response appears to be loose by comparison. Even though all necessary data be given, the probability of finding the solution of a problem appears to be extremely small, the probability being, perhaps, 0.1 or 0.01, if not, indeed, infinitesimal.

No doubt the reversal of values, or the apparent looseness of the connection between stimulus and response, is related to the increasing number of codeterminers of response at progressively higher levels of the nervous system. The spinal respiratory centers would follow their own inherent rhythm were they not under the control of the medullary centers; and the latter, although tending to follow an intrinsic innervational pattern, are influenced by the act of speaking, singing, muscular exercise, etc. To a degree, however, the relationship between higher and lower centers is a reciprocal one. The respiratory reflexes can be held in check by voluntary effort until such time as, "in defiance" of the cortex, the brain stem has regained the lead and the homeostatic functions have reasserted themselves.

It may thus be seen that the functions mediated by the highest levels of the nervous system display a high degree of *conditionality of response*. Stimulus response patterns grow increasingly flexible. They depend on conditions which can be epitomized by expressions such as: "only if ..." or "provided ..." or "unless ..." To give a simple example: A pedestrian will not cross the street unless the traffic light is in his favor, provided that no driver ignores the red light and crosses his path. On the other hand, the pedestrian will cross the street against the red light unless approaching cars take advantage of their green light; in other words, neither the red light nor the green light will of itself determine his decision. Monkeys can be trained to choose one of several objects from a tray. They will pick up an object which is odd in shape only if the board is of a certain color; and they will choose an object which is odd in color only if the tray is of a different color (*32*). A properly conditioned octopus will attack a crab but only if the bait is not mounted on an electrically charged object made conspicuous in some fashion and remembered, from previous contacts, to have an unpleasant effect upon the would-be predator. The octopus loses this ability if the highest centers of his brain are removed (*12*). In other words, the highest centers enhance the *operational dimensions* of response (roughly comparable to the mechanical degrees of freedom of a joint) or, if you wish, are endowed with *level specific resources* that make for increasing flexibility of behavior. The wealth of these resources, about whose nature we shall speculate in one of the following chapters, depends on their anatomic position.

A certain measure of adaptibility to stimuli, it is true, exists also at lower nervous system levels, in fact, in spheres of organization where nervous control is difficult to demonstrate. A given quantity of a pharmacologic substance will produce its effects only if the amount already present in the organism does not exceed a certain level. Conversely, it will produce an excessive effect only if the quantity of the same substance present in the organism is abnormally low (*76*).

In *summary*, then, higher cerebral functions

have a relatively low likelihood (or confidence coefficient) of integration, or, for that matter, of success. They are mediated by the highest anatomic levels, which, in turn, are structurally equipped to deal with a maximum number of variables of stimulation, although, it is true, not with the same degree of reliability as the lower centers deal with a minimum of variables (1). However, the lower degree of stereotypy of the highest echelons of the nervous system is associated not only with increasing error-proneness but at the same time with a certain measure of creativity, that is to say, the production of novel response patterns which take shape in the face of new and unaccustomed demands made on the organism.

Earlier in this chapter, we said that reality may be interpreted in terms of events; one category of processes, although potentially pattern forming, does not produce "end-means" systems while the other, which follows a design like course, represents integrative acts that make up the phenomena of life. We arrived at the conclusion that low level integration carries a high confidence coefficient, high level integration, a relatively low confidence coefficient. The matter may be somewhat differently expressed by saying that biological probability (that is, the probability of integration) is the reversal of mechanistic probability. Further, that biological probability is higher at the lower strata of the nervous system than at the higher grades. In a certain sense, then high level functions is a compromise between integrative action and random activity, with the general trend, however, being heavily in favour of integrative action even at the highest brain levels. Now, probabilistic viewpoints apply also to the integrative acts that created the neural arrangements of the organism, and thereby introduced a measure of anatomical and functional variability from the very beginning. The most frequent or probable organizational patterns may be expressed by the peak of a hump-backed Gauss curve, the less frequent patterns by its dispersions. At a certain distance from the central mean the patterns become more or less abnormal and, ultimately, frankly pathological.* If biological units were to be defined in terms of the totality of their individual traits, more especially, their psychological characteristics in various

* This does not, however, apply to suprastandard abnormalities. (See following.)

spheres, the graphic representation of these traits would require as many curves as there are traits. These curves would have to be oriented in different directions and to intersect at their common peak to form a "trait-cone" while the individual trait points would appear at certain distances from the peak, thereby indicating degrees of deviation from the average or normal pattern, be in a negative, *substandard* direction, or a positive, *suprastandard* direction. Lastly, the trait complex of an individual may be conveniently defined by a circumferential line. The central concept of variability facilitates the interpretation of different organizational patterns, notably those pertaining to brainedness, language, dextrality and sinistrality etc. and also the understanding of certain psychiatric syndromes. (See, e.g., figure 14).

The concept of sensory-motor dualism of the nervous system, and of systematization

"At each stratum," Jackson (38) wrote, "the sensory and motor subdivisions (or centers) appear to form *units of constitution*. . . . They are functional rather than structural although they comprise morphological elements which are arranged conveniently. . . . Since the nervous system is built in conformity with one and the same plan, the connection of the units is always the same. . . . The entire nervous system, highest centers no less than lowest, is organized as a sensory-motor mechanism. . . . However, the higher sensory centers are only predominantly sensory, and the highest motor centers only predominantly motor."

The significance of the terms *sensory* and *motor* is, of course, generally known but it may not be amiss to define them with particular reference to the concepts of *associational* systems. Sensory systems comprise chains of centers and their interconnections extending from the receptors to the cortex of the cerebral hemispheres; motor neural systems comprise those extending from the cortex to the effectors. *Sensory centers* are cell stations whose most direct connections can be traced to the individual receptors; *motor centers* are those whose most direct connections can be followed to the effector organs. *Associational connections* bring into relationship the individual sensory and motor elements and either group with one another, and since, at successively higher levels, the number of sensory and motor elements increases, the number of associational elements increases even more rapidly so that, ultimately, at the highest level, the associational neurons far outnumber the sensory and motor neurons. Hence, the differentiation between sensory and motor centers is, to a degree, arbitrary. As a rule, the morphologic structures comprise, at each level, *somatic* and *visceral* elements. Both somatic and visceral (or autonomic) centers, in turn, are composed of sensory and motor cell groups, or, for that matter, afferents and efferents.

Jackson, writing that "even the physiological basis of the mind, or the organ of the mind, is of sensory-motor constitution," carried to extremes the principle of the sensory-motor dualism of the nervous system. And Kleist, *(39)*, extending the meaning of the term motor, asserted that thinking is a dual entity made up of categorizing and formative elements. A different school of thought, which according to Binet, *(8)*, goes back to Ampère ("le grand Ampère," a universal genius whose name is associated with the measurement of the electric current), was perhaps the first to recognize the *intimate relationship between perception and thought*. Nevertheless, the concept of the sensory (as opposed to Jackson's notion of the sensory-motor) nature of the organ of the mind, being linked with the names of Bastian *(3–5)* and Broadbent *(13)*, may perhaps be best epitomized by a condensed version of the historical Bastian-Broadbent controversy. The former stipulated that the "fusion of the various perceptions together, and the evolution of an idea out of them, will be accomplished by radiation from one perception center to all others," while Broadbent maintained that "the process in question is dependent on the convergence of impressions from the various perceptive centers upon a *common intermediary cell area*, in which a process analogous to the transition of an impression [he probably meant an orimentary, primitive impression] into a sensation, and of a sensation into a primary impression, takes place. This intermediary cell area will form part of the supreme center and will be actuated in the superadded convolutions." These convolutions correspond, by and large, to Flechsig's *(26)* associational areas, which are characterized by a paucity of projection systems and are believed to be *geistige Zentren* or *Cogitationszentren*. It would take us too far afield to go

into the details of the Bastian-Broadbent argument. Suffice it to say that (with certain exceptions which do not concern us here), Bastian eventually adopted Broadbent's views. He spoke of "certain *annexes* that are *derivative developments* of certain perceptive centers." And of "a process of conception which, whilst having its roots in perceptive centers, may be completed in outgrowths thereform, that is, in parts of the brain which are in close relationship structurally and functionally with the several sensory centers, the afore-mentioned annexes of the perceptive centers." Moreover, Bastian gave Broadbent full credit for having anticipated by some twenty years, without having had the benefit of Flechsig's myelogenetic data, the concept of associational areas. "Broadbent regards the phylogenetically youngest convolutions as the latest in the order of development and on those grounds alone they may be supposed to be concerned in the more strictly mental faculties. They are the seat of the more purely intellectual functions, or the *centre of concepts and ideation*. . . . The annexes of the sensory centers tend to be developed in the direction indicated by Broadbent and Flechsig. . . . There is no sharp line of demarcation between these annexes and the several sensory centers. They are thrown into functional activity more or less simultaneously. . . . The anatomical substrate of the annexes or *elaborative centers* must be supposed to occupy a very considerable extent in the cortex of both hemispheres. . . . *More especially still, broad groups of functions may be more intimately connected with particular lobes and, if such be the case, then we believe the evidence in our possession points to the posterior rather than the anterior lobes of the cerebrum as those concerned more especially with the highest intellectual activities.*"*

The increasing size of the temporal lobes, i.e., parts of the posterior cortex which, with rise in the phylogenetic scale, grow at a faster rate than the frontal lobes, was also noted by Meynert *(51)* and has been fairly recently emphasized by von Bonin *(10)* and Gruenthal *(31)*. Interestingly enough, a similar view may be found in Schopenhauer's *(65)* writings: "If we consider that,

---

* I first became acquainted with this line of thought as a medical student in the course of an informal discussion that followed one of von Economo's lectures, but my acceptance of it .was subsequently weakened, no doubt under the influence of the vast literature dealing with mental changes in disease of the frontal lobe.

according to the latest studies, the bitemporal diameter of the feebleminded is quite small, while the same diameter is conspicuous in great thinkers (in fact, Plato's name is derived from the size and shape of his head) . . . one is driven to the conclusion that it is the very part of the brain underlying the temporal region which is preeminently concerned with the process of thought."

The *organ of the mind*, then, is neither a special associational center nor does it have a sensory-motor constitution, as proposed by Jackson. It is the *highest level of the sensory division of the central nervous system*, nothing more. As will be discussed below, the reactivity of the organ of the mind, or the readiness with which it responds to stimuli, is not a motor function in the ordinary sense of the term but, rather, depends chiefly on a specialized division of the autonomic nervous system located in the frontal lobes. Flechsig's concept of the function of the frontal association areas needs to be revised. In the words of Polyak (*57*), "Flechsig regarded the frontal association areas as uppermost in the hierarchy of cerebro-mental functions." It is true that the frontal lobes contribute a crucial quota of action to the process of thinking (see below). This quota is, however, an extraneous factor which controls the responsiveness of the highest sensory level, which is imparted to intellective processes chiefly by certain autonomic centers of the frontal lobe and, implicitly, the diencephalo-frontal system as a whole. In other words, the frontal lobes determine the volume and, to a degree, the quality of intra-sensory and of sensory-motor relations at the highest response-determining level of the neuraxis. The intra-sensory relations are the physiologic substrate of intellective functions; the sensory-motor relations, of skilled action.

It is hardly necessary at this point to expand on the diverse types of sensory and motor systems. As regards the former, Sherrington (*66*), Kleist (*41*), and others differentiate between *exteroceptive*, *proprioceptive* and *enteroceptive* systems. It may simplify matters to recognize as many sensory systems as there are varieties of receptors, and to regard, as the *core of the organ of the mind* as it were, primarily the *highest levels of the exteroceptive systems*, more especially the *visual* and *auditory systems* (telereceptor systems), that is, the cortical provinces or "annexes" which are "derivatively related" to the primary (projective) visual and auditory centers and which, for obvious

reasons—they are the most efficient analyzers—are the most important segments of the elaborative cortex in the sense of the classics. What particular physical parameters of objective reality are recorded by the sensory systems to form its image, that is, subjective reality (the experiental world of the organism) depends on the species-specific organization of the sensory segment of the nervous system, while the degree to which the data of reality are elaborated to *categorizing stimuli* (configurations and concepts) depends on the development of the highest strata of the sensory systems, or the organ of the mind. To put the matter in a somewhat different way: *Subjective reality* is an adaptively categorized image, or system of images, formed by biological recording mechanisms, of objective reality. *Objective reality*, for its part, is the product of the grouping activity of matter. It exists independently of biological recording and categorizing mechanisms.

The concept of localization of function in the nervous system

The nervous system of the vertebrate may be visualized as a three-dimensional network of nerve centers arranged as *longitudinal* (sensory and motor) *chains* and, at the same time, in the caudocranial direction, as *transverse strata* of increasing integrational complexity. Within this network of line connections and their internodia, the longitudinal chains form the *projection systems*, while the centers of equal rank, which are linked up by associational and commissural connections, form the individual *levels* of the neuraxis.

Visual functions are localized in the visual system of centers, auditory functions in the auditory system of centers, motor functions in the motor system, and so on. *Centers*, in turn, are aggregates of nerve cells which generate excitational patterns in response to exogenic or endogenic stimulation. The neurodynamic processes are transmitted to functionally related centers in a fashion which serves the biological equilibrium of the organism. Centers located at increasingly higher levels of the neuraxis are structurally equipped to deal with an increasing number of variables of stimulation. Within each system, each center contributes a specific *quota of action* to the total process of intra-system integration and, indirectly, intersystem integration, that is, each center plays its allotted part in the performance of the entire nervous system. Under pathologic conditions, it is true, high level defects may be partially compensated for by the function of lower grades; in other words, specificity of function is, within limits, relative rather than absolute. Within a given system, the *highest center* is that complex of neurons which controls appropriate quotas of action of the subordinate centers and, thus, in a certain sense, of the *entire* system. *Subordinate centers*, on the other hand, control, depending on their position in the hierarchy, less than the total of integrative acts and are, to a degree, independent of supraordinate and subordinate centers. Within a hypothetical nervous system made up of a series of more or less *equipotential segments*, stimulation of any sensory root would be propagated to any motor root but may be assumed to produce preferential patterns of response that depend on the position of the sensory root within the general context of line connections and their internodia; and appropriate synaptic connections would establish a certain measure of variability of reaction. In a *hierarchy of centers*, on the other hand, a succession of higher grades is equipped, in addition to its level-specific apparatus, with control stations for subordinate levels, while the latter appear to have lost some of their intrinsic potentialities which they would have retained in the absence of higher centers. With rise in the phylogenetic scale, and with the development of increasing cephalic preponderance within the nervous system, the lower grades lose some of their operational dimensions at an accelerated pace as it were. Accordingly, cortical lesions in man are more incapacitating than comparable lesions in animals; with increasing cephalic polarization of competency, the lower centers, both sensory and motor, become increasingly helpless. Yet the elimination, experimental or otherwise, of higher centers does not bring out, at least not in their original form, the resources of the lower grades. The latter have lost part of their independence, and, accordingly, as we have said, some of their "intrinsic" potentialities are now subserved by those centers from which they have been separated. For example, the function of the midbrain of an anencephalus does not necessarily correspond to that of a normal infant. One would imagine that certain quotas of action which, under normal conditions, are embodied in by supramesencephalic centers, are, in the anencephalus,

mediated by mesencephalic cell stations.* It should be kept in mind that the above considerations do not apply to the same degree to innate functions as to acquired functions, be they acquired by learning or by spontaneous maturation. In other words, they apply less to functions having a high confidence coefficient of integration. The latter, being reflex-like or more or less completely stereotyped, maintain, by their very nature, a large measure of autonomy.

The usefulness of the terms *center, quota of action, level-specific resources* and *operational dimensions*, is illustrated by the following experiment. Sperry tested the functional capacity of the surgically isolated cortex in cats by the removal of the greater part of the neocortex on the right side and the complete section of the corpus callosum and the hippocampal commissure, that is, by the production of an isolated right-sided "cortical remnant." Prior to the production of the cortical island on the right side, the cats had been trained to perform various discrimination tests with the left forepaw. Retesting of the animals following operation showed that the discriminations were retained and new discriminations learned if only a small frontal area was left behind. If a corresponding portion of the otherwise intact left neocortex was removed, the animals lost discrimination habits in the right forepaw. Sperry concluded from his experiments that "the establishment and maintenance of the discrimination habits performed with the left forepaw were localized mainly or entirely within the cortical remnant." This particular part of the cortex may thus be regarded to be the highest center for discrimination habits, that is, to embody all necessary quotas of action, to have all the level-specific resources, or, for that matter, to control the totality of operational dimensions involved in sensory discrimination. Centers are sometimes defined as parts of the nervous system *without* which a given performance cannot materialize. This definition misses the crucial point and is to a degree evasive. For example, cutting of a fiber tract may abolish the execution of a movement but it would make no sense to regard the nerve fibers as the centers of the movement now eliminated.

The concept of *quotas of action* contributed (within an individual system) by the individual

---

* Compare, for example, Head, and Gamper, (Chapter IV).

nerve centers to the total process of integration may be exemplified by the well-known effects of brain stem transsection carried out from infrabulbar to thalamic levels. The more extensive the remaining connections between the brainstem centers and the spinal centers, the more adaptive the responses of the experimental animals, although, needless to say, they are less adaptive than those of the intact animal; the less extensive the remaining connections, the less adaptive the responses of the animal. In fact, the phenomenon of increased *muscular* rigidity versus decreased flexibility of performance (in the restricted sense of the term) may be regarded as the most palpable expression of increasing stereotypy versus decreased adaptibility in central nervous system lesions at various levels, that is, lesions involving *any* performance field or sphere of function. Evidently, the normal motility of the animal is localized in the entire chain of centers up to and including the cerebral cortex although, as brought out by the experiments, the function of the individual centers is by no means the same.

Even the most accurate description of the deficit phenomena exhibited by the experimental animal does not imply that the intimate mechanism of central integration is fully understood. We do not know, or, perhaps, only in broad outline, what each cell station is doing in the intact animal. In this respect, we are almost in the same position as a musically minded layman who describes the poor performance of a radio set in "anthropistic" terms while only the expert is able to specify what parts of the set are out of order, in other words, what specific quotas of action are lacking.

It is thus easier to illustrate the meaning of the above terms by concrete examples than to give rigorous definitions. In any event, what can be observed in studying nervous system activity are normal and abnormal activity patterns while the existence of quotas of action, level specific resources and operational dimensions is merely inferred. The same applies to the notions of thematic and technical principles of organization, biological equilibrium etc. They should be regarded as *interpretive constructs* in biology, just as the terms energy, gravitational attraction etc. are interpretive constructs in physics, but they are necessary to "bring appearances under rules." At the same time, they enable us to view both functions and dysfunctions of the nervous system at any level of integration from a common vantage point and to discuss them in unifying language.

On the other hand, the localization of anthropistic phantom concepts, including the so called "ground-functions" (Grundfunktionen), that is, the construction of a psychological brainmap in the cortex of man attempted by Gall and others is reminiscent of Don Quixote's struggle with the windmills. The concept of functional equivalence of the cerebral cortex inaugurated by Flourens (27) and revived by Lashley (42) and Goldstein (29) has been equally overplayed. Lashley, in a subsequent version of his original thesis, spoke of equipotentiality existing, within a given system, for a given function, more especially as regards the visual system of the rat. In other words, he spoke, by implication, of the principle of redundancy of any biological substrate with respect to any function, e.g., the kidney, the lungs and the gut. The idea that, in the course of any individual response, the entire nervous system is thrown into action is equally untenable. Obviously, the olfactory system is not concerned with vision, and vice versa. On the other hand, the function of olfaction may be aided by the simultaneous visual perception of an object, as may be the visual perception by the sense of smell, and the same applies to other performance fields of the organism. In this sense, and in this sense only (disregarding for the time being sensory-motor functions), does the nervous system function "as a whole." For a detailed discussion of the history of the localization of function in the nervous system, the interested reader may be referred to the monumental work of Polyak (57) on the visual system and of Kainz (37) on the psychology of language.

As we shall attempt to explain later, the evaluative properties of the sensory centers depend on the recording of stimuli in a "technique" which, in a certain sense, may be compared to mathematical systems of notation. At the highest sensory levels, stimuli are elaborated to higher units of experience, namely, *gestalten* and *concepts*, which permit the establishment of increasingly comprehensive relationships between the primitive data of the senses. In other words, at the highest levels, the primordial grouping activity of matter comes to the fore as categorization and and manipulation of *analogs*, which are both representatives of the data of reality and instrumentalities of response determination on the part of the nervous system. If it is granted that this manipulation of data is, as we suspect, comparable to a process of calculation, mathematics, as a science, might well be the rebirth of an organizational principle in the mind of man; and central activity may be comparable to the performance of information processing devices which are nothing other than biological computing mechanisms.

The highest response-determining levels of the neuraxis have not only evaluative but, at the same time, *acquisitive* (mnemonic) and *creative* properties. As we have already indicated, the confidence coefficient of integrative acts at higher levels is low as compared with that of the subordinate strata of the nervous system. In the course of *learning* and *automatization*, the coefficient in question is increased, while, at the same time, the consciousness value of the stimuli concerned is decreased and the lower centers contribute increasingly larger quotas of action to the newly acquired, now automatic, or semivoluntary functions.* In the process of what von Economo (*23*) called *progressive cerebration* or *telencephalization*, the leading elements of nervous system functions are shifted from the lower to the higher centers of the neuraxis. Implicitly, the behavior of the animal becomes more adaptive. In a certain sense, automatization is a reversal of the process of telencephalization. It frees, however, the higher centers for the acquisition of new activities as more and more elements of a function are delegated to lower centers, and it no doubt increases the over-all adaptibility of the organism.

To be sure, learning, in the widest sense of the term at least, is not restricted to the highest nervous system centers only. As demonstrated, for example, by the formation of antibodies and antitoxins following infections, processes reminiscent of learning occur even at the cellular, if not, indeed, the stereochemical level of organization. This brings to mind a remark made previously, namely, that the nervous system is a basic mechanism which makes explicit the properties of the unicellular units of life, including the irritability of the protoplasm and its capacity to respond to stimuli in an appropriate fashion.

* The lower centers contribute crucial quotas of action to the viscero-autonomic and especially the vital functions and are, accordingly, from a functional viewpoint, the highest centers despite their location below the highest anatomic level. For example, the highest autonomic center is, according to Hess, the hypothalamus.

The concept of responsiveness of the nervous system

In addition to sensory and motor centers, more especially those of the somatic division of the nervous system, there exist certain agencies which control the *responsiveness* of the entire neuraxis. (The degree of responsiveness may, however, show differential gradations.) We are inclined to consider the agencies in question as a specialized portion of the sensory division of the autonomic nervous system (Chapter II). To forestall misapprehension, it may be stated that, in the present context, the term responsiveness does not refer to the receptivity to stimuli of individual subordinate organs such as nerves and muscles, or the excitability of individual nerve centers, as, for example, the vestibular centers; the term as we propose to use it designates more or less generalized biological states which reflect the "equilibriatory needs" of the organism. The central nervous system is not an inherently passive apparatus played upon, and reacting to, a variety of influences, and its function does not depend only on the existence and the nature of stimuli to which it is exposed but also on its *excitability*. Since the basic needs are mainly of a visceral nature, sense organs and executive devices being servants of the whole, global receptivity is largely the domain of the vegetative nervous system and, in part, endocrine glands which function in association with the former.

MORPHOLOGIC ASPECTS OF NEURAL INTEGRATION

Sensory, motor, and autonomic, including the responsiveness determinating agencies (especially the latter), are not evenly distributed over the individual segments of the neuraxis; they may be concentrated in some strata, while absent in others. For example, the heaviest concentration of autonomic centers may be found in the diencephalon. At this point, we should be in a position to correlate the above-outlined functional principles of *sensory-motor dualism, systematization, stratification* and *control of responsiveness* with the structure of the nervous system in the higher organism, and we shall attempt to demonstrate that they may be found at most levels and sublevels. It matters little, at present at least, whether every organizational factor can be actually identified throughout and, since functions must be related to substrates by which they are mediated, precisely in what anatomic terms the various strata can be expressed.

The concept of segmentation of the central nervous system, fostered by Laycock (45), was further developed by Bok (11) who attempted to show that the very same basic elements which exist in the individual segments of the embryonal spinal cord may be identified, at one or the other evolutionary stage, in the remaining segments of the neuraxis, including the cerebral vesicles and, moreover, that the archetype of neural organization is the sensory-motor spinal reflex apparatus. Bok's concept is reminiscent of the ideas Goethe, Oken, and Carus (77) of a striking analogy between the morphology of the vertebra and the bones of the skull.

The lower brain stem

In studying the intricate structure of the brain stem, the segmentally organized spinal cord provides important clues, as not only a sulcus limitans, separating the primordial sensory from the motor zone, but also *somatomotor, visceromotor, viscerosensory* and *somatozensory* zones can be identified there (Fig. 1). In the more rostral divisions of the neuraxis, these landmarks become somewhat obliterated, while there can be little doubt that the fundamental organizational plan is being maintained. Moreover, it appears that equivalents of these landmarks, to some degree at least, are visibly retained at the cortical level.

The relationship of the various components of the sensory and motor nuclei to the four zones enumerated need not concern us here, but the zonal relationships of some other nerve centers require some elaboration.

Among the various structures concerned, the *cerebellum* occupies an apparently unique position. Because of its embryologic derivation from the vestibular area of the lower brain stem and its role as a superstructure of the vestibular nuclei, it may, for the sake of simplicity, be regarded as an elaborate vestibular "nucleus." The superstructure of the vestibular nuclei, or, for that matter, the unit comprising lower and higher vestibular centers, has gradually developed to a brain possessing hemispheres, commissural fibers

and projection systems as well as extensive multilevel connections, including links with the most rostral portions of the neuraxis, particularly the frontal lobes (Fig. 3). Many pathways link the cerebellum with subcortical formations, including the inferior olive, the pontine nuclei, certain conspicuous aggregations of nerve cells in the spinal cord and the medulla oblongata, nucleus ruber, substantia nigra, globus pallidus, and others. Thus, recording of linear and angular acceleration, regulation of basic and adaptive muscle tone, maintenance of equilibrium, motor and coordinative, including postural functions, are mediated by a special apparatus, the *cerebelloextrapyramidal system*. By the method of physiologic neuronography, there has been established, in addition to proprioceptive functions, the presence in the cerebellar cortex of receiving areas for vision, hearing and tactile sensation (68 69). We are inclined to interpret these cerebellar receiving stations as an intermediary reflex level where stimuli derived from various sources are integrated and utilized in the interest of those effector responses that depend on simultaneous correlation of spatial, positional and gravitational data. Ultimately, cerebellar impulses are projected upon the frontal cortex by way of the nucelus ventralis anterior of the thalamus.

The *activating system*, experimental destruction of which causes chronic unresponsiveness, is linked up with diencephalic centers subserving the sleep-wakefulness cycle.

Somatosensory midbrain elements are the *inferior* and superior *quadrigeminal nuclei*; having extensive sensory and motor connections with other nerve centers, especially in certain mammals and birds, they are formations of a higher order than the sensory nuclei of the cranial nerves although they do not reach the complexity of the cerebellum. From an organizational point of view, the cerebellum and the structures comprising the quadrigeminal plate belong to the category of predominantly unisensory "sub-brains."

The upper brain stem

Somatomotor elements, as far as is known, are lacking.

Extrapyramidal *motor* formations are represented chiefly by globus pallidus and corpus Luysii.

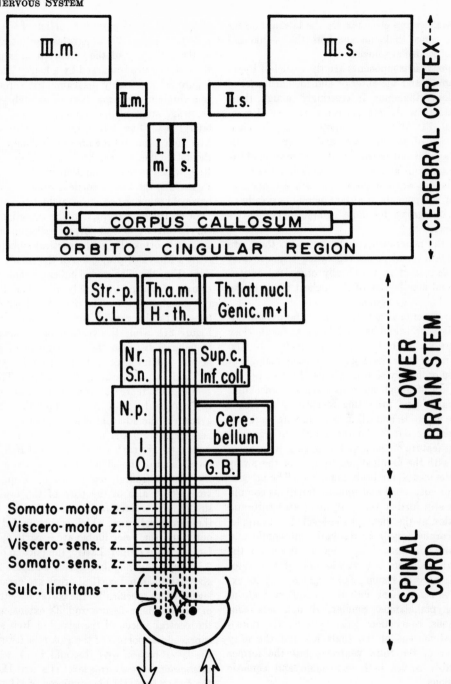

Fig. 1. The sensory-motor organization of the central nervous system.

III.m., III.s.: intellective level; II.s., II.: psycho-neural level; I.s., I.m.: sensory-motor level; i.: inner limbic arc; o.: outer limbic arc; Str.-p.: striopallidum; C.L.: Corpus Luysii; Th.a.m.: Thalamus, nucl. ant. and med.; H-th.: Hypothalamus; Th.lat.nucl.: Thalamus, nucl. lat.; Genic., m. l.: Corp, genicul. med. and lat.; N.r.: Nucl. ruber; S.n.: Substant. nigra; Sup. c.: Collicul. sup.; Inf. coll.: Collicul. inf.; N.p.: Nucl. pontis; I.O.: Oliva infer; G.B.: Goll's and Burdach's nuclei; z.: zone.

The heavy line between I.s. and I.m. indicates, throughout the present series of diagrams, the rolandic fissure.

Somatosensory elements are the lateral nucleus of the dorsal thalamus and both the medial and lateral geniculate nuclei.

Autonomic components are the nuclei of hypothalamus, and the anterior and medial nuclei of the dorsal thalamus. Interestingly enough, these centers show the highest concentration of sympathin (*74*). Within the hypothalamus, the identification of *viscerosensory* and *visceromotor* elements is difficult because of the elaboration of the hypothalamus as a highly differentiated correlation center wherein the elementary sensory and motor components of an autonomic nature have been overgrown by more complex coordinative agencies.

At the mesendiencephalic junction, there are important nodal points regulating *responsiveness* and *sleep*, that is, temporally organized activation and inactivation of the highest levels of the central nervous system.

The functional organization of the hypothalamus is complicated by the following: (a) its close integration with the pituitary body, (b) the presence of nuclei having a rich vascular supply of a type ordinarily seen in glands (*19, 25*), (c) the presence of ganglionic cells having intracellular capillary loops, indicating receptivity to blood-borne impulses, and (d) neurons having secretory functions (*2, 63*). (e) Another important organizational feature of the hypothalamus is its connection with the archipallium by way of the fornix and the medial forebrain bundle. (f) The integration of autonomic and somatic functions complicates still further the analysis of structure and function at the diencephalic level. For example, the corpus Luysii serves both autonomic and somatic functions. The anterior nucleus of the dorsal thalamus is a way-station of the autonomic nervous system, as brought out by its extensive connections with the mamillary body of the hypothalamus. Similar, though less conspicuous, connections exist between the dorsomedial nucleus of the thalamus and the gray matter of the third ventricle, but the former probably serves both autonomic and somatic functions.

The cerebral cortex

The sensory-motor level

Figure 2A represents an oblique coronal section through a cerebral hemisphere of an adult

at the level of the posterior portion of the corpus callosum. Figure 2B illustrates the lateral view of the convexity of the cerebrum in which the Rolandic fissure is marked by a heavy line, while Figure 2C is a highly diagrammatic coronal section through the hemisphere of an embryo at an arbitrary stage of development. Figure 2D is a lateral view of the left hemisphere of an embryo. The heavy line represents the Rolandic fissure; the dotted line, the cerebral sulcus of the island of Reil, which is a continuation of the former. In Figure 2E, the folded cortical ribbon of the embryonal brain has become straightened out by the "downward movement," in the direction of the curved arrow, of the corpus callosum and the adjacent cortex. Thus, the cortical ribbon represents a Mercator projection of the cortex seen on edge (Fig. 2F). The wedge indicates that the continuity of the cortex has been "severed" along the cingulate sulcus. The dotted and punctuated lines mark the various Rolandic segments as in Figure 2D, while the vertical lines indicate the boundaries between the sensory-motor, psychoneural and intellective levels, that is, levels I., II., and III. respectively (see below). The horizontal strata represent from above downward: (a) the marginal cortex surrounding the cingulate gyrus, (b) the adjacent convexity of the cerebral hemisphere, (c) the upper bank of the Sylvian cortex, (d) the cortex of the island of Reil, (e) the lower bank of the island of Reil, (f) the cortex of the inferior frontal, temporal and occipital convexity, and also of the base of the brain. The shaded area corresponds to the cross-section of the corpus callosum, which is surrounded by the outer and the inner limbic arc,—parts of the olfactory brain proper. Lastly, the bottom of figure 2 indicates the cingulate gyrus. In figure 2G, the above-enumerated cortical areas are arranged in levels. More specifically, the cortex on either side of the Rolandic fissure and its extensions, i.e., the central sulcus of the island of Reil and the supracallosal portion of the Rolandic fissure form the *lowest cortical level* (I.s. and I.m.), while the *intermediate cortex* forms level II.s. and II.m; and the *highest level* (III.) is composed of III.s, on the one hand, and, on the other, III.a. and III.e., which serve, respectively, *autonomic* and *extrapyramidal* functions. The symbols "s." and "m." indicate, respectively, "sensory" and "motor." However, for lack of space, the expression "III.m." rather than "III.a. and III.e." is used in some of the diagrams.

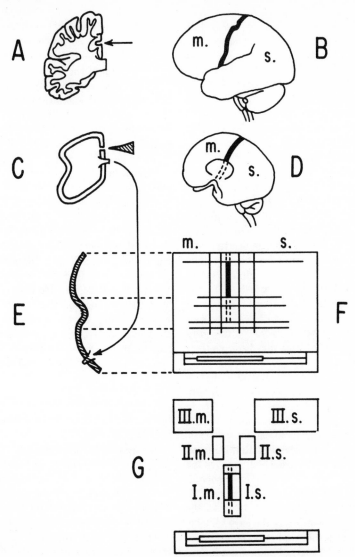

Fig. 2. The sensory-motor organization of the cerebral hemisphere in a Mercator projection, and the functional levels of the cortex. (The unlabelled part at the bottom at the figure, representing the inner limbic arc, the corpus callosum, the outer limbic arc, and the orbito-cingular region (limbic lobe) appears, on a larger scale, in fig. 1.

The Rolandic fissure and its extensions on both sides of the medial and the lateral wall of the cerebral hemispheres and the cortex of the island of Reil separates the motor division from the sensory division of the neocortex, although the line of demarcation is not considered clear-cut. The vast majority of fibers from the lateral thalamic nucleus and all fibers from the geniculate bodies project to its sensory division, including the postcentral gyrus, the parietal, occipital and temporal lobes (Figs. 3, 5). Olfactory stimuli are projected on to the gyrus ambiens and semilunaris of the archipallium.

The *sensory-motor level* (I.) proper is only indirectly concerned with the elaboration of higher cerebral functions but displays the anatomical and functional pattern of organization of the cortex in a clear fashion. It comprises essentially the somaesthetic, visual and auditory areas and their respective motor fields. (For the sake of simplicity, the discussion does not include the vestibular and gustatory cortical areas.) *The structural properties of the sensory-motor level provide for an optimum of selective reception of sensory impulses, on the one hand, and of differential innervation of certain bulbar and spinal muscles, on the other.* Intra- and subcortical association fibers subserving relatively simple sensory-motor, auditory-motor and visuo-motor reflexes connect the sensory with the adjacent motor areas. *However, the structural pattern of the sensory-motor plane is dominated by the partly overlapping motor strip and the somaesthetic area, as the former lies opposite that part of the motor cortex where the entire body is represented, whereas the other motor fields, at least in the human, are merely small cortical reflex centers which are contiguous with predominantly sensory areas.* This subdivision of the neocortex appears to be quite legitimate in spite of the presence of motor, sensory and associative elements throughout. For instance, the fact that the frontal lobes receive extensive radiations from the diencephalon does not militate against the fact that certain parts of the frontal lobe are a motor organ, just as the inflow of posterior root collaterals into the anterior horns of the gray matter of the spinal cord does not disprove their role as motor agencies.

It is well known that the Rolandic fissure straddles the supero-medial margin of the cerebral hemisphere in most cases and, in fact, in agensis of the corpus callosum, may subdivide the cingulate gyrus into rostral and caudal segments. The central sulcus of the island of Reil is an extension of the Rolandic fissure which grooves the insular cortex, as explained, on developmental grounds, by Guldberg (*30*) and Eberstaller (*21*). Thus, the anterior insular region belongs to the frontal lobe and the posterior, to the parietal lobe. Once the Rolandic fissure and its extensions are fully developed, all the cortical areas lying rostral to it form the *anterior cortex*, those located caudally the *posterior cortex*.

The Rolandic fissure extends virtually from the corpus callosum around the convexity and through the insular region. Both the somaesthetic area and the motor strip extend into the depth of the Sylvian fissure and appear to be arranged around the central sulcus of the island of Reil. The newly discovered extensions of the motor and sensory areas referred to as *second motor* and *sensory areas* (*73*) conform in general to the distribution pattern of the primary areas. Von Economo and Koskinas (*24*) found the cytoarchitecture of the anterior lobule of the insular cortex to be different from that of the posterior lobule.

According to Rose (*62*), certain segments of the anterior insular cortex, which have developed in man only, resemble architectonically the posterior portion of the third frontal convolution.

At the callosal extremity of the Rolandic line, too, there exist significant differences between the anterior and the posterior portion of the cingulate gyrus, since the latter (area 23), as pointed out by Betz (*6*) has a distinctly granular layer suggestive of receptive functions, whereas a corresponding layer cannot be identified in the rostral or motor portion (area 24). The cytoarchitectonic differences between the precentral and the postcentral lobule of the island of Reil mentioned in the preceding paragraph, and also the fact that the electrically responsive cortex lies in the region included in Brodman's area 24, while its caudal limits lie in the intermediary zone between 23 and 24, are likewise of significance in that they strengthen the theory of the sensory-motor duality of the neocortex. In summary, then, it may be said that a sensory-motor "belt" can be traced from the corpus callosum around the convexity of the brain and through the island of Reil.

The psychoneural level

By and large, the concept of a *psychoneural level of cerebral function* is based on experiences with agnostic, apractic and aphasic patients. It is well known that, in the absence of significant sensory deficit and mental impairment, an agnostic person is unable to recognize objects; that, in the absence of significant motor deficit, ataxia and mental deterioration, an apractic patient is unable to perform skilled movements; and that, under similar conditions, an aphasiac cannot understand what is said to him, cannot express himself, or is deprived of either faculty. It is true that agnosia may be combined with sensory impairment, and apraxia with weakness of the muscles to be used in performing intended movements and with mental impairment. In these instances, the diagnosis of agnosia rests on the disproportion between the inability to recognize objects and the relative preservation of sensory and higher mental functions; the diagnosis of apraxia is based on the disproportion between the patient's inability to perform skilled movements and the relative absence of weakness, ataxia and mental disturbances; and again, under similar abnormal conditions, the diagnosis of aphasia is based on the loss of speech in the absence of any significant sensory, motor and mental deterioration. Although the concept "psychoneural" goes back to certain psychopathologic observations, subsequent analysis of the underlying phenomena identified specific quotas of action mediated by the centers in question (as will be discussed in more detail in Chapter IV). The sensory group of psychoneural centers is concerned with the organization of elementary perceptual processes to those of a higher, configurational order, their motor counterpart with the integration of certain classes of movements. The two groups of centers operate in conjunction; the motor phenomena are basically the realization, or kinetic correlate, of their sensory antecedents.

Evidently, the recognition of objects and symbols is a more complex performance than perception and, moreover, depends on a level-specific factor, as the ability to recognize objects and symbols may be preserved in spite of the presence of a considerable degree of sensory deficit. By the same token, the execution of skilled movements, including articulatory movements, is a more complex performance than that of ordinary, non-skilled, volitional movements and, like gnosis, depends on a level-specific factor, as, even in the presence of considerable weakness and muscular incoordination, the general structure of the movement involved may be intact. In the sensory sphere, a level-specific factor structures elementary sensory data. The same applies to the motor sphere; elementary movements are built up to complex patterns which, even though imperfectly, realize the mental design of the movement intended.

It is a foregone conclusion that any form of recognition and skill involves psychic elements and, in this respect, is a higher cerebral function. Yet, in the category of central nervous system functions, recognition and skill occupy a unique position. Either may be selectively impaired by focal lesions (e.g., minute injuries, softenings and hemorrhages) in the same way as may a lower cerebral function, that is to say, one mediated by the Rolandic level or the brain stem. The term "psychoneural" (58) refers to this peculiarity and, at the same time, takes into account the intermediate position of the functions in question between perception and movement on the one hand,

and mentation on the other. Jackson, Pick, Liepmann, Broca and Wernicke, and others deserve credit for having segregated psychoneural disorders from the "general pool of dementia." (See Chapter IV.)

Lesions which interfere with the recognition of objects and symbols have a tendency to "cluster" in certain parts of the posterior cortex. The conclusion is inescapable that the latter is more immediately concerned with recognition than are other parts of the brain and that it thus merits the name *sensory psychoneural center*. By contrast, lesions which interfere with the ability to perform skilled movements have a tendency to aggregate in certain parts of the anterior cortex. Accordingly, these cortical provinces must be more directly concerned with the function of skill than the remaining parts of the nervous system and hence may be called *motor psychoneural centers*. The psychoneural level of cerebral function is compounded of a *sensory division* (II.s.) comprising the sum total of sensory psychoneural centers, and a *motor division* (II.m.) consisting of the sum total of motor psychoneural centers.

To the extent that the sensory psychoneural centers contribute a crucial quota of action to the process of recognition, and their motor counterpart to skilled movements, whereas, in contrast, the role of other parts of the brain in recognition and skill is nonspecific, the centers in question may justifiably be regarded not only as "centers of dysfunction" but at the same time, as "centers of function." In other words, they are parts of brain organs rather than disintegration artifacts. Wernicke's center is not only the center of sensory aphasia but also the sensory speech center, that is, one which contributes a specific quota of action to *receptive language*; and Broca's center is not only the center of motor aphasia but also the motor speech center, that is, one which contributes a specific quota of action to *expressive language* (Chapter IV). Naturally, the ability to understand language is not compartmentalized in certain sectors of the posterior sensory cortex; neither is the ability to speak located in corresponding cell stations of the anterior motor cortex, —in which case, to carry the argument to extremes, a hypothetical preparation consisting only of the speech centers and their sensory and motor connections would be capable of producing, in itself, the phenomena of speech. To throw out this absurdity is to admit that language, like any other cerebral function, is in the previously specified sense a collective performance but that, within the global activity of the central nervous system, certain cell stations play a crucial part in the integration of language while others are mere auxiliaries or do not participate at all.

The various skills, developed under the guidance of visual, tactile and auditory stimuli and facilitated and perfected by multisensory control of movements, are largely built up by training and experience, by imitation, by the individuation of mass movements and the gradual elimination of random activity. As gnosis (in the wider sense of the term) is the indispensable prerequisite of both eupraxia and speech, at least in their early stages, psychoneural activity is dependent on the transmission of impulses that travel from the regions adjacent to the primary receptive cortical fields to those lying in front of the motor area. These impulses are probably conducted along pathways which correspond to the neuronal chains utilized at the stage of learning, since experience and re-experience (apart from a certain degree of automatization involved in learning processes) are inherently identical, and the ultimate sequential structure of acquired movements is not fully dependent on the initiating stimulus. Thus, a person will write a certain letter in the same way regardless of whether he or she writes spontaneously or on command and whether the order be given in writing, orally, or by signals of any kind.

The various neuronal elements concerned with the elaboration of speech are grouped around the Sylvian fissure or, for that matter, around the central sulcus of the island of Reil, where they occupy both surface structures and concealed cortical fields. Connections between the sensory and the motor components subserving psychoneural functions, that is, speech centers and skill centers, are established by the fasciculus arcuatus, the deep insular fibers and those coursing in the external capsule. However, the fact that certain associational tracts establish functional relations between distant parts of the cortex (as has been shown, e.g., for the corpus callosum, by both section and stimulation experiments) does not exclude the role of U-fibers and even of intracortical association fibers in cortico-cortical impulse conduction between distant areas.

The intellective level

Jackson's idea that the organ of the mind has a sensory-motor constitution is brought out neither by the study of higher mental functions and their disorders nor by the comparison of the intellective level with the psychoneural level. Whoever works on the assumption that mentation has both sensory and motor aspects will find himself sooner or later in a blind alley, at least if he employs the term "motor" in its conventional sense and without further qualification. This difficulty may be avoided by assuming that the intellective level is composed of (a) a *sensory division*, or *conceptual (sub)-level* III.s., (b) an *autonomic division* (III.a.) and an *extrapyramidal division* (III.e.).* *The highest sensory (conceptual) level, or organ of the mind proper, occupies the major portion of the posterior cortex, while the two other segments occupy a large portion of the anterior cortex.* By and large, the *responsiveness* of the conceptual level is determined by the autonomic provinces of the frontal lobes and, implicitly, the diencephalo-frontal system operating in conjunction with the alerting system of the brain stem, while the *externalization* of intellective activity is dependent on the extrapyramidal nervous system. Thus, the actual exercise of mental power involves three factors which are maximally concentrated in specialized parts of the cerebral cortex. The conceptual level (or organ of the mind proper) is derivatively related to, and at the same time, "embodies," in a psychological sense, the perceptual level I.s. and the configurational level II.s. Other factors being equal, the ability on the part of the posterior cortex to form concepts, i.e., abstract relations between the data of the senses, and to operate with conceptual stimuli is dependent on the mass of III.s., which, in the course of phylogenesis, has been added to both the primitive perceptual centers (I.s.) and the sensory psychoneural centers or configurational level II.s. In other words, the ability in question depends on the proportion between the last-named sensory agencies on one hand, and, on the other, on III.s., the "elaborative cortex," or "center of concepts and ideation" of the early writers. From a technical viewpoint, so to speak, the conceptual level comprises the

* The evidence for this assumption will be given as our thesis develops.

sum total of structural provisions which are necessary to determine, or select, appropriate *responses* to psychic stimuli of various complexity and, in this sense, is the highest *selector mechanism*. Its *responsiveness*, on the other hand, is, as stated above, under the control of the autonomic provinces of the frontal lobes which, to the extent that the latter may increase the responsiveness to stimuli, may be regarded as the "motor" of the former. Thus, the autonomic provinces of the frontal lobes determine the volume of the selector-activity of the conceptual level and, inasmuch as the former is a prerequisite of goal-directed action, the volume of sensory-motor integration at the highest level of the neuraxis. The extrapyramidal provinces of the frontal cortex (III.e.) exert a facilitatory influence on volitional movements (Chapter IV).

In a wider sense, the organ of the mind may be said to extend, in a "horizontal direction," into the frontal lobes and thus to embody a wider variety of neural arrangements than the conceptual level, that is, in addition to III.s. (the organ of mentation properly so called), the cortical organs of responsiveness, III.a., and of its externalization, III.e. The three cortical agencies constitute the intellective level III. However, since, as will be explained later in this volume, III.s. includes, both psychologically and developmentally, II.s. and I.s., the intellective level extends,

in a "vertical direction," to the lowest sensory grade of the cortex as well. In the light of the above considerations, we regard the term anterior associative cortex as obsolete but have no objection to use of the terms III.s. and posterior associative cortex interchangeably. The matter will be further pursued in Chapter II., under the heading: "Anterior cortex function vs. posterior cortex function."

The question now arises whether the above levels of cortical functions can be correlated with specific cytoarchitectonic characteristics. With respect to certain areas belonging to the lowest cortical level, e.g., the motor strip and the area striata, the answer is affirmative but has to be left open in view of the fact that an "ideal cortical map" (*24*) does not as yet exist. In fact, the possibility that such map will ever be designed is remote; cytoarchitectonic and axonographic variability seems to increase almost in geometric proportion to the morphologic complexity of the cortex, which, thus far, has defied description. At present, the above-proposed scheme, although lacking a histologic basis in the strict sense of the term, should be regarded as an ordering device which makes possible correlation of ontogenetic, phylogenetic, psychological and neurologic data and which, I believe, is not contradicted by any known facts.

The derivation of higher from lower nervous system functions

In the following sections, an attempt will be made to amplify the above propositions and to show that the interpretation of higher cerebral functions involves, first and foremost, their reduction to the lower—to put it into Jacksonian terms, to show that the activity of the "highest, least rigidly organized sensory-motor arrangements" is determined by, and derivable from, the "activity of the most stereotyped arrangements."

The integrative acts mediated by the nervous system are neurodynamic processes which establish meaningful relationships between the individual parts of the organism and between the organism and its environment. Physiologically, integrative acts involve the generation of energy on

the parts of specialized sets of nerve centers and its distribution in appropriate nerve fibers. The individual functions are nothing other than the sum total of integrative acts of a similar category to which a special term is applied. The term "writing" for example, like other similar terms (including speaking, reading, etc.) is a generic one; it refers to the sum total of integrative acts concerned with the visible representation and transmission of meanings. As already alluded to, higher cerebral functions are integrative processes which, ultimately, depend on the most versatile circuits of the nervous system. *To localize a function* means (a) *to establish its process character* and (b) *to specify its relationship to individual systems and levels of the neuraxis.* In spite of their relationship to specific centers, the individual functions are *decentralized* because of the representation of their fractions at different levels of the nervous system. At the same time, they are *centralized,* as a particular "highest level center" (although it may be actuated by extrinsic stimuli) *controls the sum total of integrative acts which constitute a particular performance.* In this sense, then, one may legitimately recognize speech centers, writing centers and other cell stations which exercise ultimate control in a given sphere of function.

Thus, it is our task to demonstrate that higher functions, although ultimately dependent on the activities of the highest echelons of the neuraxis, can be traced to the function of the lower centers and that, in the present context, the term "function" derives its meaning from the relationship between physiologic activity and morphologic substrate. As expressed in *neuropsychological* terms, the psychological processes underlying a given performance reflect, in the final analysis, the activity of neurons arranged according to certain engineering principles and, since the performance of the lower strata is "repeated" by the higher, the interpretation of higher performances involves the elucidation of the relationships between structure and function at different strata of the neuraxis.

The neuropsychological viewpoint may perhaps be more accurately outlined by the following analogies.

(1) Jackson's idea that "each grade of the nervous system represents over again and coordinates in more elaborate combination the parts represented and coordinated by the grade below" may be epitomized by the analogy between the evolution of higher degrees of *integrational complexity* at higher grades of the neuraxis on the one hand, and, on the other, the acquisition of a higher degree of *structural complexity* of an organ at successive stages of its development. Just as a relatively immature embryological stage is the *structural primordium* of the stage it precedes, so, in the nervous system, a relatively low degree of integrational complexity is the *functional primordium* of the higher grade. As Goethe, taking his cue from Turpin, wrote in his *History of my Botanical Studies*": Voir venir les choses est le meilleur moyen de les expliquer."

(2) As, in the biological sciences, a given stage of differentiation should be defined in terms of (a)

its structural primordium and (b) the developmental processes leading to a *higher degree of differentiation,* so, in the field of neuropsychology, a given performance should be expressed in terms of (a) its functional primordium and (b) the specific quota of action which, at the higher level of the same system, is generated to increase its operational dimensions.

(3) As, in the development of structure, a more recent stage of differentiation supersedes the older stage but, nevertheless, still reflects the composition of its primordium, so, in the nervous system, the more adaptive functions mediated by the higher levels of a given system supersede the more primitive functions of the lower levels of the same system but *maintain the* general pattern of organization of their precursor as, for example, thought, which is an elaboration of perception.

The importance of the genetic approach to the study of higher cerebral functions was stressed by F. A. Lange (*43*) as early as 1865. "We shall easily discover", he wrote, "that in these already so complicated sequences of sensation and movements [of the spinal frog] there is afforded the beginning of an explanation of the most complicated psychological activities . . . the explanation of psychical life requires to carry it back to individual processes which are utterly and entirely distinct from the mode of action of a complete organism. . . . In our whole traditional psychology the actions of man are classified without any regards to the elements of their origin, according to certain relations to life and its aims, and indeed in such a way that the mere psychological analysis often shows clearly how little what is denoted by a single word forms a true unity. . . . The great reason why there has hitherto been no progress in our explanation of the relation of the brain to the psychical functions seems to us to lie simply in the same ground which doomed phrenology— in the reification of abstract ideas instead of the simple apprehension of the actual so far as it is possible. . . . *It is just the greatest advantage of all luminous and orderly morphology that it immediately gives us insight into funcion.*"

To a degree, Lange's remarks on the lack of progress in explaining the relation of the brain to psychical functions holds true even today. Progress is not to be expected without a profound conceptual reorientation, even at the risk of having to discard certain time honored dictionary definitions. The new system of concepts will have to be created along evolutionary lines, that is, within the framework of neuropsychology as here defined. Moreover, any statement deduced from this scheme will have to be cast in terms referring to the very same concepts that constitute its fundamentals. In other words, no statement can be deduced from it that contains concepts not represented in the system in question. This postulate will be made explicit in developing a stimulus response psychology and psychopathology, and a classification of neurosis and psychosis.

II

Affectivity

"*Les passions, suivant Bichat, ont leur siège non dans le système nerveux cerébral, mais dans le système viscéral, intestinal. C'est ainsi que Platon plaçait également dans les intestines ce qu'il appelait la troisième partie de l'âme, a savoir l'âme appétitive, source des désires et des colères. L'école des Descartes, au contraire, qui plaçait dans le cerveau le siège de l'âme, rattachait en même organ les passions et les pensées. Bichat revient à la passion de Platon, et place dans les viscères l'origine des passions. Le cerveau n'est affecté que sympathiquement. Elle est sans doute étonnant, dit il, que les passions occuppant une si grande place dans notre vie intellectual et morale, n'aient ni leur terme ni leur origine dans les organes supérieures du corps humain mais dans ceux qui sont affectés aux fonctions internes. Et cependant, c'est ce que les faits demontre. L'état des viscères modifie profondement le mode des passions, et réciproquement, les passions, dans leur effets organiques, affect en particulier les viscères.*

Flourens soutient, d'après Descartes, que les volontés sont des pensées.

PAUL JANET (432)

Given an appropriate responsiveness threshold, the organism reacts to certain categories of stimuli with *seeking response*. Thus, identical stimuli may at different times elicit different patterns of behaviour. Neglecting, for the time being, *avoidance reactions* to aversive stimuli, the consummation of seeking responses produces a mode of experience known as *gratification* which, in turn, is associated with a positive affect. (See *Elements of a stimulus psychology and psychopathology*, which follows.)

By and large, it may be stated that the changing reactivity of the nervous system is referable to the changing functionality of its elements which reflects degrees of biological equilibrium. In this respect, the nervous system behaves not unlike a neuron which, depending on its threshold to stimuli, is either excitable or refractory. In referring to the activity of the most primitive neural elements, and of the lower levels of the nervous system, we shall think in terms of *threshold*, *excitability* and *reaction*; of the highest levels of the nervous system, in terms of *responsiveness*, (receptivity), *drive* (reactivity) and *behaviour*. In other words, we regard, as the functional primordium of the responsiveness of the nervous system, the changing threshold of the ganglionic cell. *Drive is the externalized responsiveness of the organism to stimuli that have a bearing on its biological equilibrium.* Implicitly, the strength of drive is a measure of the responsiveness of the organism to biologically significant stimuli. Treshold values or, for that matter, responsiveness levels, are in turn determined by various intrinsic and extrinsic factors some of which operate periodically.

These considerations lead to a further point already touched upon in the opening chapter, namely, the regulation of drive by specific parts of the nervous system. It is well known that inordinate intensification or reduction of drive may be a prominent feature of organic brain lesions, particularly of the frontal lobe disease. Thus, the study of drive from the point of view of neuropsychology may well depend on the elucidation of frontal lobe function and the study of related mechanisms. Certain clinical experiences indicate an intimate relationship between drive and extrapyramidal nervous system. It would appear that the extrapyramidal nerve centers, whatever additional functions they serve (or might have served in the course of evolution) facilitate the externalization of the already existing receptivity to stimuli but are not directly concerned with the regulation of responsiveness levels.

One of Hauptmann's (*356*) patients with postencephalitic parkinsonism remarked: "My limbs feel heavy, like lead ... the movements do not occur of themselves as they did before, I have to think over every movement I want to perform.... If I want to execute a movement I have to get myself into some form of mental excitement ... my limbs resemble a compass whose screw has been tightened ... things are easier when I get myself into some sort of rage." Whenever one of the patients suffering from right-sided hemiparkinsonism intended to perform a movement necessitating the simultaneous use of both upper extremities, only the left side would move. Other patients, taking for granted the unity of will and movement, express surprise about the fact that their impulses and urges did not promptly produce muscular contractions. Bostroem (*101*) noted that movements which under normal conditions occur automatically, that is, in response to the awareness of a goal, had to be broken down into their individual fractions and that the execution of each component required a separate effect on the part of the patient. Cases of hemiparkinsonism prove more conclusively than other observations that the extrapyramidal system facilitates the execution of movements although stimulation experiments (*635*) have demonstrated that, within the extrapyramidal complex of centers, certain cell stations inhibit others. It should further be noted that the akinesia of the parkinsonian patient is not necessarily associated with rigidity and, hence, should be referable to a central rather than a peripheral factor. On the other hand, it is not necessarily true that extrapyramidal lesions do not alter the responsiveness level to stimuli, as may be inferred from the remarks of one of my patients who complained about the lack of "ignition of initiative." Possibly, Hauptmann's and Bostroem's above cited observations, who also noted a genuine listlessness in some of their patients, do not apply to "pure" cases of extrapyramidal disease. Experiences with postencephalitic mental changes, chiefly in children and adolescents may throw further light on the problem under study. The salient features of the postencephalitic syndrome are the inversion of the sleep curve and, apart from the disorders of attention to be mentioned below, disturbances in affect, behaviour and personality. To quote Wilson and Bruce (966): "A child of previously irreproachable character may be so transformed as actually seem a different 'person'. Impish, cruel, destructive, abusive, indecent, he may become guility of any offense from naughtiness to crime."* Apart from the derangement of the sleep wakefulness cycle, the disorders of conduct are frequently associated with polydypsia, polyuria and the adiposo-genital syndrome whereas, among a series of 60 cases studied by Thiele (900), the amyostatic symptomcomplex was found in four cases only.

The patient's attention is easily caught by current stimuli, in other words, his vigilance is increased while tenacity is lacking. The hypervigilance persists even in those cases in which, eventually, an akinetic-hypertonic syndrome supervenes. According to Werner (892), disorders of affectivity may be concealed by the generalized rigidity but may still come to the fore as fits of rage and assaultivness. At postmortem, the dominant changes are encountered in the periventricular gray matter of the third ventricle and the aqueduct. In sharp contrast, the alterations in the cortex of the cerebral hemispheres, the basal ganglia and the tegmentum of the pons are inconspicuous (584, 640, 874, 958). The above data suggest that the hyperactivity and the restlessness of the postencephalitic patient (which, needless to say, is never unilateral) is a manifestation of increased responsiveness to stimuli rather than of increased facilitation of psychomotor functions. They suggest, further, that the increased responsiveness is, in turn, the expression of an autonomic disorder because of (a) its association with neurosympathetic and neuroglandular disorders, (b) its relationship to the derangement of the sleep-wakefulness cycle, (c) both clinically and anatomically, the lack of correlation between extrapyramidal and amyostatic abnormalities and (d) the autopsy findings.

The similarity between the abnormal conduct of the juvenile postencephalitic and certain frontal lobe patients (about which more will be said

* See also Levy's (534a) recent article.

in the discussion) is unmistakable. However, it will be well to remember that disease processes may involve, concurrently, the central division of the autonomic nervous system and the extrapyramidal system; that, under normal conditions, the two systems do not function in isolation and that, for these reasons, their separation is to a degree artificial.

I shall probably never forget a patient who had a glioma of the right frontal lobe and who during the past two months of his life had shown the following abnormalities. For some time he had been annoying the members of his household by his apparent laziness. For instance, he would not get up in the morning even though he was repeatedly told to do so or when finally his blankets had been removed and the windows widely opened. He then apparently would take no notice of the icy air that streamed into the room for he would continue to lie motionless until forced to sit up. Later on he had to be dressed; otherwise he would sit about without moving for almost any length of time. When shaving he would suddenly stop, being unable to perform the necessary movements in one continuous succession. When walking in the street his attention would be caught abruptly by articles displayed in shop windows for what his wife called an excessively long time, or by advertisements of any kind, which he would read aloud. He would also make loud, tactless remarks. When reading, or appearing to do so, he would hold the paper motionless for a surprisingly long time, failing to drop it even after the lights in his room had been turned out. However he was able to report quite correctly the gist of short newspaper articles he had read and to comment on them, sometimes in a rather clever way. He was also quite oriented as to time, place and his own personality (798).

Some time afterward, having become interested in thalamic function, I attempted to reach the anterior nucleus of the thalamus in a Rhesus monkey by direct exposure in order to produce an isolated local lesion (798). Because of the small volume of the lateral ventricle and the large size of the fornix this attempt was not altogether successful in that it resulted in rather extensive damage to the medial surface of the frontal lobe on either side.* After having recovered from the operation, the monkey, apart from marked forced

* At the time the experiment was carried out, the Horseley-Clarke Instrument was not available.

grasping, (which had also been present in the above mentioned case) showed the following behaviour. Mostly, it would sit on the floor of its cage with an empty emotional expression. When frightened it would jump up on the walls of its cage and, having grasped an iron bar, maintained its posture for several minutes and appeared quite motionless during this period. When the animal started feeding itself it would move the food toward its mouth but would stop in the middle of the movement for a considerable length of time. It became evident on several of these occasions that the animal's attention had been distracted, as revealed by a sudden change in the expression of its face; the source of this distraction could not always be detected except possibly for the movements of the other animals in adjacent cages which, however, do not distract a normal monkey under similar circumstances. The animal would also seemingly forget to chew food until it was repeatedly pressed into its mouth. The animal could not see the monkey in the cage next to it except through a hole in the partition. Nevertheless, it was often found peeping through this hole in a rigid and motionless attitude even when its fellow at which it had been looking, was no longer in view.

Now everyone of us has probably seen patients suffering from frontal lobe tumors, who, in contrast to lack of drive, showed increased psychomotor activity. This activity, however, seemed to be erratic, scattered and ill-directed. This *bipolar patterning of behaviour* calls to mind mechanisms whose involvement is apt to cause the *loss of a basic regulatory function*, more especially, the balance between sympathetic and parasympathetic innervation, or the derangement of endocrine equilibrium. It is further to be noted that increased drive is apt to be associated with a heightened feeling level, decreased drive with a depressed feeling level, and that opposite feeling tones may be conditioned by the antagonistic action of certain drugs. For example, adrenaline, a sympathomimetic drug, may cause anxiety while mecholyl, a parasympathetic drug, has the opposite effect (*571*). (This point to be taken up later.)

One gains the impression that, in frontal lobe disease, a basic factor is at fault which, in the last analysis, is a homeostatic one; and that at least certain aspects of frontal lobe dysfunction, more especially disorders of responsiveness and, in-directly, drive, might be comprehensible in terms of dyshomeostasis (800, 804) if only the concept of equilibrium and disequilibrium of vital physiologic activities could be extended to include certain higher cerebral functions, more precisely the function of responsiveness to stimuli at the highest integrative level of the neuraxis.

In the human, similar disorders are apt to occur as a result of neoplastic disease of the frontal lobes and Pick's disease. But they may also follow frontal lobe injuries, frontal lobotomies, lobectomies and topectomies. (*251, 336, 531, 532, 642, 780*) The interested reader will find several hundred references in Ruffin's (*780*) and Haeffner's (*336*) review articles.

Frontal lobe damage of any kind may produce not only disorders of affectivity and drive but, at the same time, disturbances of attention, memory and mental concentration. On the other hand, similar abnormalities may occur in extrafrontal lesions. For example, in a study covering a series of 581 verified intracranial tumors conducted by the author (*799*), intellectual defitic was noted in a series of 24 right-sided (41%) and in 34 left-sided (72%) temporal lobe tumors in which, however, disorders in affect, behaviour and personality were less frequent and less severe. They indicated euphoria, listlessness and irritability, and they occurred in 33% of the right sided and 44% of the left sided neoplasms, euphoria being the most frequent abnormality. Among 211 frontal lobe tumors, the affective disorders included *euphoria, depression, puerility, lack of endurance, lack of restraint, eroticism, hyposexualism, swinging mood, increased irritability, apprehensiveness and especially listlessness.* Depending on the location of the lesion within the frontal lobe, or lobes, the disorders in question were noted in 78% of 50 bilateral extraventricular tumors, in 43% of 30 bilateral intraventricular tumors, in 58% of 36 unilateral basofrontal tumors and in 46% of unilateral neoplasms of the central white matter of the frontal lobes. *The pattern of mental disturbances with thalamic, hypothalamic and midbrain tumors* (37 cases) *resembled that in frontal lobe lesions.* An extension of the study to 23 occipital, 45 rolandic, 31 parietal and other neoplasms showed that the curve indicating the total number of psychic changes showed a steady decline as the lesion approached the rolandic fissure, using the temporo-occipitofrontal axis of the brain as a line of reference. Rolandic lesions showed the lowest incidence of mental changes, namely, 38%. Among a group of 19 tumors involving the splenium of the corpus callosum, the total incidence of mental abnormalities was 89%, and that of disturbances in affect, etc. only 26%. Considering that, for all practical purposes, bilateral extraventricular tumors involving the frontal lobes impinge upon, or infiltrate, the rostrum of the corpus callosum, the high incidence of affective disturbances in the latter (78%) as compared to the tumors of the spenium is striking. *The validity of the various data for the entire group appeared to be enhanced by the fact that the distribution patterns of mental changes produced by new growths, as could be ascertained by an extensive search of the literature, were similar to those encountered in patients with vascular and degenerative lesions and by injuries involving comparable parts of the brain.* Experimental lesions in higher primates will be discussed below. (As compared for example with the examination by means of contrast media, the localizing value of mental changes is of but little diagnostic significance, the reason being that the diverse numerical values reflects disturbance patterns for the various groups rather than for individual cases where the general pattern is apt to be obscured by chance factors.)

The above recorded data post several questions, namely, apart from the mechanics of the abnormalities, *the reason for the high incidence of both affective and intellectual disorders (including distractibility and impairment of memory) in frontal lobe lesions, the frequent occurrence of intellectual disorders in temporal lobe lesions and the appearance of the curve indicating the frequency of mental changes in neoplasms of the cerebral hemispheres.* The answer most readily given, as indeed it has been given in the past by some, is that frontal lobe are the seat of memory, a center of mental concentration, of affective control, of intelligence, in other words, the seat of higher mental functions. Other authorities, seemingly with equal justification, claim that the very same functions may be attributed to the extrafrontal parts of the cortex, if not of the entire brain. In our opinion *these questions can be answered only by a more detailed study of the organizational framework of the nervous system, already outlined in the introductory chapter, and, in line with the neuropsychological approach here advocated, the reduction of psychological to physiological concepts.* They can certainly not be

answered by the localization of abstract concepts in the brain of man and higher animals. On the other hand, if it is true that higher functions are the lower raised to a higher power, it should be possible to expand physiological concepts to cover and, to that extent as least, to "explain", the mechanism of psychological functions. We begin with the concept of homeostasis to which reference has already been made, describing, at the same time, in more detail the diverse disorders encountered.

PATTERNS OF HOMEOSTASIS

The modern concept of homeostasis as introduced by Cannon (*145, 147*) is derived from what Claude Bernard (*71, 72*) called the stability of the *milieu intern.* "In the higher organism", Bernard wrote, "where the histological elements are no longer able to adjust themselves to the physicochemical conditions as they exist in the external world, the internal environment assumes an altogether new importance. It consists in a circulating fluid which brings into relationship the organs with one another and (indirectly) with the environment of the organism. This fluid is the blood, or nutrient fluid. ... The blood is nothing other than the internal environment in which anatomical elements exist like fishes in water. ... The blood maintains the proper temperature and it provides at the same time special nutritive elements. ... The term *milieu intern* designates the blood, including its plasmatic and corpuscular elements. Certain elements of the blood are furnished by the endocrine glands." In the words of Cannon, the term "homeostasis" designates the "*coordinated physiological reactions which maintain most of the steady state of the body*". ... The homeostatic regulations act autonomously ... commonly the autonomic nervous system or that system in cooperation with the endocrine glands is called into action" [to maintain the steady state of the organism]. It may be readily seen that the term in question as employed by Cannon covers a wider variety of phenomena (many of which are cited in Cannon's article) than those forming the "milieu intern."

Now, since the stabilizing factors are under the control of the sympathetic and parasympathetic nervous system which oppose each other as it were and, further, since the tone of the two divisions varies both spontaneously and in response to the varying demands made on the organism, the homeostatic level is not a constant. There is either *sympathetic preponderance*, involving a shift of the homeostatic level toward the sympathetic extremity of an (arbitrary) scale of vegetative tone, or *parasympathetic preponderance*, involving a shift in the opposite direction. For example, during sleep, a state of parasympathetic prevalence that is, the blood chemistry, the constitution of the body fluids, the temperature of the body and other values are different from the corresponding values as they exist in the waking state. A steady state of this kind is differently patterned, but homeostasis is maintained as long as neither end of the scale is approached beyond critical points.

The point to be kept in mind is that a mean homeostatic level exists from which, however, more or less constantly, normal deviations occur under natural conditions. We have already made allusion to the fact that the term homeostatis applies also to affective levels and that affective states can be influenced by drugs acting upon the autonomic nervous system. Considering that affects are response determining factors, the inclusion of affects into autonomic phenomena would imply that they operate either within a normal range or with inordinate force or that their action is inordinately weak.

By way of *summary*, then, it may be said that the organism tends to keep autonomic and other functions related to the vegetative sphere at levels of activity best suited to demands made on its self-maintaining and self-balancing capacity. If, due to internal or external influences, a function is either intensified or depressed, a variety of mechanism is thrown into action to insure return to the *basic equilibrium*, which is the functional state best adapted to cope with internal and external environmental changes—like a bow, after the arrow has been dispatched, returns to its original (and we may assume optimal) state of tension. Defective homeostasis results in disequilibrium, the effects of which may be cumulative and, eventually, incompatible with the very existence of the organism.

The true meaning of the concept of homeostasis is not generally appreciated. Ashby (*31*), for example, contends that life processes and homeosta-

tic processes are coterminous, (he calls the "artificial brain" he built a homeostat) although homeostasis is merely one of the conditions and at the same time a manifestation of biological processes. Paradoxically, one of the functions of the higher organism is the production of "dyshomeostasic states" or goals which are superseded by the re-establishment of biological equilibrium—often at higher levels of existence and experience —and, thereby, the establishment of higher levels of organization. The extension of the concept of homeostasis by Wiener (*956*) to include tele-kinetic feedback mechanism does not seem to be legitimate; a moment's reflection shows that muscular coordination as occurs on volitional innervation does not aim at the maintenance of a steady state. On the other hand, Wiener's idea that homeostatic phenomena are, in substance, negative feedbacks has many applications. For example, Hoskins (*405*) has shown that when the titer of circulating thyroxin rises, it selectively inhibits the anterior pituitary so that the discharge of thyroxin is decreased and that, on the other hand, a deficiency state acts to augment thyrotropin and more thyroid hormone is produced.

It is in order now to consider some of the homeostatic states approaching the two extremes of the above mentioned scale. As demonstrated by the sleep wakefulness cycle already referred to, the basic biological equilibrium can be differently patterned in rough analogy to the basic setting of the regulator of a thermostat.

Other factors governing the adjustment of the basic response levels appear to be related to seasonal influence (*79, 239a*). Apart from the alternation of sleep and wakefulness and the menstrual cycle, however, *periodicity* (*95, 497*) appears to play a minor role in the physiology of the human, but seems to be brought out under certain pathological conditions. Periodic manifestations of responsiveness are codetermined by the particular phase of the cycle during which exposure to various stimuli takes place.

The close relationships between the diverse categories of dysfunction to be discussed below, namely, homeostatic disorders in the psychic sphere and the somatic sphere, appears to be suggested by their frequent association in frontal lobe lesions and the fact that they are apt to occur in an essentially similar fashion in cases of surgical interruption of the (largely reciprocal) diencephalofrontal connections (*152, 163, 165, 264, 585, 921, 927*) especially those which link the frontal cortex with the anterior and the dorsomedial nucleus of the thalamus and with the hypothalamic region. (*564, 691, 875*) It is only to be expected that the close anatomical relationship between the structures concerned will manifest itself under both normal and abnormal conditions.

Disorders of homeostasis in any sphere may however be quite different depending on (a) the individual factors involved, (b) the degree of involvement, (c) the combination in which the individual disturbances occur and, (d) the presence or absence of periodicity of dysfunction. *It appears to be of particular importance that, in analogy to disturbances of the interbrain and the endocrine gland, either plus or minus functions may develop in both the psychic and the somatic spheres.*

The responsiveness of the organism is *quantitatively* and *temporally patterned*. Quantitative patterning is manifested by decreased or increased excitability to stimuli; temporal patterning, by fluctuations of excitability, but it is worthwhile repeating that, within limits, the deviations from the mean level of excitability and constancy of performance, i.e., changing responsiveness to stimuli may be regarded as normal.

Receptivity and reactivity

In the psychic sphere, disorders of receptivity are manifested by the reduced or otherwise altered recording of stimuli commonly referred to as *disturbances of awareness*. This may range from reduced attention to profound somnolence. As compared to awareness, a more diffuse type of consciousness, attention may be thought of as "polarized" receptivity in that the recording of stimuli depends on situational factors rather than their intensity, and that stimuli that have no bearing on present, past or anticipated situations are excluded altogether or not integrated into the stream of thought. On the surface, it may appear rather far fetched to consider attention and somnolence as opposite elements of a linear series; popular usage, however, has long taken cognizance of this relationship by using the expression "to pay attention" and "to keep awake" almost interchangeably.

Distractibility is the inability to give priority to relevant stimuli. Frontal lobe lesions almost invariably give rise to difficulties in directing the train of thought which, unless it stagnates altogether, may drift along aimlessly under the influence of chance stimuli (*260, 799*).

The distractibility of patients with frontal lobe lesions manifests itself in the daily activities as well as on clinical observations. Their attention is easily distracted by any chance impression but difficult to hold by appropriate stimuli. I often have difficulty in examining the eyegrounds of patients with frontal lobe lesions for they are apt to be distracted by the light of the opthalmoscope. Similarly, they tend to follow the marker on perimetry. Distractibility has also been demonstrated in experimental animals (*233*). After bilateral removal of the frontal association areas in monkeys, the animals succeed in delayed response performances when darkness is maintained, while they fail whenever a bright light is turned on the cage in which they are kept during the delay interval of the experiments (*673*).

The term *hypovigilance* designates any type of reduction of attention. More severe disturbances of attention and therefore of awareness are seen in states of somnolence in which the recording of stimuli may be assumed to be virtually nonexistent. Somnolence in the early phases of frontal lobe tumors has been noted by many observers. The lesion does not necessarily enroach upon the region of the third ventricle (*790, 799*).

Hypervigilance or undue susceptibility to stimuli may appear in two types. *Tenacity* of attention or *pseudoconcentration* is the inability to free attention from whatever stimulus happens to enter the individual's orbit, with resulting incapacity to pay attention to subsequent impressions for any period of time. Another type of disturbance of attention, *shifting vigilance*, may give rise to restlessness and undirected psychomotor activity. In spite of the defective appreciation of pain in frontal lobe lesions, e.g., frontal lobotomies (*480*) the patient over-reacts to painful stimuli (*158*). This *over-reaction* may be caused by any unexpected and non-specific stimulus and is due to the patient's inordinately increased "immediate" receptivity.

In the psychic sphere, the abnormalities of response may be secondary to disturbances of attention, and they may manifest themselves by psychomotor retardation, i.e., inordinately decreased "immediate" receptivity. Frontal lobe lesions may increase the reaction time to stimuli and impair the ability to respond readily to sequences of stimuli (*493*). Monkeys, following bilateral removal of area 8, fail to respond to visual stimuli and tactile stimuli altogether or their reaction time is markedly slowed down (*487*). Disturbances of reactivity may range from slight degrees of inaccessibility to profound apathy. Again, in other frontal lobe lesions, the reaction time to stimuli is inordinately shortened (*635*) and all stages of restlessness from mild hyperirritability to manic-like excitement may be encountered (*799*). The matter will be taken up in more detail under the heading "The psychopathology of frontal lobe disease."

Periodicity

Kleitman (*497*), in his review article on biological cycles and rhythms, writes that a phsiological rhythm, specifically the diurnal rhythm, is essentially a metabolic cycle synchronized with the external periodicity of day and night through the influence of variations in illumination, temperature and other environmental factors and of the nervous and endocrine system. According to Rey (*755*) most metabolic and physiologic and perhaps psychological functions seem to show some degree of periodicity resulting in diurnal cycles in metabolism, growth cycles, sexual cycles and seasonal cycles. He emphasizes the morning and evening alterations of depression and euphoria, premenstrual depression and seasonal variations in the incidence of mental illness. Von Economo (*207*) speaks of the tides of awareness and the tides of the autonomic spheres of function which he found to be dissociated in encephalitis lethargica. In frontal lobe disease, intrinsic normal periodic activities may become distorted. Frontal lobe lesions may give rise to disorders of the sleep wakefulness cycle and to agrypnia which however are not as frequent as hypersomnia. Various fluctuations of symptoms and signs including sharp cycling of mood (*788*) and other opposite clinical manifestations at various stages of the disease may occur. Experience with lobotomized patients suggest that the frontal lobes dampen the diurnal autonomic rhythmicity believed to be mediated by diencephalic centers (*95*).

PATTERNS OF DYSHOMEOSTASIS

Affective dyshomeostasis

The following are preliminary remarks on the nature and physiological significance of affective states which will be discussed in greater detail in various appropriate places. (See especially *Elements of a stimulus response psychology and psychopathology*, which follows.) The dynamic bipolarity of affective states corresponds to the basic experience of pleasure and displeasure or, for that matter, gratification and frustration. Suffice to say at this point that we regard affects as "psycho-autonomic" phenomena which, by and large, are a measure of biological equilibrium, and which tend to maintain or to reestablish it by virtue of their impulse character. Thus, affects are experiences which combine the properties of signals and impulses.

In frontal lobe disease, a previously well balanced affective level may be either inordinately lowered or heightened (*556, 967*), in other words, the signals are apt to be wrong and the impulses incongruous. In emotionally imbalanced persons who sustained accidental frontal lobe injuries, the type of post-traumatic mental abnormalities may be entirely different from those prevailing during the pretraumatic period of the disease (*399, 745*) and the same holds true for patients having been subjected to psychosurgical (*260, 659, 754*) and other procedures designed to alter diencephalo-frontal relations (*805*). Periodic fluctuations of the emotional level may also occur (*788*). Apart from diencephalic lesions, disturbances in affect behaviour and personality are most common in frontal lobe disease (*799*).

Visceral dyshomeostasis

Keeping in mind the nature of affects and emotions, as we see them, autonomic disturbances properly so-called should perhaps be referred to as *viscero-autonomic*. They include both purely vegetative functions as well as products of visceral and somatic integration. In both animals and man, respiration (*38, 188, 458, 681, 744*), gastrointestinal (*115, 152, 180, 830, 897*) and sexual function (*69, 634*), circulation of the blood, pupillary reactions, pilomotor and bladder function, the feeling of hunger (*318, 485. 704*) and thirst, kidney function (*593*), blood sugar levels and other metabolic states (*897*) may be influenced by frontal lobe lesions. Among 18 cases of central nervous system disease of various etiology, which were associated with hypernatremia and hyperchloremia, 16 involved either the diencephalon of the frontal lobes (*168*). Disturbances of the sleep mechanism have already been discussed from the view-point of responsiveness. In the viscero-autonomic sphere, too, there may be observed wide fluctuations around the homeostatic level. Following frontal lobotomy carried out in patients in which such disturbances existed prior to operation, there appears to develop a certain refractoriness to various pharmacological compounds which upset the · autonomic equilibrium, such as prostigmin, eserin, ephedrine and benzedrine. At the same time, the homeostatic control as compared to the preoperative state is altered (*761*).

Viscero-autonomic disturbances are frequently associated with disorders of affectivity and it is worthy of note that both may be subject to fluctuation and cycling.

COMPARATIVE PATHOPHYSIOLOGY OF DYSHOMEOSTASIS

The diencephalo-frontal system

Disturbance in *receptivity* at the diencephalic level are represented by disorders of the sleep wakefulness mechanism, such as hypersomnia, by insomnia, and by the already mentioned inversion of the sleep curve, as seen for instance in epidemic encephalitis.

Disorders of *affect* and related abnormalities are manifested by general heightening or depression of the emotional level (*70, 614, 952*). In tumors of the diencephalon (*10, 161*), loss of restraint, irritability, fits of rage from inadequate stimuli and marked swings of mood from depression to elation have been observed. A case of a patient with a small tumor of the hypothalamus (*877*), although studied by experienced observers, was erroneously diagnosed as a typical manic psychosis. Mental changes including complete lack of initiative, irascibility, neglectfulness, swinging mood, eroticism, apprehensiveness, agitation and aggressiveness are found in primary degenerative lesions of the thalamic nuclei (*876*).

Small isolated lesions in the medial thalamic nuclei produced by electrolysis in the human (*818, 819*) and bilateral occlusion of the tuberothalamic artery supplying these nuclei are apt to be followed by loss of initiative (*818, 819*). Hoheisl and Walch (*399*) noted manic-depressive symptoms in frontal lobe injuries in a statistically significant number of cases.

Viscero-autonomic disturbances in diencephalic lesions (extensively dealt with in most textbooks of physiology and enumerated here for completeness only), include sexual, cardiovascular, gastrointestinal and various metabolic dysfunction including abnormalities of the carbohydrate and fat metabolism and of the water balance.

Furthermore, disorders of the basic setting of the homeostatic mechanism are manifested by altered responses to various drugs, in other words, by altered reactivity (*229*). Depending on the response of the hypothalamo-pituitary system in the individual case, the effects of follicular hormones have been found to be different as to type and intensity. Pituitrin administered in cases of destruction of the tuber cinereum no longer causes depression of the blood fat level. In encephalitic processes involving the region of the third ventricle, inhibition of diuresis following administration of pituitrin fails to occur and, in cases of pituitary cachexia, leucocytosis following adrenaline injection is lacking. In post-encephalitic states, barbituates have been found to be less effective. What's more, in addition to the lack or the absence of typical reactions, there were observed paradoxical responses to various pharmacological agents including barbiturates (*749*).

Disorders involving both *mental* and *physical* functions in diencephalic lesions may be present in various periods of the disease. Within a given span of time, there may occur spontaneous alternations between clinical manifestations of opposite type, such as between adiposity and emaciation, oliguria and polyuria, and between mental depression and euphoria. Adiposity may be combined with diabetes insipidus. In other cases, adiposity is accompanied by periods of depression while cachexia is associated with euphoric states and vice versa. Abnormalities of the water metabolism may alternate with emotional disturbances (*229*).

The following case of a manic-depressive patient (*488*) is of interest from various angles. (a) In depression, increased sleep was associated with salt and water retention. In the manic phases, on the other hand, sleeplessness was accompanied by the release of salt and water. (b) Following injection of pituitrin, diuresis and dilution of urine continued to occur earlier in the manic phase. (c) Depression corresponded to a normal night pattern, that is, a state of parasympathetic preponderance, while mania corresponded to a normal day pattern, or relative sympathetic hyperactivity. (See also J. L. Crammer's paper on "Water and Sodium in Two Psychotics," The Lancet, May 1959, p. 1121; 24 references.)

The last mentioned observation supports the notion of sympathico-parasympathetic imbalance involved in abnormalities of affectivity and drive. In any case, both the general picture and its modifications induced by the administration of pituitrin adduce further evidence—if such be needed—of the intimate relationship between autonomic and affective manifestations.

The above cited observations taken in conjunction with the occurrence of homeostatic disorders previously described represent a large body of evidence in support of the representation of both *autonomic* and *affective functions* in the frontal lobe and, at the same time, of an apparently quite similar role of the diencephalo-frontal system in regard to both visceral regulations and affectivity.

This concept does not, of course, exclude additional representations of visceral and affective functions in parts of the brain other than the frontal lobes.

The limbic lobe

Brown and Schaefer (*125*), Bucy and Klüver (*129*) and Smith (*846*) produced profound alterations in emotional behaviour by temporal lobe extirpations in monkeys which were for all practical purposes duplicated by Terziem and Dalle Ore (*899*) in man. Clinically, euphoria, lack of concern and overplacidity, frequently seen in patients with tumors of the temporal lobe, are comparable to the tameness and the absence of manifestations of fear in the animals operated upon (*799*). Not only have visceral and autonomic responses been produced by stimulation of certain parts of the temporal lobe, but there is both experimental and clinical evidence to suggest that the cerebral cortex outside the frontal and tem-poral lobe serves autonomic in addition to somatic functions.

That part of the temporal lobe from which *visceral responses* were obtained (*13, 157, 455, 456, 595, 596, 735, 738, 926, 927*) was found to be continuous with the posterior orbital surface of the frontal lobe, to include the anterior insula, the subcallosal region and also basal olfactory structures, namely, the uncus gyri hippocampi, the limen insulae and the anterior perforated space. Histologically, these regions, which correspond in general to Broca's "grand lobe limbique" (*118*), were found to be covered either by allocortex or transitional cortex. Those parts of the temporal lobe from which *visceral responses* were elicited belong to a large extent to the cingulate cortex. Since, following their removal, the affective responses of the animals were found to be altered (*45, 845*), and disease processes involving the anterior cingulate gyri (*42, 308, 686, 687, 688*) and cingulectomies (*954*) produce similar effects, it is very likely that the centers in question are at the same time concerned with affective reactions. The two types of cortex are extensively interconnected by a variety of fiber systems, and cannot be sharply separated from each other by cytoarchitectonic standards. Thus, visceral and autonomic functions appear to have both an archipallial and a neopallial representation. It is not unreasonable to assume that, in lower forms, visceral and "pre-emotional" experiences were mediated by the olfactory or allocortex. *With rise in the phylogenetic scale, stimuli other than olfactory were projected to the cerebral cortex via thalamus, and the thalamo-cortical apparatus, because of numerous and manifold stimuli it received from the periphery, became increasingly important. Ultimately, in man, the olfactory mechanism was relegated to a near vestigial organ.* Additional evidence for the twofold representation of viscero-autonomic and psycho-autonomic in the brain will be offered in the following paragraphs.

Herrick (*375*), who studied the problem from the viewpoint of the comparative anatomist, expressed the belief that impulses originating in the olfactory cortex activate the neocortex and thereby influence the affective tone of experience. In this connection, it is important to note that the Ammon's horn and the dentate gyrus, in whose large pyramidal cells the fornix arises, are no longer recognized as primary olfactory receiving stations, although the convolutions in question are extensively connected with the primary olfactory centers in the gyrus ambiens and similunaris. Brodal (119, 120) and Papez (665) suggested that the emotive process is "built up" in the hippocampus and transmitted to the cingulate gyrus and the remaining parts of the neocortex by way of the fornix, mamillo-hypothalamic tract and anterior thalamic radiation. However, bilateral extirpation of the hippocampus and section of the fornix performed, in dogs, by Allan (6) and, in man, by Dott (201) and by v. Wagenen and Herren (923), failed to influence emotional behaviour. Spiegel and his associates (253) who carried out similar experiments with both positive and negative findings, could not exclude the possibility of concomitant lesions to neighbouring structures, which rendered difficult the interpretation of their results. Obrader's (695) temporal lobotomies performed on two schizophrenic patients were inconclusive, the description of the operations suggesting that the fasciculus uncinatus rather than the hippocampus was severed. Brown and Schaefer (105) performed the already mentioned bilateral temporal lobe ablations in monkeys as early as 1888. The animals became tame and exhibited obvious memory and intellectual deficit in that they seemed to have entirely forgotten previous experiences. Furthermore, they showed what appeared to be increased curiosity, from which however they did not profit, and lack of understanding of sounds, sights and other stimuli. As we have already indicated these observations were confirmed by Bucy and Klüver (129) who observed, in addition, the development of carnivorous habits and of increased sexual appetite in their experimental animals. The results of Bucy's and Klüver's experiments are difficult to reconcile with those seen in cats following similar operations; in fact, Bard and Mountcastle (43) who performed these experiments, state that their results are not only at variance with Bucy's and Klüver's observations but also with Papez' theory. However, they are in essential agreement with those of Spiegel and his associates (855).

While the aggregate evidence does not fully support the views expressed by Herrick and Papez, the role of the limbic lobe including its temporal segment should not be dismissed without further consideration. It might be profitable to reformulate certain propositions and to outline the problem in question from a somewhat different angle.

The fornix is a derivative of the inner limbic arc, a primordial gyrus extending from the hippocampal formation of the temporal lobe to the septal region of the frontal lobe. The inner limbic arc having differentiated to the fornix differs from other gyri in two fundamental aspects: (a) lacking gray matter, it is relegated to a conduction or transmitting system and (b) its cortico-cortical component, which connects the hippocampal with the septal region, is reduced to a minimum while the bulk of its fibers terminates in the diencephalon as the cortico-mamillary tract. This arrangement implies that the shunt of impulses from the archipallium to the diencephalon takes precedence over the direct cortico-cortical (hippocampo-septal) route, in other words, that the mobilization of autonomic (and, perhaps, neurograndular) activity is essential in the interest of whatever function the fornix system including the anterior thalamic nucleus and cingular gyrus may subserve. Since the fornix fibers originate close to the cortical receiving stations of the olfactory sense and, possibly, also the archipallial centre of taste, it may be that the neural chains linking the archipallium with the neopallium via the diencephalon subserve neurodynamic processes underlying the satisfaction of hunger and thirst. These activities require not only the integration of somatic and autonomic functions but are associated with increased affectivity. For similar reasons as well as the importance of olfactory stimuli and the participation of obvious oral tendencies consideration should be given to the possible significance of the fornix system for the satisfaction of the sexual drive (62, 799). Reeth and his associates (750a) reported four cases of temporal lobe tumor with psychoepileptic attacks involving sexual arousal and orgasm. On the other hand, nymphomania was also observed in parasagittal tumors in which case it might have occurred incident to irritation of the bladder center in the frontal lobes.

Since the autonomic fiber connections between archipallium and diencephalon (3, 735) and those between the latter and the neocortex, especially the frontal lobes, are well established and there appears to be no valid reasons to doubt their physiologic implications—indeed the representation of the most fundamental needs in the archipallium would appear only natural—it is suggested that the absence of physiologic effects following section of the fornices is due to the existence of collateral pathways, namely, (a) the medial forebrain bundle which links the rhinen- cephalon with the hypothalamus and (b) the sys- tem of periventricular fibers which connect the latter with the dorso-medial nucleus of the thalamus.

The fornix system and the medial forebrain bundle lie in close approximation at a point where the latter crosses the mamillo-thalamic tract. Accordingly, we might expect symmet- rically placed and sufficiently large lesions to in- volve the area of virtual contact between the two fiber systems and to produce tameness in pre- viously wild and intractable animals or to abolish emotional responses altogether. This appears to have been the case in Rhesus monkeys observed by Ranson (748) in which bilateral destruction of the mamillary bodies and the lateral hypothala- mic areas (through which the medial forebrain bundle courses) was produced by means of the Horsley-Clarke instrument. Similar suppression of emotional responses was observed in cats which had been operated upon by Ingram and his associates (418) and in which, as far as can be determined from the illustrations included in their publication, practically identical lesions had been produced. It would seem, then, that the in- juries described represent the optimal lesions capable of producing lack of emotional responses although this point was nowhere particularly stressed in the two papers which deal with the problems of sleep and catalepsy. Spiegel a. ass. (858), who placed electrolytic lesions in the pos- terolateral hypothalamus in cases in which electro-coagulation of the medial nuclei of the thalamus failed to produce the desired therapeu- tic effect, and who thereby succeeded in improving the results of their original method, might have been guided by similar considerations. Meyer and Hunter (644), who produced akinetic and apathetic states in cats by lesions in the antero-medial thalamus and the mamillo-thalamic tract concluded from their experiments that the limbic system (including its subcortical connec- tions) is concerned with affective functions. (See also Ward 930).

From the foregoing we may infer that the *archipallial centers of the limbic region hold in check primitive oral and sexual reflexes, and perhaps also emotional responses of a more general nature* (799). McLean (595, 596) and Bente and Kluge (63) reported additional evidence in support of this theory. The latter observed hypersexualism associated with the uncus-syndrome while

McLean made reference to Rosvold's (775) patients who, following bitemporal lobe ablations, exhibited the tendency to eat food and non-food objects. He believes that the "limbic portion of the fronto-temporal region is organized around the oral activities of the animal as they pertain to feeding and to vocalization, attack and defense involved in obtaining food and that the memories and feelings related to Edinger's (210) *oral sense* are partially integrated and tied into the workings of the brain as a whole." McLean seems to be in essential agreement with Marshall (622) who found that feeding reactions are impaired in proportion to the extent of damage to the rhinen- cephalon and that the "basal olfactory cortex together with the associative ventral portion of the striatum and the lower centers with which it is connected are capable of elaborating feeding reactions of a highly complicated nature." Uncin- ate attacks in man in which smacking movements may be conspicuous are perhaps activated rudi- ments of the feeding reflexes described.

It is worthwhile at this point to pause in our analysis in order to speculate along more general lines.

Reflections on the Organizational Framework of the Nervous System

The above presented data, more precisely, the seemingly parallel representation in the frontal and limbic lobes of both viscero-autonomic and psycho-autonomic functions suggest the existence of a "double brain," made up of (a) an *olfactory*, or *archipallial component* and (b) of a *non-olfac- tory*, or *neopallial component*. By and large, it would seem that the former is represented by the orbitocingular cortex of the forebrain, the latter by the remaining part of the cortex. Admittedly the boundaries of the two subdivisions of the fore- brain cortex are not clear cut. The orbito-cingular cortex represents a transitional pallial formation wherein the olfactory and the non-olfactory brain "overlap." Although, with rise in the mammalian scale, the latter becomes increasingly prominent both anatomically and physiologically, the or- ganizational patterns of the two "sub-brains" which are linked together in the *archi-neopallial junction* appear to be basically identical; either is equipped with afferents and efferents; and both cortices are connected with subcortical centers, some of which (both anatomically and physiologically) are related to both divisions. The expression "double-brain" is of course not to be taken literally. Rather, in the course of evolution, the new parts of the brain which, in the words of Elliot Smith (842, 843) "were added appeared at the periphery of the older regions which, hence, became limbic and the cerebral cortex of the lower vertebrates became relegated in the mammal to the region immediately surrounding the hilum of the hemisphere, thereby constituting what is known as the true limbic lobe." Economo and Koskinas (208) were probably the first who postulated, on the basis of cytoarchitectonic studies, that the limbic lobe is concerned with olfactory-motor responses. At the same time they stipulated the representation of the autonomic nervous system in this region chiefly on the basis of the intimate connections between olfactory and autonomic functions. (See also Kremer, 513.) A more complete account of the role of the two subdivisions of the hemispheres of the brain will be attempted following the description of their connections and their physiology.

The *somato-sensory, somato-motor* and *autonomic* centers and pathways which developed in association with the cortical olfactory areas, and which were discovered by the use of modern physiological methods, are quite numerous. (a) In the *afferent* sphere, Robinson and Lennox (768) were able to record electrical responses to click stimuli chiefly from the anterior portion of the hippocampus and, following single shock stimuli to the optic nerves, additional potentials from the amygdaloid nucleus. Stimuli to the sciatic nerves produced responses chiefly from the midportion of the hippocampus and the posterior portion of the cingulate gyrus. According to Mac Lean (596) spike potentials may be evoked in receptive parts of the hipocampal formation by vagal, auditory, visual and somatic stimulation, and the limbic system has afferents related to all sensory modalities.

(b) The main *efferent* pathway from the limbic portion of the temporal lobe is the fornix or hippocampo-mamillary tract already referred to, but there is some evidence to suggest that impulses from the hippocampus may pass directly to lower centers, notably the midbrain (17, 743, 735). The amygdala discharges into the hypothalamic and septal nuclei by way of the stria terminalis. Schneider and Crosby (811) discovered a second or additional motor area at the tip of the temporal lobe of the monkey. McLean and Delgado (597) traced points yielding contraversion responses from the anterior limbic center of the cat through the internal capsule near the genu of the corpus callosum. According to Baldwin a. ass. (41), stimulation of the mesial temporal region in man is followed by movements of the ipsilateral face and the jaws if the tip of the electrode is very near the amygdala. Similar movements could be elicited in the monkey following bilateral removal of the cortical representation of the face, lips, jaws and tongue combined with bilateral removal of the lateral temporal cortex.

In addition to sensory and motor centers the limbic portion of the temporal lobe comprises chiefly the piriform area which receives olfactory fibers indirectly, that is, from the secondary olfactory cortex in the entorhinal area. The latter is believed to be an associational mechanism by means of which olfactory impulses are brought into relationship with other afferents and with autonomic stimuli. The entorhinal area and the remaining part of the hippocampal cortex are not concerned with olfactory functions only as may be inferred from the fact that they are proportionally larger in man than in macrosmatic animals, that their areal organization is more elaborate, that hippocampus and fornix are present in anosmatic or nearly anosmatic animals and also in some human cases of absence of the olfactory brain.

(c) As already indicated, *autonomic centers* in the temporal portion of the limbic lobe were found in both man and animals. Wall and Davis (926) demonstrated that stimulation of the cortex of the medial surface of the temporal lobe and the amygdala produce marked changes in blood pressure and respiration, while Smith (845) obtained marked rise in blood pressure followed by micturation in cats, and bradycardia and changes in arterial pressure by stimulation of the posterior pirifirm area in monkeys. Similar responses may be obtained from the cingulate region. According to Powell and associates (736) hypothalamic seizure activity can be elicited by stimulation of amygdala, hippocampus, hippocampal gyrus, septal nuclei and basal olfactory structures. Chapman and his coworkers (157) describe elevation of both systolic and diastolic blood pressure on electrical stimulation of the tip of the temporal lobe while stimulation of the anterior portion of the limbic lobe along with the posterior orbital surface produced not only vascular changes but also respiratory changes. Kaada, Pribram and Epstein (*459*) elicited respiratory and vascular responses from the temporal pole, the insula, the orbital surface of the frontal lobe and the cingulate gyrus in the monkey. According to Kaada and Jasper (*458*) stimulation of part of the insula, the temporal pole, anterior hippocampus and limbic cortex in conscious man produces respiratory arrest of the same character than in the monkey. In view of similar experiences with orbital-frontal lesions in man reported by Ethelberg (*215*) it is worthy of note that, in some patients, cessation of respiration was accompanied by a feeling of tiredness and sleepiness associated with a tendency to close the eyes, and with impairment of consciousness. Kaada, Anderson and Jansen (*456*) produced, by stimulation of the phylogenetically older anteromedial division of the amydala, "low level sympathetic effects" i.e., viscero-motor changes, including pupillodilation, salivation, micturition, piloerection and alimentary reflexes associated with contraversive movements; by the stimulation of the phylogenetically younger basilateral division of the amygdala, "high level sympathetic responses", including anxiety, bewilderment, fear, rage, anger and fury. On the whole, the responses resembled those previously elicited by stimulation of the hippocampal, medial prefrontal, limbic, retrosplenial and hippocampal gyrus region. These observations would seem to indicate a close functional relationship between the structures involved. In view of the relationships between the phenomena of affectivity and attention to be discussed later it is of particular interest "that the attention of the animals appeared to be fixed on something in the environment which they seemed to experience".

Lastly, certain observations suggest that the temporal portion of the limbic lobe is concerned with the regulation of *responsiveness* to stimuli, which we regard to be a specialized *autonomic function*. Sloan and Kaada (*841*) found not only that anterior limbic induced movements depended on subcortical projections but that they may influence the functions of the widespread cortical areas as evidenced by diffuse electroencephalographic responses particularly from the precentral motor cortex. Arduini and Moruzzi (*25, 26*) concluded from their experiments on cats that the olfactory and the reticular activating impulses

converge on the cephalic areas of the activating system as, after midbrain transection, the responsiveness of the isolated brain to arousal stimuli was found to be markedly decreased. Only the most active sensory modalities including olfactory stimuli were able to produce widespread disorganization of cortical rhythms. Conversely, the electric activity of the olfactory bulb may be synchronized by stimulating recruiting areas in the thalamus. A corollary of these findings is the observation that bulbo-reticular stimulation, eliciting generalized arousal reaction, is able to disorganize the thalamically induced but not the peripheral synchronization of the olfactory bulb. Thus, the above cited experiments would seem to confirm the existence of two mechanisms, an *olfactory* and a *non-olfactory*; a certain measure of independence notwithstanding, they are *centrally integrated and, at least in macrosmatic animals, jointly responsive to activating impulses from two mutually independent sources*. According to Anand and Brobeck (*16*) lesions in the amygdaloid nucleus in rats produce marked diminution of spontaneous activity and tameness while cats in which similar lesions were produced failed to develop rage reactions. Shealy and Peele (*829*) who stimulated the amygdala in cats observed autonomic and somatic behavioural reactions combining the former two. They included a state of attention, a reaction of fear or one of undirected rage. The authors concluded that the amygdaloid nucleus has autonomic and functional relations with the hypothalamus which may or may not be the exclusive channel for the amygdala effects. Weisskrantz (*842*) observed a marked increase in tameness and a weakening or disappearance of fear responses to previously aversive stimuli in "amygdala monkeys." He believes that amygdalectomy makes it difficult for animals to identify reinforcing stimuli but admits the virtual impossibility to define what constitutes the reinforcing stimulus. Olds' (*696*) view that amygdalectomy produces lack of discrimination of "motivationally significant stimuli" is likewise difficult to accept, at least introspective experiences of patients with organic lesions indicate that they recognize the motivational relevancy of stimuli in a rather abstract fashion as it were and that the affective loading of the stimuli is inadequate or discordant.

We concluded our discussion of the diencephalo-frontal system with the statement that its functional organization does not exclude the representation, in the extrafrontal parts of the brain, of visceral and affective functions. This was confirmed by the above discussed physiological investigations which, moreover, demonstrated that the temporal lobes mediate, in addition to visceral functions, somato-sensory and somato-motor functions. (See also Adley and Meyer, *3*.)

To *summarize, the forebrain of the lower vertebrates is composed essentially of the diencephalon and the archipallial (olfactory) portion. In higher vertebrates, it comprises the diencephalon, the archipallium and the neopallium.* The latter develops concomitantly with the ingrowth of neurons (serving vision, hearing and other non-olfactory stimuli) from the thalamus into the pallial portion of the more primitive brain of fishes. In other words, the forebrain cortex of the *higher vertebrates embodies the endstations of both olfactory and non-olfactory impulses which are thereby brought into mutual relationships at the highest integrative level of the nervous system. The brain of higher forms is the product of the amalgamation, at the archi-neopallial junction, of (a) the olfactory cortex with (b) the cortical provinces subserving vision, hearing, taste and the diverse somesthetic modalities shunted to it by way of the lateral division of the thalamus and its derivatives, the lateral and medial geniculate bodies.* Thus, the archi-neopallial junction which, by and large, corresponds to the limbic lobe, is that part of the forebrain where the olfactory and the non-olfactory cortex "overlap" or "merge." At the same time, the olfactory cortex proper is relegated to a near vestigial organ.

The coexistence of two "highest levels," i.e., a *unisensory* level, derived from the olfactory inflow, and a *pluri-sensory*, non-olfactory level, is a formidable complication of the basic architectonic pattern of the nervous system which renders difficult the interpretation of the relationships between structure and function. Moreover, it raises the following question: Is the twofold organization of the cerebral hemispheres a singularity or the expression of a general principle? To us, it suggests that the organism tends to develop a response determinating apparatus of a more general character at the site of any sensory inflow at any level of the nervous system and that this tendency (apart from the development of efferents) comes to the fore in the association of the *leading* afferent with secondary afferents. For

example, the leading afferents to the archineopallial portion of the temporal lobe are olfactory, while those to the cerebellum are vestibular in character. In either case, however, subsidiary (secondary) afferents are represented by visual, auditory and somesthetic pathways whose connections, in turn, may be interpreted as oriment of the elaborative cortex as defined in the introductory chapter. No doubt the term "primary cortical area of correlation" employed by Bremer (*109a*) refers to a similar neural arrangement. It designates the projection, to a sensory area, of several sense modalities which have in common their relation to posture and spatial relations. The "composite projection areas" in the cerebral cortex of the cat described by Mickle and Ades (*647a*) belong to an identical category of nerve centers. However, these data have not been made use of in the general interpretation of nervous system function, that is, in mapping out of a framework of nervous system organization.

The shift of dominance to the forebrain-"subsidiaries"especially the representation in the forebrain of the telereceptors was an event of the utmost importance in the phylogenesis of the vertebrates, in fact, its significance in biology is comparable to the birth of a new star in the history of the heavens. By contrast, the diverse non-vestibular afferents of the cerebellum (which have already been mentioned in the opening chapter) are probably of minor significance. The ubiquity of reflex collaterals, the plurisegmental projection of the motor cortex to the spinal cord and the overlapping of various sensory modalities in the lateral nucleus of the thalamus (*307*) would seem to be further suggestive evidence of the plurifocal organization of the nervous system. In sharp contrast to the universal representation of the striated musculature in the precentral gyrus in the human however, the individual *efferents* control only a limited segment of (chiefly extra-pyramidal) pathways. Moreover, as compared to the precentral gyrus, the structures in question are poorly differentiated and their functional scope is limited. This of course is not to say that the pyramidal tract is the efferent of the somesthetic sphere. On the contrary, it is the pathway which mediates responses to the integrated modalities of sensation.

The notion that a *plurality of response determinating mechanisms* exists which develop in close association with the terminals of inflow from *various sources* (and of which the archi-neopallial junction appears to be merely a special instance) may be readily correlated with Jackson's (*421*) and Sherrington's (*831*) ideas on the general organization of the nervous system. Jackson wrote that "in no two of the higher centers of the nervous system is the organism represented in quite the same way." Evidently, the organism is not "in quite the same way" represented in the olfactory and the non-olfactory centers. According to Sherrington the "rank of a center in the neural hierarchy is the degree to which paths from separate loci and of different receptive modality are confluent therein." As applied to the olfactory "center" and the non-olfactory "center" their rank is different in that the latter receives paths issuing from separate loci and of different receptive modality.

We are now in a position to apply the above formulated principles to certain pertinent aspects of nervous system organization, namely, the *subdivision of the neocortex into an anterior and a posterior segment, the differentiation of cortical motor centers into a pyramidal and extrapyramidal group, the cortical representation of autonomic functions, and to other mechanism.* For simplicity, the various features will be defined in terms of arbitrary developmental stages. (See figures 3 to 7.) The terms "stage," "differentiation," etc., should not be taken literally but, rather, regarded as constructs to be discarded once they have served their purpose to illustrate the principle that the highest levels of the nervous system are elaborations of the lower grades.

In fig. 3A, the six-layered neocortical pattern has been simplified to a three-layered arrangement of neurons comprising (a) a *superficial* (supragranular) lamina, (b) an *intermediate* (granular) lamina and (c) a *lower* (infragranular) lamina. The supergranular layer is essentially *associative*, the granular layer sensory, or *receptive*, and the infragranular layer, motor, or *emissive*. In other words, the granular layer receives afferent fibers from the same level and from lower levels, while the cells of the supragranular layer establish patterned relationships between each other and the infra-adjacent layers. On the whole, the supragranular layer corresponds to a system of associational nuclei while the granular layer represents a system of sensory nuclei; and the infragranular layer a system of motor nuclei. At a still earlier stage of differentiation of the neo-

cortex the three layers and, hence, the individual cell may be assumed to be equivalent, corresponding to a stage of organization most nearly realized in Tunicates, (*577*). A certain equivalence, however, prevails even in the differentiated, three-layered cortex. In the words of Lorente de Nò, "all cells of every layer are in contact with afferent fibers so that every layer is a receptive one; and all cells of every layer send fibers to all others, every layer associates and as, from every layer with the exception of the first fibers are going to the white substance, every layer may be an effective one."

Fig. 3B shows the subdivision of the neocortex into an *anterior* and a *posterior* portion, which is brought about by the increase of the infragranular (emissive) stratum in the former, and a concomitant increase of the granular (receptive) layer in the latter. In other words, the anterior cortex becomes *predominantly motor* and the posterior cortex *predominantly sensory*. The rolandic fissure indicates, in a general way, the boundary between the two cortices. (See also figs. 1 and 2.)

Both the anterior and the posterior cortex (fig. 3C) receive, and give rise to, fibers which serve *autonomic functions* (dotted line) and neurons which serve *somatic functions* (solid line). In other words, the two cortices are equipped with autonomic afferents and efferents and, at the same time, somatic afferents and efferents.

At a subsequent stage of development (fig. 3D) the autonomic fibers have differentiated (1) into neurons innervating the viscera, blood vessels, etc, that is, *viscero-motor* and *viscero-sensory* fibers properly so called and (2) into neurons controlling the *general responsiveness* of the three layered cellular complex.

Fig. 3E illustrates the differentiation of the two classes of autonomic fibers into an afferent and an efferent category. The subcortical connections of the autonomic afferents and efferents (fig. 3F) may be outlined as follows.

The bulk of the *viscero-sensory afferents* reaches the cortex by way of the spinal cord, the lower brainstem and a nuclear complex formed by the hypothalamus and the anterior and medial nucleus of the dorsal thalamus and the intralamellar nuclei. The bulk of the *viscero-motor* efferents may be thought of as a complex of recursive connections which reaches the periphery via the same nuclei, the lower brainstem and the spinal cord.

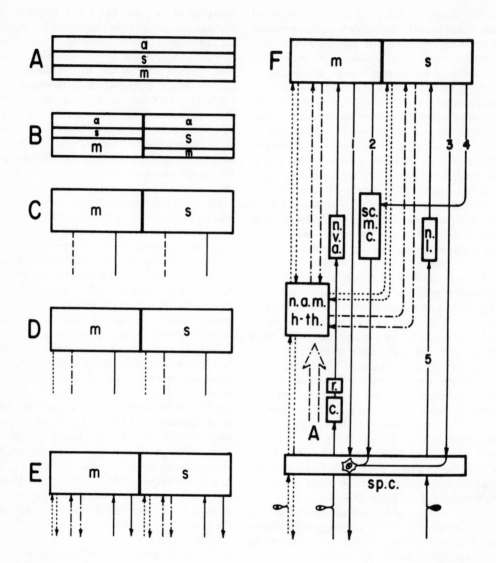

Fig. 3. The basic categories of sensory and motor cortical neurons and their subcortical connections.

A and B: a—predominantly associative cortical layers; s—predominantly sensory cortical layers; m—predominantly motor cortical layers.

C: m—predominantly motor cortex; s—predominantly sensory cortex; solid lines—somatic cortico-subcortical connections; dotted lines—autonomic cortico-subcortical connections.

D: solid lines—somatic cortico-subcortical connections; punctated lines—viscero-autonomic cortico-subcortical connections; dash-dotted lines—responsiveness regulating cortico-subcortical connections.

E: solid arrows—afferent and efferent somatic cortico-subcortical connections; punctated arrows—afferent and efferent viscero-autonomic cortico-subcortical connections; dash-dotted arrows—afferent and efferent responsiveness regulating cortico-subcortical connections.

F: c.—cerebellum; n.a.m., h-th.—Nucl. anter. and med. thalami, and hypothalamus; n.l.—Thalamus, nucl. lat.; n.v.a.—Thalamus, nucl. ventr. ant.; r—nucl. ruber; sc.m.c.—subcortical motor centers; sp.c.—spinal cord;

1: precentro-spinal tract (pyramidal tract); 2: fronto-extrapyramidal tracts; 3: postcentro-spinal tracts; 4: postcentro-extrapyramidal tracts; 5: somato-sensory tracts; Arrow A: bulbo-diencephalic activating system.

The viewpoint here taken is that the (autonomic) *responsiveness regulating neurons* constitute the *activating systems* and that they differentiate into a caudal and a cranial division. The former corresponds to the "activating system of the axial core of the brainstem" of Moruzzi and Magoun (*664*); the latter to the "diffuse thalamic projection system" of Starzl and Magoun (*865*). (For our purpose, this simplification may suffice.) We propose to call the caudal division the *bulbo-diencephalic alerting system;* the cranial division, the *diencephalo-cortical alerting system.*

(a) *The bulbo-diencephalic alerting system.* According to Starzl, Taylor and Magoun (*866*) the caudal portion, which is composed of short internuncial neurons, is distributed in the reticular formation of the medulla, the tegmentum of the pons and midbrain, the ventromedial portion of the thalamus, the subthalamus and hypothalamus. Direct stimulation of the bulbo-thalamic system produces an arousal to alertness and, electroencephalographically, a desynchronization of the electrical potentials. For further EEG data, see especially ref. 573. The effects of peripheral stimulation and those of a probing electrode are identical. When activated near its upper end, the caudal portion exerts a pronounced facilitatory influence on lower outflows so that its functions normally both in the descending and ascending direction subserving, on the one hand, facilitation and, on the other, the central alertness that characterizes the waking state (*575*). By contrast, stimulation of the lower end of the caudal division causes motor inhibition (*292, 606*). Thus, we might add, the physiology of the alerting system exemplifies the integration of autonomic and motor (including extrapyramidal and vestibulo-cerebellar) activity at lower levels of brain function. (We have already indicated that a similar arrangement exists at upper brain stem levels and also cortical, especially frontal levels. In other words, autonomic stimuli influence both the sensory and the motor systems of the neuraxis.) Acute lesions of the cephalic portion of the caudal division of the activating system abolish the electroencephalographic pattern of wakefulness (*573*). In chronic experiments, this is followed by persisting somnolence and irreversible coma (*616*). On the whole, *the system in question maintains an alert and attentive state rendering the animal capable of reacting adaptively to stimuli, and it mediates discriminatory and also* *affective responses.* Following destruction of the system, monkeys become even more unresponsive that cats and show greater disturbances in the electrical activity which, because of their higher degree of encephalization as compared to the former, suggests that the apparatus in question plays an even greater role in the human. Its multisynaptic internuncial organization makes the activating system more susceptible to anaesthetic blockade than the paucisynaptic lateral pathways (*266, 807, 867*). With increasing depth of anesthesia the electro-cortical responses are limited to the specific projection areas while arousal reactions and hypothalamic activation are absent. Barbiturates appear to block the reticular relays in the brainstem (*79, 262, 295, 296, 605*).

The discovery of the system in question was foreshadowed by older experimental and clinical experiences. Hill, Spencer and Horseley (*384*), Breslauer (*110*) and Reichardt (*752*) observed unconsciousness due to mechanical injury to the medulla oblongata. According to Foerster (*242*) digital compression of the bulb gives rise to a feeling of thirst and great fatigue. Continued pressure causes unconsciousness, bradycarcia, stertorous inspiration and, eventually, tonic fits. Kleist (*493*) believes that lesions in the region of the visceral vagal nuclei produce fluctuations between lucidity and depression of consciousness which he is inclined to attribute to changes in the interplay between sympathetic and parasympathetic stimuli similar to those operating in the hypothalamic region. Upon retraction of the cerebellar tonsil in the course of the exposure of an acoustic tumor (*803*) I observed immediate onset of consciousness which lasted over a period of 20 minutes. Claude Bernard's piqure of the floor of the fourth ventricle in unanaesthetized animals produces instantaneous unconsciousness, similar observations having been made in man in cases of injury to the bulb on attempted cisternal puncture. Other pertinent data were published by Bailey and Davis (*39*), Magoun (*604*), Macrae (*599*), Andler (*19*) and others. It must not be concluded from these observations that consciousness is "localized" in the lowest levels of the brain, but it is legitimate to infer that the physiological states underlying consciousness depend on physiological states mediated by lower brain levels.

(b) *The diencephalo-cortical alerting system* issues mainly from the nuclei of the internal and external medullary lamina of the thalamus and terminates in a more or less diffuse fashion in all parts of the cortex (321, 342, 437, 438, 594). According to Papez (707) the reticular nucleus is the last link in the non-specific path to the cortex for electroencephalographic rhythms related to general consciousness. French and associates (264) found that corticofugal fibers reach the anterior central neuraxis (evidently, the authors refer to the junction between the caudal and the cranial alerting system) from the frontal convexity of the brain, the cingulate gyrus, the orbital surface of the frontal lobes, the motor and sensory projections, the para-occipital region, the parietal area and the temporal lobe. Neuronographically, they go on to say, such connections have been demonstrated to arise from the prefrontal, cingulate, orbital, precentral, "suppressor," parietal and temporal area. *The diencephalo-cortical alerting system activates most of the very same areas which are the points of origin of recursive (descending) fibers.** There is an interplay of activity between the cortex and the central thalamus and tegmental brainstem. Diffuse disorganization of the electrocorticogram as well as behavioural arousal can be induced only by stimulation of cortical loci projecting to the reticular activating system of the axial core of the brainstem, which suggests that the very same neuronal systems operate under physiological conditions. In conclusion, they assert that "these cortico-subcortical mechanisms may then participate in such aspects of consciousness as voluntary alerting, maintenance of the arousal state, focusing of attention vigilance or perhaps 'set' and mediation and introspection. An associated function which cortico-fugal fibers may exert by way of the cephalic brainstem concerns the modulation of the sensory input to the brainstem." Of particular importance is the point made by French and his associates (264) namely, that "*these same cortical regions projecting to the cephalic brainstem are also identified with well-known important cortical autonomic fields and that, by means of their cortico-diencephalic, cortico-mesencephalic and cortico-bulbar projections, these cortical regions gain direct access to the principle autonomic stations in the hypothalamus and the neuraxis below it.*" (Emphasis added.) In other words, they call attention to the fact that the very same systems of neurons which mediate the ascending arousal mechanism is itself under the

* Emphasis added.

influence of impulses descending in the corticofugal pathways. Moreover, since most autonomic representations are found in the frontal lobes, it may be assumed that a considerable contingent of alerting fibers has a frontal orientation (263, 664, 868). According to Jasper (437), the system in question is a complex of neurons which issue "at least partially from the reticular formation of the diencephalon and midbrain and which regulate the elaboration of efferent impulses within the sensory receiving areas of the cortex." The thalamic portion of this system including its recursive connections (439, 586) may be thought of "as a mechanism for the central control of attentive processes and, at the same time, as a differentiation of the general arousal mechanism which is mediated through lower portions of the reticular formation." Loss of consciousness in petit mal attacks (440) seems to be related to excessive abnormal discharges within the diencephalic alerting system (which has diffuse bilateral projections) while excessive stimulation of its caudal segment causes convulsions. Recursive connections were also described by Graf and Magoun (316a). Baird a. ass. (40) produced, in addition to viscero-autonomic responses, a "reaction of alertness" by stimulation of the anterior nucleus of the thalamus in cats, while Hanberry a. ass. (342) found a heavy concentration of non-specific fibers in the nucleus ventralis anterior of the thalamus and, like Sharpley and Jasper (8286) maintain that the non-specific alerting system is somatotopically differentiated, that is, that arousal reactions are specific for the different sensory modalities. It would thus appear that the diencephalo-cortical alerting system is connected not only with the reticular and intralamellar nuclei but with other thalamic nuclei as well. It is with this view in mind that fig. 4 has been designed which, to maintain unity of presentation, shows the origin of the unspecific system in the major nuclei of the thalamus, including the nucleus ventralis anterior.

The neurophysiological phenomena described bring to mind certain clinical observations. Meyer and Hunter (610) found that localized electrocoagulation of the diencephalon in cats in the vicinity of the mamillo-thalamic tract and adjacent structures reduces the responsiveness of the animals. Barris and Schuman (42) saw, in addition to low level autonomic disorders, apathy, akinesia and mutism in bilateral cingulate gyrus lesions in man. (See also *898, 875, 649, 647, 648*.) Penfield and Jasper (*679*) described an exploration of the third ventricle under local anaesthesia during which pressure upon its medial wall produced an episode of transitory stupor and coma. Cairns and his associates (*130*) reported the case of a patient with a dermoid cyst of the third ventricle which had produced akinetic mutism but the evacuation of the cyst by aspiration of its contents would "awaken" the patient within a few minutes. Mettlach (*600*) described peculiar attacks of loss of consciousness, flaccidity of the extremities, pallor, short respiratory arrest, areflexia of the pupils and increased sweating which occurred in the course of frontal lobe tumors. Similar observations were published by Ethelberg (*201*).

The authors who studied the physiology of the activating systems conjectured that it has to do with attention and other higher cerebral functions but did not speculate about the intimate relationship between alerting and intellective functions. This question will be taken up later, in connection with the neuropsychology of attention and memory. (Cf., e.g., fig. 9 and accompanying text.)

(3) Certain somato-sensory afferents concerned with *equilibrating and tone-regulating functions,* that is, ascending fibertracts shunted to the neo-cortex by way of the lateral columns of the spinal cord, the cerebellum and red nucleus, reach the anterior cortex via the nucleus ventralis anterior of the thalamus (Fig. 3F). Other somato-sensory fibers enter the posterior cortex via the medulla oblongata and the nucleus ventralis posterior of the thalamus. A third group of neurones, carrying chiefly visual and auditory impulses, reach the cortex via the lateral and medial geniculate bodies, which are specialized parts of the lateral thalamic nucleus. Any of the afferent subsystems is linked up with the thalamus by recursive connection.

(4) In both the anterior and the posterior cortex, the somato-motor efferents differentiate into two sub-systems, namely, the *pyramidal* and the *extra-pyramidal*. The *former reaches the spinal cord directly, the latter by way of* the subcortical motor centers, including the *basal ganglia complex, nucleus ruber, substantia nigra, pontine nuclei and probably also the cerebellum* (Fig. 3F).

As a general rule, every predominantly afferent system is accompanied by recursive efferent fibers which "report" to the level of origin the effect of the stimuli conducted to higher levels from those lower levels where the stimuli originated. The nature of the "report" depends on the position of the level within the neuraxial hierarchy of centers and hence the function of the individual circuits of which it forms a part. One of the functions of the recursive connections or *feedbacks* is the adaptive enhancement or, as the case may be, the adaptive suppression of the input. *Associative feedbacks* participate in the formation of intralevel connections; *projective feedbacks*, which may be thought of as intra-axial reflexes of varying intensity, in the formation of level to level circuits. We may assume the general responsiveness of the cortex to be regulated by autonomic feedbacks, more precisely those represented by the caudal and the rostral alerting systems while regional fractions of responsiveness are mediated, in addition, by the recursive connections of the somato-sensory and kindred afferents as already suggested by Ramon y Cajal (*747*), Flechsig (*241*) and Wallenberg (*928*). A certain degree of differentiation however exists apparently also in the alerting systems. In a wider sense, all efferent pathways may be regarded as feedbacks responding to special classes of stimuli. The lowest intra-axial feedbacks are the gamma-fibers described by Granit (*317*) which run in the anterior nerve roots of the spinal cord and the peripheral nerves. The fibers sensitize the muscle spindels, and in this way determine their responsiveness to impulses produced by muscular contraction. The *highest intra-level feedbacks*, (as opposed to the highest intra-axial feedbacks) run in the association fiber systems of the forebrain, establishing recursive connections between cortical provinces.

Thus far, we have concerned ourselves with the "history" of Jackson's sensory-motor units of constitution to the extent that they form the neo-cortex, or non-olfactory cortex. In the following paragraphs, which are illustrated by figs. 4, 5, and 6, we propose to apply similar developmental principles to the organization of the junction of the olfactory cortex with the non-olfactory cortex, i.e., the archineopallial junction or the limbic lobe. For clarity, the development of the diverse fiber systems has been artifically isolated but a more "realistic" picture of the development of the cortex may be obtained by the superimposition of figs. 4, 5 and 6, which illustrate, respectively, the arrangement of the responsiveness regulating, somato-sensory and somato-motor systems.

Fig. 4A shows the basic organization of the spinal segment including, on the one hand, afferent and efferent somatic fibers, and, on the other, afferent and efferent visceral fibers. (The former are indicated on the left side, the latter on the right side of the cord.)

Fig. 4B illustrates the general structure of the olfactory cortex. Like the spinal segments, it is equipped with both afferents and efferents, one group of which is somatic while the other is autononic; more especially with *somatic (olfactory) afferents, somatic efferents, visceral afferents* and *visceral efferents.* In fig. 4C, the neocortex, which, in the preceding set of diagrams, forms a unitary cortical segment, is broken down into a motor, a somesthetic, a visual and an auditory unit, each of which shows similar categories of afferents and efferents.

In fig. 4D, the olfactory and non-olfactory cortex is represented as partially overlapping areas which form the archineopallial junction (a.n.p.j.). Its subcortical connections are (1) the fornix or hippocampo-mamillary tract, (2) the mamillo-thalamic tract from the mamillary body to the anterior nucleus of the thalamus and (3) the thalamo-cingulate radiation extending from the last named nucleus to the cingulate gyrus. (Note that the extension of the archi-neopallial junction into the posterior cortex is not indicated in the diagram and that the fornix issues, apparently, from the anterior cortex.)

Fig. 4 illustrates the relationship of the remaining thalamic nuclei and the hypothalamus to the cortex, with special reference to the distribution the fibers constituting the diencephalo-cortical alerting system. Activating fibers course from the hypothalamus to the medial and certain portions of the lateral nucleus of the thalamus and to the lateral and the medial geniculate bodies which relay them to their areas of destination. Thus, the thalamo-cingulate radiation, the anterior thalamic peduncle and the autonomic thalamo-postrolandic fibers are represented as members of the same class of activating fibers. (The anterior thalamic and the anterior cingulate radiation, which carry the bulk of the activating fibers subserve, at the same time, the conduction of visceral impulses to and from the cortex.)

The differentiation of the somatic afferents into a proprioceptive, a somesthetic, a visual and an auditory group is diagrammed in fig. 5.

Fig. 6 illustrates the differentiation of the somatic efferents including the pyramidal tract proper and the cortico-extrapyramidal tracts. The efferents issuing from the olfactory cortex comprise the medial forebrain bundle, which connects the baso-medial olfactory cortex with the hypothalamus, the lateral forebrain bundle being represented by the totality of neocortical pyramidal and extra--pyramidal efferents.

Apart from the archi-cortex and the archi-neopallial junction, the cortex has been shown to be composed of (a) the motor and the premotor area and (b) the primary somesthetic, visual and auditory areas. By and large, this organizational pattern corresponds to that seen in lower mammals where, apart from the olfactory division, the motor areas and the primary sensory areas occupy the major part of the forebrain cortex (fig. 7A). With rise in the mammalian scale, (fig. 7B) three developmental trends become increasingly conspicuous, namely, (a) the progressive reduction of the olfactory cortex, (b) the relative and the absolute growth of the non-olfactory cortex and (c) the differentiation of the primary sensory areas (I.s.) into cortical provinces subserving more elaborate sensory functions than the reception of stimuli from the periphery. The cortex, far from being merely a cortical retina, or a cortical cochlea, a mere recording mechanism that is, subserves, even in lower forms, the appreciation of relationships between the data of the senses and the selection of appropriate responses to stimuli. The agencies serving the appreciation and evaluation of stimulus patterns are the cortical fields previously designated as II.s. and III.s. At the same time, the motor and premotor cortex differentiates into a "motor keyboard" (I.m.) and into a higher motor organ (II.m.) which synthetizes individual movement to complexes of coordinated movements, or classes of movements, already referred to in Chapter I. In other words, the development of II.s. and III.s. on one hand, and of I.m. and II.m. on the other are correlative events. From a phylogenetic viewpoint, sector II.m. makes possible the very degree of motor realization that corresponds to the level of pattern perception on the part of II.s., and of pattern evaluation on the part of III.s. Broadly speaking, II.s. is the organ of gestalt perception (Chapt. IV) while III.s. is the organ of thought.

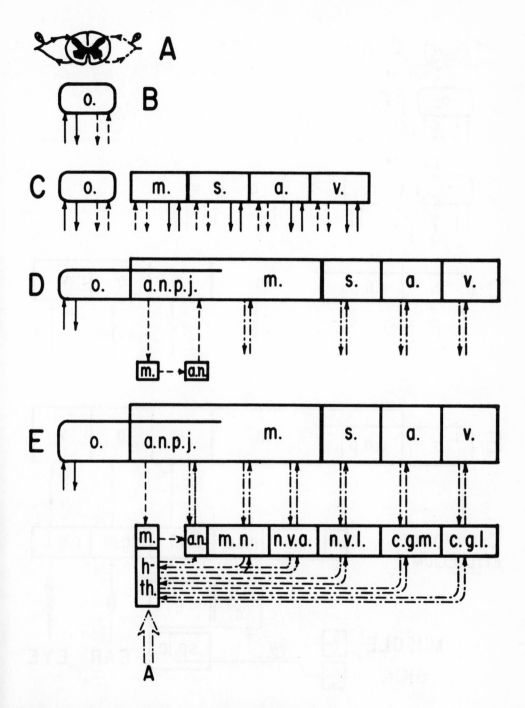

Fig. 4. General arrangement of the responsiveness regulating neurons.

o: olfactory cortex; m: motor cortex; s: somato-sensory cortex; a: auditory cortex; v: visual cortex; a.n.p.j.: archineopallial junction; m.n.: Thalamus, nucl. med.; a.n.: thalamus, nucl.-ant.; h.th.: hypothalamus; n.v.a.: thalamus, nucl. ventr. ant.; n.v.l.: thalamus, nucl. ventr. lat.; c.g.m.: corpus geniculatum lat.; c.g.l.: corpus geniculatum mediale; m.: mamillary body.

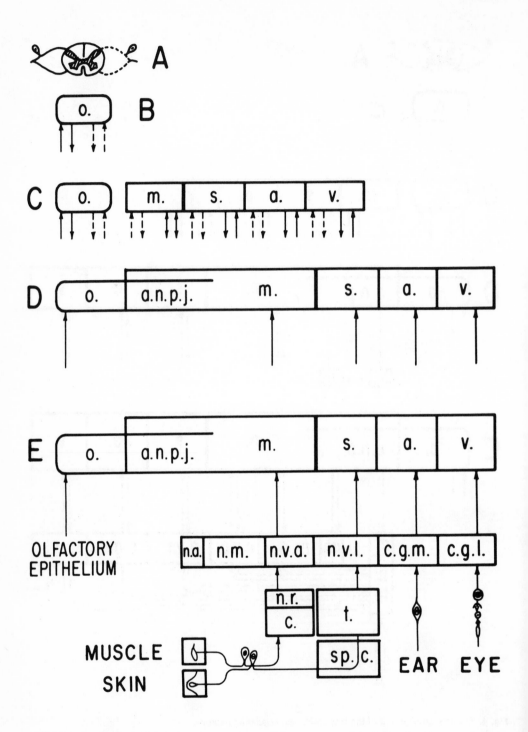

Fig. 5. General arrangement of somato-sensory neurons and allied systems.
n.r.: nucleus ruber; c.: cerebellum; t.: tectum mesencephali; sp.c.: spinal cord (compare with figs. 1 and 4).

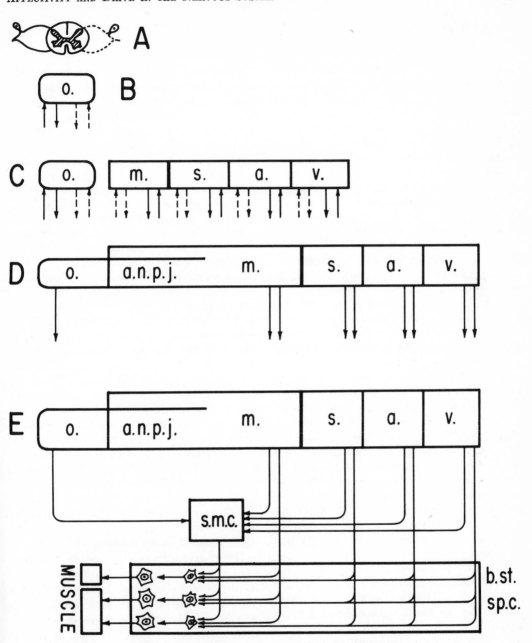

Fig. 6. General arrangement of somato-motor (pyramidal and extrapyramidal) neurons.
b.st.: brainstem; sp.c.: spinal cord; s.m.c.: subcortical motor centers (compare with figs. 4 and 5).

We remind ourselves that the so-called "counter-part" of III.s. in the anterior cortex is made up of two sectors namely, III.a., the fronto-cortical representation of the autonomic nervous system, and III.e., the fronto-cortical representation of the extra-pyramidal nervous system.

In lower mammals, I.s., II.s., and III.s. on the one hand and I.m. and II.m. on the other, overlap to a large extent. Accordingly, they show a paucity of transcortical associational connections, while their subcortical connections especially those with the basal ganglia and the thalamus are abundant by comparison. In sharp contrast, the increasing segregation in the human of the diverse functional provinces and their growth, especially the growth of III.s., is associated with an enormous increase of cortical association fibers of various order, and a relative decrease of projection fibers. However, both association and projection fibers may be found in all parts of the cortex, although in significantly different proportions.

Thus, diagram 7A illustrates that the organization of the subhuman cortex is in a sense a forerunner of the organizational pattern of the human cortex.

The above outlined "history" of the cortex demonstrates the adaptation, to special tasks, of the "units of constitution" of the nervous system as diagrammed in fig. 3, 4, 5 and 6. Although a gross oversimplification, the approach here offered permits (a) the classification of probably any fiber system connecting with the neocortex and (b) the definition of any cortical field in terms of deviation from, or, for that matter, its conformity with, an archetype. At the same time, it makes possible the specification of cortical functions in terms of connections of the cortical levels with the subcortical levels of the individual "brain organs" concerned with affectivity, thought and skill. There emerge, at successively higher levels of the neuraxis, circuit systems of increasing versatility which enhance the operational dimensions of the higher echelons and thereby the adaptibility of the organism to its environment. The non-equipotentiality of the various provinces of the nervous system is reflected by its differentiation into the "use patterns"* illustrated by the accompanying diagrams.

Although it is quite possible that we do not use the term "units of constitution" in precisely the same way as Jackson, it is useful in that makes possible to break down the maze of neuronal connections into fundamental patterns consisting, in various proportions, of the categories of neurons illustrated. It would thus depend on the proportion between the categories of "microscopic units of constitution" whether a given part of the brain is predominantly concerned with somato-motor, somato-sensory, viscero-motor, viscero-sensory or other functions, e.g., autonomic-extrapyramidal

* The term "use pattern" will be explained below under the heading "common features of limbic and extra-limbic systems."

integration, that is, whether it is, morphologically and functionally, a somato-sensory center, somato-motor center etc.

At the same time, the difference between the units of constitution may be regarded as variations on a theme as it were within one and the same species. They may help understand the different composition of the brain in different species, as certain important *species characteristics*, to the extent that they apply to the nervous system, *may be expressed in terms of relative preponderance of an afferent at a given level of the neuraxis.* In the present context, it will suffice to refer to the high development of the striatum and of the midbrain in birds, to certain anatomical structures in the medulla oblongata of fishes and to the perhaps more elaborate organization of the hypothalamus in lower mammals (*323*). In birds, extensive radiations from the large optic nerves and the geniculate bodies terminate in the corticalized tectum of the mesencephalon while the striatum receives many efferents from the thalamus (*664*). The lobus vagi, a conspicuous tubercle perched upon the superolateral aspect of the bulb in certain fishes, receives fibers not only from the vagus but, at the same time, from the sensory portion of the facial and glossopharyngeal nerves (*473*). It is not difficult to see that the sensory-motor units under consideration (to which the comparative anatomist could probably add many more) correspond, by and large, to the ideal "units of constitution" of the nervous system described by Jackson, and that the *archi-neopallial junction is nothing more than a particularly complicated fusion between two basic sensory units, namely, an olfactory unit and a non-olfactory unit.*

The brain of man is not simply an "enlarged edition" of generalized mammalian brain; and the brains of the individual species, rather than products of a linear development, would seem to be variations of a basic pattern or archetype which, although it does not exist in reality, unfolds in different directions. (One is curiously reminded of Goethe's *Urpflanze* or archetypal plant which he apparently believed to exist in reality while Schiller recognized it as a construct.) *The brain of man is the elaboration of the mammalian theme in the direction of neocortical preponderance.* The following is a *summarizing description* which applies to both the brain of man and of higher mammals.

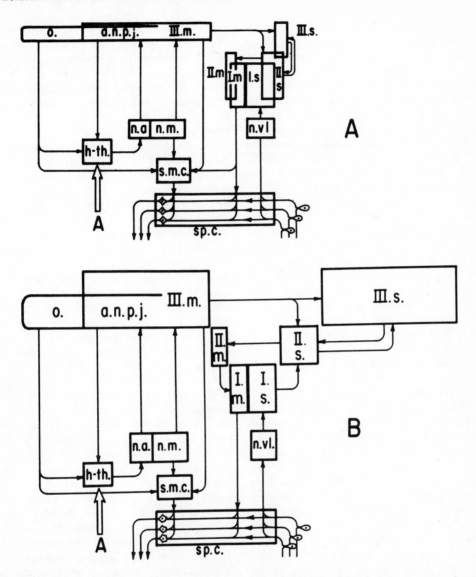

Fig. 7. The nervous system of a generalized subhuman primate (A) as compared to the nervous system of man (B). Note partial overlapping of I.m. and II.m., and of I.s., II.s., and III.s. in A. and the relative size of the motor and sensory parts of the cortex in subhuman primates as compared to the relative size of the corresponding cortical provinces in man.
Arrow A: bulcho-diencephalic activating system (compare with figs. 3 and 4).

The neopallium or neocortex. In terms of *structural and functional organization*, the neocortex may be divided into two sectors, the anterior cortex and the posterior cortex. The *anterior cortex* receives (a) proprioceptive afferents, (b) visceral afferents and (c) the majority of responsiveness regulating (autonomic) afferents; and it emits (a) pyramidal efferents, (b) extrapyramidal efferents, (c) visceral efferents and (d) responsiveness regulating (autonomic) efferents. This pattern evolves in close relationship to the somesthetic area (postcentral gyrus) in which the entire body surface is represented, and to the proprioceptive inflow into the frontal lobes. In the posterior cortex (*926*) the above described pattern is duplicated in several localities in that the cortical outflow, compounded of pyramidal efferents (544), extra-pyramidal efferents (281), visceral efferents (587) and responsiveness regulating (autonomic) efferents, is grouped around the primary sensory receiving stations of the individual receptors.

As expressed in terms of the neuron categories diagrammed in figures 4, 5, 6 and 7, the organization of the neocortex may be described as follows. (a) The somato-sensory afferents terminate chiefly in the ipsilateral postcentral gyrus and the adjacent parts of the parietal lobes. (b) The *proprioceptive afferents* terminate partly in the "predominantly motor" anterior cortex, partly in the posterior cortex. (c) The *somato-motor (pyramidal) efferents* issue chiefly from the motor area and, in a more or less diffuse fashion, from other parts of the ipsilateral and the contralateral (242) cortex. (d) In the anterior cortex, the *somato-motor (extrapyramidal) efferents* issue chiefly from the premotor area; in the "predominantly sensory" posterior cortex, on the other hand, the extra-pyramidal motor centers are organized in relationship to the primary sensory receiving stations. The so-called second or additional motor areas (893) may be regarded as regional concentrations of pyramidal and extra-pyramidal neurones in the anterior and the posterior cortex. (e) Most *viscero-sensory afferents* terminate in the frontal lobes while the remaining viscero-sensory afferents are grouped around inflow, into the posterior cortex, of the diverse receptors. (f) Most *viscero-motor efferents* issue from the frontal lobes while the balance of viscero-motor efferents take origin in the posterior cortex, in association with the fractionated extra-pyramidal efferents. (g) Most responsiveness *regulating (autonomic) afferents* and efferents, which make up the diencephalic alerting system, course in the anterior thalamic peduncle while the remaining fibers of the same system are organized in a similar fashion as the posterior groups of autonomic afferents and efferents.

Thus, the same organizational pattern which, in the anterior cortex, develops in relationship to the general proprioceptive and somesthetic inflow, is duplicated in the posterior cortex in relationship to the inflow of the receptors other than proprioceptive and somesthetic. The predominantly motor character of the anterior cortex is determined by the massive motor and premotor outflow and the role of the pyramidal tract and its extrapyramidal auxiliaries in the execution of

volitional movements; the predominantly sensory character of the posterior cortex on the other hand is established by the inflow from the various sense organs and by the relative and absolute reduction of the motor fiber tracts which, moreover, are concerned chiefly with mass movements, and cortical (visuo-motor, auditory-motor etc.) reflexes.

The brain of man differs from the brain of higher mammals in several respects, namely, by the *increased development in the posterior cortex of supraordinate sensory provinces*, i.e., of the sensory segment (II.s.) of the psycho-neural level and of the conceptual level (III.s.) and by the associated *development, in the anterior cortex, of the motor segment (II.m.) of the psycho-neural level*. The latter is concerned with the execution of both manual (non-communicative) skills and of oro-articulatory (communicative) skills, i.e., with language and speech. Corresponding sensory centers develop in the posterior cortex where they form a special category of sensory psycho-neural centers (II.s.) operating under the control of the conceptual level (III.s.). Furthermore, the brain of man differs from the brain of higher mammals in that both the associational (cortico-cortical) systems and the pyramidal system are increased in size. The latter, developing concurrently with the sensory psycho-neural level and the conceptual level, translates thought into expressive (communicative) and into manual action. Lastly, the brain of man differs from that of higher mammals by the *relative reduction of the limbic and the increased size of the frontal system*.

The limbic lobe. In a certain sense, the *fornix* and the *medial forebrain* bundle correspond to the pyramidal tract although they terminate in the hypothalamus and lower brainstem centers in line with the predominantly visceral character of the limbic lobe. The amygdala would seem to correspond to a nuclear complex concerned with both extrapyramidal and autonomic functions including the regulation of responsiveness levels. From a structural viewpoint such hypothetical complex of nerve centers is difficult to homologize with extra-limbic formations. In a general way, it may be said that striopallidum, hypothalamus, anterior and medial nucleus of the thalamus represent, jointly, the *subcortical sector of the archi-neopallial junction*, whose cortical sector is the cortex of the limbic lobe. The efferents of the amygdala would thus correspond to the *subcor-*

tico-extrapyramidal fibers and their autonomic accompaniments issuing from the striopallidum while the *cortico-extrapyramidal* fibers take origin from various parts of the limbic cortex. Either category of fibers terminate at lower extrapyramidal and autonomic levels. In other words, certain efferents of the amygdala correspond to the diencephalic efferents concerned with *autonomic* including responsiveness regulating functions, while other efferents are homologs of the *motor* outflow from the striopallidum and related subcortical formations. The above mentioned cortico-extrapyramidal tracts of the limbic lobe issue from various cell stations which, on experimental stimulation, yield somato-motor responses and, accordingly, may be regarded as homologs of the second or additional motor areas of the neocortex. Other parts of the limbic lobes are concerned with viscero-sensory and visceromotor function but the delineation of the somatosensory, somato-motor, viscero-sensory and viscero-motor sectors of the limbic cortex is even more difficult than the charting of the corresponding neocortical formations.

Common features of limbic and extra-limbic neural systems. In both the neopallium and the limbic lobes the individual somato-motor, somato-sensory, viscero-sensory and visceromotor neural arrangements, including those concerned with the regulation of responsiveness levels, are organized into *use-patterns* the most primitive of which may be studied in neuroembryological preparations. Hines and Boyton (*385*) demonstrated that, in the monkey, in the early stages of youth, certain complexly integrated reactions (which they termed use patterns) could be elicited by electrical stimulation before the animal exhibited them spontaneously. Similar observations were made by Coghill (*167*) who found that, in the simian embryo, the motor and sensory structures were recognizable prior to the development of their associative connections. Weiss (*940*) speaks of "primary motor patterns that arise by self-differentiation independent of the benefits of sensory control and guidance by experience. They are so predesigned that, when later projected into an anatomically peripheral effector system, they produce biologically adequate effects."

The physiological correlates of the use patterns are the manifold *synergies* of the organisms. Originally applied to the function of muscles which control the movement of a joint or a group of joints in a certain direction, the term synergy, as here employed, designates any group of organismic, more especially neural processes which, as explained in the introductory chapter, form concerted, interlocking patterns and, thereby, integrative acts of any level of complexity. Under pathological conditions, the synergies may be actuated in isolation (out of context as it were) and, moreover, in a more or less distorted fashion. Abnormal discharges of the use patterns are generally known as *epileptic* or *epileptiform* seizures which are practically as variegated as the individual use patterns to which they correspond. Certain synergies, especially those concerned with vital functions, are *innate* while other synergies develop concurrently with *postnatal* use patterns. Still others operate *periodically*, in connection with certain ergotropic, tropotrophic, propagative and other biological functions. Lastly, certain categories of use patterns and synergies are *permanent* or *semi-permanent* while others are more or less *ephemeral*. The concepts *synergy* and *use patterns are here extended to cover higher cerebral functions including mental functions.*

CONCLUDING REMARKS

The above reflexions on the organizational framework of the nervous system may be condensed as follows. Brain, spinal cord and peripheral nerves form a complex of neuronal line connections the unit of which is a generalized sensory-motor arrangement, rather like a generalized cell is the unit of the multicellular organism. By and large, there are as many categories of receptors as there are physico-chemical parameters of reality to which there responds, by virtue of its particular design, a given class of organisms. Elementary patterns of integration (or simple synergies) are represented by combinations of *viscerosensory* with a *viscero-motor* neuron and those between *somato-sensory* and *somato-motor* neurons. In actual fact, *somatic* sensory-motor integration is already complicated by the multiplicity of receptor categories, and *visceral* sensory-motor integration by the great variety of autonomic sources of stimulation, especially if taken in combination with endocrine function. Moreover, somatic and visceral sensory-motor processes are integrated to synergies comprising both realms of function, sceleto-muscular exercise, which requires autonomic adjustments, being a simple example. The individual units of constitution of the neuraxis form a system of interlocking use patterns which constitute the self-equilibrating "end-means-system" discussed in the introductory chapter. Special classes of integrative processes are those combining autonomic and extra-pyramidal components, which may be found at various levels of the neuraxis from the medulla oblongata up to the frontal lobes, or those combining sensory functions of various complexity, as in the posterior cortex of the cerebral hemisphere. By and large, the function of the posterior cortex is sensory although its individual neurons have both receptive and emissive properties. In a certain sense, a given population of neurons having the same over-all function as, for example, the activating and alerting system, represents an organ within an organ. Ultimately, any class of higher cerebral functions can be reduced to, or be expressed in terms of, a certain category of integrative patterns or, for that matter, combinations of certain categories of neurons which are nothing other than the units of constitution of the nervous system (figs. 3 to 7). *Affectivity* is, in substance, a manifestation of high level autonomic function; *thought*, intra-sensory integration at the highest level; and *skill*, basically, sensory-motor integration at the psycho-neural level under the guidance of the intellective level. In other words, we speak of affectivity, thought and skill as a matter- of linguistic convenience only, keeping in mind that they are generic terms which refer to certain classes of physiological processes mediated, in turn, by specialized neural arrangements.

The reflexions on the organizational framework of the nervous system suggest that its building blocks are sensory-motor units. Their archetype is formed by the combination of a receptive and an emissive neuron. The "polymerization" of adaptively modified receptive units results in the formation of *sensory centers* of a higher order, that is, of centers where sensation originally an image forming process, is potentiated to evaluative activity as a precursor of response to the stimuli by which it was elicited. A similar organization of neuron groups in the opposite direction yields *motor centers* which mediate classes of movements, more precisely, kinetic effects which realize the patterns elaborated by the higher sensory centers, including the conceptual level.

There is some evidence to suggest that the various categories of neurons are chemically different, that they have certain affinities to toxins, to pharmacodynamic compounds and to the products of endocrine glands, and that the chemical stimuli act, probably, on their synaptic connections. Further, that they have certain heredo-constitutionally determined properties, which predispose the individuals concerned to abiotrophic disease, (e.g., of motor systems) or to "integrational lability" (see *Neurosis and Psychosis*, which follows) as in certain neuroses, including the organ-neuroses and, depending on the site of the abnormalities with respect to the hierarchy of levels of the neuraxis, to mental illness. (If this concept is sound, additional categories of system diseases would have to be added to those already known.) The correlation, if any, between the histochemical properties of specialized types of neurons and their morphological properties reflected, e.g., in cytoarchitectonic features, remains to be determined. Enzyme studies and other considerations suggest that such relationships do in fact exist. Thus, Polyak (*731*) makes reference to the "different chemical constitution of the cytoplasm and its inclusions, especially Nissl's chromophil granules.' And he comments on the "functional neuronal specificity which, in turn, presupposes the ability of each neuron variety to react to a relatively narrow range of extraneous stimuli and to react dynamically to them in its own peculiar way conditioned by its own innate biochemical constitution."

A COMPARISON BETWEEN ANTERIOR AND POSTERIOR CORTEX FUNCTION

To the extent that the neural arrangements or functional building blocks of the nervous system are derivatives of sensory-motor units of constitution, the individual provinces of the brain are, in principle at least, equipotential. In actual fact, equipotentiality is reduced to a minimum by the aggregation, in specific localities, of neural arrangements that have become specialized in certain directions. Sensory provinces of the brain are cell stations where the somato-sensory elements by far outnumber the somato-motor elements, and also the various autonomic elements. In the somato-motor parts of the nervous system on the other hand, the somato-motor neurons are more numerous than the remaining neurons. Similar viewpoints apply to the relationship that exists, in the autonomic cortex and subcortex, between visceral and responsiveness regulating neural systems and somatic systems. To repeat my previous point, the billions of nerve cells resemble a cell colony whose members have assumed different tasks. We mention, in parenthesis, that specialization reaches its peak in the brain of the human adults. In the immature human organism and in animals division of labor is nascent or orimentary. This is one of the reasons why, in the animal brain and the immature human brain, restitution of function occurs more readily than in the brain of the human adult in which collateral pathways, having taken on more and more special tasks, are less numerous than in the former.

The use patterns underlying affectivity, drive and related phenomena are maximally concentrated in the autonomic provinces of the frontal and the limbic lobes and related subcortical cell stations. In man, the frontal concentration of autonomic fibers would seem to have a more intimate relationship to intellective functions than the limbic concentrations, probably because the former are younger phylogenetically and have more extensive connections with the posterior cortex than the limbic cortex. In fact, it is the great mass of association fibers between the anterior and the posterior cortex that accounts in large measure for the size of the cerebral hemispheres. It is fair to say that the responsiveness mediating anatomical systems, including those concerned with affectivity, have, apart from their multi-level representation in the neuraxis, a phylogenetically younger component in the frontal lobes, a subsidiary (collateral) component in the posterior cortex and a phylogenetically older representation in the limbic cortex.

In the following paragraphs, an attempt will be made to correlate the structural differences between the anterior and the posterior cortex, as far as they are known, with functional differences. (We keep in mind that, in this particular context, the term *frontal lobes* refers to their autonomic provinces, especially those concerned with the regulation of responsiveness levels to biologically significant stimuli.) In other words, we shall think in term of *organizational units* composed of certain categories of neurons or in terms of neural systems rather than of gross morphological subdivisions of the brain, in other words, in terms of functional rather than of descriptive anatomy.

With respect to higher cerebral functions, the differences between the anterior and the posterior cortex may be outlined as follows.

(a) In those instances in which impairment or loss of memory is confined to sensory modalities, as, for example, the formation of visual or of auditory engrams, the lesions responsible for the memory deficit involve in a statistically significant number of cases the vicinity of the primary cortical areas of vision or hearing (*493*, *521*). Thus, modality-related engram formation would seem to be superimposed upon global memory, the para-acoustic cortex to be concerned with the formation of auditory engrams, and the para-visual cortex with the fixation of visual perceptions. Interestingly enough, localized lesions interfere not only with the formation of particular engram categories but they reduce the very receptivity of the nervous system to the corresponding categories of stimuli. For example, in subcortical sensory aphasia, the patient pays no attention to auditory stimuli having a bearing upon language functions; in cortical blindness, he seems impervious to visual stimuli. In monkeys, lesions within the parieto-occipito-temporal, i.e., posterior cortex, produce "performance decrements which are modality specific" (*737*).

In *summary*, appropriately located lesions of the posterior cortex produce *partial amnestic syndromes* which are related to specific sensory modalities while lesions of the anterior cortex are apt to produce a *generalized amnestic syndrome*.

(b) Irritative lesions of parasensory areas, be they experimentally produced or caused by disease, may evoke memory images of various complexity, the most complex images being produced by temporal lobe lesions. In other words, the underlying use patterns, as brought out by the corresponding epileptiform seizure patterns, are located in the posterior cortex (*720*).

(c) Intellective processes depend on the utilization of mnemonic residues. Since there are all kinds of transitions between hallucinations, dreams, twilight states between sleep and wakefulness (hypnagogic states), and between poorly organized thinking carried by prominent visual imagery (day dreaming) and more or less well directed thought, the contents of intellective processes should be related to the functions of the parasensory cortical areas and the intervening cortex, i.e., Broadbent's "center of concepts and ideation" (*117*), or Flechsig's posterior association field (*241*). Hence, *it may be inferred that a close topographical relationship exists between the cortical fields concerned with perception and those in which the perceptual material is elaborated to higher forms of stimuli, i.e. configurations and concepts. In other words, that both processes—which represent stages in the evolvement of thought—take place in the posterior, or "sensory" sphere of the cerebral hemispheres* (*322, 343, 344, 799*).

(d) The above postulated relationship holds true for any kind of mental activity based on the elaboration of sensuous material as higher mental processes cannot be segregated from the lower, in which the factor of abstraction plays a minor role. With regard to their complexity and the element of creativity they display, intellective operations form a continuous scale, as evidenced by the psychology of recognition, of learning and of abstract thinking. Due to the inadequate activation of the selector mechanism (III.s.) in frontal lobe lesions, mental processes may be slowed down to the point where productivity ceases altogether. Similar disturbances may occur due to *involvement of associational systems* (which, in addition to direct diencephalo-cortical connections, transmit activating impulses from the intact frontal lobes to the posterior associational fields) with resulting "frontal lobe symptoms in diffuse disease processes of the brain and, as a byproduct, the erroneous concept held in some quarters that the frontal lobes have no recognizable function of their own. If, on the other hand, the *posterior cortex* is directly involved, frontal lobe impulses reach an inadequate local selector mechanism unable to establish a *system of sliding priorities* involved in mentation (*799*). Lack of productivity in frontal lobe disease is frequently mentioned in the literature. According to Freeman and Watts (*261*) the frontal poles are the "seat of creative ekstasy." Hutton and Basset (*417*) found creative imagination to be almost non-existent in a patient nine months after frontal lobotomy, and Busemann (*127*) noted a dearth of new and productive associations of ideas in cases of frontal lobe injury while the specification of concepts offered on psychological testing was relatively well preserved. Furthermore, associations in posterior cortex lesions were far fetched and irrelevant indicating, perhaps, a dissolution of concepts. Similar observations were recorded by Stoll (*883*), Kolb (*503*), Golla (*314*) and Partridge (*712*). Lack of productivity in frontal lobe lesions

is due to general listlessness or lack of responsiveness to stimuli. In other cases, the quantity of the patient's mental output may be increased in line with his inordinately increased activity, that is to say, a state of dys-homeostasis at the highest level of cerebral function. Accordingly, the quality of mentation is not matched by its quantity. A related disorder is the already mentioned distractibility of the frontal lobe patient which still further intensifies the already existing mental deterioration.

(e) Gastaut (*290*), in a review of epileptic seizure patterns, comments on the absence of any mental abnormalities (aura etc) in the classic frontal lobe seizure, that is to say, an irritative lesion of that part of the cortex which, as maintained by many authorities, is concerned with the elaboration of thought.

(f) Brickner and Stein (*116*), who reported observations of compulsive thinking in organic disease processes of the temporal lobe, called attention to Jackson's and Wilson's cases in which lesions of the temporal lobe were manifested by paroxysmal disturbances of thought, and they expressed the belief that temporal lobe lesions of a stimulatory character may result in the activation of thought processes. Similar experiences were reported by Penfield and Jasper (*721*).

In conclusion, then, the *technical* elements of thought processes, i.e., the manipulation of concepts and of mnemonic elements involved in thought may be assumed to be a function of the posterior cortex, the *dynamic* elements of the diencephalo-frontal system.

MEMORY MECHANISMS

The phenomenon of memory has many aspects only some of which will be discussed in the following pages. We have already indicated that thought processes depend to a large extent on the evaluation of past experiences. Various observations suggest that not only the activation of engrams but also their formation depends on the competency of the diencephalo-frontal system and its functional and anatomical relations with the posterior cortex of the hemispheres so that, in this particular respect, mental development is under the control of autonomic cell stations.

Experimental and clinical data

(a) Following frontal lobotomy, which severs the anterior thalamic radiation more or less completely, the patient's behaviour and psychological tests discloses a more or less marked memory deficit. The patients no longer benefit from practice during psychometric testing, they show strong tendencies to stereotyped faulty reactions and their capacity for recall is reduced (531). On the other hand, their general performance level, probably because of the elimination of inhibitory affects, may be improved (260). Bilateral disease of the frontal lobe regardless whether of traumatic, neoplastic or vascular etiology, almost invariably produce profound disturbances in memory.

The case of a patient reported by Mabille and Pitres (601) appears to be of particular interest in that the patient survived a cerebro-vascular accident over a period of 23 years. After he had recovered from the immediate effects of the disease it was noted that he had lost his memory for recent events completely but that, by comparison, his general intelligence was not markedly impaired. He was institutionalized for the rest of his life and, although living in the same surrounding, remained unfamiliar with the places in which he stayed and to the persons who attended him. As confirmed at autopsy, he had suffered from central nervous system lues. Apart from diffuse lesions of microscopic size two small softenings were found, each of which lay astride the path of the anterior thalamic radiations at a point where it leaves the anterior crus of the internal capsule and enters the subcortex of the frontal lobe.

In spite of the apparently focal character of the pathological process it is probably safe to assume that, prior to the cerebro-vascular accident, the disease had caused diffuse though only subliminal alterations and that the loss of memory may be accounted for by a concatenation of factors. From what is known about the thalamocortical connections, the largest contingent of the diencephalo-cortical alerting system courses in the anterior thalamic radiation. Because of its bilateral involvement and the diffuse nature of the pathological process, the compensatory utilization of posterior alerting fibers, i.e., the collaterals of the anterior alerting fibers, was very likely impossible. Conversely, the partial preservation of retentive memory in lobotomized patients may be accounted for by the absence of diffuse brain damage.

The case under discussion, for all practical duplicated by Zacher's (975) observation, may be compared with the effects of surgical lesions of a similar location.

(b) As early as 1896 Gudden (330) found bilateral involvement of the mammillary bodies in cases of Korsakow's psychosis.* His observations were later confirmed by Gamper (286, 287) and other workers (59) who noted that the cortical alterations were either inconspicuous or, as far as could be determined by histological examination, entirely absent. The mammillary bodies, which are connected with the archipallium by way of the fornix and the medial forebrain bundle, and with the anterior nucleus of the thalamus via the mammillary tract, discharge into the frontal segment of the cingulate gyrus (164). Williams and Pennybacker (969) found memory impairment to be most common and specific when the area surrounding the floor of the third ventricle was implicated.

(c) Lashley's (541) earlier studies yielded no evidence of functional localization in the rat's brain, but Morgan and Woods (662) found that destruction of the prefrontal areas abolishes delayed alternation habits. The authors maintain that association areas for recent memory exist even in lower laboratory animals and explain Lashley's negative findings by the large number of psychologic factors involved in maze learning. They contend that maze learning, a highly integrated function, is not localized but that localistic viewpoints are applicable to the different specific capacities. Boycott and Young (105) found that certain parts of the central nervous system (lobus opticus) of sepia are of crucial importance for retentive memory.

Disturbances of mental concentration, of memory and association following extirpation of the frontal lobes in various animals were described by Bianchi (80). Franz (254), experimenting on cats and monkeys, noticed that, following bilateral prefrontal lesions, recently formed habits were lost while long standing habits were retained. Jacobson (426), after bilateral injury to the pre-

* Recently, certain components of the amnestic syndrome were produced by the administration of JB 318, a hallucinogen (701a).

frontal association areas in primates, found impairment of those activities which "in their very nature demand integration over a long period of time." Temporal patterning fails "because the subject can no longer remember a single experience for even a few seconds in the face of new incoming impulses." The injury produces damage to a mechanism subserving logical thinking and judgement, in other words, "the capacity to organize activity of the moment in terms of the immediate past experience." Finan, (233) too, found impairment of those habits which depend on recent memory. Malmo's (613) experimental data have already been mentioned. The authors doubts that the removal of the association areas by itself impairs the capacity for delayed response and is inclined to explain the difference in behaviour by the increased susceptibility on the part of the animals to interfering extraneous stimuli during the relay time, i.e., to increased distractibility. Impairment of adaptive shifting of attention was also observed by Harlow and Johnson (345) who noted that bilateral removal of the prefrontal association areas in monkeys may prevent initiation of such simple and deep rooted performances as grasping food from a tray. Jacorzynsky and Davis (427) found that longer time is required to perceive stimuli while Campbell and Harlow (141) observed in their experimental animals that they failed to fixate and differentiate cues essential for problem solutions with result in steroetyped behaviour. At the same time, they noted increased distractibility. Lately, Harlow and his associates (344) demonstrated that, in the monkey, massive posterior ablations, which produce a lasting decrement in discrimination learning, do not necessarily interfere with delayed responses. Deficit in delayed response is characteristic of prefrontal ablations and persistent over a long period of time, the delayed response test having proved to be an extremely sensitive measure of differential damage to the frontal and posterior association areas. ("The demonstration of different and complementary frontal and posterior syndromes categorically refutes the assumption that the associative cortex is equipotential.") It is further to be noted that Carpenter (151) found in the rat "anticipatory errors" following frontal lobe lesions which he explained as a release phenomenon from frontal inhibition.

The neuropsychology of memory

The process character of memory

From the observations cited in the foregoing paragraphs, global memory, in contrast to differential or modality related memory, would appear to depend on a mechanism that is concentrated in the brainstem and which fans out into the cortex, chiefly the cortex of the frontal lobes. We may assume that the complex of neurons subserving global mnestic functions reaches the posterior cortex indirectly, by way of association fibers that connect the anterior with the posterior cortex and, to a lesser extent, directly, by way of the posterior contingent of the diencephalo-cortical alerting system (fig. 5). Accordingly, disturbances of memory may be produced by a variety of lesions, namely, those of a diencephalo-frontal mechanism and those involving the posterior association fields.

For the time being, a distant and somewhat fanciful analogy may illustrate the principle of this mechanism.

Let the material substrate of memory resemble a system of trolley cars which depend on central power supply, and let the source of electric power correspond to certain centers located in the brainstem. These centers spark the frontal lobes which, in turn, transmit the energy to the posterior cortex. The neural line connections running chiefly via the frontal lobes and, to a lesser degree, in collaterals from the diencephalon to the posterior cortex, correspond to the electrically charged tracks of the trolley system; the engrams, to the individual cars. Impairment of memory may thus be due to a variety of causes, as may be the breakdown of transportation, corresponding, singly or in combination, to lack of power supply, or damage to the tracks, or damage to the rolling stock or to more than one factor. The proposed analogy demonstrates the diversity of mechanisms underlying apparently similar effects and, at the same time, the fact that *memory is an organized complex of processes, dependent on quotas of actions mediated by diversified structural elements.* At the same time, the analogy answers the question where memory is "localized." In any case, the proposed concept appears to be more satisfactory than the theories stipulating that memory depends on the available mass of nerve substance only. For example, it is readily applicable to the memory disturbances characteristic of Korsakoff's syndrome (see below) which, as already indicated, may be caused by lesions involving the mammillary bodies (286, 287, 325, 641) or by diffuse bilateral frontal lobe lesions (150), or by bilateral tumors of the corpus callosum which implicate fiber connections between the parieto-occipital and the temporal lobes (801), and, lastly, by temporal lobe lesions (175, 506, 512, 799, 727, 917).

Dynamic properties of mnemonic processes and their structural correlates

Our own data (799), gathered from a series of 591 varified brain tumor cases, and taken in conjunction with the evidence from the literature, reveal the importance of a dynamic and a structural factor.

The *dynamic factor* involved in the formation of engrams appears to be at fault in diencephalic and diencephalo-frontal lesions. Certain clinical observations suggest that the factor in question is intimately related to the sleep-wakefulness mechanism. Gamper (286), who studied the relationship between sleep, delirium tremens and Korsakoff's psychosis, believes that wakefulness depends on the integrity of the mesen-diencephalic junction, and that the various psychic disturbances including the generalized amnestic syndrome are merely fractions of the sleep mechanisms which in turn may be identified in the transitional stage between wakefulness and sleep, in the acute delirious states of alcoholics and in Korsakoff's psychosis as a more protracted manifestation of the same disorder. The appreciation of incompatibilities and contradictions is impossible unless the patient is able to keep in mind at least two sets of data (727). This ability is characteristically impaired in Korsakoff's syndrome. It is further to be noted that the typical psychosis of encephalitis lethargica (which, as is well known, is referable to diencephalic lesions), resembles alcoholic delirium (286, 287). The different role of the *structural* factor in the causation of the disorder is referable to the interruption of the number of telecephalic line connections in diffuse bilateral lesions of the cerebral hemispheres.

FURTHER REFLEXIONS ON THE ORGANIZATIONAL FRAMEWORK OF THE NERVOUS SYSTEM

Fig. 8 illustrates the integration of two cerebral agencies, namely, the *higher sensory-motor apparatus* and the *responsiveness regulating mechanism*. The former, which mediates behavioural responses to exogenous and endogenous (non-mnemonic) stimuli is represented by circuit I.s. → II.s. → III.s. → II.s. → II.m. → I.m., while responses to mnemonic stimuli are mediated by system III.s. → II.s. → II.m. → I.m. (See chapter I.) The responsiveness regulating mechanism is compounded, on the one hand, of the bulbo-diencephalic and diencephalo-cortical (chiefly diencephalo-frontal) alerting systems (fig. 8A) and, on the other, the limbic system, its subcortical cellstations and their connections. The autonomic head ganglion, being acted upon by alerting, biochemical and oro-alimentary stimuli, controls autonomic processes by appropriate connections with the individual target organs and by hormonal stimulation. Activating impulses are concerned with the maintenance of the waking state, with attention and concentration, i.e., the receptivity to stimuli while other "trans-hypo-thalamic" impulses form, in association with alerting stimuli, the neural and biochemical basis of behaviour initiating impulses or of what will later in this chapter be referred to as "impulse components of intellective stimuli." The earliest intellective stimuli, in turn, which are of a low perceptual order, operate as releasers of instincts which satisfy vital needs of the organism. It is suggested that the neural and biochemical systems (A, B and C), having acquired a cortical representation chiefly by way of the anterior and medial nucleus of the thalamus, connect with the posterior cortex by way of the frontal lobes and, to a lesser extent, bypassing the frontal lobes, via the posterior (extra-frontal) contingent of the diencephalo-cortical alerting system. In other words, impulses generated in the brainstem reach the anterior cortex in a concentrated fashion, the posterior cortex in a relatively diffuse fashion. The diencephalon shunts streams of activity to the highest level or it diverts them to the centers subserving sleep and recuperation. If the mesen-diencephalic "gate" to the cortex is open, sector III.s., utilizing informative data transmitted to it from the sense organs via the lateral nuclear complex of the thalamus, produces conceptual

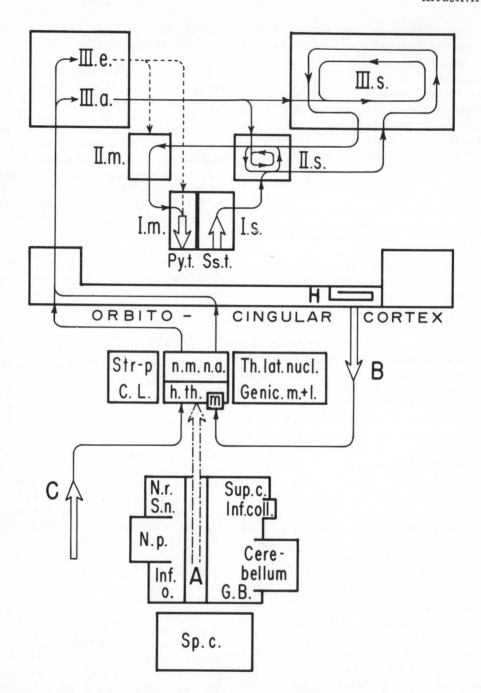

Fig. 8. The integration of mnemonic circuits (closed loops) with responsiveness regulating circuits.

III.c.: extrapyramidal part of the frontal cortex (anterior cortex); III.a.: responsiveness regulating (autonomic) part of the frontal cortex. The corresponding parts of the temporo-parieto-occipital cortex (posterior cortex) are not indicated; Py.t.: pyramidal tract; s.s.t.: somato-sensory tracts; m.: mamillary body; A.: bulbo-diencephalic activating system; B.: alimentary and sexual stimuli; C.: hormonal and metabolic stimuli.

stimuli which carry affective charges of various intensity, and which, although not necessarily of a high order, determine patterns of behaviour. The conceptual level is that part of the brain where the neurodynamic processes underlying the selection of appropriate reactions to stimuli become independent of sensory data rather as, with increasing experience, the ability on the part of a person to perform mathematical operations becomes independent on the reckoning board. The conceptual level, under ideal conditions at least, provides the instrumentalities which help maintain the biological equilibrium of the organism. Intellective activity, involving the interplay of complex rivalry-, priority-, and selector mechanism concerned with the utilization of stimuli of various order, may be thought of as localized to the extent only that sector III.s. controls the totality of neurodynamic processes involved in mentation and behaviour while the lower levels of the response determining neural mechanism contribute, to the total physiological pattern, individual quotas of action.

In *summary*, the responsiveness mediating mechanism is composed of a series of levels. Its highest level is the complex of autonomic provinces (III.a.) of the frontal cortex, which functions in close association with the autonomic provinces of the temporal lobe. The two agencies were amalgamated in the course of the fusion of the olfactory brain with the more recent, and more elaborate, cerebral apparatus built upon the telencephalic representation of the higher senses. The functional state of the highest level of the mechanism in question depends on its stimulation by lower levels. Contrarily, the functional conditions at lower levels are influenced by the higher echelons through feedback mechanisms. The functional primordium of the self-regulatory mechanism referred to above is nothing other than the metabolism of the cell serving the equilibratory needs of the protoplasm, in the already quoted words of Lillie (*504*) "a regulated system of such kind that a disturbance of the normal structure or composition determines constructive and reparative processes that tend to restore the normal condition."

The lower nerve centers discharging into the cerebral cortex are the reticular formation of the brainstem and certain nuclei of the diencephalon. Since the activating fibers are most heavily concentrated in the diencephalofrontal radiations, we regard the frontal lobes as the dominant activating organ of the cerebral cortex which determines the degree of responsiveness of the sensory segments of the cortex, including the highest and, indirectly, the externalization of responsiveness to stimuli or the intensity of drive. *Further, since the responsiveness of the sensory sphere is brought to the fore not only by its immediate reaction but also the readiness with which sensory stimuli are recorded and fixated to form engrams, mnemonic functions depend to a degree on autonomic functions.*

The existence of ascending and descending connections between the frontal lobes and the reticular formation of the lower brainstem suggests the presence of neuronal circuits already referred to in the course of the discussion of the two alerting systems. The mesen-diencephalic regions including the sleep wakefulness centers is an important internodium of this mechanism which, we may assume, cancels or reinforces streams of activity orginating in the reticular formation of the bulb. The lower brainstem controls the responsiveness of the entire neuraxis but the dominant physiological focus which exerts this control may be shifted so that, at different times, different strata of the responsiveness controlling apparatus take the lead. This temporal patterning in turn has a bearing not only upon the phenomena of sleep and wakefulness and, implicitly, of consciousness and upon the tone of striated muscles, but also upon attention, mental concentration and engram formation.

The concept of a responsiveness regulating system reconciles the cortical theories of sleep (*80, 749*) with the brainstem theories, in fact, it implies the representation of the control of sleep and wakefulness by at least two strata. The fact that certain drugs act on the cortex while others depress the receptivity of the brainstem may be regarded as further evidence that sleep can be initiated by different links of a chain of centers. The above concept suggests a continuous physiological scale whose differential ranges are (a) the refractory state of the individual cell and (b) complex inhibitory factors which produce sleep and muscular hypotonicity.

The concept of systematization of function in a succession of internodia implies that the function mediated by a given neural system acquire increasing degrees of complexity. Depending on the site of the individual center, the term function has a different meaning rather like a number which, depending on its exponent, acquires a different value. As expressed in terms of neuronal circuitry, a succession of such centers may be diagrammed as follows.

Fig. 9 illustrates the increasing versatility of response on the part of the diencephalo-frontal system, attained by a combination of a mnemonic use pattern with a responsiveness regulating use pattern.

At the most primitive "stage" (fig. 9A), a sensory stimulus, e.g., one entering the central nervous system by way of a spino-cerebral neuron, is conducted to the cortex. The stimulus thus generated does not however outlast the process of stimulation.

With increasing complexity of the system, (fig. 9B), the stimulus is fixated, that is to say, "perpetuated" as an engram. In the light of previous considerations, we may assume that the energy necessary to convert a stimulus to a memory trace is produced by the diencephalo-cortical alerting system, especially its frontal division, which, in turn, is sparked by collateral stimuli conducted to it by the lemniscus system and associated fiber tracts coursing through the lower brainstem. In other words, the stimulus to be fixated triggers the neural arrangement which makes possible its fixation.

Fig. 9C shows how the versatility of the neural arrangement or use pattern is enhanced by a feedback system extending between the engram forming (posterior) cortex and the upper brainstem. Utilizing the two way connections established in the preceding developmental stage, the brainstem either enhances or inhibits the additional inflow of impulses from the lower centers into the higher centers.

At a subsequent stage, illustrated by Fig. 9D, the posterior cortex has acquired anatomical and functional relationships not only with the brainstem but also with the autonomic segment (III.a) of the frontal lobes. The latter has become a supraordinate agency which, in accordance with the demands of the moment, either stimulates or inhibits the posterior cortex.

Lastly, Fig. 9E demonstrates how the frontal lobes control two (or, for that matter, any number) of mnemonic use patterns which are connected with the upper brainstem by individual recursive connections.

The statement that the frontal lobes acquire

anatomical and functional connections with the upper brainstem needs to be amplified. What do the frontal lobes add to the already existing operational dimensions or, for that matter, the degree of versatility of the system not yet attained at the diencephalic level?

The number of synaptic connections, is immeasurably increased at the cortical as compared to the diencephalic level. Hence, the frontal lobes tremendously multiply the conditions underlying the formation and fixation of engrams and, implicitly, the number of behavioural responses to activated memory traces. Behavioural reactions, in turn, which require an appropriate postural background and, it would seem, facilitation, are under the control of the extrapyramidal nervous system, which is likewise re-represented in the frontal lobes. Furthermore, the execution of skilled movements depends on the psychoneural level (II.) which occupies certain parts of the anterior and the posterior cortex. Ultimately, the activities in question are under the control of the conceptual level (III.s.). The more variegated the sensory representation in the organism of its internal and external milieu, the more extensive the establishment of configurational and conceptual relationships between the individual data, and the more manifold the reactions on the part of living beings to changes and events that occur in their internal and external world. Lastly, the more variegated the responses, the more complex the technical conditions of their execution and the number and interaction of stimuli, both current and mnemonic, by means of which the behavioural responses are set in motion.

The above, oversimplified and somewhat axiomatic discussion of the physiology of the organ of responsiveness illustrates the general principle that (a) the activity of a given level of nervous system function is the functional primordium of the activity of the supradjacent level and (b) that the activity at a given level is to be defined in terms of its own quota of action to the total process and of the degree of complexity of function of the infradjacent level. That the activities of the individual levels are not mere abstractions is drammatically illustrated by the effects of transections of the brainstem and the ensuing changes in the postural reactions of experimental animals. In the realm of memory functions such demonstration is of necessity conjectural but there is no reason to assume that mnemonic func-

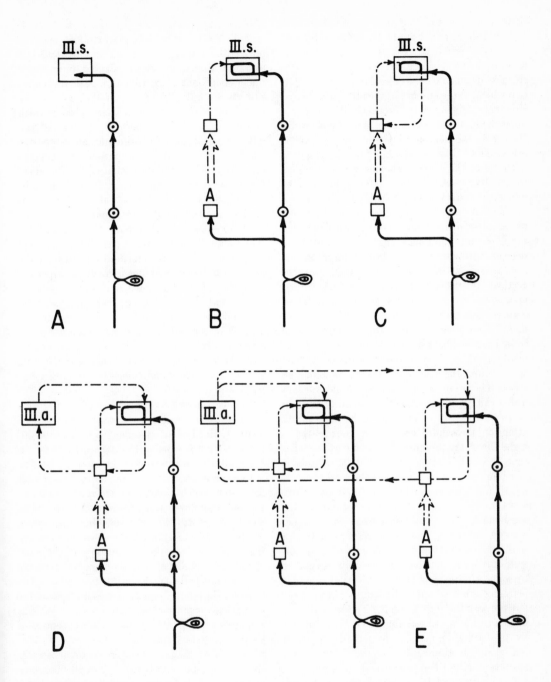

Fig. 9. The increasing complexity of responsiveness regulating circuits (dash-dotted lines) at various levels, and their integration with mnemonic (closed loop) circuits.

III.s.: conceptual level; III.a.: responsiveness regulating (autonomic) part of the frontal cortex; arrow A: Bulbo-diencephalic activating system; squares: sites of origin of the bulbo-diencephalic and diencephalo-cortical activating systems.

tions are subject to different principles, that is to say, that they are not gradually being "built up" from more primitive patterns of response. At lower brainstem levels, a critical degree of responsiveness depends on the reticular activating system which, in the absence of the above illustrated circuits, would impart the properties of the neuron upon the superimposed segments of the neuraxis. Rather as the neuron, depending on its excitability, either fires or does not fire, the response patterns of the higher echelons would conform to the all or none law as indicated in Fig. 8A. An important nodal point of this system is the mesen-diencephalic junction, which controls the sleep-wakefulness mechanism, in other words, which supplies that additional degree of freedom of reaction without which the state of unresponsiveness would be irreversible. Ultimately, at the cortical level, wakefulness is graded into *awareness, alertness, attention* and *concentration*. Thus, states of gradual awakening would seem to repeat, in an abbreviated fashion, the phylogenesis of consciousness just like the intrauterine development of man is said to recapitulate, in a short span of time, the development of the mammalian series. The brain accumulates stockpiles of data which can be shunted into the stream of thought as necessity arises. Through concentration of attention, the frontal lobes appear to repeat, at a higher level, the function of certain cortical reflex centers which involve the *immediate* utilization of stimuli in that they preserve data for the purpose of mnemic reaction (*799*). Using frontal pathways for the purpose of engram formation, the organism keeps in abeyance what would otherwise be shortlived, immediate responses. In this sense, the frontal lobes may be regarded as "organs of time" although not necessarily, as claimed by some, as "organs of planning." (What counts in planning is not so much the length of time used but the way the time is spent.) The frontal lobes introduce an additional dimension of operation by mediating temporally patterned behaviour but their function still "reflects" that of the lower centers which are concerned with immediate and stereotyped states of responsiveness. Accordingly, the ability to suppress reflex-like behaviour by anticipative and intended behaviour is apt to be abolished and a basic dimension of response is lost. Increased distractibility (which, naturally, interferes with planning and long term anticipatory behaviour) is the inability to supress reflex-

like responses, or forced attendance to existing stimuli. The resulting deficit is a twofold one. Not only is the ability to form engrams reduced but also the ability to actuate fixated impressions under conditions of existing stimulation. As a result, the frontal lobes are deprived of their role as the organs of time and the posterior cortex, which depends on frontal lobe activity, is relegated to a reflex mechanism. In principle at least, the mechanism of engram formation or "delayed receptivity" to stimuli mediated by the dien-cephalo-frontal alerting system would seem to be similar to the mechanism of perception or "immediate receptivity" to stimuli mediated by the bulbo-diencephalic system. A glance at fig. 8 shows that the apparatus serving mnemonic behavioural responses is merely an elaboration of the mechanism which mediates immediate responses. Both the engram forming agencies of the sensory cortex and their energizing diencephalo-frontal mechanisms mobilize brainstem energy in the interest of cortical activity and, *inasmuch as the attainment of concepts depends, among other factors, on the utilization of engrams, it may be said that the attainable complexity of thought is codetermined by the frontal lobes.*

In a certain sense, the effects of frontal lobe disease in man are duplicated not only by experiments performed on mammals but also on invertebrates. (See Boycott and Young's (*105*) experimental data referred to in Chapter I.) The authors concluded that the higher centers inhibit the lower, which mediate innate reflex patterns. In Sepia, the lower centers are chiefly the lobus basalis anterior; the higher, the lobus opticus and verticalis. In vertebrates, the lower centers are the brainstem reticular formation and the associated diencephalic nuclei; the higher centers, the response determining agencies of the cortex. Thus learning circuits are superimposed on the circuits mediating primitive seeking and avoidance responses: "The Intellect is indeed a beacon of the Will" (*194*).

The above described experiment demonstrates the close relationship between several functions, namely, (a) reflex-like activity sparked by impelling stimuli or releasers, (b) the formation of corrective engrams, that is to say, the modification of instinctive behaviour by learning and (c) the reduction, of a flexible performance to a stereotyped reaction following the elimination of a high level agency.

The structure of the composite psychopathological syndrome caused by frontal lobe disease, including general lack of alertness, general lability of attention, inability to fixate engrams and, indirectly, intellective deterioration, is hardly a fortuitous one. Other factors being equal, the formation and fixation of memory traces depends on quick responsiveness and sustained directional attitudes on the part of the organism. It is likewise apparent that attention and concentration depend to a large extent on *motivation,* or reward and punishment, that is to say, on *anticipated gratification* or *anticipated frustration,* as the case may be. The intimate mechanism of response depending on affective and mnemonic factors will be more conveniently discussed in one of the subsequent sections of the current chapter, in connection with critical comments on the diverse theories of frontal lobe functions, and following the discussion of certain neurotic and psychotic behaviour mechanisms.

The theory of *brainstem-cortex* relationship has an interesting history which can be traced to Franz Joseph Gall's (*285, 357*) "Anatomie et physiologie du système nerveux en générale et du cerveau en particulier, etc." (1810–1819). It is perhaps little known that Gall was the first to suggest that the central nervous system is divided into three parts, namely "those concerned with the exercise of *vital forces,* which reside in the spinal cord and medulla oblongata, those concerned with *inclinations and affections of the soul,* situated in the basal portions of the brain, and the *intellectual qualities of the mind,* associated with the cerebral hemisphere." Meynert (*1869*) thought that the primitive instincts are rooted in the brainstem. Like other prominent physicians of his epoch he was probably familiar with Schopenhauer's philosophy of voluntarism (*1819*), i.e., the relegation of the "Intellect to a slave of the Will." In modern physiological language, the Intellect is the posterior cortex, the Will the diencephalo-frontal and limbic system. Reichardt (*1918*) contended that mental performances depend on a non-psychic agency which represents, at the same time, the governing center of the entire psycho-physical organism, including the various autonomic provinces of the brain. Breslauer (*1914*) demonstrated that pressure on the lower brainstem causes immediate unconsciousness. Camus (*1922*), Spiegel (*1927*) and Haskoveč (*1929*) regarded the thalamus as the level of primitive consciousness, and Berze (*1913*) and Küppers (*1923*) as the center of driving forces. Küppers regarded the cortex as an auxiliary mechanism, that is, an instrument destined to serve the drives and instincts "vested" in the thalamus. Berze's views appear to be strikingly modern. He expressed the belief that the cortex functions under the control of subcortical centers upon which there depends its efficiency and serviceability, and that the fibers issuing from the brainstem and energizing the cortex course in the anterior thalamic radiation. Baruk's (*1947*) and Zondek's (*1944*) conception of neural and neuroglandular energy relates the early ideas which, of necessity, were more or less philosophical, to the modern neuropsychic concepts.

In 1941, Dempsey, Morison and Dempsey (*663*) described the "secondary response system" comprising thalamo-cortical circuits of neurons. In 1945, Murphy and Gellhorn (*674*) expressed the belief that the state of excitation of the associational areas which is due to the thalamic activity increases the number of active cortical neurons and, hence, the intensity of intellective and emotional functions. In 1950, I suggested that memory traces may be conceived in terms of neurodynamic processes which are by their very nature evenascent or ephemeral use patterns (*709*). That, to prevent their disintegration, engrams require stabilizing impulses generated by the diencephalo-frontal system, and transmitted to the posterior cortex by way of the frontal lobes upon recursive stimulation of the latter by the posterior cortex. Largely under the influence of Kleist's writings (*493, 494*) who contended that "thought processes have both sensory and motor aspects" I assumed the "motor" counterpart of the posterior association fields to be the above specified activating or tuning apparatus which controls the receptivity and reactivity of the posterior cortex and, by enabling it to stockpile data for the purpose of mnemic reaction, promotes its functional growth. The above quoted statement was corrected in the following year at which time I came to the conclusion that *the anterior association fields have both stimulating and inhibitory functions, that the autonomic provinces of the frontal lobes are agents of the diencephalon and that the impairment of frontal lobe function follows the derangement pattern of a homeostatic mechanism* (*801*). Starzl,

Taylor and Magoun (*1951*) suggested that the thalamo-reticular system (diencephalo-cortical alerting system) contributes to the frontal lobe function of complex emotional behaviour, higher creative activities and well organized autonomic adjustment. According to Jasper, Ajmone–Marsan and Stoll (*1952*) the same system is concerned with the mechanism of attention while French, Merzeano and Magoun (*1953*) held that the "medial system" (bulbo-diencephalic alerting system) may be involved in management of gradations of attention superimposed upon inattentive wakefulness. Gellhorn (*1954*), calling attention to Adrian's experiments (*1947*), pointed out that hypothalamic cortical discharges are increased in emotional excitement, that minor, more localized changes in the intensity of the discharge occur in the state of attention, and that still more complex psychic events such as learning and memory which are undoubtedly cortical in origin are influenced by emotional processes. In 1954, Gellhorn, Koella and Ballin postulated the interaction of sensory activity with hypothalamo-cortical discharge to be the physiological basis of sensation and a similar mechanism to underlie conscious processes, for instance those involving memory, which may occur in the absence of significant degrees of sensory excitation. Although descriptively adequate, the statements of the above quoted authorities do not throw light upon the interaction of the diverse functions to which they refer and which we attempted to elucidate in terms of Jacksonian principles.

Following a different line of thought, Penfield (*716, 717, 718*) developed the theory of a *centrencephalic integrating system*. "If anywhere,"

Penfield wrote, "it is in the centrencephalic system that Hughlings Jackson's highest level of functional integration is to be found" and where fusion of all types of sensation can be achieved. Penfield's concept was criticized by Lashley (*543*) who warned "against the present tendency to ascribe various complex functions to the thalamus and the brainstem, regions of relatively few cells and poorly developed internuncial systems." Very aptly, Lashley argued, it is impossible "for the small number of cells in the centrencephalic system to mediate or even to transmit these complexities. This system is anatomically very simple and if it fulfills its function as a dynamic center as others have called it, it has exhausted all its possibilities." (See also Chapter IV.) Spiegel (*851*), Kuhlenbeck (*524* and Walshe (*929*) voiced even stronger opposition.

Cerebral functions are built upon certain foundations both from a phylogenetic and ontogenetic point of view. Evidently, superstructures have a basis upon which to rest and, in the course of phylogenetic development, become the highest level of brain function for the very reasons for which they were established. The highest functional plane is that which, although in a sense controlled by lower strata, is structurally equipped to serve the most complex and the most adaptive performances. It is obvious that such functions depend on the existence of a neural substrate whose discriminatory and synthetizing capacities, as suggested by the microscopic study of the cortex, by experiences with conditioned reflexes and by clinical observations, far exceed those of the more primitive subcortical centers.

———————— Elements of a stimulus-response psychology and psychopathology

Thus far we have discussed diverse aspects of higher cerebral functions in more or less conventional terms. At this point, preparatory to the study of affective phenomena and related intellective functions, it is necessary from a clinical point of view, to combine pertinent data into a unifying stimulus-response psychology based on biological principles. We intend to establish a common language in which the various disorders of higher brain functions can be expressed, and

their mutual relationship made intelligible. The following is a framework of reference to be developed in more detail later in this volume. At this point, it will be outlined in a minimum of propositions and in terms of stimulus response phenomena. Moreover, to keep it within manageable proportions, we shall present it in a somewhat axiomatic fashion (expecting that it will prove its worth as our thesis develops) and divide it into introductory remarks to those topics upon which it has an immediate bearing, namely, the *psychoneuroses*, the *schizophrenias*, the *cyclic psychoses* and mental changes in *frontal lobe disease*.

Varieties of stimuli and the nature of central activity

Stimuli and responses belong to the most elementary biological phenomena. In the higher organism, stimuli, on impinging upon the sensory division of the nervous system, set up equivalent processes ranging from *mirror images* (e.g., retinal images) to *analogs*, that is, states or conditions which have the same relation-structure (*173*) as the processes which produce them. (The term "correspondance function of the nervous system" has already been commented upon in the introductory chapter.) Hence, the term stimulus refers, on the one hand, to a process in the milieu of the organism and, on the other, to the reflexion of this process in the receptive and recording elements of the neuraxis. The ambiguity of the term stimulus (which refers to both the phenomena of objective reality and their subjective counterpart) might be avoided were its meaning limited to processes occuring in the external (environmental) and the internal (somatic) milieu of the organism, and if the recording processes set up within the nervous system were referred to as nerve impulses rather than stimuli. However, the term impulse designates, customarily, a more or less elementary neurophysiological phenomenon while many psychologists use the expression stimulus in referring to both elementary and higher data, including concepts. The ambiguity of the term stimulus is a minor inconvenience which should rarely if ever lead to confusion.

For the purpose of this presentation, it will suffice to differentiate between two categories of stimuli, namely, *reflex eliciting stimuli* and *intellective stimuli* (fig. 10). The former elicit what is known as reflex responses, the latter responses mediated at the intellective level of cerebral function. Reflex eliciting stimuli give rise to reaction patterns which fall into two groups, namely, *reflex release* and *reflex inhibition*, while intellective stimuli, basically, produce either *seeking responses* or *avoidance responses*. Either response pattern may take shape at the perceptual, the configurational, or at the conceptual level of sen-

sation. It may be noted even at this juncture that reflex release *is the functional primordium of seeking reactions; reflex inhibition, of avoidance reactions*. As stated on a previous occasion, the three levels correspond, respectively, to the anatomical levels I.s., II.s., and II.s. Perceptions are the most primitive sensory experiences, or low order intellective stimuli, while concepts, or high level intellective stimuli, are the most complex data of awareness. As compared to other data of consciousness, their sensory character is at a minimum. In other words, they are impalpable rather than concrete psychisms. (To the extent that concepts are the products of abstractive mental processes they are by their very nature "abstract" even though they may refer to objects.) Configurational stimuli, i.e., sensory experiences of gestalt character, are multitudes of perceptions having spatially or temporally specifiable relationships, which makes possible their unification to groups or units of a higher order. In the scale of sensory data, gestalten, (forms or shapes) occupy an intermediate position between perceptions and concepts. *Perceptions are extrinsically generated stimuli* (mirror images or analogs) *while concepts are intrinsically generated categorizing stimuli or analogs*, wherein the term extrinsic designates the origin of a stimulus outside the nervous system; the term intrinsic, the elaboration of perceptual material within the sensory division of the nervous system. *Concepts* are representative of *invariant relations* between sensory data of a relatively lower order and, in this respect, differ from the perceptual (palpable or concrete) analogs which "mirror" the physicochemical properties of stimulus producing objects or events. *Symbols* are, ordinarily, conventionalized configurational data designed to express psychisms of any complexity for the purpose of communication.

As implied in the term *stimulus*, the physiological phenomena under study (the processes set up in the nervous system) are not inert images but have *vector character*, that is to say, both *direction* and *magnitude*. These attributes are, in the final analysis, determined by the evaluative activity of cell stations located at various levels of the neuraxis. Stereotypy of response is at a maximum at lower levels; flexibility, at higher levels (Fig. 9). The *direction* of the stimulus has a bearing upon the character of the response, which may be an act of reflex release or reflex inhibition or, for that matter, a seeking or avoidance reaction while the *dynamic element* inherent in the stimulus influences the intensity of the response. Indifferent stimuli are limiting cases wherein both direction and magnitude of stimulation is zero.

The structural provisions or inbuilt mechanisms of the central nervous system make possible, even at its low levels, the apparently automatic evaluation of, and response to, reflex eliciting stimuli. Yet reflex responses, although basically autonomous, are to a certain extent modifiable by high level activity. The nerve centers concerned operate in the fashion of *information processing devices*. The "biological computers" are the response determinating organs or selector mechanisms of "biological robots" which utilize the data fed into them for the purpose of appropriate reactions. These considerations lead to the following points.

(a) The automaticity of reflex functions is not absolute, that is to say, that even reflex functions are not completely stereotyped but, rather, dependent on certain variables,

(b) The functions of lower strata are dependent on concomitant physiological conditions in the higher echelons of the nervous system which in turn are partly identical with the variables mentioned in the foregoing paragraph.

(c) The totality of centers of an anatomical system concerned with a given performance determines or "calculates" responses, taking into account internal and external factors.

(d) The performance patterns of the higher centers exceed those of the lower in that they are able to deal with an increasing number of variables and, thereby, to operate under conditions of increasing conditionality.

To make possible these operations, especially those listed under point (d), informative data must be represented in the sensory (and at the same time response determining) mechanism of the nervous system in a suitable fashion, or in a sufficiently versatile *system of notation*. (See below.) According to Hess (*378*) "centers are devices to establish connections. . . . Nervous elements located at different levels of the nervous system may constitute a center " . . . (anatomical system) . . ." A center is represented by a series of polysynaptic connections from among which, under the controlling influence of the peripheral situation, those connections are selected which give the appropriate patterns of directed motion."

The peripheral situation, we might add, determines the action of the center to the extent only that figures determine the results of calculations rather than the choice of the mathematical method employed.

Intellective stimuli: Their affective and cognitive components

In line with the increasing complexity of the nervous system in the higher forms of life, and in the interest of enhancing the range and adaptibility of responses on the part of the organism, high level stimuli (the representations, in the organism, of events in its environment), acquire a *signal component* or *cognitive component* in addition to their impulse component. Stated in a different way, reflex eliciting stimuli are elaborated to intellective stimuli by the addition of an appropriate *parameter* or *dimension*.

The viewpoint here taken is that the newly acquired cognitive component requires a special mode of representation or recording on the part of the highest sensory level of the neuraxis, and that this special system of notation in which the cognitive component is "given" is nothing other than the irreducible quality of conscious experience. It stands to reason that the phenomenon of awareness is irreducible since the highest sensory level is at the same time the ultimate; there exists no other system of notation anywhere in the nervous system beyond that peculiar to the highest level of cerebral function, more accurately, the highest sensory level. Consciousness, then, is nothing other than the irreducible notation system of the highest sensory level of the neuraxis, while its individual symbols, the units of the system of notation, are the data of awareness. In other words, consciousness is not an entity endowed with individual existence but a "mode" or a particular state of the function of the highest sensory grade, depending, in turn, on an appropriate degree of responsiveness imparted to it by the activating and alerting centers of the brainstem. (The term "mode" designates, in common parlance, the state of a substance but its meaning is here extended to cover the state of a function, more especially the degree of responsiveness or receptivity to stimuli.) It is the versatility of this system of notation which makes possible the manipulation of psychisms in thought and, in the interest of environmental control, the establishment of pertinent relationships between the data of the senses.

To reiterate: at advanced stages of evolution, there exist two categories of stimuli namely, (a) *uni-dimensional, reflex eliciting, stimuli* and (b) *bi-dimensional, intellective, stimuli* (fig. 10). The former release or, as the case may be, inhibit reflex functions ranging from primitive neural processes to highly complex synergies. Intellective stimuli, i.e., perceptions, configurations and concepts, are represented in a special notation system. They acquire a conscious representation at the highest sensory level, their non-conscious or "unconscious" representation (which may be more or less temporary) being a secondary phenomenon to be discussed later. (See "Subsidiary sphere of mentation.") The cognitive components of intellective stimuli are analogs or equivalents of events occurring in the milieu of the organism. Their impulse component, as expressed in terms of the newly acquired system of notation, is nothing other than the affective parameter of the intellective stimulus which assumes conscious quality concomitantly with the emergence of the cognitive component. It depends entirely on the proportion between the affective stimulus dimension (which, of course may be zero) and the cognitive stimulus dimension whether we refer to an intellective stimulus as a *conative psychism* (affect) or a *cognitive psychism* (idea). The concept here offered is not entirely new. According to Hampshire (*322*), "There is nothing in Spinoza's vocabulary which exactly corresponds to the ordinary distinction between feeling an emotion and thinking . . . and every kind and phase of consciousness involves having an idea, including even the mere experience of an emotion." In a similar vein, Freud (*270*) wrote that "no mental process even 'pure' thought is quite free from affect" (G.S., V. p. 289).

The conscious character of the affective component of intellective stimuli remains to be accounted for, the presumption being that, with increasing complexity of the response determinating mechanism, the emerging, cognitive rather than the "pre-existing" affective stimulus component requires that a special system of recording be put into operation. It is probably in the interest of unity of inner experience on the part of the highest sensory level that the impulse component of an intellective stimulus is represented in the very same system of notation as its signal component, and blended with the former to a higher element of awareness, thereby adding, to subjective reality, the element of "emotional coloring" which has no counterpart in the external world. Interestingly enough, under pathological conditions, e.g., in certain forms of epileptic aura, the two elements may become segregated and, for a time at least, exist in isolation.

What, precisely, is the relationship between the acquisition of a cognitive parameter on the part of reflex eliciting stimuli, and the increasing range and adaptibility of response? In the process of determining, or "calculating" appropriate responses to stimuli, the highest recording level which is, at the same time, the selector mechanism of the neuraxis, deals with two variables, namely,

(a) the *structure of the environmental changes*, and also of certain changes occurring in the *internal milieu* of the body, both of which generate stimuli in the sensory division of the highest level of cerebral function, and

(b) the *significance of the external and internal changes* with respect to the biological equilibrium of the organism. The factor of significance, a subjective variable that is, and, at the same time, the source of the self-centered nature of the organism, is equated with the objective structure of the stimuli concerned.

The cognitive parameter of an intellective stimulus i.e., the analog (equivalent) of the stimulus generating event, is the variable represented by the prevailing state of the environment (in the wider sense of the term) that acts as a stimulus. The peculiar, experiental quality conveyed by the affective component on the other hand reflects the biological significance of the stimulus.

Now since, in the final analysis, the very state of metabolic balance is an indicator and at the same time the prototype of biological equilibrium, it may reasonably be argued that affectivity is rooted in the metabolic requirements of the protoplasm or, for that matter, that affective states, ultimately, reflect both direction and degree to which a given state of homeostasis is influenced by events in the internal and the external environment of the organism. Certain exceptions to this rule notwithstanding, it may be said that the quality of an affect is a measure of biological equilibrium.

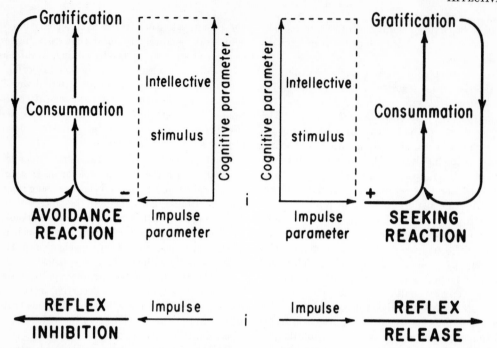

Fig. 10. The derivation of intellective stimuli from reflex eliciting stimuli, the bi-dimensionality of intellective stimuli, and the relationship between consummatory responses and gratification.
i: indifference point.

The mere recording of the biological significance of environmental changes by means of certain experiental qualities is however not the only role of affective states. *Affects are the impelling (positive) or aversive (negative) qualities of conscious experiences which not only reflect the biological requirements of living beings but which initiate reactions directed toward their reestablishment or realization.* In the absence of dynamic properties, affective states would have no recognizable function in the economy of the organism just like the vibrations of a seismograph have no influence upon the events that produced them. To repeat my previous point, there correspond, to certain physiological states, psychisms which are either impelling or aversive and which not only "express" these states but which, at the same time, tend to reduce the gradient between actual and ideal states of biological equilibrium just as, at the cellular level, biochemical factors tend to reduce the gradient between actual and ideal states of metabolic equilibrium. Needless to add that we neither stipulate a one to one correspondance between the diverse biological conditions and the various affective experiences nor,

for that matter, claim that the reactions elicited by the impulses concerned are invariably effective. Biological systems are not precision instruments but operate on a probability principle. Nevertheless, a good case may be made for the notion that affective states or, rather, the reactive processes they initiate, are patterned after biochemical feedback mechanisms having a relatively high confidence coefficient of integration.

Carrying the argument to its final conclusion, we note that, owing to the intimate relationships between metabolic and autonomic nervous system functions, the maintenance of biological equilibrium is closely dependent on the activity of the vegetative nervous system, and the same applies, in the psycho-autonomic sphere of integration, to the maintenance of *affective homeostasis* or psychobiological equilibrium.

Affective states, then, setting aside for the moment their dynamic or reactive character, reflect equilibratory needs of the body. The prototype of affective states are gradients between actual and ideal states of homeostasis so that, by and large, the degree of affective homeostasis is a measure of biological homeostasis as experienced at the highest level of integrational complexity. Kuntz (*526*), in a monograph devoted to the phenomena of visceral innervation and its relation to the personality, voiced a similar opinion. He pointed out that the "most primitive components of behaviour are essentially visceral, as they spring from the vital requirements of the organism, that such behaviour is essentially emotional, and that the higher forms of emotional behaviour have undoubtedly the same origin."

The following, is in the main, a *summary* of our remarks on intellective stimuli and their *affective and cognitive dimensions.*

(a) Reflex release and reflex inhibition operating at lower levels of the nervous system evolve, respectively, to seeking (impelling) responses and to avoidance (aversive) responses. Reflex-release is the functional primordium of the seeking responses; reflex-inhibition, of the avoidance responses.

(b) Seeking and avoidance reactions are primary behavioural response patterns elicited by impelling or aversive, i.e., affective components of intellective stimuli. The former establish behavioural trends while the cognitive components serve finer behavioural adjustments. In fact, they may reverse trends of action initiated by the inherent directionality of affects.

(c) Affects are not psychic entities in their own right. What we call an affect is that experiental quality of an intellective stimulus which is imparted to it by the homeostatic element inherent in its impulse parameter, or the manifestation of a homeostatic tendency which has, by its very nature, dynamic properties. At the same time, the affect is the vectorial component of the total (bi-dimensional) intellective stimulus which, in turn, may be of a perceptual or a configurational or a conceptual order.

(d) The functional primordium of the affect is the homeostatic element (equilibratory factor) inherent in reflex eliciting stimuli, i.e., either in reflex release or reflex inhibition so that, because of the autonomic character of homeostatic processes and, at the same time, the experiental qualities of affects, autonomic phenomena and affective states (psycho-autonomic phenomena) can be readily correlated. This correlation becomes even closer owing to the fact that responsiveness levels of the organism (the central setting of the homeostatic apparatus) are under autonomic control.

(e) In a certain sense, *affectivity*, being an inner, experiental state, is internalized responsiveness to stimuli while *drive* is externalized responsiveness to stimuli. Within the standard homeostatic range, drive is a measure of affectivity; and affectivity, in turn, a measure of responsiveness. The higher the responsiveness of the organism, the stronger the affective component of intellective stimuli. The terms *drive* and *affect*, as here employed, refer to different phenomena although "drives" (Triebe) are identical with *instinctual drives* or *instincts* to be discussed presently.

The cleavage between uni-dimensional, reflex eliciting stimuli and bi-dimensional, intellective, stimuli is to a degree artificial. Every level of animal organization, in any event, every organizational level no matter how primitive yet comparable to the human level, is equipped with sense organs and, hence, operates with at least orimentary perceptual stimuli. Furthermore, there is embodied, even in the primitive, "sub-intellective" neurodynamic processes, a nascent, cognitive component which warrants the application of the term "impulse-signal" to affective states. The "wisdom of the body" demands that even the seemingly blind nerve process and, accordingly, the seemingly blind affect, operate as a signal and, to that extent at least, has a cognitive ingredient which comes to the fore in the self-equilibrating activity of the organism.

The above outlined approach to the problem of affectivity (and, indirectly, of the nature of emotions) answers the criteria of neuropsychology formulated in the opening chapter, which stipulate that psychological phenomena, or higher nervous system functions in general, be defined in terms of (a) their functional primordium and (b) their specific quotas of action which emerge, at higher levels, to increase the operational dimensions of the former. At the same time, we have demonstrated that the more adaptive functions mediated by the higher levels supersede the more primitive functions of the lower but that, nevertheless, the "functions of the nervous system being the same at all levels," the more highly integrated functions maintain the general organizational pattern of their precursors.

The terms impulse components and signal components of intellective stimuli are of course nothing more than convenient shorthand expressions which must be made explicit in terms of physiological events. Earlier in this chapter, we spoke of three categories of "trans-hypothalamic" stimuli which form the neural and biochemical basis of behaviour (fig. 8, A, B, and C). It is precisely these processes which form the experiental basis of the impulse parameters of intellective stimuli, which is another way of phrasing the now familiar idea that affects are the mode in which there are experienced, at the highest level of brain function, the dynamic properties of intellective stimuli while the homeostatic tendencies inherent in the processes in question are the functional primordium of affective states. The neuropsychological basis of the *affective component* or *impulse parameter* of an intellective stimulus is thus a complex of physiological processes made up of (a) neural events mediated by the diencephalo-frontal and limbic systems, and (b) of correlated (hormonal and metabolic) processes. The neuropsychological basis of the *cognitive component* or *signal parameter* of an intellective stimulus on the other hand is a complex of neural events mediated by the posterior cortex, more especially its highest functional level. The most complex (impalpable) signal components are thus the domain of the conceptual level (III.s.), the less complex (palpable) components the domain of the configurational level (II.s.) and the least complex (palpable) components that of the perceptual level (I.s.). With rise in the phylogenetic scale the cognitive components become increasingly conceptualized and, at the same time, the lower intellective components "embodied" into the highest, conceptual component, which may be regarded as the physiological formulation of the principle of the "intellective nature of perception," or "Intellektualität der Anschauung" discussed in Immanuel Kant's writings. Lastly, as expressed in terms explained in the opening chapter, the quota of action underlying the impulse component of an intellective stimulus is contributed, to the composite process (the organic background of the intellective stimulus as a whole) by the diencephalo-frontal and limbic systems while the quota of action underlying the cognitive component is the product of the activity of the posterior cortex.

Instincts

The word *instinct* is a generic term referring to a wide variety of complexly integrated synergies, their experiental preconditions and accompaniments. According to Craig (*172*) and Lorenz (*583*) instinctive behaviour is compounded of two response patterns, namely, appetitive behaviour and the consummatory act. *Appetitive behaviour* is the variable introductory phase of an instinctive behaviour pattern or response; the *consummatory act*, the termination of a given behaviour pattern or sequence (*904*). It may be tentatively stated that, in terms of the stimulus-response scheme here proposed, appetitive behaviour is initiated by reflex eliciting stimuli while the consummatory act is sparked by (generally low order) intellective stimuli conventionally referred to a *sign stimuli* or *releasers*.

Appetitive behaviour or Sherrington's (*831*) *precurrent response*, which serves the quest for releasing stimuli, is apt to establish the conditions which lead to appropriate consummatory reactions. The searching movements prior to the act of feeding which may be seen in young animals are a classic example of appetitive behaviour while the consummatory act involves the actual feeding synergy. In contrast to the relatively rigid consummatory act initiated by the releasing stimulus, appetitive behaviour is said to be relatively flexible.

From what has gone before, it is apparent that *the term instinct is merely a shorthand expression covering two characteristic phases or a pattern of behaviour.* Instinctively operating stimuli involve a combination of (a) reflex eliciting stimuli which actuate use patterns involved in appetitive behaviour and (b) intellective stimuli which actuate use patterns involved in consummatory activity. Some of the use patterns are innate while others develop in the course of the maturation of the organism. It will be convenient to discuss the two phases of instinctive behaviour (including the nature of the stimuli by which they are elicited) in the reverse order of their actual sequence.

As a rule, which, however, has certain exceptions, the intellective stimulus that initiates the consummatory reaction is of a low order of complexity (*852*). It may be a primitive perception, for example, a simple olfactory stimulus. On the other hand, the affective loading or impulse value of the stimulus concerned is apt to be high, if not overwhelming. In spite of the strength of the stimulus involved in instinctive behaviour, its apparent automaticity is modifiable by *corrective engrams*. We have already indicated that, under high threshold conditions (reduced responsiveness) an otherwise releasing stimulus becomes indifferent, and that the responsiveness of the organism to low order intellective stimuli or releasers which initiate the consummatory act may depend on seasonal factors, among others. The sexual behaviour of many animals and, to a degree of man, is dependent on changing patterns of responsiveness which may display a high degree of periodicity. It is further to be noted that the intellective stimulus which releases the consummatory act is not necessarily primitive but may be spatially or temporally patterned. In animals, the specificity of the stimulus structure may be characteristic for a given species and, in man, the stimulus response pattern involved in any kind of instinctive behaviour highly individualistic, or "a matter of taste." The magnitude of the affective component of low order intellective stimuli is apt to be greater than that of high order intellective stimuli. For example, the releaser of the consummatory act is as we have said generally a low order intellective stimulus or a perception having a strong impulse component, in comparison to which the impulse component (the affective leading) of almost any concept is low. This rule however does not apply to stimuli of a conceptual order operating in strong biological needs.

Biologically and physiologically, consummatory acts are *seeking responses* and, implicitly, whenever the affectively charged precipitating stimulus is positive, are patterned after release phenomena at lower levels of integration. By the same token, the "releasing" stimulus may elicit an *avoidance response*, which is analogous to its functional primordium, namely, an *inhibitory* phenomenon at lower levels of function (fig. 10). Craig (*172*) aptly speaks of *appetites* and *aversions* involved in instinctual behaviour.

The intellective stimulus which releases the consummatory act is primarily a detector or guide, which makes possible appropriate seeking and avoidance behaviour. From this angle, the intellective level is an auxiliary mechanism erected upon the instinctive level of cerebral function, which brings out the wisdom of the word, already quoted, that the Intellect is a beacon of the Will. However, since sense organs exist at any phylogenetic level of animal organization, and, implicitly, intellective stimuli which trigger consummatort acts, the cleavage between,

on the one hand, the intellective superstructure of instinctive life and, on the other, a lower, instinctive level of cerebral function is relative rather than absolute. Further, since perceptions are the oriments of configurational stimuli which, for their part, are the oriments of concepts, Herbert Spencer's word of the "continuity of instinct and reason" is amply vindicated.

At infra-instinctual levels of function, for example, those concerned with the regulation of digestion, of blood pressure and the righting of the animal, complexly integrated mechanisms are set in motion by reflex eliciting stimuli rather than intellective stimuli. The former, which trigger highly coordinated processes are, for example, the presence of food in the pyloric part of the stomach, or changes of the pH of the blood. The processes in question are controlled by biological feedbacks. There is a significant difference (which, strangely enough, is not generally appreciated) between reflex synergies and instinctive behaviour.

Needs are the mode in which there is experienced, at the highest sensory and evaluative level of the neuraxis, the affective pressure of those reflex eliciting stimuli which initiate appetitive behaviour rather than of stimuli which initiate mere chain reflexes. A need, being directed toward an object, is a hinge as it were connecting the internal world of the organism with its external world. The satisfaction of needs establishes a biological context between living beings and their environment. On the other hand, stimuli which initiate chain reflexes connect sets of biological processes within the organism.

At this point, then, *instinctive behaviour* may be more accurately defined as behaviour *combining the features of reflexly determined responses with those of intellectively determined responses*, in that (a) the *reflex eliciting stimulus becomes an affectively loaded intellective psychism or need* and (b) the *intellective stimulus*, or releaser of the consummatory reaction, unless cancelled or modified by corrective engrams, *operates in a reflex like fashion*.

Ordinarily, needs are intrinsic stimuli while releasers are extrinsic in origin. Under low threshold conditions, the intellective stimulus operating as a releaser of the consummatory act may be represented by an ekphorized engram which, thus, takes the place of the *releaser* or *sign stimulus*. At the same time, the consummatory act assumes imaginal character.

Conflicts arise under the following conditions. The seeking reactions (appetitive behavioural reactions) ordinarily produced by intrinsically generated stimuli may be counterbalanced by avoidance reactions caused in turn by the affective components of intellective stimuli, e.g., by *complexes*. Otherwise, the effect of releasers which, ordinarily, initiate the consummatory act, is counterbalanced by intellective stimuli generated by the intellective "superstructure." In the latter eventuality, they will interfere with stimuli operating at lower levels of integration. The counterbalancing intellective stimulus or inhibitor may be of any order of complexity, ranging from perceptions to concepts. (Freud's term "antithetic ideas" covers inhibitory stimuli of a higher, complexual, nature.) By the same token, conflicts arise when avoidance reactions no matter how primitive or imposed upon by society, are counteracted by seeking reactions. In either instance, the unresolved conflict situation produces a state of *internal frustration* while *external frustration* is caused by extraneous factors. Vicious circle mechanisms may develop if external frustration initiates internal frustration or, conversely, internal frustration engenders external frustration.

The answer, to the question: "What is an instinct?" must take into account the biological, physiological, anatomical and psychological aspects of instinctive behaviour which, of necessity, overlap in various directions. The following is a summary and at the same time an amplification of what has gone before.

Biologically, instincts are behaviour patterns which aim at the maintenance of the organism and the species. The latter may take precedence over the former as parent organism may sacrifice its life to protect the young.

Physiologically, instincts are the instigators of seeking and avoidance responses subserving the biological equilibrium of the organism The impulse component of instinctive stimuli accounts for their dynamic properties; their signal component which, however, is not necessarily overt, for their directionality. The responses actuated by the stimuli in question are spatially and temporally patterned synergies. They resemble chain reflexes which are, to a degree, modifiable by experiences.

Anatomically, the synergies involved in instinctive behaviour are dependent on the presence of specific structural provisions or use patterns

which are the material substrate of the former. Some use patterns are innate while others mature in the course of the ontogenesis concurrently with the development of endocrine functions.

Earlier in this chapter, we pointed out that the "organ of affectivity," having a hierarchical organization, is compounded of three systems which can be correlated with certain physiological factors. (See fig. 8A, B, and C.) We suggested that system A or, for that matter, factor A, controls the waking state, attention and responsiveness (both immediate and delayed) to stimuli while the other two systems represent the structural and/or biochemical basis of primitive motivational, affectively loaded, impulses or instinctive needs originating in the visceral (including sexual) sphere of the organism.* It is in relation to these instinctive needs that environmental stimuli are evaluated and answered by appropriate responses. More specifically, system B mediates the flow of impulses transmitted to the visceral including olfactalimentary and "propagative" cortex (*50*) while the third system represents the stream of hormonal and metabolic (blood borne) stimuli. The three contingents of impulses play upon the hypothalamus prior to their evaluation by the cortex of the cerebral hemispheres. Hess's (*379*) investigations and those of his co-workers (*381*), suggest a specific relationship between certain segments of the hypothalamus and instinctive needs and patterns of behaviour.

In a summary of Hess' studies, Gloor (*309*) writes that some highly integrated activities which are expressive of instinctively guided behaviour and of "emotional drives" include, apart from the experimental production of the *sleep pattern, affective defense reactions, feeding responses* and *pacing responses*. "The affective defense reactions produced by stimulation of a certain part of the hypothalamus is an example of complex emotional autonomic and somatic behaviour. The pupils of the animal are dilated and there is piloerection. The cat spits and growls. If the stimulation is maintained there is sometimes involuntary micturition and defecation and finally the animal attacks a person nearby. Hess thinks that this behaviour is the expression of an internally created state of emotion. If another area of the hypothalamus is stimulated, the animal searches for food which, when presented, is eaten

---

* We remind ourselves that the affective loading occurs at higher levels of the neuraxis.

with voracity even when the animal was unwilling to take food before stimulation. If a still more posteriorly located part of the hypothalamus is stimulated, the animal becomes restless and moves around without any special goal. All observations have in common that the patterns of behaviour are displayed in perfect coordination and that they represent integrated wholes of movements associated with the experience of affect."

Hess' experiments demonstrate that, as expressed in terms of instinctive behaviour, the stimulating electrode sparks not only the central representation of reflex eliciting stimuli or needs which actuate appetitive behaviour but also the representation of the sign stimuli or releasers which evoke consummatory reactions. More precisely, experimental stimulation forces appetitive behaviour and consummatory acts upon the automaton to which the animal has been converted. (See also Olds, *696a*.)

Psychologically, the term instinct refers to the mode in which there is recorded, at the highest sensory level of the nervous system, the pressure of stimuli having a high affective charge and involved in certain vital activities. Clinical observations to be discussed presently add to our knowledge of the role of the cerebral cortex in instinctual life and, implicitly, emotional behaviour. And they illuminate the relationships between, on the one hand, the affective component of intellective stimuli and the diencephalo-frontal system (see above) and, on the other, between the cognitive component and the posterior cortex. On the supposition that the affective and the cognitive component of the stimuli in question are blended to a higher, composite, unit of experience, the cortical representation of their affective component is only to be expected.

Weil (*937*) observed that "ictal emotions," chiefly of a depressive character, which appear suddenly and without motivation, are frequently associated with epileptogenic temporal lobe disorders and he made reference to Penfield and Jasper (*721*) who evoked emotional reactions, including fear, sadness, fright and some of their accompaniments by stimulation of the temporal lobe at operation. Williams (*962*) studied 100 patients with temporal lobe lesions who felt an emotion as part of their epileptiform seizures. Sixty-one patients experienced fear, twenty-one

depression, nine a pleasant and an equal number an unpleasant feeling tone as part of their seizure or, paroxysmally, between seizures. The emotion was unrelated to any thought process and, in half of the cases, accompanied by visceral sensations and movements. Similar observations were previously reported by Jackson (*421*) and Gowers (*316*).

Now, if the bi-dimensional, intellective, stimuli are generated in the temporal lobes, a part of the posterior cortex that is, (at this juncture, Broadbent's idea of the "centre of concepts and ideation" comes to mind) it is not unreasonable to assume that temporal lobe disease may cause their dissociation so that either component of an intellective stimulus may be experienced independently. Thus one may observe either the "out of context" activation of the impulse component of an intellective stimulus as an *isolated affect*, or, alternately, of the isolated cognitive component as *intellectual aura*. In fact, affective and cognitive fractions of different intellective stimuli may be actuated concurrently so that, owing to their simultaneity, they seem to be linked together and the affect appears to be incongruous.

The aforementioned observations are of interest from various angles.

Firstly, keeping in mind that the term "localization of function in the nervous system" refers, in the final analysis, to quotas of action contributed by an individual arrangement of neurons to the total process of integration, the data in question may provide a clue as to the localization, in the temporal cortex, of impulse components of intellective stimuli. More precisely, seeking and avoidance impulses, being mediated by certain provinces of the frontal lobes as the highest level of the autonomic, diencephalo-frontal system, have become linked up in the posterior cortex with conceptually represented experiences, and thereby elaborated to affective modalities which are more highly developed than those involved in crude bipolar seeking and avoidance responses mediated by the frontal cortex. If it were possible to amputate Broadbent's centre of concepts and ideation from the remaining parts of the brain, the highest cerebral functions would be either *reflex release* experienced as seeking response unaccompanied by thought or *reflex inhibition* experienced as "thoughtless" avoidance reaction. In other words, affective experiences would not branch out into the diversified feelings and emotions which, like joy and depression, are apt to emerge concomitantly with the cognitive components of intellective stimuli and which, in contrast to the more primitive seeking and avoidance phenomena, are almost as variegated as the meanings of concepts. Interestingly enough, the type of behaviour which, we imagine, would result from the above described disorganization of brain function, develops in frontal lobe disease where, the normal interplay of anterior and posterior cortex function having been disrupted, anterior cortex function is neither refined nor modified by posterior cortex function. In frontal lobe disease, the posterior cortex does not add its quota of action to frontal cortex activity which, accordingly, displays its activity pattern in isolation as it were. As a result, the conduct of the frontal lobe patient may be expressed in terms of primitive seeking or avoidance reactions that are uninhibited or unmodified by posterior cortex control. Further, since the intrinsic posterior cortex mechanism is intact, but, to a large extent, deprived of the homeostatic, responsiveness and drive regulating influence vested in the anterior cortex, the underproductivity or inordinate overproductivity seen in frontal lobe disease may be accounted for by a dyshomeostatic factor. It is not immediately apparent why the linkage between cognitive and affective elements is a function of the temporal lobes. Owing, may be, to their association with verbalized thought, they are the very core of Broadbent's center of concepts and ideation

Secondly, the observations reported by Weil and others bring out our point that epileptiform seizures are forceful and distorted activitation patterns of synergies occurring, out of context, at any level of integrational complexity,

Thirdly, they clinical data in question permit to draw a parallel between, on the one hand, epileptiform manifestations and, on the other, the dissociation between the affective and the cognitive component of intellective stimuli occurring in dreams, in various abnormal experiences of schizophrenics and upon the administration of certain chemical compounds, e.g., adrenaline. They are not only consistent with our conception of the bidimensionality of intellective stimuli but suggest the presence of a basic mechanism involved in their fractionation.

The study of instincts has carried us to the borderline of pathophysiology and pathopsy-

chology. We shall resume the discussion of instincts in connection with the study of thinking, for instinctive activity is the functional primordium of thought. Macleary (*598*) wrote that intelligence is the essential adaptation of means to an end while instinct is the working out of results by an automatic function. It is this "working out" process which we attempted to specify and to fit into the stimulus-response scheme here proposed. Instinctive behaviour is not contingent upon the knowledge of aims. Moreover, at least in the primitive and the immature organism, the means have only to be detected rather than invented. The total response patterns is purposive and modifiable by informative stimuli impinging upon the organism both in the course of and after the completion of instinctive activity. Man, in yielding to instinctive stimuli, witnesses, from the closest possible vantage point, the play of organizational forces—of the blind yet purposive Will.

Gratification and frustration

Apposite affects involved in gratification and frustration

Gratification is the mode in which there is experienced the consummation of seeking responses caused by impelling affects or of avoiding responses caused by aversive affects. *Frustration* is experienced when seeking reactions are thwarted or avoiding reactions are forced on the organism. Thus, frustration is exper enced whenever, at higher levels of integration release is substituted for inhibition or, conversely, inhibition for release (fig. 10).

Within limits, *gratification* tends to perpetuate itself. In other words, gratification, or pleasure in the widest sense of the term, is a *potentially self-perpetuating stimulus, producing a "consummatory closed loop response."* However, since, ordinarily, gratification wanes and sooner or later, reaches the indifference point of pleasurable experience, seeking reactions are sooner or later superseded by avoidance reactions. The propensity of impelling affects to keep themselves alive (although, it is true, for a limited period of time) complicates the psychology of affects and emotions; *gratification, which flows from the consummation of a seeking reaction, assumes, for a time at least, the properties of an impelling, positive affect, which re-initiates the seeking reaction by which gratification was produced.* Similar considerations apply to inhibitory affects which however tend to perpetuate themselves almost indefinitely. A positive affect indicates that the gap between actual and ideal equilibrium is being narrowed or at least maintained. A negative affect on the other hand indicates that the gap is produced or widened.

In a certain sense, *perpetuation* is the generalized signal component of pleasurable experiences. By the same token, *termination* is the generalized signal component of painful experiences. To put it in another way, the impulse component and the signal component merge as it were as perpetuation becomes the very "significance" of pleasure and, by the same token, termination the very "significance" of pain.*

Anticipated gratification calls forth impelling ("seeking") affects or impulses while *anticipated frustration* elicits repelling ("avoiding") affects or impulses. Anticipated gratification operates in the fashion of a corroborative engram; anticipated frustration, of a corrective engram.

Seeking and avoidance responses at various levels of cognition

Gratification and frustration may be brought about by perceptual, configurational and conceptual stimuli. At the *perceptual* level of sensation, gratification is produced by consummatory responses to certain more or less elementary visual, auditory, tactile, kinesthetic, somesthetic, proprioceptive, olfactory and gustatory stimuli respectively. At the *configurational* level, it is produced by consummatory responses to certain temporally patterned auditory stimuli and spatially organized visual impressions. As will be discussed at some length in the concluding chapter, affective states produced by, and associated with, the consummation of seeking responses at the configurational level are the basis of esthetic emjoyment. At the *conceptual* level, where perception is at a minimum, gratification derives from diverse intellectual pursuits, be they followed for their own sake, like the appreciation of temporal and spatial forms in esthetic enjoyment, or engaged in for practical purposes. With

---

* As Nietzsche wrote in his "Also sprach Zarathustra"—"Leid spricht: vergeh! Doch alle Lust will Ewigkeit."

rise in the phylogenetic scale, and at all levels of cognition, especially the highest, seeking and avoidance behaviour is to an increasing degree initiated by ekphorized engrams rather than by actual stimuli, the basic motives however remaining, as at the lowest levels, (and in stimulus-bound situation) gratification or reward, and avoidance of frustration or punishment. The stronger the admixture of mnemonic elements in behaviour and the more "abstract" the engrams involved, the more human the behaviour; the weaker the proportion of mnemonic factors and the greater the proportion of concrete material, the more animal-like the behaviour. As we have already indicated, this particular type of behaviour comes to the fore under pathological conditions, more specifically in frontal lobe disease.

In a certain sense, personality types may be classified with respect to their *gratification preference*. The lowest, most primitive personality type, being closest to the animal stage—in terram pronus and ventri obediens—seeks gratification at the perceptual level, more especially in the digestive, sexual etc spheres (along the lines of Edinger's "oral sense" and senses of a comparable order) and at the conceptual level only to the extent that thinking is relegated to an instrument of the lower senses. The opposite personality type seeks gratification at the conceptual level. The well integrated personality, having sensuous, artistic and intellectual interests, seeks gratification at all levels of activity, and it may be crippled by the lack of two of them. However, at different times, different components of the personality may come to the fore, thereby establishing any conceivable transition between the unified (syntonic) personality and double and multiple personalities.

Lastly, at all levels of cognition, gratification may flow not only from the consummation of seeking reactions but also of avoidance reactions. (fig. 10). At the perceptual level, gratification is associated with the avoidance of certain elementary, non-pleasurable or painful stimuli; at the configurational level, with the avoidance of certain non-pleasurable spatially or temporally patterned stimulus groups; at the conceptual level, with the avoidance of stimulus situations which overtax the relation-generating resources of the organism or, more often than not, perhaps, of stimuli whose consummation has no obvious relationships to its biological equilibrium.

On the surface, it would seem rather odd to stipulate a causal relationship between gratification and the consummation of avoidance reactions, and it is to be admitted that gratification derived from avoidance behaviour is perhaps nothing more than the absence of frustration. Be this as it may, it is true that, with advancing years at least, life having been spent with the evaluation of stimuli and the kind of responses to be expected, the style of life is increasingly dominated by the trend to avoid pain rather than to seek pleasure.

Inapposite affects involved in gratification and frustration

Inapposite affects are impulse components of intellective stimuli which cause *inhibition* (avoidance) in stimulus situations in which the normal (apposite) response would be release (seeking) or, conversely, which cause *release* where the normal (apposite) response would be inhibition. Inapposite affects may develop either on an organic basis, e.g., (chiefly in children and adolescents) as a result of epidemic encephalitis, or they may develop as the result of frustration. In the first eventuality, the disorganization of affective states is caused by a pathological process involving the diencephalon as the chief organic basis of the quota of action underlying the impulse component of intellective stimuli. (Similar considerations apply to the changed affectivity in frontal lobe disease.) In the second eventuality, a substandard frustration-gratification ratio leads to the reorientation of affective vectors (fig. 10). *Pathological inhibitions* are caused by inapposite affects which, although they do not eliminate a need, prevent, by counterbalancing the actuating impulse, the actual consummation of seeking reactions. Pathological *compulsions* on the other hand, are caused by inapposite affects which, in producing a need, prevent, at the same time, by counterbalancing inhibitory impulses, the consummation of avoidance reactions. Briefly stated, pathological compulsions force seeking responses on the organism; pathological inhibitions, avoidance responses. In either eventuality, the conflict situation is brought to an end by defeat associated, it is true, with an element of gratification. No doubt there exists a close relationship between mechanisms involved in pathological inhibitions and compulsions, and the compromise character of neurotic symptoms postulated by the psychoanalysts.

Patterns of gratification and frustration

A person's *saturation-potential* may be expressed in terms of distance e.g., the *distance* of the indifference point of saturation from the point of initiation of a pleasurable experience. Alternatively, the saturation-potential may be defined in terms of *time*, i.e., the time at which the individual reaches a state of refractoriness to stimuli originally experienced as pleasurable.

Saturation control is a measure of the ability to postpone the inevitable transition from a state of pleasurable stimulation to a state of indifference and, eventually, non-pleasurable or painful experience.

Frustration proneness is a mental disposition which endengers the thwarting of seeking reactions and the imposition upon the organism of inapposite avoidance responses, so that gratification is crowded out as it were by frustration. As will be shown in the section of the present chapter concerned with the nature of neurotic behaviour, the response pattern in question may be brought out by frustrating experiences incident to disruptive stimulation and, by causing a substandard frustration-gratification ratio, is likely to initiate a vicious circle mechanism. Ordinarily, high frustration proneness is associated with a low saturation potential, low frustration proneness with a high saturation potential.

Frustration tolerance is the ability to maintain indifference in spite of an unfavourable or substandard frustration-gratification ratio.

Intolerance of gratification is the production of non-pleasurable affective states by a favourable frustration-gratification ratio. Freud (*270*) spoke of "neurotics who cannot tolerate success" (G.S., X., p. 370).

Dysphoria is an affective state which combines one or more of the following: low saturation potential, low saturation control, increased frustration proneness, low frustration tolerance and intolerance of gratification. In *euphoria*, on the other hand, there exists, singly or in combination, high saturation potential, high saturation control, decreased frustration proneness, increased or absolute frustration tolerance and, implicitly, low or absent intolerance of gratification. In a general way the term dysphoria designates a more or less prolonged or habitual negative affective state or mood, while the term euphoria denotes a more or less prolonged or habitual positive affective state or mood. *Aphoria* is a state of indifference or the zero point between dysphoria and euphoria.

Moods, emotions, feelings, sentiments and attitudes

Although affects have dynamic properties (their functional primordium being either reflex release or reflex inhibition—that is, responses serving homeostatic functions), their impulse value varies within a wide range. Indeed, certain affective states have only the experiental qualities of affects but, in spite of their derivation from reflexes, lack the dynamic properties of affects. They are brought out by frustration, but do not elicit remedial action; less often, by gratification which,

however, they do not tend to prolong. These peculiar states, *reactive* (secondary) *moods*, have the tendency to become not only linked up with experiences other than those by which they were produced, but to influence the general train of thought in a mood-specific direction. By contrast, *endogenous* (primary) *moods* are not attributable to any particular experience, in any case, not to any overt experience. Their influence upon cognitive data of awareness and the stream of thought is identical with that of secondary moods. Thus, it is necessary to distinguish, on the one hand, between *secondary* dysphoria, euphoria and aphoria, which are within limits normal reactions and, on the other, *primary* dysphoria, euphoria and aphoria, which are ordinarily abnormal, especially if extending beyond a certain range of intensity.

TABLE 1

POSITIVE AND NEGATIVE AFFECTIVE MODALITIES. THE AFFECTIVE LOADING OF INTELLECTIVE STIMULI

Positive and Negative Affective Modalities Pertaining to the Personal Sphere	
Affective modalities indicative of gratification:	Affective modalities indicative of frustration:
Feeling of	Feeling of
Satisfaction	Dissatisfaction
Adequacy	Inadequacy
Superiority	Inferiority
Assertiveness	Timidity
Confidence	Insecurity
Joy	Sadness
Elation	Depression
Pride	Shame
Positive and Negative Affective Modalities Pertaining to Interpersonal Relations	
Feelings of attachment	Feelings of aversion
Admiration	Contempt
Affection	Hatred
Gratitude	Resentment

Emotions occupy an intermediate position between moods and affects. They are intensified (secondary) moods but, in contrast to moods, closely linked up with the very experience to which they can be traced. In contrast to affects, they do not necessarily instigate action. *Feelings*, having a stronger cognitive component than moods, are mitigated, but protracted emotions. *Sentiments* are characterized by an even stronger cognitive element and a weaker conative elements than feelings; and *attitudes*, in turn, by a stronger cognitive and a weaker conative ele-

ment than sentiments. It is apparent that mood swings bear a close relationship to mania-depression; and attitudes, once they have become inflexible and grown to rigid believes, to paranoid reactions. The difference between, on one hand, impulse components of intellective stimuli, i.e., affects having *dynamic* properties and, on the other, passive or *inert* affective states is one of degree rather than in kind. Accordingly, the mental phenomena under study are extremes of a unitary scale. They can be traced to the affective components of intellective stimuli which, in turn, are derivatives of reflex eliciting stimuli. States of disequilibrium involving vital functions of the organism precipitate forceful affects which, under ideal conditions at least, remedy the situation instantly. By the same token, certain seeking reactions are sparked by impulses of overwhelming intensity. Clearly, it is this category of affective states which is most intimately related to reflex eliciting stimuli. By contrast, the second, "static" group of affective experiences neither remedy the situation nor do they necessarily incite action. Being pleasurable or painful experiences of relatively low intensity, they are merely a measure of emotional homeostasis or dyshomeostatis, or gratification and frustration. However, upon reinforcement, even these mitigated affects may operate as motives, and apparent pasivity flare into violent action. As expressed in a different way, abnormal moods may be associated with episodes of hyperaffectivity.

A detailed discussion of emotions, feelings, and related phenomena is outside of the scope of this investigation. In the accompanying table 1 we have contrasted affective states that apply to the self, with those that may develop in interpersonal relationships and which, to the extent that they are caused by frustrating experiences, operate in neurotic and psychotic mechanisms.

Remarks on personality organization

The term personality designates the *habitual reaction and behaviour patterns of an individual*. In the extreme case, the pattern may be so characteristic as to be virtually predictable for the behaviour of a person in a given situation. The peculiar nature of behaviour and response is primarily dependent on the affective component of the stimuli which, in turn, are determined by environmental events that have a bearing upon the biological equilibrium of the organism.

Although the stimuli produced by higher sensory centers are bi-dimensional, that is, compounded of an affective and a cognitive parameter, the latter is a personality factor which plays a minor role by comparison. What is more, the functional primordium of affective states is the homeostatic element inherent in the impulse component of intellective stimuli which, in turn, establishes a close relationship between personality patterns and the autonomic sphere of the organism.

Personality, then, is primarily, a "function" of affectivity. And inasmuch as the specificity of the affective makeup of a person may be expressed in terms of deviation from a normal standard (an ideal state or postulate rather than a reality) personality patterns may be said to fall into three broad groups, namely, an *euphoric*, a *dysphoric* and an *aphoric* variety. The individual traits characteristic for each group have already been specified. They include, among other features, saturation potential and frustration tolerance. In each group, inapposite affectivity, which establishes the "deviant" character of a given personality type, may manifest itself by the tendency to respond to stimuli with specific moods, emotions, feelings, attitudes and sentiments. Inapposite affectivity, e.g., sociopathic and aggressive trends, cruelty impulses, submissiveness, etc, may be innate or acquired. In the second eventuality, a person's affective makeup may be the result of organic disease, for example epidemic encephalitis, which produces the "psychopathic personality." Unphysiological stimulation, including exposure to neurotifying stimuli, may have a similar effect.

As we have said, intellectual traits are of secondary importance in assessing personality types. Intellectual endowment or, for that matter, the relative lack of it is compatible with any affective response pattern. On the other hand, gratification preference, as previously defined, is a characteristic feature of personality organization. Euphoric, dysphoric and aphoric personalities are entities which, in one direction, shade off into "normality"; in the other, into frank neurosis and psychosis. The *dysphrenic* (schizoid) and *hysterical* personality types will be discussed under the appropriate headings.

On the surface, the classification of personality types in terms of deviations from a normal (quasi-hypothetical) standard or mean and, implicitly, their relationship to the neuroses and psychoses may seem unnatural but a moment's reflection shows that, if dev ations did not occur, that is, if human beings would behave uniformly, the very concept of personality would hardly exist. Even the phenomenon of *double personality* can be expressed in the terms here proposed. They are produced by strong ambivalent trends which convert the affective component of intellective stimuli into vectors of opposite direction and of equal or unequal magnitude, as the case may be.

Comment and criticism

Theories concerned with the nature of instincts

Our own theory of instincts is based on Lorenz' work which we attempted to integrate into the *stimulus-response psychology* developed in the present monograph. It is noteworthy that the elements of Lorenz' theory are already present in Schopenhauer's writings. (See especially, "The World as Will and Idea," vol. II., p. 390 and 391 of the 10th Frauenstaedt Edition, 1916). The gist of the theory is embodied in a number of passages which, in translation, read as follows. "The instinct, although an outspoken striving, does not, like the spring of a watch, act from within only." [*The intrinsically generated, reflex eliciting stimulus is not the only factor involved in instinctual behaviour.*] "Rather, inst'ncts wait for an external factor necessary for action" [*the stimulus releasing the consummatory act*] "which determines the time for the manifestation of the instincts. Such external factors are, e.g., for the migrating bird, the appropriate season; for the nest-building bird, the fertilization of the eggs. . . . From which it follows that, in instinctive behaviour, intellective forces" [*the releasers, or low order intellective stimuli*] "are at work. . . . And since the activities of animals, especially of the lower forms of animal life, are released by extremely primitive factors" [*releasers are usually low order intellective stimuli*] "their brain shows a low level of organization and their overt behaviour" [*the relatively rigid consummatory acts*] "is mediated at about the same plane [*of integrational complexity*] as the diverse physiological functions which are released by relatively primitive stimuli . . ."

LEHRMAN

Lorenz' concept of instinctual behaviour has recently been challenged by Lehrman (*511*) whose criticism however, misses Lorenz' central thesis entirely. It is directed, on the one hand, against the alleged lack of emphasis on the flexibility of instinctual behaviour and, on the other, on the alleged over-emphasis on its rigid relationship to the central organization of the "use patterns" involved in it. This aspect of instinctual behaviour, i.e., the relationship between instinct and learning, is ably covered by Maier and Schneirla (*610*). A possible objection to Lorenz'

biphasic theory of instincts may be based upon the observation that the sequence of the two phases may be reversed or that they may fuse as it were into one. This may happen, for example, if the releasing stimulus acts without antecedent appetitive behaviour which, on the contrary, is seemingly aroused rather than answered by the releaser. We consider this a minor point which, conceivably, might have been brought up in one context or another by Lorenz himself.

The following are representative quotations, from which much can be learned, and which we found in the writings of various authorities, including animal psychologists, philosophers and other authorities. To most of these quotations we shall add brief comments in order to underscore important points or, as the case may be, to call attention to inaccuracies.*

MORGAN (*661*)

"Instinctive behaviour comprises those groups of coordinated acts which, though they contribute to experience, are on their first occurrence not determined by individual experience; which are adaptive, and tend to the well-being of the individual and the preservation of the race; which are due to the cooperation of external and internal stimuli; which are similarly performed by all members of the same more or less restrictive group of animals, but which are subject to variations and to subsequent modifications under the guidance of individual experiences. An instinctive act is a coordinated series of motions, recognizable as a reaction pattern, which is common at least within a species and is in general biologically useful but intuitively performed under the appropriate combination of external circumstances and internal physiological states." (Under exceptional conditions instinctual behaviour does not tend to the well-being of the individual. For example, in certain spiders the much larger female will eat the male after mating.)

WILLIAM STERN (*878*)

'An instinct is that kind of primordial drive whose direction points not only to the final end but also to the means by which this end is

* "It is a duty to judge theories in themselves, without taking into account the fame of those whose names are associated with them." (Binet)

attained. An instinctive action is a meaningful directed action which is arrived from innate needs ("propensities") and which, in attaining its ends, activates innate capabilities ("abilities") as required at the moment without necessitating conscious prevision of the ends or conscious choice, decision, and planning." One might take issue with the identification of propensities and needs. Needs arise because of certain propensities being present and, conversely, because of the presence of the latter, the former are gratified given favourable conditions. Stern cites the following example to illustrate the different biological valence of instinctive behaviour in animals and in man. If a newborn puppy is placed on a table which is then tilted forward, it will try to keep from falling down the incline by crouching back, although it has never undergone the shock and hurt while falling. A corresponding protective instinct is completely lacking in new born children; without making any countermovement they will fall. Later of course the human protective instinct also develops, but it is not easy to identify it as an instinct because it is then affected by experience and involved in acts of will." (The equilibratory reactions are not of an instinctual nature although they are biologically protective. They are righting synergies which owe their greater perfection in the newborn dog to the earlier maturation of the underlying use patterns. This does not exclude of course that preformed synergies may under certain circumstances be absorbed into genuine and still more complexly organized instinctual behaviour.)

TINBERGEN (908)

"An instinct is an hierarchically organized nervous mechanism which is susceptible of priming, releasing and directing impulses of internal as well as external origin, and which responds to these impulses by coordinative movements that contributent to the maintenance of the indiv'dual and the species." (For the precise meaning of the term "hierarchic" the reader may be referred to Tinbergen's monograph, p 102. Instinctive reponses are not limited to movements. Glandular activity may play a major role not only as instigator of appetitive behaviour but also as a component of the consummatory act.)

ROMANES (771)

"The word instinct is a generic term comprising all these faculties of the mind which lead to the conscious performance of actions that are adaptive in behaviour character but pursued without necessary knowledge of the relations between the means employed and the ends attained. (E. v. Hartmann expresses a similar view in his Philosophy of the Unconscious. "Instinct is purposive action without knowledge of the purpose.")

WILLIAM JAMES (430)

Instinct is usually defined as the faculty of acting in such a way as to produce certain ends and without previous education in the performance. Instincts are the fundamental correlations of structures. With the presence of certain organs goes, one may say, almost always a native aptitude for its use. (To the extent that the relationship between structure and function applies not only to instincts but also to reflex functions, the above definition would seem to be too wide. On the other hand, James uses the term "to act," indicating that he refers to functions integrated above the reflex level.)

RUSSEL (784)

Russel calls attention to the fact that the predisposition to attend to particular objects or events, or signs of such, is biologically significant in relation to the animals' special needs and requirements and that it is one of the essential requirements of instinctual behaviour. A particular species or group of species is predisposed, or preadapted, to attend to particular sensory signs— as a scarab to the smell of dung or the wolf spider to small moving objects. Valent objects are often distinguished in perception by means of a few characteristics such as a specific smell, size or shape, the heat radiated from them or their mode of action. These distinguishing characteristics to which the animal is instinctively predisposed are called perceptual clues or signs. Normally these signs are adequate to indicate the biologically appropriate object." (The above passage exemplifies the general statement that the releasers of the consummatory act or extrinsically generated intellective stimulus may be of an extremely low order.)

Thorpe (903, 904)

"An instinct is an inherited and adapted system of coordinations within the nervous system which, when activated, finds expression in behaviour culminating in a fixed action pattern. It is organized on a hierarchical basis both on the afferent and the efferent sides. When charged, it shows evidence of action specific potentials and of readiness for release by an environmental releaser." The action patterns are not necessarily fixed.

McDougall (589, 590)

"An instinct is an inherited or innate psychophysical disposition which determines its possessor to perceive, and to pay attention to, objects of a certain class, to experience an emotional excitement of a particular quality upon perceiving such an object and to act in regard to it in a particular manner or, at least, to experience an impulse to such action." (It is worthy of note that, unlike the other authors here quoted, McDougall emphasizes the importance of emotional factors and also the fact that, in spite of the pressure of what would otherwise be a releasing stimulus, the consummatory act does not necessarily materialize. Another author who calls attention to the emotional factors involved in instinctual behaviour is Bierrens de Haan (82).

It is worthy of note that none of the above quoted authorities makes reference to the factors of *responsiveness* and *periodicity*. We wish to re-emphasize that the initiation of any phase of instinctual behaviour depends on the responsiveness (or for that matter) the absence of refractoriness) on the part of the structural equipment that mediates the response. It may readily be imagined that both innate mechanisms and those built up in the course of maturation of the organism may fail to respond to appropriate stimuli in spite of what would otherwise be an initiating or a releasing stimulus and that, under these circumstances, the affective components involved in instinctual behaviour are likewise absent. Both internal and external (seasonal, diurnal, etc.,) conditions may depress the level of responsiveness in spite of an adequate structural equipment. In other cases as, for example, in connection with the propagation of the species, the organism develops, periodically, certain morphological traits.

Moreover, we miss any reference to the fact that, under conditions of increased responsiveness, the releasing stimulus may be imaginatively produced.

Herbert Spencer (849)

"The commonly assumed hiatus between instinct and reason has no existence . . . the highest forms of psychic activity arise little by little out of lower and cannot be definitely separated from them. The doctrine that the growth of intelligence is throughout determined by the repetition of experiences involves the continuity of instinct and reason. Relations responsed to by instinct are comparatively stereotyped and simple, while those met by reason are comparatively novel and complex.

We believe we have shown, within the framework of the theory here developed, that (a) *instinctual behaviour is an evolution of reflex action*, (b) *that it embodies and at the same time utilizes reflex functions, and that it establishes a link between the latter and intellective activity. And we expect to demonstrate that patterns of creative thought, that is to say, thought concerned with novel and complex activity is nothing other than instinctual activity and, implicitly, reflex function, raised to a higher power*.

Theories concerned with the nature of affective states

Viscerogenic Theories of Emotion

Affects and emotions are so intimately related to autonomic functions that they have been identified with the awareness of innervational states of viscera and blood vessels. James (429) denied that "mental perception of some facts excites the mental perception called the emotion and that the latter state of mind gives rise to the bodily expression. Rather, the bodily change *follow* directly the perception of the excitatory fact and our feelings of the same changes as they occur *is* the emotion. We feel sorry *because* we cry, angry *because* we strike afraid *because* we tremble." Lange's (533) and Darwin's (178) views, namely, that profound bodily changes occur during emotional excitement can hardly be questioned. James on the other hand committed an epistemological error; he thought that states of awareness are expressible in the "language of the periphery." Had he defined the psychological experiences "red" or "blue" in terms of retinal processes, the error would have been obvious and, what later became known as the James-Lange theory of emotions, would soon have fallen into oblivion. The doctrine in question was challenged by Cannon (146) who was able to demonstrate that experimental animals displayed all signs of emotional excitement in spite of the severance of the entire sympathetic inflow into the central nervous system. Dana (177) reported the case of a patient who was completely paralyzed and insensitive below the level of cortical lesion yet manifested joy, grief, displeasure and affection. Since the publication of Dana's paper, many more pertinent observations might have been reported.

THALAMOGENIC THEORY OF EMOTION

In the words of Cannon (143), which we wish to quote rather in full, an external stimulation excites receptors and the consequent excitation starts impulses toward the cortex. Arrival of the impulses there is associated with conditioned processes which determine the direction of the response. Either because the response is initiated in a certain mode or figure and the cortical neurones therefore stimulate the thalamic process, or because of their inward course, the impulses from the receptors exert thalamic processes, which are aroused and ready for discharge. The thalamic neurones do not require detailed innervation from above to be driven into action. Being released for action is a primary condition for their service to the body—they then discharge precipitately and intensely. Within and near the thalamus the neurones concerned in an emotional expression lie close to the relay in the sensory path from periphery to cortex. Cannon assumes that when the former discharge in a particular combination, they not only innervate muscles and viscera but also excite afferent paths to the cortex by direct connection or irradiation. "The theory which naturally presents itself is that *the peculiar quality of the emotion is added to simple sensation when the thalamic processes are aroused*. When the thalamic discharge occurs the bodily changes occur almost simultaneously with the emotion experience. . . . When the thalamic centers are released the processes aroused in them become a source of vivid affective experiences."

Cannon based his theory largely on Head and Holmes (358) experiences with patients suffering from lesions in the lateral thalamic nucleus, which is the common relay station for most somatosensory stimuli that pass on their way from the receptors to the cortex of the cerebral hemispheres. In Head's patients, otherwise indifferent or near indifferent stimuli applied to the skin were experienced as intolerably disagreeable or painful on the affected side, while similar stimuli impinging upon the normal side failed to elicit abnormal sensations of any kind.

Recently, Blau (86), following, apparently, Cannon's line of reasoning, found that the pair of autonomic visceral activities subserved by the sympathetic and parasympathetic nervous system "becomes expressed as imbalance and balance, dissatisfaction and satisfaction, pleasure and displeasure. Outwardly, he goes on to say, these are expressed as emotions." Blau who, for all practical purposes, equates visceral balance with satisfaction, and visceral mbalance with dissatisfaction, telescopes physiological processes occurring at different planes of integration into one or, for that matter, expresses high level integrative acts in the language of low level integrative acts.

EPIPHENOMENALISTIC THEORIES OF EMOTION

McDougall (590) holds that "emotions are the conscious aspects of instinctual activity or an experience consciously felt by the individual while an innate impulse dominates its behaviour." If this were true, emotions would be merely a recording device, lacking any kind of inhibitory or impelling quality. The most striking aspect of emotions is their dynamic bipolarity and is precisely this feature in which their biological significance is rooted.

DISORGANIZATION THEORY OF EMOTIONS

In spite of what Leeper (549) called its "absurd inadequacy," the disorganization theory which regards emotions as disorganized or disorganizing response has many followers, including Dockeray (195), Woodsworth (970) and others. Dockeray writes that "when the behaviour of the organism becomes disorganized as the result of the occurrence of a situation for which he has no ready response, we may call the disorganization emotion. (This may hold true for those cases in which the organism is helpless when confronted with a task with which it is unable to cope. On the other hand, the product on of new responses may be an eminently gratifying experience. Moreover, ready made responses, be they responses satisfying elementary needs or those serving highly integrated skill and intellectual activities may have a high degree of affective loading.) In all fairness to Woodsworth it should be noted that he considered "emotions and feelings as temporary states of the individual associated with motifs and together with motions, comprising what are called desires."

DISTRESS THEORY OF EMOTION

Whitehorn (953) prefers to employ the term impulsion rather than emotion. By impulsion, he means to indicate primarily the psychological experience, vague but intense, of an unpleasant physiological state which is the signal of biological need. He goes on to say that "impulsion, as a psychological experience, is not highly developed in man, where the suppression of extreme subordination of action patterns necessitates a more insistent signal of distress. Relief of impulsions, if obtained by appropriate and successful behaviour, is a pleasant experience, but a pleasing anticipation of success develops only with repeated experience. The primary impulsion, that which is a general trait in experiences recognized as definitely emotional, tends to disturb, confuse and disconcert a person. In practical everyday life emotional phenomena are regularly taken as indication of unpreparedness." Thus Whitehorn's concept of the emotional process appears to be closely related to the disorganization theory and we are inclined to reject as one sided his contention that pleasantness and unpleasantness do not appear as equally fundamental features of man's affective life; that unpleasantness, the signal of distress that is, is a primary factor while unpleasantness is a secondary effect dependent on the relief of an impulse. Moreover, Whitehorn's theory strikes us as somewhat dismal in outlook and, fortunately, not quite in keeping with the experiences of every day life. He believes in a dynamic unipolarity, rather a bipolarity of emotions. He recognizes their motivational character but, erroneously, shifts their signal character from the cognitive to the affective sphere.

MOTIVATIONAL THEORY OF EMOTION

Duffy (202) contended that "in their capacity to release energy in a given direction, those phenomena which we call emotion, are a form of motivation." According to Leeper (549) emotional processes operate primarily as motifs. They are processes which arouse, direct and sustain activity. Emotional processes are the fundamental means of motivation that rests on relatively complex neural activities rather than primarily on definite chemical states or definite receptor stimulation as in the case of bodily drives or physiological motifs such as hunger and thirst. Both Duffy and Leeper come close to the *"impulse-signal theory"* of emotion here developed which permits to specify the position of affective stimuli in the scale of response determiners ranging from reflex eliciting stimuli to intellective stimuli of the highest order. What might have been brought out more clearly is the relationship between inhibitory and impelling affect, including their vector character, their relationship to the phenomena of gratification and frustration and a more specific reference to their relationship to lower and higher response determiners. (See fig. 10.) For a more extensive discussion of the theory of affects and emotions the interested reader may be referred to Arnold's (29) excellent review article.

—————— **Neurosis and psychosis**

GENERAL CONSIDERATIONS

Experimental neurosis

Masserman and Pechtel (625) subjected monkeys to "psychologically traumatic or motivational conflicts between learned feeding patterns and presumably innate reactions of fear aroused by the exhibition of a toy snake. This was accomplished by precipitating the animal to operate the switches of a food box in the usual way but, then, just as it reached for the award, exposing it to the emergence of the forepart of the phantom snake through a curtained aperture at the back of the box." By these means, the investigators produced in their experimental animals neurotic behaviour characterized chiefly by "various inhibitions, regression, phobias, compulsions, organic dysfunctions, neuromuscular disabilities sexual deviations and alterations in social relationships.'

For reasons which will become apparent later, we propose to classify the symptoms in question to be listed in greater detail below into viscero-autonomic dysfunctions, psycho-autonomic dysfunctions, and abnormalities of behaviour.

The *viscero-autonomic* dysfunctions include gastrointestinal hypermotility, diarrhoea and respiratory irregularities. Weight loss, cachexia, polyneuritis, sceletal osteoporosis and decalcification were probably secondary to the nutritional disturbances caused by the first named dysfunctions.

The *psycho-autonomic disorders* (designated as such because of their close relationship to anxiety states) consisted in mydriasis, horripilation, persistent palpitations, motor restlessness, stereotyped pacing and guttural low voice vocalization. In addition, there were noted disorders of defecation and micturition.

The *behavioural abnormalities* in the *alimentary sphere* manifested themselves by the refusal of costumary food or by gulping it down, or grasping it tightly without an attempt to eat it; in the *sexual sphere*, by almost complete cessation of heterosexual behaviour and increased autoertism; in the *social sphere*, by violent threatening discharges against the experimenter, exaggerated suspiciousness and, save for assualtiveness, avoidance of all contact; and lastly, in the *mental sphere* proper, by general decrease of spontaneous activity and interest and by the manipulation of imaginary objects. Paraplegia, hemiplegia and impairment of basic coordination might have been secondary to polyneuritis.

The following is a brief survey of experimental work antedating Masserman's and Pechtel's investigations which, being a convenient framework of reference for other experimental and clinical observations, were quoted in the opening paragraphs. In rats, exposure to conflict situations may cause convulsions and other abnormalities. According to R. N. F. Maier (*609*), frustrated behaviour is an end in itself. It is in sharp contrast to motivational behaviour, nonconstructive or actually destructive. Punishment increases the

strength of many frustrated responses which therefore become more and more fixated. Compulsive behaviour is characteristic of a state of frustration. In Pavlow's (*714*) early experiments, the following conditions lead to neurotic behaviour in dogs. An insoluble problem, bodily confinement without avenue of escape, the necessity of choosing between two stimuli which could not be ignored and, lastly, continued and repeated exposure to this situation. In Lidell's (*567*) experiments neurotyfing conditions were "self-imposed restraint on the part of the animals, that is, the strain of waiting for the signal for punishment which inevitably and repeatedly occurs." (See also Gannt (*288*).

According to Tinbergen (*908*), conflict situations may give rise to *substitutive responses.*' Their remarkable stereotypy, the fact that they resemble innate motor patterns of instincts other than those frustrated and their typical occurrence in a given species suggest that the motivation of a frustrated instinct finds an avenue of response by means of the discharge of centers serving a different instinct." For example, the stickleback makes irrational attempts to dig a nest when he can neither fight nor run away from an enemy. Thus, *conflicts* produce disorganization of behaviour and atypical modes of response (*288*). In dogs, conspicuous experimentally produced disorders of behaviour may last over a period of ten years (*44, 407*). A number of observers are inclined to invoke *constitutional factors* as determiners of experimentally produced neuroses. "Whether or not an animal breaks down," Pavlow (*714*) writes, "depends on the constitution of its nervous system. Different breeds of dogs behave differently in standardized test situations and statistically significant differences among the various breeds indicate that special training and experience may be secondary to basic etiological factors in the causation of behaviour disorders." According to Russel (*785*) *hereditary factors* play an important part in determining the behaviour of animals under conditions of stress. Disorganization of behaviour due to a variety of causes is often associated with a generalization or spread of symptoms to other modalities of behaviour. Frustration of feeding behaviour in young rats causes abnormal hoarding of food in the adult animal, and puppies which are not allowed to complete sucking activity lick and claw other objects (*413, 414*). Exposure to stress situations of a particular kind influence the attitude toward future stress situations by lowering their threshold (*621, 785*).

The above data illustrate the production of abnormal reactions to experimentally produced frustration which, as previously defined, is experienced when seeking reactions are thwarted or avoiding reactions are forced upon the organism. It is well to remember that the prototype of seeking responses is reflex release, of avoiding reactions reflex inhibition, and that both seeking and avoidance responses are involved in instinctive behaviour. Although the anatomical substrates of most reflex responses are innate use patterns while those of many seeking and avoidance reactions are to a large extent acquired, any use pattern, be it preformed or integrated in response to the demands of the moment, is the anatomical substrate of a synergic response.

It follows from what has gone before that, in so far as seeking and avoiding responses are synergic processes, *frustration is caused by the inhibition of physiological functions.* In turn, any type of stimulation that prevents the realization of the process is question is disruptive. With special reference to instinctive behaviour, *disruptive stimuli are those which, by inhibiting consummatory acts, substitute "dys-synergic"* (inappropriate) *reactions for "synergic"* (goal-leading) *reactions to biologically significant stimuli.* The same viewpoints apply to the inversion of avoidance reactions.

Neurotic behaviour is the sum total of abnormal reactions produced by frustration, more especially, by a substandard frustration-gratification ratio. In experimental animals, frustration is caused by the thwarting of goal directed responses and the imposition of avoidance reactions. The same holds true for life situations which are apt to cause neurotic behaviour in man. In the following paragraphs, we shall bring together several generalizations some of which have already been formulated in various appropriate places while others are based on the above reviewed experimental data.

(1) Synergies are compounded of individual components mediated in turn by hierarchically organized levels of the central nervous system which, singly or in combination, contribute their specific quotas of action to the total process of integration. However, each level, or system of levels, having maintained the early segmental pattern as it were, consists of its own afferents, central regulatory mechanisms and efferents, and is, to a degree, autonomous. In the following table, the individual synergies are arranged according to various anatomical, physiological and developmental viewpoints. They may be grouped according to the participation of *somato-motor* centers into

    a) *pyramidal* synergies,
    b) *extrapyramidal* synergies, and
    c) *pyramido-extrapyramidal* synergies,

according to the *level of their integration*, into

    a) *subcortical* synergies,
    b) *cortical* synergies and
    c) *cortico-subcortical* synergies,

according to the *functional divisions* of the nervous system involved in their integration, into

    a) *visceral* synergies
    b) *somatic* synergies and
    c) *viscero-somatic* synergies,
    d) *somato-visceral* synergies,

according to the *dynamic value of the stimuli* by which they are set in motion, into

    a) *seeking responses* and
    b) *avoidance responses,*

according to the *physical properties of the stimuli* by which they are called forth, into

    a) synergies actuated by *oral* (olfactory, gustatory, oro-tactile) *stimuli,*
    b) synergies actuated by *tactile stimuli*
    c) synergies actuated by *proprioceptive stimuli*
    d) synergies actuated by *visual stimuli*
    e) synergies actuated by *auditory stimuli*
    f) synergies actuated by *vestibular stimuli* and
    g) synergies actuated by *enteroceptive stimuli*
    h) synergies actuated by *sexual stimuli,*

according to their *genesis,* into

    a) *innate* synergies and
    b) *acquired* synergies,

according to the *organs involved in their execution,* into

    a) *alimentary* synergies
    b) *propagative* synergies
    c) *locomotor* synergies
    d) *postural* synergies
    e) *equilibratory* synergies
    f) *attitudinal* synergies and
    g) *manipulative* synergies
    h) *communicative* synergies,

according to the *degree of automaticity* into

    a) *reflexes*

b) *instinctual* activities and

c) *volitional movements,* including *skilled movements,*

according to the *organizational complexity* of sensory stimuli into

a) synergies involved in the formation of *perceptions*

b) synergies involved in the formation of *configurations* and

c) synergies involved in the formation of *symbols* and *concepts.*

The synergic character (or process character) of the psychisms listed in the last group will be explained later. The above survey amplifies our remarks on the various types of sensory-motor arrangements as the structural background of synergic processes but it would take us too far afield to specify each synergy here listed in anatomical terms; indeed, any attempt in this direction would necessitate the virtual rewriting of many chapters of physiology.

(2) The term synergy may be profitably extended to include not only motor and sensory-motor functions but also those mediated by the sensory division of the nervous system, more especially the grouping of relatively low level intellective stimuli to concepts. As a corollary, the formation of concepts is dependent on the establishment of use patterns at the highest sensory level (III.s.) of cerebral function.

(3) Under conditions of normal stimulation, the highest levels of the nervous system exert a regulatory influence upon the activity of the subordinate levels. Contrarily, under stressful stimulation, the effect of high level activity upon the indirectly involved lower levels may be reversed and their performance patterns disorganized. *Stress is a process or condition provoked by any factor that inhibits, derails or otherwise interferes with synergic functions at any level of the nervous system and which, sooner or later, overtaxes the adaptive capacity of the organism.* In other words, stress is the effect of unphysiological stimulation. Stressors are stress producing stimuli which are either liminal or supraliminal. In all likelihood, there exist not only subliminal physiological stimuli but also subliminal unphysiological stimuli.

(4) *Inter-level symptoms* are caused by the abnormal influence of the higher, primarily involved, strata upon the subordinate levels of the neuraxis. (The reverse mechanism does not concern us here.) *Intra-level symptoms* on the other hand, reflect the abnormal function of a given level within its own performance field.

(5) Since, under conditions of abnormal stimulation, low level activity is adversely affected by the dysfunction of the primarily involved (supraordinate) strata, certain disorganization patterns of the higher levels "embody" those of the lower echelons. The principle of anatomical and physiological subordination and supraordination makes possible to classify the neuroses according to the "comprehensiveness" of their symptomatology and, at the same time, to establish the continuity between (a) the individual neuroses and the neuroses as a group and (b) neurosis and psychosis in general.

(6) The experimentally produced *viscero-autonomic* syndrome corresponds to the *organ-neuroses* in the human, while the *psycho-autonomic* syndrome is the equivalent of the *anxiety-neuroses;* and the *behavioural abnormalities* of experimental animals have their counterpart in certain *hysterical* and *psychotic* symptoms.

The nature of psychogenic and "functional" abnormalities

In the light of the above considerations, we regard psychogenic symptoms and signs as expressions of biological disequilibrium forced upon the organism by the blocking of need-directed synergies, in other words, the blocking of the discharge propensities of use patterns involved in instinctual behaviour. Thus, psychogenic symptoms are interference effects, preventing the self-realization of the organism in one or more spheres of function. In the present context, it is of secondary importance whether or not the blocking of synergies, or only its effect is a conscious experience, that is, whether or not the patient is aware of the source of his symptoms. Now, functions are not entities endowed with independent existence. They depend on the structural provisions by which they are mediated, in other words, "functional" symptoms have, of necessity, a structural basis. For this reason it is necessary to extend the meaning of the term "structural" or "organic" to cover postulated changes at the ultravisible level. It is only in this way that one may account for the lability of integration under stress, that is, for the variegated and shifting phenomena of "integrational organicity," or organicity existing in the absence of microscopic and macroscopic changes.* The viewpoint here taken is that, in the neurotic, the confidence coefficient of integration is low by comparison although not necessarily low in every sphere of integration; that it is still further reduced by experience, associated with the blocking of need-directed synergies, and that the various "functional" abnormalities reflect the precarious (physiological or, for that matter, organic) equilibrium that existed from the very beginning, that is, prior to the period of disruptive stimulation. In the presence of the biological abnormalities here postulated, the probability of malfunction prevailing to a degree even in the normal organism is enhanced. Thus, a combination of needblocking stimulation and the presence of postulated microstructural changes in the *biochemical range* is apt to depress the confidence coefficient of integration still further. It is natural to assume that, in the extreme case, malfunction will develop without apparent cause, that is, in the absence of an ascertainable precipitant. The intimate mechanism of stress induced dysfunction is unknown but the role of an endocrine factor appears likely, if the changes in endocrine function in normals are taken into consideration and, at the same time, the difficulty of drawing a line between episodic manifestations of stress and organ-neurotic conditions. The notion that an inferior biological substrate is the organic background of "functional" symptoms is supported by the relative frequency of somatic stigmata in neurotic individuals and also of neurotic and psychotic traits in the family of the proband. Evidently, the predisposition per se—an abstract term—cannot be transmitted from one generation to another. What can be transmitted is only the behaviour of abnormal molecules which, in turn, derives from their abnormal structure. Lastly, the notion of an organic background of neurotic reaction under conditions of blocking of need-directed functions is supported by the observation that certain individuals, as has been demonstrated both in experimental animals and in man, do not develop neurotic reactions in spite of the

stress to which they are subjected. To sum it all up, diversity of response under indentical conditions cannot not occur in a structural vacuum. It presupposes an organic factor, just like the different behaviour of any material under mechanical stress presupposes different physical properties. Now, the stress-induced disorganization of physiological functions may be brought to the fore not only by the malfunction of individual organs but also by the disorganization or the very patterning of needs, or the establishment of disequilibrating tendencies. Ultimately, reaction to stimulation may become destructive. In other words, frustration substitutes abnormal needs for normal needs and, implicitly, abnormal goals for normal goals. Further, since normal needs are components of instinctive activity, neurotic behaviour resembles, in a certain sense, instinctive behaviour.

Frustration-aggression mechanisms and related response patterns in the human

General nature and trend of neurotic aggression. Frustration-induced abnormalities may involve processes occurring within the organism, such as cardiac action, respiration, etc. or behavioural responses which, directly or indirectly, disorganize the relationship between the organism and its social setting. By far the most frequent although by no means the only type of reaction to frustration is aggression (824). The following are the salient points of the *frustration-aggression theory* of neurosis as developed by Miller a. ass. (653) and other workers in this field (288, 714). Miller maintains that aggressive action, not always recognizable as such, is a manifestation of frustration; the reverse, however, is not necessarily true. Complaints, beating, the spreading of rumours, cruel joking, swearing, murder and even suicide are forms of aggressive behaviour. Incitement to aggression, however, should be differentiated from aggression, for the latter may be temporarily inhibited by stimulation to other responses incompatible with aggression. Indeed, under certain conditions, these latter responses may weaken the stimulation to the response that was frustrated. Fear of punishment may also inhibit aggressive action. Aggressive feelings may be handled in many ways, some of which may provoke profound personality conflicts. Displace-

---

* This line of reasoning will be resumed in the course of the discussion of the etiology of schizophrenic illness and of the question of pathological changes in idiopathic schizophrenia. (See *considerations*.)

ment of the object of aggression and catharsis may result. Deterioration of the psychomotor aspects of behaviour may follow simple conflict situations experimentally produced in human subjects. This may be brought out by prolonging the reaction time and by increasing response oscillations (621, 711). A subject confronted with insoluble problems may experience aggressive impulses; regression, resignation and stereotyped fixation may develop, reproducing the frustration reactions that tend to occur under "natural" conditions. The provocation of a special frustration-induced stimulation, the goal response to which is aggression, is but one of the effects of frustration. The following are action sequences or effects of frustration upon future behaviour that may occur: (a) The instrumental act directed toward the same goal response may be repeated or (b) an attempt may be made to achieve the same goal response by a different type of mental act or (c) a different set of instrumental acts may be provoked, in order to set the organism so that it may perform a different goal response from that from which it was originally frustrated. Substitutive responses may or may not have certain features of the originally frustrated goal responses; they may dominate the strength of the primary instigation. Under certain conditions, however, not only may frustration prevent further action toward the original goal response but the inhibition itself may involve even the substitutive response. Here, stimulation to alternative responses having no relationship to the original response may become dominant. The frustrated individual may have a whole repertory of frustration reactions. He may react differently at different times to the same provocation. Where the frustrating agent is absent, another object must be selected for the purpose of relieving aggressive feelings generated in the frustrating situation. Not all frustration give rise to aggressive responses in the sense that hostility is discharged against a social subject or its substitute. Moreover, acts that typically provoke aggressive behaviour in certain persons may affect other persons differently. Frustration may result from failure to establish effective social relations. For details, consult the above cited monograph.

It may be readily seen that certain trends and actions caused by frustration are countermeasures instituted by the neurotic patient, and intended to attain gratification in spheres other than those frustrated, that is to say, by the substitution of secondary goals for primary goals in spheres of activity where the subject is not likely to meet defeat. Evidently, there is a basic similarity between, on the one hand, behavioural abnormalities and other types of dysfunction produced in experimental animals and, on the other, neurotic behaviour in the human subjected to frustrating experiences. It is only the superior integrational complexity of the human brain which multiplies the manifestation of neurosis.

Neurotifying social and interpersonal settings

It is a truism that rivalry factors operate in any group, be it within the family, in competitive settings imposed upon by sexual needs, or within professional hierarchies where, like in certain animal societies, a "pecking order" is the natural correlate of social organization. Hence, any member of the group is both a potential object of aggression and a center of counteraggression. Although the individual "foci" may discharge in any direction, the very nature of social structures favours the transmission of frustration from the higher to the lower echelons. Accordingly, the individual members are apt to be relegated to convenient substitutes, or victims of aggressive tendencies on the part of the less vulnerable "initiators" of frustration which, in turn, are, or have been, the victims of their superiors—now, perhaps, resting in peace. In certain minority groups which are victims of discrimination and which yearn for equality (but which they by no means deserve), sub-minorities are created and forced to play the role of (god-sent) sub-underdogs. Unfortunately, the dog-underdog-sub-underdog organization of society is a harsh fact. Unless the chain reaction is broken by a favourable concatenation of factors, perpetual *intragroup neurotification* ensues. An additional pathogenic mechanism is *cross-neurotification*, i.e., the emergence of aggressive mechanisms that operate in overlapping social systems, including family settings which are, of necessity, interconnected with other groups. In any social milieu or the combinations of settings, inapposite affectivity of any individual may become an autonomous focus of neurotification, threatening, potentially, any other member of the group. It is pertinent to point out that inapposite affectivity is not necessarily frustration-induced. It may be innate or produced by central nervous system disease, e.g., encephalitis. The role, as pestcarriers, of psychopathic personalities, including devout egomaniacs, pathological liers and swindlers (with or without cruelty instincts) and other antisocial individuals can hardly be over-estimated. They become particularly dangerous if conflict producing levels of abnormal traits, including the saturation potential, the saturation tolerance etc of the individuals involved is associated with superior intelligence. If, in any social setting, moral standards are mere postulates, hypocritically enunciated to cover up selfish designs or, at most, temporary expedients, the group may sooner or later be dominated by subcriminal or frankly criminal psychopaths whose position, for a time at least, is assured by factors of natural selection and the survival of the fittest. In the extreme case, they become leaders with which the members of the group identify themselves by a process of introjection or at least support them as long as they provide the means of satisfaction of basic needs and guarantee a reasonable measure of security. By and large, neurosis is a sociogenic disease developing in predisposed individuals, especially those trapped in a social milieu in which the only stable factors are mutual distrust, hypocrisy, fanatical opportunism and a shifting criss-cross pattern of hostility.

The frustration theory of neurosis was inaugurated by Freud (253), who maintained that "the most immediate, the most easily discerned and most comprehensive exciting cause of the onset of neurotic illness lies in the external factors which may be generally described as frustration. The person is healthy as long as his erotic needs are satisfied by an actual object in the outer world. He becomes neurotic as soon as he is deprived of his object and no substitute is forthcoming." Freud's thesis would be generally valid if frustration mechanisms operated in the sexual sphere only. The extension of the concept of libido to encompass non-sexual aspects of gratification does not establish the validity of Freud's conception of neurotic illness. According to Schoenwald (764), "energy, bound to the maintenance of pleasure and the reducing of tension, is sexual, that is, sexual in a sense unknown to any past user of the term and that sexuality's range of meaning covers the individual, normal as well as the abnormal, from toothless thumbsucking to toothless pipe-smoking." Naturally, a good case

may be made for the identification of the sexual instinct and the instinct of self preservation, the integrated total of all other instincts. In fact, at an early phylogenetic stage, life and propagation were identical. This was the stage at which "self-maintenance, homeostasis and a balanced metabolism were basically identical autokatalytic processes, and propagation was an excess anabolic phase of the life process."* Yet, since this primordial stage, the process of differentiation has been going on in many directions. It established a great variety of biological needs which, although perhaps not as powerful as the sexual instinct, exist in their own right. Accordingly, any attempt to bring them upon a common denominator and the claim that, ultimately, human behaviour reflects the functional and motivational dynamics of bodily orifices, more especially those concerned with propagation, is bound to result in confusion. Freudian mechanism account for the neurotification of society to the extent only that sexual rivalry mechanisms are special aspects of social rivalry situations in general, that, in certain personality types, psychopathic traits predominate in the sphere of the sexual instinct and that, ordinarily, sexual needs are motivating forces of overwhelming power.

In *summary*, the viewpoint here taken is that neurotic behaviour is primarily the effect of a substandard frustration-gratification ratio caused in predisposed individuals by an inordinate measure of frustration or, for that matter, an inordinate lack of gratification, either of which overtaxes the frustration tolerance of the organism. Learning mechanisms, inferiority complexes and cultural settings may be contributory factors. Indeed, they may well account for neurotic behaviour in sporadic cases but attempts at explaining neurosis on the basis of theories that lack a broad biological foundation are entirely too one sided. The validity of the frustration theory of neurosis is brought about by the peculiarities of behaviour under competitive conditions, including the trivial conditions of daily life or, as formulated in terms of instinct pathology, in an environment in which appetitive behaviour is readily aroused but consummatory reactions are blocked sufficiently often to prevent the self-realization of the organism. Under conditions of disruptive stimulation, there

* This was discussed at some length in the opening chapter.

develops a vicious spiral as the tolerance to noxious stimuli decreases with the intensity and the duration of frustrating experiences and, by increasing the frustration-proneness of the individual, raises, to abnormal levels, its already existing sensitivity to noxious stimuli. Be it on heredoconstitutional grounds or under the cumulative effect of frustrating experiences or a combination of both factors, certain individuals develop a low frustration tolerance, that is to say, an increased sensitivity to frustration. Thus, depending on the subject's degree of sensitivity, neurosis may be defined either as an *abnormal response to normal stimuli* or as a *natural reaction to disruptive stimuli*. The organism which reacts to normal stimuli in an abnormal fashion may be said to show a predisposition to neurosis. Maximal abnormality of behaviour under minimal stress suggests a high degree of predisposition; normal behaviour under maximal stress, absence of predisposition. Of necessity, neurotic reactions will be intensified whenever abnormal stimuli impinge upon a nervous system being hypersensitive from the very beginning or sensitized by the stress and strain of life.

We have already indicated that *organ neuroses* are caused by the predominant involvement of the visceral sphere of integration while the basis features of *anxiety neurosis* are disorders manifesting themselves primarily in the abnormal functionality of the vasomotor apparatus, including cardiac action. The symptomatology of *hysteria* is even more comprehensive. It encompasses (a) dysfunctions of somato-sensory, somato-motor, visceral and vaso-motor mechanisms, and (b) disorders of affectivity, behaviour and conduct (which are the accompaniments of the specific hysterical symptoms to be discussed later) and which represent the *psychopathological core* of hysteria. In a general way, it may be said that hysterical illness "includes," in addition to its own level specific response patterns, that is, its intra-level symptoms, certain elements of the anxiety neuroses and, implicitly, the organ neuroses, while anxiety neuroses "include," in addition to their own level specific response patterns, certain organ neurotic elements. In a diagrammatic fashion, this relationship may be represented as follows:

```
┌─────────────────── Hysteria
→     ┌─────────── Anxiety neuroses
→     └───→        Organ neuroses.
```

It is matter of experience that, in neurosis, including organ neurosis, anxiety neurosis and hysteria, the individual symptoms and signs occur in various proportions and in shifting combinations. At the same time, innumerable gradations may be encountered between, on the one hand, normal and neurotic behaviour and, on the other, neurotic and psychotic behaviour. Easy as it may be to categorize the neuroses in conformity with neurophysiological guide concepts, considerable difficulties may arise in applying theoretical principles to individual cases. In general, one may proceed as follows. One may classify a given case in somewhat the same way as a mixed tumor, that is, either according to its most malignant or to its predominant cell type. Either method has its merits. The former takes into account a significant—potentially dangerous—developmental trend; the latter, the basic pattern of abnormal response to stress.

In the following paragraphs we propose to discuss the above mentioned varieties of neurosis, postponing, because of their close relationship to schizophrenia, a consideration of the obsessive compulsive neuroses.

ORGAN NEUROSIS

There is, as we have said, no sharp dividing line between stress-induced, natural overreaction and imbalance of autonomic functions on the one hand, and the organ-neuroses on the other. Yet, in spite of the many transitions between the extremes of a single scale, it is necessary to set apart the two conditions at some point of the continuum extending from the normal to the pathological. One would certainly regard, as organ neurotic symptoms, overreactions that occur under minimal stress and which tend to persist even under the cessation of the cause. Normal biochemical conditions existing in the autonomic nervous system maintain a standard value of integration in the visceral sphere of the organism. Under stress on the other hand, and in the presence of an as yet hypothetical biochemical factor (which, moreover, may be of a composite nature) integration drops to substandard levels. Stress-induced visceral or vegetative neuroses are dys-autonomias of individual organs. According to Bauer (*45*), they are functional alterations which arise from primary disorders of the nervous control of an organ. Although they are caused by unresolved conflicts and by frustration, they do not express or symbolize them. "The vegetative neuroses," Alexander (5) wrote, "are not an attempt to express an emotion but the physiological response of the vegetative organs to constant or to periodically returning emotional states. . . . It is most improbable that internal organs express ideas."

We are primarily concerned with the clarification of basis viewpoints.* Accordingly, we shall not expand on the symptomatology of organ neuroses and the tissue alterations (allegedly the result of abnormal states of innervation of the organs involved) nor on the highly controversial correlation between specific personality types and the propensity to develop certain types of organ neurotic dysfunctions. As an illustration of the foregoing it suffices to call attention to the fact that the gastrointestinal tract is one of the most frequent target organs of abnormal discharge on the part of the highest level of the neuraxis. As early as 1913, v. Bergmann (65) called attention to the fact that the pain and discomfort associated with gastric and duodenal ulcers is not necessarily the cause of the patient's nervousness but that, on the contrary, the patient's tenseness may be the very cause of the anatomical changes. Other classic example of psychosomatic disease are anorexia nervosa or, singly or in combination, symptoms referable to the respiratory, the genito-urinary and the endocrine system. Sexual neuroses are closely related to inhibitory mechanisms of a hysterical nature (see below) while the neuroses of the endocrine organs, e.g., the thyroid gland, may have widespread effects in the entire autonomic sphere. However, since only the adrenal medulla and the posterior lobe of the pituitary gland are supplied with autonomic nerve fibers, the mechanism of functional alteration of the remaining endocrine glands secondary to disorders of emotionality remains to be elucidated. Perhaps, the responses in question are mediated by general stress mechanisms discussed by Selye (825) which, however, function in an abnormal fashion.

It is likely that the "choice of the target organ" is determined by constitutional factors. Lacey and his associates (527) speak of a specific symptom selection in psychosomatic neuroses. "The

* This applies to the neuroses, the psychoses and to their interrelations. A straightforward textbook type of presentation is not intended.

autonomic nervous system responds, to experimentally produced stress, as a whole in the sense that all autonomically innervated structures seem to be activated, usually in the direction of apparent sympathetic predominance. But it does not respond as a whole in the sense that all autonomically innervated structures exhibit equal increment or decrements of function. Striking intra-individual differences are found in the degree of activation of different physiological functions when the different reactions are expressed in equivalent units. . . . There is relative response specificity. . . . For one physiological function an individual may be markedly overreactive; for another, average in reactivity; and for still another, markedly underreactive. . . . Some individuals are so constituted that they will respond with a given hierarchy of autonomic activation; others will show greater fluctuations from stress to stress although they will exhibit now one pattern more frequently than another; still other individuals will randomly exhibit now one pattern now another."

ANXIETY NEUROSIS

Anxiety is a dysphoric state ranging from mood to paroxysm and produced by the anticipation or the recall of frustration and insecurity. The anxiety producing experiences are precipitated by situations with which the organism is unable or has been unable to cope, and which involve the thwarting of seeking reactions or the forced inversion of aversive impulses. In other words, anxiety is a state of dysphoria which, although existing in the absence of an actual threat, actuates avoidance reactions to the anxiety producing stimulus. Naturally, the stimulus, whenever real rather than imagined, will intensify the (negative) affect involved in the experience of the state of anxiety which, in turn, given the reality of the threat, is a limiting case of fear, or a reaction to an actually existing threat to the organism.

The tendency to develop anxiety reactions may become generalized even if the organism is unaware of a specific stimulus which poses a threat, or which has posed a threat in the past. In these instances, anxiety, or seemingly empty fear, is the counterpart of a specific or directed fear precipitated by a concrete stimulus posing a threat to the individual.

In actual fact, fear and anxiety are, as already alluded to, the two extremes of a scale which have in common the quality of the experience associated not only with the psychic responses but also with the somatic reactions to the stimulus in question, and which involve both the psycho-autonomic and the viscero-autonomic spheres of activity.

Accordingly, *anxiety neurosis* may be defined as a condition characterized by the propensity to react, in both spheres of function, either with stimulus-precipitated dysphoria (even though the stimulus may be merely imaginary) or with habitual dysphoria. Further, since the inner experience associated with anxiety is identical with the feeling of fear, and the viscero-autonomic more especially cardio-vascular accompaniments of fear and anxiety are likewise identical, *anxiety neurosis is a condition characterized by the propensity to react with viscero-autonomic dysfunctions including predominantly organ-neurotic responses mediated by the cardio-vascular system.* (See also Braun, *109*, Hoch, *389*, and Kardiner, *472*.)

Phobias are avoidance responses which are not generalized but center around certain objects or situations having acquired symbolic significance. In other words, phobias are caused by complexes. *Hypochondriasis* is anxiety, anticipatory or otherwise, produced by proprio-ceptive and/or entero-ceptive rather than extero-ceptive stimuli or anxiety centering around the self. However, to the extent that hypochondriasis may be related to a specific stimulus, it is a manifestation of fear rather than of anxiety.

We have already indicated that the "higher" forms of neurosis embody the "lower" forms. It would appear, then, that anxiety neurosis is the supraordinate abnormality which includes the organ neuroses, in other words, that the organ neuroses grow to anxiety neuroses by the addition of the psychic element of anxiety to the apparently organic elements involved in the abnormal functionality of various organs of the body. In the present context, it is pertinent to point out that Freud (*270*) in his article entitled "The justification for detaching from neurasthenia a particular syndrome: the anxiety neurosis" segregated the latter from neurasthenia, in turn a nosologic "entity" comprising no less than 53 individual symptoms. Prior to this separation, then, the anxiety neuroses embodied two syndromes, namely, the organ-neurotic syndrome and the anxiety-neurotic syndrome. Ferraro (*227*), in an article on the nosological position of neurasthenia in psychiatry, maintains that, once the anxiety syndrome is separated from the over all concept of neurasthenia (a nosological concept created by Beard in 1869), the disorder is reduced to the simple expression of a few somatic symptoms. At the same time, he reviewed the concepts (none of which however appears to be adequate) of a great many authorities on the nature of neurasthenia. We would suggest that the nosologic concept of neurasthenia be maintained and applied to a mitigated form of anxiety neurosis, that is to say, a disorder compounded of a low grade organ neurosis and a mild form of anxiety neurosis. For a discussion of the psychiatric aspects of anxiety the interested reader may be referred to Fromm-Reichmann (*275*) and May (*627*).

Thus, the appreciation of the relationships between anxiety and fear is essential for the understanding of the clinical manifestations of anxiety neurosis, variously described to include "pallor, sweating, trembling and increased frequency of bowel movements and urination" or "cold shivers, a sense of pressure on the heart and precordial region, profuse sweating and palpitations of the heart" (*475*). Darwin (*178*), in his monograph on the expression of emotions in animals and in man, pointed out that young children do not tremble but go into convulsions under circumstances which would induce trembling in adults. "Of all emotions," he wrote, "fear is notoriously the most apt to induce trembling." The tremor of Parkinson's disease may be exacerbated by the injection of epinephrine. (See below.) As already noted by Cannon (*144*) "the visceral changes which accompany fear and rage are the result of discharge by way of sympathetic neurones. Differences in visceral accompaniments are not noteworthy . . . there is indeed obvious reason why they should be alike . . . these emotions accompany organic preparations for action and just because the condition which evoke them are likely to result in flight or conflict (either of them requiring perhaps the utmost struggle) the bodily needs in either response are precisely the same."

In discussing the hierarchy of response levels of the nervous system, mention has been made of the fact that the affective component of the more complex responses mediated by the intellectual level is the quota of action contributed, to the total process of response, by certain higher brain-stem centers, by parts of the frontal lobes and the limbic lobes. At the same time, attention was called to Hess' (*359*) experiments who produced fear and rage reactions by posterior hypothalamic lesions. Likewise, anxiety can be precipitated by the injection of adrenaline which appears to act not only at the psycho-autonomic but at the viscero-autonomic level. It may give rise to a feeling of being afraid, of anxiety, that may be referred to events in the past life of the individual, a feeling variously described of nervousness, tenseness and excitement, of the anticipation of an emergency, of nameless fear, etc., while the hyperactive state of the viscero-autonomic level produces palpitations of the heart, a rapid pulse, coldness of the hands and feet, shaking of the extremities and trembling of the voice. It is worthy of note however, that anxiety may be produced experimentally by infusing epinephrine in amounts too small to evoke gross somatic changes (*13*). It may be readily seen that, under clinical conditions, a similar state develops spontaneously. It is only to be expected that the physiological "fear-rage-complex" should have not only a hormonal basis but a neural substrate as well. Thus, empty fear may occur as aura preceding psychomotor seizures caused by temporal lobe (limbic) lesions (*721*), in other words, as an abnormal, organically determined dissociation between the impulse component and the cognitive component of an intellective stimulus.

To sum up, anxiety neurosis is an organ neurosis which derives its special coloring from the fact that fear, to which anxiety is closely related, is linked up with cardio-vascular dysautonomias. The feeling of anxiety is however linked to the function of higher centers. In experimental animals, the ganglionic chain can be removed without abolishing the expression and, as far as can be known, the experience of fear. Moreover, as already noted in the course of the discussion of affective states, emotional experiences may occur in patients suffering from high cervical cord lesions (*177*).

HYSTERIA

Because of the complexity of the clinical manifestations of hysteria, a definition of hysterical illness at the present state of our thesis is not feasible. It will have to be deferred until after the discussion of the diverse symptoms and signs. What can be said at this point is that the manifestations of hysteria fall into three broad groups, namely,

(1) symptoms of *organ neurosis*,

(2) symptoms of *anxiety neurosis*, and

(3) certain effects of disruptive stimulation existing in addition to those comprising the first two groups of abnormalities. The third group of symptoms may be subdivided into two categories, including

(a) inter-level effects of disruptive stimulation, or *inter-level symptoms*, and

(b) intra-level effects of disruptive stimulation, or *intra-level symptoms*, i.e., the *psychopathological core of hysterical illness*.

By and large, inter-level symptoms correspond to the *conversion reactions* of clinical psychiatry while the intra-level symptoms are identical with the so called *dissociative reactions*. However, since it is doubtful whether the term "conversion reaction" is applicable to all inter-level symptoms it appears to be preferable to discuss the matter in terms which do not prejudge the issue and which are consistent with the neuro-psychological approach here proposed. The terms "dissociative reactions" and "intra-level symptoms" will be used interchangeably. The individual symptoms and signs to be discussed below occur in various proportions and, moreover, in shifting combinations. There exist not only innumerable transitional forms between individual cases of hysteria but an inexhaustible number of gradations between hysteria on the one hand and normal behaviour on the other. For the purpose of general orientation, we note that both the inter-level symptoms and the intra-level symptoms of hysterical illness are basically inapposite seeking and avoidance reactions and, to a degree, potential means of expression of the very frustrations and conflicts by which they are generated.

The organ-neurotic symptoms of hysteria

They include a variety of autonomic nervous system abnormalities which may be grouped as follows:

(1) Vasomotor instability. (Edema of the skin, cyanosis, etc.)

(2) Disorders of secretion. (Hyperhydrosis, increased salivation.)

(3) Intestinal disorders. (Meteorism, constipation, diarrhoea, anorexia nervosa, vomiting, oesophagism, pharyngism or globus hystericus.)

(4) Respiratory disorders. (Bronchospasm, tachypnoea, hiccough.)

(5) Urinary disorders. (Retention of urine.)

(6) Sexual disorders. (Impotence and frigidity.)

Whether the sexual abnormalities are organ-neurotic symptoms proper, in which case they would belong to the syndrome of neurasthenia, or avoidance responses which belong to the group of inhibitory interlevel responses can be determined only by a full investigation of the individual case.

The anxiety-neurotic symptoms of hysteria

They include the symptoms and signs listed under the heading "Anxiety neurosis." *Anxiety hysteria* is a form of hysterical illness in which the clinical picture is dominated by anxiety but which, in addition, exhibits clinical manifestations that are specifically hysterical in character. (See below.)

The psychopathological core of hysteria

Immaturity and aggression. The hysterical personality

The following considerations are intended to supplement what has already been said about the *euphoric*, the *dysphoric* and the *aphoric* personality structure. The hysterical personality combines, in a peculiar fashion, traits of both euphoria and dysphoria, including cruelty traits. Features of immaturity and puerilism (which may be readily expressed in terms of euphoria and dysphoria) were noted by many observers. They were discussed in detail by Kretschmer (*514, 515*) whose ideas we wish to quote rather in full. Kretschmer makes reference to Freud's (*270*) theory of the early infantile trauma which, however, he is inclined to minimize somewhat on the ground that unhappy infantile experiences are so frequent in the general population that their incidence is out of proportion to the small number of hysterical reactions. He stresses the relationship between *somatic stigmata* on the one hand and *hysterical behaviour* on the other. In particular, his line of

reasoning runs as follows.* The effects of childhood trauma persist beyond the period of puberty in those individuals in which somatic and psychic growth, having proceded in an erratic fashion, resulted in developmental retardation. Whenever partial bodily infantilisms and juvenilisms appear as components of the psychological constitution, they are, because of the production of tensions and countertensions, apt to be associated with discrepancies and ambivalent instinctual attitudes. The latter, in turn, are apt to inhibit the development of harmoniously integrated personality patterns. In the somatic sphere, the probands show one or more of the following: signs of blocked or uneven function and maturation in the endocrine sphere, dysgenital and intersexual stigmata of the bodily build, partial masculinisms, feminisms and infantilisms, eunuchoidism, anomalies in the distribution of hair over face and body, abnormalities of secretion and of the distribution of fat, local hypoplasias, retarded, irregular and painful menstruation, retardation or inordinate acceleration of bodily growth, of sexual function, abnormal development of the voice and other abnormal traits. Now since, in the normal subject, the maturation of the instinct proceeds in the course of puberty in typical phases, the persistence of an early instinct is an anachronism and "yesterday's instinct may be tomorrow's neurosis." In the retarded subject, there persist not only general affective attitudes but the active engrams of emotional traumas. Emotional traumas experienced by neurotic individuals in their childhood are neither different nor more severe than in those subjects which fail to show the above stigmata; rather, the persistence of traumatic experiences is referable to the fact that, in normal subjects, infantile experiences lose their affective loading concurrently with the natural changes of instinctual life occurring in puberty. As a result, the traumatic experiences in question become meaningless in terms of the meanwhile acquired instinctual maturity. With persisting infantile or juvenile instincts on the other hand, the influence of early trauma persists with unremitting strength, and, inasmuch as, in the retarded individual, early infantile affective life patterns continue to operate beyond the period of puberty (at which time

* Author's translation from the German edition (1922).

they should have become obsolete), the early life experiences become pathogenic under "favourable" conditions. A significant proportion of hysterical reactions are paroxysmal instinctual defenses of the immature, or only partially mature, personality against instinctual demands with which it is unable to cope. They challenge the resources of the personality in general and its sexual components in particular. The weakness of instinctual organization and the failures, disappointments and discouragements incurred in attempting to cope with the most vital demands of life, (including the establishment of social relations) are incompatible with the maintenance of self respect. Feelings of insufficiency which alternate with frenzied attempts at overcompensation, with feelings of self-assertiveness and clumsily exaggerated efforts to cope with the tasks of life are caused by the oscillations and ambivalent dynamics inherent in the weak instinctual background. In summary then, the infantile trauma becomes pathogenic in those individuals which remain more or less infantile, that is, weak, or otherwise abnormal, in the somatic sphere. The term *"hysterical personality"* refers to the aggressive, obnoxious and socio-pathic features of hysterical conduct rather than to those manifestations of the disease in the visceral, somatic and other spheres of function which constitute the clinical syndrome of hysteria. In fact, these features may exist more or less independently of the clinical symptoms and signs of hysteria so that, for all intents and purposes, hysterical individuals may appear to be "otherwise" healthy.

No matter how different the views of the authorities on the nature of hysterical illness, they are agreed that the hysterical personality resembles, in many significant respects, the personality of the child. Kraepelin (510) wrote that certain hysterical character traits are immediately reminiscent of the behaviour of naughty children, e.g., the jumpiness, the superficiality of attention and thought, the curiosity, stubborness and moodiness, greediness and unconcerned selfishness. The following is a representative sampling of opinions expressed on the subject by various authorities. Hysterics remain children, having the aspirations of grown ups, and they play their roles one of which is that of the child (460). Hysterical individuals display strong dependency needs and susceptibility to suggestion. In some way, the behaviour and the reactions of the person with strong hysterical personality traits may be compared with those of the spoiled child. The hysterical person is demanding, vain, inconsiderate, selfish, impulsive and juvenile (545). Hysteria develops in people who have an immature emotional approach to life (651). Hysterical character traits are appropriate to the level of maturity belonging to young children (140). The hysteric is physically and emotionally immature and has an excessive demand for security (651). Her childish egocentricity and inner fantasy poorly fit the hysteric for adult reality (692). Immaturity and a dependency upon guidance is a characteristic feature in the majority of hysterical patients (1). The hysterical individual lies either for the sake of lying or the habit can be traced to the lies of children where they represent a defense mechanism against the demands of reality which the child finds difficult to face (460). The hysterical person invents memories freely to satisfy pressing psychological needs (692). Many authorities hold that hysterical persons are outright sociopaths, and that mendacity, nymphomania and pseudologia fantastica are specific hysterical features. The silly, habitual lying and evasive talk of the hysterical country bumpkin and Ganser's syndrome of past-speaking displayed by hysterical criminals are the two extremes of one and the same scale.

That hysteria is more common in females than in males (Aristotle thought the illness to be caused by the meanderings of the uterus searching for gratification) is undoubtedly due to the fact that both men and women are sexualized children— the latter more so than the former.

We wish to conclude this section by quoting from Anna Freud's (267) writings. By and large her description of the behaviour of the child is applicable to the hysterical patient and, in many respects, similar to Kraepelin's description already quoted. "The child is frightfully inconsiderate of others and egotistic; he is only concerned with getting his own way and satisfying his own desires; he is quite indifferent as to whether he hurts others or not . . . he is quite curious about the things other people wish to conceal from him. He is greedy and will steal dainties. He is cruel to all living creatures weaker than himself." If the view that the hysterical patient is in many respects an adult child is correct, hysteria would be the anachronistic persistence, on a grand scale, of preformed mechanisms; and childhood hysteria the accentuation of certain behaviour patterns encountered in normal childhood.

Conversion reactions

Since the intellective level receives messages from, and sends directives to, the lower levels of the neuraxis, the inter-level relationships and their disorders are either sensory or motor in character. The latter may be divided into two subgroups, namely, (1) *hypaesthesias, anaesthesias, hypalgesias and analgesias* and (2) *hyparaesthesias and hyperalgesias.* The motor abnormalities include (1) *paretic* and *paralytic* phenomena on the one hand and (2) *irritative* or *hyperkinetic* phenomena on the other. The sensory and the motor symptoms of hysterical illness are both *ideogenic* and *ideomorphic.* The term ideogenic indicates that the symptoms are caused by mental abnormalities while the term ideomorphic refers to the peculiar feature that they conform to the patient's idea of a functional unit rather than the distribution of a peripheral nerve or a spinal segment of which, ordinarily, the patient knows nothing. In spite of the fact that both the sensory and the motor inter-level symptoms are psychogenic, the mechanism of certain sensory deficit phenomena is fundamentally different from that of the motor inter-level symptoms. They are in actual fact partial dissociative reactions of which mention is made in the present context only for the purpose of comparison with their motor "counterparts."

Symptoms of sensory deficit include disturbances of glove and stocking type, amblyopia, blindness, constriction of the visual fields, deafness, anosmia and disturbances of taste.

Symptoms of *sensory irritation* comprise various types of hypersensitivity which may involve the somatic and visceral sphere. They involve, e.g., mastodynia, a special form of what is familiarly known as hysterical topalgia.

Paretic and paralytic phenomena are flaccid or spastic paralysis, astasia and abasia, contractures of the extremities, glossospasm, laryngospasm and aphonia.

How do the neurodynamic processes underlying mentation "gain access" to the semi-independent (subordinate) strata of the neuraxis? It is convenient to apply the term *somatization* to the production of motor effects which conform to, and which translate into reality, corresponding sensory patterns. It is true that the term in question has been pre-empted by the psychosomatic school of thought, and that it designates the somatization of a conflict or a stress situation, that is, the production of tissue changes (or at least abnormal functions) by psychic factors. Nevertheless, for want of a better term, we shall employ the term somatization in referring to a psychological phenomenon, the most complex of which is the *translation of thought into action.* To give a simple example. In executing appropriate movements, we *somatize* the idea of a triangle by translating it into its pictorial representation. Drawing of a triangle is a psychosomatic process in the physiological sense of the term or, for that matter, the somatization of an idea. Now, acts of somatization are synergies compounded of movements which, to the extent that they are volitional and "replicating" in character, are mediated by the pyramidal tract but which, for smoothness of performance, depend on *proprioceptive, extrapyramidal* and *vestibulo-cerebellar mechanisms.* What's more, every volitional movement is accompanied by *vasomotor* adjustments and, if involving a sustained effort, by *metabolic* processes which satisfy concurrently increased tissue needs. Thus, volitional movements are compounded of a (a) *leading* or *primary synergy* mediated by the *pyramidal system,* (b) *subordinate or secondary synergies* subserved in part by auxiliary motor systems and (c) by certain divisions of the *autonomic,* including *cardio-vascular system.* That the subordinate organs are "sensitive" in responding to the precurrent sensory blueprints or *ideational plans* of those very movements which they are designed to translate into action may be gathered from the altered functionality of the striated muscles, the sweat glands, the blood vessels etc, that occur in response to the forerunning idea of the intended movements. (These phenomena can be detected by electrophysiological and pletysmographic methods.) Briefly stated, the total synergy "volitional movement" depends on the harmonious integration of individual synergies comprising a variety of levels of the neuraxis and the corresponding neural arrangements in the periphery of the organism. Under the influence of disruptive stimulation on the other hand, the repatterning of the very same functional arrangements may reach a point where the very plan of intended movements is no longer recognizable. (It is precisely this type of repatterning which may be seen in experimental animals and, under clinical conditions, in the human.) Similar considerations apply to mimetic movements which, too, encompass pyramidal, extra-pyramidal, vestibulo-cerebellar and auto-nomic mechanisms. If organic disease or physical or mental stress interferes with somatization, the integrative acts which make up the movements in question are disorganized. In the light of the concept here developed, certain *conversion symptoms may be regarded as the selective activation of those components of a somatization synergy which serve the function of expression, or the realization of an attitude*. Thus, *tremor* would represent the inordinate preponderance and, at the same time, the dysfunction, of *extrapyramidal* mechanisms while *blushing* would represent the inordinate preponderance of *vasomotor innervation*. (The phenomena in question, some of which are related to schizophrenic mannerism, will be dealt with in more detail under the heading "deviant channeling of impulses.") If, on the other hand, avoidance attitudes utilize the *pyramidal* system, the resulting *paralysis* renders pointless the use of subordinate mechanisms. It is important to keep in mind that only some of the above described dys-somatization reactions are expressive conversion symptoms while others are non-expressive. In fact, considering the meaning of the term "conversion," a good point may be made for restricting it to expressive conversion reactions and to regard conversion symptoms as a subgroup of dys-somatization reactions. (As is well known, conversion is generally regarded as the transformation of a repressed affect into somatic symptoms which are symbolic expressions of repressed ideas.) Now, it is difficult to accept that all symptoms of neurosis or, for that matter, of hysteria are means of expression. Rather, it would seem that many of them are the effects of mental stress in the somatic sphere and, in this respect, correspond to the neurotic symptoms in experimental animals. For example, Abse (*1*) described the case of a hysterical patient who developed a left sided paralysis, and which the analyst attributed to the fact that he was emotionally attached to a person who used to sit on his left side. Abse's interpretation may well hold true for this particular case but the psychoanalyst would be hard put to interpret, e.g., the variegated symptoms of one of Taylor's and Martin's (*898*) patient who was

"analgetic, tactually anesthetic, without muscle sense, deaf in one ear, weak-visioned in one eye and color blind." In other patients, weakness, involving now the left side, now the right side, may alternate with paraplegia. What kind of a conflict could possibly be expressed by such variety of symptoms? To sum up, certain dys-somatization symptoms are expressions of psychic conflicts, in which case the term conversion reaction is legitimate but not all somatic symptoms of hysteria are expressive in character. They are the reflection of inter-level disorganization caused by stress. (For a detailed discussion of conversion- and dissociative reactions along convention lines the interested reader may be referred to Laughlin (*516, 517*).

The concept of *defective somatization* as here developed has recently gained strong support by the production of hysteriform symptoms following the administration of prochlorperazine, a tranquilizing drug. Delay (*186, 187*) observed, in the motor sphere, various "excito-motor" symptoms of extrapyramidal type, weakness in the mimetic muscles simulating facial paralysis hyperreflexia, somato-sensory and neurovegetative changes. The hysteriform character of the abnormalities was accentuated by anxiousness, puerility, increased suggestibility, disturbances of volition and changes in consciousness. Shannon (*828a*) reports that the administration of perphenazine may produce seizures consisting of stiffness of the neck and fixation of the head in an abnormal position, protrusion and distortion of the tongue, increased salivation, anxiety, crying and moaning. The symptoms produced were originally mistaken for hysterical seizures. (Cf. the appearance of catatonic symptoms during recovery from insulin shock).

Hyperkinetic phenomena include pathological postures, bizarre, theatralical attudinizing and opisthotonus, clonic and choreiform movements, tics, tremors, torticollis, convulsions, rhythmic movements of various parts of the body, including nodding and head rotation.

The hyperkinetic phenomena occur, singly or in combination in the course of *hysterical seizures*. According to Kretschmer (*516*), hysterical seizures are patterned after two basic mechanism, namely, the *Bewegungssturm*, or "kinetic tempest" and the *Totstellreflex*, or "death feigning reflex," which he is inclined to interpret as an exaggeration of the startling reaction and the immobilization reflex seen in animals. The kinetic tempest is an attempt to *escape* from a threatening or intolerable situation; the death feigning reflex, an attempt to *avoid* it. Both phenomena are protective reflexes. It may be assumed that, in the hysterical seizure, the protective reflex has become elaborated to a protective synergy, which embodies various elements of the subcortical automatisms already described and which, whenever it involves higher levels of integration, may be shot through with elements expressing the very trends and motives that precipitated the attack. Thus, hysterical, subcortically integrated mechanisms are utilized whenever, under the impact of an intolerable situation caused by frustrations and conflicts, rational means of solution are not practicable or irrational means preferable. The very same mechanism is thrown into action whenever the necessity becomes imperative to reduce tension, and to give more or less veiled *expression* to its underlying cause.

That hysterical symptoms are a means of expression was emphasized, among others, by Kraepelin (*510*). Hence their constant coming and going and their relationship to emotionally charged ideas. Hysterical *laughing* and *crying spells*, he wrote, are pathologically distorted discharge of moods, be they joyous or sad; hysterical *vomiting*, of disgust; and hysterical *muteness*, *dyspnoea*, *pharyngism*, *palpitation* and *sweating* of anxiety. Hysterical *paraplegia* is reminiscent of the loss of power in the legs while hysterical *ataxias* resemble the trembling of the limbs associated with fear; and hysterical *fainting spells*, the clouding of the senses in emotional excitement. *Generalized hysterical seizures* have many features in common with the temper tantrums of children, while hysterical *contractures* resemble the muscular rigidity occurring in rage and despair. At the same time, Kraepelin, referring to Darwin's (*178*), already quoted studies, voiced the opinion that the manifestations of the emotions are rudiments of phylogenetically old protective and defensive synergies actuated by environmental conditions. It is not difficult to see significant relationships between the synergies in question and certain products of dys-somatization whose mechanism has already been discussed. Under *normal* conditions, the old movement patterns are relegated to subordinate synergies while the leading component of the total movement pattern are taken over by the pyramidal system of neurones. Under *abnormal* conditions on the other hand, there emerge "suitable" components of the total movement pattern, which subdue as it were the onto- and phylogenetically younger components.

Dissociative reactions

Like motivational conflicts, a substandard frustration-gratification ratio may interfere with the function of the intellective level. It may give rise to a variety of mental changes or *dissociative states*, including, among others, *hysterical amnesia*, *fugue states*, *somnambulism*, and *dual personality phenomena*. The understanding of these abnormalities is predicated upon the clarification of certain basic concepts, including the concept of the "*self*," of the "*will*," of *conscious* and *nonconscious mental* processes, of the processes of *engraphy* and *ekphory*, of *psychopathological complexes* and their influence upon human conduct, of the phenomena of *dominant* and *subsidiary mentation*, of *axial* and *marginal awareness*, of *suggestion*, *suggestibility* and *hypnosis*. To avoid ambiguity of terms, which would perpetuate the existing confusion, rather lengthy theoretical discussion will be necessary. They will make intelligible the *intra-level symptoms* (better known as dissociative reactions) of hysterical illness and indirectly, the disorganized relationship between the intellective (more especially the conceptual) level on the one hand and the subordinate echelons of the neuraxis on the other. Actually, since certain *inter-level symptoms* are referable to intra-level disorganization, the order of presentation might have been reversed. On the other hand, the sequence here adopted will facilitate the connection of the present section with the following, which is devoted to the discussion of schizophrenic illness.

THE OVERT SYSTEM OF NOTATION AND THE MNEMONIC SYSTEM OF NOTATION OF STIMULI

The representation of intellective stimuli at the highest sensory level of the brain conforms in a certain sense to the flow of time, in that stimuli generated by current environmental processes and those having been generated by past events are represented in different systems of notation. Primarily at least, the first group of stimuli is represented as *perceptual processes* or *psychisms;* the second group as *mnemonic processes* or *psychisms*. In response to the demands of the moment, the processes in question may however be converted into one another. The term *"engraphy"* designates the translation of a psychism from the overt into the mnemonic system of notation; the term *"ekphory,"* the reverse process (fig. 11). Ordinarily, perceptions do not outlast the processes by which they are produced, but are reversibly eliminated after the environmental or internal perception generating process has come to an end. Since perceptual stimuli have a special representation by virtue of their synchrony with current events occurring in the orbit of the organism, the sensory division of the neuraxis may be said to operate in the fashion of a recording device. Biological recorders are able to store stimuli in an inactive state, to reactivate them, and to correlate them, somewhat in the fashion of an information processing mechanism or computer equipped with what is known in technical language as a memory register.

Supplementing what has been gone before,* consciousness may be defined as that mode of representation of data or, for that matter, that system of notation in which there are recorded (a) primarily perceptual stimuli, the crude material of our experience that is, and, secondarily, their configurational and conceptual derivatives, and (b) ekphorized engrams. The representation, in the nervous system, of data in different systems of notation enhances the adaptibility of behaviour. Diversity of notation makes for increasing complexity of response, including anticipatory behaviour, which is shaped in accordance with past experiences, and which depends in large measure on the articulation of current psychisms with the mnemonic residues of stimuli. There operate, with data lacking conscious quality, lower organisms and, in the advanced forms of life, the individual echelons of the neuraxis below that sphere of activity of the highest level which uses the overt system of notation. The utilization of conscious, i.e., perception-like processes and their elaboration to configurational stimuli and concepts is a biological stratagem which opens additional parameters of objective reality and, at the same time, increases the performance range of the organism.

* Cf. "Intellective stimuli: their affective and cognitive component."

In *summary*, then, the term "consciousness" refers to that system of notation of stimuli which is put into operation by the highest sensory level of the neuraxis for the purpose of recording of stimuli, of the interaction of existing stimuli with those having been generated in the past, and lastly, with those stimuli that are anticipated on the basis of those known. For the purpose of interaction with existing overt psychisms, mnemonic stimuli are translated into the very same system of notation to which the term "consciousness" is applied. And since the system of notation to which the term in question refers is, at the same time, the notation system in which perceptions are recorded, and, further, perceptions are the immediate data of awareness, the conscious state is the ultimate, irreducible mode of awareness. The notation system analogy of stimulus representation (to be amplified in the course of the discussion of the mathematical fields of thought) has many advantages which, although perhaps difficult to appreciate at the present stage of our thesis, may be listed below for ready reference.

The *notation-system-analogy* is the least anthropistic. It takes into account the fact that

(a) stimuli are represented in the fashion of symbols of increasing inclusiveness, i.e., perceptions, configurations and concepts, and that the latter, which are the most inclusive psychisms, resemble the incorporative symbols of algebra

(b) that the symbols in question represent at the same time increasingly complex "analogs" of the stimuli by which they are generated

(c) that there are two basically identical classes of phenomena, namely, *calculations*, and the *selection of appropriate responses* on the part of the nervous system which, in turn, involves the manipulation of sensory stimuli

(d) that the manipulation of both mathematical and non-mathematical symbols follows certain operative laws

(e) that notation systems are interconvertible and

(f) that, with a certain degree of complexity of incorporative symbols, their interaction takes place in a quasi-automatic fashion. This interaction resembles the activity patterns (or follows the operative laws) of stimuli which lack a conscious representation.

It is worthy of note that Leibniz, in his "De arte combinatoria" published in 1666 proposed to "create a general method in which all truth of reason would be reduced to a kind of calculation" (*879*).

THE DOMINANT AND THE SUBSIDIARY SPHERE OF MENTATION

The. study of certain phenomena to be dealt with below suggests a *division of labor*, within the highest level of the neuraxis, into two spheres of activity which we propose to call, respectively, the dominant and the subsidiary sphere of mentation. *Dominant mentation comprises* the totality of mental processes which are represented in the overt (conscious) system of notation, which are concerned with the recording of stimuli, with the elaboration of perceptions to configurations and concepts and the selection (determination) of responses. The *subsidiary sphere of mentation* on the other hand does not record stimuli directly and it uses, for the purpose of determination of response, data represented in the mnemonic rather than the overt system of notation (fig. 11). However, subsidiary mental processes are by no means an "unconscious edition" of overt processes and vice versa. On the contrary, dominant and subsidiary processes, having specific tasks to perform, use different techniques. The dominant sphere of mentation operates with perceptions of various complexity (including gestalten) and with concepts, i.e., with both palpable and impalpable psychisms. The subsidiary sphere of mentation on the other hand derives informative data from the dominant sphere, and it utilizes material which, apart from the fact that it is represented in a different notation system, may have only a very loose connection with current stimuli. In this fashion, highly complex responses requiring the utilization of concepts may be worked out by, or with the aid of, the subsidiary sphere long after the initiation of the process of response determination on the part of the dominant sphere. In other words, subsidiary mentation is concerned with responses to stimuli which appear to have been forgotten but, nevertheless, may be presumed to be operative while attention is paid to existing stimuli not necessarily related to the (seemingly forgotten) stimulus situation. On the other hand, it is true that the latent stimuli are more likely to be activated and made to interact with those current stimuli which are related to the apparently forgotten stimuli, no matter how

remote this relationship may be. From the viewpoint of normal psychology, the fact that a problem may be solved at a time it has apparently been forgotten is one of the main reasons for stipulating two categories of mental processes, namely, a conscious (dominant) category and a non-conscious (subsidiary) category of psychisms. It is implied in the foregoing that the subsidiary sphere of mentation influences the dominant sphere and thereby the behaviour of the organism.

To put the matter somewhat differently: The overt system of notation operates in that experiental mental state in which perceptual data are recorded. It operates with stimuli of which we are aware, i.e., psychisms having *conscious quality*. In sharp contrast, the stimuli operating in the *subsidiary sphere of mentation* are represented in a system of notation which differs from that in which perceptual material is registered, i.e., in the *mnemonic system*, the elements of which are non-experiental. More accurately, we are not directly aware of the processes that go on in the subsidiary sphere of mentation. It is only the products or the results of subsidiary mental activity that are transmuted into the very same system of notation in which immediate reality is recorded. Evidently, this translation occurs to make possible the *interaction of past stimuli with existing stimuli*, and is a synthetizing (synergic) process serving the generation of novel data out of those already known. (This process, which is a problem for further discussion, will be taken up in Chapter III.)

Concerning the *mnemonic system*, we assume that engrams are dormant unless translated either into the dominant sphere of mentation or the subsidiary sphere; it is difficult to imagine that problem solving in the course of thought processes in which the subsidiary sphere of mentation plays a part, should be possible without the activation of mnemonic material. (As we have already indicated, the psychisms involved in subsidiary mentation are likewise represented in the mnemonic system of notation, fig. 11.) In other words, since both dominant and subsidiary mentation are concerned with the determination of behaviour, and responses are co-determined by engrams, the residues of previously experienced stimuli are translated into *active dominant psychisms* or, as the case may be, *active subsidiary psychisms*.

The translation, into dominant (conscious or perception-like) psychisms of both mnemonic and

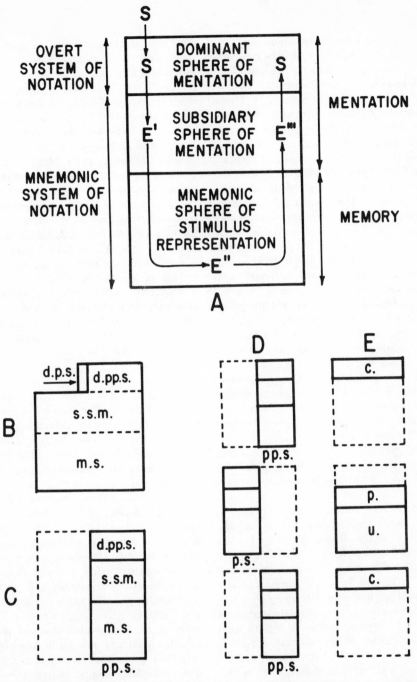

Fig. 11. The functional organization of the mental apparatus. Engraphy and ekphory. Dissociative reactions.

A.: waking pattern of the mental apparatus;

B.: Partial dissociation of the self. d.p.s.—dominant sphere of mentation of the personal self; d.pp.s.—dominant sphere of mentation of the para-personal self; s.s.m.—subsidiary sphere of mentation of both selfs; m.s.—mnemonic system of both selfs.

C.: complete dissociation of the self.

D.: alternating selfs.

E.: "Horizontal" dissociation of the self.

subsidiary psychisms may be rapid and complete, in which case a person may suddenly become aware of a relationship thus far unknown or it may occur in a shadowy and fragmentary fashion. The term *Bewusstseinslage* introduced by Marbe (*619*) designates a state of awareness whose contents are either unspecifiable or, at most, conceivable in vague outlines only. At the state of *Bewusstheit* the maturation of meaning proceeds to a stage where awareness qualities become differentiated into individual elements of whose relationships the subject is already becoming conscious and which form the general framework of the emerging thought process. According to Ach (*2*), *Bewusstheiten* are complex awareness contents whose structure, while fully known to the subject, do not as yet permit their verbalized formulation. Weininger (*938*) spoke of *"henids,"* that is, phantom-like awareness contents which vanish before they can be "fixated."

Mentalization is the translation of a stimulus from the somatic into the perceptual (conscious) notation system, say, the translation of a retinal process into a perception and its conceptual derivatives. (Needless to add that mentalization is not identical with mentation, the manipulation of psychisms in the dominant or the subsidiary sphere of the mental apparatus.)

The dominant sphere of mentation is not uniformly structured. As already suggested by William James (*430*) and others, we may compare the dominant sphere of mentation to a stream, for its contents are ordinarily in a state of fluxion. Moreover, certain data of awareness occupy the axial current of the stream of thought while others "drift" in its periphery. Accordingly, it is convenient to distinguish between *focal* or *axial awareness* on the one hand and *marginal* awareness on the other, both of which are by definition conscious processes. (Apart from their state of fluidity, they correspond more or less to what Wundt (*792*) called *Blickpunkt* und *Peripherie des Bewusstseins.*) Marginal awareness must not be confused with subsidiary mentation, which lacks the attributes of consciousness and of whose activity we are only indirectly aware. For example, a person writing a letter in noisy surroundings may suddenly discover the solution of a problem which is entirely unrelated to the contents of the letter, the solution having been arrived at by subsidiary mentation. The contents of the letter on the other hand are elements of

dominant mentation which, in spite of potentially distracting stimuli was kept organized into sets of focal and marginal elements. Carpenter (*153*) was "informed by John Stuart Mill when his *System of Logic* was first published that he had thought out the greater part of it during his daily walks between Kensington and the India House. And he himself met Mr. Mill more than once in Cheapside, at its fullest afternoon time, treading his way among the foot passengers with which its narrow pavement was crowded, with the air of a man so deeply absorbed into his own contemplations that he would not recognize a friend and yet not be jostling his fellows or coming into collision with lamp posts." Thus, the *System of Logic* must have been worked out by the axial stream of mentation, reinforced and supplemented, at the appropriate time, by the products of subsidiary mentation and mnemonic elements while the marginal stream of mentation helped John Stuart Mill to avoid lamp posts and, maybe, even to overlook his friends.

To *summarize*: In conformity with the principle of division of labor, the stream of mentation bifurcates into a *dominant* and a collateral, or *subsidiary* current. The former is concerned with reactions depending on demands made on the organism by situational factors of *recency* and *immediacy* which, to be answered at the intellective level, require perceptual awareness. Subsidiary currents of the stream of mentation are concerned with *mnemic reactions*, which do not necessarily depend on the conscious representation of the data to be evaluated. The subsidiary stream is a mental system that is rather more adapted to cope with delayed reactions which, in order not to interfere with current stimulation, are experientially segregated until such time as the subsidiary process has come to fruition. (See also "Intuitive Thought," Chapter III.) It is precisely at this moment that the products of subsidiary activity are made available to the dominant (conscious) stream of mentation. No doubt subsidiary mental activity serves its purpose best by being kept out of the realm of awareness and by not being burdened with the load of perception. It is not difficult to see that the subsidiary stream of mentation is a derivative of mnemonic activity. (At this point of the argument, we perceive, in dim outlines at least, the relationships between experiental engrams, instinctual engrams and complexes.) To reiterate, the *axial* stream of thought, then, comprises stimuli which elicit more or less immediate psychic processes or, as the case may be, psychomotor reactions while the *marginal* current is represented by stimuli of which we are by comparison not distinctly aware and which elicit responses only on sudden change of the environmental setting. The stream of *subsidiary thought* is comparable to a collateral yet invisible undercurrent which, in a more or less unpredictable fashion, may "join" the dominant stream and which, at almost any time, may furnish data seemingly out of nowhere. Since thought is the antecedent of action, the data involved in this process may influence behaviour in the same way as those generated in the sphere of dominant mentation or conscious thought. Either stream of thought is reinforced by affluents from the large subterranean reservoir of *engrams*. Figure 11 is a "crossection" through both the overt (axial and marginal) stream and the subsidiary flow of mentation while the store of engrams is represented, for simplicity, as a static, although not necessarily permanent, system of psychisms.

Since dominant mentation is a conscious process while subsidiary processes and dormant engrams are non-conscious psychisms, they are ordinarily said to comprise the "Unconscious." We have avoided using this term because of its many conflicting connotations. Rather, we prefer to think in terms of, on the one hand, "non-conscious mental processes," i.e., subsidiary mentation (which includes ekphory into the subsidiary sphere) and, on the other, inactive mnemonic representation. It would be a mistake to assume that every act of problem solution and of determination of behaviour on the part of the intellectual level is worked out by subsidiary mentation or, for that matter, its apparent equivalent, the "Unconscious." Apart from other considerations such misconceptions has indeed arisen in some quarters owing to the fact that, a subject is ordinarily not aware of the mechanism of creative thought even if he should have solved the problem upon which he had concentrated by a process of conscious mentation.

THE STRUCTURE OF THE WAKING STATE

The terms "awareness," "consciousness," and "wakefulness" are for all practical purposes synonymous. A person who is awake is conscious and, at the same time, more or less aware of his body and his surroundings. What is the structure of the waking state? We have already indicated that we are focally aware of some stimuli while we are only marginally aware of others. The stimuli which are focally, or, as the case may be, marginally represented, may be of any degree of complexity. A focally represented stimulus may be a mere perception, say, a blue, cloudless sky. It may be an intensely pleasurable sensation or a sharp pain. For a time at least, any of these perceptions may form the content of our awareness to the virtual exclusion of all other experiences. Or the content of consciousness may be a configurational perception, such as an abstract design, which, being an object of esthetic enjoyment, gives rise to a state of intense mental absorption. Lastly, dominant mentation may be occupied with the manipulation of concepts while the perception of marginal stimuli is reduced or virtually suspended.

Under ordinary conditions however the structure of the waking state is complex and variegated. As a general rule, we respond to perceptual and configurational stimuli in a way that requires *recognition*, that is (in the human at least) *conceptual awareness*. At the same time, we may be concerned with the utilization of concepts which are unrelated to what we see, hear and feel and with the selection of responses to whatever stimuli happen to be "leading." Thus, the structure of the waking state depends, apart from a critical level of generalized receptivity, on selective responsiveness to stimuli, i.e., on focal awareness, and the establishment of conceptual preponderance necessitating, in turn, the correlation of perceptual and configurational material with the appropriate conceptual framework. If the general level of responsiveness is reduced, as in transitional stages between the waking state and sleep, the recording of stimuli falls below critical levels. Moreover, the general lowering of responsiveness is apt to obliterate the boundaries between focal and marginal awareness, which reduces the reliability (or confidence coefficient) of the mechanism underlying behavioural responses.

The representation of stimuli in a particular system of notation is determined by *priority principles*. Ordinarily, the waking state is characterized by the preferential representation of those stimuli, be they perceptual or conceptual in character, which have an immediate bearing on the biological equilibrium of the organism and, at the same time, by the preferential ekphory of engrams which are translated from the mnemonic into the overt system of notation for the purpose of interaction with current stimuli. Contrariwise, the structure of the waking state is disrupted by the shift of priority (a) to stimuli which in the interest of response should be relegated to the marginal currents of awareness or (b) to contextually unrelated engrams and other (ordinarily indifferent) stimuli. Absentmindedness, distraction and mental confusion ensue. Under normal conditions, similar states develop in the transitional stages between the waking state and sleep. (See above.)

Now, whatever psychisms interact with one another constitute what is called a unitary *self*, which is nothing other than the *expression of synergic activity at the highest sensory (intellective) level of the neuraxis*. This unity, however, may break down under the impact of disruptive stimulation.

THE SELF

The unity of responses to stimuli is rooted in the above outlined organization of the intellective level. To say that unity of behaviour depends on the unity of the self is a convenient shorthand expression although one not entirely free from the danger involved in the reification of abstract terms. Speaking in more detail, *the term "self" designates the mode in which there are experienced the interaction-and interdependence relationships of the psychisms operating in the dominant sphere of mentation, and also the articulation of the latter with the subsidiary sphere and with the mnemonic system of stimulus representation*. As we have already alluded to, the relationships in question belong to the category of *intra-sensory synergies*. The psychisms involved in this process are data of various complexity. The axial stream of thought is that segment of the dominant sphere of mentation where the relationships in question are most closely knit and most distinctly experienced, that is to say, where, concurrently with the intensified interaction of the sensory elements concerned, the degree of awareness is maximised. Moreover, the *interaction relationships per se remain unchanged* in spite of the changes of reality, which is in a state of virtually constant

fluxion, in other words, the *formal properties of the process of interaction do not depend on the contents of the interacting psychisms*. Neither are they changed upon being interrupted by sleep and similar conditions, the continuity of mentation being re-established by the mnemonic reinstatement of data which participated in the process of interaction. Ultimately, the interacting elements are of a conceptual order of complexity. Accordingly, the self of man is, in substance, a conceptual one while the self of the lower organism is made up of perceptual and configurational data. Neglecting, for the time being, that animals, too, can think, (although, it is true, at a lower level), they experience the world perceptually; they see, feel, hear and smell the world. Man, on the other hand, "thinks" the world. At still lower levels of life and, no doubt, in the human infant, in the very early stages of development, the self is of a primitive, perceptual rank. Moreover, continuity relationships are nascent and they develop only with increasing maturity. In the still more primitive, non-perceiving organism, that is to say, in living beings in which stimuli have not as yet acquired a cognitive component, the self exists in a nascent stage, at a level of reflex function unified by organizational control. Moreover, the human self is reduced to the perceptual level in states of fading awareness. Ultimately, it is abolished and man is reduced to a reflexly integrated organism. In any case, at whatever level of complexity they occur, the interdependence-and interaction relationships which, under normal conditions, underly the experience of the self, refer to relationships between the data of awareness and are, accordingly, of a sensory order.

What may be the biological significance of awareness or, for that matter, of the waking state? How is it that mentation does not take shape (in any case, not in the same fashion) at a non-conscious level, as do other, highly complicated processes of life? We have already made reference to the rationale of conscious experience while discussing the affective and the cognitive parameter of intellective stimuli. We remarked that the acquisition on the part of reflexly operating stimuli of a cognitive parameter (which is established in the interest of increasing adaptibility of living beings to complex environmental conditions) requires a special system of notation on the part of the highest sensory level of the neuraxis. Rather like certain mathematical operations depend, technically, on the invention of suitable symbols, the synthesis of the data of reality to concepts are predicated upon precisely that system of notation which has an experiental, conscious, quality. In so far as concepts embody, or incorporate, perceptions, man sees, or, rather, "thinks" the world in terms of "incorporative symbols," and his responses to reality are dependent on the manipulation of conceptual symbols according to certain operative laws. (See Chapter III.) This is not to say, however, that the formation of concepts is invariably a conscious process.

THE WILL

The term "will" is a shorthand expression applied to the *experience of sensory-motor dependence relationships established at the highest level of response determination*, namely, the dependence of movements on precurrent, evaluative, processes mediated by the intellective level. Thus, the relationships in question belong, in contrast to those underlying the self, to the category of *sensory-motor synergies*. Further, since the experiental agency involved in evaluative processes is the self, volitional movements are as a matter of linguistic convenience said to be carried out by the self. (It would be an anthropistic fallacy, amounting to the projection of man into his own brain, to say that the "self wills.") Implicitly, the will is, at the same time, the mode in which there is *experienced*, at the highest sensory and responsiveness determinating stratum of the nervous system, the *apparent possibility of freedom of choice between, and response to, stimuli whose impulse components operate as motives*. The experience of the will being free is attributable to the fact that, in a given situation, (be it regarded anterospectively or retrospectively) different actions are imaginable. The same would seem to apply to the imaginal inhibition of motives by countermotives. Jones (*448*), in discussing Freud's views on the freedom or, rather, lack of freedom of the will, speaks of a "gigantic reflex arc which is commonly not being recognized as such partly because of the difficulty in tracing

the ultimate sources of the stimulation which fortifies the illusion of spontaneity."*)

In *summary*, then, the conceptual analysis of the term *self* reveals that it is not an entity endowed with independent (not to speak material) existence. It is an "agency" which, although rendered phasically discontinuous by the sleep-wakefulness cycle, can be defined solely in terms of experiental identity and constancy. This unitary system of reference is put into operation whenever the responsiveness of the highest sensory level of brain function reaches a critical level. Experiental identity is maintained in spite of the difference between the individual experiences and the fact that they are in that state of partial fluxion which reflects the changes in objective reality, that is, which mirrors the correspondance between the latter and subjective reality. The experiental reference system encompasses the dominant sphere of mentation, the subsidiary sphere of mentation and the ekphorized engrams of the mnemonic system. In spite of the fact that the interaction- and interdependence relationships involved in perceptual and configurational awareness and even in abstract thinking may be experienced as autonomous, activity is no essential attribute of the self. Figuratively speaking, it may be merely an observer. The *will*, like the self, is not an entity endowed with independent

---

* As regards the question of the freedom of the will, the *agnostics*, represented by Bridgeman, philosopher and physicist, maintain that the problem is insoluble "since, once a decision has been made, there is no possibility to prove that, in this particular instance, a different decision had been possible." (Quoted by P. R. Hofstätter, "Psychologie," Fischer Verlag, Frankfurt a.M., 1957, p. 67.) The quantum physicist P. Jordan, a representative of the modern *indeterministic school*, claims that atomic events are not subject to the law of causality (P. Jordan, "Die Quantenmechanik und die Grunprobleme der Biologie," Naturwissenschaften, 1932, 20:815, and "Zur Quantenbiologie," Biologisches Zentralblatt, 1939, 59:1) as, in the sphere of microphysics, any cause may have any effect so that the individual effects are "free" and only collectively subjected to the law of cause and effect. Consequently, the "events in the living organism including the acts and decisions of man are governed by structures in the atomic range and are, accordingly, free." W. H. Westphal insists that the indeterminists prove nothing "since man's actions although he be free from the laws of causality, would be slaves to the vagaries of atomic events." ("Deine tägliche Physik, Ullstein Verlag, Frankfurt am Main. 1957, p. 175–176.)

existence, nor indeed does the will control the self or vice versa. Rather, the term "will" refers to the somatization of precurrent ideas, or of the products of evaluative processes which are experiental in character owing to the fact that they materialize at the highest level of brain function. They are calculations performed by biological computers; and the results of these calculations, the intellective antecedents of action that is, are linked with volitional movements in essentially the same way as the sensory inflow into a spinal segment is coupled with the motor reaction it precedes. The lowest imaginable level of reflex activity, which is the least versatile, deals with a minimum of variables and its responses attain a maximum of stereotypy. It is the most reliable but least productive. In either eventuality, the reactions are determinate, i.e., the experiental, volitional, responses are subject to the very same laws of causality as the non-experiental involuntary reactions—the subject has willed precisely what it has done. The highest level, on the other hand, operates with that system of notation without which it could not synthetize elementary stimuli to concepts* and which, for technical reasons, has the quality of conscious experience. In *conclusion*, then, the terms *self* and *will* are reification artifacts, or products of language structure. They refer to certain relationships between experiental stimuli and, at the same time, to synergic processes or integrative acts. With this mental reservation, the terms *self* and *will* may be used for the sake of brevity.†

---

* As already noted, the subsidiary sphere of mentation may have some preparatory function as regards concept formation (see Chapter III).

† Thus, the term "self" refers to a relation between psychisms, more precisely, to the mode in which the relation of mental experiences is represented at the highest sensory level of integration. In other words, the term "self" does not refer to an independent entity (as stipulated by the substantialization-theory of the self), and statements to the effect that the self organizes data, that it is narrowed, etc. would seem to involve a contradiction. In actual fact, we shall speak of the self as if it were an agency only as a matter of linguistic convenience, that is, use the expression in question as an auxiliary term. In other words, in every instance in which the term is used as a shorthand expression, its definition can be substituted for it, but such usage would result in extremely cumbersome expression.

DISSOCIATION OF THE SELF

If it is true that the term *self* is a name for the experience of interdependence- and interaction relationships between intellective stimuli, it should also be true that a *loosening of these relationships* (an instance of what will be discussed in Chapter IV as "temporal dissociation of function") will alter the functional organization of the self, and that, as the result of this "vertical cleavage," which may assume various depths, the self will lose its original unity and become converted into a *dual system of relational experience*. As a matter of convenience, we propose to call these *secondary systems* the *personal self* (ps) and the *para-personal self* (pps). Further deliberations concerning the degree of cleavage suggest that a relatively mild degree of dissociation of the central experiental agency may involve the *dominant sphere* of mentation only; a more profound dissociation, the *subsidiary sphere* in addition to the dominant sphere; and the maximal degree, the *mnemonic sphere* as well (fig. 11).

In the first eventuality, the dominant sphere of either of the two selfs would maintain, although on a reduced scale, their relationships (a) with one another (either directly or by way of the subsidiary sphere of mentation) and (b) with the mnemonic system.

In the second eventuality, some sort of communication between the two selfs would be maintained by their common stock of engrams.

Lastly, if the dissociation of the self reaches a maximum, certain engrams would be accessible to and utilized by the personal self only; others, only by the parapersonal self.

HISTORICAL NOTE

The concept of non-conscious mental function goes back to antiquity (*565, 620, 693*). If one were to write a historical essay on the development of this concept, the matter might appropriately be discussed under three headings, namely, (a) early concepts, (b) the ideas of the non-analytic theorists and (c) the ideas of Freud and his immediate forerunners.* St. Augustin stated that certain psychological observations indicate the

---

* This was attempted in the original version of the manuscript, but this section was eliminated because of its length.

presence of unconscious elements (431), and similar ideas were subsequently expressed by other philosophers and naturalists, including Leibniz (650a), Hume (410), Kant (467), Schopenhauer (see esp. "Die Welt als Wille und Vorstellung," vol. I., pp. 227–228; vol. II., pp. 148–149, and 457–458), Brodie (121), Maudlsey (626), Carpenter (153), Maine de Biran (611), and Hamilton (340). Ed. von Hartmann (340) who sketched the history of the concept in his *magnum opus* (see vol. I., p. 13 ff.), acknowledged that his "Philosophie des Unbewussten" was inspired by Leibniz. Among the non-analytical theorists, we mention Bernheim (75), Janet (433, 434), Prince (740), Muensterberg (671), Sidis (832, 833), Myers (677) and Mills (655). Freud's theory of the unconscious is an elaboration of Breuer's ideas, derived, in turn, from Helmholtz's system of physics and Bruecke's (73, 519) system of physiology and from the teachings of the French psychiatrists, especially Pierre Janet's doctrine of the "subconscient." (See also Jerusalem, 455, and Lipps, 576.) The Freudian concept of the unconscious was further developed by Bleuler (87) and by Jung (246, 517, 450, 209) who introduced the terms "personal unconscious" and "collective unconscious" respectively.

Although the meaning of the Freudian terms "conscious," "preconscious" and "unconscious" is generally known, it is worth while pointing out that according to Freud the unconscious consists largely of repressed complexes of an unsocial, immoral, especially incestuous nature; that it represents the infantile part of the mind; that its laws differ widely from those that govern the operations of the conscious; that ideas, strivings, decisions differ from conscious mental activity only by the absence of the conscious quality; that the unconscious may serve the most complicated and the most rational processes in spite of the fact that they contradict outer reality; that the unconscious is unaware of inner inconsistencies; that there is no relation between its elements, no sense of doubt and certitude; that it has no sense of time and only the present exists; and that opposite ideas do not influence each other. These statements are repeated over again both in Freud's own writings and in those of his pupils.*

It is difficult to see how the most complicated and the most rational processes can go on in a mental system that lacks a sense of time, where there is neither contradiction nor negation, and where wishes are fulfilled by mere phantasy. Partly because of these inconsistencies and partly because of the fact that the terms "subconscious," "intra-conscious," "co-conscious," etc., coined by other writers have been completely pre-empted and their number has grown so large that it would be difficult to keep their meanings in mind (even if they were established by mutual consent) we deemed it advisable to refer to the totality of non-conscious mental processes believed to be in an active (though subliminal) state as the subsidiary sphere of mentation, and of non-conciouss mental processes believed to be in an inactive (latent) state as the mnemonic system of stimulus representation. The preconscious does not correspond to the subsidiary sphere of mentation, nor does the unconscious correspond to the mnemonic system. In a nutshell, the unconscious is a source of inconvenience for the patient, while the mental processes comprising the subsidiary sphere of mentation and the mnemonic system (which establishes a link between the physiological and the psychological spheres of integration) are primarily components of a mnemonic action mechanism. Furthermore, non-conscious mental processes should not be equated with the Id, nor the self with the Ego. In the words of Masserman (590) "Freud's own precedent of using key terms such as instinct, ego, cathexis, transference and so on with different connotations in successive writings or sometimes even in succeeding paragraphs has been followed by many subsequent writers in this field. Sometimes this has lead to curious situations as when various writers solemnly agree on a formula to which they obviously attach different meanings or indulge in heated polemics over verbiage when they are in essential operational agreement."

At this point it is possible to define the intra-level symptoms of hysterical illness. They are disorder characterized chiefly by *complex-determined dissociative reactions* involving the intellective level which, in turn, produce independent or

---

* *Origin of the contents of the unconscious.* (a) Early concepts: (683), p. 247.–(270), vol. XIII., p. 412, and vol. IV., p. 25.—Later concepts: (448), vol. II., p. 346, vol. I., p. 403, and (446), p. 247.–(471).

Contents of the unconscious. (448), vol. II., p. 321, and (270), vol. IV., p. 25.

Properties of the unconscious. (270), vol. IV., p. 25, vol. V., p. 610, vol. X., p. 266, and vol. VII., p. 86. (448), vol. II., p. 225 and (796), p. 271.

semi-independent systems of intellective stimuli or separate selfs. We add that, except for the inordinate intensification of the affective loading of the stimuli involved, the pathological process leaves intact their intrinsic structure whereas, in schizophrenia, in addition to the dissociative process, the production of the two selfs that is, the structure of intellective stimuli (more accurately those which constitute the para-personal self) is disorganized in a characteristic fashion. Pierre Janet (*433*) defined hysteria as a "form of mental disorganization characterized by the tendency toward permanent and complete division (dissociation) of the personality. Things take place as if the system of the psychic phenomena which form the personal perception with all men were, with these individuals, disintegrated and giving birth to two or more simultaneous or successive groups, mostly incomplete, and robbing each other of sensation, images and consequently, movements, which should normally be united in one and the same consciousness and the same form." (Hollingworth's translation, *401*.) According to Abse (*1*), Janet connected the predisposition to hysteria with an inadequacy of mental tension to hold together, under conditions of stress (toxic, exhaustive or psychological) partial systems of thought which thus separate from the main body of consciousness.

We are inclined to believe that, spontaneous dissociative states are ordinarily initiated by *complexes*, that is, intellective stimuli whose impulse parameter of affective loading is increased well beyond the normal (homeostatic) range. *Complexes are produced by certain life experiences involved in gratification, or its denial, of needs; and they influence, for reasons rooted in the personal history of the individual, emotional homeostasis, thought and conduct.* In predisposed persons, they precipitate certain seeking and avoidance reactions encompassing a variety of functional levels of the neuraxis. In hysteria, the reactions in question are "unconsciously motivated," that is to say, motivated by complexes operating in the subsidiary sphere of mentation. Breuer and Freud's (*111*) studies on hysteria suggest that the spontaneous dissociation or splitting of the mental apparatus is due to the representational incompatibility of specific mental contents. This in turn would indicate that the dissociative process is basically an avoidance response aiming at the exclusion of certain data from the interaction

with others. To put it in another way, the dream like repatterning of the para-personal self makes possible the imaginal consummation of mental seeking reactions coupled with avoidance responses directed toward opposing elements. As applied to hysterical dissociation phenomena, the psychoanalytic concept of wishfulfilment (the wish being a complex operating in the subsidiary sphere of mentation) appears to be preferable to Janet's notion of inadequacy of mental tension. On the other hand, Janet's hypothesis seems to provide a more suitable explanation for states of organically induced dissociation.

Alternating Selfs

It may well be imagined that, within an already dissociated self, the interaction of intellective stimuli is temporarily discontinued either in the personal self or the para-personal self. In the first eventuality, the para-personal self will become active, in the second eventuality, the personal self; in fact, the activity of one is the correlate of the inactivity of the other. Alternating states of dissociation of the self include (a) conditions in which the structure of the waking state is maintained in both the personal self and the para-personal self, whichever happens to be active, and (b) conditions in which the structure of the waking state is maintained, or fully maintained, in the personal self only. The first group comprises the double (or multiple) personalities properly so called; the second group, states of primary hysterical amnesia, in which the personal self is inactive while the para-personal self asserts itself.

ALTERNATING DOUBLE AND MULTIPLE PERSONALITIES. The individual selfs may or may not be aware of each other, that is, they may be *communicating* or *non-communicating*. Since, in pure cases at least, the two personalities exist at different times, communication, if any, is established by way of mnemonic mechanisms. In a recent study, Taylor and Martin (*898*) advance many reasons for the genuineness of the observations made in various countries, and said to comprise close to 100 cases. The first case reported is probably that of Mary Reynolds, who was born in 1793. She was "melancholy, shy and given to solitary religious meditations. When 18 years old, she would change periodically into a buoyant, witty girl, fond of company and a lover of nature. Five weeks later she lapsed into her old (personal) self and from that time the two selfs would alternate at irregular intervals. Ultimately, the second state (or pps) became permanent and continued until her death. There having been mutual amnesia between the two selfs, the case may be classified as one of *alternating, non-communicating dual personality*. Miss Beauchamp, to whom Prince (*740*) devoted a long monograph, has aroused exceptional interest. Miss Beauchamp "herself" was the ps. "Sally," (the pps), was "the exact opposite, a mischievous girl, whose behaviour would have shocked Miss Beauchamp, a lady raised in the best Victorian tradition. Moreover, Sally tormented Miss Beauchamp with practical jokes, such as the mysterious disappearance of some money. She was considered a "distinct personality in the sense of having a character, train of thought, memories, perceptions, and mental acquirements different from Miss Beauchamp. . . . Accordingly, the two selfs willed, acted and thought along opposed lines. During the time when the ps has vanished, Sally was, for the time being, the whole conscious personality having taken the place of the other. (In other words, the dissociation involved not only the dominant and the subsidiary sphere of mentation but also the mnemonic mechanism.) . . . At other times, however, the two selfs would to some degree coexist. "Sally would then know what Miss Beauchamp thought; she would hear what she said, read what she wrote and see what she did," which indicates the presence of two selfs, more precisely, a pps embodying the ps. A similar case, Anna O., a classic hysteric, was observed by Breuer (*111*). As in the case just quoted, the patient's pps was a naughty and troublesome child. Thigben and Cleckly (*302*) reported the case of a patient in whom *unidirectional communication* could be ascertained by the therapists between the ps, Eve White, and the pps, Eve Black. For all intents and purposes, the trouble started with a trip for which Eve White had no memory. However, in the course of treatment it became apparent that the duplication of the personality went back to early childhood. Several days after the disappearance of Eve White, a letter was received to which a childish postscript was appended (by the pps). Eve White was a "circumspect, matter of fact person, meticulously truthful and consistently sober and serious about her grave troubles." Surprisingly, during an interview (as the ps vanished to be supplanted by the pps), a profound change in her bearing, indeed in her whole appearance took place. She said "Hi, there Doc!" and commenced speaking of herself as "she" or "her." When asked about her own name, she replied: "I am Eve Black." She was "shrewd, provocative, and frank" and displayed a sexual appeal which Eve White lacked entirely. She freely told of episodes of mischief or disobedience and she lied glibly and without compunction. Jane, a third personality, comprised both Eve White and Eve Black. R. L. Stevenson's legendary figures Dr. Jekyll (the ps) and Mr. Hyde (the pps, which however, eventually gained the upper hand) are a classic example of an *alternating, communicating, dual personality* either of whom know of the other at all times. The two characters are depicted as follows. "Dr. Jekyll was the familiar guest and entertainer of his friends; and whilst he had always been known for charities, he was no less distinguished for religion." Mr. Hyde was "cruel, callous and violent"—and "tales came out of his life, his strange associates and of the hatred that seemed to have surrounded his career." Dr. Hyde, referring to himself, spoke of "a secondary form and countenance substituted none the less natural to me because they were the expression and bore the stamp of lower elements in my soul". . . . Another passage reads as follows: "He (Hyde) knew himself more wicked, sold a slave to his original evil." He realized that "all human beings as we meet them are comingled out of good and evil and Edward Hyde, alone in the rank of mankind, was pure evil . . . Henry Jekyll stood at times aghast before the acts of Edward Hyde . . . but it was Hyde, after all, and Hyde alone, that was guilty . . . and Jekyll would make haste, where it was possible, to undo the evil done by Hyde." Toward the end of the story, Dr. Jekyll, referring to Mr. Hyde, remarked: "He, I said—I cannot say I. That child of Hell had nothing human, nothing lived in him but fear and hatred . . . these two base passions raged in him like a tempest . . . I hated and feared the thought of the brute that slept within me." In the alternating, non-communicating dual personality, the pps (for example, Sally in the Beauchamp case and Anna O's alter ego) is amnesic for the actions and experiences of the ps, and vice versa.

PRIMARY HYSTERICAL AMNESIA. This form of dissociation develops spontaneously, without an antecedent state of somnambulism or fugue. The subject (the pps) is oriented but has forgotten its past, that is to say, lost its personal identity. A precipitating factor, usually a painful experience, has interrupted the continuity of the self. Primary hysterical amnesia is an avoidance reaction which, however, may be limited to the precipitating event, for example, a crime committed by the subject—now the "victim" of amnesia. It is apparent that primary hysterical amnesia and the non-communicating type of double personality are closely related.

Coexisting Selfs

Dissociation of the self producing concomitant splitting of the personality fall into two main groups, namely, (a) dissociation syndromes that occur *spontaneously* and (b) *experimentally produced* dissociation syndromes. The former include *somanmbulism, fugue states* and certain forms of *automatic writing*, the latter *hypnotic states* which, although strictly speaking not a symptom of hysteria, will be discussed in some detail because of their theoretical interest and their similar psychopathological structure.

In both the personal self and the parapersonal self the waking state is repatterned as will be illustrated below under points (a) and (b). In the former, the dominant sphere of mentation appears to be reduced to some sort of tubular or polarized consciousness limited to the mirror like recording of certain stimuli, and permitting but limited access if any to the psychomotor apparatus. All possible gradations of constriction of consciousness may occur. Within the parapersonal self, the dominant and the subsidiary sphere tend to merge. Moreover, both the *ekphory-potential* and the *engraphy-potential* are increased, which results in increased fluidity of the mnemonic apparatus. In other cases, the fluidity of engrams is decreased, in fact, engraphy and ekphory may be blocked entirely. The possibility of access of the pps to the psychomotor apparatus varies. By and large, the wakeful state of the pps assumes dreamlike features. The term *trance* designates the peculiar condition of the state of *double consciousness*, i.e., the *constricted state* of awareness of the personal self which coexists with the *dreamlike state* of consciousness of the para-personal self.

COEXISTING SELFS FORMING SPONTANEOUSLY. As already indicated, spontaneous (endogenous)

splitting of consciousness into two non-equivalent spheres is the psychopathological background of somnambulism, fuge states and certain forms of automatic writing.

SOMNAMBULISM AND FUGUE STATES. In the state of somnambulism, (741, 853), the subject walks and usually avoids obstacles. At the same time, it engages in complex activities which he subsequently does not remember. His eyes are open and his actions seem to have a definite goal. He may or may not respond to questions or commands directed to him. Upon more or less forceful stimulation, he may regain his normal state of consciousness. Somnambulism is more frequent in childhood and adolescence than in adult life. The dominant sphere of mentation of the personal self is polarized in conformity with the intentions of the dream like consciousness of the para-personal self, in other words, *the para-personal self maintains a precarious contact with objective reality by means of the dominant sphere of the personal self, which functions as a channel or guide to objective reality*. In fugue states, which may last up to several months, the patient appears to be confused and his activities are rather disorganized. It is not unreasonable to assume that somnambulism is a seeking response while fugue states are avoidance reactions both of which, as we have said, are actuated by complexes. In either condition, psychic puerilisms come to the fore. They often reflect trends and wishes which are acted out and imaginatively gratified in a symbolic and theatrical fashion. The acting agent is the para-personal self.

AUTOMATIC WRITING. The element of expression is evident even more clearly in automatic writing and drawing. The following description is taken from Prince's (740) monograph and, like that of alternating personalities, supplemented by our own remarks specifying the respective roles of the personal self and the para-personal self. The subject's mind (the mind of the ps) is absolutely unclouded. He (the ps) may watch with unconcerned curiosity the vagaries of the writing pencil (used by the pps, the active agent). In other words, he (the ps) is in possession of his normal waking intelligence." (The ps is unaltered.) "Meanwhile the hand (of the pps) automatically performs perhaps long discourses of diverse content. But he (the very same ps) is entirely unaware what his hand '(the pps)' is writing and his first knowledge comes after readng the manuscript" (having been composed by the pps). In other words, the former watches the activities of the latter as if it would observe another person. In fact, it may engage in conversation while the hand is doing its work. In some cases "the automatic writer may be entirely unaware of what the hand is writing, in others, at the moment of writing, ideas corresponding to written words surge, apparently from nowhere, without logical association, into his mind—there being, apparently, a last minute communication between the two selfs, namely, from the pps to the ps." The subject, (the ps) is in doubt whether she writes the sentence volitionally or whether it is written automatically entirely independent of her will." The subject is unable to communicate her ideas showing that she does not really know what the hand (giving expression to the pps) "was about to write." In other cases however, which we are inclined to consider as transitional stages between the coexisting variety and the alternating variety of dual personality, the personal self is in a drowsy condition. The automatic writer imperfectly orients his surroundings and if he is reading aloud he is only dimly conscious of what he is reading. He (the ps) "may not hear when spoken to or feel when touched. He reads on mechanically and without consciousness of the matter he is reading, he has become deaf and actually anesthetic and blind to everything (his dominant sphere of mentation is constricted) but the printed characters on the page before him, and even for these mind blinded. In this state then, there is practically extinguishment all sense perception and intellectual thought and finally the impairment of consciousness may be carried so far that he (the ps) actually goes to sleep. "... If, then, the automatic writer" (the pps) "is asked what "he" (the ps) is doing he may answer that "he" (the ps) "has gone to sleep." "If we examine the contents of the writing we may find that it is made up of memories of past experiences which were entirely forgotten by the original intelligence No. 1 (the ps) and gives evidence of a personality differing in character, volition, sentiment, moods and points of view; of a character differing in a large degree from that of the waking intelligence." In cases of this kind, the dissociation of the "mind" is complete, involving all three "layers" of the mental system. The writing, Prince goes on to say, may be an original composition involving thought and reason com-

parable to that exhibited by a normal mind. . . . Such compositions throw light upon the origin of secondary (para-personal) personalities. If we speak to intelligence No. 2 "(the pps)" "it answers intelligently in writing, though intelligence No. 1 (the ps) fails to respond. In the motor sphere, the loss of function is not so great as that which has befallen intelligence No. 1, for it has lost only a general coordinating control over the whole body. "Automatic writing does not consist of words, phrases and paragraphs which might be mere repetitions or memories, whether physiological or psychological, but even consist of elaborate psychical compositions. Sometimes they exhibit mathematical reasoning shown by the solution of mathematical problems. And they indicate a personal character with varying moods and temperaments. Feeling and emotion, whether of anger, hatred or malice, kindness and amiability are often exhibited. . . . In certain types of hysteria, the script is very easily obtained. Script may contain references to, i.e., reproductions of experiences which have long been forgotten by the subject and which cannot be voluntarily recalled. Mrs. Verall reproduced numerous instances of English, Latin and Greek script which investigations showed to be forgotten citations from an author previously read. (Because of its unique value for the appreciation of the phenomena in question, Prince's description of automatic writing has been quoted rather in full.) According to Löwenfeld (578) a "hysterical person engaged in conversation may be induced to answer in writing (even though her hand is screened off) to questions which she (the ps) seemingly does not hear. Under similar experimental conditions she (the pps) may write a perfect letter without (the ps) being aware of it— neither while she (the pps) is writing, nor afterwards; or she may carry out mathematical operations, including multiplications." Froebes (273) calls attention to similar observations made by Pierre Janet, Binet and Féré.

EXPERIMENTALLY PRODUCED COEXISTING SELFS. Experimental (exogenous or hypnotic) dissociation of consciousness is initiated and maintained by the verbal suggestion given by the hypnotist. For all intents and purposes, the contents of the suggestion correspond to, and play the role of complexes that initiate and maintain states of spontaneous dissociation. Although endogenous dissociation is initiated in the subsidiary sphere of mentation while experimental dissociation operates by way of the dominant sphere, a portal of entry as it were, there are good grounds for believing that the dissociation of the self is dependent on a certain predisposition of the subsidiary sphere of mentation, which is the basis of suggestibility. (See below.) The existence of a state of trance in both spontaneous and experimentally induced dissociation of the self into coexisting subsystems would seem to be substantiated by the theory, first formulated by Charcot (160) and later by Bernheim (75) and Babinski (35), that hypnosis is an artificially produced state of hysteria. As is well known, Charcot produced gross physical symptoms by hypnosis.

OBJECTIVE AND SUBJECTIVE ASPECTS OF HYPNOSIS. Forel (247) distinguished between three stages of hypnotic depth, namely, *somnolence*, *hypotaxia* and *somnambulism*. Somnolence is a feeling of pleasant passivity and gradually increasing heaviness and flacicity of the limbs. Hypotaxia is a state of intermediate sleep during which orders are carried out and which is characterized by catalepsy, analgesia, hallucinations and delusions. There is preservation of hearing, vision and the ability on the part of the medium to observe his own alterations of consciousness, including, ordinarily, a general inhibition of thinking which will be described in detail below. *Somnambulism* is a state of deep sleep and amnesia which, however, does not interrupt the rapport between the hypnotized person and the hypnotist. It may be readily seen that somnolence and hypotaxia resemble in many respects the state of transition between waking and sleeping. The psychopathology of somnambulism is controversial, in fact, the theory that hypnosis is a *sleep deviant* is rather generally abandoned; at most, it is maintained by some only with certain qualification. The galvanic skin resistance, the cardio-vascular and respiratory functions show a waking rather than a sleep pattern (365). The EEG taken during hypnosis does not as a rule show any fundamental changes from that taken in the waking state. Hypnotic modification of seeing does not influence the electrocortical activity which, however, may be modified in some subjects by emotional arousal (245, 205). It should further be noted that the classification of the hypnotic state is not uniform, different classifications having been proposed by Charcot (160),

Liébault (569), Bernheim (75), Janet (433) and Bramwell (108).

How does the experimenter know that the medium is not feigning? The most convincing proof is the absence of startle and pain reactions, including a negative dilator response of the pupils. Moreover, muscular rigidity (catelepsy) may be extreme and abnormal positions of the extremities may be maintained for a surprisingly long time.

SUGGESTION AND SUGGESTIBILITY. Jaspers (441) and Stern (878) regard hypnosis and, indirectly, suggestibility as an imitation reflex, while Moll (657) stresses the importance of expectancy and the arousal of an idea and Stransky (886) the role of kathathymic (emotional) factors. Wundt (972) attached great importance to the *narrowing of the field of consciousness which prevents the formation of associations opposing the suggested idea*. According to Löwenfeld (578) the idea awakened by suggestion takes effect because of the peculiar condition of the associative apparatus. Hence, he holds, suggestibility is a disposition of the mind which manifests itself by the dropping out, or at least by the weakening, of associative processes which would otherwise emerge in response to certain ideas, that is to say, by the lack of criticism. Suggestion, then, is the idea of a "psychic or psychophysiological situation which, owing to the lack of diminution of associative processes ordinarily provoked by it" (and, we might add, potentially opposing it), "acquires extraordinary force and which, by the realization of the situation in question, assumes a compulsive character." Somewhat different definitions were offered by Eysenck (219) and Furneaux (283).

Wundt's and Löwenfeld's ideas would seem to provide a clue which is worth while following, and which may well be brought into harmony with the approach here proposed. It may be pointed out that even more primitive mechanisms play a part in suggestion, especially *autosuggestion*. To mention two simple examples. Fear of blushing may cause blushing. In adolescents, the effects of fear materialize with such frequency that they can hardly be considered abnormal. On the other hand, fainting produced by fear of fainting is frankly pathological, although the underlying mechanism must be similar to the mechanism of blushing. In either case, the translation of a psychism into its physiological or pathological correlate, that is, its somatization, would suggest the presence of a *preformed mechanism* which, in some persons, especially under conditions of stress, may be readily actuated. (See Kretschmer's "dead feigning reflex.") A more complicated mechanism which is, to some degree at least accessible to introspection, operates under the influence of a wish or, for that matter, a complex, that eventually silences whatever logical grounds may be mobilized against it. Let us assume that we think of buying an object which we like and wish to own. The idea that it will serve some useful purpose may predominate, while the true reason underlying our wish remains in the background. And if, although our resistence is weakening, the idea fails to gain sufficient strength to act as a motive, we may nevertheless be readily persuaded to buy the object by someone who knows well how to exploit states of indecision. In this particular instance there would not seem to be much difference between autosuggestion, that is, stressing the reasons put forward by ourselves, and exogenous suggestion, reasons which, we feel, may not be as valid as they sound but which happen to conform to our own wish. Now, it is quite possible that the purchase of an object has a meaning of which we are not aware, and which is in actual fact a substitute response in which case a non-conscious wish would be reinforced by an extraneous agent. It would seem to be a far cry from the trivial type of suggestion, which operates in daily life, to the verbal suggestion given by the hypnotist, powerful enough to produce a dissociation of the self. On the other hand, the presence of certain common features in either variety of suggestion is unmistakable. Both forms are dependent on the constriction of the dominant sphere of mentation, except from certain concordant elements and its virtual isolation from the subsidiary sphere and the mnemonic system. The idea is translated into action as soon as has no longer to compete with the countermotives which would block it in the absence of dissociation caused by the actuating complex.

Sidis (832) distinguishes between normal and abnormal suggestibility. The conditions of experimentally verified normal suggestibility include (a) fixation of attention (as translated into the terms of the stimulus response scheme, the sharp delineation of the axial stream of awareness), (b) distraction of attention, (the polarization of the already reduced axial stream of awareness), (c) monotony, (the elimination of the marginal stream of thought), (d) limitation of volitional movements, (which supplement and reinforce the above listed conditions—especially those listed under points b and c), (e) limitation of the field of awareness, according to Sidis a result of the former, (f) inhibition, (the elimination of opposing motives) and (g) immediate execution, a short circuiting process to be discussed below. It may be readily seen that the conditions of normal and of abnormal suggestibility are essentially identical.

In *summary*, then, concurrently with the above described isolation of the dominant sphere of the personal self, there originates a sub-system of the self, or a para-personal self which interacts with the contents of the verbal suggestion and which corresponds to the para-personal self emerging, spontaneously, in endogenous dissociation. The core of the para-personal self is in all likelihood a latent wish or, more generally, an attitude of compliance, and the hypnoid state of the para-personal self thus established a natural correlate of the artificially produced constriction of the dominant sphere of mentation of the personal self which, under normal conditions, holds in check whatever compliance tendencies there may be. In sharp contrast to spontaneous dissociation, the para-personal self acts under the influence of the hypnotist. In spontaneous dissociation, the para-personal self asserts itself, more accurately, the complexes assert themselves which form its core. In the experimental situation, the para-personal self carries out the suggestion of another person. Otherwise, passive or induced dissociation of the self is patterned after spontaneous dissociation mechanisms not only with respect to sensory interaction but also to sensory-motor sequences. To the extent that the dominant sphere of mentation becomes restricted and isolated from the appropriate interaction with other, potentially competing, intellective stimuli and with the psychomotor apparatus or the "will," the para-personal self or, rather, the hypnotist, gains access to the medium's "organ of volition."

MOTOR FUNCTION UNDER HYPNOSIS. By means of suggestion, voluntary movements cannot only be produced but inhibited. Bleuler (90) gives the following account of his own introspective experiences. His resistance to the hypnotist's suggestion was gradually overcome and a state of complete automatism supervened. When the hypnotist elevated Bleuler's arm and gave the suggestion that he would be unable to lower it, he met at first with little success. However, his resistance lessened after the arm was re-elevated and a new suggestion given. Contractions of antagonists occurred against his will whenever he (the ps) tried to perform a movement other than that suggested while the protagonists failed to contract no matter how hard he tried. Ultimately, because of the effort involved, he (the pps) no longer attempted any spontaneous movements and felt compelled to follow the suggestion to walk from one room to another. According to Sidis (833) the hypnotized person is indifferent to the actions of its own body; the latter (pps) acts by itself. Some of his experimental subjects state that they were more spectators of all the experiments performed on them and of all the strange actions, dramas that transpired during the trance. It seemed to them as if they themselves, their personality (their pps) retreated far away. One of them remarked that the conscious controlling "I" seemed to retreat far away from the world—as, we assume, the ps was virtually eliminated. Another subject declared: "I appeared to act automatically, by an impulse foreign to myself. It was certainly another (the pps produced by the hypnotist) which had taken my form and assumed my functions." One of Klemperer's (498) patients declared: "In hypnosis I can't think. . . . It seems that I have no control over my voice whatsoever. It is as if I had no mind. To explain it: I am sitting here and you ask me a question. I can think before I speak but in hypnosis that is impossible. . . . I can't think. The voice just answers. My mind feels as if it were cut in half. . . . You are helpless. When you are asked questions there is no thinking process, a voice just answers that is my voice."

The above statements lend color to the belief that hypnosis produces a double personality one of which is a powerless observer while the other is an instrument of the hypnotist . . . "my mind feels as if it were cut in half." As expressed in terms developed in the present monograph, the state of trance involves a repatterning of the dependence relationships of those stimuli which emerge, as the "will," at a critical stage of sensory-motor integration at the highest level of brain function. The suggestion given by the hypnotist intrudes, as an extraneous stimulus, into what would otherwise be an autonomous process. It deranges primarily the interaction of those psychisms which, at the highest response determining level of the neuraxis, precede efferent discharge and, secondarily, the dependence relationship between sensory (intellective) and motor stimuli. And, since the "will" is nothing other than the mode in which these relationships are felt at the highest level of brain function, more especially its conscious segment, the hypnotized subject has the experience of being deprived of its will.

Depending on the depth of the trance, the state of consciousness of the hypnotized subject resembles (a) that of a person about to fall asleep, as the dominant sphere of mentation is gradually being isolated from the remaining parts of the self, (b) that of a person who knows that he is dreaming, in which case the dominant sphere of mentation of the personal self is relegated to a mere observer and, (c) of a person who is dreaming but lives through the content of the dream as if it were reality. In this instance, he has no power to intervene or to participate actively but, on the contrary, has the feeling of complete passivity. The constriction of the personal self has thus reached a maximum and the dream experiences are exclusively those of the parapersonal self.

Yet, within limits, the personal self retains a certain measure of conscious control which serves protective functions. The individual cannot be made to perform any actions which he would not perform under otherwise normal circumstances. However, this rule, too, may have its exceptions. Watkins (933, 934) and other experimenters produced anti-social compulsions in a number of subjects of which they had every reason to believe they were otherwise incapable. It should also be noted that, ordinarily, a person cannot be hypnotized "against his will," and that only rarely a state of trance be produced in a person in spite of his or her opposition. In fact, in the absence of an appropriate seeking attitude, or at least an attitude of complete compliance on the part of the subject to be hypnotized, the production of a hypnotic state is virtually impossible. In fact, some psychologists invoke intense dependency strivings as a prerequisite of hypnotizibility.

VISCERO-AUTONOMIC FUNCTIONS IN HYPNOSIS. If the suggestion of physical effort is given, the heart rate will be accordingly altered. It has been reported that, in a few cases, the hypnotist succeeded in producing skin blisters by direct sugestion. Ullman (*314*) reported the case of a hysterical soldier in whom a second degree burn with blister formation was induced by the suggestion that a cold object placed against his skin would burn him. Subsequently, a herpetiform eruption was produced in the same person 24 hours later after the suggestion was given in deep hypnosis. However, Heilig and Hoff's (*363*) studies in the experimental production of herpes labialis indicate that emotions induced by means of hypnotic suggestion are capable of producing changes of a pathological nature which cannot be produced by direct suggestion under hypnosis, and Pattie (*713*) is of the opinion that blister formation is an alleged fact that needs stronger experimental evidence than the clinical investigations thus far afford. Tuckey (*912*) was able to demonstrate tonic contractions of the small arterioles and of the capillaries of the skin in deep hypnotic trance which would account for the fact that skin folds pierced by a needle failed to produce hemorrhages. Mabille (*600*) produced ekchymoses similar to those seen in hysterically stigmatized persons. The bodily temperature can be elevated or lowered.

SENSORY FUNCTIONS IN HYPNOSIS. Both lower and higher sensory functions can be either reinforced or inhibited. For instance, the subject can be made *paragnostic*, that is, it can be made to see a picture on a blank paper or to feel to taste sugar on eating salt. Moreover, the hypnotist can evoke sensory experiences which have the vividness of dream images, i.e., a sensory quality rarely if ever attained under normal conditions of imagination. For example, the hypnotized person may be made to believe that he or she is in a church, or a concent hall or a department store. Furthermore, the hypnotist may be able to produce partial dissociative states, including anesthesia of the cornea and of the pharynx, blindness and analgesia, that is to say, to eliminate certain perceptions form the para-personal self. In the present context it is of interest that, of the 76 cases of patients with spontaneous sensory disorders reported by Taylor and Martin (*898*), five displayed various types of sensory deficit. One of them (the pps) was analgesic, tactually anesthetic, without muscle sense, deaf in one ear, weak visioned in one eye, wholly color blind and so on. Sally, (Miss Beauchamp's para-personal self) was hemianalgesic, indicating the presence of dissociation of sensibility within an already dis-

sociated system, i.e., an alternating self. *Negative hallucinations*, or non-perceptions belong to the same group of phenomena, except that the "negative scotoma" produced by hypnotic suggestion is a more complex one. Erickson (*200*) defines *negative hallucinations* as unresponsiveness of deeply hypnotized persons to stimuli ordinarily effective or the inability to perceive actual stimuli. Both auditory and visual non-awareness may be produced, and both objects and persons attending the experiment can be made to disappear either partially or completely. The following is a sampling of experiments reported by Bernheim, Binet, Féré (*226*) and others. If the subject is shown five cards, two of which are marked with a cross and the suggestion given that the marked cards are invisible, the subject (pps) will count only three cards. After the cards have been turned around, he will count five. Yet after the cards have been brought back to their original position, he will again count three. Similar phenomena may be observed after the hypnotic suggestion of unilateral blindness. The subject, (or rather, the pps), on being asked to look at a drawing with one of his eyes having been made blind by appropriate suggestion, will claim not to see anything. It is only after the eye, upon appropriate suggestion, has regained vision, that he (now the ps) remembers to have seen the drawing. Erickson (*214*), after deeply hypnotizing a subject and inducing a somnambulistic state, gave the suggestion that one of those present would leave the room, that is, the subject was instructed to become unaware of a selected person. The hypnotized person then stared with a "blank gaze" at the "absentee" who was sitting directly in front of her. When, subsequently, the supposedly absent person shook the subject's hand, she (the pps) stated to have a hallucinatory experience. If addressed by the invisible one, she did not pay attention to him and, upon being asked to sit in the chair occupied by him, expressed astonishment and was puzzled at finding herself on an invisible lap. According to Löwenfeld (*578*) negative hallucinations are not necessarily complete as the subject, while walking in the room in which the allegedly absent person is standing, may avoid to collide with him, in which case, we might add, the hypnotized person behaves like a sleepwalker who avoids obstacles. How are the above the described phenomena to be accounted for? Pierre Janet (*433, 434*) believe that the impressions were transferred from ordinary consciousness into the subconscious of which the ordinary consciousness knows nothing, but it is doubtful whether this interpretation does justice to the complexity of behaviour described by the various observers.

We are inclined to believe that the constricted dominant sphere of mentation of the personal self not only perceives the object but that the personal self has at least some access to the psycho-motor apparatus, as evidenced by the fact that it avoids obstacles. It can only be the personal self that maintains some measure of contact with reality. The perceptual world of the para-personal self has been changed, i.e., deprived of the "interdicted" object. More accurately, the para-personal self does not perceive the person or object because of the interaction of intellective stimuli involved in the process of *identification*, indeed, in pure cases of negative hallucination, the verbal suggestion blocks the very process of *perception*. Thus, the behaviour of the medium must be a compromise between conflicting trends induced, in turn, by conflicting data. For example, Löwenfeld (578) mentions the following episode. A medium, in accordance with the suggestion given, did not see a person sitting on a chair but insisted that the chair was covered with a plaid. Yet, that the medium has in some way seen the interdicted object is proven by the fact that it is able to ekphorize the impression by a change of conditions in subsequent experiments. Moreover, the impression can then be made available to both the personal self and the para-personal self, doubtless because of their communication with the mnemonic system which they have in common.

At this point we wish to refer the reader to the discussion of the *psychology of recognition*. The explanatory diagrams reproduced in Chapter IV (figs. 42 and 43) will enable him to follow the description of the mechanism underlying the phenomena of non-recognition and of negative hallucination. First of all, it is essential to distinguish between the different role of the ps and the pps. If, in the course of a hypnotic experiment, the *suggestion of identity of actually uncongruous, i.e., non-identical stimuli is given*, the feedback-processes which, ordinarily, play between the x-stimulus (the object to be identified) and its ekphorized engram are crowded out by competing processes. The latter operate, between, on the one hand, the representation of the

x-stimulus in the dominant sphere of mentation of the *para-personal* self and, on the other, the stimulus implanted there by the hypnotist. The implanted stimulus, in turn, is to blame for the misidentification of the x-stimulus on the part of the medium. Misidentification is produced by forced compliance with the suggestion given by the hypnotist, that is, by the resultant failure on the part of the medium to appreciate the diversity between an impression and an ekphorized engram. (The possibility that hypnosis produces gestaltblindness appears unlikely, as in this particular instance at least, the stimulus to be identified can subsequently be recalled under changed conditions.) Now, while all this goes on in the mind of the *para-personal self*, a comparing feedback, which is instrumental in the identification of the x-stimulus, operates also in the dominant sphere of mentation of the *personal* self, which is not under full control of the hypnotist, in other words, the x-stimulus is recognized by the personal self. So much about the phenomenon of *non*-recognition. If, on the other hand, the *suggestion of the non-existence or absence of an actually existing stimulus* is given, no engram will be ekphorized, at least not in the para-personal self and, for want of an ekphorized engram, no comparing feedback actuated. As a result, the para-personal self sees the x-object, but as an unknown (something unrelated to a specific class concept). As expressed in configurational terms, he sees the x-object like a pattern hidden in a more complex pattern which he cannot break down into meaningful, component parts. As in the preceding experiment (producing non-recognition), the negative hallucination on the part of the para-personal self does not interfere with the recording of the "absent" object on the part of the personal self. It is only in this fashion I believe that we can understand the behaviour of the hypnotized person who "stares blankly" at the object he does not see, yet, nevertheless, tends to avoid. The degree of imbalance between the experiences of the personal self and the coexisting para-personal self depends among other factors on the depth of the trance. For example, the medium which insisted that a chair on which someone was sitting was covered with a plaid might have fully accepted that no one was sitting in the chair had it been in a deeper state of trance, or conversely, insisted to see the person had it been in a lighter state of trance.

The already mentioned *positive hallucinations* are ekphorized engrams. Owing to the dreamlike character of the state of consciousness of the para-personal self, they are unusually vivid, which illustrates the statement referring to the *increased ekphory-potential* of the para-personal self and the *intensified fluidity of engrams* in general. The "transformation" of the medium to an imaginary, earlier ontogenetic state known as *age regression* during which the subject, (the pps) acts in an emotionally and intellectually appropriate fashion is referable to the production of positive hallucinations. However, the resemblance to a child is apparent rather than real since the situation is not identical with the situation of a subject at an earlier age but is composed of memory images ranging over a long period of time and supplemented by suitable confabulations (*699*). If the suggestion is given that the subject has been transformed into another individual, he will impersonate him like a good actor. If the suggestion is given that he is an animal, he will walk on his four limbs. The subject's intellectual capacity can be increased or decreased not only at the perceptual level but also at the conceptual level.

MNEMONIC FUNCTIONS IN HYPNOSIS. The hypnotized person can be made to ekphorize engrams which under normal conditions are beyond voluntary recall. For example, Stalnaker and Richardson (*864*) found that their subjects (pps) were able to recall verses and prose passages which they had learned a year previously much better under hypnosis than in the normal state. The reanimated memory traces may attain the plasticity of dream images. Moreover, the subjects could be made to remember what they experienced in the course of previous hypnotic experiments even though they might have been performed in the remote past, or what they had experienced during hysterical seizures and twilight states. On the other hand, depending on the depth of the hypnotic state, they could be made to forget things they have learned, for instance how to read and write. Indeed a person can be made to forget his own name; that is, otherwise available engrams can be excluded from the general intrasensory context. As far as introspection serves me, loss of control over ekphory processes may occur in dreams, especially anxiety dreams. *Posthypnotic phenomena* involve the execution on the part of the medium of suggestions

ordered in the hypnotic state at almost any time after its termination. In a state of trance, for example, the medium may be asked to raise his right arm some time afterward or to perform more complex acts, either of which will then be executed at the appropriate time. On being asked to give reasons for what he did, the subject may remark that he was requested to do so while in a hypnotic state, or he may rationalize his actions; indeed, a specific rationalization may be suggested to the subject by the hypnotist. Thus the subject may say "I do not know why I did it, it was just an idea" or "I simply had the feeling that I had to do it." Otherwise, the medium may act as if he were in a state of somnambulism or he appears to be absent minded while carrying out the posthypnotic suggestion. He may be distracted and only dimly aware of what he is doing, or altogether unaware, which would indicate that the state in which the suggestion was given continues up to the moment at which it is being carried out and that the term "posthypnotic suggestion" is not entirely accurate. Sometime prior to carrying out the hypnotic suggestion the medium may have the more or less vague notion of an impending task. (See *Bewusstseinslage* and *Bewusstheit*). If rehypnotized some time during the interval, the subject is unable to indicate at what point of the time scale (see above) the suggested act is to be performed, but he knows how much time has elapsed since he was hypnotized or how many hours are yet to elapse before the request is to be carried out. Although it is doubtful whether a uniform explanation of posthypnotic phenomena is possible, it appears certain that engrams can be implanted by hypnotic suggestion and ekphorized at the appropriate time from the common pool of engrams. The process in question becomes part of a wider problem namely, of the as yet poorly understood mechanism of the initiation of delayed reactions.

To *summarize*, the subject's behaviour resembles, in significant respects, the actions of a person in spontaneous dissociative states. Sensory phenomena become vivid and dreamlike or they are selectively abolished. Both compulsive and inhibitory complexes may be induced. The ekphory potential is either increased or decreased; memories can be selectively eliminated. Abnormal communications are established between, on the one hand, the activity of the subject's intellective level and, on the other, motor and viscero-autonomic functions. Lastly, the sensory-motor dependence relationships to which, commonly, the term *will* is applied, are supplanted by the communication between the hypnotist and the para-personal self. To state the matter somewhat differently: The common denominator of spontaneous and induced dissociative states is the segregation of a unitary mental system into a constricted personal self and on the one hand and, on the other, the repatterning of the waking state of the para-personal self, i.e., the relationships between (a) the dominant sphere of mentation, (b) the subsidiary sphere of mentation and (c) the mnemonic system. At the same time, the functional relationships between the intellective level and its motor instrumentalities are modified, and abnormal communications are opened between the intellective level of cerebral function and certain autonomic centers.

In the original version of the section devoted to the problem of dissociation of consciousness, we worked on the assumption that the split of the self occurs in a horizontal direction as it were (fig. 11); that there are formed a conscious self (then believed to be the dominant sphere of mentation) and non-conscious or subconscious self, compounded, supposedly, of the subsidiary sphere of mentation and the mnemonic system. This hypothesis however proved to be powerless to explain the phenomenon in question and was discarded. While reviewing the present section with particular attention to both the description of the behaviour of alternating selfs and of the accounts of hypnotists subjects of their experiences in a state of trance, the reader will find that, basically, coexisting selfs are patterned after alternating personalities. In either group, dissociation must have occurred in a vertical direction resulting in the production of two selfs (two nearly complete selfs in the former, repatterned selfs in the latter) rather than the formation of two half-selfs, or horizontal layers of the mental apparatus.

Pierre Janet (*433, 434*) believed that post-hypnotic phenomena are manifestations of dissociated subconscious processes outside and independent of the personal consciousness. He limited the meaning of the term "subconscious" (subconscient) to ideas that are in actual activity but of which the personal self of the hypnotized subject was not aware, and he compared the phenomena in question to the depersonalization phenomena of psychasthenics or what was then included into the so-called "accidents hysteriques." Although the subject was not aware of the split-off ideas, Janet found is possible to communicate with the dissociated mental system (the secondary self or pps) and to recover memories which were unremembered in the normal state. He developed the theory that hysteria is a dissociation of the personality analogous to that experimentally produced by hypnosis and since a dissociated self was apparent in either condition, regarded hypnosis a spontaneous dissociation of the self. Significantly, he *attributed this dissociation to an upsetting event and assumed that hysterically reacting persons tend to keep certain ideas apart.* (See "intra-level dissociative reactions.") As regards the mechanism of dissociation, he expressed the belief that the *personal consciousness was unable—or unwilling—to interconnect all sensory data and that, if a large number of impressions becomes split-off, the dissociative experiences may form* active aggregates which grow to a secondary self capable of independent function, e.g., automatic writing. Janet considered the unity of consciousness a criterion of mental health, the splitting of the mind as a sign of psychasthenia and defined consciousness as "an act by which a multiplicity and diversity of states is attached to a unity."

From all this, it appears that Janet postulated dissociation mechanisms operating in a "horizontal" rather than a "vertical" direction. Be this as it may, the concept of personality dissociation has a much wider applicability than was hitherto assumed to be the case, and we shall study the phenomenon in question from a somewhat different angle in the discussion of productive thinking and of artistic endeavour and realization.

THE SCHIZOPHRENIAS

Most authorities invoke both *psychogenic* and *physiogenic* factors in the causation of schizophrenic illness. Thus far, the nature and relative importance of these factors has not been elucidated. To quote Hoffer (*397*): "The schizophrenias have proved so baffling in their variety and scope that as yet no rational hypothesis has been developed to satisfactorily synthetize the wealth of published data regarding them. The etiology is unknown but the etiologic hypotheses are numerous. They vary from purely psychologic to purely organic. . . . So much of the data appear contradictory that it seems a hopeless task to reconcile the host of accurate observations into a consistent hypothesis of schizophrenia." The present state of ignorance, we might add, is likely to continue until such time as the role of the physiogenic and psychogenic mechanisms is specified, and their relationship to heredo-constitutional and environmental factors brought to light.

We intend to discuss the schizophrenias under three headings. In the first section, we shall review various pertinent clinical and other data collected by the followers of either school of thought. However, since most authors discuss schizophrenic illness as if they were referring to a *generalized form* rather than to particular varieties, we shall, for the present at least, work on the assumption that a generalized form of schizophrenic illness does in fact exist. Any other course of action would deprive us of the benefit of using "the host of accurate observations" to which Hoffer made reference. In the second section, we shall attempt to resolve the contradiction involved in the preliminary assumption by establishing *individual varieties* of schizophrenic illness based on etiologic considerations; further, to relate them to various, apparently inconsistent data, to specify their relationship to one another, to the second, major, group of functional psychoses, that is, *mania-depression*, to other *psychoses*, to the *neuroses* and to the group of *psychopathic personalities*. Lastly, we shall discuss the merits and shortcomings of representative physiogenic and psychogenic theories.

Etiological and clinical aspects

Heredo-constitutional factors

The popular belief that hereditary factors play an important part in the causation of mental illness in general and of the schizophrenias in particular has been substantiated by the investigation of leading geneticists whose findings are summarized below.

SOMATIC STIGMATA AND NEUROLOGICAL DISEASE ASSOCIATED WITH SCHIZOPHRENIC ILLNESS

In one and the same family, there may occur combinations between schizophrenia and hereditary, non-schizophrenic dyskinesias (*643*). Physical abnormalities which are usually regarded as the expression of degeneration were found in 74% of the cases. (Saiz, quoted by Kraepelin, *511*.) According to Kraepelin, this corresponds well enough to the general experience that patients with dementia praecox are apt to show *physical stigmata*. They include weakliness, small stature, youthful appearance, abnormalities of the cranium and of the ears, high narrow palate, persistence of the intermaxilliary bone, abnormal growth of hair, strabism, deformities of the fingers or toes, polymastia, defective development, irregularity of the teeth and the like. Gibbs' (*302*, *303*) findings in 137 cases indicate a disturbance of sexual development and a failure of sexual maturity which is most marked in patients admitted to the hospital during the year of puberty and adolescence. Patients admitted at an early age give the impression of unevenness of sexual growth, the development of the sexual character lagging behind that of the testicles. In women, masculine hair is interpreted as the surface manifestation of a more profound and interrupted biological disturbance which influences behaviour and which is not confined to the ovaries. Such an interpretation is supported by the rather frequent occurrence of other evidence of *endocrine disturbance* in patients with the psychosis appearing in close relation to puberty or after a period of psychopathic behaviour beginning in puberty. Schizophrenics, either by measurement or by impression, are most frequently of the asthenic type. Schizophrenics with asthenic habitus least frequently have syntonic (i.e., well integrated) premorbid personalities. According to Sands (*791*) adolescent schizophrenics are often stunted in growth and immature in sexual development. Among a population of 5223 schizophrenics, Kretschmer (*518*) found the following constitutional types. Pycnic types, 13.7%; leptosomes, 30.3%; athletic types, 16.9%; dysplastic types, 10.5%; others, 8.65%. The corresponding figures among a population of 1361 manic-depressives were 64.6%, 6.7%, 1.1% and 8.4%.

HEREDO-CONSTITUTIONAL RELATIONSHIPS BETWEEN SCHIZOPHRENIA AND OTHER PSYCHOSES

The presence of schizophrenia in the ascendency and in collateral side lines increases the number of non-schizophrenic psychoses among the progeny while the presence of non-schizophrenic psychoses increases the number of schizophrenics among the descendents (462). Ruedin (779) calls attention to the great predominance of collateral and discontinuous inheritance.

HEREDO-CONSTITUTIONAL RELATIONSHIPS BETWEEN CONSANGUINEOUS SCHIZOPHRENIC INDIVIDUALS

Unless otherwise stated, the subsequent data are based on Kallmann's (462-465) investigations and those of this coworkers. (a) The subtype of schizophrenia present in individual members of one and the same family may or may not be identical. Within whole groups of schizophrenics, there may exist separate hereditary strains, or consanguineous members of schizophrenic families are apt to develop similar psychoses. For example, Rainey and Carson (746) described paranoid reactions in three generations and Freyhan (272) three cases of schizophrenia among siblings one of whom grew up separately. (b) In certain families, schizophrenic psychoses occur with striking frequency. According to Kallmann the statistical evidence in support of the genetic etiology centers around the well established fact that the disease occurs much more frequently in families which include a known case of schizophrenia (index case) than in the general population, that is, any group of persons who are not distinguished by blood relationships to an index case. All observed variations are correlated with the different degree of consanguinity to a proband. The incidence of schizophrenia tends to be higher in blood relatives of schizophrenic index cases than in the general population. (See below.) That heredity determines the individual capacity for development and control of schizophrenic psychosis is demonstrated still more clearly if the similarities in extent and outcome of the disease are taken as further criteria of comparison.

HEREDO-CONSTITUTIONAL RELATIONSHIPS BETWEEN SCHIZOPHRENIC COUSINS, SIBLINGS AND TWINS

All observed variations in the schizophrenia rate are correlated with the different degrees of consanguinity to a proband.

Incidence rates

Cousins	2.6%
Half sibs	7.1%
Full sibs	11.5%–14.3%
Bi-ovular twins	15.0%
Uni-ovular twins	86.2% (Slater, 840: 76.00%)

If the uniovular twins are separated for five years or more the incidence rate was 77.6%; if they are not separated, 91.1%. That twins may develop schizophrenia almost at the same time although they live in different localities and have lost all contact was mentioned already in one of Wilman's (965) publications who reviewed the literature up to 1922. In the discordant monozygotic twin on the other hand, one member of the twin set tends to be free if there is a definite physical difference as to body weight, strength, etc (463).

Types of Schizophrenic Psychosis

In a series of 38 sibling sets comprising a total of 92 patients, including five sets of four schizophrenic siblings, 19 sets of siblings, four of which were twins, showed 50 similar psychoses while 19 sets of siblings including two pair of twins showed 42 dissimilar schizophrenic psychoses (976). As regards the clinical features, there were certain significant resemblances between blood-related pairs. Affective illnesses among the relatives of schizophrenics most frequently took the form of involutional depression and in many of them affective symptoms of the schizophrenic type were seen (840).

HEREDO-CONSTITUTIONAL RELATIONSHIPS BETWEEN SCHIZOPHRENIC PARENTS AND SCHIZOPHRENIC CHILDREN

Concerning the offspring of schizophrenic index cases, it has been shown that their morbidity ranges from 16.4% to 61.1%, that is, from 19 to about 80 times average expectancy according to whether one or both of their parents are schizophrenic. Approximately 30% of the children do not transmit the disease (464). The risk of mental illness for the binovular twin is greater if one or both of the parents were mentally abnormal (840).

INCIDENCE OF SCHIZOPHRENIA IN NON-CONSANGUINEOUS MEMBERS

The taint figures for the marriage partners (2.1%), step-siblings (1.8%) and fosterchildren of schizophrenics are all close to normal.

INCIDENCE OF SCHIZOPHRENIA IN THE GENERAL POPULATION

The incidence of schizophrenia in the general population is 0.85%. The probable incidence of schizophrenia is 19 times as high as in children of schizophrenics than in the general population, and for grandchildren, nephews and nieces five times as high.

Environmental factors

A. Meyer (*638, 639*) was probably the earliest proponent of the psychogenicity of schizophrenia. Although his ideas far antedate those expressed by Kallmann and other geneticists, they are shared by many modern writers. Langworthy (*539*) maintains that schizophrenia, rather than a disease, is a reaction type or a way of life, or adjustment to life, adopted by people who are unable to make satisfactory interpersonal relationships. Meyer had asserted that schizophrenia is a maladjustment, or habit disorganization, that withdrawal from reality is logically understandable in terms of the patient's experiences and life history, and the result of repeated failures of the individual to react (appropriately) to its environment and of his inability to face important concrete situations. However, Meyer did not overlook that schizophrenic reactions are apt to develop in certain constitutional types. According to Fromm-Reichmann (*275–276*), whose words we wish to quote rather in full, the schizophrenic is painfully resentful and distrustful of other people due to severe early warp and rejection he encountered in important people in infancy and childhood, as a rule mainly in a schizophrenic mother. (At this point, one may well ask what caused the schizophrenia in the parent.) During his early fight for emotional survival, she goes on to say, he begins to develop the great interpersonal sensitivity which remains his for the rest of his life. His initial pathogenic experiences are actively, or by virtue of their interpretation, the pattern of a never ending succession of subsequent similar ones. Finally, he crosses the threshold of endurance. Because of his sensitivity and his never satisfied lonely need for benevolent contacts this threshold is all too easily reached. The patient's partial emotional regression and his withdrawal from the outside world into an autistic private world with its specific thought processes and modes of feeling and repression is motivated by the fear of repetitional rejection, his distrust of others, and equally so by his own retaliative hostility which he abhors as well as deep anxiety promoted by his hatred. Bellak (*57*), referring to the investigations of Spitz (*860*) and Mahler (*607*), writes that infants who do not have a maternal object, that is, who suffer from lack of maternal stimulation, develop a schizophrenic psychosis, and he attributes (a) *childhood schizophrenia* and (b) *backward cases of dementia praecox* showing both somatic aberrations (including a leptosomic habitus) and defects of the whole adaptive mechanism to early disturbances in the relationship of the infant to the mother or mother figure. In his opinion, neuroendocrine and possible other somatic disturbances involving perhaps the general deficiencies of the adaptive mechanism are due to the impact of severe emotional deprivation. At the same time, the authors do not entirely exclude the possibility that somatic symptoms, more especially disorders of the carbohydrate mechanism, may be secondary to concurrent emotional problems. According to Clardy (*161*) the effects of environmental factors in the child's early personality integration, especially parental attitudes (as evidenced by the overpossessive, oversupervising anxious domineering mother) appears to be an unusually prominent etiological factor in childhood schizophrenias. However, in considering the etiology, physiological makeup and organic findings cannot be neglected. Jenkins (*444*) asserts that the schizophrenic is a victim of parental tendencies which make it more than usually difficult for a child to establish or maintain some sense of individuality in the autistic withdrawal and fantasy. (See also Oltman a. ass., *698*.) Bosselman (*100*) states that there develops primary narcissistic depression in infants deprived of their mothers during early infancy. At this time, when the ego is taking form and is differentiating itself from the outer world, it is particularly important that it meets with adequate stimulus and recognition. Bowlby (*104*) holds that if the child is deprived of "warm intimate and continuous relationships with his mother or permanent mother substitute, a syndrome may develop consisting of anxiety, withdrawal and regression to more infantile behaviour. There are apt to occur dazed stupor, insomnia, anorexia, loss of weight and sometimes intercurrent infections and death. If the child survives it may become a juvenile schizophrenic, a delinquent or a psychopath. On the other hand, Hotchkiss and his associates (406) found that the common conception of a mother of a schizophrenic as oversolicitous, overanxious and domineering was not brought out by a group of 22 mothers who visited their schizophrenic sons in an institution. Only three of them could be so classified while the behaviour of almost one half of the group were lacking in concern and solicitude. Menninger and Chidesh (599) discuss the role of financial loss in the precipitation of mental illness. Mayer-Gross (629) enumerates, as precipitating factors, various emotional conflicts, including the loss of close friends and relatives, professional failure, extreme mental and physical exhaustion, threat to life, the breakup of the family circle or the strain of facing grave decisions of marriage and occupation. He cal.s attention to the importance of predisposition upon which the psychic events act as a trigger. If the predisposition is present, the response of the predisposed person to a situation of stress may take the form of schizophrenic illness. On the other hand, the number of cases where such predisposition is plausible is small. A. Hoch (389) admits that one cannot legitimately invoke psychogenic causes unless the contents of the precipitating cause is also found in the contents of the psychosis which, in his opinion, is a relatively rare occurrence. However, he adds that such relationship between causes and psychosis must be more frequent than the view based on the merely superficial aspect of cause and psychosis would let one to believe, namely, sexual demands which the patient does not meet and those which stir strong subconscious wishes. Like many other writers, he postulates an "organic deficiency the nature of which is however obscure." According to Jung (451) it is impossible to make evident an exclusively physiological origin of the disease. "We may have a strong suspicion as to the organic aspect of the primary symptoms but we cannot omit the well established fact that there are many cases which develop out of an emotional shock, a disappointment, a difficult situation, a reverse of fortune etc, and also that many relapses as well as improvements are due to psychological conditions." Freud (270) stressed the paramount importance of sexual frustration as the cause of regression which is a fundamental in the field of schizophrenia. Noyes (692) lists as

causative factors early conditioning experiences, intra-psychic conflicts, insistent but consciously rejected demands of various instinctive drives and urges, feelings of guilt, emotional and sexual immaturity, as well as long standing and troublesome problems and frustrated purposes that have given rise to anxiety.

According to C. Schneider (804) a psychic trauma itself will never produce the illness but merely precipitate its already impending onset. Kraepelin (511), Jacobi (424) and E. Bleuler (see below) believe that the trauma merely brings into the open an already existing psychosis. Jacobi found that among a group of 605 male and 583 female patients, only 44 cases in which psychic factors produced the disease. He holds that the psychic trauma makes manifest a psychosis or mobilizes its symptoms only if the disease is at least latently present. The psychic trauma however can exert this effect only in the presence of an already active somatic process which underlies the disease. Jacobi never observed the onset of the disease in connection with an acute psychic trauma in the absence of a hereditary constitution and prae-psychotic manifestations. The latter were present in 26 cases, in 20 of which a hereditary predisposition was operative. He regards as the main cause of the disease, an unknown somatic heredoconstitutional disposition. Of the 12 patients who were manifestly schizophrenic prior to the psychic trauma somatic predisposing factors were present in nine instances. They existed in all five cases who failed to show mental abnormalities prior to the onset of the disease. The psychic trauma was acute in 36 of the 44 cases, chronic in seven cases. (One case is unaccounted for). A. Meyer (637), on the basis of his experiences in World War I, claims that the trauma which releases schizophrenic reactions will hardly if ever give rise to pathogenic complexes, and that Jung's cases were characterized by the fact that the patients derived the contents of their thought from the most different aspects of every day life which were unrelated to the alleged trauma. E. Bleuler's (89) views may be epitomized by the following quotations from his monograph. "Schizophrenia appears to be independent of external conditions and circumstances. It is seen among the poor as well as among the rich, in all walks of life and in the most varied conditions, whether orderly or disorderly, fortunate or unfortunate ... it is probable that such psychic irritations can help make the disease manifest. But usually the conditions are such that these people are never satisfied with their lives, occupations and positions just because they are sick."

Childhood schizophrenia.
The schizoid personality

Schulze (*817*) noted that over one half of childhood schizophrenics were from the beginning psychopaths and that they exhibited a shy and, especially in the female sex, an irritable capricious character while others were quiet and reserved. Bradley and Bowen (*106*) considered as the most prominent symptoms of childhood schizophrenia seclusiveness, bizarre behaviour, regressive nature of personal interests and sensitivity to command and criticism. Irritability, diminution in number of personal relationships, interests and physical activ.ty appear secondary to seclusiveness. According to Despert (*193*) the onset of childhood schizophrenia may be acute or insidious. Significant deviations from the normal are early emotional detachment and lack of social relationships, excessive dependence on the mother or mother substitute, early bizarre behaviour, tendency toward non-functional play, exaggerated interest in word form detached from the emotional and intellectual content which these forms normally carry and lastly anomalies of voice, pitch, rhythm and modulation of voice. He notes that the acute onset may often be hyperthermic but that in his opinion the elevated temperature does not necessarily point to an organic etiology of the disease. Silver (*835*) believes that childhood schizophrenia is a profound disturbance of maturation with the retention of basic patterns of function seen in the embryo. They involve difficulties in establishing homeostasis, autonomic and respiratory equilibrium, difficulty in motility, poor muscle tone, distorted perception and basic anxiety. Bellak (*57*) differentiates between a pre-adolescent psychosis up to 9 or 10 years at the most, and an adolescent psychosis from then on. Practically all the pre-adolescent psychoses have factors with them strongly suggestive of somatic etiology. On the other hand, the majority of adolescent schizophrenias with the median age of 12 seemed to contain predominantly psychogenic factors. Malamud (*612*) epitomizes the relationship between somatic and psychic factors as follows.

The early schizophrenic reaction develops on the basis of two factors, namely, (a) a constitutional weakness which some children may have brought with them into the world and which makes them particularly vulnerable in their adjustment to life stress, and (b) environmental stress situations that are apt to be especially damaging in case of such vulnerable constitution. Kleist (*491*) found a schizoid personality in about two thirds of his cases. Most of his patients were described as having been oversensitive, unsocial and irritable, or domineering and emotionally blunted. More than one half of the individuals who later became ill showed a poor scholastic achievement. (See also O'Neal and Robins, *654a*.) A similar praepsychotic character is believed to be reflected in the psychosis. According to Kallmann (*463*), the "inadequacy of the home does not seem to be directly responsible for a pre-adolescent onset of schizophrenia any more than an adequate home can be trusted to prevent it in vulnerable children. There is no simple correlation between the inadequacy of the parental home and pre-adolescent onset of schizophrenia. A late onset of the disease is not always associated with unfavourable home conditions in childhood." Hendrickson (*369*) refuses a unilateral view as untenable. He contends that an underlying biological deficit is present and that there is no scientific validation for a definite causal relationship between early mothering and schizophrenia. And Partiff (*710*) writes: "The conception of schizophrenia in terms of maternal rejection appears quite unwarranted. "There are several in this series who enjoyed happy childhood homes, who grew up in healthy surroundings with every prospect of satisfaction and success, who were outgoing, active and competent, virile and well formed or lovely to look at until they were struck by the disease of devastation." (See also Anderson (*8*).

In *summary*, then, the adherents of the physiogenic school of thought assert that schizophrenia is basically an organic disorder but admit (at least they do not deny) the pathogenic role of psychogenic factors. Only a few exclusivists maintain that schizophrenia is an entirely organic disease in the conventional sense of the term, that is, a disease caused by structural nervous system alterations. The follwers of the *psychogenic school* on the other hand, maintain that schizophrenia is basically a functional disorder but fail to specify the nature of the organic factor.

Whatever the interpretation of its etiology, the *psychopathological core* and, beyond any doubt, the symptomatologic core of the "generalized form of schizophrenia" is a mental syndrome. Further, since no single somatic abnormality is present in every case of schizophrenia and, hence, cannot be regarded either as the cause (at least not the only cause) or as the effect of the psychopathological abnormalities and lastly, the existence of a heredo-constitutional factor is established, we shall regard, (for the time being at least) the abnormalities in the bodily sphere as *heredo-constitutional accompaniments of the psychopathological core of schizophrenic illness.* At this stage of our thesis, then, we shall work on the assumption that *schizophrenic syndromes are compounded of more or less conspicuous somatic heredo-constitutional abnormalities and of mental abnormalities which, too,* are *heredo-constitutionally conditioned.* More specifically, we propose to differentiate between two groups of abnormalities, namely,

A. *Somatic heredo-constitutional abnormalities,* including
   (I) those of the *bodily build,* of *endocrine functions* and of *maturation,*
   (II) *autonomic nervous system* and *metabolic disorders,* and
B. *Psychic heredo-constitutional abnormalities.*

Categories of schizophrenic symptoms

The symptoms of schizophrenic illness to be discussed in the following paragraphs comprise those listed under points A.(I) and A.(II).

Organ-neurotic, visceroneurotic and metabolic symptoms and abnormalities of schizophrenic illness

ORGAN-NEUROTIC AND VISCERO-AUTONOMIC DISORDERS

(1) Vasomotor instability. (Edema of the skin, cyanosis, etc.)
(2) Disorders of secretion. (Hyperhydrosis, increased salivation.)
(3) Pupillary abnormalities, (Change in size and shape of pupils in catatonia)
(4) Hematologic disorders, (Abnormal sedimentation rate)
(5) Decreased blood coagulation time

METABOLIC DISORDERS

(1) Abnormal response range to thermal stimuli
(2) Abnormalities of carbohydrate metabolism
(3) Abnormalities of liver function
(4) Abnormal blood cholesterol, fatty acids and serum cholinesterase levels
(5) Abnormal NPN values
(6) Decreased response to insulin and epinephrine
(7) Low cerebrospinal fluid rise upon histamine administration.

For additional data, the interested reader may be referred to Keup's (*484*) recent review and also to Hoagland's (*386, 387*) and to Huszák's (*416*) publications.

Metabolic and *pharmacodynamic studies* and the examination of various reflexes reveal either a great variability in the individual values that is, *extra-homeostatic ranges of function* or a decreased reaction to stimuli. The widest extra-homeostatic ranges were found to involve the basal metabolic rate, the regulation of circulation, the galvanic skin reflex, the size of the pupils, temperature regulation, pulse rate, sedimentation rate, body weight, blood pressure NPN, blood cholesterol, fatty acids and serum cholesterinase. The reactivity to insulin and epinephrine is decreased and the rise in cerebrospinal fluid pressure on histamin administration is low (*258, 836*). In general it may be said that the schizophrenics as a group are less than normally receptive to a variety of stimulating agents both as to levels reached and promptitude of reaction, and that their adaptive capacity is thereby reduced. Moreover, the schizophrenic patient is ill equipped to maintain a steady state even under normal conditions of existence. In various metabolic functions the average variability ranges from about one and a half more to twice that in normal persons of similar ages (*405*). According to McFarland and Goldstein (*591*) the schizophrenic is a highly variable individual. In practically 80% of the variables exam ned the intra-individual variations of the schizophrenic is greater than that of the normal controls. Frantze a. ass. (*253*), who investigated adrenal cortical functions in chronic schizophrenic patients, found that the responses are uneven with a far greater individual variation than in normal subjects. In no case however were all indices in both tests clearly normal or clearly pathological (indicating a minor degree of adrenal insufficiency) but normal, uncertain and clearly insufficient responses were seen side by side in the same case. The authors leave open the question as to whether the adrenal insufficiency is (a) an original constitutional trait which facilitates the manifestation of schizophrenia, or (b) whether it arises simultaneously with the disease as a result of a provoking stress or (c) secondary to the psychosis caused by inactivity or (d) as a part of complex metabolic disturbance which is the cause of the psychosis. Lastly, they consider the possibility that the adrenal insufficiency is an accompaniment of the psychosis.

The question of the relationship of the adrenal insufficiency to the schizophrenic process is merely a particular aspect of a wider problem, namely, as we have said, of (a) the relationship between the various manifestations of the disease and (b) of the nature of the psychic heredo-constitutional component of the schizophrenic syndrome.

We turn now to those symptoms of schizophrenia which we listed under point B. They comprise anxiety-neurotic symptoms and other mental changes.

The anxiety-neurotic and hysteriform symptoms of schizophrenia

Because of the similarity between schizophrenic behaviour and frustrated behaviour it may reasonably be argued that schizophrenic reactions may be precipitated by frustrating experiences. The following is a further sampling of representative views on the subject.

Jenkins (444), one of the most eloquent proponents of the frustration theory of schizophrenia, writes that anxiety is usually one of the first signs of reaction to a frustrating problem insoluble to the patient, in fact, that it is a typical prodromal symptom of an acute schizophrenic process although not all patients with acute anxiety develop schizophrenia. According to Williams (963) the early schizophrenic is constantly emotionally aroused and external psychological stress further increases his level of emotional arousal. Myerson (678) asserts that inner turmoil is very marked in the earlier phases of the schizophrenic process and that apathy appears only later. Social drives, when thwarted, distorted or exaggerated, cause

inner turmoil, anxiety and schizophrenia. A. Meyer's views have already been outlined early in his section. Malmo and Shergass (614), who studied certain physiological reactions in normals and in psychoneurotic and schizophrenic patients, found that, in most of the physiological reactions investigated, the early schizophrenic resembled the group of anxious neurotics to stress more than any other person. They quote Cameron (138) who described hyperactive patterns of nonspecific early symptoms of schizophrenia including such complaints as worry, uneasiness, apprehension and tenseness. L. Bender (58) writes that anxiety is the nucleus of the problem of schizophrenia in its earlier stages. According to Arieti (27) the case histories of schizophrenic patients are all similar in that a severe state of anxiety, having originated in childhood and symbolically spread later in life, has not been resisted by other defenses. Sullivan (895) asserted that, in the history of every case studied, there has occurred a disaster to self-esteem, that this event was experienced by the patient as a state of panic and that the complex etiology of the disorder has invariably culminated in a situation in which the sexual adequacy of the individual according to his own ideals was acutely unsatisfactory.

In general, the relationship (to be extensively discussed in one of the following sections) between anxiety and disturbances of thought is a reciprocal one; either may be the cause of the other. Welch and Diethelm (943) found that patients of high intelligence are unable to reason well during episodes of anxiety which may be brief or prolonged. In their experimental subjects, anxiety affected inductive reasoning adversely in psychoneurotic, psychopathic, depressive, elated, paranoid and schizophrenic patients. On the other hand, the presence of anxiety does not affect reasoning invariably. Moreover, the significance of the influence of anxiety on reasoning must be considered in schizophrenic patients in forming any concept of a specific schizophrenic thinking disorder. Clinical signs which may indicate the adverse effect of anxiety on reasoning are vagueness, circumstantiality, rambling and inadequate definitions. (The reverse relationship, namely, anxiety due to distortion of perception and confusion of thought, will be dealt with in connection with the effects of hallucinogens.) Anxiety symptoms undistinguishable from those of anxiety states are so common as to be almost uniform in patients seen early (*710*). In the initial stages of the disease, many patients are irritable, hyper-emotional, sensitive, morose and easily offended. Affective reactivity appears to be increased in the direction of displeasure. Anxiety, oppression, angry hyperexcitability, irrascibility and moodiness prevail. There exists a state of "affective hyperalgesia" which however is entirely one-sided. The result is a mixture of anxiety and bewilderment (*76*).

In discussing hysterical illness, we have worked on the assumption that hysteria embodies organ-neurotic and anxiety-neurotic symptoms. The reader will have gathered that we consider the schizophrenias (the "generalized form of schizophrenic illness" that is) as a disorder which encompasses an even wider range of dysfunctions than hysteria. Accordingly, their relationship to the psychoneuroses may be diagrammed as follows:

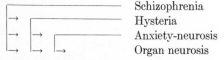

Schizophrenia
Hysteria
Anxiety-neurosis
Organ neurosis

The existence of transitional forms between the psychoneuroses and schizophrenia is attested by numerous observations. Hoch and Polatin (*392*) and Axel (*33*) described the clinical picture of *pseudo-neurotic schizophrenia*, i.e., a variety of conditions including anxiety neurosis, obsessive compulsive neurosis, dysphoria and sexual maladjustment. The disorder progresses to schizophrenia in about one third of the cases. According to Noble (*689*) there is a continuity of disturbances ranging from frank hysterical illness to the disorganizing schizophrenic process. Max Loewi (*580*) reported the case of a soldier in whom hysterical symptoms were associated with equally characteristic schizophrenic symptoms. Miller (*654*) observed that early cases of schizophrenia may resemble familiar syndromes of neurosis, which he interpreted as stages on the way to even more severe disorders, developing in turn, to schizophrenic illness. Carl Schneider (*804*) wrote that disorders of movement seen in schizophrenia resemble in many respects the emotionally determined (psychogenic) disorders of hysterical patients. "Between dementia praecox, mania depression, and simple psychopathy there is an uncertain territory. In the absence of severe basic

symptoms or acute episodes, schizophrenia may be undistinguishable from a psychoneurotic reaction. Sometimes, there is a sense of different diagnosis over several years, in one case hysteria, then depression, then mania, then recurrent mania and finally schizophrenia" (*710*). Normal behaviour shades off into schizophrenia without any essential chasm. There is continuity between the normal and the neurotic. Hence the common occurrence of anxiety, hypochondriasis and compulsive behaviour as precursors or early symptoms of schizophrenia (*138, 139*). The difference from the functional neuroses is so vague that a mild schizophrenia may give the impression of a hysteric or neurasthenic for a long period of time (*77*). The emotional indifference of many schizophrenics resembles the "belle indifférence" of many hysterics and the explosive excitement in dementia praecox the explosive affects of hysteria. The difficulty is enhanced by the fact that, occasionally, hysteria may usher in schizophrenic psychosis and that there is, in the former, a sense of disturbance of reality of a psychotic degree, though it is transient and there is usually no march to fixed schizophrenic disorganization (*451*). Many schizophrenics begin with hysterical or compulsive mechanisms and it is for this reason that many of them first look like psychoneurotics and are diagnosed as such (*130*). In Partiff's (*710*) series there were two examples of fugue and amnesia among schizophrenic patients. Of 66 psychoneurotics diagnosed at the Boston Psychopathic Hospital 22 turned out to be psychotics of whom 12 were schizophrenic. According to Neubauer and Steinert (*682*) many neurotics are schizophrenic. Harrowes (*349*) holds that neurotic reactions occur as precursors of schizophrenia. Mueller (*668*) observed a series of psychoneurotic patients over a period of 25 years. Out of a total number of 27 patients, seven became schizophrenic while two became manic-depressive. Finke (*234*) believes that schizophrenic illness is apt to be preceded by a neurotic state. Although the authors are well aware of the close relationship between neurosis and schizophrenia they did not establish a "natural system of progression" which would permit to indicate, on a unitary scale as it were, the position of the various forms of biological deficit under consideration (see above).

In line with the concept here proposed, we concerned ourselves, firstly, with the organ-neurotic, viscero-neurotic and metabolic symptoms and, secondly, with the anxiety-neurotic manifestations of schizophrenic illness. At this point, then, it would appear logical to deal with the hysterical component of the schizophrenias, more especially, (a) the "inter-level effects" and (b) the "intra-level effects" of disruptive stimulation. However, since the last named symptoms are profoundly influenced by the schizophrenic thinking disorder it will be necessary to defer the discussion of what would otherwise be straightforward hysterical reactions.

At this point, then, it is our task to specify the nature of the schizophrenic thinking disorder, or the psychopathological core of the disease which, in combination with the organ-neurotic, anxiety-neurotic and hysteriform manifestations represents the full blown picture of schizophrenic illness. It has long been recognized that schizophrenic thinking is closely related to mentation in dreams. As Hoskins (405) succinately put it: "If we understood adequately the mechanism of dreams we might have the key to schizophrenia."

The psychopathological core of the schizophrenias and its relationship to the disorders of conduct

The Disintegration of Concepts

As will be more fully explained in the following chapter, thinking involves essentially (a) the grouping of experiental data to concepts or "categorzing stimuli" and (b) their manipulation in generating relationships between them. The structure of concepts is determined by the priority value of their components which, in turn, depends on their goal leading properties that come to the fore in the course of mental operations. In general, it may be said that concepts embody elements which prove to be useful in pursuing the goal of thought and those which are apt to lead the train of thought astray. Figuratively speaking, the former occupy the *core* of a concept, that is, they are, ordinarily, active elements involved in thought while the latter are apt to be neglected and are distributed in the *fringe* area, seemingly at random. According to Wernicke (949, 950), "every concept is composed of a firm nucleus, i.e., a group of constantly reappearing memory traces and its various jags (Zacken) and extensions

which represent the memory traces of the non-essential properties of concepts. A concept is the sum total of all individual impressions." (The term "fringe," as used in the present context, corresponds to what Wernicke calls "jags and extensions" and should not be confused with W. James (430) "fringes of consciousness." Neither should it be identified with the "marginal stream of thought.") Now, the solidity of the core of a concept is a relative one, as the *priority value* of the individual elements of a concept may have to be kept sliding. The assignment of changing priority values, in turn, varies with situational factors. As N. R. F. Maier (608) said, "In some situations a dime may mean two nickels, in others a screw driver." To put it in another way, core and fringe are not sharply delineated but in a state of *adaptive fluxion*. The fluidity of fringe-core relationships is even more conspicuous in the course of the development of concepts as, by and large, those elements tend to gravitate toward the core-area which survive as the fittest as it were while the remaining elements are relegated to the fringe region. The situation existing prior to the relative consolidation of the fringe-core relationship or *core-dominance* may be illustrated by the following example.

On being introduced to a visitor, one of my friend's children asked her to turn around and let her see her back. It soon became apparent that she treated the visitor in the way her parents a phonograph record. However, marginal material may come to the fore even after the maturation of concepts. The other day someone said in the operating room that the eye of the French type surgical needles frays the silk. It occurred to me that what was referred to as the eye of the needle might perhaps better be called a slit into which the silk is squeezed rather than threaded. On the other hand, I said to myself that the term eye may still be appropriate, as certain animals have an "open" orbita which communicates with the temporal fossa of the skull. The common element of the two concepts, namely, of the eye of the needle and the orbita, was their defective circumference, the association between "eye" and "orbita" being still further reinforced by their close anatomical relationship.

The technique of thinking varies with the degree of responsiveness of the highest sensory level to stimuli or, for that matter, with the level of the waking state. As a general rule, concepts are impalpably represented psychisms. In the process of dreaming, which is a state of partial wakefulness, i.e., of reduced receptivity to environmental stimuli, the core-fringe-relationship tends to become reversed. At the same time, the fringes of concepts tend to become perceptualized and to be expressed and represented in a symbolic fashion as it were. In extreme cases, thought emerging in the course of dreaming is the passive awareness of relationships between visual images which may be enlivened by auditory and bodily sensation. In other words, thought becomes emancipated from the laws of logic by the restructuration and the symbolic concretization of concepts. Moreover, the images, palpable contents of awareness that is, may follow each other in time and arrange themselves in space in almost any combination. In contrast to logical elements, the grouping of which follow certain relation generating principles, pictorialized elements of awareness depend to a large extent on the vagaries of shuffling and reshuffling. This is not to say that thought carried by imagery is necessarily illogical —in fact, visualization of thought material in certain mental operations is essential as, for example, in those involved in problems of projective goemetry, roentgenological diagnosis, etc. Nor is the process of recombination of images an entirely fortuitous one; it is apt to be influenced by complexes which tend to activate fringe elements. Lastly, there exist transitions, namely, those between dreamlike thinking and thinking in the waking state which resemble the former rather closely.

Hypnagogic states, having been experienced, probably, by most persons, resemble, on the one hand, the clouding of consciousness in states of extreme mental fatigue and, on the other, mentation in dreams. According to C. Schneider (*804*) hypnagogic hallucinations and schizophrenic thinking have many features in common.

Quite recently, while listening to a concert transmitted over the radio at a rather late hour, it occurred to me that it was about time to "turn the page" of the musical score. This hypnagogic experience may be taken to indicate that a fringe element of the over all concept "music" became a prominent element of awareness although it was inapplicable to the given situation. To put it in another way, a central element of a concept was crowded out by a peripheral element. A minute or so later I had the experience that the sounds of the music were identical with the contents of some of my notes lying on a nearby table, i.e., that the table and the notes were not only representative of the music but that they actually *were* the music. The perception-like feeling of identity, conveyed as it was by a visual image, was an immediate one; the image merged with the sounds of the music to a unitary psychism. On another occasion, I had the hypnagogic experience of identity of a melody with a brain operation both of which were represented as sensory impressions.

It is probable that hypnagogic experiences involving the experience of identity are related to the "meaning laden" delusions or "meaning spells" of the schizophrenic patient to be discussed later. Froeschels (*274*), who gave a very readable description of his own hypnagogic hallucinations, came to the conclusion, which is well in accord with our own, that "all of them show an identification of appearances which to the waking mind are phenomenologically as well as logically well differentiated." In other words, *remote relationships between items are apt to establish the semblance of partial or complete identity*.

THE INFLUENCE OF FRINGE DOMINANCE ON THE EXPERIENCE OF REALITY

Objective reality is the sum total of objects, events and their relationships existing independently of their perception on the part of living beings—just like the material events underlying sounds, sights and kindred phenomena do not require recording mechanisms to be realities. *Subjective reality*, on the other hand, is the representation, at the highest level of cerebral function, of the data of objective reality. Man's consciousness, unless he happens to be in a state of vivid daydreaming, encompasses only one subjective reality, and the same may be said about the dreamer—up to the point at least where he realizes that he is dreaming. In hypnagogic states of consciousness, on the other hand, two subjective realities oscillate sharply; one, *personal*, subjective reality, having no correlate in the physical world, disrupts the fabric of the true subjective reality. The disrupting subjective reality is *invalid*, in sharp contrast to the *valid subjective reality* (the representation in the organism of objective reality) which we share with other people. Ordinarily, the data of subjective reality may be compared with the images produced by a mirror. It is well known of course that the mirror "consciousness" does not show events at the time of their occurrence only; that it may form, i.e., anticipate images before their objective correlates come to be, or reproduce them after they have ceased to exist. What is the relationship of these images or sensory data to thought processes? *Recognitive, anticipative* and *reconstructive thought* depends on the synthesis, on the part of the highest recording mechanism of the neuraxis, of perceptions to concepts or "intrinsically generated categorizing stimuli" and their appropriate manipulation which precedes reaction. To put it in another way: concepts are the most complex symbols of the system of notation in which the data of reality are recorded and manipulated by the highest sensory (evaluative) level of the brain. The notation system "consciousness" (its most elaborate or "incorporative" symbols are conceptual data) enables us, (as was already discussed under the heading "Intra-level symptoms of hysteria") to "think" objects within an over-all framework of reference. Moreover, it enables us to be aware of them, i.e., to think of them either as individual entities or as representatives of a class, even though we do not perceive the objects at the critical time, that is, at a time they exist outside the recording range of our nervous system. In the final analysis, the contents of consciousness are represented by conceptualized thought processes, that is to say, the manipulation of conceptual stimuli as antecedents of appropriate responses. Responses in turn, unless left in abeyance, may be either immediate or mnemonic.

The contents of dreams belong as a matter of course to the realm of subjective reality. However, in contrast to its legitimate (valid) variety, "dream reality" is not representative of environmental relations. Under conditions of reduced wakefulness, the *representational* or *correspondance function* of the highest sensory level is cancelled and its relation generating properties disintegrate. Because of these peculiarities, and its distant if any relationship to the process of response determination (which it is ill equipped to serve), states of reduced awareness interfere with the production of reality-oriented ideas and their relations.

Now, what is the relationship of response determination integrated at high levels to other physiological (low level) functions of the organism? In so far as thinking under conditions of wakefulness involves the manipulation of sensory (intellective) stimuli according to certain rules, (although not necessarily the rules of formal logic) the manipulation of conceptual stimuli is a *synergic process*. The "movements" of dream images in *oneroid thought* on the other hand occurs in a more or less dys-synergic fashion.

It may be readily seen that schizophrenic thinking is contaminated with oneroid elements although the prevailing level of awareness is not necessarily reduced. The intrusion into subjective reality of elements lacking representational value causes a breakdown of the correspondance function of the highest sensory, i.e., the conceptual level of brain function. The process of dissolution interferes with the recording of objective reality, the evaluation of data and the determination of responses to environmental stimuli, just as the notation of non-existing objects falsifies a map and renders difficult or impossible the task of orientation.

The Influence of Fringe-Dominance on Directionality and Content of Thought

The goal of thought is the attainment of a state of biological equilibrium at the intellective level, which is established in response to a state of disequilibrium. And since, at the highest sensory level of the nervous system, disequilibrium is caused by the presence of unknown relations, (comparable in a certain sense to a positive scotoma) *the goal of thought is the replacement of unknown relations by known relations*. The goal of thought, whose attainment re-establishes equilibrium at the conceptual level, is either an end in itself as it were (the elimination of the scotoma) or a means to an end, that is to say, the forerunning idea of an action. The precurrent idea is either *repetitive*, i.e., dependent on the reinstatement of mnemonic material, or *creative*, in which case its emergence depends on the synthesis of ekphorized memory traces with appropriate observations.

In a given situation, the goal of behaviour calls forth the intellective antecedents by means of which it is realized, just as a state of bodily disequilibrium determines the choice of the muscles that re-establish it by their contraction. In advance of what will be discussed more fully in the following chapter, we note that according to

Ach (2) the "ordered or goal directed course of mental happenings is the effect of *determining tendencies*." This is true but leaves unanswered the question of the origin and nature of the directive trends postulated by the psychologist. Determining tendencies are generated as directed, i.e., equilibrating processes, that is, generated by states of biological disequilibrium at the intellective level. The nature of disequilibrium calls forth *orienting feedbacks* (see Chapter III) which are processes likely to lead to its restitution. Other than its reduction to its prototype or functional primordium (a pattern of lower nervous system function), there is no "explanation" for the directionality of thought. Like other functions of the organism, thought involves the initiation of appropriate, i.e., re-equilibrating *causes*—and thereby of re-equilibrating *effects*—at the appropriate time, if only under ideal conditions and, more often than not perhaps, in steps of approximation. Like other organismic processes, thought is a system of "timed actuation of synergies."

Earlier in this chapter we made reference to the crucial role of core-elements of concepts in goal directed thought—indeed the very character of these elements as core-material was said to depend on their goal directed, i.e., re-requilibrating property. Contrariwise, the inordinate preponderance of fringe-elements is bound to derail the train of thought as may be illustrated by the following example. A man looks in vain for a cigarette. For a moment he has a fleeting picture of a door being opened, of a hallway, of a carpet covering the floor between his apartment and the elevator, and of a nearby store. (It is of no concern at present whether or not he translates thought into action centering around the above ideas or mental images.) Under conditions of fringe dominance on the other hand, a person may actually think that he sees the carpet and may perhaps start wondering whether it was imported. He may visualize as in a dream the boats on which goods from overseas are carried, sea gulls that accompany it, and so on. What has happened is that some of the fringes of the concepts used here have become pictorialized and that his thoughts have become deflected particularly if, owing to some superficial resemblance apt to produce associations by similarity, the fringe material involved should happen to become "hooked up" with the fringes of other concepts.

One of Berze's(76) patients, an early schizophrenic, described his experiences as follows: "Two or more thoughts are in the foreground where they produce a circle as it were. They converge and point at each other. One is forced to combine one's thoughts regardless whether one wants to and no matter whether they are related. Very often, the silliest ideas emerge." Another patient spoke of the "appearance of gruesome, inextricably intertwined skeins of ideas which cannot be intelligibly expressed." One of C. Schneider's (804) patients described a feeling of extreme confusion and scattering of thought. "For example, if I think it is 3 a.m. in the morning another thought will interfere before the first one is concluded. I can no longer control the flow of thought. Very often, my thoughts are not clear at all—there are thoughts one has not got, which touch one only tangentially but which, one knows, have some meaning. Apart from the main stream of thought there are collateral currents which confuse it—one does not get anywhere. It becomes stronger and stronger, everything is topsy turvy. All of a sudden, a thought may lose every sense or it may be linked with another thought in an entirely illogical fashion. The result is complete nonsense. I can no longer direct my thoughts, they jump and become confused. I cannot help but laugh about all that being possible. I have the feeling of impoverishment of thought. Everything I see and think appears to be colorless, insipid and a little unilateral. Other sentences intrude into what I say. The whole thinking is somewhat different. I feel a pressure of thought. At the same time I have the feeling that my own thoughts do not belong to me any longer. The individual ideas are *more picture-like than before.* (Emphasis added.) Sometimes they occupy the entire ideational space in which case I no longer think about anything. *I merely see.* (Emphasis added.) Beringer (67) reported the case of a patient who said that he no longer really thought, and that his thoughts were semi-visions which soon disintegrated. "Sometimes my thoughts swim away. At other times, they are slowed up. It is like a car which got stuck in the snow. The motor keeps on running but the wheels no longer turn. Formerly I used to have definite thoughts. Now just the opposite happens. Everything that goes on around me distracts me—and I jump on it. I used to conclude my thoughts. Now I do not come to any conclusion." The following are utterances of some of Partiff's (710) patients. "I cannot sort my ideas out.... I can't get my thoughts straight.... I get so muddled and I cannot arrange my thoughts ... my thoughts won't work ... thinking is so difficult.... I get so mixed....However long it takes I cannot get ideas.... I find it so difficult to keep up high level work."

The attainment of the goal of thought would thus seem to depend (among other factors) on the utilization of the more or less impalpably represented core elements of concepts. However, as Kekulé's (480) now legendary dream (see Chapter III) and similar observations indicate, goals of thought may be attained by the utilization of picturable fringe elements. In these instances, as indeed sometimes under conditions of dimmed awareness, constructive thought involves the establishment of relations between items which are not obviously related—or apparently unrelated.

THE INDIRECT EFFECTS OF FRINGE DOMINANCE UPON THE CONTENTS OF AWARENESS

The intrusion into the waking state of oneroid elements gives rise to experiences of *derealization*, *depersonalization* and other *primary delusions*. Mental fatigue, inability to concentrate and impoverishment of thought are readily ascribable to fringe dominance which renders the concepts involved too unwieldy to serve relation generating purposes. To a degree, the *oligophrenic* component of the schizophrenic thinking disorder may well be secondary to the *dysphrenic* element with which we are primarily concerned at present. The experience on the part of the patients that *thoughts are being taken out of their head* and the phenomenon of *blocking* reflect their inability to concentrate, that is, to follow up a goal directed association of ideas by appropriate linkage of psychisms —if not by any association. *Pressure of thought* complained of by some patients is a phenomenon peculiar to the state of dreaming. If I may generalize from my own experience, ideas may race through the dreamer's mind and disintegrate before they can be grasped, or page after page of printed material may be scanned with unnatural speed without being apprehended. It is not unreasonable to assume, although not always possible to prove, that (in line with Freud's and Jung's ideas) there are pictorialized, or rendered

palpable, primarily those concepts which are related to the patient's complexes in a similar way as they are symbolized in the dreams of normals. The fact that trivial perceptions may appear to be *loaded with meaning* and thereby gave rise to *paranoid ideas* may be attributed to the interaction of genuine data with oneroid material. For example, a schizophrenic patient declared that the sight of the twisted legs of a table signified the twisted state of world affairs (630). The study of dreams will show that trivial sensory data may acquire symbolic meaning, which still further reinforces the similarity between schizophrenic thinking on the one hand and dreaming on the other. Another frequent abnormality met with in schizophrenia are *distorting delusions* or *dysmorphopsias* of existing objects. They may be referable to the involvement of sensory functions lying somewhere at the borderline between thinking and gestaltperception, while the symbolizing delusions may be dysfunctions involving borderline processes between non-symbolic and symbolic mental processes. The experiences in question evoke associations which utilize fringe elements of concepts and which are unintelligible in proportion to the fringe-core "distance." Müller-Suur (670) differentiates between the following *varieties of delusional experiences*. (a) The most primitive and generalized degree of delusional alteration of awareness involves the *lack of meaning* of the things that make up the world; all experiences appear to be strange and mysterious. Things have lost their conventional meaning without however having acquired a new one. (b) The *normal meaning of experiences is cancelled* and substituted by the suspicion that they have acquired a *new but elusive significance*. (At the same time, the patient may be convinced of the absolute, though unknown, determinism involved in all happenings.) "It has a mysterious, incomprehensible meaning or significance that this tree stands here, that this flower blossoms here, that a stone lies here in a certain fashion, that a cloud passes by in this way, that this house stands here in that peculiar way, that this man walks in the way he does." Everything, every trivial matter is experienced as being loaded with *some* meaning. (c) Experiences may assume a *specific* meaning, although one which they ordinarily do not possess. For example, the swaying of a flower signifies the movements of a sailing boat on the Adriatic Sea and, at the same time, the dream-like mood of a young girl. Or the noise of a chain binding a dog to a gypsie's wagon on an icy plain signifies the icy character ("iciness") of a Jesuit priest. (The relationships between "meaning spells" and the phenomenon of fringe-dominance are evident.)

For all intents and purposes the experiental world of the schizophrenic patient is walled off from the world of the normal by a complex barrier compounded of *fringe material*, (and implicitly by the tangential association of ideas), of *personal symbolization* and *personal verbalization* as expressed in the patient's neologisms. In fact, it may reasonably be argued that the patient, living concurrently in a world of reality and of delusion is in actual fact *bi-phrenic* rather than schizophrenic. Moreover, he may be fully aware of his own twofold existence and distinguish between the genuine elements and the intruding elements of his consciousness.

One of my patients, on being asked what he was doing (he was found as usual to kneel motionless in his bed and to stare out of the window with his hands folded as in prayer) answered drily: "I am halluzinating." Later on, the genuine data of awareness are crowded out or overgrown by the products of oneroid thought. After recovering from an acute episode, one of Kronfeld's (*522*) patients, a college teacher, reported that the disease started with mental confusion. "My thoughts jumped this way." . . . "One day, during an outing in the company of two ladies, I was suddenly overcome by a feeling of great joy. I was in an exhuberant mood. I threw an apple high up in the air. While it fell down, it occurred to me that it moved faster than one would expect. The law of gravity was punctured, a law of nature had ceased to be valid! Everything around me seemed strange like a miracle. I asked someone: Do you know me? Do you know who I am? He answered in the negative. I was astonished. At this very moment the delusions occurred . . . the idea of grandeur. They were associated with a feeling of tremendous elation. I had the feeling of being a Duke, an Emperor. I was quite sure of myself and very calm. It occurred to me that the proclamation announcing that I was made Emperor must be out by now. Is it not true that there had been two revolutions and that two dynasties were fighting each other? All this appeared all of a sudden in my consciousness. *At the same time, I knew where I was and what my surroundings were,* (emphasis added), the only difference being that

the persons I saw appeared to be idealized, transfigured,—in short, peculiar. I heard the bell strike from a nearby churchtower which I felt had some relationship to myself, but as I said it was merely a feeling; it was not clear. I thought it had something to do with the war, perhaps with armistice negotiations. I saw everything in an atmosphere of transfiguration. I concluded with phantastic logic: The soldiers are representatives of the army. If they follow me it will be evident that everything goes well. *And now, all of a sudden I realized the utter nonsense of all these ideas. I apologized. My mind was quite clear again—the whole thing was over.*" (Emphasis added.) After a relapse, the patient gave the following account of his experiences. "At night, I hardly slept. I was quite restless. I dreamed a lot, mainly about things related to the war. Everything was quite lifelike. I could almost say I literally saw everything. In fact everything was so vivid that I mistook the dream for reality. Apparently, I could not with any degree of certainty differentiate between dream and reality at that time." On being questioned about hallucinations, the patient declared: "As I said, I never had any massive hallucinations. I have, so to speak, formed the images myself. For example, I made a person out of the shadow I saw on the wall. At the same time, I knew that it was just a game I was playing."

The effects of oneroid disorganization (*628*) of thinking may be insidious, or they may be dramatic, involving a feeling of *bewilderment, anxiety* and *terror* rather than a feeling of elation (Table 2). No doubt it is the occurrence of conflicting data on the map "consciousness" which is to blame for the *secondary falsifications* (and indirectly the helplessness and confusion on the part of the patient) rather like dizziness results from conflicting data concerning the position of the body in space. (Cf. also the recent studies of Korchin and his colleagues, concerned with the "experience of perceptual distortion as a source of anxiety" *405*.) The *interpretive delusions* already alluded to, which rationalize the contents of the primary delusions, include *ideas of reference* and of *influence*. They may be codetermined by contents of the patient's complexes and, setting up a vicious circle mechanism, intensify his feelings of anxiety. Accordingly, they may provoke actions which, although logical from a subjective viewpoint, are by all normal standards irrational.

Abnormalities of Behaviour Caused by Fringe Dominance

We are inclined to believe that the intrusion of oneroid thought into the waking state and the resulting disorganization of reality awareness elicits, in addition to the above described thinking disorder, a variety of abnormal behaviour mechanisms. At this point, it is well to remind ourselves on (a) the role of *affects* as response determiners, at least as baselines of response determination, (b) the relationship between *affects and instincts* and (c) between *instincts and thoughts*.

(1) The relationship between the *cognitive* and the *affective* component of intellective stimuli is customarily referred to as congruity of appropriacy of affect. The term *thymo-noic concordance* would seem to express more precisely the relationship between the two components in question. In the course of the maturation of the organism, there are apt to emerge more or less apposite relationships between the two components of intellective stimuli. Moreover, it is pertinent to point out that intellective stimuli of a complexual nature, which are represented in the mnemonic system of notation are characterized by a highly personal and, more often than not, discordant thymo-noic relationship.

We are inclined to interpret the *abnormal conduct* of the schizophrenic as follows. Realizing that conventional standards of behaviour not only fail to gratify his instincts but make impossible his very contact with reality, let alone control of reality, the schizophrenic patient "adapts" his behaviour either in a *random fashion* (he acts like an animal in a puzzle box) or he designs a *new system of behaviour*. Either stratagem is an attempt at escape. In other words, the impulse values of intellective stimuli fluctuate or individual values become systematized as if determined by a new formula which is the basis of the patient's now changed attitude toward reality. The oscillations of impulse values become manifest in unpredictable abnormalities of motivation, i.e., as abruptness and impulsiveness of behaviour, while the more rigid reversal of habits causes repolarized and rather stable thymo-noic relationships which may become compulsive in character. Figuratively speaking, *ambivalence* may be thought of in terms of the bifurcation of the impulse vector of motivation which controls

attitudes of seeking and avoidance, and the tilt of the branches, which are the products of this dichotomy, into opposite directions (fig. 10). The secondary vectors may or may not retain their original magnitude: further more they may co-exist or alternate. As expressed in conventional terms, the above phenomena are intimately related to disorders of volition. For example, C. Schneider (*804*) distinguishes between (a) blocking, (b) disorders of volition in the more restricted sense of the term and (c) fluctuation phenomena. Blocking interrupts simple movements, complex psychic motor acts, "inner resolutions," decisions and mere intentions. Fluctuations are characterized by a continuous change in the direction of behaviour, the absence of motives to account for them and the [apparent ?] lack of congruity between the patient's thoughts and his actions.

It is pretty generally accepted that schizophrenic patients may lack the feeling of activity and of the exercise of normal willpower. There being however no such entity as "the will" operating in motivated behaviour, there arises the question as to the nature of the so called *disorders of volition*. The following facts have a bearing on the present problem. (a) The transformation of the dreamer (and hence, of the "daydreaming" schizophrenic) from an active subject to a mere observer, that is to say, to an individual lacking the feeling of activity, is a familiar phenomenon which, being obviously related to the disorder under study, may be dismissed without further comment. (b) The cognitive component of an intellective stimulus may be virtually absent, even though the patient is awake at the critical time, and there remains, as a consequence of the dissociative process, an isolated affective component. More specifically, there operate blindly propelling or, as the case may be, inhibitory processes. (c) Ambivalence is an additional source of disorders of volition. (d) The lack of feeling of activity may be caused by the awareness of the contrast between, on the one hand, the effects of fringe-determined behaviour and, on the other, of core-determined activity and the resulting lack of progress toward the goal of thought. This may well explain why, in the words of C. Schneider (*804*), as here translated, the patient may "feel to be made to make" decisions, to form intentions and to execute movements. In addition to the symptoms caused by the re-proportioning of affective values, including *oscillations* and *reversal of affects*, we find symptoms caused by the *re-orientation of instincts*, i.e., *aggression, withdrawal, resignation* and *perversions*. The changes involving both the direction and the magnitude of the "affective vector" of intellective stimuli are far-reaching and revolutionary as, largely as a result of frustration, standardized values are either re-evaluated or abandoned. Indeed, it may be imagined that, ultimately, *gratification*, as experienced by the schizophrenic patient, has ceased to be the mode in which there is felt the consummation of seeking reactions caused by impelling affects and, by the same token, *frustration* has ceased to be the mode (as would be expected to be the case in a normal person) in which there is felt the thwarting of seeking reactions, or the forcing, upon the organism, of avoiding reactions. The *vectorial re-orientation* on the part of the schizophrenic produces patterns of conduct which account for his bizarre behaviour—and the lack of empathy on the part of normals. "The schizophrenic acts as if convinced that his changes of equilibrium lie in the direction opposite to that of the society around him" *(696)*.

(2) Owing to the close relationship between affects and instincts (the heavy affective loading of instinctive stimuli) it is only natural that the factors operating in the re-proportioning of the affective component of intellective stimuli govern, at the same time, the re-orientation of instinct-based conduct. Accordingly, we find that, in terms of the frustration-aggression theory of neurotic behaviour discussed earlier in this chapter, conflict situations give rise to *substitutive responses* on the part of the patient. Further, that the motivation of frustrated instincts finds an avenue of response by the discharge of centers serving a different instinct, that substitutive responses may or may not have certain features of the originally frustrated response, that they may dominate the strength of the original instigation and that, lastly, under certain circumstances, frustration may not only inhibit further action toward the original goal response but that this inhibition may in turn involve even the substitutive response.

(3) *Thinking* is instinctual activity having become intellectualized. To be precise, it is the goal directed (i.e., re-equilibrating) manipulation of concepts in the course of seeking and avoidance responses of a higher order, especially those fashioned in accordance with personal experi-

ences; the very same factors which control the *re-orientation of instincts* determine the *re-drafting of the goals of thought*. Accordingly, the "adapted" instincts reflect certain trends, including attempts at escape, at the intellectual level. Clinically, they encompass, in the milder cases, certain types of non-conformity among which, perhaps, may be counted diverse "-isms" in the arts and their underlying philosophy; in the more severe cases, they involve weird flights into fantasy, preferentially into realms of thought which thrive in a dreamlike atmosphere. Some of the "new" trends may be understood in terms of *regression*, the role of which in schizophrenic thought and behaviour however has been overplayed. Needless to say that, owing to the breakdown of his conceptual equipment and the resulting scattering of the thinking process, the patient will fail to reach his objectives (goals of thought) which, nevertheless, are somehow reflected in his conduct and in his *verbal, pictorial, mimetic and attitudinal expressions*. In other words, the contents of schizophrenic thought give rise to the bizarre functioning of those lower levels of the neuraxis which are to a large extent under the control of the intellective level, and which thereby produce *oro-articulatory, verbal, mimetic, postural and manipulative* mannerisms. Klaesi *(486)*, who studied 21 patients exhibiting stereotyped mannerisms, found that nine of them were defenses against delusions and hallucinations, two autistic purposive actions and six relics of preformed activities. This study would seem to bring out our point that "the contents of schizophrenic thought give rise to the bizarre behaviour functioning of those lower levels of the neuraxis which are under the control of the intellective level." (The magic defenses bear some resemblance to the symptoms of obsessive compulsive neurosis. See below.)

DISSOCIATION OF THE SELF IN SCHIZOPHRENIC ILLNESS

The mechanism of dissociation into a *double personality*, that is to say, its dissociation into a *personal self* (ps) and a *para-personal self* (pps) was already discussed under the heading "Hysteria." We remind ourselves that there are two main types of double personality, a *coexisting* and an *alternating type*. Under conditions of more or less complete remissions, the schizophrenic's ps takes the lead while his pps is virtually elim-

TABLE 2
Schizophrenic Symptoms and the Dynamics of their Formation

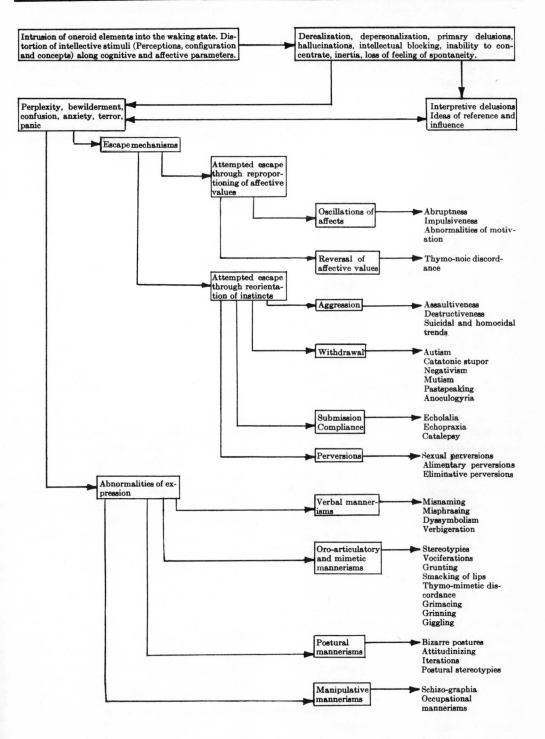

Intrusion of oneroid elements into the waking state. Distortion of intellective stimuli (Perceptions, configuration and concepts) along cognitive and affective parameters.

Derealization, depersonalization, primary delusions, hallucinations, intellectual blocking, inability to concentrate, inertia, loss of feeling of spontaneity.

Perplexity, bewilderment, confusion, anxiety, terror, panic

Interpretive delusions Ideas of reference and influence

Escape mechanisms

Attempted escape through reproportioning of affective values

Oscillations of affects → Abruptness Impulsiveness Abnormalities of motivation

Reversal of affective values → Thymo-noic discordance

Attempted escape through reorientation of instincts

Aggression → Assaultiveness Destructiveness Suicidal and homocidal trends

Withdrawal → Autism Catatonic stupor Negativism Mutism Pastspeaking Anoculogyria

Submission Compliance → Echolalia Echopraxia Catalepsy

Perversions → Sexual perversions Alimentary perversions Eliminative perversions

Abnormalities of expression

Verbal mannerisms → Misnaming Misphrasing Dyssymbolism Verbigeration

Oro-articulatory and mimetic mannerisms → Stereotypies Vociferations Grunting Smacking of lips Thymo-mimetic discordance Grimacing Grinning Giggling

Postural mannerisms → Bizarre postures Attitudinizing Iterations Postural stereotypies

Manipulative mannerisms → Schizo-graphia Occupational mannerisms

141

inated or dormant, in other words, the two selfs alternate. Otherwise, both selfs coexist, in fact, it is precisely this state of frank dissociation to which there applies the term *schizophrenic* or, for that matter, the expression *bi-phrenic*. There exist, in one and the same mental apparatus, two sets of mental contents or two mental systems. At a given time, one or the other system may come to the fore while the "companion" system is reduced to some sort of background activity. In the concurrent type of double personality, the two systems are the coexisting ps and pps which may or may not be in (uni-directional or reciprocal) communication. In schizophrenic illness, the personal self is that part of the mental apparatus which represents what is conventionally referred to as the still preserved part of the personality; the pps on the other hand, is that part of the mental apparatus in which the waking state is *repatterned* and conceptual data and implicitly, *thought processes* are fringe-oriented. The repatterning of the state in question accounts for the dream-like vividity of its mental contents, i.e., the patient's hallucinations and delusions which contaminate the dominant sphere of mentation of his pps; the fringe-oriented thought, for the bizarre products of its mentation. The concept of double personality, which is both concurrent and communicating, explains the patient's awareness of the irreality of his experiences. At the same time, the dissociation of the personality is reflected in the patient's behaviour and conduct which are to a large degree controlled by the pps. For example, the agitated catatonic's excitement reflects the lively, dream-like activity of his pps; while the negativistic catatonic's lack of psychomotor activity and his resistance to passive movements results from his withdrawal from reality. And just as, in hysterical dissociation, the pss may abruptly give way to the ps (the patient becomes "himself" again), so, in the catatonic, the stupor may all of a sudden disappear. A patient, having resembled a living statue for days or weeks, or having given the impression of being completely demented may rather abruptly start moving about in a natural fashion. In spite of the delusions and hallucinations experienced at the critical time, he may talk coherently and prove to have been aware of his surroundings. K. Schneider (*810*) described the case of a catatonic schizophrenic who came out of her stupor as soon as an air raid alarm was

sounded, who behaved intelligently during the raid—and who relapsed into stupor after the raid had ended. Thus, in the more frequent transitional states between complete and partial stupor, that is to say, under conditions of coexistence of the two more or less active selfs, the catatonic, after "awakening" from his stupor (after the ps had reasserted itself) may give a more or less precise account of the events that took place in his environment or, rather, the surroundings of his (now dormant) pps. In schizophrenic *twilight states* which, depending on their depth, merge with states of stupor, the patient may move about or rest and, on superficial examination, appear to be rational and oriented. Yet, depending on the degree of abnormal fluidity of the mental contents of his pps, and the degree to which the dominant sphere of mentation of his pps is overcrowded with dreamlike material, he will appear confused and out of contact with reality.

SCHIZOPHRENIA ILLNESS AND OBSESSIVE-COMPULSIVE NEUROSIS

The intimate relationship between obsessions and schizophrenic symptoms is well documented by Rosen's (*773*) recent study and a number of earlier publications (*138, 139*). Rosen found obsessional symptoms in 30 out of 848 cases of schizophrenia. In some of them, the obsessive symptoms preceded the onset of schizophrenia over a period of many years; in others, the two categories of symptoms appeared at about the same time. Obsessional symptoms may be experienced as being implanted by someone else. Eventually, they are held to be true. It would thus appear that the symptoms of obsessive-compulsive neurosis are more closely related to schizophrenia than to the psychoneuroses and, in this respect, resemble the mannerisms described by Klaesi as defenses against delusions and hallucinations, in other words, magic rituals practised by primitive man for the purpose of producing desirable effects or of averting disaster. More especially, the obsessional states studied by Rosen (*773*) included, among others, magical thinking, compulsions, touching rituals, looking rituals and other behaviour rituals. Rosen believes that the predisposition to schizophrenia must be much more frequent among the obsessional than among the general population. In 25 out of the 30 patients marked depressive symptoms were present

at times. What is the rationale of ritualistic practices in modern man, especially the compulsive
neurotic? We believe that, under normal conditions, the appreciation of cause-effect relationships can be traced to the experience of contiguity from which it volves by a process of
logical elimination of antedents, as convincingly
demonstrated by David Hume (410). In modern
man, the reinstatement of the contiguity principle
affords a means of reality control which, although
imaginary, is used as a magic tool. To quote Spinoza (341): "The mind is reluctant to accept
whatever reduces the power of the body." By the
same token, the mind is only too prone to accept,
if not forced to believe, in the opposite, however
absurd it may be. Primitive man believes in the
rationale of his ritualistic practices; so does the
compulsive neurotic (797). At the same time, he
does not. Yet, because of the dissociation of the
patient's personality this contradiction is more
apparent than real. Originally, the obsessive compulsive patient is a communicating type of double
personality in which the pps, thinking along irrational lines, subjugates the ps. The compulsive
rituals are the result of this subjugation. With the
appearance of a non-communicating type of
double personality at the more advanced stages
of the disease, the ps is unaware of the rationale
of the symptoms and as, with further increasing
dissociation, oneroid mechanisms operating in the
pps and unknown to the ps become still more
powerful, the patient's constricted ps misinter-
prets the obsessive ideas, and there occur transitions from obsessions to delusions. The obsessional
ideas (which may or may not lead to compulsive
behaviour) are produced by complexes operating
in the subsidiary sphere of mentation of the pps
and, as such, are manifestations of hypersymbolism and parasymbolism. Further, since the
"choice" of a particular symbol on the part of
the patient may be highly individualistic, the
nature of his compulsive thoughts and behaviour
may be unintelligible. Interestingly enough, a
patient treated by Freud under the diagnosis of
obsessional neurosis and published in a special
report later turned out to be a schizophrenic
(773). It remains to be mentioned that obsessive
thoughts are not necessarily psychogenic. The
obsessive states associated with the oculogyric
crises in metencephalitis are an example of the
mobilization of oneroid mechanisms by organic
brain lesions.

THE PSYCHOGENIC BACKGROUND OF NEUROTIFORM SCHIZOPHRENIC REACTIONS

The distintegrative effects of abnormal stimulation are clinically and experimentally established.
In studying the schizophrenias in terms of frustration effects (and there is ample evidence that
the schizoid, dysphoric, personality has a low
frustration tolerance), it should be taken into consideration that, *in analogy to the lower strata of
the neuraxis, the intellectual level is nothing other
than an instrumentality of the organism which, like
other biological instrumentalities, may break down
under the impact of frustration. This is precisely
what constitutes the schizophrenic reaction wherein,
as may be inferred from the early disorganization of
concept formation and thought, disruptive stimulation involves, first and foremost, the highest sensory
level while its functional relationships with the lower
levels of the neuraxis break down only secondarily.*
(Concerning the chronology of symptoms it is
worthy of note that even those writers who tend
to minimize the importance of the psychic trauma,
including Kräpelin, E. Bleuler and K. Schneider,
emphasize the early appearance of the thinking
disorder and its role as a primary or cardinal
symptom of the disease.) The previously
described dys-somatization symptoms in the
sphere of expression etc., are a special category of
breakdown products. The pathogenic mechanism
would seem to operate as follows. Given a certain hereditary constitution or biological weakness and, implicitly, a state of frustration-proneness, oneroid elements intrude into the waking
state. This is another way of saying that, on the
basis of a certain heredo-constitutional predisposition, frustration (the thwarting of instinctual
seeking reactions and the imposition upon the
organism of avoiding (responses) splits the personality into a personal self and a para-personal
self, and it breaks down the boundaries between
the fringe elements and the core elements of the
concepts operating at the intellective level of the
"separated" part of the personality. As expressed
in physiological language, it disorganizes the
synergic "movement" or grouping of stimuli at
the highest sensory level of the parapersonal self.
Thus, frustration causes disintegration *within* the
intellective level of brain function. In principle,
disruptive stimulation may derange either already existing use patterns or synergies mediated
by the subordinate grades of the neuraxis, or it

may interfere with the formation of intellective stimuli, i.e., use patterns formed by, and operating at, the highest level of brain function. In the first eventuality, the pathogenic mechanism generates neurotic symptoms and signs; in the second eventuality, disruptive stimulation produces dyssynergic patterns of function, including a wide variety of dys-somatization effects, notably the mannerisms involved in mimetic and attitudinal expression.

Summary

Correlating the above, we see that the pathophysiology of schizophrenic disintegration may be outlined as follows. Basically, the functions of the individual parts of the organism represent integrative acts or synergies, that is, processes maintaining biological equilibrium by the establishment of meaningful relationships between the organs of the body and between the organism and its environment. Accordingly, the term "function" refers to specific classes of biological phenomena (integrative acts of a similar or identical category), such as the physiological processes concerned with the regulation of circulation and respiration, with muscular coordination, etc. In other words, every function "consists" of integrative acts or synergies. The synergies in turn, especially those of a higher order of complexity, depend on the formation of use patterns, of appropriate connections between neural arrangements which are either innate or established in the course of the maturation of the organism and in response to the factors of need and motivation. As mentioned in the introductory chapter, H. Jackson distinguished between lower nervous system functions, which are the "most highly organized" or most automatic, and higher functions, which are the "least highly organized" or least automatic. As expressed in modern statistical language, the most highly organized functions have a high "confidence coefficient" and vice versa. For example, out of a given number of integrative processes involving certain sets of muscles the vast majority of skilled movements take shape in a harmonious fashion. On the other hand, a similar perfection is not to be expected with respect to an equal number of neurodynamic events presumed to underly mnemonic functions, let alone thought processes. Applying the above

viewpoint to the process of mentation, especially the grouping of elementary sensory data, the formation of concepts that is, it may be said that, under normal conditions, the "demarcation" of fringe elements from the core elements and, in response to the demands of the moment, the adaptive shifting of the individual elements, is a synergic function having a standard confidence coefficient. (Indeed, since the core elements of concepts are more likely to be goal leading than the fringes, the very establishment of core and fringes is a goal directed, synergic, process.) Now if, under the impact of frustration, the confidence coefficient in question drops below standard values, the boundaries between fringe and core become blurred and mentation assumes an oneroid character. The inadequate grouping of sensory data in the process of concept formation is patterned after a preformed mechanism, namely, the pattern of mentation prevailing in dreams. It will bear repetition that the other, correlated component involves, in addition to fringe dominance, the pictorialization and personal symbolization of data which enter into the formation of concepts and which thereby interfere with abstractive and directed thinking.

The study of abnormal thought and conduct in the schizophrenic has demonstrated that the disease process vitiates the formation of intellective stimuli, more especially of concepts. Now, it should be kept in mind (a) that concepts are the most highly developed intellective stimuli developing by a process of abstractive generalization from configurations and perceptions and (b) that every intellective stimulus has not only a *cognitive* but also an *affective* parameter. In the following paragraphs, we shall concern ourselves with certain aspects of abnormal affectivity in schizophrenic illness.

INVOLVEMENT OF THE AFFECTIVE COMPONENT OF INTELLECTIVE STIMULI

At this point, it is pertinent to recall that the symptoms of schizophrenia fall into two main groups, namely,

A. *Somatic heredo-constitutional abnormalities*, including
   (I) those of the bodily built, of endocrine and of maturational defects, and
   (II) autonomic nervous system abnormalities and metabolic disorders, and
B. *Psychic heredo-constitutional abnormalities*.

As we have attempted to demonstrate, the latter produce *the psychopathological core of the schizophrenic syndrome or the schizophrenic (oneroid) thinking disorder.* The symptoms listed under "A.(I)" represent preferential linkages of traits which, in turn, are apt to be associated with the autonomic nervous system abnormalities listed under "A.(II)." Is there any relationship between the autonomic nervous system disorders and the psychic abnormalities referred to under point "B"?

We are inclined to stipulate such relationship and, moreover, to relate it to the bi-dimensional composition of intellective stimuli. As we have explained earlier in this chapter, affectivity reflects the state of equilibrium of living matter. Without invoking a one to one relationship between the phenomena under consideration, we hold that affective experiences are states of awareness asociated with certain physiological conditions of the organism. In fact, we stipulated that the quality of affects can be traced to, although not necessarily identified with, the needs of the tissues of the body—which is another way of saying that psycho-autonomic phenomena or affective states are derivatives of visceroautonomic and, ultimately, metabolic phenomena. Further, unless affects, in addition to their experiental qualities, tended to provoke immediate impelling or inhibitory responses in order to narrow the gap between actual and ideal states of biological equilibrium, it would be difficult to account for the phenomenon of affectivity on general biological grounds; it would be redundant in the economy of the organism. It is the twofold nature of affective states as experiental data and impelling or inhibitory determiners of response that establishes their character as "impulse-signals." In essence then, not only intellective stimuli are bi-dimensional in character, but (at a lower level it is true) their affective components as well. It is fair to say that, originally, affective states associated with experiental data are the only determiners of seeking and avoiding reactions, or primitive patterns of behaviour and conduct. By comparison, the cognitive component of intellectual stimuli is an analog, in the physical sense of the term, of the stimulus generating event as is, no doubt, (with certain well known exceptions) the signal component of affective experiences with regard to biological equilibrium. In sharp contrast to the signal component of

affects, the cognitive component of intellective stimuli does not operate in a near automatic fashion. It is used for the process of "calculating" responses of a more adaptable nature than those precipitated by affective trends which, thereby, are apt to be superseded (or at least modified) by response determiners of a higher order. *In the course of maturation of the organism, however, a state of concordance, conventionally referred to as appropriacy of affect, tends to develop between the affective trends and the cognitive parameters of intellectual stimuli which in turn facilitates appropriacy of response by eliminating potentially conflicting trends.* In principle, any intellective stimulus, be it a perception, a configuration or a concept, partakes of the bi-dimensionality in question. As such, it may initiate seeking, or as the case may be, avoidance reactions some of which are of a highly complex nature but which, nevertheless, like the more primitive reactions, depending on whether or not they are consummated, give rise either to gratification or to frustration. Now, certain biological deviants tend to react, more or less habitually, to stimuli or experiences either with gratification or with frustration and, hence, either with euphoria or with dysphoria. The former do not concern us here. In the latter, dysphoria may be produced by any experience. This state of dysphoria (and related states of anxiety) may well account for the shyness and withdrawal of the pre-schizophrenic adolescent even if it should occur in the absence of "actual" conflicts and frustrations. This seems to have been the case in some of Sullivan's (*894*) patients who described their condition as follows: "E. K. suffered a prevailing, all encompassing affective state of markedly disagreeable character for years prior to the occurrence of the panic.... V. H. experienced a long period of discomfort.... S. I. was for the best part of 12 years markedly unhappy.... I. O. experienced an intensive unhappiness early in adolescence and, in G. H., there existed intensely unpleasant affects prior to his behaviour disorders extending backward over many years." Scores of similar cases must have been reported in the literature. Indeed, Sullivan himself points out that the psychiatrists of the Kraepelin period were quite familiar with the pre-psychotic mental state in question.

In view of the autonomic derivation of affective states psycho-autonomic phenomena inapposite affectivity may be thought of as another facet of autonomic stigmatization, or *affective dysautonomia* which, in turn, would establish a close relationship between points "B" and "A.II." It is perhaps not a coincidence that, according to Meadow and his associates, abnormal thought ("abstractive deficit and looseness of association") and abnormal autonomic reactivity are highly correlated in schizophrenic patients with poor outcome (*631*).

Once the existence of an *affective component* of intellective stimuli has been established, there arises the question of its *relationship to a specific pathophysiological mechanism and a morphological correlate.* Hess' (*379*) observations made on experimental animals and Cushing's (*176*) and Foerster and Gagel's (*244*) experiences with neurosurgical patients suggest that the upper brainstem, more especially the hypothalamus, contributes that physiological quota of action to intellective stimuli which, as expressed in the language of the highest sensory level, is their feeling tone or affective component. (Assuming that the derivation of affective states from experiences associated with states of homeostasis is correct, this observation is not surprising.) Because of its dysaesthetic, unpleasant "thalamic" quality, we are inclined to regard this particular experiental constituent of the total stimulus complex as the most elementary form of dysphoria. It may be said with some justification that dysphoria is dys-aesthesia associated with intellective stimuli and that, by the same token, dys-aesthesia is dysphoria associated with perceptual stimuli. In this connection, it is perhaps significant that patients with upper brainstem lesions describe the feeling tone associated with perception in a way which is remarkably similar to the description of dys-aesthetic experiences on the part of the schizophrenic (*62*, *487*).

According to Alsen, (*11*) patients suffering from central ("thalamic") pain are self-absorbed and impervious to environmental stimuli. They tend to assume bizarre postures and may be extremely irascible. At other times, the patients, display a complete lack of emotional expression although they describe the pain as agonizing in severity, and the associated feeling as unpleasant in the extreme. Alsen noted that central pain may be associated with diverse vegetative abnormalities, including increased or decreased sweating, palpitations of the heart, abnormalities of the pulse rate, precordial oppression, dyspnoea, short bouts

of tremor of the entire body resembling chills, increased intolerance to heat, low tolerance to cold, disorders of sleep, (including the reversal of the normal sleep curve) constipation, disorders of micturition, diminished libido, attacks of imperative thirst, anorexia nervosa and nausea. Moreover, there is some experimental evidence to suggest that the dysaesthesias or, if you wish, the thalamic quality of sensation, is related to the abnormal functionality of the hypothalamus rather than the postero-lateral nucleus of the thalamus. Spiegel and his associates (*852*), who called renewed attention to the increased severity of thalamic pain under the influence of emotion and to the vegetative disturbances associated with it, expressed the opinion that the entrance of pain conducting impulses into the hypothalamus plays a crucial part in the genesis of the Dejerine-Roussy (*184*) syndrome and that the classic concept of the genesis of thalamic pain needs, to be revised. At least this is their conclusion based on the observation that, in their experimental animals, the electrolytic destruction of the posterior ventral thalamic nuclei increased the potentials evoked in the hypothalamus by the stimulation of afferent nerves. A parallel situation, it would seem, exists under clinical conditions as a result of the deflection of pain impulses into the hypothalamus. In *summary*, then, the authors attribute "thalamic" dysaethesias and hyperpathias to the abnormal functionality of the hypothalamus secondary to spontaneous or experimentally produced thalamic lesions. Interestingly enough, Berze (*76*), in an already quoted passage "speaks of *affective hyperalgesia* which, however, is entirely onesided." Thus, the unpleasant feeling tone or dysphoric element associated with the perceptual experiences of the schizophrenic may well be due to a primary rather than an experimentally produced dysfunction of the hypothalamus, as already suggested by the presence of diverse signs of inadequate central autonomic regulations. Ultimately, dysaesthesia associated with perception is identical with dysphoria associated with sensory experiences of any complexity as the higher intellective stimuli, i.e., configurations and concepts, are nothing more than elaborations of perceptions. To conclude this paragraph, it would be the hypothalamic quota of action which, being "transmitted" to the posterior cortex, (chiefly by way of the anterior and medical nucleus of the thalamus and the anterior cortex) establishes the abnormal, dysphoric, character of intellective stimuli of any complexity.

INVOLVEMENT OF THE COGNITIVE COMPONENT OF INTELLECTUAL STIMULI

In the foregoing paragraphs, we have concerned ourselves with intellectual stimuli as regards the abnormality of their affective component. At this point, we shall elaborate on the abnormality of their cognitive component which, in association with the former, constitutes the inner experience of the stimulus complex as a whole. Further data will be adduced in support of the contention that, in addition to the *affective dysautonomia*, the crucial factor involved in schizophrenic illness is the fashion in which reality is recorded at the perceptual, the configurational and the intellectual level of sensory integration, in other words, that the schizophrenic process interferes not only with the formation of concepts but also of their forerunners, i.e., perceptions and with stimuli of a configurational order.

Abnormalities of Perceptual Awareness

They include both *somato-sensory* and *viscero-sensory delusions* and *hallucinations*. Although the difference between the two forms of abnormal experiences is not always clear cut, it is fair to say that *delusions are falsifications of the analog value of sensory stimuli* while *hallucinations are the conversion, into oneroid elements, (a) of engrams and (b) of psychisms represented in the subsidiary sphere of mentation*. As a result, either category of data assumes a palpable character. The following examples are taken from the writings of Kraepelin (*511*) and Mayer-Gross (*630*). *Somato-sensory delusions* are alterations in the quality of sounds. For example, of the sounds of voices which assume a quality described as metallic, bright, chirping, "hyper-acoustic," tuning-fork-like or organ-like. Other vitations of elementary somatic perceptions are modifications of color similar to those produced by mescaline. On the other hand, the patient may not be aware of objects in his environment even though they lie in the field of vision. *Somato-sensory hallucinations* occurring at the perceptual level are visions of colored lights, experiences of smell and taste, and a feeling of intense heat or cold localized in various parts of the body. The fact that stimulation of the lateral aspect of the temporal lobe in patients operated upon under local anesthesia (*720*) may produce a change in the interpretation of the distance of sounds and sights, feelings of familiarity and strangeness and other abnormalities of perception suggests that the patient's experiences are the mental correlates of somatic processes occurring in the posterior cortex. *Cenaesthesias* are *viscero-sensory* delusions and hallucinations, i.e., peculiar visceral sensations in various parts of the body. They are often related to the sex organs and may involve a feeling of artificially produced orgasm.

Abnormalities of Configurational Awareness

As in the above mentioned delusional and hallucinatory processes, the mechanism underlying abnormal configurational awareness may be assumed to involve, respectively, the *delusional repatterning of actually experienced stimuli, and the conversion, into oneroid psychisms, (a) of configurational engrams* and (b) of *structured psychisms represented in the subsidiary sphere of mentation*. Configurational hallucinations involve the experience of simple noises and of complex acoustic phenomena, including zooming, knocking, crying, shooting, of the sounds of musical instruments and of voices. The latter may appear to be localized in the patient's ear, his head, his legs or, for that matter, in any part of his body. (On occasion they appear to be synchronized with the carotid pulse.) Other disorders of configurational awareness are *pareidolias, dysmorphopsias, metamorphopsias, distortions of the body scheme*, and certain abnormalities perhaps best referred to by the terms "*hypersymbolism*" and "*parasymbolism*." *Pareidolias* are strange visions resembling fantastic cloud formations while *dysmorphopsias* are delusional distortions of objects which appear as if reflected by an uneven mirror but which do not convey any meaning. *Hypersymbolism* is the propensity to convert impalpable psychisms into palpable (concrete) awareness contents, while the term "para-symbolism" may be conveniently applied to the highly individualistic configurational elements representing abstract meanings. To the extent that symbols are configurational data of awareness to which, conventionally, certain meanings are assigned, the already discussed "primary delusions" or "meaning spells" of the schizophrenic patient are disorders of configurational awareness, as any structured experience may suddenly become loaded with meaning. "There may occur primary delusions of "significance, clairvoyance, of reference, of inferiority, of messianic mission, and of universal recognition, which may puzzle the patient but which, nevertheless, carry with them their own sense of conviction." (630). Similar experiences may be produced by the canabis indica. For example, one experimental subject tore to pieces a cigarette which was offered to her, the reason being that it symbolized the nature of the role she was forced to play and which she resisted to the utmost. "The cigarette forced me to become an officer's wife," she said, "that's why I tore it up" (250). The relative inability to visualize on command, or the weakness of imagery studied by Zucker and de Hubert (980), is in strange contrast to the seemingly spontaneous or paroxysmal (delusional or hallucinatory) ekphory of structured perceptions, which may attain the vividness of dream images. "Upon being asked to picture diverse objects, schizophrenic patients may remark that nothing appears, or that the desired picture may appear only after a long delay. Moreover, the picture may disappear almost immediately after its emergence. Additional abnormalities are the complete inability to visualize in the ordinary way, to keep the picture unaltered even for a few seconds, and the simultaneous appearance of experiences from several sensory spheres. The patients may find it difficult to tell about any alterations in their imagery. Sometimes, they speak of a threatened interruption or loss of clearness of the image. After a little delay, the picture may appear again, or a similar picture or several pictures emerge. As the cases become more severe, the pictures that appear later bear less and less relationship in their meaning to the first one, as is particularly noticable in the picturing of scenes." Obviously, there exist significant similarities between looseness of association and looseness of imagery and also between weakness of imagery in agnosia and in schizophrenia.

Abnormalities of Conceptual Awareness

For completeness, we repeat that the corefringe relationship of concepts is distorted and that concepts exist in the patient's mind, more accurately, in the pps, as pictorialized fringes of the conceptual framework. In other words, impalpable elements of awareness are converted into oneroid psychisms. Other conceptual disorders are represented by what is known as *secondary* or *interpretive delusions*. They must be differentiated from the above mentioned *primary delusions* or *meaning spells*. Intellectual auras occurring in temporal lobe lesions resemble in many respects schizophrenic disorders of thinking. Prior to an epileptic seizure, one of Penfield and Jasper's (720) patients "would hear someone from his hometown give him orders. Other patients reported that thoughts came crowding into their minds, that they experienced strange ideas which they found difficult to explain, compulsive ideas that they had to manipulate, objects they happened to see, that they felt they had to think about something particular, that their thoughts become fixated, that they lost control over their thoughts, and lastly, the feeling that they observed their own thoughts from the sidelines.'"

The nature of schizophrenic illness and its relationship to neurosis

The pathophysiological basis of the schizophrenias is the disruption of synergic processes at all levels of integrational complexity. The organneurotic and the anxiety-neurotic symptoms of the disease are the expression of defective integration in the visceral, including the cardio-vascular sphere of function while the hysteriform symptoms reflect both inter-level and intra-level abnormalities of integration as previously defined. More especially, the dys-somatization symptoms of hysteria (which are, to a degree, identical with conversion reactions) correspond to the schizophrenic mannerisms. The hysterical and the schizophrenic dissociative reactions, too, are basically identical. In the virtually complete remissions occurring in certain forms of schizophrenia there come to the fore, although not at the same time, the intact, or almost intact, personal self, (the "healthy core of the personality") and alternately, the para-personal self, in other words, the remitting forms of the disease may be expressed in terms of double personality mechanisms. In the other extreme, namely, the nonremitting more or less steadily deteriorating forms, both selfs exist at the same time although, it is true, not necessarily in the same proportion. However, the specific feature of schizophrenic illness is neither the alternation of the two selfs nor their coexistence nor the presence of any one gradation between the two extremes but, rather, the *disruption of integrative acts mediated by the intellective level of the para-personal self, in other words, the defective formation and manipulation of stimuli at its intellective level*. Both the affective and their cognitive parameter are involved. Implication of the former accounts for inapposite affectivity, including, e.g., ambivalence; of the latter, for the various disorders at the perceptual, the configurational and the conceptual level. Like in other types of central nervous system dysfunction, the symptoms in question may indicate either *integrational deficits* or *abnormal discharges*. Deficit phenomena are, e.g., difficulties in visualization; discharge phenomena, delusions and hallucinations at various levels of sensory integration.

Thus far, we concerned ourselves with the *primary symptoms* of schizophrenic illness. Interpretive delusions and paranoid ideas are *secondary symptoms*. The *autism*, regarded by some (perhaps because of its frequency) as a primary symptom is in actual fact imposed upon the patient by the contents of the abnormal mentation of its para-personal self which constitute the patient's private world, or for that matter, his non-valid subjective reality. In addition to primary and secondary symptoms, there may be recognized those of *mixed origin*, for example anxiety, which is by far the most frequent expression of (primary) inapposite affectivity and, at the same time, the repercussion of derealization and depersonalization incident to abnormal perception.

By and large, the psychoses are characterized by one or more of the following abnormalities, any of which indicates the presence of intrinsic disorders at the intellective level. (a) *Dissociation* of the self, (b) abnormalties of the affective component of intellective stimuli, i.e., *parathymic* disorders (see below) and (c) certain abnormalities of the cognitive component of intellective stimuli, or *dysphrenic* disorders.

In the introductory paragraphs to the present section, we made reference to two competing schools of thought, a psychogenic school and a physiogenic school both of which attempt an interpretation of schizophrenic illness. In their extreme form, the psychogenic school stipulates that the disease is caused by psychic trauma; the physiogenic school, that it develops independently of an external precipitant, that is, as a result of a heredo-constitutional predisposition. We assume that either etiologic form is a reality and suggest, for the psychogenic variety, the term *neurotiform schizophrenia*, for the physiogenic variety, the term *idiopathic schizophrenia*. The existence of the former may be stipulated on the ground that there are innumerable transitions between psychoneurosis and schizophrenia; and because of the well attested observation that the disease may follow a psychic trauma, which makes virtually certain its psychogenesis in at least certain instances, especially if the nature of the trauma is reflected in the patient's hallucinations, delusions and paranoid ideas. The existence of idopathic schizophrenia on the other hand rests on the equally well established fact that the disease may develop without an external precipitant and, above all, on the data of genetic studies.

Although the disease attacks the highest central nervous system levels, its nature, a peculiar integrational deficit, can thus be outlined on a broad biological basis. What's more, the definition of the disease in terms of a stimulus-response scheme applicable to all central nervous system functions eliminates the necessity of using a separate framework of reference for the organ-neuroses, the anxiety neuroses, hysterical illness and the schizophrenias, which comprises the former.

Schizophrenia and mania-depression. Catatonic and epileptic psychoses

In the following pages, an attempt will be made to categorize the individual forms of mental illness into *predominantly cognitive* and *predominantly affective disorders*, and their *combinations*. In studying psychopathological syndromes, one encounters a great many transitional forms whose nosological position and interrelationships needs further clarification. As we have said, psychoses may be regarded as disorders of the formation and utilization of intellective stimuli, chiefly those of a conceptual order. Predominant abnormalities in the cognitive sphere give rise to *dysphrenic psychoses;* in the affective sphere, to *parathymic psychoses*. It stands to reason that, owing to the close association of the two components of intellective stimuli, i.e., the cognitive and the affective components pure forms will be the exception rather than the rule. Further, because of the relationship of the affective component of intellective stimuli to the function of the diencephalofrontal system, which controls many periodic functions of the organism, it is not surprising that parathymic psychoses are more likely to occur periodically than dysphrenic psychoses, and more frequently in females than in males.

The term *parathymia* refers to abnormal affectivity and abnormal *mood levels*. We remind ourselves that moods are derivatives of affects which, having both direction and magnitude, have properties of vectors. In analogy to the abnormal setting of a homeostatic mechanism in the viscero-autonomic sphere, leading, e.g., to hyperthermia or hypothermia, abnormal affectivity and abnormal mood levels may be expressed in terms of dyshomeostasis in the psycho-autonomic sphere. Parathymia manifests itself (a) either in *hyperaffectivity* or *hypoaffectivity*, i.e., "vectorial imbalance," or (b) in *inapposite* affectivity, or "vectorial reversal" (fig. 10). In the first eventuality, the magnitude of the vector representing the impulse component of intellective stimuli is either inordinately increased or decreased; in the second eventuality, an impelling affect and, hence, a seeking response is substituted for an inhibitory affect or vice versa. Changes in mood comprise *euphoria, dysphoria* and *aphoria*. Parathymia may be either *primary* or *secondary*. The former is due to organic disease of the neural substrate of psycho-autonomic homeostasis, i.e., the diencephalofrontal system and, probably, the limbic lobes; the latter, to disruptive stimulation. Inapposite affectivity in metencephalitis is an example of primary parathymia, reactive depression of secondary parathymia.

The term *dysphrenic* refers to the oneroid disorganization of the cognitive components of intellective stimuli, including perceptions, configurations and concepts. The latter are restructured in the direction of *fringe dominance*, and, moreover, apt to be converted into *palpable psychisms* represented by more or less individualistic symbols. Furthermore, the term dysphrenia refers to *hallucinations, illusions* and *delusions* and to the *oneroid, tangential associations of ideas* as evidenced by the *dreamlike* patterning of thought. In other words, the term dys-phrenia applies not only to the faulty *formation* of intellective stimuli, more especially their cognitive components but, at the same time, to the erratic *activation* of the use patterns or synergies underlying the stimuli in question. The fact that, in dysphrenic disorders, the formation of stimuli has become a dys-synergic process while their activation occurs out of context as it were, establishes a link between hallucinations and *epileptiform* phenomena. The term *oligophrenic* refers to the primitive character if concept formation and the limited complexity and range of thought.

In the sphere of *consciousness*, increased reactivity to stimuli may cause increased *psychomotor excitement*, which is a frequent accompaniment of *delirious states*. Decreased responsiveness on the other hand is manifested by *apathy, drowsiness, semistupor, stupor, semicoma* and ultimately *coma* or complete unresonsiveness to exogenous and certain endogenous stimuli. *Confusion* and *incoherence of thought* is not necessarily a measure of clouding of consciousness but may be caused by oneroid mechanisms. Psychomotor overproductivity and underproductivity indicate extrahomeostatic ranges of responsiveness on the part of the highest sensory level of cerebral function. By contrast, *dyskinesia, hyperkinesia* and *hypokinesia* have a strong subcortical component. According to Kleist (*490*) *parakinesias* are distortions of volitional and expressive movements which occur in the so called motility psychoses and which should not be confused with the *iterative* and *stereotyped* movements of catatonics. Automatic phenomena occurring in hysterical illness and epileptic twilight states have a strong psychic component. Before a general classification of mental illness is attempted it will be necessary to discuss certain relationships between (a) schizophrenia and mania depression, (b) the nosological position of periodic catatonia and (c) between periodic and epileptic psychoses.

SCHIZO-AFFECTIVE DISORDERS

The two psychoses, conventionally referred to as *endogenous*, form a continuous scale of mental abnormalities. In fact, it is held by some that the transitional forms by far outnumber the pure cases. Although a psychosis may have begun with a "typical" manic or depressive syndrome, the patient may become a "typical" deteriorated schizophrenic several years later. Furthermore, patients who, as far as could be judged from the general course of the disease observed over a prolonged period of time, appeared to belong to the manic-depressive group, may show transient symptoms which are for all intents and purposes schizophrenic in character (*821*). Leonhard (*562*) and others regard as untenable the fundamental differentiation between dementia praecox and manic-depressive psychosis as propounded by Kraepelin (*511*). Lange (*535*) and Urstein (*915, 916*) deal with the very same problem in their monographs entitled, respectively, *Catatonic Manifestations in Mania Depression* and *Dementia Praecox and its Relationships to Manic-Depressive Illness*. Zendig (*977*) who collected a large number of striking observations of what, ultimately, had to be considered as terminal stages of schizophrenia having been preceded by a periodic course of the disease, rejects as unjustified a sharp distinction between the disorders in question. In our opinion, the classification of the endogenous psychoses into the two groups "mania-depression" and "schizophrenia" is not necessarily obsolete. Pure cases no doubt exist in spite of the fact that, at one time or another, the clinical picture may be dominated by manic-depressive or schizophrenic symptoms, or that features of either group of disorders may occur in combination more or less at the same time.

The symptomatology which determines the diagnosis mania-depression may be arranged somewhat in the order of the integrational complexity of the functions involved (Cf. the discussion of schizophrenic symptoms). In depressive disease, the functions in question include autonomic abnormalities, such as hypoacidity, constipation, loss of weight and insomnia. The patient looks aged and the turgor of his skin is reduced. By contrast, the manic patient appears vigorous and the above named autonomic symptoms are absent. The mental changes, including euphoria, over-productivity and psychomotor hyperactivity are too well known to warrant a detailed description, and the same applies to the mental changes in depression, evidently the negative of the former. According to Ewald (*217*) manic-depressive patients show changes of their basic metabolic rate, disorders of the cholesterol metabolism, of blood sugar and of the elimination of water. In depression, the blood sugar levels are elevated and the sugar tolerance is increased. The

manic phase may be heralded by an increase in weight. Mania is supposedly indicative of ergotropic or sympathico-mimetic preponderance; depression, of vagotonia. (See also Stenstedt (*873*).) Klein (*488*) reported the case of a patient with mania-depression to whom reference has already been made early in this chapter. It will be recalled that the phases of depression were associated with salt and water retention and that, in the manic phase, sleeplessness was accompanied by the release of salt and water. Moreover, the injection of pituitrin had different effects depending on whether the hormone was administered in the manic or the depressive phase. At the same time, Klein noted the presence of parasympathetic preponderance in depression and of sympathetic hyperactivity in mania. Further data concerning the abnormalities of viscero-autonomic and homeostatic functions may be found in Bellak's (*56*) monograph. Reference has also been made to Cushing's (*176*) and Foerster and Gagel's (*244*) observations on the effects of hypothalamic stimulation in patients operated on under local anaesthesia, and to Stern and Dancey's (*877*) case of a patient with a small hypothalamic tumor which produced the clinical picture of a manic psychosis. Because of its periodic character and the derivability of mania-depression from a scheme (Figs. 12, 13) which renders intelligible the above mentioned transitional forms between schizophrenic and mania-depress'on, or *schizoaffective disorders*, mania-depression is not only related to schizophrenia in general, but appears to be especially related to *periodic catatonia* where phases of relative freedom from symptoms alternate with phases of stupor. (See below.)

In terms of the theory propounded in the present chapter, the inherited factor and, at the same time, the leading symptom of mania-depression would seem to be the inability on the part of the organism to maintain a homeostatic level in both the viscero-autonomic and the psychoautonomic sphere of function. To be more explicit: in mania, the affective component of intellective stimuli is inordinately increased in a positive (sympathetic) direction; in depression, in a negative (para-sympathetic) direction (fig. 10). In any case, the thinking disorder, including flightiness of ideas and other abnormalities is secondary to the disorders of affect, and there exists a gross disproportion between the affective component (or vector) of intellective stimuli and their cognitive component. To put it somewhat differently, both content and speed of thought depends on the direction and magnitude of the impulse parameter of conceptual stimuli. Not only does the prevailing affective disorder determine the chain of associations, but the analog-character of stimuli is vitiated by the inordinate magnitude and direction of the affective element involved in thought. In schizophrenia, the affective and the cognitive component of intellective stimuli are concurrently involved. Hence, the dysphoria and the intrusion of oneroid elements into the waking state. In mania-depression, the primary element is the affective dys-autonomia which comes to the fore in opposite directions while the cognitive component of intellective stimuli is implicated secondarily.

In *conclusion*, then, the concept of level-hierarchy of the nervous system and of the bi-dimensionality of intellective stimuli proved useful not only in the interpretation of nervous system functions in health, but also of the nature of neurotic and psychotic disorders, and lastly, of the transitional states that may occur in a common field of disintegration.

THE NOSOLOGIC POSITION OF PERIODIC CATATONIA AND RELATED DISORDERS

Periodic catatonia may or may not occur in combination with the non-catatonic varieties of idiopathic schizophrenia. Gjessing (*305*), who studied periodic catatonia chiefly from the viewpoint of nitrogen metabolism and other metabolic functions differentiates between the *reaction phases* (catatonic stupor and catatonic excitement) and the *free intervals*. He believes that either type of reaction phase is precipitated by an abnormal stimulus, acting primarily upon the diencephalic nuclei of the autonomic nervous system, secondarily upon the cortex of the cerebral hemispheres. It depends on both the intensity of the stimulus (the nature of which is as yet unknown) and the functional condition of the diencephalic centers whether abnormal stimulation causes stupor or excitement. (At this point, Wilder's "Law of Original Value" comes to mind

(*960, 961*).* The thyroids and adrenals are involved indirectly. Some changes may represent various phases of Selye's (*825*) adaptation syndrome. Gornall and his associates (*315*) found that periodic catatonics show abnormalities of the urinary excretion of certain hormones, presumably a reflexion of their production by the adrenal cortex. In Gjessing's Type A, the reaction phase develops during nitrogen retention, in Type C, during nitrogen excretion. Type A tends to show akinetic stupor; Type B (which is transitional) and Type C hyperkinetic excitement. From a physiological viewpoint, the *free interval* is a state of *parasympathetic* (cholinergic) preponderance, the *reaction phase* a state of *sympathetic* (adrenergic) preponderance. In the latter, autonomic, electrolytic and nitrogen retention occur at the same time. (For details and electro-encephalographic covariations see Roth, *776*). The transition from the free interval to the stuporous state may occur suddenly, while the development of the hyperkinetic state is as a rule prolonged. The pattern of the symtomatology and the course of the disease is fairly constant for each patient. The symptoms of the reaction phase are mydriasis, salivation, tachycardia and cyanosis. There is retention of urine and feces. The BMR is increased. The temperature may climb to 104 F. The type of fever is swinging. The patient's hands are cold and clammy. Although psychomotor excitement may grow to blind rage and the patient's utterances be entirely incoherent he may answer questions correctly. His memory for recent events is impaired but his memory for events of the remote past appears to be preserved. Significant psychopathological symptoms include oneroid experiences, ideas of reference and of influence. The patient seems to identify himself with his behaviour. Apparently, he has no changed feeling of his own activity. In the *free interval*,

---

* "In its broadest formulation, this law, or rule, may be expressed as follows. The alteration of any function of an organism in response to stimuli depends not exclusively, but in the first place, on the level of this function immediately prior to the stimulus. If the stimulus is of excitatory nature, the response, (rise in function) will be weaker if the original level of function is higher; stronger, if it is lower. With an inhibitory stimulus, the response (drop in function) will be greater with a high original level; smaller, with a low original level. In more extreme original values we see frequently no response or reversal of the usual effect of the stimulus, e.g., a drug. (Paradoxical reaction.)"

somatic and mental symptoms and signs may be entirely absent or limited to some degree of emotional blunting and inertia. The patient may die during his first attack or catatonic stupor or excitement may be an isolated episode. Because of the complete or nearly complete remission in some cases and the absence of specific abnormalities at autopsy (see below) Gjessing does not believe that the psychosis is caused by a destruction of neurons. For a more complete account of the symptomatology of catatonic stupor and excitement the interested reader may be referred to the standard texts.

In interpreting the nosologic position of periodic catatonia, the following points are pertinent. Roy (710) pointed out that a schizophrenic psychosis may follow a cyclothymic-like evolution. Ossipow (621a) lists the following transitional forms:

(1) Cyclophrénie à éléments schizophrenics
2 cases
(2) Schizophrenie à évolution maniaco-depressive
4 cases
(3) Schizophrenie hallucinatoire périodique
3 cases
(4) Schizophrenie à évolution maniaco-depressive intermittente
4 cases
(5) Schizophrenie à évolution depressive
3 cases
(6) Schizophrenie à évolution maniaque
1 case
(7) Schizophrenie à évolution intermittente
2 cases

Similar transitional forms were described by Mayer-Gross and Slater (630), Lange (534), K. Schneider (810) and, as already mentioned, by Urstein (915), Schwab (821) and especially by Leonhard (560).

Knoll (501), in a final evaluation of his own studies and Stauder's (869) investigations, calls attention to the similarities between the psychotic features of periodic catatonia and idiopathic schizophrenia. At the same time, he mentions the frequent occurrence of manic-depressive episodes while Bumcke (131) makes reference to manic depressive features and a cyclic course and, moreover, notes the presence of hysterical twilight states in a small group in his own material of 716 catatonics in 399 of whom the disease occurred in episodes separated by intervals of varying length. According to Knoll, the role of a psychic precipitant in periodic catatonia may be discarded. The periodic symptoms of idiopathic schizophrenia and periodic catatonia including headaches list-

lessness, poor sleep, vasomotor disturbances, undue fatigability, hypersensitiveness and moodiness resemble the neurasthenic symptom complex. One of the first symptoms of periodic catatonia may be the feeling of impending diaster, or overwhelming anxiety. Apart from the symptoms already mentioned, the somatic manifestations include cardio-vascular disturbances, leucocytosis, relative lymphopenia, increased sedimentation rate and petechiae whose rapid development may precede the onset of mental symptoms. Petechiae unrelated to injury were found in 41 out of 151 cases constituting Knoll's series. Tachycardia was found to be independent of agitation. Stupor may be initiated by a short period of psychomotor excitement. Knoll does not indicate how many of his cases of periodic catatonia terminate fatally, his material, among which there were only four survivors, having been deliberately selected. The causes of death in *pernicious catatonia* were peripheral vascular collapse in 107 cases, cardiac insufficiency in 23 cases and cardio-vascular insufficiency in 17 cases. A brain autopsy was obtained in 93 cases. The brains were described as being entirely normal in 63 instances. In the remaining cases, in which brain swelling was found, the changes were unspecific as were the abnormalities of the inner organs. Among the schizophrenic psychoses occurring in the consanguineous members of the family, pernicious catatonia occurred more frequently than in other forms of schizophrenia. Among those probands who underwent at least one catatonic episode, manic depressive psychoses were more frequent than in the general population. The same applied to periodic catatonia with an admixture of manic-depressive features.

It follows from what has gone before that *periodic catatonia is related not only to idiopathic schizophrenia but also to mania-depression.* (Its relationship to idiopathic epilepsy will be discussed below.) Approaching the problem from a neurophysiological and psychopathological viewpoint, periodic catatonia may be regarded as the clinical manifestation of a *distorted waking pattern.* The reaction phase of periodic catatonia is a carricature of the waking state, i.e., a state of *sympathetic preponderance* characterized, in the *agitated form,* by *release* of the psychomotor apparatus; in the *stuporous* form, by its *inhibition.* In either instance, we are dealing with a pattern of disordered responsiveness leading, in the first eventuality, to an *extrahomeostatic intensification of drive* in the *positive direction;* in the second eventuality, in the *negative direction*. It is not unreasonable to assume that the basic mechanism underlying the normal sleep-wakefulness cycle is a negative feedback process and that a similar process operates in the catatonic cycle. The activity of the sympathetic (ergotropic, adrenergic) cell stations, having continued for a certain period of time, sets up a stimulus which triggers the opposite (tropotrophic, cholinergic) centers, thereby producing sleep including its autonomic and somatic accompaniments. Conversely, parasympathetic activity, having prevailed over a certain period of time, generates a stimulus which in turn actuates the opposing, sympathetic centers, and thereby reverses the functional relationship involved in the waking state and in sleep. Needless to say that the basic cycle may be influenced by countless low level and high level modifiers. During the phase of sympathetic preponderance, the receptivity of the organism to stimuli is increased. The externalization of stimuli (reactivity) is facilitated by the extrapyramidal system and, at the same time, adaptibility of response maximised by the pyramidal system. In periodic catatonia, excitement is produced by the actuation of sympathetic mechanisms trespassing the homeostatic range of unction. In the state of catatonic stupor, receptivity and reactivity are dissociated as, in spite of adequate responsiveness levels, the externalization of responsiveness is inhibited. (Cf. the definition in the opening paragraphs of the present chapter.) It is precisely this dissociation which accounts for the fact that the patient's ability to give an account of what happened in his surroundings after the stupor has subsided. Under normal conditions, dissociation between responsiveness to stimuli and reactivity may occur in states of fractionated awakening which are well documented by Forel's (*247*) and Troemner's (*911*) self-observations.

The presence of autonomic nervous system abnormalities, the periodicity of the disease, the absence of an extraneous precipitant, genetic considerations and last, but not least the high mortality rate establish the organicity of periodic catatonia. The viewpoint here taken is that neurotiform schizophrenia is related to periodic catatonia in the same way as inapposite affectivity produced by frustration to inapposite affectivity incident to diencephalic lesions. Stress and structural changes, then, may produce significantly similar syndromes. At the same time, periodic catatonia is related to neurotiform schizophrenia in the same way as memory disturbances due to hypothalamic disease are related to the amnestic syndrome incident to diffuse lesions of the cerebral hemispheres, in other words, psychopathological symptoms caused by focal lesions may mimic those incident to diffuse lesions.

In actual fact, neurotiform schizophrenia and periodic catatonia are not mutually exclusive, but rather extremes (although, it is granted, more or less overlapping extremes) of a unitary scale, and they may be "converted" into one another by emphasizing or, alternately, minimizing crucial parameters of the syndromes in question.

The abnormal, catatonic, behaviour of the *neurotiform schizophrenic* is motivated by complexes and set up by a mechanism which can be described in psychopathological terms. (See table 2.) Apart from the material basis of integrational organicity, as we see it (see below) the organic features of *neurotiform schizophrenia* are the diverse heredo-constitutional including autonomic nervous system abnormalities described in this chapter. In this particular form of schizophrenic illness, whose variegated symptoms reflect widespread intra-level and inter-level disorganization (and which derives its specific coloring from the dissolution of concepts in the direction of fringe-dominance and from the concurrent abnormalities in the affective sphere) the highest level takes the lead in shaping the mental symptoms of the disorder. Hence, the contents of the psychosis are organized around complexual material and, in some of the paranoid varieties of schizophrenia at least, form a more or less coherent system.

In *periodic catatonia* on the other hand, the brainstem centers are the target organ of an endogenous noxious agent which is in all likelihood of a biochemical nature. Accordingly, the viscero-autonomic and psycho-autonomic disturbances take the lead in precipitating the disease and they determine its psychomotor and oneroid components. In the extreme form of neurotiform schizophrenia, stress produces a parapersonal self which shapes the abnormal behaviour of the schizophrenic. In the extreme forms of periodic catatonia on the other hand, the pps is produced by oneroid mechanisms which stem from the above discussed disorders of the sleep wakefulness apparatus. This hallucinating self, in turn, which may or may not coexist with the personal self, constitutes the patient's abnormal mental experiences and, thereby, gives rise to abnormal reactions. Stated once more in a different way, the pps, the product of a distorted sleep-wakefulness mechanism and, at the same time, a distorted pattern of dream consciousness, is organic in origin. Whatever complexes might have existed prior to the outbreak of the disease, play a pathoplatic rather than a pathogenic role. *Summarizing* these considerations, we may say that emphasis on the organic aspects of neurotiform schizophrenia establishes its continuity with periodic catatonia, while emphasis on the functional aspects of periodic catatonia establishes its continuity with neurotiform schizophrenia.

THE RELATIONSHIP BETWEEN PERIODIC CATATONIA AND THE EPILEPTIC PSYCHOSES

The responsiveness of the highest sensory level of the neuraxis to stimuli is dependent on a certain functional state of the bulbo-diencephalic and diencephalo-cortical alerting systems. The lateral portion of the reticular formation of the axial core of the brainstem facilitates the discharge of the inframedullary centers by way of the lateral reticulo-spinal tracts while the medial portion inhibits the same centers via the medial reticulo-spinal tracts. In a similar fashion, the reticular formation controls the suprabulbar centers so that its influence extends not only upstream but also downstream. The action of the reticular formation upon the remaining centers of the neuraxis is dependent on its own intrinsic pattern of excitation. In a certain sense, the, activity of the medial portion, being inhibitory, is the most primitive pattern of para-sympathetic function and, by the same token, the activity of its lateral portion the most primitive pattern of sympathetic activity. It is not unreasonable to assume that autonomic activation will be associated with a generally increased muscle tone; inactivation, with a generally decreased muscle tone. Accordingly, the *lower brainstem* embodies the most primitive centers serving autonomic and extrapyramidal integration, while the *upper brainstem*, more especially the diencephalon, comprises more adaptable complexes of vegetative and extrapyramidal motor centers; and the *cerebral cortex*, especially the frontal cortex, not only the most highly differentiated (autonomic and extrapyramidal) neural arrangements but the pyramidal system as well. Moreover, according to Allan

(7) upon whose studies the present account is based, and who discussed, among other points, the relationships between the reticular formation and the energizing function of the cerebellum (see also Gauthier a. ass. *292*), the autonomic and extrapyramidal centers, including nucleus ruber, substantia nigra etc. develop from a common matrix. The cells of the activating system are "left over cells," that is to say, neurons that have not been used up in the process of development of the local brainstem nuclei and of other, more or less sharply circumscribed cell stations.

In one of the preceding paragraphs, we took up the idea, propounded by Gjessing, that, in periodic catatonia, an abnormal, presumably metabolic, stimulus acts upon the autonomic centers of the diencephalon, and that catatonic stupor and catatonic excitement represent a disordered waking state. We submit that, in epilepsy, a pathological, probably metabolic, stimulus acts upon the combined autonomic and extrapyramidal cell stations of the lower brainstem which disorganizes the most elementary pattern of autonomic-extrapyramidal integration. It may well be that, *in grand mal epilepsy*, loss of consciousness is due to temporary inactivation of the lateral division of the reticular formation and, further, that the associated tonic and clonic movements represent an abnormal functional pattern generated by the stimulation of the lowest centers. The abnormal motor phenomena may be fractions of reflex release and reflex inhibition occurring alternately, and involving the use patterns which underly primitive mass movements. Secondarily, the higher centers are activated. Like any form of epileptic discharge, the grand mal attack brings to the fore preformed synergies operating in an exaggerated and distorted fashion. According to Gastaut (*290*), whose monograph should be consulted for further details, convulsive predisposition is due to increased permeability of the synapses and all cerebral structures, somatic and visceral alike, are involved in the convulsive seizure. Presumably, loss of consciousness is due to the interruption of normal impulse transmission during discharge. Penfield and Jasper (*720*) on the other hand think in terms of a primary disturbance at the site of the epileptic discharge believed to be in the diencephalon.

In the present context, the loss of consciousness, i.e., the paroxysmal loss of the highest sensory level of brain function is of particular interest. Unconsciousness is either superseded by sleep, or consciousness is repatterned in post-seizure confusion or, for that matter, in some epileptic twilight states. In the reaction phase of periodic catatonia, the involvement by the abnormal stimulus of the diencephalic target organ and the disorganization of the waking pattern occurs simultaneously; in idiopathic epilepsy, in succession wherever the primary site of the seizure may be. In either instance, organic disease produces a para-personal self. In catatonia, the ps and the pps may coexist, in which case the patient, having become temporarily "bi-phrenic," is aware of the fact that he is hallucinating; in epileptic post-seizure states, (as indeed in hypnosis and hysterical dissociative states) the ps is constricted, and its communication with the pps reduced to a minimum or completely interrupted. We do not agree with Penfield and Jasper's statement that postepileptic automatisms indicate loss of consciousness; the patient is conscious to the extent that he acts. "The patient is judged unconscious," the authors write, "not because he will have no memory for the period but because when examined he shows no evidence of awareness of the significance of what he does and what he experiences. . . . A man who is automatic may walk, avoid traffic and carry out a habitual or even formerly intended activity . . . without giving any evidence of present consciousness or with evidence of impaired consciousness." Now it is quite possible that a person may be able to execute some highly automatic movement such as fumbling with his clothes and the like, without being aware of what he is doing, but, he must have at least some degree consciousness to avoid running into a car. What's more, a patient, his state of consciousness having returned to normal, may be unable to recall what happened in the epileptic twilight state but may remember, in a subsequent twilight period, what occurred in an antecedent twilight period in which he acted automatically. In this respect, he behaves like a medium which, having been rehypnotized, remembers what had happened in the previous hypnosis. Loss of memory for recent events in which the pps is the active agent, indicates a dissociation of all layers of the self including the dominant and the subsidiary sphere of mentation and of the mnemonic system (fig. 11). This dissociation, however, does not separate the pps from its own memory registers.

The symptomatology of epileptic psychoses, including epileptic clouded states, dream and twilight states, delirious confusion with hallucinations, "conscious delirium," furor etc can be expressed, on the one hand, in terms of dysphrenic and parathymic disorders and their combination and, on the other, of dissociation of consciousness. Epileptic psychoses may be undistinguishable from catatonic psychoses, which fortifies the impression that the two conditions are closely related. Moreover, catatonia may be associated with epileptiform seizures. The following is a tabulation, of various factors involved in schizophrenic, epileptic and postepileptic mental states. (Table 3.)

Classification of mental disease

The entities of clinical psychiatry are to a degree *classification artifacts*, that is to say, *shifting or semi-stable combination patterns of basic psychopathological components*. This is brought out by the frequent revision of the original diagnosis made in the course of follow-up studies, amounting, for example, in Masserman's (*623*) material to no less than 40%, by the enormous literature on the transitional forms of the textbook types of mental illness, the widespread rebellion, initiated by Hoche (*293*) in 1912 against too rigid classifications, and the chaotic terminology, compared, by some, to the Tower of Babel.

In ideal system of classification should take into account (a) the *etiological and phenomenological* aspects of the psychoses, (b) their *nosological position*, (c) the underlying *pathophysiological mechanisms*, even though hypothetical at present, (d) *borderline conditions* between psychosis, neurosis and abnormal personality types, (e) the relationships between *structural* and *integrational organicity* which make up the pathogenetic background of the disorders concerned, (f) the relationships between the *periodic* and the *nonperiodic* psychoses and (g) those between *spontaneous* psychoses and abnormal mental conditions produced by *psychotomimetic drugs*. In other words, an ideal diagnostic system should reflect the continuum of mental illness in its various aspects. Lastly, it should be "surveyable" like a map from which the position of any symptom complex can be read off at a glance. Clearly, such system of classification requires that the individual data be arranged in a *panoramic* rather than in a linear fashion. Once mapped out, the system of classification can be analyzed in a variety of ways which reveal significant relationships be-

TABLE 3

SOME FUNCTIONAL AND ORGANIC MENTAL SYNDROMES AND THEIR RELATIONSHIP TO PSYCHOPATHOLOGICAL MECHANISMS

	Receptivity	Reactivity	Memory (Delayed reaction)	Motor and vasomotor manifestations	Active psychic agent(s)	Affect	Oneroid experiences
Grand mal	abolished	abolished	abolished	tonic and clonic mass-movements	none	none	none
Petit mal	reduced or abolished	reduced or abolished	reduced or abolished	minor	ps	not characteristic	none
Myoclonic petit mal	,,	,,	,,	myoclonic twitchings	ps	,,	,,
Psychomotor automatisms	,,	,,	potentially present in subsequent automatic states	complex volitional movements	ps	variable	present or absent
Deja vue	increased to oneroid experiences. Otherwise reduced	reduced	preserved	not characteristic. (Usually absent)	pps	,,	present
Epileptic clouded states, psychoses and allied conditions	reduced, abolished or increased	reduced, abolished or increased	partially preserved	complex volitional movements with admixture of automatisms	pps concurrently or alternately with ps	variable (ecstatic, anxious, destructive)	present or absent
Catatonic excitement	,,	,,	,,	complex volitional with admixture of stereotypies, parakinesias etc.	,,	,,	present
Catatonic stupor	,,	greatly diminished or absent	,,	vasomotor abnormalities	,,	variable (ecstatic, anxious, destructive)	,,
Posttraumatic (including postconcussive) states	reduced or increased	reduced or increased	Temporarily inhibited (retrograde amnesia)	Psychomotor excitement	,,	variable	present or absent

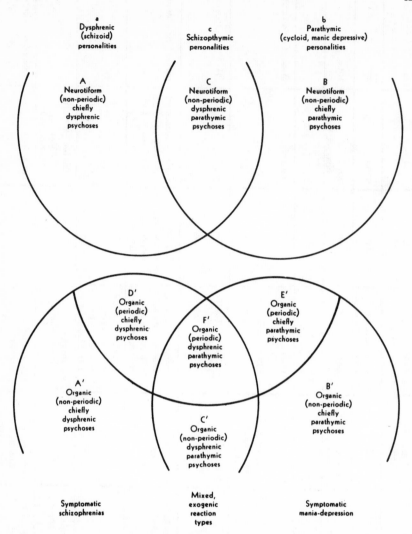

Fig. 12. Principles of classification of mental illness. (see text)

tween its component parts. (See figs. 12, 13).

(1) From the viewpoint of *periodicity*, the periodic psychoses D′, E′, F′ may be set apart from the non-periodic psychoses A, B, C and A′, B′, C′.

(2) From an *etiological* viewpoint (cf. "Etiological considerations") one may distinguish between

   Group   I, (comprising A, B, C), the *neurotiform psychoses*,

   Group II, (comprising A′, B′, C′) the *idiopathic psychoses* and the (endogenous and exogenous) *symptomatic psychoses*, and

   Group III, (comprising D′, E′, F′) the *periodic idiopathic psychoses*.

(3) The axis of the panoramic continuun of mental illness is formed by the *pluri-symptomatic*

or combined psychoses, i.e., subgroups C, F′, C′; its wings, by the *pauci-symptomatic* psychoses, i.e., subgroups A, D′, A′ and B, E′, B′.

(4) The left wing of the system is formed by the predominantly *dysphrenic* psychoses, the right wing by the predominantly *parathymic* psychoses.

(5) The top layer (a, b, c) of the scheme comprises psychopathological syndromes having a minimum of organic background; its bottom layer (fig. 12 A′, B′, C′ and fig. 13 A′-s, C′-s, B′-s) psychoses associated with various disease processes and allied conditions (e.g., intoxications) whose organic background ranges from biochemical and microstructural alterations to gross destruction of brain tissue. The intervening

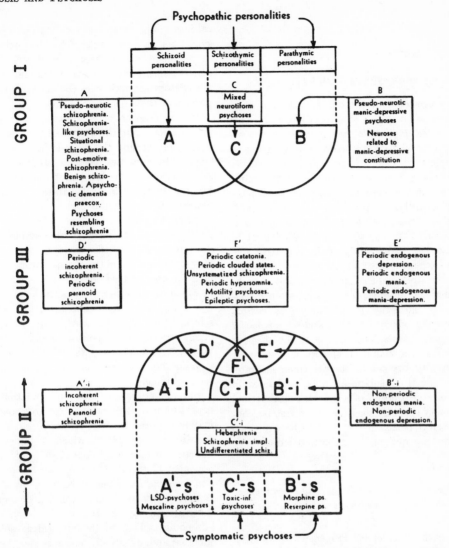

Fig. 13. Relationship between psychopathic personality and the functional psychosis, and between the ideopathic and the symptomatic psychoses. (see text)

abnormalities occupy the space between abnormal personality types and frank organic disease.

(6) The psychic abnormalities indicated in the top layer of the two diagrams 12 and 13 may be associated with any degree of, including superior, mental endowment. With increasing distance from the top layer, on the other hand, oligophrenia, amnesia and clouding of consciousness becomes increasingly frequent and the organic mental syndrome more and more conspicuous.

(7) Apart from the fact that, with increasing organicity, oligophrenic symptoms are combined with dysphrenic and parathymic elements, Groups II and III may be regarded as more severe forms of Group I. To put it in another way, Groups II and III include the latter, just as neurotiform schizophrenia includes hysteriform, anxiety-neurotic and organ-neurotic elements; and the neurotiform parathymias include, for their part, affective disorders of a lower grade than the full blown manic and depressive syndromes. (To avoid complicating diagrams 12a. 13, Group I, the neurotiform syndromes, have not been included into Groups II and III, but the close relationship between them is indicated by the choice of appropriate symbols, e.g., A and A' for the dysphrenic group, B and B' for the parathymic group, etc.)

GROUP I

NEUROTIFORM PSYCHOSES

(*Subgroups A, B, C*)

We suggested that the *crucial factor operating in the neurotiform psychoses is an exogenous precipitant and that the heredo-constitutional predisposition does not of itself produce the disease*. The role of complexes is both pathogenic and pathoplastic. In the extreme case, the disease is caused by minimal stress in the presence of maximal predisposition. Contrarily, the psychosis remains dormant if minimal stress coincides with a minimal predisposition. The *neurotiform element* inherent in the disorders under study is the causative role of the exogenous precipitant; the *psychotic* element, the stress-induced disorganization of mental functions. More especially, the *cognitive component of intellective stimuli undergoes oneroid* (dysphrenic) changes, the *affective component parathymic changes*. The changes in the affective sphere and the cognitive sphere, if developing concurrently, are not necessarily commensurate. Any of the three subgroups may be defined in terms of accentuation of a subclinical, abnormal personality type. By the same token, any psychopathological personality type may be expressed in terms of a mitigated psychotic reaction.

Subgroup A: Neurotiform, chiefly dysphrenic psychosis

Pathogenetic background: Propensity to develop stress induced dysphrenic reaction.
Symptoms: Dysphrenic reactions with minor parathymic accompaniments.
Subclinical types: Schizoid personalities.

In a general way, the term neurotiform schizophrenia covers psychopathological syndromes which are essentially identical but which were described in the literature under various names, such as "pseudo-neurotic schizophrenia" (*33, 392*) as "psychoses resembling schizophrenia" (*709*), as "schizophrenic-like psychoses" (*468*), as "situational schizophrenias" (*649*) as "postemotive schizophrenia" (*698*), "benign schizophrenia" (*944*) and "apsychotic dementia praecox" (*685*). See also Kantor a. ass., (*469*) and Papanek's article (*667a*) in which reference is made to physi-

cal forms of periodic depression (Schick), physical symptoms as equivalents of the depressive state or manic-depressive disease (Karliner), pseudo-neurotic forms of depressive psychosis (Gutheil), ambulatory schizophrenia (Zilboorg) and schizophrenia without psychosis (Beck).

In the absence of a substandard-frustration gratification ratio, the neurotiform schizophrenia remain latent; and the somatic heredo-constitutional abnormalities isolated stigmata of the schizoid personality. If integrational deficiency is brought to the fore by frustration, it does not necessarily involve the highest levels of brain function to produce the complete psychopathological core of the schizophrenic syndrome. Indeed, integrational deficiency, for a time at least, may manifest itself at the organ-neurotic, anxiety-neurotic and hysteriform level of disorganization in which case the heredo-constitutional (somatic dys-homeostatic etc.) stigmata of the potential schizophrenic are associated, respectively, with organ-neurotic, anxiety-neurotic and hysteriform features. At most, the patient will be considered a borderline schizophrenic or pseudo-neurotic schizophrenic.

In a diagrammatic fashion, the relationship of neurotiform schizophrenia to the psychoneuroses may be expressed as follows. Let X and Y be two coordinates (fig. 14) of which X indicates the direction of *increasing stigmatization of biological deviants; Y*, the direction of *increasing integrational complexity* of the functions involved. Deterioriation extends in the direction of increasing integrational complexity, i.e., from the viscero-autonomic sphere to the intellective sphere of function and, eventually, encompasses the entire range of integrative levels of nervous system functions up to and including those concerned with the formation and utilization of intellective stimuli. As expressed in clinical terms, deterioration proceeds from the organ-neurotic level to the psychotic level. A glance at fig. 14 reveals that schizophrenia includes hysteria, that hysteria includes the anxiety neuroses and the latter the organ-neuroses. Any case that answers the above criteria of biological deterioration (or typical case) may be found on line t. For example, the schizophrenic patient S shows a greater variety of organic features than the hysterical patient H. At the same time, the schizophrenic displays, among other defects, disorders of the affective element and the cognitive element of concept

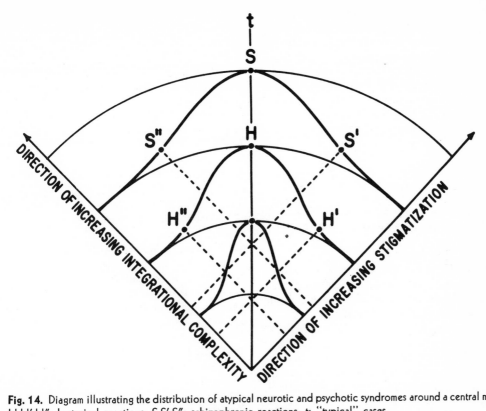

Fig. 14. Diagram illustrating the distribution of atypical neurotic and psychotic syndromes around a central mean. H,H′,H″: hysterical reactions; S,S′,S″: schizophrenic reactions; t: "typical" cases.

formation, and dissociative states involving the more or less complete dychotomy into a personal self and a para-personal self with the attending restructuring of the dominant and the subsidiary sphere of mentation. Patient H on the other hand fails to show disorders of concept formation and his organic stigmata are less prominent than those of the schizophrenic. Allowance should be made for the existence of atypical cases in both hysterical and schizophrenic illness, that is to say, for a certain measure of scattering. For simplicity, we limit the discussion to the two above named conditions.) It is suggested that (a) in each sector representing a basic pattern of disintegration, the distribution of atypical cases follows a dispersion curve, (exemplified by symbols S′ and S″ and H′ and H″) and (b) that the degree of non-conformity is represented by the distance of points S′ and H′ from the two summits S and H on one hand and S″ and H″ on the other. Thus, patient S′ shows many organic (somatic heredo-constitutional) abnormalities but relatively few mental changes. Contrarily, patient S″ is a schizo-

phrenic who, in spite of the paucity of organic stigmata, shows the full blown psychopathological picture of schizophrenic illness. Similarly, patient H′ exhibits many organic stigmata while dissociative phenomena are conspicuous by their absence. Patient H″ on the other hand, displays only a few hysterical stigmata in the somatic sphere but definite signs of hysterical dissociation. Either case fails to show impairment of concept formation and the type of thinking disorder which would warrant the diagnosis of schizophrenia. In *summary*, then, line "t" symbolizes the *contiguity of typical disintegration patterns* while the dispersion curve illustrates the distribution of *atypical and transitional cases.*

Subgroup B: Neurotiform, chiefly parathymic psychosis

Pathogenetic background: Propensity to develop stress induced, parathymic reactions.

Symptoms: Parathymic reactions with minor dysphrenic accompaniments.

Sublcinical forms: Parathymic personality.

Neurotiform depressions embody organ-neurotic, anxiety-neurotic and hysteriform features in the same way as the neurotiform dysphrenic psychoses. Reactive mania is a paradoxical reaction to a psychic trauma (537). The neurotiform parathymic psychoses were described in the literature as "pseudo-neurotic manic-depressive psychoses" (479) and as "neuroses related to manic-depressive constitution" (483). (See also Shagass a. ass. (827) and Papanek's (667a) article.

Subgroup C: Neurotiform, dysphrenic-parathymic psychoses

Pathogenetic background: Propensity to develop stress induced dysphrenic-parathymic reactions.
Symptoms: Dysphrenia-parathymia.
Subclinical forms: Schizo-parathymic personality.

In the mixed neurotiform psychoses both elements, although not necessarily present at the same time, are equally prominent.

Are there any periodic neurotiform psychoses? Stähelin (813) describes neurotiform conditions which sooner or later develop to periodic psychoses. One group of patients become dipsomanics or poriomanics, while others show, at intervals, mixed dysphrenic and parathymic symptoms associated with viscero-autonomic abnormalities. (We mention in passing that both poriomania and dipsomania may develop as sequelae of chronic encephalitis.)

GROUP II

IDIOPATHIC PSYCHOSES AND (EXOGENOUS AND ENDOGENOUS) SYMPTOMATIC PSYCHOSES

(Subgroups A', B', C')

The reason for grouping together a variety of mental disorders is the similarity between, on the one hand, certain experimentally produced toxic psychoses and, on the other, endogenous psychoses developing on the basis of a heredo-constitutional predisposition, the inference being that, in either case, the crucial factor is of a biochemical nature and that, in contrast to the neurotiform psychoses, psychogenic precipitants play a minor role if any. Exogenous, predominantly dysphrenic psychoses comprise the symptomatic schizophrenias; exogenous, predominantly parathymic psychoses, the symptomatic manias and symptomatic depressions, while the mixed type

corresponds by and large to "acute somatogenic reactive psychoses." In the older literature, the last named conditions were referred to as toxic delirious state or amentia, i.e., "psychoses characterized by motor excitement, incoherence, hallucinations, deep confusion and at least some degree of clouding of consciousness" (890) More recently the psychoses in question are being referred to as "acute, confusional deliroid reactions" or "acute, hallucinatory confusions" (692). The term "exogene Reaktionsformen" was coined by Bonhoeffer (97, 98) who called attention to the fact that toxic infective processes, autointoxications, chronic intoxications and severe contusions of the brain are apt to cause more or less typical reaction patterns, especially delirious and stuporous conditions associated with anxiety and twilight states of an epileptiform and catatoniform type. He believed that the delirious states are caused by toxic metabolites produced, in turn, either by the inner organs or by the injured brain and acting on the central nervous system either directly or by way of "intermediary etiologic links." With the cessation of the cause, exogenous reactions subside either rapidly or gradually and are followed by a neurasthetic-like symptom-complex or an amnestic syndrome of the Korsakoff type.

Thus, a further breakdown of the psychoses constituting Group II would yield the subgroups shown in the following table.

Idiopathic Psychoses	Symptomatic Psychoses
Subgroup A'-i *idiopathic* dysphrenic psychoses	Subgroup A'-s *symptomatic* dysphrenic psychoses (including the symptomatic schizophrenias)
Subgroup B'-i *idiopathic* parathymic psychoses (508)	Subgroup B'-s *symptomatic* parathymic psychoses (including the symptomatic manias and symptomatic depressions)
Subgroup C'-i *idiopathic* dysphrenic-parathymic psychoses	Subgroup C'-s *symptomatic* dysphrenic-parathymic psychoses (including the psychoses of the Bonhoeffer type)

The subdivision of the *symptomatic psychoses* into a *dysphrenic* and a *paratthymic group* is an oversimplification proposed to establish some semblance of order. In subgroup A'-s, the dysphrenic element predominates and, as far as known, the quality of the affect corresponds to the patient's oneroid experiences. In subgroup B'-s, on the other hand, affective changes are primary, intellective changes secondary. Lastly, in the mixed forms, which are by far the most frequent, the action of noxious agents appears to be more or less generalized.

Certain symptomatic psychoses known as *symptomatic schizophrenias*, (e.g., the model psychoses) mimic, to a degree, the idiopathic form while the symptomatic manias and depressions resemble genuine manic or depressive psychoses respectively. On the other hand, symptomatic psychoses may be complicated by oligophrenic and amnestic symptoms and, moreover, differ from the "corresponding" idiopathic varieties by disturbances in consciousness. (In the following pages, the abbreviations "o-phr." indicates an admixture of oligophrenic symptoms; "O-PHR.", the oligophrenic rather than dysphrenic character of the intellective changes; "amn.", the presence of an amnestic component; and "consc.", disturbances in consciousness.) The model psychoses will be discussed below. Symptomatic psychoses may occur periodically. For example, Thiele's (*900*) case concerned an extremely polymorphous dysphrenic-parathymic psychosis attributable to vascular disturbances. Between the attacks, the patient was completely free from neurologic and psychiatric symptoms. According to Stähelin (*861*) *periodic symptomatic psychoses* may be precipitated by diseases of the brainstem. Postencephalitics may at certain intervals develop episodic states of increased salivation and increased diuresis, intensifications of the signs of parkinsonism and mental changes. In other patients, the beginning of the menstrual cycle may be associated with attacks of anxiety and dipsomania. In principle, then, there exist two types of symptomatic psychoses, namely, A'-s, B'-s and C'-s on the one hand, and A'-s (per.), B'-s (per.) and C'-s (per.) on the other. Thiele's case belongs to category C'-s (per.), Staehelin's case to category B'-s (per.).

Idiopathic schizophrenia is an autochthonous psychosis or morbus sui generis while *symptomatic schizophrenia* is a complex of psychopathologi-cal syndromes which develop incident to injury or disease, and which mimic the idiopathic variety more or less closely. Diagnostic errors are apt to occur if the neurologic concomitants of the psychic symptoms are inconspicuous. Symptomatic schizophrenia must be differentiated from *secondary idiopathic schizophrenia*, which is likewise precipitated by an organic disease process. Bostroem (*102*) and others believe that the psychic abnormalities occurring in *symptomatic schizophrenia* are caused by the localization of the pathological process in the central nervous system; in *secondary idiopathic schizophrenia*, primarily by the patient's premorbid disposition brought to the fore by a noxious agent. The prognosis of at least some forms of symptomatic schizophrenia is relatively favourable while the course of secondary idiopathic schizophrenis is apt to be as progressive as that of primary idiopathic schizophrenia. Kleist (*464*) believes he has found a heredo-constitutional predisposition even in the exogenous psychoses, more especially in the psychoses associated with influenza which tend to run in families. In the present context, the case of a patient reported by Holt and Tedeschi (*420*) is of particular interest. It concerned a young man who, without ascertainable cause, developed a schizophrenic episode from which he recovered. Some 18 years later, he developed symptoms of schizophrenia which, as demonstrated at autopsy, were caused by a diffuse demyelinating disease of the brain. Possibly, there existed a latent predisposition to develop the disease which, initially, was brought to the fore by a non-organic and, subsequently, an organic stress situation. In other words, the first episode might have been a primary form of idiopathic schizophrenia, the second episode, a secondary form. The following is a selected list of publications dealing with the problem of symptomatic schizophrenia. The cases on which the reports were based were either diagnosed as primary idiopathic schizophrenia but proved to be symptomatic at autopsy, or the symptomatic nature of the illness was recognized during life as the mental disturbances developed incident to a known organic disease process. Schizophrenic symptoms were found in *allogenic intoxications* by Glauss (*306*), Roeder-Kutsch and Schulz-Wölfling (*769*), in *autogenic intoxications* (incl. uremia) by Thiele (*900*), in *endocrine* disorders by Glauss (*306*), in *bacterial* and allied infections (incl. syphilis) by Jacob (*423*), in *virus* infections (incl. epidemic encephalitis) by Lemke (*555*), in *neurodegenerative* and *demyelinating* diseases by Polatin a. ass. (*742*), Ferraro (*228*), Roizin, a. ass. (*770*), Holt and Tedeschi (*400*) and Frowein and Kruecke (*278*), in *hematogenic* disorders (incl. pernicious anemia) by Buessow (*132*), in *neoplasms* by Guttmann and Hermann (*333*), in cranio-cerebral injuries by Feuchtwanger and Mayer-Gross (*231*), Elsässer and Gruenewald (*213*) and Shapiro (*828*) and, following *carotid ligation*, by Deboor (*182*). (See also Bruetsch (*127*), Menninger (*632*) and Murphy and Neuman (*675*).

As expressed in terms here developed, *psychotomimetics*, whose action will be discussed below, produce a particular form of symptomatic schizophrenia which, depending on the predominance of dysphrenic or parathymic features, belongs either to group A'-s or B'-s. In group C'-s, both elements exist in combination.

The terms *symptomatic mania and symptomatic depression* refer to psychoses which, because of the presence of mood changes, psychomotor hyperactivity or hypoactivity, mimic the idiopathic forms so closely that they may be confused with idiopathic mania or idiopathic depression respectively. Classic examples of symptomatic mania are the parathymic states caused by marihuana and symptomatic depression caused, or accentuated, by reserpine. In analogy to the symptomatic dysphrenic psychoses, symptomatic mania or depression are either genuine exogenous disorders in which case they are produced by biochemically active agents or by palpable, microstructural or macrostructural brain lesions or lastly, by the activation of a preformed mechanism by unspecific organic injury or disease. In the first eventuality, we are dealing with cases of *exogenous mania* or *exogenous depression;* in the second eventuality, with *secondary idiopathic mania or depression.* Gagel (*284*) reported the case of a 19 year old dwarf with atrophy of the genitals and diabetes insipidus in whom "classic mania" was caused by a craniopharyngeoma invading the third ventricle. As far as can be judged from the relatively small number of publications, symptomatic parathymic psychoses, e.g., those caused by Stern and Dancey's (*877*) case of diencephalic glioma (already referred to) and by Gagel's case, are rare but the concept of symptomatic parathymic psychoses finds some support in experiences with chronic encephalitis and Foerster and Gagel's and Penfield and Jasper's above noted experimental observations.

GROUP II

IDIOPATHIC AND SYMPTOMATIC PSYCHOSES

Subgroup A'-i. Idiopathic (non-periodic) chiefly dysphrenic psychoses
  Pathogenetic background: Habitual propensity to develop endogenous dysphrenia
  Clinical varieties:
  a. *Incoherent schizophrenia* (*491*)
  b. *Paranoid schizophrenia.* (*Phantasiophrenia, progressive hallucinosis.* (*491*).

Subgroup A'-s. Symptomatic (non-periodic) chiefly dysphrenic psychoses
  Pathogenetic background:
  1. Primary metabolic disorders
    a. Familial amaurotic idiocy (O-PHR.)
    b. Phenylperuvic amentia (O-PHR.)
    c. Progressive lenticular degeneration (O-PHR.)
  2. Avitaminoses and deficiency state
    a. Cachectic psychoses
    b. Nicotinic acid deficiency delirium
  3. Intoxications
    a. Allogenic: Alcohol (chronic intox.), copper, lead, arsenic mercury, benzene
    b. Autogenic: uremia
    c. Hallucinogenic: LSD-25, mescaline adrenochrome, adrenolutin, marihuana.
  4. Pharmacodynamic action
    a. Stimulants: strychnine, amphetamine
    b. Depressants: barbiturates (chronic intox.), scopolamine, bromides
    c. Analgesics: codeine, morphine (acute intox.), cocaine
    d. Euphoriants: morphine
    g. Tranquilizers, (ataractics): reserpine (see also under parathymia)
    h. Others: atropine, isoniazid, akineton (*422*, *955*), iproniazid (Marsilid) (*174*).
  5. Endocrine disorders
    a. Puerperal psychoses
  6. Infections
    a. Bacterial infections
    b. Viral infections
  7. Neurodegenerative and demyelinating diseases
    a. Involutional paranoid reactions
    b. Diffuse sclerosis
  8. Vasodegenerative and circulatory disorders
  9. Hematogenic disorders
    a. Kernicterus
  10. Dysplasias
  11. Neoplasms and malformations with blastomatous growth
    a. Tuberous sclerosis (O-PHR., para-thy.).
  12. Craniocerebral injuries

Subgroup B'-i. Idiopathic (non-periodic) chiefly parathymic psychoses
  Pathogenetic background: Habitual propensity to develop endogenous mania or endogenous depression

Clinical varieties:
 a. *Non-periodic (endogenous) mania*
 b. *Non-periodic (endogenous) depression*

Subgroup B'-s. Symptomatic (non-periodic) chiefly parathymic psychoses
Pathogenetic background:
1. Primary metabolic disorders
2. Avitaminotic and deficiency states
3. Intoxications
 a. Allogenic: Muscarine, alcohol, lead (chronic intox.)
 b. Autogenic
 c. Hallucinogenic
4. Pharmacodynamic action
 a. Stimulants: caffeine
 b. Depressants: barbiturates (acute intox.), bromides (chron. int.)
 c. Analgesics: opium
 d. Euphoriants: morphine
 e. Tranquilizers (ataractics): reserpine
 f. Endocrine preparations: ACTH, cortisone, insulin
 g. Others: acetanilid
5. Endocrine disorders
 a. Basophilic adenoma
 b. Addison's disease
 c. Pancreatic hypoglycemia
 d. Thyroid dysfunction; Graves' disease
 e. Disorders of the sex glands: climacteric manic-depressive psychoses, psychoses of puberty, lactation psychoses
6. Infections
 a. Bacterial infections: Sydenham's chorea
 b. Viral infections: epidemic encephalitis
7. Neurodegenerative and demyelinating diseases
8. Hematogenic disorders
9. Dysplasias
10. Neoplasms and malformations with blastomatous growth
 a. Diencephalic tumors
11. Craniocerebral injuries
 a. Chronic frontal lobe lesions

Subgroup C'-i. Idiopathic (non-periodic) dysphrenic-parathymic psychoses
Pathogenetic background: Habitual propensity to develop endogenous dysphrenia and parathymia
Clinical varieties:
 a. *Hebephrenia*
 b. *Simple type of schizophrenia*
 c. *Undifferentiated type of schizophrenia*

Subgroup C'-s. Symptomatic (non-periodic) dysphrenic-parathymic psychoses
Pathogenetic background:
1. Primary metabolic disorders
2. Avitaminoses and deficiency states
3. Intoxications
 a. Allogenic: nicotine, lead (chronic intox.), arsenic (chronic intox.), mercury, alcohol, (chronic intox.) carbon dissulfid
 b. Autogenic: uremia
 c. Hallucinogenic

4. Pharmacodynamic preparations
 a. Stimulants
 b. Depressants: scopolamine (acute intox.)
 c. Analgesics: morphine, opium, cocaine
 d. Euphoriants: morphine
 e. Tranquilizers (ataractics)
 f. Endocrine preparations
 g. Others.
5. Endocrine disorders
 a. Due to pituitary dysfunction: Simmond's disease
 b. Due to thyroid dysfunction: cretinism
6. Infections.
 a. Bacterial infections: pneumonia, typhoid fever
 b. Viral infections: influenza, epidemic encephalitis.
7. Neurodegenerative and demyelinating diseases.
 a. Multiple sclerosis
 b. Huntington's chorea
 c. Pick's disease
 d. Alzheimer's disease.
8. Vasodegenerative conditions and circulatory disorders.
 a. Arteriosclerotic psychoses
 b. Cardiac decompensation
9. Hematogenic disorders
 a. Pernicious anemia
10. Dysplasias.
11. Neoplasms.
12. Craniocerebral injuries (Posttraumatic delirium).

Group III

Periodic Idiopathic Psychoses

Subgroup D' is a phasically modified form of A'; subgroup E' of B'; and subgroup F' of C'. Oligophrenic, catatonic and amnestic features are more common than in the remaining groups

Subgroup D': Periodic, chiefly dysphrenic psychoses
Pathogenetic background: Periodic propensity to develop endogenous dysphrenia
Symptoms: periodically occurring dysphrenic reactions
Clinical varieties:
 a. *Periodic form of incoherent schizophrenia (722)*
 b. *Periodic paranoid schizophrenia (722).*

Subgroup E': Periodic, chiefly parathymic psychoses
Pathogenetic background: Periodic propensity to develop endogenous dysphoria or euphoria
Symptoms: periodically occurring depressive, manic or cyclothymic reactions
Clinical varieties:
 a. *Periodic endogenous depression*
 b. *Periodic endogenous mania*
 c. *Periodic endogenous mania-depression*

Subgroup F': Periodic dysphrenic parathymic psychoses
  Pathogenetic background: Etiology periodi-
    cally occurring propensity to develop
    dsyphrenic-parathymic reactions
  Clinical varieties:
  a. *Periodic catatonia*
  b. *Epileptic psychoses*

The following is a fairly representative selection of *atypical psychopathological syndromes*
which illustrates the advantage of a pluridimen-
sional classification of mental illness. *Periodic
clouded* states which combine certain features of
catatonic and epileptic psychoses were described
by Kleist (*491*), Ewald (*218*) and other authors.
In Kleist's series of 18 patients, clouding of consciousness developed as a rule without any external precipitant and, recurring many times, lasted
on the average over a period of five days. Mental
clouding, initiated by fatigue and increased irritability, was complicated by assaultiveness, ecsta-
tic affects, hallucinations, delirium, hyperkinesia
and hypokinesia, insomnia and attacks of severe
headaches. In some of the cases the psychopathological syndrome was combined with fugue states
and, in each instance, terminated by prolonged
sleep. Three consanguineous members of the
family were epileptics. Ewald emphasizes the
rapid onset of the psychoses, the similarity of the
attacks in one and the same patient, and he confirms the presence of the terminal hypersomnia.
Monroe (*659a*), in a recent study on episodic behavioural disorders, makes reference to a "diagnostic category intermediate between epilepsy
and schizophrenia" and he "assumes a clinical
continuum which is a reflection of a similar
physiological one." Other transitional forms of
psychosis, which combine features of subgroup F'
and E', are the *unsystematized schizophrenias*
described by Leonhard (*560*). They are, over a
period of many years, associated with manic
features which in turn are superseded by an
equally prolonged psychopathological syndrome
associated with depression. The heredo-constitutional character of these atypical psychoses which,
according to Leonhard, may be a manifestation
of somatogenic, phasically operative noxae, is
more prominent than that of the non-periodic
forms of schizophrenic illness. Other transitional
forms, which combine symptoms of subgroups E'
and F', are the *periodic hypersomnias* reported by
Grosch (*319, 320*). As a rule, the patients are tall
young males with signs of hypogenitalism in
which attacks of encephalitic-like hypersomnia
associated with increased thirst, nycturia and
dysphoria occured at intervals of four weeks duration. Among some of the consanguineous members
of the family, epilepsy, hypomania and mania depression were noted. Grosch believes that cyclothymic disorders may occur in the guise of
periodic insomnia. Habel (*334*) reported the case
of patient with true infantile dwarfism in whom
hysterical and anxiety states alternated with various viscereo-autonomic syndromes. Nonnenbruch
and Feuchtinger (*690*), who studied patients in
whom euphoria was associated with loss of weight
and depression with adiposity, consider the clinical syndrome as a borderline condition of the
classic cyclothymias. The case of a manic-depressive psychosis reported by Klein (*488*) was already mentioned under the heading "Comparative pathophysiology of homeostatic functions."
Lastly, reference may be made to the *motility psychoses* (*490*), some of which, the *recurrent hyperkinetic motility psychoses*, may be associated with
the menstruel cycle while the *cyclic motility psychoses* exhibit alternating hyperkinetic and hypokinetic phases. Non-periodic motility psychoses
are the *protracted motor excitements* and the *akinetic motility psychoses*. The former are characterized by parakinesias, which should not be confused with the iterative and stereotyped
movements of catatonics.

The so-called "generalized form of schizophrenic illness", tentatively assumed to be a
reality, can now be broken down in various ways
depending on whether one wishes to emphasize
the dichotomy between the

  (a) *neurotiform* and *idiopathic* variety,
  (b) the *pure* (dysphrenic) and the *mixed*, (dys-
      phrenic-parathymic) variety, or, lastly,
  (c) the *non-periodic* and the *periodic* variety.

Combining points (b) and (c), one would thus
recognize the following categories of idiopathic
schizophrenia:

  Non-periodic idiopathic schizophrenia (dys-
      phrenic subgroup A'-i), including
  a. *Incoherent schizophrenia and*
  b. *Paranoid schizophrenia.*
  Periodic idiopathic schizophrenia (dysphrenic
      subgroup D'), including
  a. *Periodic incoherent schizophrenia and*
  b. *Periodic paranoid schizophrenia.*
  Non-periodic dysphrenic-parathymic psychoses
      (subgroup C'-i), including
  a. *Hebephrenia*

0

b. *Schizophrenia simplex and*
c. *Undifferentiated schizophrenia.*
Periodic, dysphrenic-parathmic psychoses (subgroup F'), including
a. *Periodic catatonias*
b. *Periodic clouded states and allied conditions.*

Lastly, a glance at fig. 13 shows that a classification of the *parathymic psychoses* (or, if you wish, a "generalized form of manic-depressive disease") including the transitional forms C, F' and C', would likewise include the mixed, dysphrenic-parathymic psychoses. They may thereby be grouped (as *combined* or *transitional forms* of *endogenous psychoses*) with either main group of endogenous psychosis, that is, either with the *dysphrenic* group, or, alternately, the *parathymic* group.

Concluding Remarks

In the foregoing pages, the division of schizophrenic illness into a neurotiform and an idiopathic variety was extended, that is, applied to the parathymic psychoses. We thus established two main groups of disorders (Group I and Group II, fig. 12, 13) each of which consists of two relatively pure subgroups and one mixed subgroup. The fact that each form of idiopathic psychosis may be either periodic or non-periodic, adds another main Group (Group III) and raises, to nine, the number of subgroups, that is, three varieties of neurotiform psychosis and six varieties of idiopathic psychosis. Furthermore, there exist transitions between the neurotiform psychoses and the neuroses, between the latter and the psychopathic personality and between the idiopathic and the symptomatic psychoses. The inclusion of the latter into the scheme here proposed brings to twelve the total number of subgroups of psychotic illness. The general *psychopathological structure* of psychoses (as opposed to its "clinical entities") may be expressed in terms of three main deviation patterns concerning respectively, (a) the affective component of intellective stimuli (b) the cognitive component of intellective stimuli and (c) natural fluctuations in the responsiveness in various spheres of organization, including the intellective level. In a certain sense, *parathymia* is a carricature of normal *conation*, dysphrenia of normal *cognition*, and *periodicity* of disease a distorted pattern of normal life cycles. We remind ourselves that the three terms are merely names applied to certain

categories of integrative acts mediated, respectively, by the posterior cortex and the diencephalo-frontal system. As a corollary, schizophrenia should be a disease process involving more or less the entire brain, which will be discussed on the following pages.

Physical and laboratory findings in schizophrenic illness

At this point we propose to review the diverse non-psychic abnormalities that may accompany the psychopathological core of the "generalized form" of schizophrenia, that is to say, the dysphrenic disorganization of thinking and the related affective disorders. Thus far, we considered most of the concomitant symptoms as heredoconstitutional abnormalities largely on the ground that they were not consistently present, and that it would be difficult to interpret them as either the cause or the effect of the disease. It would appear that the abnormalities in question occur more frequently in some forms of the illness, less frequently in others, and that this diversity may be etiologically significant.

Inaugural Manifestations

According to Ewald (*217*), Bleuler, Staehelin (*861*) a.o. the onset of the mental symptoms may be preceded by general vegetative symptoms, including headaches, disturbances of sleep, vasomotor disturbances, attacks of syncope, undue fatiguability, gain or loss of weight, elevated temperature and slight, unspecific cerebrospinal fluid changes.

Somatic Abnormalities

(See also "Organ-neurotic, viscero-autonomic a. metabolic symptoms", where the abnormalities in question were discussed chiefly from the point of view of dys-homeostatis.) Muehlig (*667*) found neurological symptoms in 65 out of 500 cases. They included irregular pupils in 16 cases, sluggish pupils in 12 cases, unequal pupils in seven cases and dermographism in 22 cases. He concluded that the type of sign found are for the most part non-specific and often seen in apparently normal individuals, and that some of the isolated signs reported are likely due to coincidental disease or secondary complications. Runeberg (781) found pyramidal tract signs in two out of 400 cases. Bumcke (131) described a diminution of the psychoreflexes of the pupils. Westphal (895) observed, chiefly in catatonics, unilateral or bilateral mydriasis or miosis which may or may not be associated with a distortion of the pupils. Levine and Schilder (533) attributed the pupillary abnormalities to sympathetic-parasympathetic imbalance. According to Loewenstein and Westphal (951) the pupillary abnormalities in schizophrenia resemble those encountered in postencephalitics but are due to constitutional weakness rather than structural changes of the reflex mechanism concerned. Angyal and Sherman (21) found differences between vestibular postural reactions as compared to normal controls which, they believe, reflect either the depressed activity of the underlying nervous mechanism or a diminished muscular tone of the schizophrenic patient. Furthermore, they found the nystagmic response to caloric stimulation and to rotational stimuli to be markedly less in schizophrenics than in the group of non-schizophrenic patients. Surprisingly, they attribute the abnormalities described to "withdrawal" (20) on the part of the patients and suggest that the meaning of the term be extended to include a diminished range of reflex activity including vestibulo-ocular and related reflex functions.

METABOLIC FUNCTION TESTS

According to Wilder (959) a certain blood cholesterol curve is found in normals. It consists in a rise between morning and noon and a drop later in the day. This curve is reversed in melancholic depression as well as in depressive states in the course of schizophrenic and other psychoses, but normal in reactive depression. The pathological reaction precedes the clinical symptoms by almost two weeks. Pincus and Hoagland (729) described a failure of normal adrenal stress responses in the schizophrenic individuals as compared to the normal population. The failure occurs principally at the level of the ability of the adrenal cortex to respond to adrenocorticotrophine. Psychoneurotic patients respond to the injected substance in a normal fashion.

ELECTROENCEPHALOGRAPHIC ABNORMALITIES (383)

In a series of cases studied by Kennard and Levy (482) abnormal EEG records were quite definitely more frequent in the group of cases in which the psychopathic process was most severe as indicated by early onset, long duration, and a positive family history of psychological disorders. "These are the findings which may be expected if the schizophrenic process is thought of as progressive disorder which, ultimately, profoundly affects performances of all organic systems including that of the cerebral cortex." Chamberlain's and Russel's (156) findings appear to indicate that there is an incidence of EEG abnormalities in the total group of near relatives of schizophrenic patients which is somewhat in excess of the expected rate of the general population. "The incidence of the abnormalities among the siblings was significantly greater than that of the control group. The overall incidence of abnormal records among the siblings was not markedly different from that of the patients though, in general, the severity of the abnormalities was much less. The siblings of patients with abnormal records show a much higher incidence of abnormalities than was the case with siblings of the patients whose records were normal. The results generally may be said to indicate that the pattern of EEG abnormalities is to some extent determined by hereditary factors." According to Finley and Campbell (236) a significantly greater percentage of borderline and abnormal records was found in the schizophrenic group of 500 patients as compared to 215 normals. Blum (94) believes that schizophrenia involves actual changes in brain function which closely resemble the states produced by demonstrable pathology in organic patients. The changes in schizophrenics appear to consist in reduction of cortical responsiveness to external stimulation. F. A. Gibbs (304) on the other hand, categorically denies the existence of EEG abnormalities in schizophrenic patients. Indeed, he holds that they may be, if anything, "more normal" than in a group of comparable, non-schizophrenic probands.

CEREBROSPINAL FLUID AND PNEUMOENCEPHALOGRAPHIC ABNORMALITIES

Moore and his associates (660) found the cerebrospinal fluid pressure to be top normal or higher in the majority of cases and the ventricular system and cisterns to be enlarged to a varying degree. The tendency to selective atrophy involved the parietal lobes and the Island of Reil. To some extent, the atrophy paralleled the mental deterioration. The ventricles were enlarged in 25 out of 60 patients studied. No forms showed a normal pattern. Jacobi and Winkler (*425*) differentiate between two groups of schizophrenic patients, namely, those who on pneumoencephalography show signs of brain atrophy in the temporal and temporo-parietal lobes even after an illness of only a few months duration and those who show no abnormalities whatsoever even after an illness of many years duration. In Huber's (*408*) series of 63 cases, the third ventricle was enlarged in 80% of the cases. The enlargement was slight in 15 cases, moderate to marked in 36 cases. Of ten cases in which there was no enlargement of the third ventricle nine showed practically complete remissions. In the 36 cases with moderate or marked enlargement on the other hand, 26 patients showed marked schizophrenic defects. Borenstein a. ass. (*99*) found cortical atrophy and some degree of ventricular changes in 88% of their cases; 26 showed marked schizophrenic defects. In a subsequent study devoted to both schizophrenic and parathymic psychoses, Huber (*409*) called attention to the following points. In purely cyclothymic depression with complete remission, the PEG was found to be completely normal while chronic cases with personality changes showed as a rule abnormalities of the third ventricle and the lateral ventricles. Ordinarily, the relationship between the degree of remission and the PEG findings was identical with respect to atypical endogenous psychoses and the schizophrenias. Endogenous psychoses with complete remissions failed to show abnormalities in the roentgenograms regardless whether they belonged to the schizophrenic or the cyclothymic group of psychoses in that the findings were normal in 84% of the case. In sharp contrast, 84% of all "defect-schizophrenias" and 100% of all periodic atypical "defect-psychoses" showed pathological degrees of brain atrophy. Of the low grade "defect-schizophrenias", 74% showed brain atrophy on pneumoencephalographic examination; of the high grade forms, 95% − 100%. In 18 cases in which there developed mental defects, repeat pneumoencephalograms disclosed an intensification of the atrophic process. As regards the suggested etiological classification of the psychoses it appears to be of particular significance that brain atrophy developed not only in the deteriorating schizophrenias but also their counterpart, the parathymic psychoses.

Biopsies and postmortem findings

According to Pool (*734*) and Rinkel a. ass. (*762*) the inspection of the brain prior to frontal lobotomies and topectomies carried out for schizophrenia reveals in a significant number of cases gross abnormalities including atrophy of the cortex, excessive subarachnoid fluid and gray milky appearance of the meninges. However, David (*181*) claims that the microscopic examination of biopsy specimens yields no conclusive results. The problem of brain changes in idiopathic schizophrenia was discussed in some 600 articles the most important of which were reviewed by Wolf and Cowen (*469*). The reviewers arrived at the conclusion that "the changes found in the brain of the patients having died from idiopathic schizophrenia are neither obvious nor equivocal, that the reported microscopic abnormalities have been challenged as non-specific by a group of competent histologists and attributed to misjudgements of the limits of normal variations, misinterpretations and artifacts, or the uncritical attribution of special significance to casual, incidental findings." (See also Braitenberg *101*.) In sharp contrast, Winkelman (*911*), who stressed the frequent occurrence in the brain of schizophrenics of cortical atrophy associated with a hypoplastic cerebrovascular system, contended that "the organic nature of the disease cannot be disproven by the observation that the schizophrenic process can be restored to normal for hours since the patient suffering from myasthenia gravis, the organic nature of which is established beyond doubt, can also be restored to normal at least by the injection of appropriate amounts of neostygmin." Most authorities agree with Spielmeyer (*859*) and Scholz (*814*) that a pathological anatomy of schizophrenia is non-existent. (Cf., in addition to Wolf and Cowan, Peters (*724*) and Weinstein (*339*.) Heyck (*382*), who studied the anterior and mediodorsal nucleus of the thalamus by the Nissl method failed to confirm the findings of C. and O. Vogt. As is well known, the Vogts found Schwundzellen (dwarf cells) in the above mentioned parts of the brain and in other localities. They do not claim that the abnormal cells are specific for schizophrenic processes but are convinced that the pathological diagnosis of schizophrenia can be made if a large number of ganglinonic cells, chiefly in the thalamus, the cingulate gyrus and the basofrontal cortex are implicated. Hopf (*403*), who examined the striopallidum of ten catatonic schizophrenics and of several controls, encountered histopathological (chiefly symmetrical) changes in the globus pallidus in each case of catatonia. He agrees with the Vogts who hold that the cells in question are particularly characteristic. Interestingly enough, he observed that, in four of the cases of catatonia, the ganglionic cells of the globus pallidus were quite small without being degenerated. Rather, he thought they might have failed to mature fully. (At this point the question arises whether the cells under study belong to the group of somatic heredo-constitutional abnormalities.) On the other hand, according to David (*181*), the Vogts do not identify the dwarf cells with the concept of a cerebral lesion. They regard them as reversible alterations which, in case of spontaneous recovery, may revert to more or less functionally intact cells. Dwarfcells were also seen in the thalamus of young catatonics who died within three weeks after their first admission to the hospital. According to David's account, the Vogts infer that this is a congenital metabolic dysfunction of the nerve cells rather than a concomitant abnormality or, perhaps, the result of prolonged psychotic behaviour. Presumably, the cell changes in question are, according to David, the expression of a metabolic derangement which leads to the catatonic syndrome or, alternately, psychotic behaviour may produce the variable, non-specific, lesions which are often seen in diverse parts of the brain in schizophrenic patients. Fuenfgeld (*279*) studied the anterior nucleus of the thalamus, Baeumer (*36*) the medial nucleus and Buttlar-Brentano (*135*) the innominate substance. Although the members of the Vogt team of investigators encountered diverse intravitam changes and dwarfism of ganglionic cells in what they believe to be a statistically significant number of cases, they are well aware of the fact that the results of their studies have thus far been modest in scope and in need of confirmation. They are likewise conscious of the general methodological difficulties, discussed in considerable detail by the Vogts themselves, and the many pitfalls involved in the search for a histopathological substrate of the disease, one of which is the lack of familiarity with the normal characteristics of the ganglionic cells in the various regions under study (*921*).

The above data illustrate the variety of conflicting opinions expressed in the literature. On the other hand, certain changes, e.g., certain encephalographic and pneumoencephalographic abnormalities would seem to be mutually corroborative. Obviously, it would take years of concentrated effort on the part of many teams of workers to prove or disprove the validity of the pathological, clinical and laboratory data and to evaluate their significance. In the absence of this information, one may use a shortcut as it were and suggest that the following statements are more likely incorrect than their opposites: (a) All cases which form the basis of the above reported data belong to the group of symptomatic schizophrenia. (b) All reported abnormalities are observational errors. (c) Although not necessarily observational errors, the data in question are etiologically insignificant.

It is more likely that only some of the cases belong to the group of symptomatic schizophrenia, that not all reported abnormalities are observational errors and that at least some of them bear significant relationships to etiological factors. To put it in another way: the viewpoint here taken is that, more likely than not, *at least some of the reported abnormalities are genuine although not necessarily specific or, for that matter, pathognomonic.* Spielmeyer (*859*) pointed out that the possibility on the part of the nerve cells to respond to noxious agents is limited and that, as far as can be ascertained with purely histological methods, neurons react to a variety of abnormal stimuli in an identical fashion. If this concept is sound, some schizophrenic and non-schizophrenic noxae would probably cause similar abnormalities while other schizophrenic noxae would not necessarily cause histological changes.

Etiological considerations

In one of the preceding sections of the current chapter, we suggested a classification of the psychoses into a *neurotiform*, an *idiopathic* and a *symptomatic* variety any of which, depending on the predominant involvement of the cognitive or the affective parameter of intellective stimuli, may have either a dysphrenic or a parathymic orientation. In the mixed, dysphrenic-parathymic form on the other hand, the two basic dysfunctions are more or less evenly balanced. Further considerations based on the above survey of abnormal clinical and laboratory data suggest that, apart from symptomatic schizophrenia, the idiopathic and neurotiform types have a different etiological background. In fact, we have already attempted to answer the question as to the different etiology of the psychoses in a rather general way; we surmised that the crucial factor operating in the neurotiform psychoses is an exogenous precipitant, by which we mean a crucial level of frustration, whereas, in the idiopathic psychoses, the etiological factor is a metabolic error of some kind. The presumed differences between the two forms of genuine schizophrenias and the symptomatic form may now more accurately be formulated as follows.

(a) The etiological background* of *neurotiform schizophrenia* is a deficit of an ultra-microscopic (biochemical) nature which, in turn, causes synaptic imbalance; and the symptoms of neurotiform schizophrenia are the expression of malfunction at the synaptic level. (See below.)

(b) The etiological background of *idiopathic schizophrenia* is a *metabolic error*, which may or may not cause visible structural alterations and, at the same time, the above mentioned laboratory, clinical, biopsy and postmortem findings. These changes however are not necessarily specific or, for that matter, pathognomonic. If present, they exist in addition to the stipulated, ultramicroscopic changes which, in turn, are the crucial etiologic factor in neurotiform schizophrenia. In other words, idiopathic schizophrenia would be a more severe form of the neurotiform variety.

(c) In *symptomatic schizophrenia*, the schizophrenogenic noxae cause changes ranging from "zero" to gross, naked eye tissue alterations.

Additional data pertaining to the three forms of schizophrenic illness are assembled in table 4.

The above drawn distinction between the three groups of schizophrenic illness is hypothetical but would not have been suggested unless it arranged,

* Thus, the term *pathogenetic background*, as here employed (see above, under "Subgroups"), refers to clinical abnormalities; the term *etiological background*, to structural, including ultramicroscopic changes, without which the clinical abnormalities would not occur.

as we believe it does, a host of otherwise unconnected data into a tolerably consistent scheme. Whether or not the synaptic lability (or "integrational organicity") assumed to be present in neurotiform schizophrenia is, ultimately, the expression of some sort of metabolic error rather than a factor in its own right (which, thus, to a degree might obliterate the differences between the former and the idiopathic variety) is a moot question at present. Be this as it may, there are good grounds to upheld the above distinction. In neurotiform schizophrenia, the biochemical processes at the synapse are, under standard conditions of stimulation at least, adequate. In idiopathic schizophrenia on the other hand, decompensation occurs of necessity, as a direct result of the metabolic disorder just as, in certain types of symptomatic schizophrenia, the derangement of synaptic function occurs as a consequence of an exogenous intoxication. The crucial differences between the three forms may be illustrated by the following analogy. *Neurotiform schizophrenia* is comparable to congenital halisteresis, that is, low calcium content of a bone which, however, will not break unless subjected to a degree of stress that will not damage a normal bone under similar circumstances. *Idiopathic schizophrenia* may be compared to the abnormal calcium metabolism of a bone, more accurately, a congenital metabolic error that exists in addition to the already present increased fragility in which case even ordinary or subliminal strain will produce a fracture; in other words, the fracture occurs for all practical purposes of necessity. Thus, the difference between neurotiform schizophrenia and idiopathic schizophrenia would be one of degree. Lastly, *symptomatic schizophrenia* is comparable to a fracture occurring as the result of, say, an invasive tumor that attacks normal bone (primary symptomatic schizophrenia) or an already diseased bone (secondary symptomatic schizophrenia.)

What particular observation suggests that neurotiform schizophrenia is conditioned by synaptic lability, and that idiopathic schizophrenia is probably an intensified form of the neurotiform variety? In a certain sense, the relationship between the neurotiform and the idiopathic type resembles that between *catatonia* and certain *postencephalitic syndromes*. In spite of many criteria that facilitate the differential diagnosis between catatonia and postencephalitic parkinsonism, certain basic similarities make difficult the differentiation of

TABLE 4

NEUROTIFORM SCHIZOPHRENIA, PRIMARY AND SECONDARY IDIOPATHIC SCHIZOPHRENIA AND SYMPTOMATIC SCHIZOPHRENIA

	Organic background	Precipitant	Microscopic and macroscopic changes	Premonitory signs and preexisting conditions	Neurologic signs	Stigmata	EEG and PEG abnormalities	Hereditary background
Neurotiform Schizophrenia	Synaptic malfunction	Substandard frustration-gratification ratio	If present, unrelated to organic background	Schizoid personality. Somatic heredo-constitutional abnormalities present or absent	None or unrelated	More frequent than in general population	None or if present probably unrelated	Present, depending on degree of consanguinity
Idiopathic Schizophrenia (primary)	Synaptic malfunction Metabolic error	Spontaneous modification of metabolic error, periodic or non-periodic	If present potentially related	Schizoid personality. Inaugural somatic states present in some instances	Present (potentially related) or absent	,,	Probably related if present	,,
Idiopathic Schizophrenia (secondary)	,, (subliminal) intensified by intercurrent disease	Intercurrent disease	Depending on nature of brain damage	Schizoid personality?	Caused by noxious agent or brain disease	Not necessarily more frequent than in general population.	Related to intercurrent disease	Probably present
Symptomatic Schizophrenia		Primary (neurogenic) or secondary (somatogenic) brain damage	,,		,,		Related to brain damage	?

the two forms in the individual case. Gerstmann (*299*) and Gerstmann and Schilder (*301*) made a comparative analysis of catatonics and postencephalitics which exhibited motor disorders suggestive of an involvement of the extrapyramidal system. They admit that it is impossible to be certain about the organic or the psychic character of catatonia, and they express the belief that the picture of catatonia may be produced either by organic or by psychic factors.

Now, the similarity between catatonia and the psychomotor syndrome of postencephalitis is too obvious to be coincidental. On the other hand, the examination of the brains of catatonics failed to show any changes which would indicate the presence of lesions comparable to those responsible for postencephalitic phenomena; in fact, they may not show any changes at all. How can we reconcile the conflicting views on the nature of catatonia which, some observers believe, is a "functional" disorder while others stipulate an organic background?

Appropriately located lesions in the upper brainstem disorganize local neurodynamic processes which, under normal conditions, are integrated with fronto-cortical synergies to more adaptive movements. In other words, abnormal motor phenomena caused by anatomically verified lesions are, as experiences with postencephalitic parkinsonism demonstrate, caused by structural deficit. (We do not agree with Leupp's (*563*) recent statement that the movements of the catatonic are preformed synergies; they are, like the abnormal phenomena in postencephalitic parkinsonism, effects of disintegration of function.) Now, motor symptoms undistinguishable from those caused by organic lesions may occur in the absence of demonstrable histological changes and, since the similarity between the motor symptoms in catatonia and postencephalitic dyskinesias may be virtually complete, it is natural to assume that *the location of the pathogenic factor is for all practical purposes identical*. In the present context, the histopathology of postencephalitis is of no particular interest except for the fact that, in spite of the permanency of the lesions, some of the corresponding symptoms may fluctuate in response to psychic stimuli. On the other hand, they never disappear completely. In sharp contrast, catatonic symptoms may disappear from one moment to the next either in response to psychic stimuli or without apparent cause.

Combining two propositions, namely, (a) the interpretation of *organ-neurotic symptoms* as expressions of heredo-constitutionally determined ultra-microscopic changes which depress the confidence coefficient of integration and (b) the fluctuating character of the *motor symptoms of catatonia*, one realizes that both may be interpretable in terms of "integrational deficit" which, in the first eventuality, causes dysautonomias of inner organs, in the second eventuality, disorganizes the channeling of psychomotor impulses. It is well known that the impulses in question may be mischanneled even under physiological conditions, e.g., under conditions of fatigue or distraction of attention, in the absence of an organic lesion that is, and that the pattern of volitional movements is apt to change. Although fatigue may be caused by toxic metabolites, its effects, in the early stages at least, can be overcome by psychic factors suggesting a psychic origin of motor and other signs of fatigue. Distraction of attention creates an unfavourable psychological setting, rather as the position in which the Romberg test is performed makes difficult the maintenance of the equilibrium of the body. In either instance, functional abnormalities are apt to occur in the absence of any structural alterations. The "abnormal channeling theory" is consistent with the general neurophysiological principle that, within the natural limits of organization, even normal functions are mediated by a preferential, modifiable, rather than a fixated association of neurons, and that the normal pattern of innervation shades off from the state of near perfection to less and less perfect conditions. For example, a person's handwriting may be more or less legible at different times—indeed it may look bizarre on occasion—and the same applies, although not to the same degree, to other performances including distinction of articulation, quality of intonation, artistic performance and also semi-volitional acts including emotional expression whose "adequacy" may fluctuate rather widely without apparent cause. Frankly *abnormal channeling of impulses* would seem to occur whenever the normal leeway of response is being exceeded, and the fluidity of association of impulse conducting elements trespasses the functionally tolerable range of precision that underlies integrative action. The same holds true for the manipulation of concepts which, like other nervous system functions, are, from a neuropsychological viewpoint, integrative processes. At this point, it is apparent that a link exists not only between schizophrenic and hysterical mechanisms but also between schizophrenic behaviour and normal behaviour.

Briefly summarized, we have encountered the following varieties of defective integration, namely, those responsible for

(a) organ-neurotic symptoms, or *dysauto-nomias* of inner organs (including the cardio-vascular system) in the sphere of peripheral visceral innervation,

(b) the inter-level symptoms (including the conversion reactions) of hysterical illness, or *dys-somatization phenomena*,

(c) the *motor symptoms* of catatonia, and

(d) the *faulty formation of percepts, configurations and concepts*, including those occurring under experimentally controlled, i.e., toxic conditions.

It may be readily seen that the disintegrative processes referred to form a more or less continuous scale and that, in each eventuality, in the presence of abnormal biochemical conditions anywhere in the nervous system, the likelihood of faulty integration that exists even under normal circumstances will be enhanced.

Now, if standard response patterns or synergies of any complexity, including those mediated by the highest, intellectual level, fail to gratify the instinctive demands in response to which they are actuated, that is to say, fail to maintain or produce biological equilibrium, the organism "abandons" as it were acquired synergies in favour of performance patterns which fall outside the normal leeway of organization. The experimental evidence in support of this contention has already brought forward in the section dealing with the frustration theory of neurosis. In other instances, we submit, deviant channeling of impulses occurs even in the absence of stress; the mere use of the response mediating mechanisms, presumably because of their heredo-metabolic weakness, causes their deterioration. In neurotiform schizophrenia with catatonic features, deviant channeling of impulses comes to the fore in the bizarre abnormalities of volitional movements, and also in expressive including articulatory movements. At the same time, the pathological process manifests itself in the sensory sphere. It involves not only the most complex use patterns (the very formation of concepts reflects the appropriate synergic grouping of their components into core and fringe elements) but also configurational and perceptual elements. Disorders of abstraction and concept formation may be interpreted as dyssynergies involving the realm of stimuli generated at the highest level of cerebral function—the over all pattern of misuse and disorganization is identical throughout. It is apparent not only in the process of dys-somatization but also of dys-mentalization, the abnormal structuring and use of conceptual, configurational and even perceptual data.

It is tempting to apply these ideas not only to the psychic heredo-constitutional abnormalities but also the *somatic heredo-constitutional* defects exhibited by many schizophrenics. Not only the various functions of the organism are integrative acts but, in a certain sense, also the morphogenetic processes underlying its formation in space and time. It is this very *disorganization* and *mischanneling of integrative acts* which renders the schizophrenic a deviant in a "functional" and also in a morphological sense. However, like in other heredo-constitutional abnormalities, functional and morphological features may become segregated in the course of their heredo-constitutional transmission and, moreover, appear in their respective spheres in varying intensity and in different proportions.

The concept of dys-somatization is not entirely new; it is, if not expressively formulated, at least implied in the writings of Gerstmann and Schilder (*301*), Gerstmann (*298*) and, perhaps, of others. The former note that the extrapyramidal motility reacts to psychic stimuli and that inferiority of, or lesions to, the motor mechanism favours the appearance of organic symptoms which, ultimately, are precipitated by psychic factors. (In catatonia, psychic factors cause organic symptoms in the constitutionally inferior sphere of extrapyramidal functions.) Gerstmann believes that the nervous system may be damaged either by organic or psychic agents and that psychic factors may give rise either to abnormal psychic or abnormal organic phenomena. (Conversely, unquestionably organic motor symptoms as, for example, certain bizarre disorders in post-encephalitics, may resemble neurotic symptoms.) Being caused by psychic factors, functionally induced organic changes are "physiogenic neuroses" rather than organic nervous system diseases. (Inasmuch as the term "physiogenic neurosis" applied by Gerstmann to the disorders in question suggests a somatic rather than a functional origin, it is perhaps not a very happy one. The disorders are not physiogenic neuroses but psychogenic somatoses.) Organic symptoms produced by psychic factors presupposes an appropriate disposition of the symptom-producing mechanism. Most likely, he goes on to say, the vulnerability to psychic stimuli is rooted in some inferiority of the neural substrate concerned but the factors responsible for this inferiority are as yet unknown. Conceivably, they are "molecular, dynamic, chemical or nutritive" in character. The above expressed theories are supported by the observation that catatonic symptoms, including Schnauzkrampf and grimacing occur in insulin coma (85), after awakening from elektroshock (84), that is, after a temporary disturbance of the nutritional state of the tissues, that striking parkinsonian attitudes may be observed in war neuroses (472) and that, in the state of remission, somatic and psychic symptoms of schizophrenia may be produced under hypnosis (479). The application of Gerstmann's ideas to the pathophysiology of catatonic symptoms would justify their interpretation as an organic neurosis of the extrapyramidal system. Some of the bizarre features would be accounted for by the fact that the system in question is concerned not only with coordinative and motor functions but also with attitudinizing and expression. The organ-neurotic character of the disorder would be established (a) by the absence of demonstrable tissue alterations and (b) the absence of extracerebral pathology causing secondary involvement of the central nervous system. In other words, the basis of catatonic symptoms in neurotiform schizophrenia may be attributable to a "integrational deficit", or malfunction referable to increased synaptic lability.

THE ROLE OF THE SYNAPSES IN THE MISCHANNELING OF IMPULSES

One would assume that the deviant channeling of impulses is made possible by the very abundance of synaptic connections, which multiply the probability of integrational error inherent, to a degree, in any nervous system process. (In the present context, it is of interest that Young suggested two varieties of synapses, namely, those which a high probability of transmission from the pre-synaptic to the post-synaptic fibers and those with a low probability of transmission (974). Under normal conditions, mischanneling is kept within natural limits but it may be increased in fatigue, in transitional states between sleep and wakefulness, etc, all of which lower the confidence coefficient of integration. We have already made allusion to the fact that, in the vast network of neurons which mediate higher brain functions, appropriate channeling of impulses or success is merely a limiting case of the innumerable ways of potential failure. Depending on the degree of heredo-constitutional inferiority of the substrate concerned, the mis-channeling of impulses that supplants normal, synergic function, occurs either under any condition or under conditions of disruptive stimulation, that is, stimulation causing cumulative biological disequilibrium chiefly by the thwarting of instinctive seeking reactions. Organic lesions, on the other hand, produce symptoms even in the absence of a heredo-constitutional predisposition.

As we said, synaptic activity is involved in any type of nervous system function including the highest mental processes. Not only the translation of thought into action but also thinking itself is a synergic process (although no doubt one more likely to be derailed than any other physiological activity). It cannot be divorced from its material substrate; it is the functional correlate of morphological use patterns. To quote Herrick (373): "The apparatus of totalizing function evidently includes many diverse components of which one of the most obvious is the neuropil which, in primitive vertebrates pervades the entire brain so that activity in any part of it may affect the whole fabric. . . . This dispersed tissue is not homogenous and it is not equipotential. It is doubtless always active and in diverse ways and different places at different times. Such localization of function as it exhibits can best be conceived in dynamic terms, that is, in terms of what intercurrent volleys act upon it, momentarily changing places, rhythms and intensities. We are dealing here with an equilibrated dynamic system comprising many activated fields in interaction and this interplay is in patterns quite different from those of the stable locally differentiated centers and tracts. It is more labile, and the patterns of performance are not stereotyped. Nevertheless, the fields are not structurally identical, and each one has distinctive physiological properties correlated with the histological differences. . . . In higher vertebrates these local differences are accentuated; the segregation of the synthetizing apparatus is carried farther, and its tissue is locally differentiated in a radically different way from that of the analytic apparatus as best exhibited in the associational tissue of the human cerebral cortex." In a different context, Herrick (374) writes as follows: "In the human cortex, the enormous masses of unspecific tissue are everywhere abundant; it varies in structure from place to place and its function from moment to moment. *It integrates all cortical activities, synthetizes experience and provides the plasticity of the structure requisite for learning and higher mental processes in general.* (Emphasis added) ... Permeating a stable architectural fabric, there is an enormous mass of neuropil. ... *It serves the higher mental processes including the semantic and symbolic activities* (Emphasis added) ... Diversification of structure and pattern of activation is essential." In a third article, Herrick (376) makes reference to a "localization of fields within which various recurrent patterns of performance or schemata are known to be fabricated, and in which inhibition, modification or conditioning of these patterns takes place. These tissues yield dynamic schemata. The manifestations of any scheme at any particular time is always the function of a configuration of nervous elements which has localization in space. And a very similar scheme may at another time be exhibited by a different structural configuration, whose locus in space is by no means identical with the first. Our present technique is adequate to delineate the fields within which the schemata are operative but it has not as yet clarified the exact mechanism involved."

It is evident that the schemata correspond to the use patterns and, implicitly, the synergies underlying higher mental processes. However, Herrick's ideas, which have been quoted at some length, are inapplicable to the present problem in that "inhibition, modification, conditioning, intercurrent volleys etc." are of themselves powerless to account for higher cerebral mechanisms. On the other hand, the anatomical data furnished by Herrick are of the utmost importance. See also Polyak (686a).

SYNAPTIC DYSFUNCTION IN SCHIZOPHRENIC ILLNESS

If it is true that, owing to the very complexity of synaptic arrangements, synaptic functions may become temporarily disorganized even under ordinary conditions of (stimulation in any case under conditions which fall into a normal range including for example, integration under conditions of fatigue) it should also be true that the probability of synaptic transmission going astray will be increased under frankly abnormal conditions, and that it will result in more widespread and intensified mischanneling of impulses. In the absence of precise knowledge what produces abnormal synaptic events (one might consider, e.g., the presence of abnormal chemical transmitter substances) it may be advisable to speak of increased synaptic vulnerability. Now since, ordinarily, activity at the synaptic level yields synergic phenomena, including those underlying higher mental function, *frustration, resulting for the most part from the inhibition of biologically significant seeking reactions or synergies,* will increase the likelihood of dys-synergic responses. At least this can be shown to occur with some regularity in experimental animals and in man under the influence of frustrating experiences. Given a certain heredo-constitutional predisposition, the experiences in question are apt to produce deviant, indeed, self-destructive patterns of behaviour and conduct which, eventually, overgrow the self-equilibrating activity of the organism. It is suggested that an essentially similar mechanism causes neurotiform schizophrenia. We reiterate that *neurotiform schizophrenia* is conditioned by two factors, namely (a) *increased synaptic lability* and (b) an *external precipitant, more especially a substandard frustration-gratification ratio and, further, that the increased vulnerability of synaptic function is heredo-constitutionally determined.* In the absence of an increased frustration-gratification ratio, increased synaptic vulnerability may be assumed to remain latent so that deviant channeling of impulses need not occur. On the other hand, in the presence of a higher degree of vulnerability at the synaptic level, in *idiopathic schizophrenia* that is, deviant channeling of impulses sooner or later occurs with necessity, as a result of the very activity of the synaptic net even under ordinary conditions of stimulation or the normal stress and strain of life. In this respect, idiopathic schizophrenia would resemble the abiotrophic processes of classic neurology. It is hardly necessary to add that, in idiopathic schizophrenia, deviant channeling of impulses is even more likely to occur under conditions of frustration just as dormant abiotrophic disease may be precipitated by physical stress. Since, presumably, the biochemical basis of idiopathic schizophrenia is a higher degree of synaptic vulnerability caused by metabolic error of some sort, the disorder may be regarded a more severe form. It follows that the distinction between the two forms (figs. 12 and 13) can be maintained only with certain qualifications.

What are the relationships between idiopathic schizophrenia and other heredo-constitutional disorders, especially phenylperuvic dementia? In the former, the central metabolic error assumed to be the biochemical core of the disease is associated with other heredo-constitutional abnormalities in the metabolic sphere. At the same time, it is the cause of the mental changes. In phenyl-peruvic dementia, too, the mental defect is the direct result of metabolic derangement. Its nature is well known while the intimate mechanism of the corresponding factor assumed to operate in idiopathic schizophrenia is as yet purely understood, indeed, in Kallmann's (465) words, "the primary physiodynamic substrate of the psychosis remains baffingly obscure." According to Alvord and Stevenson (14) the metabolic error in phenyl-peruvic dementia is contingent on the recessive inheritance of a defect in an enzyme that para-hydroxylises phenylalanine to tyrosin. The mental changes are associated with fair coloring of hair, sensitivity of the skin to light, an aboral configuration and size of the head, increased reflexes, eczema, abnormal skin pigmentation a rigid posture, increased muscle tone and hyperkinesia (291).

In *symptomatic schizophrenia*, abnormal metabolic conditions would be produced by the underlying disease process, intoxication or injury, either directly or indirectly, possibly by way of Bonhoeffer's "indirect etiologic links." In what is known as *secondary idiopathic schizophrenia* on the other hand, the metabolic error may lay dormant until activated or released by accidental factors. It is entirely consistent with the concept here proposed that the intensification of metabolic derangement may convert neurotiform schizophrenia into the idiopathic variety. Furthermore, it is intriguing to consider the possibility that (a), ultimately, the metabolic changes influence the structure of the cell so that at least some cellular changes alledged to occur are due to, although not necessarily specific for, idiopathic schizophrenia,

and (b) that the changes may be reversible in those instances in which the disease shows a fluctuating course, as is the case in periodic schizophrenia. Given a different degree of vulnerability of different types of ganglionic cells, the factor of differential vulnerability may conceivably apply to the dwarfcells described by the Vogts (920, 921), by Hopf (403) and other observers. (The existence of congenital hypoplasia of the cells in question would be an alternative explanation.)

We have already indicated that neurotiform schizophrenia is related to idiopathic schizophrenia in the same way as neurotiform (exogenous) depression and mania is related to idiopathic (endogenous) depression and idiopathic (endogenous) mania respectively. As a corollary, in different mental forms of mental illness, different synaptic fields should be involved in different proportions. In the predominantly parathymic psychoses, the synaptic nets constituting the diencephalofrontal and limbic system should be primarily involved. In the predominantly dysphrenic disorders, those constituting the posterior cortex and, in the parakinetic disorders, the extrapyramidal system. Thus, in a modified fashion at least, Kleist's (491) concept that schizophrenias are system diseases, may be accepted; indeed, it may be extended to the cyclothymic disorders.

That disorders of synaptic function are of a submicroscopic order i.e., that they occur in the biochemical range, is made likely (a) by their temporary reversibility by biochemical means, (b) their experimental induction by hallucinogens in the dysphrenic group, (c) the fact that their action can be neutralized by antagonistic chemical compounds, by (d) the experimental production of euphoria in the predominantly dysphoric psychoses, and also in the dysphrenic psychoses having a strong parathymic element.

EXPERIMENTALLY PRODUCED REVERSIBILITY OF SCHIZOPHRENIC SYMPTOMS

Loevenhard a. ass. (577) showed that inhalation of carbondioxide by mute or stuporous patients can temporarily restore them toward normal. In schizophrenics, hallucinations may disappear during inhalation of the gas. Altschule (12) changed the position of hallucinating schizophrenics by alternatingly lowering and raising the table. On increasing the cerebral blood flow, the hallucinations disappeared and the patients had full insight. When the table was raised, the hallucinations reappeared, and visual memories were activated concomitantly with the decreased blood flow. He concluded from his experiments that hallucinations are not entirely psychogenic in origin but that metabolic changes, by making one or the other area abnormally active, can be responsible for their occurrence. What may be the mechanism of "supression" of hallucinoses? It may reasonably be argued that the increased carbon-dioxide content of the blood renders ineffective a chemically active agent which produces the hallucinations or, to put it in a more general way, interferes with the complex conditions that produce them and, at the same time, engender the pictorial representation of engrams. In other words, a certain combination of factors would disorganize the function of the neural arrangements or use patterns concerned with normal concept formation and thought. Furthermore, it would produce abnormal discharges (now blocked by chemical means) as the correlate of the patient's abnormal experiences. The irritative processes might be regarded as biochemical events occuring at the synaptic level.

The action of carbondioxide is far from specific. According to Fulcher a. ass. (280) arecoline produces a lucid interval, its mode of action being that of a parasympathetic stimulation of the brain. Presumably, the authors argue, a naturally occurring anti-schizophrenic metabolite may likewise have a parasympathetic effect. At the same time, they point out that reserpine produces symptoms of parasympathetic (muscarinic) stimulation. Fabing (221) demonstrated that Frenquel, an isomer of meratran, may dramatically influence hallucinations not only in acute schizophrenia, in alcoholics, senile and arteriosclerotic individuals but also LSD-25 induced hallucinations. Similar effects were obtained by Schwartz a. ass. (773) with megaphen.

EXPERIMENTAL EVIDENCE FOR THE THEORY OF SYNAPTIC DYSFUNCTION IN SCHIZOPHRENIC ILLNESS

Marazzi (616) and Marazzi and Hart (618) demonstrated that abnormal phenomena within the purely neurophysiological range of function and, presumably, also at higher levels of the nervous system, may be caused by interference with synaptic functions. They showed that epinephrine in microgram quantity produced inhibition of synaptic transmission in the central nervous system, as does serotonin, bufotenin and, in much larger quantities, adrenochrome. (See also Hart, Langfit and Marazzi (351).) Chloropromazin is apparently able to prevent mescalin-like inhibition of synaptic transmission to a considerable degree with little depressant action of its own on the transmission process. The same applies to Frenquel which does not alter synaptic transmission. Marazzi and Hart compared the effects of adrenaline, amphetamine and mescaline (all of which may cause mental disturbances) on synaptic transmission. They claim that an empirical correlation exists between, on the one hand, the synaptic inhibition and, on the other, the disturbances of conduct observed on administration of mescaline to the unaesthetized cat (see esp. p. 365 of Marazzi and Hart's article) and the marked hallucinations induced in man. At the same time, they call attention (a) to the similarities between adrenochrome, a breakdown product of adrenaline believed by some to be involved in the production of hallucinations (b) between LSD-25 and (c) between serotonin which, according to Wooley and Shaw (971), is a central metabolite whose deficiency may be responsible for schizophrenia. Ultimately, Marazzi and Hart came to the conclusion that *certain hallucinogens produce synaptic inhibition or a generalized defect, that is, a function of variations in synaptic thresholds*, which, however, may be secondary, incident to a primary lesion of the cell bodies. Although the authors, like Evarts a. ass. (216), think in terms of partial inhibition of neuronal activity rather than a mischanneling of impulses, the two concepts are not necessarily incompatable, especially since Marazzi and Hart invoke, as a result of synaptic inhibition, a "pattern of over all activity which would be a function of the variations of synaptic thresholds," and maintain that "derangements owing to partial inhibition could readily result in release from restraining influences with consequent stimulation." Brodie a. ass. (123) consider the possibility that "disequilibrium could result from a chemical imbalance at synapses in one or more functional units of the brain, with the process perhaps spreading over a considerable number of interlocking neurons of the central nervous system.

The synaptic disturbance could result from an over/or underproduction of a particular neurohormone, its impaired storage, its impaired release or from too slow an inactivation after its release.... One or more neurohormones may be involved."

Significantly, different points of departure, i.e., clinical considerations centering around the similarities between postencephalitic and catatonic phenomena on the one hand and biochemical studies on the other lead to the conclusion that the clinical manifestations of schizophrenic illness are referable to ill-balanced and precarious synaptic mechanisms. This is perhaps only to be expected; the nervous system is compounded of energy generating units, the ganglionic cells, and line connections, their processes, which, articulating by means of literally billions of contacts, enhance the possibility of error by their sheer number. Yet even if future research should fail to confirm, in every detail, the results of the above quoted investigations, the concept of deviant channeling could still be upheld on clinical as well as general biological grounds, that is, based on the probabilistic approach to the concatenation of events which constitute the organism. (See Chap. I.)

Schizophrenia is not the only central nervous system disease in which synaptic dysfunction is believed to be an etiological factor. We have already mentioned that Gastaut (290) attributed the spread of epileptic seizures to an abnormal permeability of the synapses. Moniz developed the somewhat crude concept that abnormal synaptic adhesions to the body of the ganglionic cells cause the abnormal fixation of ideas which can be eliminated by frontal lobotomy. On the other hand, the following passages quoted from one of Moniz' (628) relatively recent article, are significant. "The impulses pass through the neurons via the fibrils and in the synapses alterations are produced which, in turn, are projected into many other cells.... On the basis of this anatomical concept, which we owe to Ramon y Cajal, I arrived at the conclusion that the *synapses, repeated in countless cells, constitute the organic basis of thought.... Normal psychic activity depends on proper synaptic function, while mental disturbances derive from derangement of the synapse.... Mental activity is interconnected in direct ratio to the functioning and interplay of these fibrillary activities.* (Emphasis added) ... Held's bundles, at their point of contact, rest upon an intercalary separat-

ing substance, a membrane or, more probably, a colloid substance, in which chemical and electric phenomena take place and possibly other phenomena of unknown nature. These factors give the impulse current new qualities, or they contribute to the modifications within the cell body. In this manner, the impulse passes on to other cells, where again new alterations occur.... The terminal points at the level of the synapse do not function at the same time. We are still unable to prove this and even less able to explain the intimate mechanism which conditions them.... Both exogenous and endogenous intoxications and also alterations in the products of the internal glands ... exert an ultimate effect on the synapses.... *The activity of the zones which are especially associated with psychic phenomena depends on the increased quantity of synapses of highly varied neurones which play a part in the production of psychic phenomena* (Emphasis added. Cf. Herrick's neuropil or synaptic fields.)

Correlation of psychopathological and pathophysiological data

It is a truism that the most complex integrative acts are the most vulnerable just as, in the course of ontogenesis, malformations are most likely to occur in localities where the most involved developmental processes take place. Translated into terms of synaptic transmission, one would assume that certain specialized performances require a high degree of functional differentiation on the part of the elements by which they are mediated. Further, that the corresponding dysfunctions can be traced to normal performances in somewhat the same way as malformations to the structure of a matrix that has developed in an abnormal direction, or a primordium having been arrested in its development. Briefly stated, we assume that patterns of disorganization reflect, in a certain sense, patterns of organization, and that the former are apt to develop at critical points, or critical phases, of specialization of nervous system function.

In the following paragraphs, an attempt will be made to show that symptoms occurring in psychiatric illness with some regularity reflect the inability on the part of the nervous system to perform basic neurophysiological functions at higher levels of integrational complexity.

DYSPHRENIA AS DERANGEMENT OF OBJECTIVE
CORRESPONDANCE RELATIONS

Under ideal conditions, perceptual, configurational and conceptual stimuli are analogs (equivalents) of events whose biological significance is evaluated by the highest relation generating level of the nervous system. Certain relationships are represented by data of a conceptual order. The formation of concepts (intrinsically generated categorizing stimuli) in turn is dependent on the grouping activity of the highest sensory level which organizes low order intellective stimuli into the core and the fringe of concepts. Thus, dysphrenic disorders involve not only the manipulation of concepts in the course of determination or "computation" of response but the very formation of concepts including the flexible arrangement of their elements into core and fringe (or center and periphery) of the over all framework of the concept. In other words, they comprise (1) the segregation of concept forming elements including, in response to the demands of the moment, their adaptive shifting from the periphery to the center and vice versa and (2) the utilization of concepts in the course of actual thought processes. As will be explained in the following chapter, the utilization of concepts is facilitated by the formation of *procedural schemes*, i.e., learning sets and thinking sets. Moreover, the formation of concepts or the grouping of sensory data to units of a higher order involves the replacement of palpable (concrete, perceptual and configurational) elements into impalpable (abstract, conceptual) data of awareness. In oneroid or dysphrenic thought, the derangement of concept formation and related functions manifests itself in the following fashion. (1) As can be shown for both spontaneous and drug-induced psychoses, the correspondance function of the highest sensory level breaks down in that perceptions, configurations and concepts loose their character as analogs. (2) Concepts are crowded out by more or less vitiated data of a lower, perceptual and configurational order. (3) Since symbols used in the process of thinking and expression have configurational properties associated with conventionalized meanings, and certain configurational stimuli acquire symbol character, the thinking of the schizophrenic is to a large extent carried by highly individualistic symbols, i.e., contaminated by hypersymbolism and parasymbolism. (4) Active response determination or goal directed thinking is replaced or at least hampered by the autonomous (uncontrolled) activity of sensory elements, i.e., in the milder forms of dysphrenia by daydreaming, in the more severe forms by delusions and hallucinations. Occurring "out of context and in a forceful and distorted fashion" the phenomena in question are no doubt abnormal discharges on the part of the highest sensory level, and they establish a link between schizophrenic and epileptiform disorders. The reproduction of similar phenomena by electrical stimulation of the temporal cortex and their spontaneous occurrence in temporal lobe lesions suggests that, in the final analysis, both hallucinations and epileptiform discharges involving mental phenomena are produced by abnormal temporal lobe mechanisms at the synaptic level.

Thus, dysphrenia is caused by the derailment of integrative acts or synergies at crucial points of integration at the highest sensory level which, had they developed in a normal fashion, would have established objective correspondance relations between the organism and its environment. Ordinarily, derailment of the correspondance function takes place in oneroid states that occur under conditions of gradually diminishing responsiveness at the highest sensory grade of the nervous system, that is to say, in the transitional forms between wakefulness and sleep.

PARATHYMIA AS DERANGEMENT OF SUBJECTIVE
CORRESPONDANCE RELATIONS

In the process of determining appropriate responses to biologically significant stimuli, the highest sensory stratum of the neuraxis deals with two variables, namely, the *structure of environmental changes* that generate intellective stimuli or analogs and the *relationship of the recorded events* to the biological equilibrium of the organism. The *cognitive* (receptive) component of an intellective stimulus mirrors the variable represented by environmental events; the *affective* parameter, on the other hand, is the peculiar quality of the experience that elicits aversive or impelling responses. More accurately, that quality which represents a primitive baseline of response in equating the objective structure of an event with its subjective aspects, that is to say, those aspects which have a bearing on significant, especially vital spheres of the organism. The affective quality or "feeling tone" of experiental data is the correlate of the egocentric organization of living beings, the experience of a disembodied spirit would be purely cognitive. The functional primordium of the *affective component* of an intellective stimulus is the homeostatic element or equilibratory factor inherent in the "blind", reflex eliciting stimulus. The *cognitive component* of an intellective stimulus is a potential modifier of the affective (impelling or inhibitory) component which, in turn, can be traced to reflex release and reflex inhibition respectively. Thus, *parathymia* may be interpreted as return to a more primitive way of response determination and, in this sense, especially if compared with response patterns of the immature organism and those of lower forms of life, appears to be related to developmental arrest rather than to the derailment of developmental processes.

DISSOCIATION OF CONSCIOUSNESS AS DERANGEMENT OF MNEMIC ACTION MECHANISMS

In conformity with the principle of division of labor, the stream of thought, (in its simplest form an apperceptive function, that is, a running record of reality) bifurcates into a *dominant* and a *subsidiary* arm. The former is concerned with the representation of stimuli in the overt system of notation and with the determination of responses to immediate data of awareness; the latter, with the preservation of data in the mnemonic system of notation and, by interacting with the dominant arm of the current of thought, with the formation of mnemic reactions in which are utilized the mnemonically fixated data after their translation into the overt system of notation. To a degree, however, certain data represented in the mnemonic system of notation acquire a measure of autonomy and, thereby, form the subsidiary sphere of mentation. Under conditions of abnormal stimulation, the above outlined working arrangement is apt to be superseded by the more or less complete segregation of the psychic apparatus into two points of condensation as it were, namely, the personal self (ps) and the para-personal self (pps), each of which is compounded of a dominant sphere of mentation, a subsidiary sphere of mentation and a mnemonic system of stimulus representation (Fig. 11). The two selfs

may control the determination of responses to stimuli either jointly, or, more often than not, antagonistically or, lastly, as in hysterical twilight states followed by amnesia, in an alternating fashion. In other words, the ps and the pps form the cores of the so called (communicating or noncommunicating) double personalities. Moreover, the working arrangement between the dominant and the subsidiary sphere of mentation, including the mnemonic system, may be maintained only within the ps. In the pps on the other hand, the relationship between the two spheres of mentation and the mnemonic system of stimulus representation is apt to be repatterned in an oneroid fashion. The restructuring of the waking state characterises the schizophrenic thinking disorder and abnormal (psychotic) reality recording in general. In neurotiform schizophrenia, the predominance of the pps is stress-induced, in other words, dys-synergic processes are caused by frustration; in idiopathic schizophrenia on the other hand, the disorganization of the mental apparatus is primarily determined by the derangement of brain centers which control the responsiveness of the highest sensory level (and thereby make possible the normal patterning of the waking state) or by the combination of an extrinsic precipitant and intrinsic factors. In the periodic forms of idiopathic schizophrenia (subgroups D' and F') the pps re-emerges at intervals. Its appearance is provoked by the very same factors which determine the periodic maladjustment of the organism in the viscero-autonomic and certain somatic spheres of integration.

In contrast to *dysphrenia*, which exemplifies the derailment of a developmental process, and to *parathymia* which, in certain respects, resembles a process of regression, *dissociation of consciousness may be traced to the misdirected division of labor in the central nervous system.* Under normal conditions of specialization, there emerge two agencies working in coordination. Under abnormal conditions, the subsidiary sphere of mentation of the pps becomes redundant and the leading response determinating agency.

CONVERSION PHENOMENA AS INTEGRATIONAL DEFICIT

A further sphere of potential weakness are integrative processes involved in somatization, the translation of thought into action. Dys-somatization (corresponding in a general way to the conversion phenomena of depth psychology) is the expression of integrational malfunction involving the intellective level and its organs of execution, including, potentially, their autonomic auxiliaries. In other words, it is possible to bring upon a common denominator the following phenomena: The effects of integrational deficit within the intellective level (causing dysphrenia, parathymia and the dissociation of consciousness) and integrational deficit involving the coordination of the intellective level with its organs of execution. Psychotic and neurotic mechanisms can thus be expressed in unifying language.

Spontaneous and drug induced disorders of time experience

The discussion of disorders of time experience is added here as they occur either spontaneously, chiefly in schizophrenic illness, or as a result of drug intoxication. The nature of time is an age old problem which cannot be discussed here in any detail. Mach (602), assuming that the sensation of time is inherent in the individua: sense qualities, recognized an immediate sensation of time to be differentiated from what he called *"urteilsmässige Zeitauffassung"*, or knowledge of time arrived at by reasoning. Bergson (66) spoke of *"durée toute pure"* and E. Strauss (887) of an elementary experience of duration. Cooper and Erickson (169) asserted that "subjective experience seems to be inseparately interwoven with time sense." In a previous study (802), I defined the concept of time as an abstraction covering experiences that involve the element of change. No matter how varied experiences may be, they have in common this particular feature. It is this unique parameter of experience, then, which we keep in mind when we speak of time. Now, under abnormal conditions, the experience of change may fail to produce the experience of time or, for that matter, a uniform experience of duration. For example, to various persons watching, say, a chemical substance undergoing metachromasia the change in color may appear to occur with "natural speed"; to others, it may appear either accelerated or decelerated, or all phases may seem to be concentrated into a single moment. Lastly, and most puzzling of all, the phenomenon in question may fail to yield the experience of time in spite of the experience of change. Now, if it is true

that the experience of time is inherent in the very process of perception, which, because of the nature of objective reality, involves the awareness of changes in the external and the internal world of the organism, it should also be true that the abnormal experiences of the flow of time should in some way correspond to the perceptual disorders. Yet, to my knowledge at least, such relationship has thus far not been established. It is therefore an open question whether the above suggested definition of the concept "time" covers the phenomenon of time experience as a whole or applies to one of its particular aspects only.

The following is probably a fairly representative sampling of utterances of schizophrenics who described their experiences in a more or less intelligible fashion.* Fischer (238) *Case 3:* "My arms and legs seem to increase in size and become inflated. I experienced a terrible pain in my head. Time seemed to stand still. At the same time, I became aware, in an almost superhuman fashion, of the deeper meaning of this very moment. Subsequently, time continued to flow as usual. However, time, while standing still, was like a door through which the new experience entered." *Case 5:* "At 11.30, I felt that it was 11 o'clock again. However, not only did time come back, but the very content of time, or the time gone long ago. This was associated with the dreadful feeling of expectancy that I might be dragged into what had past, or the past would overwhelm me. I experienced the dawn of a strange, unfamiliar time. I wished the wrong time would disappear again." *Case 5:* "I am attempting to efface time so that it would be possible not to distinguish between day and night any longer but I did not succeed." *Case 6:* "Time no longer flows. The watch keeps on going as before but I can no longer imagine the flow of time. I wish I could run inwardly so as to make time flow again. One cannot reach the future. One can talk about the present and the past but one can no longer imagine it. Time is standing still. One oscillates between the past and the present. It is a boring, drawn out time." *Case 7:* "Is there anything like the future? Previously, there has been something like it. Now, it becomes more and more contracted. The past is so obtrusive, it throws itself upon me. It draws me back. I am like a machine that is standing still and does not move forward. The machine works

---

* The following passages were, with some difficulty, translated from the German.

with such furor that almost anything goes to pieces. I wish time would slow down, recline and relax." *Case 8:* "Time dropped out and was standing still. Actually, it was not quite like time re-emerging the moment it had disappeared. The new time was immeasurably more variegated and kaleidoscopic. Thought was arrested. Everything was standing still as though time had ceased to flow. Time was motionless like a dragon fly in midair. I appeared to myself like a being without a soul, like a mathematical formula." The above quoted examples show that disorders of the appreciation of the flow of time may be either isolated, or that they may occur in association with thinking disorders, meaning spells (e.g., in case 3) and with various hallucinations and delusions.

To bring some semblance of order into the disturbances of time experience, it will be convenient to assume that, under normal conditions, changes in the external and the internal world of the organism are projected upon a *subjective time scale* which is rather loosely synchronized with the *objective*. The objective time scale in turn is based on the evaluation of environmental changes that occur with a certain regularity and is measured by means of mechanical devices. Under ideal conditions which, however, rarely obtain, the "event points" indicated on the subjective time scale and the corresponding event points of the objective time scale are superimposable. The experience of *duration* would correspond directly to the distance of events on the subjective time scale; the experience of *sequence,* to their fixed arrangement or "spatial" relationship. The fact that the position of event points on the subjective time scale is (a) either immediately experienced or (b) recalled or (c) determined by a process of reasoning would seem to indicate that, in the appreciation of time, not only *perceptual* but also *mnemonic* and *intellectual* factors play a part. In the following paragraphs we shall regard the diverse *disturbances of the appreciation of time in terms of incongruity, or non-correspondence, of the subjective and the objective time scale at various levels of mentation* (Fig. 15).

PERCEPTUAL DISORDERS OF TIME EXPERIENCE

Ordinarily, the congruence between the subjective and the objective time scale is a rather loose one in that the former may be either shortened or lengthened. Kant remarked that a time span in which but a few events occur may be experienced as inordinately long in one's immediate awareness but short in one's recollection. Modern psychological investigations (*897a*) have brought out the validity of this thesis, indicating that a certain measure of asynchrony, as found by Kant by introspection, is physiological. The following observations refer to pathological incongruence.

Shortening of the Subjective Time Scale

Klien's (*499*) patient, an eight year old boy, had peculiar attacks during which he believed that "everything moved fast." He would then run to his mother and exclaim excitedly, "Now everything goes so fast again! Am I really speaking so fast? Do you, mother, speak faster?" During these spells, which would last about five minutes, the patient did not talk with more than usual speed. The peculiar states were accompanied by delusions consisting of the sensation that his whole body became thicker. Wagner's (*924*) patients had the impression that the physicians and nurses on the ward would walk with lightning speed. Music and speech, too, appeared to be "terribly accelerated." (At other times, however, the gait of those passing by appeared to be unnaturally slow). Beringer (*68*) studied experiences of time awareness induced by mescaline. One of his subjects, while walking downstairs, had the impression that "everything happened so fast that it was almost impossible to follow. My friends who had just a moment ago walked near me, all of a sudden were a whole flight of stairs below. I found myself continuously faced with a new situation. In the dark room, the tip of a burning cigarette appeared to describe wild circles." Sturt (*892*) described the experiences of a British Officer during the first World War. After "going over the top" at daybreak and leading his soldiers in an attack on enemy positions, it occurred to him that the sun could now be seen on the opposite point of the horizon. This made him aware of how rapidly the time had flown by. In this particular case, no retrospective falsification had occurred; rather, the surprise caused by the "discovery" that the sun had changed its position resulted from the altered appreciation of time during the immediate past, in other words, from the awareness of the "shrinking" of the subjective time scale.

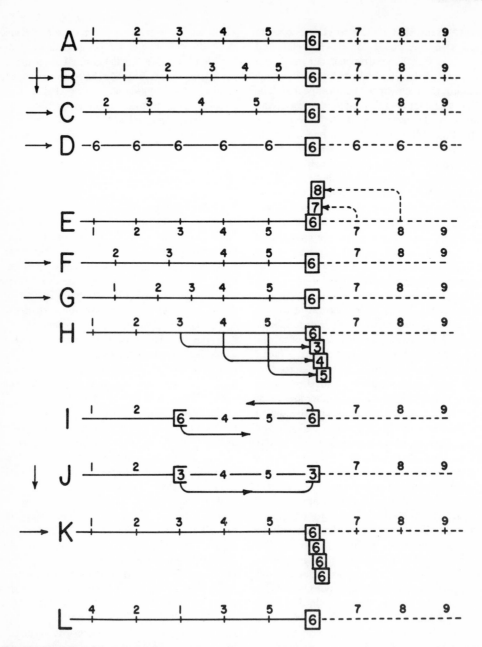

Fig. 15. Disorders of time experience.

1–6: the past; 6: the present; 6–9: the future; A: objective time scale and synchronized subjective time scale; B: shortening of the subjective time scale; C: lengthening of the subjective time scale; D: obliteration of the subjective time scale; E: concentration of the subjective time scale; F: retrospective lengthening of the subjective time scale; G: retrospect shortening; H: time lapse paramnesia; I: reduplicative paramnesia; J: Déja vu; K: reverberating paramnesia; L: reshuffling of the subjective time scale; Bold face numbers: abnormal position of event points on the subjective time scale; curved arrows: movements of event points on the subjective time scale; vertical arrows: defective appreciation of time occurring during, or as, psycho-epileptic seizures; horizontal arrows: defective appreciation of time induced by drugs.

Lengthening of the Subjective Time Scale

Clarke (166) reported the case of a patient who was under the influence of Hashish. "Ascending the stairs from his sitting room to his bedchamber seemed to occupy enough time for a journey from Washington to Boston and it required a century for the winding of his watch." One of Beringer's subjects reported that the simple process of forming the answer, "yes", appeared to last hours while another subject described how a cigarette he smoked would not get smaller and that a sheet of paper upon which the physician who examined him wrote, never seemed to get filled. An object which fell from a roof hardly moved. He had the impression of creeping rather than walking. Hoch (390) and his associates found that, under the influence of lysergic acid, there was apt to occur a slowing of the subjective recognition of the flow of time. To one of Jones' (449) patients, who was put to sleep with chloroform, all movements appeared to be much longer than they actually were. In the induction stage of the anesthesia, a slight movement of the tongue seemed to be magnified "at least ten times." Carr (86) described a patient suffering from psychoepileptic attacks, during which his sense of time appeared to be magnified. The apparent duration of the stages of "trance" varied between wide limits. Sometimes the state was "judged to last for hours and hours, or days and days, and twice for years and years." Klien made brief reference to a patient who had the delusion, produced by Hashish, that the beginning of a sentence he spoke lay a long time back. The opium eater, de Quincey, thought that in one night he had lived a period of from 80 to 100 years.

Obliteration of the Subjective Time Scale

It is evident that the objective time scale becomes meaningless in the absence of a subjective. Obliteration of the latter would seem to occur in Korsakoff's psychosis and in other organic mental syndromes. According to Gamper (286), the patients are "able to concentrate but they fail to form the kind of spatio-temporal background established under normal conditions by means of which a given experience complex is related to mnestic continuum." However, Gamper's statement that the stimulus to which the patient directs his attention is fixated in his memory (festgehalten) is difficult to reconcile with the idea that the patient fails to form a mnemonic background to which the stimuli in question are related. At most, his statement can be accepted with the qualification only that the structure of his background itself has been fundamentally altered. From the patient's reaction, one would judge that he lives in a timeless world; in other words, in a perceptual "now" which neither merges with the past nor extends into the future. Whatever the patient does remember might have happened at any time; the place values on his time scale have become equivalent, indicating that the awareness of duration and sequence has ceased. As far as can be known, the patient's mental state resembles that of someone who, having just awakened from a deep sleep, has no actual awareness of duration but, rather, the feeling that his inner world is static; he has the experience of self and also of his surroundings but, as far as introspection serves me, the awareness of changes in one's environment fails to convey the experience of time. One of Beringer's subjects remarked that there was always noontime, the flow of time having ceased. Another person who watched test figures moving with constant speed, failed to appreciate that the events observed occurred in succession. Rather, all changes appeared to occur synchronously as "succession coalesced into an unmoved present." It is of interest to note that the obliteration of the subjective time scale does not take place in a uniform fashion but may manifest itself in a variety of abnormal phenomena. "After having mounted a flight of stairs and seen several people," one of the persons observed by Beringer remarked, "the continuity of time appeared to have vanished. The entire sequence appeared to have disintegrated into a number of individual events which subsequently could be interrelated, just like fragments of a film which, however, during its actual exposure and also immediately afterward, appeared to have no connection with one another. Strangely, events seemed to coexist rather than to succeed each other. They had no place in time; the concept of time had lost its very meaning." The obliteration of the time scale in the case of a patient reported by Grünthal and Störring (326) manifested itself within the general setting of a profound disturbance of retentive memory which, in turn, occurred following exposure of the patient to carbonmonoxide. All awareness contents faded without leaving a trace after little more than one

186

second. Thus, it may be stated that the patient saw little more than one point of the time scale "at one time", that his "spacious present" was almost punctiform and, hence, the subjective time scale practically non-existent. Heimann and Heimann (364), who re-examined the patient some 25 years after the accident, confirmed Grünthal and Störring's original observations.

Concentration of the Subjective Time Scale

In panoramic states of vision or hearing both present events and certain happenings of the past appear to occur synchronously, as if they were objects seen simultaneously from a great height. In other words, *past event* points and *present events* appear to be concentrated into one single monent. Apparently, imaginal *anticipation* of events may also occur, for many composers and poets, among them v. Beethoven (53), Mozart (665) and Goethe (310), narrated that some of their works stood suddenly before their mental eye, and that all that remained for them was to record what they saw or heard. Mozart, for example, describes his states of artistic inspiration as follows: "The whole, though it be long, stands almost complete and finished in my mind, so that I can survey it, like a fine picture or a beautiful statue, at a glance. Nor do I hear in my imagination the parts successively, but I hear them all at once ... the actual hearing of the *tout ensemble* is after all the best."

Mozart's description gains added significance when compared not only with those of other artists but in particular with the phenomenon of time lapse paramnesia, (see below) and the well known concentration of the subjective time scale in dreams. It is well authenticated that artists may almost synchronously see or hear sequences of events which one would assume to occupy a reasonably long period of time. In other words, future segments of their subjective time scale may be concentrated into the "spacious present." In the opinion of Humphrey (232a), Mozart's experiences are an example of "impalpably given knowing" for the tout ensemble of which the composer speaks must have been a fundamentally imageless experience. We disagree with Humphrey for the following reasons. Firstly, we cannot apply ordinary standards to the workings of the brain of the man of genius, more especially as regards its individual sensory spheres, in fact, the brain

mechanisms in question, under ordinary circumstances at least, are entirely beyond the realm of our experience, rather as the olfactory experiences of macrosmatic animals.* Secondly, sensuous experiences of any kind lie of necessity outside the sphere of imageless thought. Mozart could have experienced his work in an abstract fashion only if, by some miracle, the mathematical framework of his composition had been converted into complex incorporative symbols, in other words, by a process of algebraization.

In general, it may be stated that the image of the objective and hence, the subjective reality is not static; it is recorded by the highest level with approximately the same speed as that with which events take place both in the environment and the internal milieu of the organism. Thus, synchrony of the subjective and the objective time scale is merely one aspect of the correspondence that prevails between subject and object; and disturbances of the appreciation of time, as we have ventured to suggest, those of a particular parameter of the "correspondence function" of the nervous system. They are true, or primary, disturbances of consciousness.

MNEMONIC DISORDERS OF TIME EXPERIENCE

The flow of thought processes and the speed with which memory images appear (and which, unlike precepts, have of course no direct representation in the external world) take place with "conventionalized" speed. What's more, temporal sequences appear to be preserved in memory in a scale which corresponds roughly to their original arrangement. (At this point, we disregard the fact that different persons think with different speed and that one and the same person will think, or remember things, with different speed on different occasions). In other words, events, to the extent that they are remembered, are brought into relationship with both the subjective and the objective time scale in their original chronological order, a radical rearrangement or reshuffling being uncommon. Only events of the remote past might have to be reconstructed with the aid of reasoning processes. (See below.) However, these relationships, too, may undergo remarkable changes as will be shown in the following paragraphs.

---

* At most, insight into the mechanism in question can be gained indirectly (see Chapter III).

Retrospective Lengthening of the Time Scale

Wilbrandt (957) mentions the case of a patient who depicted her time experience as follows: "Something that might have happened ten minutes ago appears to me as if it occurred three hours ago or longer. Right after you had left I do not know whether it was an hour ago I saw you, or today, or yesterday, the day before, or at any other time you visited me." This patient had not "lost" her subjective time scale but the time elapsed since a given moment appeared to be indefinitely extended. One of Beringer's (52) subjects, having been left alone for five minutes, estimated the period of time as having lasted several hours. Bechterew (51), referring in particular to chronic alcoholics, asserted that although their state of consciousness may be otherwise undisturbed, their inability to estimate the length of time elapsed since a given moment is striking. By contrast, their memory appears to be intact in respect to events that anteceded their illness. One of his patients was taken from the Wolga to Kasan, a distance of about 7 kilometers. After recovering from his illness, he declared that the trip appeared to have lasted 100 years.

Retrospective Shortening of the Time Scale

Other patients, after their confusional state had cleared up, estimated experiences which lasted ¼ to ½ hour as having lasted only seconds. One of them said that an hour's drive had lasted two minutes only; another patient that it had lasted one second. The night had passed so quickly that it apparently "never existed"; and events of the remote past happened "only recently."

The above data should be interpreted with caution, for we cannot be certain that the awareness of time was not *primarily* inadequate. However, in view of the fact that similar distortions of time experience, although to a relatively minor degree, may also occur in normal persons, pathological degrees of non-correspondence between the subjective and objective time scale may be genuine.

Time Lapse Paramnesia

Reports of the rapid flow of memory images during moments of mortal danger, for instance during falls from great heights or imminent drowning should not be lightly dismissed. Among other testimony, they are substantiated by an infantile reminiscence of Charles Darwin (179) recorded in his autobiography. "I walked off and fell to the ground," Darwin wrote, "but the height was only seven or eight feet. Nevertheless, the number of thoughts which passed through my mind during this short but sudden and wholly unexpected fall was astonishing and seemed hardly compatible with what physiologists I believe proved about each thought requiring an appreciable amount of time." Frankl and Pötzl (252) reported the case of a laborer who fell down from a height of about 25 meters. Feeling the scaffold on which he was standing give, he yelled: "We are done for." At this moment, he saw only the sky and his friend at the same level as himself and only a short distance away. Immediately afterwards he had visions of scenes that followed each other in quick succession. They were quite pleasant and more natural than dreams. They were not fragmented but connected like scenes one might see in the movies. He saw himself as a boy, playing with his friends; he saw the home of his parents; he saw scenes he had witnessed on the battlefields of France and in Poland. It occurred to him that he had made a date before going to work the same morning. Lastly, he thought about what his mother would say on learning what had happened. Toward the end of his fall he clenched his fists and waited for the inevitable crash. While falling, he did not have any fear whatsoever and at no time did thoughts of death enter his mind. He never lost consciousness during the accident. Reichardt (751) made brief reference to a patient who during an attempted cisternal puncture sustained an injury to her medulla oblongata. After coming to from a period of unconsciousness lasting from 15 to 20 seconds, he reported that "she saw herself and that her whole life would fly past her with lightning-like speed." That she had actually sustained an injury to her medulla oblongata could be demonstrated by motor and sensory changes. For all intents and purposes, the states described, although perhaps more vivid, are akin to the wealth of visual images which may be crowded into dreams lasting but a few seconds.

Reduplicative Paramnesia

One and the same event may be referred to two separate points of the time scale. According to Pick (728) reduplicative paramnesia is "characterized by the fact that a continuous series of events in the patient's remembrance subsequently falls into manifold experiences. The isolated events, though they remain pretty clearly in his memory, are impressed on him as repetitions." One of Pick's patients said he had been "in another clinic in another city which was exactly like the one he was in, and that it was headed by a chief of the same name." In the second case "the patient did not duplicate the chief and his assistants but asserted something similar in regard to the arrangement of the clinic and a number of events. However, she had no doubt as to the identity of the chief as the administrative head of both clinics." The patients, then, feel sure that they actually experienced identical earlier situations. "They construe a delusional memory image which duplicates an actual experience more or less faithfully." Reduplicative paramnesia appears to be related to what Kraepelin (409) called "identifizierende Erinnerungsfälschung", a phenomenon which he believed may occur in normal persons. Bleuler's (87) "Kryptamnesia", the exact opposite of reduplicative paramnesia, is a state of awareness in which a recollection is mistaken for an original experience.

Déjà Vu

The temporal delusion known as déjà vu differs from reduplicative paramnesia in that it occurs in episodes, or attacks, during which the subject has not only the impression of having lived through exactly the same situation before but the "intruding" experience so dominates his mind that the duplicated awareness content may be all but crowded out by the duplicating. The *past itself* rather than past events appears to have returned, leaving no room for the "legitimate" present. The delusion of familiarity may be so compelling that the subjects, as the scene "rolls off," believe they are able to predict if not actually envision what is about to happen. Their state of mind resembles that of a person who, attending a motion picture for the second time, is always one or two jumps ahead; occasionally they may have the delusion to "know to have known" what would happen.

Reverberating Paramnesia

The disturbance in question, which occurs under the influence of Dibenamine, resembles in some respects reduplicative paramnesia; in others,

déja vu. One of Arnold and Hoff's (30) experimental subjects gave the following (katamnestic) description of his experiences under the influence of the drug. "I was lying on the electroencephalographer's couch. The door opened and the secretary entered carrying a lot of books. Hesitating for a moment, she asked, "Pardon me, may I walk through the room?", tiptoed past me and left through another door. She had hardly disappeared when she reopened the door through which she had entered (as if she had flown back through the room in 1/1,000,000 of a second) reappeared with a lot of books under her arm, hesitated a monent and asked, "Pardon me, may I walk through the room?", tiptoed past me and left the room through the other door. Again, within the fraction of a second, she re-entered the room through the first door and every detail repeated itself with absolute precision some 15 times. The speed with which she walked appeared to be quite normal but, as previously mentioned, the intervals between the stereotyped scenes were unnaturally short.

As compared to the diverse forms of defective appreciation of time involving the perceptual sphere, all of which are primary disturbances of consciousness, those involving mnestic functions are of a variegated character. Time lapse paramnesia, reverberating paramnesia, and déjà vu are primary disturbances of consciousness while retrospective shortening and lengthening of the time scale and also reduplicative paramnesia may be regarded borderline conditions as is, for example, profound absentmindedness approaching confusion. Unlike déjà vu, reduplicative paramnesia is not a potentially overwhelming state of disturbance of consciousness; it is the dichotomy of an event and its projection upon disparate points of the subjective time scale. It is admittedly difficult to separate phenomena of reduplication of time from those of place and person (for "objectless" reduplication is hardly conceivable) but the concept of reduplication should not be watered down to include trivial instances of mental confusion and misidentification. From the point of view of the psychopathology of memory or, for that matter, of time, it is not the duplicated event that is of interest but the very phenomenon of reduplication. On the other hand, psychoanalytically oriented writers feel that the contents of the delusions should be given more attention than they have received in the past.

Intellective Disorders of Time Experience

In referring to the intellectual aspects of time experience it is appropriate to speak of the knowledge rather than the awareness to time. (Cf. E. Mach (602).) For example, in trying to reconstruct the sequence of events in a particular case we conclude, on logical grounds, that the events in question must have either preceded or followed other events about whose position on the objective time scale we are not quite certain. On the other hand, if the disease has demolished the system of reference, no chronological sequence can be worked out. Inability on the part of the patient to apply the law of contradiction will eliminate the logical component of time awareness. In states of confusion, acceptance of the statement that event A has followed event B does not invalidate the opposite statement. Random reshuffling of event points on the subjective time scale is likely to occur and, to the extent that the significance of an objective time scale is at all appreciated, any type of non-correspondence is accepted without hesitation as actual or possible. Thus, the experience of sequence might have to be reconstructed with the aid of thought processes; conversely, the concept of time could never have developed without the capacity to appreciate the flow of time and the aid of chronological memory.

Psychotomimetics

Stoll (882) discovered accidentally that *LSD-25*, a derivative of ergot, produces mental symptoms. The effects of the drug were subsequently studied in a systematic fashion by Stoll and Hoffmann (884) and other workers. The effects of *mescaline* are well known since Beringer's (68) classic investigations. There is a considerable chemical and potency difference between the two hallucinogens. Mescaline is a tri-methoxyphenyl-ethylamide, and LSD-25 a d-lysergic acid diethyl-amide tartrate. The former produces mental symptoms in doses of 500 to 1000 milligrams while mere traces of LSD-25 produce similar effects with doses of from 1 to 1½ micrograms per kg body weight. Other hallucinogens are *adrenochrome, adrenolutin* and *adrenotoxin*. Although the clinical affects of mescaline and LSD-25 are not exactly alike (see below) the differences may for simplicity be neglected. In normal individuals, the drugs produce temporary schizophrenia-like symptoms. In fact, the artificially induced symptoms resemble the schizophrenic symptoms so closely that the following data, especially if arranged in an appropriate fashion, will read like a recapitulation of the description of the psychopathological core of schizophrenic illness.

If the drugs are administered to schizophrenic patients who are in a state of remission, the psychoses is reactivated, and the clinical picture intensified in acute and subacute cases while chronic schizophrenics show behaviour abnormalities similar to those in the acute phases of the illness. Catatonic and paranoid features are intensified in certain cases. It is worthy of note that the symptoms produced by hallucinogens can be counteracted by chlorpromazine (159, 822). There is rapid diminution of psychomotor activity and aggressiveness but tolerance quickly develops in some patients. The following account is based on the investigations of Denber and Merlis (190), Schwartz a. ass. (822), Hoch a. ass. (390, 391), Rinkel a. ass. (762), De Shon a. ass. (192), of Savage (792) and Bercel a. ass. (64). Solms' (848) and Hoffer's (397) recent articles may be consulted for further information.

Hallucinogens disorganize the process of response determination both at reflex levels and the intellective level. The former, which are apt to precede the appearance of mental changes following the administration of the drug, are for all intents and purposes limited to the viscero-autonomic sphere, while the formation and manipulation of intellective stimuli involves both their affective and their cognitive components including perceptual, configurational and conceptual processes. It is to be noted however, that anxiety and other affective changes may be reactive, i.e., secondary to the perceptual disorders (as, indeed, may be the case in genuine schizophrenia) and that, on the other hand, the intellectual impairment may be due to primary anxiety. Both inter-level effects of disruptive stimulation (dys-somatization reactions) and intra-level effects (dissociative reactions) are either inconspicuous or difficult to ascertain because of the scattering of thought and the looseness of associations. The abnormal mental experiences may be related to stimuli from the environment, projection of subjective feelings or symbolic representations of thought, in that previous thoughts may be represented as hallucinations (64).

(a) *Viscero-autonomic changes* are nausea, increased perspiration, chilliness, throbbing, flushing, sexual excitement, need to urinate, diuresis, mydriasis, vomiting, malaise, headaches, dizziness, fall in blood pressure and bradycardia.

(b) *Psycho-autonomic changes* are primary anxiety associated with palpitations and a subjective feeling of trembling, depression, lability of affect, alternating euphoria and depression, irritability, uneasiness and restlessness. It is worthy of note that autonomic, particularly adrenergic system derangement always precede the occurrence of mental changes while falling adrenaline concentration seems to be associated with relaxation and euphoria.

(c) *Inter-level symptoms* are ataxia, a positive Romberg sign, dysarthria, slurring and slowing of speech, and unexplained smiling.

(d) *Perceptual symptoms* are delusions and hallucination, a feeling of numbness, coldness, warmth, hyperacusias, hallucinations or colors and flashes of light, depersonalization and derealization.

(e) *Configurational* (primary) *delusions* are dysmorphopsias, hallucinations of geometrical figures and patterns, fantastic hallucinations, hallucinations of animate and inanimate objects, auditory hallucinations, and distortions of the body image. Both space relationships and time relationships are distorted. Anxiety and depersonalization experiences may be secondary to the perceptual and configurational distortions or to the vitiation of the correspondance function of the sensory sphere while increased or decreased verbal activity may be secondary to anxiety.

(f) *Conceptual* (secondary or interpretive) *delusions* and *disorders of thought* include impairment of concentration and of thinking ability, blocking, hesitancy, indecision, pressure of thought, increased evasiveness, scattering, irrelevancy and dreamlike alteration of thinking. Hostility, aggression, resentment, mutism, negativism and antagonism may well be secondary to the interpretive delusions and to the morbid ideas produced by the drug.

Bercel and his associates (*64*) studied the reaction of 25 normals to LSD-25. It will be convenient to group the symptoms produced by the drug into those resembling (1) various abnormal experiences of schizophrenics, (2) epileptiform manifestations (3) phantom limb experiences (4) components of the thalamic syndrome and (5) miscel-laneous abnormalities. (6) Lastly, the authors observed certain electroencephalographic phenomena. To facilitate the comparison with the data discussed in the preceding paragraphs, we prefer a simplified classification to the one proposed by Bercel and his collaborators, neglecting as irrelevant in the present context certain autonomic changes, e.g., mydriasis, which occurred in each case, and motor changes, namely, twitchings in various muscle groups observed in isolated instances.

(a) *Perceptual and configurational hallucinations* included micropsias, metamorphopsias and heteromegalomorphopsias, that is, changes in the size of actually seen objects. The visual experiences were apt to be complex in character, of an extraordinary variety and seemed to follow what may be called a fringe dominant pattern. For example, one subject reported that the green colors of a stained Gothic window which he saw with his eyes closed turned into autumn leaves, which in turn turned into peacock feathers. Another subject, having looked at a picture, saw it contracting in size, coming out of its frame and retracting into it in a rhythmic fashion, the movements described occurring synchronous with his breathing. At times, the subjects would react to their experiences with exhilaration but the prevailing emotional response was one of apprehension. A number of subjects developed paranoid reactions; they claimed that the food was poisoned, that the examiner's voice influenced their visions, delusions and bodily sensation and that he subjugated and controlled their train of thought. One subject reported that the red color "means something", and complained about the examiner's "ice-cream talk." Another subject complained about a "hole in the middle of his forehead and that the examiner, while talking, blew the cold air of his breath into this hole, thus influencing the function of the subject's brain and his thinking." On the basis of their own subjective experiences, time appeared to some subjects either "much longer or much shorter." A feeling of depersonalization and estrangement of a vague character, and associated with anxiety was noted in six subjects. The most characteristic language change was condensation of words and confusion over opposites. The choice between these opposites in the thinking of the subject was openly admitted. Circumlocution of the amnesic aphasic variety and echolalia was also noted.

(b) Among the drug induced sensations resembling "sensory seizures or psychosensory seizures (715) commonly seen in *psychomotor epilepsy*" (and reproduced by Penfield and others by electrical stimulation of the cortex) the authors mention "primary visual hallucinations, delusions, visions, pareidolias micropsias, metamorphopsias and heteromegalopsias, kaleidoscopic pictures, vertiginous attacks, auditory, gustatory, olfactory, perceptual anomalies, auditory and visual reverberations, feelings of familiarity (déja vue) and unfamiliarity. Other abnormal sensations consisted in alterations of perspective associated with perceptions of propulsions and retractions. Alterations of the experience of the flow of time occur not only in schizophrenia but also in temporal lobe epilepsy as evidenced by the following remarks of epileptic patients. "Time seems to stand still . . . time rushes by . . . it seems to last forever but is only a moment" (722).

(c) The following *phantom* limb-like sensations were described. One subject declared that his "left arm had a disconnected feeling . . . the right arm seems to be more connected to the body than the left . . . both arms and legs feel detached . . . the left foot appears half as long as the right . . . the left arm feels numb, pulled into a knot."

(d) As described in the subjects own words, sensations reminiscent of certain components the *thalamic syndrome* included the following. "The right half of my body feels as if it were 6 o'clock in the evening, whereas the left arm feels as if I had just gotten up early in the morning." Another subject reported that the left half of his body including every organ felt detached and entirely different from the right, as if it had been split into two and put back the wrong way. Even the left hemisphere of the brain felt different from the right.

(e) *Miscellaneous abnormalities* were synaesthesias, chiefly the influence, upon optic sensations, of auditory stimuli which were apt to induce paranoid reactions. The authors make much of these sensory abnormalities which they considered the main source of the ideas of influence induced in their experimental subjects. They are inclined to attribute the effect of one stimulus upon another to "cross-talk" between the individual sensory pathways and, depending on the complexity of the stimuli involved, invoke either the thalamic or the cortical level of sensory integration.

It is interest to note that the subjects participating in this study were aware of the unreal character of their experiences. The same however may apply to schizophrenics although, it is true, some patients, while under the influence of the drug, reported that the ensuing sensory abnormalities resemble the sensations they had experienced in the early stages of their illness. Other schizophrenics however, even in the advanced stages of the disease, distinguish between reality and hallucinatory experiences. The above data corroborate the impression that significant similarities exist between (a) drug induced phenomena on one hand and schizophrenic and organic disease processes on the other, including the production of personal and a para-personal self, and (b) between schizophrenia and organic nervous system disease.

(f) As regards the electroencephalographic phenomena, the authors state that "the widespread disturbances in mood, feeling tone, alertness, reality testing and perceptual acuity are bound to influence the behaviour of the spontaneous electrical activity of the brain, if only in response to various sensory stimuli. Unlike the situation in epileptic phenomena . . . in LSD psychosis no evidence of synchronized excessive electrical discharge could be detected. The complete absence of any abnormal electrical event in LSD psychosis even when the site of origin is presumed to be the convexity (rather than the under surface) of the temporal lobes, has been uniformly confirmed. There is no excessive discharge and resultant electrical abnormality."

Perhaps, the simulation, on the part of certain drug actions, of the symptoms of idiopathic schizophrenia may be referable to their affinity to the very same cell stations which, in the last named disorder, are heredo-constitutionally inferior and, one may suppose, apt to break down under conditions of stress. By the same token, other neurotropic drugs, e.g., the toxins of diphtheria, have an affinity for the morphological substrate of lower cerebral functions. That the very same drug effects may simulate symptoms of neurotic schizophrenia, an *integrationally organic* disorder that is, may be attributable to the biological inferiority and the ensuing stress-induced or spontaneous disintegration of certain cerebral agencies. On the other hand, the fact that the very same drug effects may mimic symptoms of (macro)-*structurally organic* nervous system disease (including epileptiform manifestations, phantom limb experiences and components of the thalamic syndrome) may reflect the limited "symptomatological repertoire" of neuronal circuits even though they operate as units integrated to systems of enormous complexity.

The following *historical note* is of interest with regard to the effects of psychotomimetic drugs. In 1892, Kraepelin (*508*) remarked in his monograph entitled "Uber die Beeinflussung einfacher psychischer Vorgänge durch einige Arzneimittel." . . . "The methods employed in the present study enable us to quantitate mental processes and to reduce them to certain elementary disturbances. . . . We may assume that the use of new methods of investigation will throw light upon other aspects of the abnormal mental states produced by drug intoxication and, thereby, to complete what we have learned thus far. Conversely, we may expect and this would seem to be a considerable advantage of this '*Psychopharmakologie*') to grasp the essence of certain mental process by equating them with the specific effects of those experimentally studied drugs whose effects are known. . . . If motor and intellective functions depend on parts of our nervous system whose chemical composition materially differ from one another, it is obvious that the changes of the individual functions produced by the individual toxins will likewise be different."

Concluding remarks

Considerations of space do not permit a detailed discussion of the theories of schizophrenic illness.* Suffice it to say that they fall into two main groups: *physiogenic theories* and *psychogenic theories*. The former may be subdivided into (a) *topologically oriented theories* (*15, 237, 491, 496, 559, 806, 920, 921*), (b) *biochemically oriented theories* (*32, 64, 81, 133, 185, 212, 221, 228, 232, 289, 359, 360, 375, 387, 389, 396, 397a, 416, 511, 484, 603, 712a, 733, 760, 762, 763, 764, 906, 971*) and (c) *genetically oriented theories* (*96, 131, 404, 463, 464, 465, 779, 776, 837, 838, 839, 840*) while

---

* A discussion of these theories in the original manuscript has been omitted to keep the monograph within managable proportions. The individual numbers refer in part to the articles and monographs in which the individual theories have been formulated, in part to comments to be found in the various publications in which they were critically examined.

the psychological approach comprises the (a) *psychologically oriented theories properly so called* (*76, 77, 78, 327, 328, 354, 792, 804, 805, 886*), (b) the *psychoanalytically oriented theories* (*27, 52, 76, 88, 89, 100, 268, 319, 326, 451, 452, 453, 511, 794, 795, 796, 804*), (c) the *anthropologically oriented theories* (*239, 885*), (d) the *psychobiologically oriented theories* (*60, 83, 222, 539, 638, 639, 756, 894, 895, 896*) and (e) the *psychosomatically oriented theories* (*93, 272*). As implied in the term "oriented", the above outline is an oversimplification, neglecting the *mixed, multifactorial, theories* (*27, 55, 56, 710*).

A perusal of the literature led to the conclusion that the topologically oriented theories do not fit into any acceptable concept of central nervous system function, that they neglect the difference between neurotiform and idiopathic schizophrenia, and that they fail to account for the psychological intelligibility of certain symptoms of the disease. Furthermore, they leave un xplained the relationship between schizophrenic illness on the one hand, the relative paucity and the shifting character of organic symptoms on the other and, implicitly, the modifiability of at least some symptoms by psychological factors. Moreover, certain topological theories are too narrow in that they regard lesions of the highest autonomic cell stations as sufficient to produce the variegated clinical picture of schizophrenia. At the same time, they are too schematic in that they invoke lesions of "specifically human" (*676*) parts of the brain. Still other topological theories attempt a correlation between psychoanalytic and localistic concepts (that is, between incommensurate categories) or a correlation between certain ad hoc postulated functional systems (*559*) and anatomical systems.

The findings of the geneticists, on the other hand, are of the highest importance as, if taken in conjunction with the biochemically oriented theories, they make virtually certain the etiological role of one or more biochemical factors. Obviously, *what is inherited is a biochemical condition*, and it is precisely this condition that establishes a close relationship between schizophrenia and metabolic disorders. As Pauling (*671a*) wrote in a recent article: "In a sense, every hereditary disease is a molecular disease because genes are molecules and an abnormal gene is then an abnormal molecule. . . . Mental illness is [probably] the result of a quantitative molecular abnormality."

Full credit should be given to Kleist (*491*) for having called attention to the relationship between schizophrenia and inheritable metabolic disorders, e.g., phenylketonuric dementia.

Our considerations lead to the hypothesis that the heredo-constitutionally determined disposition to schizophrenia is a synaptic malfunction in the biochemical range. If the malfunction is subliminal, the deficit remains latent in the absence of stress but creates a picture of neurotiform schizophrenia under stressful conditions. If the malfunction is liminal or supraliminal, it gives rise to idiopathic schizophrenia even in the absence of stress—or in the presence of what would otherwise be subliminal stress. (Predisposing and precipitating factors have been postulated by many authorities, including Mayer-Gross (*629*), A. Hoch (*388*), Jung (*451*), Jacobi (*424*), Malamud (*612*) and Hendrickson (*369*), indeed, even by psychoanalytically oriented writers, e.g., Bosselman (*100*), but the nature of the predisposing factors has not been specified.) The relative intensity of dysphrenic and parathymic elements in endogenous psychoses may well be correlated with the predominant site of synaptic instability; this, in turn, would explain the similarity between certain unquestionably organic conditions and schizophrenic symptoms, e.g., between postencephalitic parkinsonism and catatonic stupor (*58, 112, 186, 187, 195, 197, 249, 332, 402, 443, 490, 494, 563, 630, 781, 812, 870, 871, 872, 888, 950*) but the validity of this hypothesis remains to be tested. Nielsen (*397a*), who recognized certain similarities between diencephalic deficit phenomena and schizophrenic symptoms (cf. Ewald (*218*), noted the absence of tissue changes in fatal cases of schizophrenia. From this fact, Nielsen rightly concluded that "organizational patterns" are involved in spite of the absence of alterations of the individual neurons that form the patterns in question. From a wider, biological, angle, it may be said that the synaptic malfunction of neural arrangements underlying the formation of intellective stimuli (more accurately their affective and cognitive components) depresses the confidence coefficient of integration at the intellective level. Depending on the degree of malfunction, the depression comes to the fore either spontaneously or under the influence of disruptive stimuli. In other words, the relatively low confidence coefficient of high level integrative action that exists even under standard conditions of stimulation is still further reduced under abnormal conditions at the synaptic level of neuronal activity and under abnormal conditions of stimulation. The symptoms comprising the psychopathological core of schizophrenia are in all likelihood the expression of synaptic malfunction which may be either progressive or fluctuating and which may or may not show an overall tendency to progression.

A critical examination of the *psychogenic approach* to the problem of schizophrenic illness leads to the following conclusions. The symptomatology of neurotiform and of idiopathic schizophrenia cannot be fully accounted for in terms of early infantile experiences, emotional deprivation, etc., nor can it be explained in terms of regression or of psychoanalytic mechanisms. We submit that the common denominator of psychologically stressful situations is frustration and that a substandard frustration-gratification ratio precipitates the disease, given a certain heredo-constitutional predisposition. To reiterate, if the predisposition is marked, even subliminal frustration, indeed, the ordinary stress and strain of life, is apt to be a pathogenic factor. On the other hand, if the heredo-constitutional predisposition is subliminal, the disease is likely to develop only in the presence of supraliminal frustration. The idea that the predisposition must have been strong because of the trivial nature of the trauma or, indeed, its absence, may be regarded as circular reasoning but genetic studies render inescapable the assumption of an inverse relationship of the intrinsic and the extrinsic factor. Frustration may or may not involve the sexual instinct, but the notion that, ultimately, every instinct is sexual in nature is powerless to explain the causative mechanism. Frustration may block the self-realization of the organism in any sphere of function, especially those functions (including, of course, the sexual) which go into operation under overwhelming instinctual pressure.

One of the chief weaknesses of the psychogenic theories of schizophrenic illness is the lack of a definition of the somatic etiological factor and the emphasis on the psychic trauma, especially the childhood trauma, in spite of the fact that "traumatizing" childhood experiences, however severe they may have been, may fail to produce the disease. Another weakness of the psychogenic theories is their failure to explain somatic and physiological abnormalities in psychosomatic terms, as certain significant somatic features precede rather than follow the psychological symptoms of the psychosis. The concept of regression has been ably criticized by Allers (9), Cameron (139) and Partiff (710). Finally, it should be noted that the psychological theories neglect the relationships between the schizophrenias and the neuroses, and that they describe the symptoms of schizophrenic illness in terms of traditional psychology, for example in terms of abnormalities of volition, in other words, that they fail to use a unifying framework of reference based on the analysis of physiological brain mechanisms and their disturbances at the highest levels of integration.

The psychopathology of frontal lobe disease

By and large, the symptoms of frontal lobe disease fall into three main groups, namely, (a) *mental and behavioural* changes which, jointly, constitute the much discussed personality changes of the frontal lobe patient, (b) *viscero-autonomic* disorders and (c) *cerebello-extrapyramidal* abnormalities. The last named symptoms, being only remotely related to the disorders of higher cerebral functions, do not concern us here. The study of viscero-autonomic symptoms early in this chapter enabled us to demonstrate the autonomic nature of affective states and the fact that their disorders follow the derangement pattern of a homeostatic mechanism. It is understood that the concept of dys-homeostasis does not designate constancy of dysfunction but, rather, the absence of a normal level of function, that is, deviations from normal behaviour in either direction which, moreover, may occur in an unpredictable fashion.

We propose to discuss the psychopathology of frontal lobe disease under two headings, namely, (a) the *mechanism of mental changes* and (b) the *mechanism of abnormal behaviour*. As the two groups of symptoms cannot always be sharply be differentiated, some of them will be listed under either heading. That frontal lobe lesions are apt to attack primarily the affective rather than the intellective component of the personality may be inferred from the patient's relatively well preserved intelligence in the early stages of the disease. As a result, the affective and behavioural changes, for a time at least, are more conspicuous than the intellective changes. We are inclined to attribute this dissociation of symptoms to the fact that the attainment of concepts is dependent to a large extent on the resources of the posterior cortex and that concepts have already been formed prior to the onset of the disease, during a period of competency of both the anterior and the posterior cortex. Thus, as already stressed by Russel (786), early isolated frontal lobe damage may have more serious consequences in childhood than in adult life. Similarly, the effects of epidemic encephalitis in the intellectual sphere are more crippling in young children than in adolescents (948). In advanced stages of frontal lobe disease both intellective and emotional deficit is prominent.

As a rule, the psychologic functions of the frontal lobes are described in conventional terms. For example, Strong and Elwyn (840) write that the "frontal lobes bestow upon the individual the ability to plan and to look ahead, a capacity for perceiving a stimulus or a problem not only as an event of the present but in relation to past experiences and anticipation of future possibilities, an ability to adjust oneself agreeably to one's neighbours and to control emotional reactions." Unfortunately, these terms are (and are probably meant to be) descriptive rather than explanatory. The mental functions of the frontal lobes and the psychopathology of the frontal lobe syndrome remains obscure unless expressed in terms of stimulus and response.

THE MECHANISM OF MENTAL CHANGES IN FRONTAL LOBE DISEASE

The mental changes which are the basis of the behavioural abnormalities in frontal lobe disease comprise (1) *parathymic disorders*, (2) *disorders of attention and memory* and (3) *thinking disorders*.

Parathymic disorders

The *parathymic disorders* may be divided into (a) *disorders of affectivity* and (b) *mood changes*.

It is chiefly the parathymic changes which reflect the lack of homeostasis in the psycho-autonomic sphere of function while those of attention, memory and thinking are secondary. In contrast to the memory changes in localized posterior cortex lesions, the memory deficit in frontal lobe disease is generalized.

Disorders of affectivity

We have repeatedly made reference to the fact that affects (derivatives of the homeostatic element inherent in the impulse components of intellective stimuli) have vector character, i.e., both direction and magnitude and that, for convenience, affective changes may be expressed in terms of *vectorial derangement*. More especially, *vectorial inversion* corresponds to inapposite affectivity, i.e., the substitution of impelling affects for aversive affects and vice versa, while *vectorial imbalance* corresponds to hyperaffectivity or hypoaffectivity, that is to say, the inordinate weakening or intensification of an apposite affect. Paradoxical or perverted reactions are elicited by inapposite affects; overreactions, by hyperaffectivity.

Mood changes

Phenomenologically, moods, feelings, and emotions are derivable from affects as explained earlier in this chapter. Etiologically, primary mood changes, like primary affective changes, are caused by organic (structural and, presumably also ultra-microscopic) involvement of the diencephalo-frontal and limbic system. Abnormal moods comprise *dysphoria, euphoria* and *aphoria*, the latter being conventionally referred to as indifference or emotional blunting. Both dysphoria and euphoria tend to be associated with hyperaffectivity and overreaction to stimuli while aphoria is usually combined with hypoaffectivity. The following is a list of symptoms encountered in frontal lobe disease (*799*).

Symptoms referable to primary dysphoria
   Depression, apprehensiveness, despondency
   Unsociability, argumentativeness, increased
      irritability, fits of rage
Symptoms referable to primary euphoria
   Inapposite hilarity (moria), boastfulness,
      facetiousness, jocosity, puerility
   Vulgarity, obscenity, eroticism

   Talkativeness, overactivity
Symptoms referable to primary aphoria
   Indifference, fatuous equanimity
   Emotional dullness, lack of affective response
   Listlessness, lack of interest, lack of ambition,
      lack of initiative
   Disorders of volition, lack of perseverance
   Slowness and catatonic like immobility.

The above mentioned parathymic abnormalities may be associated with disturbances of attention and memory and with thinking disorders whose mechanism however is, to a degree, dependent on the prevailing changes of affectivity.

Disorders of attention and memory

Disorders of attention and memory in the dysphoric and the euphoric group

Both dysphoria and euphoria are states of increased affectivity. Increased affectivity, in turn, should increase the responsiveness of the organism to stimuli, and, by intensifying attention, enhance the formation of engrams. On the other hand, it is an established fact that responsiveness falling outside the homeostatic range leads to hypervigilance, or increased receptivity to chance stimuli and, hence, relatively diminished receptivity to appropriate stimuli. Thus, contrary to what may be expected on theoretical grounds, the overloading of the brain with sensory data and the resulting disorganization of the recording and synthetizing mechanism is apt to decrease rather than to increase the formation and fixation of engrams. In the behavioural sphere, hypervigilance manifests itself in the already mentioned distractibility and scattered overreaction of the frontal lobe patient. That a dysphoric state is not conducive to the formation of engrams is an every day experience. This does not, however, apply to engrams having a mood-related cognitive parameter.

Disorders of attention and memory in the aphoric group

Hypoaffectivity and diminished responsiveness in the aphoric group causes inattention which, for its part, is associated with relative lack of perception and reduction of engram formation.

Disorders of thinking

Disorders of thinking in the dysphoric and the euphoric group

It is a matter of experience that the content of thought is influenced by prevailing mood disorder that vitiates the generation of relationships between stimuli. This disturbance of thinking is still further enhanced by defective attention and memory.

Disorders of thinking in the aphoric group

The hypoactivity associated with aphoria manifests itself in reduced responsiveness to any stimulus which, in turn, gives rise to mental sluggishness. Kleist (495) refers to this type of disorder as *alogic thought disorder*. Freeman (256), obviously referring to the same phenomenon, speaks of the "reduction in the richness of associations and the termination of thought processes in an unfinished state"; Lidz (568) makes reference to a "severe limitation of the associative range and diminution of the ability to shift from one associative trend to another." Brooding, described by Wimmer (967) is referable to the inability to change the set, or pseudoconcentration met with in dysphoric states. The inability to plan described by Penfield and Evans (719) may likewise be explained by a combination of alogic thought, poor memory and distractibility which, however, need not come to the fore in the routine activities of daily life. In any case, the inability to plan or to look ahead is not an autonomous symptom of frontal lobe disease but a deficit that appears under certain conditions of stimulation. Confusion of thought is a higher degree of the same disorder. Halstead (339), who studied frontal lobe function from the viewpoint of factorial psychology, distinguished between an A factor and a P factor. The former, or the capability for "abstracting universal or rational concepts seems to be a general property of the cortex in man that is maximised in the cortex of the prefrontal lobes. The cerebral power factor P also seems to be represented throughout the cortex but again is maximised in the cortex of the prefrontal lobes." (See below.) We do not agree with Halstead that factor A is a capability in its own right but rather, assume that its apparent absence reflects the failure on the part of the frontal lobes

to add their quota of action to the activity of the posterior cortex, the organ of thought properly so called.

MECHANISM OF ABNORMAL BEHAVIOUR IN FRONTAL LOBE DISEASE

Abnormal behaviour in the dysphoric and the euphoric group

Dysphoria is associated with hyperaffectivity, inapposite affectivity or a combination of both varieties of parathymic disorders.

Originally, impelling affects tend to elicit behaviour patterns leading to immediate gratification while aversive affects give rise to gratification indirectly, that is to say, by the initiation of suitable avoidance reactions. With increasing maturity of the organism, behaviour is no longer dominated by immediate needs only. It is decisively influenced by the evaluation of past and anticipated experiences represented in turn by the ekphory of corroborative or, as the case may be, corrective engrams. Thus, impelling affects, operating concurrently with the data of memory, tend to elicit behaviour patterns involving reward, even though reward is known to be *preceded* by frustration. By the same token, aversive affects tend to suppress behaviour patterns involving immediate reward if reward is known to be *followed* by frustration. Stated in a different way, the pleasure principle is superseded by the reality principle.

Abnormal behaviour develops if, as described below, the impelling or inhibitory value of affective states is inordinately increased. More especially if, as result of primary (organic) derangement of psycho-autonomic functions, (a) apposite affects associated with the awareness of primary *gratification* are reinforced beyond the homeostatic range or (b) apposite affects associated with the awareness of primary *frustration* are inordinately intensified so that, in either instance, the relative strength of potentially corrective engrams is reduced. Briefly stated, the patient acts as if corrective engrams did not exist. In normal persons, the net effect of the behaviour pattern described would in all likelihood be frustration. In frontal lobe disease on the other hand, where the very baseline of affective response is unstable, frustration does not necessarily occur. The patient acts like a child which pursues a pleasurable short term policy. For example, a patient of my observation (461) in whom a right frontal meningioma was completely removed at operation and, to make possible the exposure of the tumor, a large portion of the frontal lobe amputated, showed the following abnormalities as described by his daughter six years after the operation. "He acts like a child, He is stubborn and does not listen to reason. He is impatient and abrupt in his actions." According to Jarvie (435) the "development of the personality is such that when it reaches completion in early adult life some socially undesirable tendencies may persist, so that social control can only be achieved by their continued inhibition. It is these tendencies which seem to come principally to the surface after frontal lobe injury. . . . There is insight into the new pattern of behaviour but control over it is minimal or negligible."

Certain types of abnormal behaviour in frontal lobe disease appear to be carricature of *immature behaviour*, especially lack of restraint, rudeness, tactlessness, lack of decency and, in sense, even obscene behaviour, uninhibited sexual aggressiveness and outright criminal acts. Tactlessness is the inability to forego readily accessible sources of gratification. In our culture, tactlessness, perhaps, involves lack of endurance. Frank criminal behaviour in frontal lobe disease was described by de Crinis (183), Cossack (170), Wimmer (967), Faust (223), Haefner (336, 337), Knepel (500), Lenz (557, 558) and other writers. As a rule, the patient has insight into his own moral defect as illustrated, for example, by Wimmer's observations. His first patient developed deceitfulness, a tendency to lie, to roam about and to steal. In the second case, there was noted a tendency to lie, to steal and an increased sexual urge. The patient was impervious to admonition and reproach. The third patient became destructive. In all three patients however the social concepts were well preserved as none of them had any difficulty in answering questions concerned with ethical and social problems. A similar dissociation between "knowledge and virtue" may occur in metencephalitic children (782). "Scio meliora proboque, deteriora sequor." Lenz reported the case of a soldier who had sustained a bilateral frontal lobe wound but recovered sufficiently to travel by railroad. He happened to be present when an amputee was refused a seat by a civilian. The brain injured soldier threatened to kill the civilian unless he gave his seat to the cripple. The former declined again, laughing derisively—and was hit by a deadly bullet from the soldier's gun.

Conceivably, the mechanism of abnormal behaviour will grow more complicated if, as result of the dyshomeostatic effect of frontal lobe damage, inordinately increased (though apposite) affects operate in conjunction with *inapposite affects*. Thus, antisocial and criminal behaviour may not necessarily be due to hyperaffectivity but, rather, as discussed under the heading "Elements of a stimulus response psychology and psychopathology" earlier in this chapter, to the *vectorial inversion* of the impulse parameter of intellective stimuli. The behaviour disorder may be further complicated by the combination of the abnormal affective states in question with disorders of attention, memory and thinking. In the extreme case, potentially corrective engrams may not be ekphorized so that the rivalry mechanisms which ordinarily play between, on the one hand, the impulse parameters of intellective stimuli and, on the other, the affective loading of the engrams in question are not put into operation in the first place. Lastly, the dyshomeostatic character of the affective changes may be accentuated by the fluctuations of the affective level already referred to; one and the same patient may be euphoric at one time but dysphoric or, for that matter, aphoric at other times. (Accordingly, the division of frontal lobe patients into three groups is somewhat schematic and may have to be supplemented by the addition of a fourth, dysphoric-euphoric group.)

Abnormal behaviour in the aphoric group

Aphoria is commonly associated with hypoaffectivity or decreased responsiveness to stimuli. Whenever affects become too weak to elicit behaviour patterns apt to produce immediate or delayed gratification, the patterns in question are eliminated from the performance repertory of the subject. It is this group of patients which are said to suffer from lack of drive, who have ceased to will, and act as if they knew neither joy or grief.

In *summary*, then, emotional dyshomeostasis produces polar opposites of behaviour wherein one extreme is comparable to puerile behaviour patterns of conduct while the other extreme resembles a state of emotional blunting, apathy and exhaustion. The former is an apparent regression to an earlier state of behaviour organization while the latter which, fortunately, has no counterpart in the history of human development, may be confused with neurotic reactions.

At this point, brief reference may be made to those cases in which, allegedly, frontal lobe lesions failed to cause any demonstrable abnormality of mentation. In these instances, the lesions were either unilateral or, although bilateral, did not destroy the entire frontal lobes (*311*). Even granting the absence of mental changes, the negative findings would hardly indicate that, as held in some quarters, the frontal lobes have no recognizable function. The anatomical and physiological considerations developed in the present chapter indicate that the material substrate of affectivity and drive is most heavily concentrated in the anterior cortex and its subcortical connections but that, as in other spheres of function, the principle of collateral organization applies equally to the representation of activating factors, especially the direct connections of the activating and alerting system with the posterior cortex or, for that matter, of Halstead's power factor P. The adaptibility of the neural tissue to gradually increasing damage must of course be taken into consideration. In slowly growing tumors of the foramen magnum, for example, the medulla oblongata may be compressed to a ribbon but signs of medullary compression may be scanty in proportion to the degree of deformity of the bulb encountered at operation or autopsy. Several years ago, I operated upon a patient with a large frontal lobe meningioma, who while at work as a laborer three days prior to his admission to the hospital, had struck his head against a beam. Following the injury, he developed epileptiform seizures. Air studies demonstrated a large filling defect of the right frontal horn of the lateral ventricle, which excluded the diagnosis of uncomplicated posttraumatic epilepsy. Because of the slow growth of the lesion, personality changes, if any, were minimal both preoperatively and postoperatively. The statistical evidence is overwhelmingly in favour of the role of the frontal lobes in affectivity, setting aside, at this point. the correlated changes already described. A comparison of 30 verified bilateral tumors of the genu of the corpus callosum with 20 verified bilateral tumors of the splenium disclosed that emotional disturbances in tumors of the splenium were not only less frequent than those in

the anterior group but that they were mild by comparison. In the anterior group, euphoria was noted six times, puerility four times, hypersexualism twice, depression six times, listlessness 18 times, and irritability four times. In the posterior group, lack of restraint, eroticism, listlessness, swinging mood, irritability and apprehensiveness were noted in one instance each.

COMMENT AND CRITICISM

For a discussion of the early theories of frontal lobe function the interested reader may be referred to Feuchtwanger's (*230*) and Rylander's (*787, 788*) monographs. The authors point out that Meynert and Hitzig regarded the frontal lobes as an organ of abstract thought, Bianchi (*80*) of psychic synthesis, Wundt of apperception; and Ferrier of mental concentration. In the words of Rylander (*788*) the opinion of the various writers who studied the clinical symptoms of frontal lobe disease are directly opposed to one another, and his own (Rylander's) investigations "partly confirm and partly deny the assumption of each of these authors." "It can be agreed with Baruk," Rylander writes, "that changes in emotion and personality are very conspicuous in nature, with Feuchtwanger that pathological traits in the volitions are also present, with Foerster and Kleist that the volitional defects are considerable and with Brickner as well as Goldstein and v. Woerkom that the higher intellectual functions are deteriorated." Rylander himself did not attempt to find the "rationale" of the variegated symptomatology of frontal lobe disease; in fact, he declined to speculate on the "duties of the frontal lobes in mental life and the nature of the normal functions which, when damaged, give rise to the pathological features" he found among his 32 patients with frontal lobe ablations. Significantly, he encountered emotional changes in 30 out of his 32 patients studied, changes in volitional and psychomotor activity in 22 cases, and intellectual changes in 21 cases.

Some of the earliest and most valuable observations were recorded in Harlow's (*396, 347*) papers which deal with the now legendary "crowbar case", and in Leonore Welt's (*945*) article on the effects of severe baso-frontal injuries. We mention the two publications in passing only for they have been widely quoted in the literature and have received the attention they deserve. In recent years, theories concerning the mechanism of abnormal behaviour in frontal lobe disease were promulgated by Feuchtwanger, Kleist, Goldstein, Brickner, Freeman and Watts and Denny-Brown, which will be taken up presently. For a critical evaluation of Hebb's (*361*) and of Hebb and Penfield's (*362*) theories the reader may be referred to Goldstein (*311, 312*) and Denny-Brown (*191*) and for a criticism of Hebb's (*361*) and Kanzer's (*470*) views to my article on mental changes in intracranial tumors (*799*). At this point, it will suffice to note that, conceivably, mental changes occurring in the course of organic brain disease may reflect the patient's attempts to adjust himself to a new life situation. However, this mechanism can hardly be of significance if, as in the average case of frontal lobe tumor, the mental changes *precede* the other manifestations of the disease. Neither is the severity of the mental changes proportional to the severity of the organic changes, as one might expect of Kanzer's theory were correct, for they are notoriously rare in incapacitating posterior fossa lesions.

Feuchtwanger: (230)

Feuchtwanger examined 200 cases of frontal lobe trauma, which he compared with 196 cases of injury to the extra-frontal parts of the brain. He arrived at the conclusion that, in frontal lobe disease, the basic mental defect involves primarily volitional and affective functions while the intellectual deficit is secondary. He deliberately abstained from any attempt at defining behavioural changes in terms of structure-function relationships. By contrast, he explained the equilibratory functions of the frontal lobes and their disturbances by the fact that, as suggested by Anton (*23*), both the cerebellum and the frontal lobes are parts of a unitary coordinative mechanism. Thus, the representation of equilibratory functions in the frontal cortex would appear to be quite logical while the role of the frontal lobes with regard to human behaviour, at least as far as suggested by a perusal of Feuchtwanger's work, lacks any physiological rationale; indeed, it appears to be coincidental. His approach to the problem under study demonstrates the futility of developing an adequate framework of reference without due regard to neuropsychological criteria, and his notion that behaviour disorders in frontal lobe disease are primarily emotional in origin is,

although true, left hanging in midair. Oddly enough, Feuchtwanger does not stick to his own idea of the primacy of volitional factors in the causation of frontal lobe symptomatology; he sees the source of emotional attitudes (and, by implication, their perversions) in *abstract knowledge*. Only in this sense can we understand his statement that the defective inhibition of instincts (including polyphagia and sexual aggressiveness) is attributable to the loss of the sense of judgment and that loss in turn of judgment can be attributed to a loss of "sense of value."

Kleist (492, 495)

In sharp contrast to Feuchtwanger's approach to the problem of behaviour abnormalities in frontal lobe disease, Kleist's theory is based on the interpretation of structure function relationships in both the somatic and the psychic sphere. Kleist very early recognized the close morphological and functional affinity between the baso-frontal and the cingulate cortex and also of the importance of the fiber connection between the diencephalon and the frontal lobes. As regards the functional significance of these relationships, he gave credit to Le Gros Clark (*162*) who had insisted on their importance in his comparative anatomical studies on the thalamus. Kleist expounded the view that both the orbital and the cingulate cortex and their subordinate centers are related to ego-functions (a shorthand expression applied to the instinctual and emotional life of the organism) while the convexity of the prefrontal lobes is concerned with psycho-motor and intellectual activities. "The anatomical data," Kleist writes, "permit us to recognize in the orbital and the cingulate (including the retro-orbital) cortex the basic ego functions which in turn are rooted in enteroceptions (Innenempfindungen) and in the reactions thereto." Biologically, the ego is made up of three "layers" comprising (a) the lower emotions and drives (Gefühls-Ich and Trieb-Ich), (b) the somatic sensations (Körper-Ich) and, (c) the higher emotions and character traits, sentiments, beliefs, moral and religious attitudes (Gemeinschafts-Ich, Welt-Ich and religiöses-Ich). The individual "layers" of the ego have both sensory and motor aspects, the former comprising feelings, drives, enteroceptions and attitudes, the latter the various kinetic phenomena such as movements related to drives, volitions, etc. In his somewhat capricious terminology, which makes a translation of his writings quite difficult, Kleist describes pathological alterations of the diverse ego components. (Incidentally, his terminology has given rise to the considerable misapprehension, particularly to the story that the individual egos are located in specialized cytoarchitectonic areas). For example, defects of the social ego or Gemeinschafts-Ich are those of social traits, including deceitfulness, unreliability and faithlessness, the tendency to cheat and to lie, etc., while defects of the Selbst-Ich are puerility, inappropriate hilarity and sexual aggressiveness; and defects of the somatic ego, dysphoria and euphoria as expressions of pathological fluctuations of the receptivity of this particular layer of the ego. Concerning the localization of the ego disturbances, Kleist expresses the belief that they are due to structural changes of the diencephalon, the orbital and the cingulate cortex, and that even the highest ego functions are rooted in the interbrain. ("*Auch das höhere Ich senkt seine Wurzeln bis ins Zwischenhirn.*") Apparently, the diencephalic components of all functional layers of the ego are so organized as to respond to injury with fluctuations in the excitability of the structures in which they are represented. In this respect the centers in question react in a manner similar to that of the cell stations mediating sleep, wakefulness and temperature regulation. Kleist deals extensively with the phenomenon of *Antrieb*, whose importance was first recognized by Bayerthal (*49*), and which comes to the fore not only in the psychomotor sphere but also in language and thought.

Kleist's studies on the function of the frontal lobes, which are an outstanding contribution to the subject, are for the most part based on experiences with war injuries. They would be worthy of more lengthy quotation than is feasable both for considerations of space and because of the already mentioned difficulty of an adequate translation. I have epitomized his ideas in a section devoted to the criticism of frontal lobe theories to throw Feuchtwanger's psychologizing approach into sharp relief. At the same time, I wish to acknowledge my indebtedness to Kleist. Differences of opinion concern the interpretation of drive, or *Antrieb*, which, I believe, is ultimately autonomic rather than motor in origin, that is, imparted to the extrapyramidal system by the autonomic nervous system. The extrapyramidal system, in turn, plays a facilitatory role in psychomotor motility.

GOLDSTEIN (311, 312, 313)

According to Goldstein, frontal lobe deficit consists in varying degrees of failure to use the abstract attitude and in the inability to shift back and forth between the abstract and the concrete attitude. In taking the concrete attitude, objects are apprehended in their entirety as just what they appear to be. For example, a key is not taken to be the instrument "key" but as an object in a specific setting, briefly, a particular key right then and there. In taking the abstract attitude on the other hand, certain qualities of an object such as size, color and shape may be apprehended and set apart from the individual circumstances under which the object appears. (Perhaps, the abstract attitude is best defined as the ability to deal with certain aspects of objects, of events, and of situations as representatives of a class rather than as perceptions or individual experiences.) As a result, the concrete attitude also suffers. Further, Goldstein differentiates between mood changes and emotional disturbances: of these, only the latter are allegedly caused by changes in the abstract attitude while mood changes are believed to be disorders caused by injury to the fronto-thalamic system. Lack of drive, or akinesia, (roughly corresponding to what Kleist calls "Mangel an Antrieb"), is a secondary disorder, that is, one due to confusion and indecision on the part of the patient. The resulting hesitancy and slowness is likewise a manifestation of his inability to take the abstract attitude. As to the equanimity displayed by the patient, his "affective state must necessarily be more amiable, since many situations are not grasped conceptually, which makes him appear blunted." Allegedly, lack of initiative, of foresight, of activity and the ability to handle new tasks and the impairment of voluntary shifting and choice are likewise dependent on the impairment of the abstract attitude. Thus, Goldstein denies the primacy of emotional changes upheld by Feuchtwanger.

In evaluating Goldstein's theory, it is important to keep in mind that the *impairment of the abstract attitude is nothing other than the inability to think in concepts*, while the difficulty in shifting from the abstract to the concrete attitude and vice versa is more likely due to the "psychic akinesia" inherent in the alogic thinking disorder. It is not altogether clear why this particular defect should lead to emotional changes and how it would possibly explain the hyperactivity rather than the hypoactivity observed in some patients. Neither is it apparent how the inability to take the abstract attitude should account for akinesia in experimental animals in which it is just as conspicuous as in humans. The distinction between emotional and mood changes appears to be artificial, at least in the particular context concerned.

BRICKNER: (113, 114, 115)

The patient described by Brickner underwent a bilateral frontal lobectomy forward of area 6 and 44. He showed "(a) defects in complex, synthetic functions the existence of which depends on the synthesis of simple engrammatic units and (b) the manifestations referable to the separate activation of single engrammatic units which formerly were synthetized. . . . A single theme runs throughout, intact simple units of thoughts are unsynthetized into coherent complex aggregations." Follow up studies showed that "the patient had lost control over his emotions including the uninhibited nature of his jocosity of which he was well aware and that he was alternately boastful, angry, aggressive, negativistic, etc. In the intellectual sphere, he showed some degree of impairment of the power of synthesis and analysis but his lack of appreciation of the severity of the situation was out of proportion to his other defects of appreciation and judgment." In another connection, Brickner writes that frontal lobe deficit becomes manifest by the "conscious inability to synthetize separate thought processes which places a limit on the degree of attainable complexity of thought and on the number and possible associations between engrams which have already been synthetized to a complex degree in another part of the nervous system." As may be read from Brickner's diagram, the engrams have been aggregated in the posterior associative cortex, and are literally transferred to the anterior cortex. He believes that most if not all clinical manifestations of frontal lobe deficiency can be explained by difficulties in the synthesis of thought, and that the synthetic process, as opposed to more primitive thought, is elaborated by the frontal lobes.

Thus, Brickner is in essential agreement with Goldstein who, we remind ourselves, claimed that the primary defect in frontal lobe disease involves the cognitive rather than the emotional sphere. Brickner believes that the "individual must be able to *conceive* (italics mine) of emotional compensation for the emotional sacrifices which are required." Earlier in this chapter we have shown that the integrity of social concepts does not influence the patient's behaviour in the least. In other words, the patient fails to make use of whatever insight into his own condition he may have; whatever insight he does have, does not carry force. The Socratic approach to the interpretation of behaviour disorders in frontal lobe disease—for Socrates taught that virtue is knowledge—is not the only weak point of Brickner's theory. The notion that engrams can be transported from the posterior cortex to the anterior cortex, there to be put together to higher mental processes, is an anthropistic fallacy; it implies that engrams can be literally shipped from one part of the brain to another. Further, Brickner claims that one must be careful to ascribe a symptom to the lack of the part of the brain which has gone. Yet this is precisely what he himself is doing for, clearly, removal of the frontal lobes eliminates the very organ which supposedly synthetizes engrams to concepts. It is further to be noted that Brickner places undue emphasis on the capacity to form a maximum of associations and, implicitly neglects the problem of the quality of thought. The value of Brickner's work lies chiefly in the graphic description of the patient's behaviour. It should be read in conjunction with Beringer's (69) equally excellent account of a comparable case of a patient with a bilateral frontal lobe meningioma. The two carefully recorded observations convey a much more vivid impression of a frequent behaviour abnormality encountered in extensive frontal lobe damage than the results of psychometric tests. In the presence of gross clinical abnormalities, negative tests prove nothing except their own uselessness: if positive, they merely confirm the clinical impression. Tests cannot possibly measure the patient's potential behaviour abnormalities in life situations which, to be successfully handled, require that conflicting motifs be delicately balanced. The description of the patient's behaviour by a child may be more enlightening than the result of the most elaborate tests. It is not without interest that Brickner's patient survived his operation for well over twenty years and that, at autopsy, there were found multiple small meningiomas scattered over the convexity of the occipital lobes. Unexpected as these findings undoubtedly were, they do not diminish the value of Brickner's description of frontal lobe deficit in the least. Not only is his case strikingly similar to those of frontal lobe tumors in which no other lesions were found (and of which scores have been collected) but it is extremely unlikely that the occipital lobe meningiomas were present at the time of the clinical observation.

FREEMAN AND WATTS (259, 260, 261)

"The prefrontal region longcircuits our actions," the authors write, "make for deliberation and delay to the end that the decision shall be mature and the results measure up to expectation. They improve caution and restrain any action until we are as certain as possible of the future implications of the action." On the surface, the above formulation of basic frontal lobe deficit appears to be plausible. In actuality, mere delay does not guarantee appropriacy of response. Lack of appropriacy of response is the result of the derangement of a far more complicated mechanism than the elimination of delay circuits although, in determining appropriacy of response, delay may no doubt play a major role. In this particular respect, Freeman and Watts do not add anything to the subject; they fail to specify both the nature of the rivalry mechanisms which ordinarily operate in the delay interval and the criteria which determines the solution of the conflict. On the other hand, the following statements are important contributions to the theory of frontal lobe function. (a) The occasionally observed postlobotomy deficit in the intellective sphere is not due to a primary impairment of intelligence but, rather, to the inability, caused by the operation, to make use of the existing mental capacity owing to the emotional changes and the reduction of drive. (However, the opposite statement may also be found: The patient, having lost his anxiety and his inhibitions, uses his intellectual capacities more freely.) (b) Hunt (415), who tested Freeman and Watt's patients, mentions poor attention and lack of initiative as causes of the poor test scores. (Accordingly, her opinion that lobotomy causes impairment of abstract thinking and of the higher intellective faculties is not completely substantiated by the outcome of the tests.)

DENNY BROWN (191)

The author is in essential agreement with Brickner that "restraint in behaviour is itself a product of intellectual operation." If this were true, Napoleon Bonaparte would have acted almost like an imbecile; when his valet gave him a uniform which felt too tight, he would fly into a fit of rage and tear it to pieces. Denny Brown asserts that failure in reaction following frontal lobe lesions appears to be "the absence of a normally predictable stimulus the properties of which should ultimately be accurately definable"; that "it is the reaction to the projection of the consequence in space and time that is at fault"; that "the whole future setting or Gestalt fails to resolve as a stimulus for an act"; and that, "in the last analysis, the behaviour of frontal lobe deficit is one of visualization or, for that matter, of gestaltperception." Yet, since lack of gestaltperception does not correlate with behaviour disorders, one is left in the dark about the nature of the particular form of gestaltblindness that makes the patient act in the fashion described.

PENFIELD AND EVANS (719)

"It may be concluded that the anterior frontal cortex has no motor or sensory functions; nor is it employed in the recording mechanisms of memory. It is utilized in conscious mental processes that are essential to well planned initiative and which provide the individual with understanding of future consequences of present action." It is true that the anterior frontal cortex is utilized in conscious mental processes involved in planning but it remains obscure how planning can occur without the ekphory of appropriate engrams. Experimental and clinical evidence does not support the contention that mnemonic processes are a function of the anterior cortex only. Lastly, the understanding of future consequences does not guarantee appropriacy of conduct.

GOLLA (314)

The last-developed mental function (sense of responsibility and mental judgement) depends on the integrity of the last-developed structure of the cerebrum, the prefrontal lobe in its relation to the thalamic system of emotional resonance. This statement is an example of how frontal lobe function should not be interpreted. Not only are the prefrontal lobes not the phylogenetically most recent part of the brain but Golla fails to account for the presence of severe ethical defects in persons in which the frontal lobes and the thalamus are intact.

Hertz a. ass. (377)

The authors report the case of a young male who developed an abscess of unknown origin in his left frontal lobe. Following enucleation of the abscess, the patient's immediate postoperative behaviour was similar to that of a patient after a frontal lobotomy. Confusion, dullness and retardation were present for a few days, followed by laziness, irritability and lack of interest. He was discharged four weeks after the operation and returned to his work as manager of an office after another four weeks. His behaviour was unlike his old self, the main abnormalities being lack of interest in his duties and poor judgement. Moreover, he squandered his own money and developed an increased sexual urge approaching satyriasis. However, he had full insight into his own condition and promised his wife "to behave in the future." Four years after the operation the patient was readmitted to the hospital for psychiatric treatment. There it was concluded that "this man's developmental history was of primary importance in understanding his behaviour" the implication being that, with a different history, the sequelae of the disease would have been different. In my opinion the personal history shows nothing that might not have occurred in any man's life. Moreover, in spite of his allegedly traumatic experiences early in his life ("a most traumatic childhood . . . blows to self-esteem") the patient "prior to the operation" had been a "good and steady family man", and again, "prior to the time of the operation" (the authors, probably, mean to say "prior to the onset of the disease") "his marriage has been ideal. They were well adjusted to each other and quite happy." It is the thesis of the three authors who wrote up this case report that the structural frontal lobe damage was only *one factor* which determined the behaviour and the personality changes following the operation on the left frontal lobe. Unfortunately, they do not specify to what extent the organic factor determined (or even conjecture to what extent it might have determined) the patient's behaviour. In fact, it would appear from their account of the case under consideration that the abnormalities described were purely psychogenic and the involvement of the frontal lobe coincidental. They express the *other factors* in terms of Ego defense, anxiety, deeply repressed feelings of helplessness, rejection and abandonment undoubtedly originally associated with early loss of his mother, feelings of inferiority, of insecurity, intense dependency longings and, ultimately, regressive (primitive) defenses, overcompensation, striving for success and prestige, outlet of ego strivings in spheres he felt he could be successful, namely, in sexual and certain social areas. Moreover, "the sexual outlet represented an acting out of hostility because of his obvious dependency on his wife." (Strangely enough, the marriage was a happy one and mutual adjustment perfect." (See above.) The pathological, sexual and social behaviour, the authors go on to say, also may have served as a defense against the emergence of his infantile separation anxiety. In conclusion, they assert that personality changes after "brain damage can in no way be understood in terms of the actual damage alone, a dynamic neuropsychiatric approach is required properly to understand and treat such patients." Unfortunately, the authors neglect any reference to the personal history of other patients with structural brain damage and to the fact that, as documented by a great many case reports, the very type of behaviour they themselves describe occurs precisely in other patients with frontal lobe damage. If personality changes after brain damage can in no way be understood by the structural changes alone, (in which statement there is no doubt some truth) the changes described should occur (a) as a result of damage to any part of the brain, including, e.g., the cerebellum, and (b) they should not precede the incapacitating symptoms of the disease as they do in most cases. It is to be hoped that we shall read further progress reports concerning both the patient himself, who is just about beginning to behave under psychiatric treatment, and also his wife who is undergoing "case work therapy by a psychiatric social worker—first once a week and now only every other week for one hour."

JARVIE (436)

Jarvie studied intellectual and behavioural changes in 71 men with wounds of the brain in 46 of whom the frontal lobe were damaged. Certain permanent changes took place only when the frontal lobes were injured but this happened in only in nine of the 37 cases of frontal lobe injury. (It is worthy of note that as far as known only one frontal lobe was involved.) Restlessness was noted in five instances, increased drive, stereotyped actions, impulsive actions, and loss of anger response in one each, increased sexual activity in three, talkativeness in eight, inappropriate talk in five and emotional blunting in two instances. He stressed the point that personality changes of a distinctive type occurred only in 25% of the cases, adding that the explanation cannot be purely anatomical, that, in his opinion, "the men who developed behaviour changes were in some way different from those who did not, and that the difference might have been rooted in the pre-morbid personality, more especially, that the injury brought to the fore a previously concealed conflict. "Certain features in their personalities that were formerly kept under control came to the surface as though the breaking power in respect of these features had become less effective." This, he adds, was well understood by most of the patients. He regards the loss of inhibition as very characteristic and to be dependent on interference with the normal functioning of the prefrontal cortex. The loss of inhibition did not extend to every part of the patients' behaviour but only seemed to occur in relation to those aspects over which they had to exert a special vigilance.

As expressed in neurophysiological terms, the inordinately strong affectivity of the probands, presumably, was compensated prior to the injury. After the injury, the compensatory process broke down. Apposite affects associated with the awareness of primary gratification were (although, because of the compensatory process, in a latent fashion) inordinately strong or, by the same token, inapposite affects dominant but suppressed by compensatory rival mechanisms. Prior to the injury affective equilibrium was so to speak artificially maintained. In a certain sense, then, the explanation of the abnormal behaviour is not purely anatomical. Nevertheless, it rests on an anatomical basis provided the frontal lobes are

assigned a psycho-autonomic function which, in disease, reflects the derangement pattern of a homeostatic mechanism.

TRIZARD (910)

Trizard, in a recent article devoted to the psychological effects of frontal lobe lesions, critically examines diverse interpretations of frontal lobe function, chiefly those based on experiences with lobotomized and lobectomized patients. While offering no solution of her own, she maintains that the theories of frontal lobe functions thus far proposed are inconsistent with the "modern holistic approach." I for one rather doubt that Trizard appreciates the significance of certain clinical data. For example, minimizing the value of Rylander's observations, in fact, calling attention to what she apparently believes to be a basic contradiction, she writes that, in Rylander's own words, "the most frequently registered symptoms were emotional lability and loss of interest but, whilst many patients became euphoric and tactless, others became depressed and withdrawn." In actual fact, the apparently inconsistent symptomatology reflects the disturbance pattern of a homeostatic mechanism, and, thereby, throws light upon the very nature of frontal lobe deficit, indeed, it is one of the most important clues to the interpretation of frontal lobe function.

CONCLUDING REMARKS

Apart from the contention that the frontal lobes have no recognizable function of their own, the most obvious mistakes made in interpreting frontal lobe symptoms in the mental sphere may be epitomized by the following statements to which brief comments are added.

(1) Mental changes in organic brain disease including frontal lobe lesions are difficulties of adjustment to the somatic disability produced by the former. (Kanzer)—In most cases, mental changes in frontal lobe disease antedate the organic disability; in others, they are the only symptoms. Accordingly, they cannot be attributed (at least not in a great majority of cases) to somatic disability, or the necessity on the part of the patient to adjust himself to a new life situation. In fact, the patient may be utterly unaware that a new life situation exists, and be happier than ever before.

(2) Mental changes in frontal lobe disease can be satisfactorily explained only by the evaluation of both psychological and somatic factors. (Hertz a. ass.)—In their own case, the investigators make no attempt whatsoever to determine the respective role of the somatic factors but, rather, study the symptoms presented by the patient on an exclusively psychodynamic basis, implying that the involvement of the frontal lobe was purely coincidental.

(3) The changes in volition are primary, the intellective changes secondary. (Feuchtwanger)— The intimate mechanism of this relationship remain unaccounted for.

(4) The intellective deficit, e.g., the inability to take the abstract attitude, is primary, while the mood changes are caused by the former. (Goldstein)—The inability on the part of the patient to take the abstract attitude cannot account for either euphoria or dysphoria. Moreover, following frontal lobe lesions, the mental changes are basically identical in man and in animals whose attitude is apt to be concrete.

(5) The intellective changes are caused by the failure on the part of the frontal lobes to synthetize engrams formed by the posterior cortex. (Brickner)—For comment, see above.

(6) Frontal lobe deficit can be expressed in gestaltpsychologic terms. (Denny-Brown) For comment, see above.

(7) Observations made on frontal lobe patients without concurrent evaluation of a "sufficient number of controls" are invalid. (Trizard)—The study of controls is certainly desirable but, to the degree postulated by Trizard, (see her original article) hardly practicable. Neither is it essential. For example, Brickner's and Beringer's already quoted publications are classic descriptions of mental and behavioural abnormalities in frontal lobe disease. Their value would not be enhanced by comparing the personality changes, which were identical in both cases, with the behaviour of normal controls of an identical or similar socio-economic background, intelligence, professional activity, age, sex and what not.

It is not a coincidence that personality changes in frontal lobe disease have been described in identical terms (in terms of traditional psychology) wherever they have been observed. It is true that similar changes may occur in extrafrontal lesions but the large number of concordant observations in frontal lobe disease is significant both statistically and symptomatologically. Although the frontal and extra-frontal syndromes do to a degree overlap, frontal lobe patients, as a group at least, differ from others.

The interpretation of frontal lobe function here offered may be more complicated and, at least without due evaluation of neuropsychological data, more difficult to understand than, say, the statement that the frontal lobes are the *seat of the highest intellectual functions*, so that frontal lobe damage causes intellectual deficit, or the *seat of the highest ethical functions*, in which case the patient, rather naturally, becomes a criminal. The authors who make such statements do not bother with a definition of the terms intellectual and ethical, presumably because the meaning of these terms is "generally known"; nor do they explain why the functions under study should have a seat in the first instance. In truth, mental changes in frontal lobe disease are not referable to any one factor. They are caused by the lack of coordination of specific factors which, under normal conditions, cooperate to maintain *affective homeostasis, normal responsiveness of the highest sensory levels of the brain* and a *normal volume of sensory-motor relations at the highest level of brain function*. In this respect, the derangement of the interaction of the factors involved in normal frontal lobe function resembles the diverse mechanisms of heart failure and other pathophysiological conditions which can be grasped in terms of complexly interacting events only. The individual disturbance patterns are however not necessarily stereotyped but, owing to the great many factors concerned, show manifold interrelations.

III

Thought

Once unleashed, thought grows to a torrent that carries us irresistibly with it.
LUDWIG FEUERBACH

NATURE OF THOUGHT

Thought, being the function of an organ of the body, is a special segment of the total life process. It is a means by which the higher organism is able to find its way through reality, that complex of interacting forces and events which constitutes the external world and its hazards. The manifold which we call the physical world is made up of traces and imprints of things that have been happening and, still going on in the present, are the nascent future. Hence, reality is not only the sum total of existing things but also of their determinants projected upon past and future cross sections through the stream of events flowing around us. Thought is the representation, in the brain of man, of these interacting things and events some of which have passed while others are unfolding or are yet to evolve. It embodies the awareness of relationships at the same time as it develops new ones, preeminently those which have a bearing on the fate of the organism.

If it is true that thought is an instrument of goal directed behaviour, it is legitimate to infer that *the attainment of similar goals requires similar actions or responses on the part of the organism.* Further, that they depend on the *ability to differentiate between likeness and difference, and to establish categories comprising similar data and their relations.* (Hippocrates' saying that "it is the business of the physician to know, in the first instance, things similar and dissimilar" has universal applicability.) The assumption, then, that *thought is concerned with the discovery of similarity and difference* may be chosen as an appropriate point of departure. More accurately, that it is concerned with the discovery of similarity and difference at the *conceptual level of experience* even though, in a certain sense, the very formation of concepts is already an act of thought.

The more prominent the factor of productivity, of discovery and invention, the stronger the element of *thinking* in the awareness of conceptualized relations; the more prominent the factor of reproduction, remembering and recall, the stronger the element of *learning.* Learning and thinking form a continuous scale but are by no means identical. In simple language, learning may be defined as the acquisition of knowledge and skill by means of observation, instruction and participation. Since the most primitive forms of learning involve the modifiability of instinctive behaviour by corrective engrams and, in the lower organism, behaviour is adapted by means of perceptions rather than of concepts, learning and thinking and, at the same time, perception and thought, or "instinct and reason" cannot be sharply set apart but, on the contrary, are in many respects interrelated. For all intents and purposes, then, learning and thinking may be brought upon a common denominator.

CATEGORIES OF THOUGHT

For the time being it will be convenient to express learning in terms of thinking and, depending whether the *mnemonic system*, the *dominant* or the *subsidiary sphere of mentation* takes the lead, to differentiate between three main categories of reasoning, namely, *reproductive, reflective* and *intuitive* thought.

(1) *Reproductive* thought may be conveniently subdivided into (a) repetitive thought and (b) recognitive thought.

(a) *Repetitive thought.* Its essence is the spontaneous reproduction of mnemonic material. One of the most primitive forms of repetitive thought in which, accordingly, the factor of thinking properly so called is at a minimum, is the ekphory of nonsense syllables while higher forms of repetitive thought, in which ekphory is combined with observation, are more or less productive. A person who, some time ago, has found his way through a maze of streets, may be once more confronted with the task to orient himself in a city looking almost as unfamiliar as ever before.

(b) *Recognitive thought.* Its essence is the object-induced, (exogenic) ekphory of mnemonic material, and the correlation of ekphorized engrams with corresponding objects or events. This correlation produces what is known as feeling of familiarity or *perceptual recognition*, while the *conceptual recognition* of an object involves its correlation with a supraordinate system of reference. A simple form of recognitive thought is the recognition of an object in a familiar setting; of a more complicated form, in an unfamiliar setting. (See Chapter IV, *Disorders of recognition and skill* and figs. 42 and 43.)

(2) *Reflective thought* is predominantly a function of the axial stream of mentation, i.e., it is dependent on a maximum of attention and concentration and, at the same time, the reinforcement of the axial stream by its mnemonic undercurrent at appropriate phases of the thought process. Reflective thinking falls into three main groups, namely, *apperceptive, reconstructive* and *anticipative* thought.

(a) *Apperceptive thought* is concerned with "things that go on in the present" and "with interacting things and events", in other words, with the appreciation of *existing* relations and those *developing* under the reasoner's eyes. (Owing to the infinitesimal character of the present, the two varieties of apperceptive thought cannot always be set apart.) A simple example, illustrating the appreciation of existing relations, is the experience that the effort to lift a box increases not only in proportion to its size but also to the weight of the objects it contains. The original experience was based on a generalization which was only conditionally correct—in a certain sense, *experience may be regarded as a system of corrected generalizations*. The same applies to apperceptive thought concerned with the appreciation of developing relations, for example, the rules of a game.

(b) *Reconstructive thought* is concerned with "things and events that have passed." It involves the appreciation of causal relationships if only the last link of a chain of events is known or, alternately, if the last link and one or more immediate links are known, in other words, reconstructive thought encompasses conclusions from the effect to the cause.*

(c) *Anticipative thought* is concerned with "things and events which are as yet to evolve," i.e., the awareness of cause effect relationships within a chain of events if the first link is known or the first link and, with the exception of the last or final event, one or more subsequent links are known.

(3) Intuitive thought is predominantly a function of the subsidiary sphere of mentation which interacts, in a way to be discussed later, with the dominant sphere of mentation and the mnemonic system. The intuitive technique of thinking plays a crucial part chiefly in reconstructive thought and other forms of productive mental activity. It does not depend on attention and concentration but, on the contrary, is apt to take shape in a setting of relaxation of attention, indeed, sometimes in directing attention to other matters. (See Chapter II, fig. 11.)

There may be a subtle difference between the terms *thinking* and *reasoning* but we see no objection for using them interchangeably. The term *imagination* refers to the element of productivity

in both reflective and intuitive thought, the term *discursive reasoning* to verbalized thought.

The question now arises: Are there any common mechanisms involved in the various forms of reasoning? And is it possible to trace them to elementary nervous system functions as their functional primordia? Further, what is the intimate mechanism of creative thought in daily life and in science? (Creativity in the arts will be studied in a separate chapter.) Can it be expressed in terms of the "stimulus response scheme?"* The more recent investigations devoted in part to the problem of creativity (*39, 147, 333*) offer a wealth of data but, unfortunately, fail to elucidate its nature, as already pointed out in several review articles, notably those by Kline (*61*), Newman (*244*) and Nagel (*242*). Earlier publications will be discussed under the heading "Comment and Criticism."

We hope to find a common basis for the study of the *diverse categories of thought processes*, to be able to specify the relationships between *instinct and thought*, between *thinking* on the one hand and the role of the individual *spheres of mentation* on the other and, finally, to examine the interrelation between thinking, the *structure of the waking state* and the possible role of the *dissociation of the self*. For the time being, we shall keep comments at a minimum and avoid going into controversial matters too deeply. Suffice to refer to R. N. F. Maier's (*214*) remark made in his paper on the solution of problems in the human and its appearance in consciousness. "A problem which is different from one solved in the past but which has the same principle involved in the solution cannot have the solution explained by similarity until both solutions are known." We expect to show that, given a certain concatenation of factors, the problem is solved, or apt to be solved (for the nervous system operates on a probability basis) by the similarity between two relation-structures, regardless whether the subject is aware of it or, indeed, ever will be aware of the common features and principles concerned. In other words, the common mechanism involved in various forms of thought are *associations by similarity* and, we might add, related *associations by contiguity* regardless whether they materialize in the dominant or the subsidiary sphere of mentation. These associations, it is true, are of a different order of complexity and their structure may not be immediately apparent.

---

* This procedure is frowned upon by logicians but it is doubtful whether they had lived long enough to reach the frowning stage had they consistently followed their own principles.

---

* See Chapter II, "Elements of a stimulus response psychology," and related subjects.

For reasons which will become apparent later, the *non-mathematical fields* of thought must be set apart from the *mathematical fields* before the principles underlying the two varieties of thinking can be integrated. The following paragraphs are concerned with the processes of *association*, *redintegration*, *thinking* by *generalization and analogy, induction and deduction*, and their interrelations.

Association by similarity and contiguity

The principle of association by similarity and contiguity, the prototype of the association of relations, is indispensible to the investigation of more complicated thought processes. I beg the reader's indulgence for reporting some personal experiences which, no doubt, he will readily supplement by some of his own.

Shortly after graduation from medical school, I visited Rome. Descending the steps from one of the Piazzales, I saw two women approaching. As they slowly mounted the steps, it seemed to me that I had seen the younger one before; and when finally I saw her up close, the impression became compelling that I was seeing the classical features and the far away look of the models Anselm Feuerbach had immortalized in many of his paintings. For a fleeting second I felt that by some miracle the young woman had come alive and had stepped out of the frame of a picture. Ever since then, on seeing a photograph of the Piazzale or one of Feuerbach's paintings, or the two large volumes in which his letters are collected, I seem to live through the whole scene again.

Only recently I attended a lecture delivered by a visitor from England. She wore black gloves which, although an unimportant detail, seemed peculiar and somewhat distracted me from the subject she was discussing. A week later, while riding in a bus, I saw a woman who happened to be wearing black gloves. Immediately, I recalled the lecture and, at the same time, that the speaker had mentioned a book on an important subject. Having been interested in that problem, the train of thought initiated while listening to her was instantaneously reactivated.

The first example demonstrates the role of similarity both in evoking antecedent experiences and in determining future associations; the second example, *the power of association by similarity to evoke an entire train of thought by "redintegration" (132).* Everyday experience demonstrates the tendency of the mind to actuate successions of memory images under certain conditioning circumstances or to reestablish a set of data by their repetitive linkage. The role of associations in thought, although not generally admitted from a theoretical viewpoint is, nevertheless, somehow taken for granted. Who has not, during an oral examination, avoided bringing up a matter that might lead the examiner to ask an awkward question? And who has not, having forgotten what he wanted to do a moment ago, gone back to the very same place where he just *did* know what he wanted, expecting to reproduce the "lost" association? Given an appropriate stimulus, associations may be produced with almost reflex-like regularity.

The following examples illustrate transitions between *associations by similarity* and *thinking by analogy.*

The other day I found my refrigerator so well stocked that it seemed hardly possible to squeeze a small piece of butter onto its crowded shelves. Eventually, I placed the bar of butter on one of the shelves by standing it upright. At that moment, I recalled having read a curious item about George Clémenceau's last will. Truculent even in death, the celebrated French statesman had requested that his casket be lowered into his grave in an upright position, there to stand erect for the rest of the ages.

Dr. Charles Mayo (32, 231), while repairing a fistula of the intestines, found that he could not suture it, and that the defect had to be walled off, which reminded him of hogs getting out of their pen and being hemmed in by a fence. (I mention this well documented episode to demonstrate that I am not the only one who is given to odd association of ideas.)

Pearl Buck writes in one of her novels that a Chinese lady was very pleased with her maid because she never swept dust into corners but picked it up with a shovel and carried it out of the room. For a long time afterward, whenever I saw dust in a corner, I thought of Pearl Buck's novel, most of which, incidentally, I have forgotten.

While looking at Cleopatra's Needle in New York's Central Park I noticed that the four corners of the base of the obelisk were cut off and that the niches were occupied by sculptures representing giant crabs. This episode recalled a pleasant summer day spent, in part, watching people catch crabs somewhere along the shores of Long Island.

Grillparzer (99) had forgotten the plot of his play "The Golden Fleece." It so happened that he played a melody with which the forgotten idea had been associated. The music brought the plot back to this mind.

During the recent hospital strike in New York City, I was carrying two large bottles from one laboratory to another. A colleague of mine, who happened to pass by, remarked: "You remind me of Rebecca carrying her jars to the well." The following is another example of an even more remote but still intelligible association. Some time ago I awoke at night and, wondering what time it was, turned on my flashlight, but the batteries were almost exhausted, and I could not read the dial of my watch. However, I could use the flashlight to locate another one lying in a near by drawer. At that monent, I recalled an article discussing the production of a machine by another, similar machine, that is, the problem of machine propagation.

David Hume (136) wrote: "It is evident that there is a principle of connection between the different thoughts or ideas of the mind and that in their appearance to the memory or imagination they introduce each other with a certain degree of method and regularity. ... To me, there appears to be only three principles of connection of ideas, namely, *resemblance, contiguity in time and place and cause and effect.*" On another occasion he expressed his ideas on the subject in the following fashion: "We have arleady observed that nature has established connections among particular ideas and that no sooner one idea occurs in our thoughts than it introduces its correlate, and carries our attention towards it by gentle and insensible movement. These principles of connection or association we have reduced to three— namely, *resemblance, contiguity* and *causation* which are the only bonds that unite our thoughts together and beget that regular train of reflection or discourse which, in a greater or lesser degree, takes place among mankind."

The above recorded associative processes were certainly induced by resemblance, although the element of similarity was faint. (See "fringe-dominance", Chapter II, Part III.) It is hardly necessary to quote further instances of associations by

similarity and contiguity. In any case, there exist two types of associations; namely a *relevant* and an *irrelevant* form; ordinarily, the tendency to produce the first named, potentially goal leading, variety is stronger than the trend to form irrelevant associations.

Associations of any kind would be pointless without the notion of *causality*, which has crystalized from the observation of a habitual (unidirectional) linkage of certain events in time, and which is thereby derivable from the principle of association by contiguity. Causality is the central notion around which thought revolves and which lends it content and weight; it is the gravitational reference system of thought without which relationships would disintegrate into a cloud of meaningless homogeneity.

The following are examples of reasoning by generalization and analogy in which the elements of similarity plays a significant role. We deliberately choose some more or less well known biographical episodes which, for the sake of simplicity, will be stripped to their bare structure.

Generalization and analogy

Archimedes was asked to measure the volume of the crown of his friend and sponsor, Hiero, Tyrant of Syracuse, who suspected that it might not have been made of pure gold. One day, while taking his bath, it occurred to Archimedes that his body displaced a volume of water equal to its own. Given the volume of the crown and knowing the specific weight of gold, he could then determine how much the crown weighed and, at the same time, find out whether its weight equaled that of an identical volume of gold.

Newton (245) knew that the Earth attracts objects and, while observing the legendary fall of the apple in the orchard at Woolthorpe, the effects of terrestrial attraction was brought visibly to his mind. Up to this moment, he had not known what keeps the moon within the orbit of the Earth, and the planets circling the sun—Galilei having previously raised the question why the heavenly bodies move in circular rather than in straight paths. At the moment the apple fell near him, Newton became aware of the fact that the very same force which attracts the satellite toward the center of the Earth keeps the smaller cellestial bodies within the orbit of the larger. He explained the circling movement of the smaller around the larger by the fact that the satellites have a momentum of their own which, however, at each moment of their motion, is influenced by the gravitational pull of the dominant body, hence, that their path is the resultant of two forces, their own momentum and a pull acting perpendicularly to it.

Darwin (62) knew that breeders attempting to produce useful strains of animals select certain individuals as mates. He did not know the factors producing new species under natural conditions but was convinced that species are not immutable, and that individuals differ in innate qualities. (They are at present believed to be caused by mutations.) Malthus treatise on the *Principle of Population* called his attention to the continuous struggle of living beings in a world which, unfortunately, fails to provide sufficient food for all. Thus, he theorized, only the fittest transmit their innate traits to their progeny. In other words, Darwin saw the identity of the effects of artificial and natural selection.

More complicated examples of reasoning by analogy are Herschel's (127, 257) anticipation of Faraday's discovery, namely, the influence of magnetic and electric forces upon polarized light (145) and Einstein's theory of a path of a particle in the space time continuum which he fashioned in analogy with Newtonian dynamics (60).

The concept of wave mechanics, inagurated by De Brogie and Schrödinger (273) rests on a simple analogy with the physics of standing waves washing to and fro within the atom. Benjamin Franklin, experimenting with Leyden jars, recognized the similarity between electric sparks and lightening. Goethe (315) reasoned by analogy in comparing the bones of the skull with the vertebrae of the spinal column. Many inventors are convinced to have been guided by analogies and similarities with known principles (235, 273). Ellis (79) points out that Boole traced the analogy between logic and algebra, just as Descartes between geometry and algebra. And Jevons (145), in referring to Descartes' analytical geometry, writes: "Every geometrical curve represents some algebraic equation and even the discovery of the differential calculus was mainly due to geometrical analogy." According to McCurdy (205), Leonardo da Vinci recognized the similarity between sound and light waves. "Just as a stone flung into water becomes the center and the cause of various circles, and a sound produced in the air spreads itself out in circles, so each body situated in the luminous air is spread out circlewise and fills the surrounding parts with infinite images of itself and is present all in the whole and all in every part" (125). At the same time, Leonardo pointed out that there is a great similarity between waves of water and the waves caused by the wind across a grain field, which waves we see moving onward while the grain remains stationary.

The first three instances of reasoning by analogy can be represented by the accompanying relational proportions:

Case 1.	$\dfrac{\text{Volume of the crown (x)}}{\begin{array}{l}\text{Volume of water to}\\ \text{be displaced (a)}\end{array}}$	=	$\dfrac{\text{Volume of Archimedes (b)}}{\begin{array}{l}\text{Volume of displaced}\\ \text{water (a)}\end{array}}$
Case 2.	$\dfrac{\begin{array}{l}\text{Circling path of the}\\ \text{moon (x)}\end{array}}{\text{Terrestrial attraction (a)}}$	=	$\dfrac{\text{Straight fall of the apple (b)}}{\text{Terrestrial attraction (a)}}$
Case 3.	$\dfrac{\begin{array}{l}\text{Spontaneous transmu-}\\ \text{tability of species (x)}\end{array}}{\begin{array}{l}\text{Deliberate production}\\ \text{of animal species (a)}\end{array}}$	=	$\dfrac{\begin{array}{l}\text{Survival value of innate}\\ \text{inheritable qualities (b)}\end{array}}{\begin{array}{l}\text{Breeding value of desirable}\\ \text{traits (c)}\end{array}}$

The following diagram (fig. 16) is a symbolic representation of the reasoning processes described.

The analysis of the *pre-solution phase* (or problem phase) reveals the presence of three elements, namely, the awareness of the problem (or x) i.e., the gap in knowledge to which the two known data have as yet no fertile relationship. (To simplify matters the various as yet "scattered" factors involved are shown as if they had already moved into the "position" they occupy in the productive phase.)

In the *productive phase*, there appears a new awareness content which "closes the figure" in the

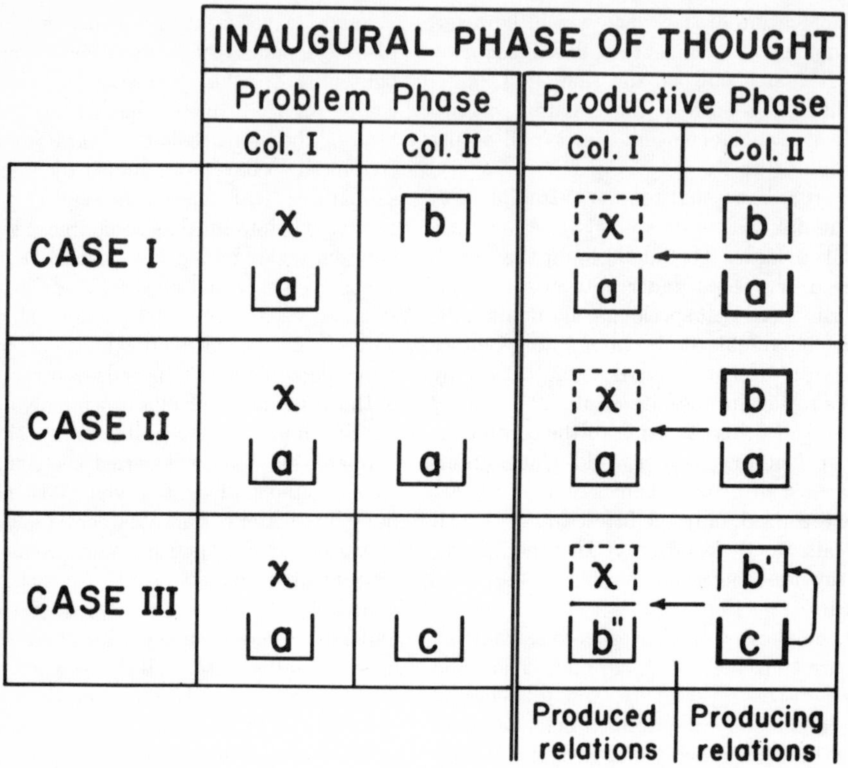

Fig. 16. Apparent gestalt mechanisms in productive thinking. Its relationship to association by similarity.

second column of the diagram. This new element or *actuating event* is either an observation or an ekphorized engram. As a result, the figure shown in the first column is likewise closed and the pre-solution phase converted into the solution phase.

The pattern represented in the second column is the *generating term*, that in the first column the *generated term*. *Insight* is the awareness of the suddenly emerging produced relation. The crucial event in the process of reasoning by generalization and analogy is the generation of a new *relation within the framework of the total relationstructure and its perception on the part of the reasoner*.

The above comment may have conveyed the impression that the reasoning processes under study may be fully understood in terms of gestalt-perception. This might be true had the reasoner actually looked at columns I and II while someone was completing the patterns indicated in column II of the productive phase, and he (the reasoner that is) had become aware of the similarity of the two terms of the relational framework at the moment of its completion. Yet, the reasoner

is confronted with *relations between assertions* rather than figures and, although assertions may be conveniently demonstrated by symbols, every individual assertion stands for a specific relation between a subject and a predicate. Thus, the diagrammatic illustration of reasoning by generalization and analogy indicates that either process involves a relation of a higher order, i.e., the *identity between two sets of relations*, or between *two terms of a proportion*. At the same time, it demonstrates the production of a new assertion or, for that matter, a new relation, within the generated term. The fact that the new experience or insight may be diagrammatically represented by the closure of a figure suggests a relationship of some kind, most likely a derivative relation, but does not imply that thinking and gestaltpercep-tion are identical. As will be shown later, the above interpretation of productive thinking combines in a way features of the gestalttheory and the associational theory of thought.

Thus far, then, the analysis of productive thought has disclosed that a variety of factors

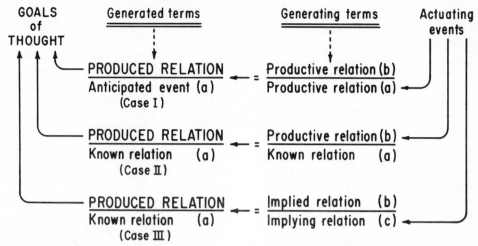

Fig. 17. Actuating events, generating terms, generated terms and produced relations in productive thinking. Their relationship to association by similarity.

can be isolated namely, (1) *productive relations*, (2) *generating terms*, (3) *generated terms* and (4) *produced relations*. For convenience, we apply the expressions "producing" and "produced" to the *individual relations*, and the expressions "generating" and "generated" to the two terms of the equation or to *relations between relations* (fig. 17).

A further study of the subject shows that, in spite of their uniform structure, the generating terms are not identical and that the same holds true for the generated terms.

In case 1, the *generating term* is composed of the relation between the productive relation (a) and an observation (b). The *generated term* is composed of the relation between an anticipated event (a) and the produced relation.

In case 2, the *generating term* is composed of the relation between the productive relation (b) and a relation known to the reasoner (a). The *generated term* is composed of the relation between the same relation (a) and the produced relation.

In case 3, the *generating term* is composed of a relation between, on the one hand, a relation known to the reasoner (c) and, on the other, a relation (b) suggested by the very same relation (Fig. 16, arrow). The *generated term* is composed of the relation of another relation known to the reasoner (a) to the produced relation. The expression "known to the reasoner" may be taken to mean that the data in question are (or, up to the experience of insight might have been) represented in his subsidiary sphere of mentation. (See below.)

At the same time, we realize that, in case 1 and 2, the productive relation was produced by an actual observation. In case 3, on the other hand, the productive relation was produced by an ekphorized engram. In other words, the producing relation itself was in each case initiated by the *actuating event*.

Lastly, the study of the three instances of productive thinking shows that certain phases of thought bear a resemblance to association by similarity. In *case 1*, (a) and (b) are similar, and so are (b) and (x). In *case 2*, (a) and (a) are similar. In *case 3*, (c) and (b) are similar. On the other hand, the reasoning processes under study cannot be *fully* expressed in terms of association by similarity for (b) resembles (x) neither in *case 2* nor in *case 3*. *It is true that the process of induction of the generated term by the generating term involves a principle similar to that operating in the process of association by similarity*. On the other hand, the item generating process, being based on the *appreciation of abstract relationstructures* rather than of perceptions or configurational data, is of a higher order than the process of association by similarity. *For the time being, we note that associations by similarity are in some way incorporated into the processes of reasoning by generalization and analogy which, in turn, may be interpreted as associational processes raised to a higher power.*

In spite of the above mentioned lack of uniformity of the generating and the generated terms, (and hence, of the reasoning processes themselves) reasoning by generalization and analogy may be expressed in terms of relational identity of the two terms of mathematical proportions, or of equations of the type.

(1) $x/a = b/a$ wherein a is known, and x becomes known at the moment the value of b is given; and

(2) $x/a = b/c$ wherein both a and c are known, and c implies b; and wherein x becomes known as soon as c (and therefore b') is given.

It may be readily seen that the relational proportions indicated under (2) are more complex than those indicated under (1); indeed, it may be imagined that *increasingly complex proportion patterns may be worked out by a process of extrapolation*. We are unable at this time to provide any concrete examples of more complicated reasoning processes than those already cited but shall return to this problem in the course of the discussion of superior mental ability.

What, exactly, is the difference between reasoning by generalization and reasoning by analogy? According to Aristotle (*6*), "analogy or proportion is when the second term is to the first as the fourth to the third." According to Kant (*152*), analogy is the "full similarity of two relationships between entirely different things." (Analogie ist eine vollkommene Ähnlichkeit zweier Verhältnisse zwischen ganz unähnlichen Dingen.) By the same token, generalization, or proportion, would be "when the second term is to the first as the fourth to the second", or "the full similarity of two relationships to identical (rather than to different) things." Jevons (*146*) expressed the difference in question as follows: "There is no distinction but that of degree between what is known as reasoning by generalization and reasoning by analogy. In both cases from certain observed resemblances we infer, with more or less probability, the existence of other resemblances. In generalization, the resemblances have great extension and usually little intension whereas in analogy we rely upon the great intension, the extension being of small amount. In analogy, we reason from likeness in many points to likeness in other points. The qualities of points of resemblance are now numerous, not the objects." (See also *255, 260, 265, 277, 323*.)

As already noted, actuating events, which, for their part, generate the productive relations, emerge in the thinker's mind either spontaneously, as the result of the *ekphory* of engrams, or they may be produced by *observation*. For example, Wallace (*338*) arrived at the idea of the origin of the species by natural selection while recalling Malthus' work with which he had been familiar for some time, while Darwin had only just read it and it was fresh in his mind. And Newton might well have come upon the idea of universal gravitational attraction *without* having seen the apple fall; rather, at one time or another, he might have spontaneously become aware of the fact that unsupported or unsuspended objects fall, and that the same force acts upon the moon and all other satellites, indeed, any particle of matter.

THOUGHT AND INSTINCT

To say that the ekphory of engrams functions as an actuating event raises the question of the role of the non-conscious mental processes in problem-solving and, implicitly, of how creative thought is related to neurointegrative processes of a lower order. No doubt there exists a one to one relationship (which can hardly be fortuitous) between certain components of instinctive behaviour and the individual steps involved in creative thinking, which lends support to *Spencer's* (*314*) *notion of the continuity of instinct and reason*. We remind ourselves that (a) instinctive behaviour is compounded of *appetitive* behaviour and the *consummatory act*, (b) that the former is initiated by a *reflex eliciting stimulus* experienced as *need*, while the consummatory act is set off by a (low order) *intellective stimulus* or *releaser* and (c) that appetitive behaviour is relatively *flexible* while the consummatory act is more or less *stereotyped*.

As applied to mental processes eventuating in the production of new relations, the *intellective need* initiated by the gap in knowledge, i.e., the state of disequilibrium at the conceptual level of cerebral function, corresponds to the *instinctive need*. The conventional term "directionality" of thought denotes nothing more than the self-regulatory property of thought processes which establishes, or re-establishes, biological equilibrium at the highest level of brain function.

Intellectual curiosity, the functional primordium of which is the exploratory behaviour of animals, corresponds to *appetitive behaviour* in the sphere of instincts. Investigative behaviour in man which, like appetitive behaviour, is flexible and highly individualistic, results primarily in the representation of impressions in the dominant sphere of mentation. Yet, to the extent that, as a result of many and partly unrelated activities in which the organism is engaged, more and more stimuli from various fields of experience at one time or another come to be represented in the dominant (conscious) segment of the mental apparatus, problem related data, temporarily at least, are shifted into the subsidiary (non-conscious) sphere of mentation i.e., "side-tracked" to be handled by *mnemic action mechanisms*. This shift, in turn, may be assumed to occur indirectly, that is, by way of engraphy of the stimuli concerned.

The *actuating event*, which is either an observation or an ekphorized engram, corresponds to the (low-order) *intellective stimulus* which releases the consummatory act in instinctive behaviour or, as expressed in terms of thinking, to the concluding phase of thought.

The *procedural scheme*, comprising (a) the formation of the generating term, (b) the ensuing emergence of the generated term having an identical relation-structure and (c), the conversion of "x" to a known, (figs. 16, 17) corresponds to the *consummatory act*. The term "scheme" refers to the relative rigidity involved in the establishment of the relational proportion of terms which, as we have said, matches, to a degree, the relative stereotypy of the consummatory response. And, just as the latter removes the instinctive need, so, the production of new relation, for a time at least, satisfies, by filling in the gap in knowledge (a positive scotoma as it were), the intellective or exploratory need.

According to Wallas (*339*), the creative process comprises four phases called, respectively, preparation, incubation, illumination, and verification. In terms of the stimulus response scheme here proposed, *preparation* would correspond to engraphy in the course of appetitive behaviour; *incubation*, to the period of activity, (though it may not be overt) that precedes the actuating event; and *illumination* to the emergence of the new relation within the framework of the procedural scheme. The process of *verification* or validation will be discussed below. Unfortunately, Wallas' account of productive reasoning, no matter how useful it may be for the purpose of preliminary orientation, is purely descriptive. The metaphorical expressions incubation and illumination have no explanatory value and they render difficult the integration of Wallas' ideas into a comprehensive and, ultimately, neurophysiological framework of reference.

DIVISION OF LABOR WITHIN THE SUBSIDIARY SPHERE OF MENTATION

Why do we distinguish between, on the one hand, the mnemonic sphere of stimulus representation, that is to say, between a mental system composed of non-ekphorized engrams and and, on the other, ekphorized engrams which are represented in the subsidiary sphere of notation? (Fig. 11) Is this differentiation justified although the contents of both the subsidiary and the mnemonic sphere of the mental apparatus are represented in an identical system of mentation? On a previous occasion we spoke of non-conscious mental processes which are by no means merely "another edition" of conscious processes represented in a different, non-conscious, compartment of the mind. We pointed out that the processes in question have a specific function in the process of response determination. They are concerned with the elaboration and preparation of mnemic reactions while immediate reactions cope with current situations. It is not unreasonable to assume that the preparatory processes concerned with delayed reactions presuppose, if not a state of activity, at least of readiness made possible by *a subliminal representation of the psychisms in question, in other words, an adaptive patterning of data represented in the mnemonic system of notation*, and resulting in the formation of a problem related group and an unrelated group of non-conscious psychisms. At the moment the actuating event materializes, pertinent data would already be represented in the subsidiary sphere of the "prepared mind" while the threshold of unrelated engrams is kept high. Another reason for differentiating between subsidiary, *potentially active*, mental contents and, *dormant engrams* is the well known observation that certain persons have an excellent mechanical memory while their creative ability is below par. Lastly, the necessity to differentiate between the two elements in question will suggest itself in the course of the study of intuitive thought.

It is apparent that the nature of the subsidiary elements, i.e., of the subliminally represented psychisms, differs with different problem situations concerned. In the subsidiary sphere of his mind, Archimedes "knew" not to know the volume of the crown. Newton "knew" that the Earth attracts objects and, further, "knew" not to know what keeps the Moon within the orbit of the Earth and the planets circling around the Sun; and Darwin "knew" the nature of certain breeding practices, that species are not immutable and that they differ in innate qualities; and he "knew" not to know the factors producing new species under natural conditions—up to the point of ekphory of data emerging seemingly out of nowhere. In reality, they existed, as subliminal stimuli, ever since he had studied Malthus's work. We mention, in advance of a more detailed discussion of the problem of productive thinking, that Darwin's discovery may well have been an act of intuitive thought—the scientist was unaware of the factor which ekphorized the crucial engram and thereby created an actuating event.

THOUGHT AND THE PROBABILITY PRINCIPLE IN NEURAL INTEGRATION

It may be readily imagined that the very complexity of the processes involved in productive thinking entails a high degree of *vulnerability* of the psychic processes involved, and that the premature termination or the derailment of the process of reasoning may be due to a variety of factors. For example, appetitive behaviour or, for that matter, intellectual curiosity does not necessarily produce engrams and existing engrams are not necessarily activated. Moreover, even though appropriate memory traces may be formed and, under low threshold conditions, be represented in the subsidiary sphere of mentation, they may fail to react with the actuating event. Simply put, the intellective mechanism may be *non-receptive* or *non-responsive* so that, for want of the interaction of appropriate subsidiary elements, and in spite of the presence of an "actuating" event, no generating term is called into being. Further, if low threshold conditions and high threshold conditions occur at random, appropriate elements are less likely to interact with one another. Lastly, even though the formal conditions inherent in the procedural scheme may be fulfilled, the produced relation may prove to be invalid. The scheme in question is merely a framework wherein the relational identity of terms is but one condition of the correctness of the produced relation. It is far from being the only criterion of validity. On the other hand, the very leeway inherent in the procedural scheme raises it above the level of the consumma-

tory act, and it facilitates learning and thinking by *transfer* or *transportation*.

The concept here offered makes possible a *factorial definition of intelligence*. To the extent that intelligence and creative thinking run parallel, intellective yield depends on the following factors: (a) engraphy, (b) the selection of appropriate engrams prior to their translation into the subsidiary sphere of mentation as low threshold psychisms, (c) the responsiveness of the factors involved in the formation of the procedural scheme or the item generating relational proportion and (d) on the verification of the produced relation. Thus, intelligence would be a function (in the mathematical sense) of the stimulus response scheme here proposed.

THE TENTATIVE CHARACTER OF GENERALIZATION AND ANALOGY

As implied in the foregoing, reasoning by generalization and analogy may be a spectacular performance, but their results are by no means self-validating; a verified analogy may turn out to be a glorified guess. There is no logical calculus of reasoning either from the particular to the *general* or from the *particular to the particular*. Either form of reasoning must be deductively tested. This does not, it is true, apply to those cases in which generalization, as in the Archimedes episode is of a mathematical nature that is to say, where the relationship in question involves magnitudes only. Newton's conclusion, on the other hand, was by no means self-evident. The verification of his hypothesis of terrestrial attraction depended on the then unknown length of the meridian and it was not until after many years that Newton was able to prove its validity. And Darwin might have thought: it is quite possible (although not necessarily true) that spontaneously appearing traits are inheritable, that some of them have a greater survival value which increases the likelihood of their hereditary transmission, while those having a negative value might be eliminated. Many authorities believe that Darwin's hypothesis is merely a rough approximation to the truth as the "fittest" are by no means those which necessarily survive. In human societies at least, certain weaker individuals may be the better protected.

As explained above, reasoning by analogy is a limiting case of reasoning by generalization, and the two processes are therefore interdefinable. Neglecting the more subtle points of formal logic, *induction is generalization based on many observations yielding confirmatory conclusions, or the enhancement of the probability-value of generalization by superimposable experiences.* In the early stages of mental development generalization is indiscriminate, the maker of the naive world of the child. The reflex-like tendency to generalize is gradually superseded, although not entirely replaced, by inductive reasoning.

In *summary*, then, generalization, induction and reasoning by analogy are apt to lead to the discovery of significant likeness and, no doubt, may yield relational sameness in spite of the fact that they proceed by trial and error, and that error, for a time at least, may be more frequent than success. At the conclusion of the productive phase of thought, a person may recall instances of deceptive reasoning undistinguishable from mental processes that were goal leading in the past. To quote Edison (75): "I have constructed countless theories in connection with the electric light, each of them reasonable and likely to be true. Yet only in two cases did my experiments prove the truth of the theory."

ANALOGY AND WITTICISM

Earlier in this chapter, we mentioned the odd similarity between two pictures, namely, a bar of butter placed upright on a refrigerator shelf and Clemenceau's casket lowered into the grave in an upright position. The way the two ideas matched and clashed at the same time must have contained a humorous element; a friend, to whom I gave the manuscript to read found it very funny, although the reference to the two situations had not been meant to be a joke but, rather, an illustration of the transition between association by similarity and thinking by analogy. No doubt, the effect on the reader was produced by the *combination of contrast and concordance* involved in the two notions. *Witticism* stems from the clash between disparity and analogy produced at the very moment the former is brought to the fore and made the dominant element in the interplay of two otherwise similar relations. In the course of an evening spent with friends, I heard someone question the competence of a certain surgeon. In the ensuing discussion most of those present agreed that he did routine work quite well but that he showed a deplorable lack of ingenuity when faced with unfamiliar situations. One of the physicians, who had thus far sat in silence, remarked, "I would not say that he never had an idea; he invented an operating table which, by pushing a button, can be converted into a casket."

The analysis of this macabre joke (fig. 18) reveals a *primary idea*, the invention of a surgical procedure in response to an urgent demand, and a *companion idea*, suggested by the former, i.e., the invention of a device. However, the companion idea involved a *pseudo-confirmatory element*, produced by a tangential association by similarity originating in the fringe region of the concept "inventiveness." Lastly, the study of the joke reveals the *abrupt deflection of the primary idea* under the impact of a contradiction that "hit" it from an entirely unsuspected direction. It should, however, be kept in mind that, in spite of the sharp "angulation" of the primary idea, the parallelism between the two propositions continues, if only in an imaginary fashion (fig. 18 p') since, considering the ineptness of the surgeon at whom the joke was aimed, the convertible operating table represented a useful innovation. Without the temporary preservation of the analogy relation—the ghost like existence of the already exploded primary idea—the witticism would have no point. In general, the punch of a joke increases with the degree of concordance of the primary and the secondary ideas and the degree of tangentiality of the association produced by the former, that is, with the degree to which the position of lines d and p' approximates a right angle. On another occasion, when the question of the same surgeons's general ability came up, some one remarked: "Actually, his position in surgery corresponds to that of Immanuel Kant in philosophy." And when his listeners, already smiling, looked a bit puzzled, he added: "Is it not true that Kant was called the 'Alleszermalmer' [all-crusher]?"* The primary relation was the question of the surgeon's ability; the companion idea, Kant's role in philosophy. Again, the companion idea was suggested by a fringe association yielding in turn an epithet which, when applied to a surgeon, had a deadly connotation. The element of spite is mitigated, although still recognizable, in the answer to a question put to a physician regarding his relationship with the psychoanalysts in his com-

---

* By the poet, Heinrich Heine.

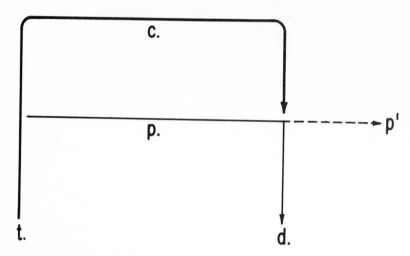

Fig. 18. Mental processes involved in witticism.

p.: primary relation; c.: companion relation; t.: tangential association; c.: deflection of the primary relation; p′: imaginal persistence of the primary relation.

munity. "I do not share their creed but I eat their steaks." The parallelism of the two relations rests on the idea "keeping company" (be it in spirit or otherwise), which is denied in the first proposition but affirmed in the second, so that contrast and concordance are, as before, combined. A further element of apparent contradiction lies in the implied juxtaposition of "creed" and "science." The reference to the good meals psychoanalysts serve their guests implied that what they pretend to be science is, at least in the opinion of some, not only a creed but a lucrative one at that. Lastly, the physician wished to express the fact that he considered the matter so unimportant from a scientific point of view that his opportunism was a minor issue. Not only did he not conceal it but, if anything, displayed it openly. (As long as they give me good things to eat it does not really matter what they think and do.) By and large, harmless jokes have the same effect as the malicious varieties (which are a socially acceptable means of aggression), provided they involve a similar combination of contrast and concordance: A man is groaning under the weight of an old-fashioned grandfather clock that he is carrying. Just as the man puts the clock down to rest for a while and wipes the sweat from his forehead, a passerby pauses, points to his own wristwatch and says, "Look, my dear fellow, this is the kind of watch people wear nowadays." The parallelism between the two situations is the time piece; the contrast, the disparity between carrying and wearing. In

actual fact, the two parallel ideas are replaced by two apparently identical situations whose concomitant contrast is brought out by the absurd notion that the man is "wearing" the grandfather clock as one would a wristwatch. Lastly, a witty effect may be produced by *slips of the tongue*, in which case the companion idea is in some way "assimilated" by the primary idea. In studying a case history submitted to me, I found the sentence "Claimant developed a lump sum on his head", that is, the combination of "lump" as a result of an injury and a "lump sum settlement" suggested by the claimant's attorney. On another occasion, I heard a radio commentator say: "Russia is flexing her missiles", and a politician remarked: "We have to take these accusations with a grain of fault."

Witticism is converted into *comicality* in that an expected situation is replaced by an unsuspected situation with which, however, it has something in common. The sight of a man wearing a woman's hat will make everybody laugh, and the sight of a man falling downstairs will affect at least some persons in the same way. Laughter is the response to the shocklike surprise experienced from the combination of contrast and concordance, be it ideational, as in wit, or situational, as in comicality. It is an "expression of emotion in man," an expression which is partly mimetic (if not generalized, involving most muscles of the body), and partly audible, but the equivalent, if any, of this "expression of emotion in animals" is uncertain. Its counterpart may well be a warning in response to surprise or to sudden danger.

The above considerations on witticism and comicality are, of necessity, somewhat sketchy. Even Freud (*270*), who studied the mechanism of about 150 jokes, suspected that he may have missed one or another variety of "joke-techniques." I agree with him that dream and wit are equivalent but I agree only to the extent that fringe elements of concepts play a part in either phenomenon. Hence, the apparently far-fetched, if not utterly absurd associations in dreams, and the tangential associations which, in witticism, provide a shattering explosive. For the same reason, namely, the fringe orientation of the associations of schizophrenics, certain of their utterances are witty and funny at the same time. Wit is undoubtedly a higher cerebral function. To have Voltaire's wit, one must have Voltaire's intellect; the opposite however is not true: many a great mind is a bore.

Let us, after this apparent digression, continue where we left off, that is, let us return to our main topic, the question of verification of the products of generalization and analogy.

Inductive and deductive reasoning

Children who are old enough not to apply, in an indiscriminate fashion, past experiences to new observations eventually reach the state of legitimate generalization. They develop concepts by abstracting everything "different" and assembling everything "similar" into representative ideas. For instance, in observing that both people and animals have legs, the child forms the concept of "legs of living beings." At about the same time, it has observed or learned that not only animals but also chairs and tables have legs and accordingly develops, by a similar process of abstraction and generalization, the concept of "legs of pieces of furniture." Eventually, it finds that all kinds of legs have certain common properties and forms the over-all concept "leg." No doubt the process of concept formation was materially aided by the application, to a variety of experiental contents, of an identical verbal symbol which the child has learned from its environment.

Now let us assume that the child happens to see unfamiliar looking furniture and, during a visit to a zoo, strange looking animals. We have little doubt that it would recognize the legs of both inanimate and most animate objects, but the situation is somewhat different when the child sees an animal that does not fit into any familiar category. While looking at a seal the child may be intrigued by the animal's fins. He may then test his hypothesis that they are legs (this is apt to be the first idea that leaps to mind because of the element of similarity involved) by observing the creature. Since the concept "legs of living beings" implies their use for the purpose of locomotion, he will "diagnose" the animal's legs as soon as the seal begins to shuffle about. Or the child may throw him food and verify his hypothesis experimentally. Either process is an example of primitive deductive reasoning and the experimental verification of hypotheses wherein the use of concepts as guide structures plays a crucial part.

SOME ASPECTS OF CONCEPT FORMATION

At this point, it is necessary to resume the discussion of the nature of concepts. (See also under "The mathematical fields of thought.") Concepts are data which embody one or more of the following:

    (a) *identical, or near identical experiences* (fig. 19A and B),

    (b) *superimposable parameters of basically different experiences* (fig. 19C) and

    (c) *non-superimposable parameters of similar experiences,* (fig. 19D).

The various attributes of a concepts are neither equivalent nor equipotential as, under ordinary circumstances, concepts are less likely to be formed by non-superimposable parameters of similar experiences than by other elements. Thus it is necessary to distinguish between the *core* of a concept and its *fringes* already referred to in the preceding chapter.

Concept formation involves the abstraction of what is identical or similar from a total stimulus complex. For example, the concept "horizontal" may be thought of as an abstraction from the totality of awareness contents illustrated by fig. 19E, the concept "vertical" as an abstraction from fig. 19F, the concept of "obliquity" as an abstraction from figs. 19G and E. In a similar fashion, the concept "angle" is derivable from E and F, and from G and H respectively. Fig. 19I

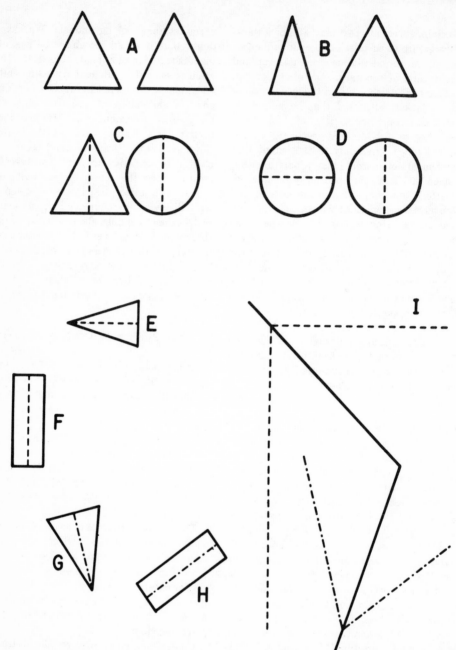

Fig. 19. Concept formation at levels of increasing abstraction (cf. fig. 26).

illustrates the formation of an angle formed by two lines, derivable, in turn, from the bisection of two angles oriented in a certain fashion and, hence, the formation of an abstraction of a higher order. In parenthesis, we add that not only the angle in question but the process of its derivation can be conveniently represented by a symbolic expression.* At this point, for the "concept of

---

* The matter will be taken up in more detail in the paragraphs dealing with the formation of algebraic, more especially incorporative symbols.

concept" has many aspects, we shall regard concepts as *products of abstractive grouping activity involving sensory data and comprising similar elements, including perceptions, patterns and relations.* The products of the grouping activity are identical with the "intrinsically generated categorizing stimuli" already referred to.

It may seem a precarious undertaking to base on a fictitious example the history of concept formation and the role of class concepts in deductive reasoning. On the other hand, it can be readily shown that a mechanism similar to that described in the Zoo eipsode operates in concrete situations of problem solving, and also in the process of verification of hypotheses. To illustrate this point we might choose an example of diagnostic reasoning taken from our personal experience. Although the particular field of problem solving is somewhat technical we are convinced that the reader will be able to follow the train of thought developed below.

THE FORMATION OF CLASS CONCEPTS BY INDUCTION AND THEIR ROLE IN DEDUCTION

It is well known that the interpretation of roentgenograms may not involve any difficulty whatsoever; pathological conditions may be immediately recognized, much in the same way as pictures of familiar objects. They are "seen" to be virtually superimposable upon the ekphorized engram of comparable abnormalities (cf. fig. 42).

The following problem may illustrate the train of thought in the roentgenologic diagnosis of a brain tumor. In the case of brain tumor suspect, in which ventriculography had been performed, a series of x-ray films were taken, three of which, namely, the profile views (Fig. 26A) and a sagittal view proved to be particularly useful. The *first profile view* showed the posterior portion of the lateral ventricle as the familiar crescent-shaped image which, had it not been for a rather inconspicuous abnormality of its curvature, might well have appeared normal. The discrepancy was discovered by "superimposition" of the actual image upon a memory image (fig. 20B) their synchronization and matching having been "reflexly" produced through *association by similarity.* The two images, namely, the actual and the mnestic, were by no means strikingly different but their incongruence was sufficient to arouse attention. Since similar though less marked ventricular

abnormalities had previously been seen in cases of thalamic tumors, the rule was formulated that the lesions under consideration are apt to produce the ventricular changes and hence the roentgenologic abnormalities described. The study of anatomical specimens put this rule, or generalization, which could now be used as the basis of *deductive reasoning,* on a reasonably safe ground.

The *second profile view* (fig. 20C) showed air in the anterior portion of the lateral ventricle and the interventricular foramen. Under normal conditions, the anterior segment of the lateral ventricle resembles a comma whose tip points backward, and the foramen interventriculare, unless the third ventricle is also visualized, a short, gradually fading out process extending from the lower concave border of the comma backward and downward. The roentgenogram under study appeared to be normal in that the anterior portion of the lateral ventricle conformed to the above given description, except for the fact that (a) its lower outlined was somewhat s-shaped rather than curved and (b) that the image of the interventricular foramen did not flare out but had the shape of a funnel, thereby suggesting compression of its outlet by a mass lesion. The difference between the anterior portion of the pathological ventricle and a normal ventricle (fig. 20D) had again been determined by superimposition of a percept upon a memory image, that is, through *association by similarity,* and the evidence obtained considered confirmatory. Although, as far as known, an s-shaped outline of the anterior horn of the lateral ventricle had never been encountered, it was legitimate to attribute it to a neoplasm causing distortion of the adjacent ventricle; in the present case, to a thalamic tumor encroaching upon the frontal horn. To put it in other words: as a constructive step of *generalization,* the two images could be readily correlated because (a) of the partial similarity between the appearance of the ventricle in the case under study and, (b) of the general appearance of a cavity encroached upon by a mass lesion.

At this point, the presence of a thalamic tumor was considered a practical certainty, and the *sagittal view* (fig. 20D) studied in the expectation of discovering abnormalities consistent with those described, and to find additional evidence of such lesion. In a certain sense, the evaluation of this film was an *experiment* designed to bring out additional constituents of the roentgenologic concept

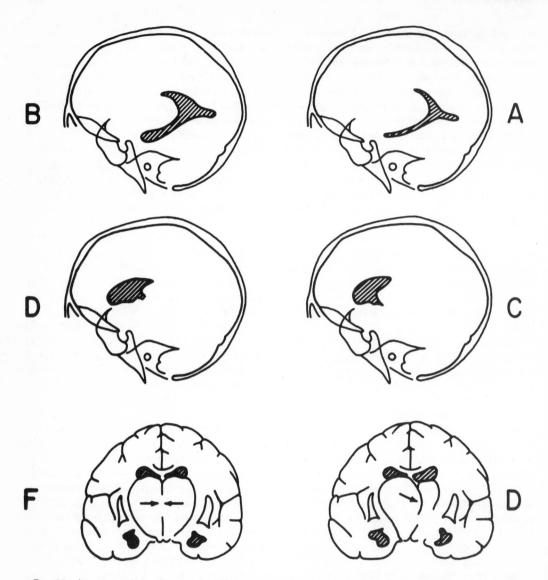

Fig. 20. Association by similarity and contiguity, and their relationship to inductive and deductive reasoning in a diagnostic problem involving visualization.

"thalamic tumor". Guided by previous experiences, the roentgenologic features of thalamic tumors had been worked out by a process of *inductive* reasoning; and, from the concept "thalamic tumor" thus developed, the presence of certain other abnormalities was expected to be found in the sagittal view by the reverse process of *deduction*. Now the leading abnormality as seen on sagittal views is a crescent-like distortion and a sharp displacement across the median plane due to the tumefaction of the thalamus and its bulg-

ing into the ventricle (Fig. 20E). It was therefore disconcerting to find that the anticipated deformity was absent. However, on closer inspection, the x-ray films showed a filling defect not only in the ipsilateral but also the opposite lateral ventricle and pathognomonic of a symmetrically placed tumor (fig. 20F). Thus, the lack of displacement of the third ventricle could be readily accounted for by the fact that the twin neoplasm counterbalanced the pressure they exerted on the midline, indeed it confirmed the general rule that tumors located on opposite sides of the median plane and exerting pressure effects of approximately the same magnitude fail to cause a demonstrable midline shift. The awareness of the normal position of the midline structures was again an act of *recognition*, as evidenced by the *subsumption* of this particular case to a class-concept.

In the course of the above outlined thought processes, associations by similarity were instrumental in recognition, generalization and induction; associations by contiguity, in deductive reasoning; reasoning deductively, the thinker, guided by contiguity associations, was "working his way" within the framework of the concept "thalamic tumor" from one constituent to the other. He was trying to discover their correlation in the roentgenograms, in other words, he was matching his observations against the elements of a *conceptual guide-structure.*

The above description should not convey the impression that it did not take longer to interpret the roentgenograms than to read the above paragraphs. In reality, the diagnostic process extended over a period of at least two weeks for neither were the crucial details on which the diagnosis was based immediately seen nor were they evaluated as soon as they were discovered. What's more, the idea that one or the other detail may be of crucial importance would emerge not during the actual study of the films but, rather, in the intervening periods, at a time when I was occupied with other matters. In fact, some of the details were "seen" some time after the films have been returned to the file clerk.

FURTHER REFLECTION ON PROBABILITY FACTORS INVOLVED IN THOUGHT

Having followed the description of thinking from the psychological point of view, the reader may have gained the impression that, given a certain set of roentgenograms and a certain level of experience on the part of the examiner, diagnostic processes develop with the inevitability of chain reflexes. This indeed is the opinion held by the ultra-mechanistic school of associationists which will be more extensively dealt with later. (See Chapter III, *The general organization of thought processes and the problem of intuitive thought.*) We reiterate that appropriate thought sequences might have failed to form altogether; and, since the correct perception of pathological

changes does not necessarily bring to mind either appropriate memory images of normal conditions nor, for that matter, indicates the significance of the abnormalities involved, the reasoning process might have come to an end at any stage. Moreover, even though pathological alterations may be identified and their possible implications recognized, clues may be disregarded and, owing to the cumulative effect of apparently conflicting impressions, or the distraction of the reasoner by non-essentials, associations of ideas derailed. It is a matter of experience that a given psychism will not necessarily produce appropriate associations, no matter how similar the individual elements to be associated may be, or how frequently they were associated in the past.

It is only under ideal conditions that the individual steps follow each other in a way that leads to the rapid attainment of the goals of thought. The composite nature and vulnerability of thought processes can be appreciated under abnormal or, perhaps, experimental conditions only. On the other hand, we have pointed out that dreamlike associations of a practically unlimited range may form even in states of full ludicidty. We do not mean to imply that the likelihood of marginal associations is high. On the other hand, it is unpredictable just when they will form and, if this be the case, they will disrupt the fabric of thought. *Like other self-equilibrating functions of the organism, productive thinking, or the generation of relationships, has a certain confidence coefficient of integration, in other words, it follows the laws of probability operating in the organism at large.*

In the above quoted example of diagnostic reasoning, two phases could be recognized. In the first, *inaugural phase of thought*, the reasoner formed an opinion which was verified in the second, *concluding phase of thought*. The former was initiated by association by similarity and, once the second phase had started, the "flow" of thought maintained by association by contiguity.

ASSOCIATION BY SIMILARITY IN TRANSFER MECHANISM

Now, what is the nature of the factor which initiates the second phase, that is to say, connects it with the first phase? It is not difficult to see that the *connection was brought about by association by similarity.* In fact, since we are dealing with an act of recognitive thought, the produced relation (diagnosis) or the last step of the first, inaugural, phase was identical with the first step of the second, deductive, or concluding phase of thought. In other, more complicated reasoning processes the two steps are not identical but they are more or less similar, there being all gradations from patent likeness to remote similarity.

The greater or the more complete the similarity between the two items concerned, the greater the probability of a "reflex like" association between the inaugural and the concluding phase of thought; the more remote the similarity, the less likely. The greater the frequency with which fertile, remotely similar items are associated (or hypotheses formed) the more intelligent the individual; the greater the frequency with which inapplicable, remotely similar items are formed, the less intelligent the reasoner—other factors being equal.

Now the term association would seem to imply that the item to be associated is known to the reasoner and that it has only to be remembered to connect the two phases of thought. In actual fact, the crucial item that initiates the concluding phase of thought does not need to be the exact reduplication of a previous (manifestly or remotely) related experience. It may be an *applicable element generated by abstraction from a previous experience* (or, for that matter, from more or less superimposable experiences) *which is transferred to an existing problem situation*. The more appropriate, i.e., transferable the abstractions formed and applied to an existing problem situation, the more intelligent the reasoner; the less appropriate the abstraction, and the more frequently applied to a problem in spite of frustrating experiences, the less intelligent the reasoner—again, other factors being equal.

The matter may again be illustrated by a simple example. On a visit by a group to the laboratories of the Bell Telephone Company, where we had occasion to watch the performance of various "thinking machines," we parked our car on the lawn in front of the building. On leaving, we noted that it had been raining. The wheels of the car had sunk into the ground, and we were unable to get it going. We called a truck from a nearby station, connected the two vehicles with a chain and the truck pulled the stalled car on to the driveway. The question came up whether the machines we have just seen could have solved the simple problem with which we were faced, that is to say, could they have reasoned anticipaticely by the activation of appropriate engrams. (The answer to this question does not concern us here.) The act of anticipative reasoning, namely, the awareness that the car would be freed upon exerting an adequate pull, was, of course, not the literal application of previous experience, for none of us, as I was told, had ever freed a car that had sunk into a wet lawn. What happened was that each of us knew that an adequate pull would overcome a resistance. The produced relation was arrived at by reasoning by analogy or, if you wish, the application of a rule to a specific instance.

Kline (*167*), in his already quoted review of Polya's (*259*) work, writes that "in mathematics, plausible reasoning . . . is only the prelude to deductive proof. How does a mathematician proceed from one to another? On this crucial point Polya's discussion is forced and unsatisfactory. He presents some obvious truths and suggestions noticing among other things that the inductive process itself sometimes suggests deductive proof or at least gives insight into the problem. But he has little to say about how mathematicians discover a method of proof when it is not apparent." We take note of the fact that the inductive process (the inaugural phase of thought) may suggest the proof, the deductive or concluding phase. Further, we assume that this suggestion is brought about by *transfer*, the carry over of a response pattern from one stimulus situation to another, the mechanism of which will occupy us later. Suffice to call attention to Lashley's (*181*) experiments which demonstrate that transfer mechanism, indeed, transfer mechanisms at a high level of abstraction, operate also in animals. He trained monkeys to discriminate between triangles of different shape and those of different color. Following experimental lesions to the temporo-parieto-occipital cortex, the animals failed in either task but were able to differentiate between triangles of different *color* after having been retrained to recognize those having a different *shape*. By contrast, control animals were unable to discriminate between either category of stimuli. Thus, the postoperative training of the animals, aiming at the recognition of shapes only, produced the wider concept of non-identity. The above experiment is a classic example of substitutive application of experiences to novel stimulus situations. It is not difficult to see that repetitive transfer operations will establish more or less habitual but neverthe-less flexible trends in reasoning, and that abstraction of superimposable elements from similar patterns of transfer will increase the adaptibility and range of thought. We submit that, in the final analysis, any transfer process is based on the process of association by similarity of superimposable parameters of remembered items, i.e., items represented in the mnemonic system in notation. To put it in another way, the associations in question take shape in the subsidiary sphere of mentation of the reasoner, unknown to him. He is as unaware of the integrative activity of subsidiary psychisms as he is ignorant of the interplay of muscles in the course of the execution of a skilled movements.

The derivation of elaborate thought patterns from primitive thought patterns

We suggested that reasoning by generalization and analogy and deductive reasoning are patterns of thought which, under ideal conditions at least, operate in coordination and which are instrumental in the awareness and generation of relationships. At this point an attempt will be made to trace the two processes to primitive central nervous system mechanisms. No doubt they did not appear abruptly at some stage of development but are products of gradual evolution.

The Functional Primordium of Reasoning by Generalization and Analogy

Thus far, we have shown that associations by similarity are instrumental in reasoning by analogy and generalization. Similarity associations are embodied in higher response determining mechanisms, just like primitive reflexes are incorporated into more adaptive patterns of response. The question now arises: Is it possible to identify central nervous system mechanisms which are still more primitive than associations by similarity? The latter is a sort of mental diplopia wherein the associating image is an actual impression; the associated image, a partly superimposable ekphorized engram. Since, in a certain sense, the impression is experientially generalized, the generalization being brought about by the actuation of mnemonic material, generalization

may be said to encompass, potentially at least, those pairs (or sets) of stimuli whose degree of experienced incongruity does not exceed a critical value. Now, as far as can be determined by the reaction of experimental animals in conditioned reflex situations (more accurately, as far as can be inferred from their identical reactions) the animals experience similar stimuli as identical stimuli. For example, if an animal is exposed to the sound of a buzzer (stimulus A) the same effect may be obtained by any noise (stimulus B). On the surface, the difference between association by similarity and what is conventionally called *stimulus generalization* is the following. In the former, a stimulus actuates a partly superimposable engram, the "double image"; in the latter, a partly superimposable stimulus gives rise to an identical reaction. Yet it may well be that the identical reaction is caused by the experience, on the part of the animal, of the conditioning stimulus B (e.g., the sound of a buzzer) as partly superimposable upon, or similar to, the originally conditioning stimulus A; in other words, that the animal does *not* experience A and B as identical. If this is granted, the mechanism of association by similarity in the human may be traced to, and perhaps identified with, an intervening experiental phase that operates in a primitive stimulus response situation.

The mechanism in question is of interest from various angles. (a) In the early stages of human development, there correspond, to the generalization of reactions, generalizations of meanings. It is trivial observation that infants and children identify objects on the basis of certain similarities which, in the light of subsequent experiences, appear to be superficial and which, little by little, are sifted out by the activation of corrective engrams or, for that matter, corrective feedback mechanisms acquired largely by trial and error. As expressed in terms of partial congruity, training and experience result in the gradual reduction of the critical value of stimulus incongruence, that is, that degree of diversity which causes misidentification. In other words, training and experience enhance discriminatory capacity. The relationship between the incongruent parameters of similar experiences to the fringe elements of concepts (which are redundant in the early phases of mental development) is immediately apparent, as is their role as connecting elements of different data. The counterpart of the gradual reduction of the critical incongruence value in the human is the gradual increase of the discriminatory capacity of experimental animals in the stimulus response situation. For example, if, following exposure of an animal to the stimulus B, feeding is discontinued, the conditioned reflex will fade even though the degree of similarity between stimulus A (the unconditioned stimulus) and stimulus B is greatly increased. For example, if stimulus A be represented by a sound of 1000 vibrations, the similar, previously reflex eliciting, stimulus B will be rendered ineffective if the difference between the frequency of the two stimuli is only about 1% (347).

In *summary*, then, it appears that association by similarity cannot be reduced to a still more primitive nervous system mechanism; rather, it represents a quasi-stereotyped response pattern operating in primitive stimulus response situations. It is likely that the response is generalized because the stimulus is also generalized, i.e., answered in the same way as stimuli having superimposable parameters and that, under suitable conditions, the stimulus is not generalized (or misidentified) unless the degree of superimposability between the two critical stimuli reaches a crucial value. Further, there is some evidence to suggest that the original pattern of primary generalization is still maintained in the process of recognition and that it is followed by secondary differentiation. We submit that recognition is a *bi-phasic* process wherein the first phase involves the potential misidentification of stimuli while the second phase consists in the immediate initiation of a corrective feedback process, that is to say, the reinstatement of an engram which brings to the fore the non-superimposable parameters of the items involved. Corrective engrams establish the experience of similarity rather than of identity or, if you wish, convert the latter to the former. Under *normal* conditions, misidentification and its immediate correction are fused as it were into one process. As far as introspection serves me, they may be experienced for a fleeting moment under conditions of fatigue and distraction of attention. Under frank *pathological conditions* on the other hand, primary misidentification is not followed by corrective feedbacks. For example, a hospitalized patient may believe to be at his home. He responds "automatically", i.e., without immediate correction to the similar features in his environment and of his home, neglecting, at the

same time, crucial differences. He does not actuate corrective engrams and, accordingly, neglects crucial differences. In other words the critical value of incongruence is increased (See chap. IV, fig. 42).

THE FUNCTIONAL PRIMORDIUM OF DEDUCTIVE REASONING

We have already made reference to the fact, which was illustrated by various examples, that *deductive reasoning may be reduced to association by contiguity*. This makes it superfluous to repeat the whole argument. At this point, we are confronted with the problem of tracing the process of association by contiguity to an even more elementary process of nervous system mechanism. It is immediately apparent that association by contiguity operates in the fashion of the classic conditioned reflex. Just as a dog secretes saliva on hearing a bell ringing because this noise has several times been followed by feeding, so a person concentrating, at a given time, on a particular component of a concept is apt to ekphorize other components as, in the past, the association of the remaining (more especially the relevant attributes of the very same concept) was instrumental in problem solving and, potentially at least, rewarding. In this process or, for that matter, in the process of deductive reasoning, random associations are reduced by the the elimination of data which, with increasing experience, prove to be irrelevant. At the same time, primitive *thinking sets* are built up by transfer of relevant (goal leading) aspects of past situations to current problems. Clearly, there exist intimate relationships between the process of "sifting" and the formation of core and fringes of concepts which, in this particular instance, are not only categorizing stimuli but also adaptive patterns of response. If, in the course of problem solving, certain response schemes are found to be useful although applied to apparently unrelated problem situations, (especially as connectors of the inaugural and the concluding phase of thought) the response schemes become "fixated" to *thinking sets*, that is, more or less standardized schemes, strategies and techniques. Because of the continuity between learning and thinking, and the fact that they are instrumental in a variety of thought processes, including reconstructive and anticipative thought, thinking sets are reducible to Harlow's (*108*) *learning sets*. Thinking sets create a certain measure of economy in response determination. They polarize awareness, promote alertness and produce a feeling of expectancy and familiarity with the problem situation. Figuratively speaking, they start out as trails which, eventually, become the speedways of thought. Their general significance lies in the facilitation and the rapid establishment of complex response patterns found to have been goal leading in the past and, a certain measure of stereotypy notwithstanding, in their adaptibility to novel situations. Some of the energy necessary to generate new data having been already spent in the process of learning or "set building", thinking sets make possible productive thinking with a minimum of corroborative effort.

The relationship between the notion of *causality* (invariable antecedence) to the process of association by contiguity or, for that matter, to the conditioned reflex, can now be specified as follows. It is known that an otherwise indifferent (neutral) stimulus, say, the sound of a bell, may become a conditioning stimulus, in other words, that previously indifferent (now significant) stimuli may produce biologically significant effects. Contrariwise, the stimulus becomes indifferent (a) if the temporal sequence between the unconditioned stimulus and the conditioning stimulus is reversed or (b) stimulation fails to be followed by feeding (*347*). In the final analysis, then, the notion of causality would seem to be derivable from the elimination of irrelevant associations and, at the same time, the concomitant recognition of signicant antecedants emerging in the process of inductive reasoning in general, and in certain stimulus response situations in particular.

In *summary*, then, we have made likely (apart from the empirical nature of the concept of causality) the existence of a hierarchy of response patterns involving the reduction of

(1) reasoning by generalization and analogy to association by similarity, and of

(2) deductive reasoning to association by contiguity; and of the latter to certain primitive conditioned reflex mechanisms.

(3) We have found that deductive reasoning is
(a) initiated by transfer mechanisms and
(b) compounded of association by similarity and contiguity which operate in a coordinated fashion.

Since thinking consists of two phases, namely, one involving reasoning by generalization and analogy, and one involving deductive reasoning, or, for that matter, an inaugural and a *concluding phase of thought* (at least if the act of thinking is to be completed) the mental operations in question can be reduced to derivatives of relatively primitive central nervous system mechanisms, namely, a process operating in stimulus generalization and the induction of conditioned reflexes.

The reader may call into doubt broad generalizations established on the basis of a few examples. Considering that there exist many varieties of reasoning as, for example, reasoning in daily life, in science, in the professions, in business and industrial enterprises, in games and puzzles (*191*) etc., one will realize that, thus far, the inductive basis of our argument has been quite narrow and that we might have sinned against the very same principles of induction which we said emerge with increasing maturity of thought. Nevertheless, for the present at least, we may do well to leave our conclusions stand as they are, to assume that the basic pattern of thought (rooted in reflex-like associations and evolving to the most complex reasoning sets) are identical throughout, and that the "speedways of thought" differ only in their adaptation to local pecularities of the ground over which they extend. Meanwhile, whatever doubt the relative paucity of observations might have raised in the reader's mind might well be dissipated by the testimony of authorities. For example, Einstein (*77*) remarked that "the whole of science is nothing more than a refinement of every day thinking." And Thorndyke (*327*), that the "same general laws that explain how a child learns to talk or to dress himself and why he gets up in the morning and goes to bed at night also explains how he learns geometry or philosophy and why he succeeds or fails in the most abstruse problems." Conceivably, the above summarized inferences intended to bring out the unitary character of thought processes are applicable to certain techniques only. Whether this is true or not will be left to future considerations.

Thorndyke's notion of the universality of the laws of thinking links the subject matter of the present section with that of the following pages which are devoted to the mathematical fields of thought.

In spite of Thorndyke's dictum, the laws of reasoning, perhaps, may not be entirely applicable to mathematical thought. In many important aspects, mathematics is autonomous. Its realm is difficult of access. Its heights, for the ordinary mortal at least, are unapproachable; and its peaks shrouded. On the other hand, certain principles involved in mathematical reasoning are relatively easy to grasp. They are here discussed because of their bearing upon the formation of *concepts*, the mechanism of *non-mathematical thought* and, as already referred to in various places, the phenomenon of *consciousness*.

The concept of number

Traditionally, discussions concerned with mathematical thought begin with an analysis of the concept of number. About this basic idea mathematicians have argued since the day of Gauss (*88*) and his predecessors. In fact, they argued among themselves since the early period of Greek philosophy (*45*). In the following pages, an attempt will be made to trace the *derivation of number concepts from non-numerical concepts*.

Non-mathematical concepts are psychisms which lack the properties of vivid mental images; at most they are their indistinct residues. Heidbreder (*121*) contended that conceptual processes are modifications of perceptual experiences, especially of those involved in the perception of objects. Galton (*86*) and Külpe (*176*) and other workers on the other hand demonstrated that meaningful mental processes may take shape at the conceptual level in the absence of any mental imagery. As Philiatros in Fernel's (*80*) famous dialogue said: "I do not try to look by actual vision at what I follow in a train of thought." Very often, it is true, the perceptional elements of thought tend to become reinforced more or less in proportion to the complexity of the relations involved; in fact, in the history of human thought, even the "concept of concept" became perceptualized. Euler, who was entrusted with the task to teach Queen Cristina of Sweden logic, indicated concepts by circles and, whatever different concepts had in common, by an area of overlapping. In verbalized thought, the area in question and,

potentially at least, also the peripheral extensions (see Wernicke, Chapter II) are represented by a symbol. Cohen's (*52*) statement that concepts are "signs (mainly visible and audible words or symbols) pointing to invariant relations, i.e., relations which remain identical despite the material in which they are embodied" can therefore be excepted with certain reservations only. The same holds true for Stoehr's (*303*) definition who regarded concepts as identical reaction patterns.

Symbols are not merely tools which enable us to convert meanings into words but, at the same time, implements upon which there depends both the realization of more complicated thought processes and the communication of meanings. In a way, symbols bear the same analogy to concepts as paper money to its coverage. The smaller notes stand for objects; the larger, for class concepts and relationships of various order. If necessary, larger notes can be converted into smaller units at will. Comprehensive mental operations involve the handling of large units which, of course, have a meaning only to the extent that they express concrete entities. However, notes gradually acquire a value of their own; similarly, abstract thought is facilitated by manipulating semi-emancipated symbols.

As already noted, reasoning does not in general depend on more or less vivid memory images although, under certain conditions, the awareness of relationships may be made easier by reactivating the original elements used in concept formation, and by converting thought into perception, somewhat in the fashion large notes may be exchanged into coins. On the other hand, whenever thought depends on the utilization of abstract concepts, the reinstatement of original experiences will hamper its flow in proportion to the appropriate degree of abstraction. In a certain sense, the relationship of image-bound to imageless thought bears analogy to that of arithmetic to algebra. Either procedure has its applications.

How did the concept of number and its symbolization come to be? We would assume that it has branched off from the processes of general concept formation and symbolization. Needless to say that, in examining the concept of number, we shall not talk in terms of mathematical history but that the derivation of the concept in question as described below is pure fiction designed to save the reader lengthy discussions of a technical nature. A somewhat naive presentation of the matter may be vindicated by the contradictory views of professional mathematicians, logicians, and philosophers (45). According to Waismann (335) the concept of number (and, implicitly, of the nature of mathematics) has been interpreted in four different ways; indeed, if Waismann's own theory is added to those discussed in his monograph in five ways. In the present context, it will suffice to differentiate between two schools, namely, an *empiristic* and a *non-empiristic*. The former is represented chiefly by John Stuart Mill and Mach, the latter by Kant, Poincaré, Frege, Cantor, Dedekind and others (45).

An account of the "development" of the concept of number may be attempted along the following lines. A person interested in the morphology of plants studied their roots, seeds, leaves, etc., and eventually arrived at concepts of the classes of things he set out to investigate. For instance, he developed the class-concept "leaf" by placing leaves of various plant species one on another and he associated the invariant elements with a perceptualized equivalent or symbol. Another person became interested in altogether different aspects of plant morphology, namely, the study and symbolization of relationships between magnitudes. He considered a grove of fir trees of roughly identical size as suitable material for such investigation and, concentrating on their trunks only, disregarded their roots, seeds, etc., already studied by his colleague. He cut the trees down and sawed their branches off; he trimmed the first trunk down to a stump of, say, one foot in length; the next, two feet in length; the third, three feet in length, etc., until he had produced a set of stumps of various length. Starting with the shortest, he arranged them according to length and made their long axes equidistant. Having lined up as many stumps as he could physically handle, he decided that the game could be conveniently continued with the aid of paper, pencil and ruler. He drew a horizontal line upon which he represented the perpendicular axis of the individual columns as lines of increasing length. He connected the tips of the lines by an oblique line and observed that it crossed their common baseline, that it could be extended beyond it, and that he could produce a similar pattern by drawing a set of lines below the base. Subsequently, he drew horizontal lines dividing the vertical lines into units of equal length. He discovered that the right half of his drawing represented regularly increasing quantities and its left half regularly decreasing quantities, and that at the point of intersection between the oblique line and the baseline there was no quantity at all. He invented arbitrary names for each vertical line. For the first, he chose the name "one"; for the second, "two"; for the third, "three", etc. Of necessity, the lines extending above the baseline had to be differentiated from those extending below it. He chose the symbol + for the former, − for the latter, and for the point of no quantity the name "zero." For convenience, he replaced the names with symbols, namely, $+3$, $+2$, $+2$, 0, -1, -2, -3 and so on. At this point, he had arrived at the concept of *nought* and of positive and negative *integers*. No doubt he realized that, apart from representing quantities, the symbols would be meaningless unless their relationship could be readily surveyed. For example, plus 4 means twice 2, or four times 1; and plus 6, means twice 3 or 6 times 1, illustrating the *ratio meaning* of numbers; while the fact that 4 means, at the same time, 3 added to 1 and five, 3 added to 2, brings out their *relational meaning*. This meaning is equally evident in the observation that plus 7 minus 5 equals 2, and plus 7 minus 7 equals zero. Furthermore, he found that numbers have a series meaning, in that 2 means 1 *more* than 1; and 3 one *more* than 2. . . . Lastly, he discovered that numbers have a *collective meaning*, in that 3 means a *total* of 3 units, or a group of 3, and 5 a *total* of 5 units, or a *group* of 5. By contrast "0" taken any number of times, indicates the absence of a quantity, a positive and negative. In other words, the mathematician discovered not only that he could count but that he had developed the concept of *ordinal* and *cardinal* numbers and their various meanings, and that he had become aware of the significance of zero.

At the same time he realized that the concept "3" can be applied either to as many identical *units* created by him or to three different *objects*, as, for example, his paper, pencil and ruler; or that the concept "5" can be applied (a) either to the *sequence* of 5 lines or (b) to a *group* of lines; that it can be applied (a) to the 5 fingers of his hand—a convenient *counting device*—or (b) to the whole *group* of fingers. In applying the concepts

"3" and "5" to the corresponding number of *identical units*, or *pure quantities*, he was operating in the sphere of *pure or formal mathematics;* in applying the above concepts to whatever *objects* they may be made to refer, he was operating in the sphere of *applied mathematics*. Both branches of mathematics have the following in common: "3" indicates under all circumstances 3 times as many elements of whatever nature, and the same holds true for "5" and other positive numbers, for they refer to quantities regardless of the nature of the constituent units. In the final stage of abstraction, he realized that the concept "1" stands for the irreducible concept of *unity;* that the concept "2" applies to two entities of any kind, in other words, that it has come to designate all *pairs* regardless of the nature of what constitutes the pair; that the concept "3" applies to every *threeness* regardless of what constitutes it and so on ... which brings us to Bertrand Russell's (*279*) definition of number as the *"class of classes": the number 1 is nothing other than the symbol for the class concept of all existing unities; the number 2 nothing other than the symbol for the class concept comprising the totality of all existing pairs, the number 3 nothing other than the symbol for the class concept embodying the totality of all existing triads and so on.*

For an explanation of the terms fractional numbers, rational and irrational numbers, real numbers, imaginary numbers, complex numbers, finite and transfinite numbers see esp. Cooley (*56*) and Kramer (*173*).

Thus, the analysis of the mathematical fields of thought disclosed the *crucial role of class concepts*, as did the examination of the non-mathematical fields. Where then, did the ways of non-mathematical and mathematical thought separate? In the diagrammatic representaticn of concepts by Euler's circles their mutual overlapping indicated but partial identity, as the constituents of concepts, by virtue of their individual differences, retained their semi-independence from the core. *The concept of number, we submit, differs from other concepts by the equality of the individual components, achieved in turn by the artificial elimination of differences and, hence, by the complete absence of "fringes."** Accordingly, *each individual component represents* the whole, and it depends on the number of units only what symbol we choose to

---

* I am aware of the fact that this is a laymans' suggestion.

express it. In other words, mathematics has "branched off" from the non-mathematical fields of thought by the *elimination of marginal elements of individual concepts;* it has endowed them with maximal conciseness and their relationships with maximal validity—indeed necessity. *Mathematics, more especially pure mathematics, became sceletized logic expressed in a language whose words are symbols, whose thoughts and sentences represent relationships between measurable magnitudes and whose syntax mirrors the specificity of these relations.* In exploring them and letting the laws of mathematical thought unfold, an almost unbelievable variety of numerically expressible relations has been brought to light.

It can hardly be a matter of surprise that other interpretations of mathematical thought have been offered. For example, Waismann (*335*) holds that "mathematics contains a series of deductive systems which develop the inferences of arbitrarily chosen assumptions." No doubt he discards the possibility, which may perhaps be inferred from his own definition, that the assumptions in question are not necessarily related to the data of reality, or that they may contradict them; if one were to assume that points 1, 2, 3, etc., of the number axis are non equi-distant, or one would make other changes, the inferences of arbitrarily chosen assumptions would not square with the data of the physical world, in fact they may not even form a self-contained logical system.

The simplest mathematical operations are arithmetical, the most elementary of which in turn are counting and computing with numbers. In algebra, the inclusiveness of operations is established by the introduction of alphabetical symbols to which different values are assigned so that, in contrast to the results of arithmetical problems, those of algebraic problems can be applied to many cases. However, while a given *algebraic expression*, because of the inclusiveness of the alphabetical symbols, represents potentially an *infinite number of particular operations*, it remains inherently arithmetical in character, just like the maneuvers of formations of infantry can be broken down to individual steps of its soldiers; furthermore, the movement patterns of a group remain identical irrespective of the number of individuals that form it. The chief characteristic of algebraic expressions is *symbolized generalization*. For example, "the algebraic formula expressing Newton's law of universal gravitational attraction is the translation of the *general* fact of gravitation into a language which, at the same time, expresses its particular instances" (*145*).

Mathematical notations

The discovery of algebraically definable relations depended, among other factors, on the use of appropriate symbols. Gradually, these symbols have grown into a system of notation permitting the expression of relations of increasing complexity. In advancing from relatively simple systems to more complicated systems or relations and, eventually, relations of relations, it became essential to create appropriate symbolic expressions for them. Cajori (*40*), in an essay on the growth of mathematical notation systems, distinguishes between *primitive* and *incorporative* symbols. The former represent abbreviations of words and various pictorial and ideographic signs; the latter, combinations of two or more mathematical ideas such as, for example, ∫ (summa) indicating the "sum of an infinite number of infinitely small magnitudes of elements." The totality of these elements, however, represents not only the *quantity* to be determined by integration but, at the same time, the sum total of an infinite number of *operations*. The symbol Σ, on the other hand, represents merely the sum total of a number of finite magnitudes. With the evolution of algebraic language, symbols become increasingly "condensed", indeed, some of them no longer include an infinite number of particular and similar but, instead, many diverse simultaneous and successive operations. It is not difficult to see that incorporative symbols *correspond to the "schemes, techniques and strategies"*, that is, the *"thinking sets"* previously discussed.

In general, as explained by Cajori, Rignano (*273*), Whitehead (*352*) a.o., symbols enable an otherwise long written statement to be compressed within a small space for convenient and rapid mental survey and they place and keep logical relationships before the mind. Their relative superiority depends on the adaptibility to changing viewpoints and varying needs as, for example, Leibniz' ∫, which has admitted of incorporative devices in integration while Newton's □ could not admit so easily (*273*). Cajori, in commenting on the potency of symbols, states that they may stimulate intellectual experimentation and lead to vital extension of ideas. Ideal nota-

tion systems are characterized by a maximum of inclusiveness and specificativity; by convertibility and fertility; further, by their capacity to promote not only the interaction and articulation of relationships between magnitudes but also their condensation—readily to be broken down to elementary units whenever necessity arises. Thus, *notation systems are elaborate and at the same time flexible devices* permitting the establishment, summation, commutation, substitution and specification, briefly, the *representation* and *manipulation of meanings*.

Under ordinary conditions, the operative laws of the various symbols do not fully determine the line of reasoning, like associations by similarity and contiguity alone fail to account for the directiveness of thought processes. Neither does syllogistic reasoning of itself determine the train of thought in spite of the close relationship between mathematics and formal logic. Mathematical truth, as stressed by Keyser (*159, 160*) in a magnificent oration delivered before an audience of Columbia students, is never found by the mechanical application of rules only, nor is mathematical thought a "syllogistic mill." Pierce (*253*), when asked about the role of formal logic, answered: "Ratiocination? It is merely the smooth pavement upon which the chariot rolls." Helmholtz (*123*) described the effort involved in productive mathematical thought as follows: "I must compare myself with a mountain climber who, without knowing the way, mounts slowly and painfully; often, I must turn back if I can go no farther. Sometimes through intuition, sometimes through accident, I discover a trace of a new way. This leads me forward again for a short distance and finally I reach my goal. Then I discover to my shame the royal road upon which I could have travelled if I had only been clever enough to find it from the beginning."

The algorithm

In spite of the element of intuition involved in mathematical thought, the suggestive power of mathematical symbols is far more compelling than the associative trends of non-mathematical psychisms. The difference may be readily accounted for by the fact that mental operations involving fringe-less conceptual material represent relationships which, although they are not necessarily obvious, exist of necessity. They are nothing more than tautological transformations.* In this respect, the associative mechanisms involved in mathematical thought are quasi-imperative as compared to those operating with both central and marginal elements of non-mathematical concepts. The directiveness and conciseness of the associative mechanisms in question has forged them to a time and energy saving tool, the *algorithm* (*53*). *Algorithmic thinking operates not only with relations, but with systems of relations whose meaning has become fixated and which span vast reaches of thought at a height from which details are no longer visible—indeed, relations which span an apparent void.* In general, the term *algorithm* signifies the ability to calculate in any system of notation. As here employed, it designates the seemingly autonomous origin of relationships between mathematical concepts and, indirectly, of more and more complex mathematical ideas. Thus, response determination at the highest level of abstraction re-acquires certain characteristics of *automatic* functions. Somewhat paradoxically, there exist common features between, on the one hand, abstract mental performances and, on the other, the functions of the lower, purely physiological levels of the nervous system where self-regulating processes take shape outside the sphere of consciousness. In other words, *algorithmic thinking seemingly reinstates the technic of mechanical response determination in the very same sphere where, in fact, the element of choice of response has generally reached its maximum.* Later on, we shall consider the possibility that, under certain conditions, algorithmic mechanisms may operate in non-mathematical thought as well.

To summarize, the study of mathematical thinking has brought forward the following facts.

---
* Bertrand Russell.

(1) Mathematical concepts are derivable from perceptions; they have a meaning only inasmuch as they can ultimately be related to the data of reality. This statement may satisfy Cassirer's (*45*) postulate that "the concept of space and the concept of number, geometry and arithmetic, must be systematically deducible from one and the same principle, for otherwise that union by virtue of which they had not only developed side by side historically but also had interpenetrated and enriched one another would hardly be understandable."

(2) Algebraic operations correspond to the generalizations in the non-mathematical fields of thought.

(3) Notation systems are conventionalized expedients which serve primarily the symbolic representation of meanings. In addition, they have unifying and synthetizing functions; they promote, at the same time, the generation of meanings of different complexity into which many individual elements may enter. The elements out of which notation systems are composed may or may not have a one to one correspondence to the realities to which they refer but the representational property and operational laws of mathematical notations permits the item generating manipulation of the symbols which compose them. Although mathematical thought may become emancipated from empirical data its results, nevertheless, are applicable to the physical world.

(4) Since the manipulation of mathematical concepts is controlled by the operative laws of symbols, mathematical thought carries with it an element of automaticity. In this sense, we may interpret Hertz' (*128*) dictum, that mathematical formulae have an independent existence and an intelligence of their own.

The general organization of thought processes and the problem of intuitive thought

The following is a brief recapitulation of the first part of the current chapter and, at the same time, an introduction to the problem of intuitive thought. For reasons which will become apparent presently, the psychological analysis of intuitive thought had to be deferred pending the clarification of certain mathematical concepts.

PHASE SEQUENCES OF THOUGHT

The immediate appreciation of *perceptual relationships* occurs for all practical purposes in one step while a complete sequence of thought, i.e., the appreication and validation of *conceptualized relations* involves two phases, namely, the *inaugural* phase and the *concluding* phase. Needless to add that, in the course of problem solving, any number of bi-phasic sets may emerge in succession. In fact, alternative sets may for all practical purposes be worked through simultaneously.

The inaugural phase of thought

The previously given examples of reasoning by generalization and analogy have brought forward the following points.

(a) The inaugural phase of thought is composed of two subordinate phases, namely, the *presolution phase* (or problem phase) and the *productive phase*.

(b) In the presolution phase, no fertile relations exist as yet between overt and subsidiary psychisms. Under certain conditions, *productive relations* may be called into being by actuating events which, in turn, are either observations or ekphorized engrams.

(c) The productive relation creates the *generating term* and, indirectly the *generated* term by a process that is traceable to, although not identical with, association by similarity. The generated term embodies the *produced relation*. Prior to the attainment of the goal of thought, the inaugural phase comprises two as yet non-articulating psychisms. Now, since the productive relation, which converts x into a known, is ordinarily represented by an observation, while some of the remaining factors involved in productive reasoning are subsidiary psychisms, *insight produced by generalization or analogy mechanisms may be defined in terms of articulation of conscious (dominant) with non-conscious (subsidiary) processes.* However, there are good grounds for believing that new data may be generated not only by the above discussed mechanisms of generalization and analogy, by reflective reasoning that is, but also by intuitive thought. *Intuition is the product of the interaction of one group of non-conscious mental processes with another non-conscious group. It is only the attainment of the goal of thought i.e., the product of this interaction* which *is a conscious process*, that is, one represented in the dominant sphere of mentation, or the overt system of notation (Fig. 11). Preparatory to the study of the insight producing interaction of non-conscious psychisms, we shall attempt to combine the various approaches to the problem of conscious versus non-conscious mental processes.

The notation system "consciousness." A comparison with mathematical notation systems

It can hardly be questioned that both conscious and non-conscious mental acts have a physiological basis and that they are to a certain extent "interconvertible." We know that the functions of the receptors may be expressed in physical terms, for example in terms of wave-frequencies, and that, phenomenologically, a given frequency is altogether different from the color perception to which it gives rise. Nevertheless, there prevails, in general, a rather consistent (if not rigid) correspondence between physiological and psychic phenomena involved in perception. For instance, in the course of events intervening between the peripheral and the central recording of stimuli, specific wavelengths are transposed into colors of equal specificity. In the foregoing chapters we defined consciousness in rather general terms, namely, as the way objective reality is recorded by the highest levels of the nervous system, or as the state of a function of the highest sensory level of the neuraxis. At the present stage of the argument, and in the light of experiences gained by the analysis of mathematical concepts, symbols and notations, a further clarification of the nature of consciousness may be attempted.

(a) In the periphery of the organism, stimuli are recorded in a relatively simple fashion, that is, as low-order analogs, and their integration with motor neuron function at the reflex level is, by comparison, a primitive process. It is fair to assume that, at increasingly higher levels of the neuraxis, the process of sensory-motor integration becomes increasingly complicated and that, to cope with the increasing complexity of stimuli, and to determine appropriate responses which depend on an increasing number of determiners (or variables), sensory data are incorporated into more versatile and more inclusive systems of reference as it were just as, in algebra, whenever more complex operations are to be carried out, elementary units are incorporated into more comprehensive systems of notation. To define events at the reflex level, a relatively simple framework of reference is adequate, (for example sounds and colors may be defined in terms of wavelengths) while the definition of events occurring at higher levels, could they be expressed in terms of man systems of notation, would require the use of incorporative symbols of a higher order.

(b) In adaptation to the specific purposes for which they have been designed, mathematical notation systems can be converted into one another. Similar viewpoints would seem to apply to the systems of notations established at the various sensory levels of the neuraxis. Accordingly, engrams have a potential consciousness value, while overt psychisms have a mnemonic value. In other words, if engrams and overt psychisms be recorded in interconvertible systems, states of awareness and states of non-awareness would be nothing more than different *modes* in which data are recorded by various central mechanisms, or, for that matter, "given" in different systems of representation.

(c) To say that an engram is ekphorized means, in actual fact, that the psychisms concerned is translated from the mnemonic system of notation into the overt system, while process of engraphy may be expressed in terms of translation from the latter to the former. Now since engrams are ekphorized in the interest of appropriacy of response to stimuli, *consciousness* may be thought of as a *state of a function* (or mode), more especially a state of a function of the highest sensory level of the neuraxis, the other, alternative state being *non-consciousness*. The conscious state is instituted whenever the recording of similarity and dissimilarity requires reference to appropriate residues of experiences, and their articulation with recent stimuli. This is merely another way of expressing the fact that a *particular mode of recording of data on the part of the highest sensory (intellective) level brings into mutual relationship the sphere of objective and subjective reality not only along the dimension of space but also of time.* The determination of appropriate responses on the part of the highest selector mechanism presupposes a setting in which past, present and anticipated determiners of behaviour coexist, for it is chiefly this specific setting wherein the intellective level computes the neurodynamic processes that determine the action of the effector mechanisms. We add, by way of repetition, that the term "mode" designates originally, the "state of a substance", e.g., ice and water are different modes of one and the same chemical compound. However, it is profitable to extend the meaning of the term to cover the *state of a function* as well. For example, if the vibrations of a cord be regarded as its function, different intensities of vibration would be different states of an identical function.

(In fact, it would be an alternative way of visualizing the relationship between conscious and non-conscious mental processes, not unlike one already suggested by Newton's contemporary Sir Robert Hooke, to regard engrams as inaudible vibrations, conscious mental processes as audible vibrations. Yet the notation system analogy is the least anthropistic and, moreover, most appropriate in view of certain similarities between biological and man made computing mechanisms.)

The fact that, at the highest sensory level, subjective and objective reality are correlated along the dimensions of both space and time may in a different way be expressed as follows. At the highest level, appropriacy of response, or choice, depends on a state of brain activity put into operation whenever the adaptive behaviour of the organism (in contrast to reflex response) requires the anteroceptive and retrospective evaluation of the data of reality. It would be pointless if the organism were to operate in a system of notation in which reality is recorded unless there existed the necessity to evaluate the data in question and to establish contact with reality. (In point of fact, states of awareness in which all experiental data are overtly and simultaneously represented are unimaginable although, to a degree at least, similar mental states are realized in panoramic awareness.) Conversely, "withdrawal" from reality may be understood in terms of reduction of awareness, such as lack of attention, of alertness and, eventually, transitional states between the waking state and sleep. In states of reduced awareness, the physical world is recorded in a fragmentary fashion, i.e., in a modified and generally less versatile system of notation. From this particular viewpoint, intuitive thought that takes shape in states of reduced awareness is a shortcut, for response determination is still dependent on the institution of engrams in spite of the fact that it bypasses conscious mental activity.

To sum it all up, consciousness may be thought of as representation of certain high order nervous system processes put to use whenever the interaction between the subjective and the objective sphere requires that both percepts and engrams be manipulated in appropriate combinations. In parenthesis, it may be noted that, since both engrams and overt psychisms enter into the formation of concepts, and not only man but also animals evaluate percepts and engrams in determining the nature of response to certain stimuli, that s, since both man and animals act consciously, both the actions of man and, in principally the same fashion, certain segments of animal behaviour are guided by concepts. Further, the various techniques involved in the recording of reality on the part of the highest sensory level and mathematical systems of notation have certain interrelated properties. They include (a) *correspondence* between the stimulus and its analog, (b) *convertibility*, the capacity to transform a given analog value into a corresponding value which is more convenient operationally, (c) *comprehensiveness*, the property to incorporate significant data or aspects of the stimulus into analogs of a higher, "algebraic" order, (d) *versatility*, the fluency of manipulation of analogs in the course of the generation of relationships, and (f) *fertility*, the generation of relevant relations which is inherent in the composition of the analogs or symbols involved.

The above considerations stress certain *formal properties* between biological and mathematical notation systems but are not intended to conceal the limitations of the simile here proposed. If a mathematician describes certain physical relationships in the language of symbols, the symbols do not, unless he uses ideograms, resemble the data of the external world with which he is concerned. Still, the same applies to concepts, the highest category of analogs or recording symbols which are impalpable data of awareness and, accordingly, bear no resemblance to the stimuli they represent, so that, in this respect, the analogy does not necessarily break down. The crucial difference between the symbols of mathematics and symbolizing central nervous system processes is that the latter are "aware" of the symbolized stimuli and thereby resemble mirror images (if such existed) that are aware of the data of reality they duplicate. (That objective reality is independent of its subjective counterpart is brought out, among other observations, by the fact that countless generations of biological recorders have vanished while objective reality is persisting; further, that experimental tempering with the recording mechanisms of the brain, e.g., electrical stimulation of the posterior cortex sets up local dysfunctions while the recording mechanism of the posterior cortex of the experimentalist continues to operate in a normal fashion as mirror of objective reality.)

It is up to, and exclusive of, the point made previously that the notation-system analogy of consciousness can be carried, namely, to the awareness character of the recording data, or the awareness character of an apparent central point (the "self") to which they are referred. The problem of how material events produce psychic events, which has vexed not only generations of philosophers but also modern physicists and physicians (see, e.g., references *177, 256* and *315*) is unanswerable if formulated in this fashion. Indeed, the very phrasing of the question is based on a preconceived notion, which makes it a self blocking question. Conscious phenomena represent a technique of recording of informative stimuli, a technique developed, on the part of higher biological units, as the most effective means to deal with stimuli in certain situational settings. Consciousness is merely one of the instrumentalities of the organism which serves its biological equilibrium and, in this respect at least, the property of certain type of biological equipment. It is no more of a mystery than the neural arrangements which relax the pyloric sphincter in certain phases of digestion. It is a fact that, just like the pyloric muscles, the recording equipment serving the highest, including the most sublime functions, may be disorganized by physico-chemical influences. To make this idea more palatable, one might say that consciousness is a name applied to certain working arrangements at the highest sensory level, established to cope with the data of the external and the internal world in the most versatile fashion possible, maximal versatility of notation having been achieved by the brain of man. Yet, in spite of the different perceptual organization of the various phyla, which opens up different parameters of the objective world, certain basic data are represented in their nervous systems in a practically identical fashion. That man can fight an eagle, an octopus and a shark in perfect coordination can hardly be explained by empathy as some would have us believe. Rather, it indicates the extensive overlapping of at least their visual, kinaesthetic and motor worlds. Man can deal with these animals in spite of the fact that their brain is organized in a different way because the highest levels of the nervous system, even though they may be represented by different strata of the neuraxis, produce, in each phylum, basically superimposable representations of the

238   THOUGHT

world as it is in itself, that is, of *ultimate reality*.*)
Nature has developed different methods of how
to form a "world scheme" in the organism, just as
she has invented at least four methods of flight,
namely, flight in birds, in insects, in bats and in
sauropsides, not to speak of the methods which
she invented "indirectly", through the medium
of the human mind. Romanoff, in a fascinating
lecture devoted to the fundamentals of evolution,
confussed to be baffled by the fact that, in some
phyla, the "soul" seems to reside in the cortex;
while, in others, the "seat of the soul" appears to
be the corpus striatum; and, in a third group of
organisms, in the midbrain.

After this digression, it is pertinent to call renewed attention to the effects, upon the contents
of consciousness, of unphysiological stimulation of
the sensory division of the nervous system that
extends from the receptor organs to its highest
sensory plane. Irritation of the labyrinths of the
inner ear when the sea is rough may cause not
only fantastic distortions of the "images" but
even the delusion that the organism itself, the
seemingly stable core of subjective and objective
reality, is distorted, increased in size or experi-
ended as a whole or in part in an abnormal
fashion difficult to describe. Pressure on a peripheral nerve may vitiate the data "transmitted to
consciousness." A minimum amount of psychotropic drugs or of extra-homeostatic blood levels
of certain metabolites causes gross distortions at
the perceptual, the configurational and the conceptual level of sensation. Moreover, toxic substances may change not only the cognitive but
also the affective parameter of intellective stimuli
so that the entire structure of the experiental
world is altered concurrently with the feeling tone
with which we respond to it. Unless physical and

---

* As is well known, Kant (*152a*) considered ultimate reality as unknowable. "Das transzendentale
Objekt, welches den äusseren Erscheinungen
imgleichen das, was der inneren Anschauung
zugrunde liegt, ist weder Materie noch ein denkendes
Wesen and sich selbst, sondern ein uns unbekannter
Grund der Erscheinungen." However, adequacy of
response is difficult to grasp without the assumption
that objective reality is a limiting case of ultimate
(or absolute) reality; and subjective reality, for its
part, in each phylum, a limiting case of objective
reality. Thus, the diverse subjective realities are in
a sense true images of ultimate reality although
they are not superimposable throughout but depend,
in each biological form equipped with a sensory
apparatus, on its particular sensory organization.

chemical influences acted, like in a testtube, on a
physicochemical substrate, it would be impossible
to account for the phenomenon in question, i.e.,
the distortion of the mirror images of the external
world and sometimes even the internal world of
the organism. The accuracy of the recording
equipment of living beings is determined by the
material state of its component parts which serve
the function of recording. It is a multiplicity of
material factors on which there depends adequate
recording activity or, for that matter, the adequate functioning of the highest sensory mechanism of the nervous system.

Now, it is a unique feature of the biological
equipment described, that it combines, figuratively speaking, the properties of a mirror with
those of a photographic emulsion. Objects that
have entered the perceivable orbit of the organism
are more or less permanently and faithfully preserved in the form of "invisible images", so that
their cumulative superimposition to the point of
uselessness is prevented. What's more, the data
of the past which are fixated in this fashion are not
inert. If re-converted into the overt (visible) system of notation, they may interact with recent
data. Indeed, they interact even if they remain
in the state of invisibility, as stimuli represented
in the mnemonic system of notation. They behave like purely physiological processes which
never become conscious, which go on automatically, or blindly, reminiscent, in a way, of algorithmic operations which "span an apparent
void."

Intuitive thought

Whatever insight into the relationships between
conscious and non-conscious processes the above
deliberations have yielded may be applied to the
study of the relationships between, on the one
hand, reasoning by generalization and analogy
that occur *reflectively* and, on the other, *intuitive
thought*,* which takes shape in the absence of reflexion as a conscious process. In the former eventuality, the reasoner is more or less clearly aware
of the existence of the gap in knowledge, just as
of a positive scotoma in his field of vision. In the

---

* It is convenient to discuss intuition under the
over-all heading "The inaugural phase of thought."
This does not imply that intuition does not play a
role in the concluding phase or, for that matter, in
connecting the two phases in question.

latter eventuality, the goal of thought exists as a non-conscious mental state or, for that matter, as a phase of a delayed action mechanism. In other words, the goal of thought exists in the subsidiary sphere of mentation. If the reasoner deals with the problem reflectively, he has two distinct experiences. He is aware of the goal, or state of disequilibrium, at the cognitive level of experience and, at the critical moment, of the attainment of the goal. (It matters little at this point that the solution of the problem may be tentative.) In states of intuitive problem solving on the other hand, the "reasoner" is unaware of the goal of thought or the gap in knowledge; or, to put it in another way, he has a negative rather than a positive scotoma. It is only the sudden, unexpected solution of the problem that reminds him that the goal now reached, or apparently reached, has ever existed. At the moment of intuitive illumination, a person might have been occupied with some routine matter, or been in a related or hypnagogic state, or dreaming, or sleeping—perhaps even sleeping without dreaming.

The following are examples of sudden illumination occurring in various states of awareness ranging from full lucidity to deep sleep.

Over a period of many years, Gauss (*88*) had been trying to solve a mathematical problem. At long last he succeeded, as he put it, "not by dint of effort . . . but by a sudden flash of light." However, he was unable to "point to the threat which joined what he know previously to what he succeeded in doing." The wording of the above quoted passage indicates that Gauss, although at the critical moment not concerned with the problem, was nevertheless convinced that the idea which leaped to his mind was related to what he knew before.

To Helmholtz happy ideas came unexpectedly, and, strangely enough, not when he was working at his desk but "readily during a slow ascend of hills on a sunny day" (*123*).

Poincaré (*34, 258*) solved a difficult mathematical problem (subsequently termed the Fuchsian functions) while stepping into a bus; and Hamilton (*24, 95, 105*) solved an algebraic problem (quaternion algebra) while walking over a bridge and talking to his wife about trifling matters. "I then and there felt the galvanic circuit close; and the sparks that fell from it were the fundamental equations . . . about which I had thought for at least fifteen years." Hadamard (*100*) solved an

involved mathematical question while being rudely awakened in the morning without, as he said, having had time to think about it, indeed, about anything. The scientists had given countless hours of conscious but futile thought to their problems some time prior to their solution. "When I settle down to the hard thinking," Heisenberg remarked, "I may get stuck and annoyed and give up. Next morning, the solution comes through—just as if I'd had been thinking about it all night." (Newsweek, August 24, 1959, p. 82.)

Kekulé v. Strachonitz (*161*) gives the following account of one of the most important discoveries ever made in organic chemistry. After having worked all day long on his textbook, he got tired and sat down in front of his fireplace. "I turned my chair toward the fireplace and sank into a doze. Again the atoms were flitting before my eyes. Smaller groups now kept modestly in the background. My mind's eye, sharpened by repeated visions of a similar sort, now distinguished larger structures of varying forms. Long rows frequently closed together all in movements winding and turning like serpents. And, see, what was that? One of the serpents seized its own tail and the form whorled mockingly before my eyes. I came awake like a flash of lightning. This time I spent the night working out the consequences of the hypothesis", (the ring-like structure of the benzene molecule).

Inaudi (*141*) often dreamed about figures and would solve mathematical problems while sleeping. Both Heaviside (*120, 184*) and the Indian prodigy Srinivana Ramanuyan, whose life was described by Sir Oliver Hardy (*105*), arrived at mathematical results of considerable complexity without going through a conscious process of proof. Like Newton (*245*) and Laplace (*179*), he sometimes solved mathematical problems while asleep and would record the result on awakening. Like Gauss, he was not always able to supply an immediate mathematical proof.

What may be the mechanism of intuitive thought?

Let us assume that, in ordinary, reflective, reasoning, the reasoner made an effort to solve the problem by "thinking of it all the time" (as Newton said he had done before discovering the law of gravitation) whereas, in those cases in which the problem is solved by intuition, the "reasoner" has apparently forgotten all about it and the goal of thought is represented by a non-conscious mental state. Nevertheless, the suddenness with which the solution (or the tentative solution) is experienced, characterizes either variety of thought, and the frequent use of the terms "sudden" and "flash" by persons who had the experience of illumination is hardly a coincidence.

At this juncture, we have become sufficiently familiar with the fact that, in reasoning by generalization and analogy, the experience of achievement coincides with the completion of the generating term which, for its part, completes the generated term and culminates in the attainment of the goal of thought. By the same token, insight gained by intuition, although a product of nonconscious activity, can be accounted for by a similar alignment of terms. The difference between intuitive and reflective thought may be specified as follows.

(a) In the former, the actuating event is an engram which is ekphorized into the subsidiary rather than the dominant sphere of mentation. This engram enters into the formation of the generating term and is instrumental in the production of the generated term.

(b) The emergence of the produced relation, the goal of thought (now reached) which is translated into the overt system of notation, produces an *arousal reaction* usually referred to as *illumination*, or *flash of insight*.

Accordingly, the only component of intuitive thought represented in the dominant sphere of mentation is the new, produced, relation. The reasoner is aroused by the conversion of "x" into a known quantity that occurs within the relational framework of the generating and the generated term (Fig. 16, 17). In other words, he is aroused by the appearance of a new mental content in the dominant sphere of mentation. At this crucial moment, there occurred a transposition of the newly produced item into the notation system operating at the highest sensory level, the item searched for having become "visible" like a number that leaps up on a score board. Apparently, it is of no consequence that, in intuitive thought, the producing relation is a physiological process which lacks consciousness value. (In reflective reasoning, we remind ourselves, the producing relation was either an observation of an ekphorized engram.) Thus, inasmuch as switching over to the notation system consciousness presupposes the completed alignment of relations, both varieties of reasoning can be derived from an identical mechanism; in either case, physiological processes would attain consciousness value at the moment the produced relation is called into being. If this interpretation is accepted, *intuition should be a borderline case of the awareness of relational identity which, in turn, is the core of reflective reasoning by analogy and generalization;* furthermore, one may expect to find transitional forms of thought wherein the difference between the two varieties of productive thought is infinitesimal. The following observations are suggestive evidence of the postulated borderline mechanisms.

In some of the cases of reasoning by intuition it is at least possible that an outside clue called forth, or helped produce, the formation and juxtaposition (figs. 16, 17) of a relationally identical pair of terms. For example, "the idea of motion in geometry came to Descartes while he was lying in bed and watching the movements of a fly crawling near an angle of the room, and the position of which he observed at any moment could be defined by its perpendicular distance from the ceiling and the two adjacent walls" (*321*). Otto Loewi (*194*) awoke one night and scribbled a few words on a sheet of paper before falling asleep again. Unfortunately, the note was so poorly written that he was unable to decipher it next morning. It so happened that he awoke the following night apparently with the same idea, and recorded it more carefully—the concept of chemical transmission of nerve impulses had come to him in his sleep. (A few hours later he verified the hypothesis by a simple but ingenious experiment). In this case, we may interpret intuition as repetitive thinking by analogy for, some twenty years prior to the episode described, Loewi, while talking to one of his associates, had mentioned in passing that nerve cells act upon one another chemically, in the fashion other cells do, but, as he told me, did not pursue the matter any further.

In the Descartes' episode, then, the actuating element was an observation, (the crawling fly) although one so remotely related to the sphere of geometry that it can hardly be considered an observation properly so called. By the same token, Kekulé's dream was only symbolically related to the subject of chemistry. It is therefore a debatable issue whether the idea of motion came to Descartes through reflective reasoning by analogy or by intuition—indeed it may be argued that, as we have already indicated, Darwin's theory of the survival of the fittest and of the origin of species was a product of intuitive thought. The following passages of his autobiography (*62*) are pertinent. "I was well prepared to appreciate the struggle for existence which everywhere goes on . . . it at once struck me that under these circumstances favourable variations would tend to be preserved and unfavourable ones destroyed. The result of this would be the formation of new species. But at that time I had overlooked one problem of great importance . . . this problem is the tendency of organic beings descended from the same stock to diverge in character as they become modified . . . *and I can remember the very spot in the road whilst in my carriage when to my joy the solution occurred to me.* (Emphasis added) The solution as I believe is that the modified offspring of all dominant and increasing forms tend to become adapted to many and highly diversified places in the economy of nature."

In the Loewi episode the actuating event and, hence, the productive relation was in all likelihood an engram ekphorized during a dream; even so, the element of transition between reflective reasoning by analogy and generalization and by intuition (based on the same mechanism) is unmistakable. The idea that analogy-like mechanisms operate in intuitive thought as well, i.e., that (a) the item-generating alignment of terms occurs in the subsidiary sphere of mentation, (the mnemonic system of notation that is) and (b) that the generated term is subsequently transposed into the overt system of notation, may be inferred from Poincaré's (*258*) account of the discovery of Fuchsian functions which we now quote rather in full. "We entered the omnibus," he wrote, "to go to some place or other. At the moment I put my foot on the step, the idea came to me without anything in my formed thoughts having paved the way for it that the transformation I had used to define the Fuchsian functions was *identical* with those of non-Euclidian geometry . . ." (Thus, the transformation used to define the Fuchsian functions was an intuitive mathematical discovery, and Poincaré noticed the *relational identity* of the two terms only later. Only later did he become aware of the fact that the transformation of non-Euclidian geometry had evoked those used to define the Fuchsian functions).* "I turned

---

* It should perhaps be added that the solution of the problem was the definition of the Fuchsian functions, which antedated the "bus episode," at which time Poincaré became aware of the previously obscure logical background of the solution.

my attention to the study of some arithmetical questions, apparently without much success and without suspicion of any connections with my preceding researches. I thought of something else. One morning, walking on the bluff, the idea came to me with just the same characteristic of brevity, suddenness and immediate certainty that the arithmetic transformations of the indeterminate ternary quadratic forms were *identical* with those of non-Euclidian geometry." (In other words, the transformations of non-Euclidian geometry had produced those of the indeterminate ternary quadratic forms.)

Like probably most of my readers, I have only a very dim notion of the nature of the mathematical problems with which Poincaré had to deal. Nevertheless, it is apparent that the celebrated scientist, although at the critical moment occupied with another matter, solved the problems as if suddenly aware of the identical relationstructure of his new discovery and a certain theorem of non-Euclidian geometry. Hence, it is not unreasonable to assume that the relationship between the latter and the quadratic forms can be expressed in terms of analogy or, perhaps, of generalization.

The well attested observation that a person may solve a problem in the state of sleep suggests the following *interpretation of non-conscious* productivity. Sleep may be defined in terms of dissociation of the self into a personal self and a para-personal self or a ps and a pps. Depending on the depth of sleep, (the degree of reduction of responsiveness of the highest sensory level of the brain which acts, at the same time, as a selector mechanism) the ps may be constricted to the point of virtual elimination from the mental apparatus, as, indeed, may be the pps, in which case sleep is dreamless and deep. In sharp contrast, the state of dreaming, apart from the above mentioned modification of the pps, is a limited and modified state of wakefulness of the pps. It is a mental state characterized, among other features (relatively unimportant at present) by an increased fluidity of psychisms, especially by the increased fluidity of engrams, which, moreover, as soon as ekphorized, are apt to be represented in the dreamer's dominant sphere of mentation in a perception-like fashion. Although certain persons have an extraordinary power of visualization, a picturable type of ekphory approaching the vividity of dream images does not occur under ordinary conditions of wakefulness. On the other hand, the dream content may be formed by more or less abstract thought or an intermingling of both palpable and impalpable psychisms. The dreaming pps continues to be aware of the gap in knowledge, in other words, the state of disequilibrium at the conceptual level persists. One may suppose that, in analogy to what happens in the full state of wakefulness, the actuating event (an observation on the part of the pps being impossible) is an engram which is ekphorized into the dominant sphere of mentation of the pps, and which initiates the generating term, the generated term and the produced relation. The newly generated idea, which is an awareness content represented in the dominant sphere of mentation of the pps, re-establishes the unity of the self, in other words, the self is aroused to full wakefulness. Otherwise, the newly generated psychism is represented in the common mnemonic system of the ps and the pps. Upon reestablishment of the unity of the self on awakening, the newly generated psychism is recognized, that is, incorporated into the dominant sphere of mentation and brought into relationship with the ultimate system of reference. We might add that, owing to the perception-like character of the psychisms involved, and the fact that symbols are ordinarily configurational data, the newly generated item, as illustrated by Kekulé's dream, may be formulated in a symbolic fashion. (He readily deciphered the significance of the "snake-symbol.") In the second eventuality, then, the self becomes aware of the item in question on awakening rather than on arousal. In the third eventuality, the self, on awakening, becomes aware of having dreamed but does not quite know what. The fact that dream contents are apt to be forgotten is another way of saying that, in line with the trivial observation having been made by nearly anyone at one time or another, the fixation of engrams on the part of the pps is more or less ephemeral. At the same time, the comparison of the modified wakeful state with hypnotic states suggests that engrams are more likely to be ekphorized in the very same ("hypnoid") state of limited and modified wakefulness in which their engraphy has taken place. In fact, a subject may have to be rehypnotized to recall what it experienced in the course of previous hypnotic sessions. It is probably not without significance that Otto Loewi recalled in subsequent dreams (rather than in the waking state) what he had dreamed in his first productive dreams. Only later did he recall the new item by which, indeed, he was ultimately aroused to full wakefulness. Interestingly enough, episodes of scientific and especially of artistic creating have been known to occur in trance-like states which differ from dreaming only by the fact that the ps is not completely eliminated but which, with respect to the state of the pps, resemble each other rather closely.

Carrying this line of reasoning one step further, we suggest that *intuitive thought that takes shape under condition of full wakefulness may be likewise expressed in terms of dissociative mechanisms.* If this concept is sound, the presence of a problem in the reasoner's mind would set up a state of limited dissociation into a ps and a pps and, concurrently, the accumulation of pertinent material in the subsidiary sphere of mentation. Off and on, the two selfs may communicate while, at other times, the existence of the problem has apparently been forgotten. A superficial communication between the ps and the pps may result in the awareness of a problem and, concomitantly, a certain degree of mental distraction on the part of the ps. In fact, it may result in mental depression referable to the frustrating experience of disequilibrium at the conceptual level of cerebral function. Under conditions of more extensive communication, the products of the activity of the pps are transmitted to the ps, which experiences them as ideas coming seemingly out of nowhere. If the newly generated item is verbalized, the person may have the impression that a new idea has been "whispered into his ear."

The new idea may not necessarily embody the generated term, but, rather, may be related to the second, concluding, phase of thought, that is to say, the establishment of a *guide structure* against which the item generated in the inaugural phase of thought is matched and, depending on the outcome of this comparison, either accepted or rejected. Or the new idea may indicate the way the inaugural phase of thought should be made to articulate with the concluding phase. In other words, the new idea may embody the *transfer mechanism* discussed in the early part of this chapter. In *summary*, then, we may assume that there occurs, ultimately, both in reflective and in intuitive reasoning by generalization or analogy, a translation of data from the subsidiary into the dominant sphere of mentation or, to put it in another way, from the mnemonic into the overt system of notation. *The transmutation of data occurs at the moment neuro-integrative processes have matured to a stage at which they are ready to fulfill their function, namely, to correlate the data of subjective reality with the facts of objective reality.* Once the correlation has been established, the organism is able to construct a tentative baseline of response which, in the concluding phase of thought, is tested either empirically or deductively.

The concluding phase of thought

In so far as the concluding phase of thought is dependent on the ekphory of engrams, it is a more complicated mental process than the inaugural phase. In classifying a plant, for example, it is necessary to recall the essential features of the species embodied in the appropriate class concept. In ascribing a combination of clinical symptoms and signs to the disease by which they are produced, one must know, and must be able to remember, the characteristic clinical manifestations condensed in the particular syndrome. The classification of a crime as burglary requires that its legal definition is known.

In other fields of knowledge, for instance in astronomy, the appropriate test situation must be discovered with the aid of thinking sets based on the appreciation of cause effect relationships. These relationships in turn must be implied in, or suggested by, the problem situation. In the present context, the term "implied" indicates that *appropriate sets, having been found through association by similarity, that is to say, the actuation of a transfer mechanism, are to be injected into the stream of thought and evaluated, step by step, through association by contiguity.*

In establishing the fact that light needs time for its propagation, Olaf Roemer (*275*) was guided by the observation that the distance between the Earth and Jupiter (which revolves around the Sun within a period of approximately 169 years), is either diminishing or increasing. At the same time, he found that the duration of a periodically occurring event in the orbit of one of Jupiter's moons varied; the inter-eclipse intervals became shorter as the distance between the Earth and Jupiter decreased while they became longer as their mutual distance increased. Roemer, assuming the time of revolution of the eclipsed moon

around its planet to be constant, concluded that light needed a varying period of time to reach the Earth, in analogy to the simple observation that it takes a messenger longer to reach an individual (who, in the course of traveling, increases its distance from the sender), than a person which, traveling in the opposite direction, meets the messenger half way. In this particular instance, then, the relationship of the inaugural to the concluding phase of thought may be outlined as follows. In the former, Roemer noted what appeared to be significant differences in the length of the inter-eclipse intervals. He knew, further, that the distance between Earth and Jupiter varies. He stipulated a causal relationship between the two observations. In the inaugural phase, through reasoning by analogy, he inferred that the time interval between the two eclipses becomes shorter whenever the distance between the two planets decreases. In the concluding phase, he verified the assertion formulated in the inaugural phase by measurements carried out at appropriate intervals. Thus, he arrived at his results by a combination of reasoning by analogy, by generalization and by the application of familiar cause effect relationships to cosmic events.

In the experimental sciences, the situation necessary to initiate the concluding phase of thought must be *designed* by a "transfer" process rather than left to chance or awaited for. By contrast, the inaugural phase is very often the product of a fortuitous combination of circumstances. In the two following instances of reconstructive reasoning the hypotheses in question were experimentally verified.

It is well known that sedimentous rocks, when examined under a special petrological microscope, are found to be composed of grains of rounded or worn fragments while igneous rocks display little crystals formed out of a molten material, for example quartz or mica. It so happened that, at the glass works of Leith, a large mass of material was by accident allowed to cool too slowly, which resulted in the production of a hard rocky crystaline mass rather than of glass. After having been reheated and rapidly cooled however, the material acquired a normal glassy character. By a step of ingenious generalization Sir James Hall (*104, 186*) concluded that all igneous rocks had a common type of origin in the molten rock of the interior of the Earth, and that the difference of structure and crystal size was due to the rate of cooling. The hypothesis was verified by the heating and cooling of lava from the Vesuvius and from certain regions of Scotland.

Pasteur (252) prepared cultures of the microbe responsible for chicken cholera but, having been shortly thereafter occupied with other matters, left them untouched in his laboratory. On resuming his work, he found that neither healthy chickens inoculated with the preparation developed the disease nor chickens inoculated with both the old and meanwhile prepared fresh material. By contrast, chickens inoculated with fresh material died. By a bold stroke of reconstructive reasoning (that is, reasoning from the effect to the cause) he inferred that weakened and dead germs have immunizing properties. He subsequently verified his idea by the successful application of the same principle in the protection of sheep against anthrax.

In either case, then, the scientists reasoned by generalization; they reconstructed the sequence of events and succeeded in establishing the reality of the causative relationship they had stipulated.

The famous Michelson experiment (234, 253) which was later repeated by Morley, was based on the tentative analogy between a swimmer moving against a current, and a ray of light moving against the ether. The medium in which the movement occurs should influence the movement of either "object." The speed of light moving against the stream of ether should be decelerated; conversely, it should be accelerated if moving with the stream of ether.* It is well known that the speed of light was found to be constant in all directions and that the ether theory had to be abandoned.

The analysis of the concluding phase of thought demonstrates the production of the awareness of consistency, or inconsistency, with the assertion formulated in the inaugural phase. For example, the wave theory of light could not be corroborated by the result obtained in the concluding phase, the velocity with which light travels having been found constant regardless of the relative movement of the observer in relation to the source of light. *Now, the awareness of consistency or contradiction is nothing more than that of similarity and*

---

* It would take us too far afield to discuss the influence of a medium on "cross-current-movements" and the construction of the interferometer used by the experimenters. For a full discussion of the experiment see e.g., J. A. Coleman (52a).

dissimilarity on a higher level of abstraction; and thought, in this particular sense, is merely an elaboration of perception, or the combination of actual with reinstated sensations. As already noted, recognition of sense data is replaced, at increasingly higher levels of abstraction, by the recognition of relations. *Nevertheless, there operate, both in perception and thought, two fundamental processes, namely, acceptance based on identical appearance, or consistency; or rejection, based on different appearance or contradiction.* In attempting to bridge the gulf between perception and thought and by treating their relationship in a more systematic fashion we shall work (in fact we already have operated) on the assumption that *contradiction is dissimilarity in the sphere of abstraction, or the experience of incompatibility derivable from dissimilarity; in other words, that it is dissimilarity raised to a higher power.*

THE DERIVATION OF THOUGHT FROM PERCEPTION

Disregarding for the time being that there are pitfalls not only in thought but in perception as well (142) we remind ourselves that the former is for all practical purposes *self-validating* while correct thinking is predicated upon the *evaluation* of data. In other words, we realize that, in the sphere of sensation including configurational perception, identical data represent identical entities whereas, in the sphere of thought, identity of terms may be an apparent one. With certain exceptions, sensory data have an "absolute pitch" whereas, in thought, the experience of congruity may be misleading. In sharp contrast to the act of identification involved in perceptual processes, the assertions which constitute the inaugural phase of thought are tentative. The validity of an assertion depends on an additional dimension of operation, namely, the elimination of contradictions in the concluding phase, that is, the establishment of definitive "identity."

These postulates however would be literally true only if perception and thought were as fundamentally different as here presented for the purpose of preliminary orientation. Being, in reality, differential ranges of an identical scale, perception and thought are linked together by numerous transitional phenomena. The following observations, each in its own way, are reported to illustrate the derivation of thought from perception.

(a) Perceptual awareness precedes conceptual awareness both ontogenetically and phylogenetically. The utterances of the child, of primitive man and of certain animals involve, for the most part, states of perceptual awareness, whereas, in the maturing organism of man and, very likely, of higher animals, perceptual awareness acquires conceptual elements.

(b) Perceptual awareness and conceptual awareness may alternate or they may coexist in various proportions. They may fluctuate, and visual daydreaming and abstract thought may merge with each other. On awakening, conceptual awareness does not ordinarily reach its peak until after some time; before falling asleep, it may be crowded out by hypnagogic hallucinations which interrupt the fabric of thought, like patches of an odd material break the continuity of a regular though subdued design. In conceptual awareness we may imaginatively see what we think; in perceptual awareness we think only what we see.

(c) Perception includes elements of thought to the extent that thought is interpretive. Although the "ingredient" of thought varies, any object that forms part of our customary surroundings may under certain conditions have to be "interpreted"; for example, if it should happen to lie in an odd place, and the illumination is poor. Once the object is recognized, that is to say, integrated into the general conceptual knowledge of one's surroundings, the contents of perceptions are found to be "determined" by what we know. In a similar manner, the importance of interpretation in perception becomes manifest whenever we are confronted with altogether unfamiliar objects. The visual experiences of a layman visiting an exhibition of machines should not be different from that of an expert; in either case, identical stimuli are conducted to comparable parts of the visual cortex of the brain. Yet, in the naive visitor, as it happens to me while strolling through the Ford Plants, perceptual awareness produced merely chaotic impressions.

(d) From a different angle, the inadequacy of "thoughtless" perception can be demonstrated by disturbances in copying. While senile individuals do far better than agnostics, they fail whenever the correct copying of test patterns depends on counting. The patients are able to count on command but it does not occur to them to do so spontaneously; they fail to grasp the conceptual relationships inherent in perceptual processes (283).

(e) Monkeys can be trained to experience vague differences as definitely heterogenous and to convert insignificantly different perceptions which, for all practical purposes, may be regarded as identical, into meaningful biphasic thought contents. Experiments performed by Harlow (109–113) demonstrated that the animals, although initially misled by the apparent identity of the test patterns exposed, were eventually able to discriminate between actual and apparent likeness. In a series of trials the animals were shown a board of a certain color and three objects, one of which was *odd in shape;* in another series, they were confronted with a board of a different color and three objects one of which was *odd in color.* Initially, the perception of diversity, if any, was probably extremely vague as both patterns appeared to be identically "indifferent." However, after a series of rewarding tests, the animals grasped the conditional nature of the identity of the two categories of stimulus groups, the reason being that stimulus patterns signalled reward only if, in the presence of a board of a certain color, the object chosen was odd in shape or, in the presence of a board of a different color, the object was odd in color. In terms of transition of perception to thought the results of the experiments may perhaps be described as follows: in the monkey, *inaugural phases* of thought, or hypotheses, are induced by the experience that grasping a certain object is rewarded only if presented in a certain combination with other objects. In the *concluding phase,* on the other hand, the hypothesis is verified by the experience that the act of taking hold of different objects presented in the same combination is unrewarded. At this moment, previously homogenous combination of objects became meaningful and, as far as can be inferred from the effects of interpretive activity in the human, definitely different to the perceiving eye. Insight into the conditional nature of similarity is achieved by operating with primitive thinking sets based, in turn, on the appreciation of cause-effect relationships or through association by continuity in time, and with the aid of impressions of dissimilarity. By focusing upon initially vague differences, which however must have become increasingly obtrusive after the hypothesis is verified, there is formed a more complex mental experience. Thus, in properly motivated animals, *thought converts insignificantly different patterns into significantly different situations.* Indeed, the experience in question may well mark the crucial phase of transition in the continuum or, if you wish, pseudo-continuum "perception-thought." Thus, we would assume that perception and thought can be unified and, at the same time, set apart by expressing the former in terms of *monophasic thought* and the latter in terms of *biphasic*, or *pluriphasic*, perception.

(f) The relationship between perception and thought is reflected in the development of their respective organs. Phylogenetically, the organ serving the awareness of *conditional identity* is an elaboration of the mechanism subserving the awareness of *non-conditional identity;* in other words, the posterior associational fields are an elaboration of the primary cortical receiving stations (see Chapter II) and recognitive reasoning, the differentiation between similarity and dissimilarity or, at the higher level, the capacity to choose between acceptance and rejection is roughly proportional to the ratio between the evaluative and the receptive cortex.

The above cited examples show that animals, depending on their cortical and therefore intellectual organization, are able to learn how to sift apparent from actual identity and that thought is not a privilege of man.

The young Schopenhauer (*285*) introduced his doctoral dissertation with the following, somewhat ponderous sentences: "The devine Plato and the astonishing Kant join their grave voices in emphasizing a guiding principle of philosophy, indeed, of every kind of knowledge. . . . They say that one should satisfy both the law of homogeneity and of specification rather than follow any of the two at the expense of the other. The former demands to grasp similarities and congruities, thereby to establish the concept of groups of an increasingly higher order . . .; the latter, on the other hand, decrees to break down seemingly all-inclusive concepts to their subcategories, until one arrives at the concept of the individual; yet even the concept of individuality can be understood within the context of the general only rather than by its reduction to mere perception."

As the previously cited performance tests show, the ways of higher animals and of man in dealing with homogeneity, and in breaking it down, are not materially different. Clearly, there exists a continuous scale, beginning with the lowly organism which responds within its small world to identical stimuli in a practically stereotyped fashion. The scale extends to the pattern discriminating animal which can be thought to differentiate between actual and conditional identity. And it culminates in man, who utilizes sensory data in concept forming and, by progressive emancipation from the world of perception, eventually operates in more or less abstract spheres of knowledge. There, the process of deeper and ever more detailed resolution of apparent homogeneity, of objective reality that is, is continued step by step until the resolving power of the mind has reached its temporary limits. However, new assaults upon the seemingly homogenous structure of reality are made. Similarity once again becomes diversity—as "seemingly all inclusive concepts are broken down to their subcategories and, eventually, to that of the individual, to be seen within the context of the general."

COMMENT AND CRITICISM

I intend to discuss representative theories of thought with particular reference to the *gestalt-psychologic* and the *connectionist* approach to the problem of higher brain functions, and to mention the *muscular theory*, discussed, in all earnest, in Humphrey's (*137*) and Vinacke's (*333*) monographs for the sake of curiosity only. In the words of Humphrey, the "essential work of the thinking process would seem to be muscular work, of very small amplitude indeed, but still essentially muscular." Vinacke wrote that "there is an impressive weight of evidence in favour of the motor theory of thinking, that it offers an extremely convincing explanation of thought processes about which obviously little is known" but "that it could well be that the neural system in the brain alone, organized as a result of learning, that handles the actual thinking process." Having just watched the stunning performance of the Russian Ballet at the Metropolitan Opera House, I am more than ever convinced that muscular coordination depends to a high degree of intelligence, but that the reverse is not true. Quadruplegic patients are still able to think as are those afflicted with a bilateral paralysis of their laryngeal muscles. One of my most intelligent patients was a girl suffering from progressive muscular dystrophy with involvement of the locomotor, manipulative, oculogyric and articulatory apparatus. Muscular activity in the course of thinking, which can be experimentally demonstrated, indicates that the neurodynamic processes underlying mentation irradiate, to a degree, into the muscular apparatus. They indicate at the same time the close linkage between response determination and response. Indeed, the movements in question may be plainly visible in persons who inaudibly move their lips while reading. This occurs particularly in unexperienced readers who are rarely great thinkers.

A theory of thinking which is of interest because of the experimental elimination of the element of learning was proposed by Heibreder (*121*). "The term *"thinking"*, she contends," refers not so much to a process than a result. It is assumed that thinking has occurred when an organism has produced a response having the following characteristics. It must be adequate, adequacy of response being particularly useful in distinguishing it from a reverie. Moreover, the response must be novel and invented and the result of activity implicit as opposed to overtly motor." In Heidbreder's experiments, thinking occurred under conditions which reduced mental activity to "mere" thinking, that is, "thinking without the aid of previous experiences with the material would contribute." Heidbreder's thesis may be challenged from various angles. It is only under exceptional conditions that products of thought enter the reasoner's mind "ready made." More often than not (as brought out by Heidbreder's own protocols) the thinking process is a laborious one. We have already mentioned that Edison formed countless false ideas before he succeeded in inventing the electric bulb. Kekulé's and Otto Loewi's experiences demonstrate that important discoveries can be made in the course of a reverie. Moreover, it is doubtful whether the response must be novel. A student, struggling with a difficult problem, may find (having returned to the very same subject some time later) that he has forgotten most everything and, for all practical purposes, does not know more about it than when he first started. In this case, the second attempt to master the subject is repetitive rather than novel. Heidbreder's experiments were designed in such a way that her subjects did not have the benefit of thinking sets, that is to say, of the application of condensed and, at the same time, categorized thought material applicable to novel situations, as occurs, for the most part, in the innumerable transfer situations involved in the thinking in daily life. Lastly, it is worth while mentioning that Heidbreder took issue with Dewey's (*66*)

"five phase scheme" of thought which comprises the following points. The recognition of a situation, the finding of the problem, the search for a solution, the determination of the best solution and, as the final phase, the test by action. She found no case in which the subject systematically thought out all the implications of a situation and investigated them with any thoroughness. In other words, the situations were not systematically examined and varied. This is entirely consistent with the ordinary type of thinking in which trial and error mechanisms play a prominent part.

Field theories of thought

According to Koehler (*170*), "problem solutions consist in finding the fitting part which will relieve the existing stress. . . . When the solution of a problem has been found, the forces are better balanced, the problem stress is relieved. . . . Reorganization of the field has taken place. When one grasps a problem situation, its structural features and its requirements set up certain strains, stresses, tensions, in the thinker. What happens in real thinking is that these strains and stresses are followed up, yield vectors in the direction of improvement of the situation and change it accordingly."

In Duncker's (*69, 70*) own words, "a phenomenologic or physiologic content comes from insight, since its relevant traits are immediately determined by intrinsic traits of the stimulus content; a problem solution results from insight because its relevant traits are immediately determined by those traits of the problem situation they satisfy. The process itself, which leads from the stimulus situation to the response, may be called insightful provided it directly shapes the content of the response according to the intrinsic traits of the situation. *The gestalt theory rejects the assumption that, in the stimulus-response scheme, the stimulus can release only ready-made responses owing to original endowment or set up by learning.*" Thinking, Duncker believes, "is a process which, by insight into a problem situation, leads to appropriate responses. After the problem situation as such has been fully comprehended, the thinking process sets in, with penetration into the conflicting circumstances of the problem situation. There it is essential that the cause of the conflict bear intimate and obvious relations to the conflict." Duncker goes on to say that penetration, terminating in the functional value of the solution (the positive elaboration of the presentation) contains the essential features of the required device, i.e., that which is of functional relevance in a final solution. For instance, if an ape finds that his arm is too short to pull a banana into a cage and it occurs to him that something elongating would do the trick, the "elongating something" is the functional value. It is thus the dynamical demand in the functional value or field-stress (*Gestaltdruck*) that makes for the singling out of the particular aspect which need not have been singled out before. Realization, or solution of the problem, can occur in two ways. Either the realization comes immediately by glancing around, by taking something from the immediate inventory of the problem situation, or it comes from taking recourse to something that overlaps the problem situation, that is to say, to the stock of memories. According to Duncker, the second type of realization is brought about by gestalt-druck upon neural residues.

Duncker thus denies the crucial role of transfer or transposition. Yet his reference to the preponderance of what he terms the second type of realization contradicts his own statement that he was unable to find evidence of transfer from similar cases, which is all the more surprising as he recognizes the importance of memory in problem solving. Subsequently, Duncker suggests that the experience of similarity occurred only *after* the solution, or *along* with it, and that the similarity between problems was not necessarily recognized by his subjects even after similar problems were deliberately chosen and the subject, after solving the problem, were asked what the similarity had been. Yet since the actuation of unknown relations by known relations (which emerge either through observation or ekphory) does not imply that the subject is familiar with the mechanism controlling the relational alignment of terms (just as the ability to perform skilled movements does not depend on the theoretical knowledge of skeleto-muscular mechanisms) the subjects, in retrospect, may or may not have been aware of the element of similarity that accounts for the attainment of the goal of thought. Gauss, for example, having found the solution of a problem, remained for some time unaware of the line of reasoning; and Poincaré, after solving problems by intuition, did not recognize their relationship to known mathematical data until some time afterwards.

It is fair to assume that, in the problems devised by Duncker, the element of transfer played a crucial part, although his subjects may not have been aware of it throughout. In the "drillhole-saw" problem, for example, the subject had to bore five oblique but strictly parallel holes through a thick wooden board. Duncker holds that the best solution, suggested by several subjects, would be to place a block with a hole at the desired angle in it on top of the board and to use it as a guide. After one of his subjects had solved the problem, the experimenter asked him and others whether they had thought of a similar case. No, was the answer in most cases. After that, one of his subjects described a certain sawing device which he himself had used in the laboratory shop, namely, two parallel boards with vertical slits to guide the saw so that it would cut exactly square pieces of wood.

Duncker denies that these elements were identical. Now they are certainly not identical in the same way that photographs of the two contrivances would be; they would not show identical elements on their superimposed outline tracings. The truth is that the principle applicable to both problems, namely, the guidance of a potentially deviating system by a fixated or bracing system, operated at the abstract rather than the concrete level. In so far as the relationships that can be condensed into the formulas "Guide-holes: Non-deviation" equals "Slit-Holes: Non-deviation" are identical (in that they express the *general principle* of non-deviation) the process of reasoning which led to the solution of the problem was based on a process of generalization. The subject had formed the class concept "guide system" in which the elements "slit-guides" and "hole-guides" were linked up, and the solution of the problem was found by the above specified relational alignment of terms.

We agree with Duncker that a number of isolated elements having necessarily an enormous number of potentially associated traits in common could not have led to one of the few definite arrangements of traits constituting an appropriate solution, but it is precisely the appropriateness of these arrangements that characterizes physiological processes anywhere in the organism. The field-stress invoked by Duncker to account for the appropriacy of combinations is itself a manifestation of appropriateness rather than their cause. It is further to be noted that Duncker is aware of the importance of memory in problem solving and that the relationship between memory and transposition is obvious.

Fieldstress is not an explanatory principle in problem solving. Problem solving mechanisms are *mnemic action mechanisms* in which the element of transfer plays a vital part. The response is not determined by *one* stimulus, but by the applicability, to a given situation, of a selected parameter or aspect common to a *group of stimuli*, one of which is the recent stimulus. In the final analysis, the response is dependent on association by similarity, which, we have good grounds to believe, is the very core of transfer mechanisms no matter how complicated they may be.

In the course of the examination of Duncker's approach to the problem of thought, we have chosen an example which makes manifest the role of associational mechanisms. Considerations of space do not permit a more detailed discussion of the subject. What's more, it would be difficult to offer alternative explanations for every Duncker problem. One would have to know the background of his experimental subjects, indeed, one would have to have a complete record of the mental processes occurring in the course of the experiments. More especially, one would have to know the peculiarities of the individual *thinking sets utilized* by the persons taking part in the experiments. Interestingly enough, Duncker contended that *the problem situation signals, or suggests, those models of search for the reasoner which involves past experiences.* Thus, he himself introduced an element of associationism, for the mere restructuring of the problem could hardly lead to a solution unless it can be linked to specific experiences or familiar data. The terms restructuring, recentering, and reorganization, as used by Duncker, are purely metaphorical; *the statement that mnemonic material can be recentered in the same way as figure elements and background elements change their position in the field, is powerless to explain the appropriacy of the changes under study, even granting that a recombination of data has taken place.* For example, we read that in certain solutions of the pendulum-problem, "the space of suspension suddenly comes to have a connection with the length of the pendulum although there was no previous connection between these two moments." By the same token one may claim that, in a (fictitious) rain-problem the place of the water,

having been previously in the clouds, suddenly comes to have a connection with the earth. Duncker epitomizes his position as follows: "Every solution rests on some kind of change in a given situation. This is change not only of this or that feature of the situation but, in addition, there is change in the psychological total structure of the situation or of special partial regions." This leaves one completely in the dark for, again, we do not learn anything about the forces which transform the total structure in an appropriate fashion. Even if we were willing to go along with Duncker and to express problem solving in terms of restructuring, we would have to account for the fertility of some acts of reorganization and the sterility of others.

In illustrating the basic concepts of their theory, the gestaltpsychologists prefer to use mathematical, especially geometrical, examples of problem solving. (See especially Duncker's second publication (*70*) and Wertheimer's (*350*) book on *Productive Thinking*.) Geometrical problems appear to be most suitable, as their nature can be fully *represented* by visual data; yet, it is a debatable issue whether they can be fully *expressed* in visual terms. It is easy to design figures whose essential features can be grasped by process of counting only, i.e., by the initiation of an act of thought, since their crucial features surpass the power of gestaltperception (Figs. 44, 45). What's more, the gestaltfactor appears to be absent in solving arithmetical problems at the non-conscious level where the two terms loose their meaning altogether, there being no trace of either figure or background.

Now it is of interest that mathematical problems formulated in algebraic equations may acquire properties of geometrical figures (*124*) and algebraization may very closely approach an extreme case of geometrization. In dealing with algebraic problems it is not only the suggestive power of the symbols and their laws of operation but, at the same time, the arrangement of the terms which creates certain trends in thought and which, although they are not of themselves goal leading, build up a strong directional pressure. By the "ruse" of algebraization, relationships between quantities can be readily surveyed and they become more easily comprehensible. On the other hand, there exist countless cases where comprehension of the problem depends on abstract concepts rather than simultaneous surveying and where, particularly in inventive mathematical reasoning, thought has to go far beyond the limits of visualization. The wholesale identification of simultaneous surveying and comprehensibility, on which Duncker insists, has given rise to a great deal of confusion. Wertheimer (*350*) chose nearly all his test situations from the field of geometry or from arithmetic which, to a degree, lends itself to geometrication (see for example "The Story of the Young Gauss") or from mathematical physics. It is of some interest that Wertheimer subjected, to a searching analysis, the development of Einstein's idea which lead to the theory of relativity. Yet it is doubtful whether the crucial points of Einstein's argument can be adequately covered by the terms "structure" and "restructuring" which Wertheimer uses freely and, no doubt, literally. We suspect that the terms in question fail to do justice to a process of inventive thought which must have proceeded at the highest levels of abstraction, and that the metaphorical expressions centering around the ideas of figure and structure conceal the crucial points of Einstein's argument. The latter felt that the important steps had come to him intuitively and, in a letter to Hadamard (*100*), confessed his inability to judge how far Wertheimer's psychologic analysis had caught the essential points.

The gestalt theorists attempt to apply the laws of fieldforces not only to the phenomenon of problem solving in the most abstract spheres but also to the problem solving capacity of animals. The reader is no doubt familiar with Koehler's experiments from which he concluded that chimpanzees manage to get food beyond their immediate reach by the use of implements, the functional value of which he believed to be experienced by insight into the relationship between the animal, the tool and the food. The experiments were criticized on the ground that the apes had not been born in captivity and that their previous experiences with tools, conceivably achieved by previous trial and error rather than insight, could not have been known. Birch (*22*), working with chimpanzees born in captivity, tried to determine the question whether "insight arises directly from the effect of a given situational structuring of an animal possessing a cortex of a given innate complexity, or whether the experimental background of the organism plays a significant part in determining the way in which it will perceive and manipulate external reality." The animals were first tested as to

their ability to solve problems involving the use of securing food. Only two out of six animals solved the problem within a 30 minute test. The chimpanzees were then given a number of sticks in their home enclosure and it was found that, in the course of three days' playing with the sticks, and on subsequent testing, everyone of the subjects succeeded in solving the problem within 30 seconds and that, moreover, the functional relations which were perceived in the situation were fundamentally modified by the general experience in stick-using. The author concluded that the functional relationships perceived in a given problem by the animal (which, at the same time, serve as the basis for insightful response) are determined not only by the objective features (the structure or gestalt quality of the situation) but also by the available repertoire of experience. The results are in essential agreement with Kluever's (*169*) views and appear to support the thesis that the animals generalize inasmuch as they make use of the specfiic knowledge of the property of an object. According to Birch the animals reorganize previous experiences in accordance with the requirements of a new problem situation, they are able to select from the available repertoire of recall, and they reorganize, into new patterns of response, previously learned but not contiguously acquired items of experience: in other words, the behaviour of the animals, which is determined by both perceptions and reinstated memory traces, cannot be expressed in terms of chain reflexes.

The above quoted data show that neither Birch nor Kluever share the uncompromising views of the left wing gestaltpsychologists, Duncker, Wertheimer and Köhler. The same may be said about N. R. F. Maier (*212, 219, 221, 222*) who holds the view that rats are able to combine and spontaneously to assemble never before associated habit fragments under the influence of a goal, in other words, that they can reason. In examining what causes a new pattern to be formed, Maier, using as a point of departure Shepherd's and Foglsong's (*300*) experimental work concerned with the association of syllables, invokes, in addition to the goal, a "common element." This element is the recognition of essential likeness and difference which stands out and becomes more intense. (Cf. the factor of overlapping mentioned by Duncker.) However, Maier makes no reference to the relational alignment of terms that occurs in the process of problem solving. Hull (*134, 135*), in his examination of Maier's theory of reasoning, points out that at least some forms of insightful behaviour are nothing more than a special though somewhat complicated association between stimulus and reaction; and Maier (206) himself concludes his most recent paper on reasoning in the human with the statement that the mechanism of equivalent stimuli has its limitations but that, in the solution of creative problems, its fundamental importance in the process of generalization and in the transfer of training must be recognized.

Ultimately, then, the gestalttheory appears to have undergone a process of considerable dilution (approaching autolysis) of its first principles and it looks as if it were about to be absorbed by connectionist theories.

As has been mentioned on several occasions, the fieldtheorists make much of the sudden and compelling feeling of achievement accompanying both the experience of closure of a figure and the solution of a problem. Yet, the closure of a figure by means of fitting parts is natural (even the phenomenon of optic delusions has been invoked in support of the views of the gestalttheorists) while the feeling of conclusiveness which terminates reasoning processes may be entirely unwarranted. We have repeatedly called attention to the fact that, in contrast to the inaugural phase of biphasic thought, perceptual (monophasic) thought may be self-validating. In other words, to distinguish between plausibility and truth, *gestaltperception must be carried to the higher power of gestalevaluation.*

The difference between the perception and the evaluation of gestalten may be illustrated by personal experiences in the field of neuroradiology. In studying roentgenograms, one may see only some of the visible patterns, or all of them, in which case one may spend hours in writing long descriptions or in tracing a maze of lines and shadows. Up to this point, everything depends on gestaltperception without which further progress is of course impossible. To appreciate the significance of roentgenologic abnormalities, one may have to recall experiences with similar cases, which enable one to read the films in somewhat the same way as one might read letters or words. In the latter eventuality, the diagnostic process is repetitive rather than productive in nature. However, if the significance of changes seen is not immediately apparent, pattern perception must be followed by *pattern evaluation,* a crucial step re-

quiring mental activity *based upon* visual data rather than upon mental processes which reduplicate visual experiences. This activity, although initiated by visual impressions, is not visual in nature, and, in this respect, resembles certain mathematical operations previously referred to; they involve visual material, but cannot be fully expressed in terms of visualization. The solution of the diagnostic problem depends on the discovery of *relational relevancy* rather than on the previously mentioned *perceptual fittingness.* Correct results are produced by a much more complex mechanism than, for example, one involved in the perception of an incomplete circle as a closed circle. It is true that the experience involved in finding a correct solution may be sudden and just as vivid as that produced by distinguishing a figure from its background yet the feeling of achievement common to both does not prove the identity of insight with the experience of closure and Prägnanz. Moreover, the feeling of achievement may be produced by arriving at any solution, be it correct or incorrect, and is neither validating nor necessarily stable. The other day, I was shown a set of x-rays which I interpreted correctly, as subsequent surgery proved. However, when one of my colleagues suggested preoperatively an alternative interpretation, I changed my mind, for the diagnostic value of the various data upon which my opinion had been based seemed quite suddenly questionable. In this particular problem situation, the feeling of achievement experienced by my colleague had been as deceptive as mine had been unreliable for after he had pointed out certain facts, I saw the situation in a new, different, light. In my own mind, the processes of "closure" of the figure had followed each other in quick succession. It is true that both processes were legitimate by gestalttheoretic standards but one result only was correct.

CONCLUDING REMARKS

If the gestaltpsychological approach to the process of thinking had any validity, the concluding phase of thought would be redundant. In other words, if problems were solved by the play of field forces in the inaugural phase of thought, the concluding phase would be unnecessary. Hypotheses would not have to be verified either in daily life or in the various fields of science. A child, assuming that the fins of a sea lion are legs would not chase the animal about but would rely on the simple similarity between legs and fins. A roentgenologist, suspecting that the profile view of a skull shows an abnormality would not attempt to verify it in the sagittal view. Had the discoveries of Roemer, Loewi, Pasteur, Hall, Michelson and other scientists been made by a simple act of restructuring the field, their verification by a second act of thought would have been superfluous and their experiments a waste of time. Thought cannot be expressed in gestaltpsychologic terms, except in a derivative sense. The processes involved in gestalt perception lack the operational dimensions of thought processes just as the neural crest of the embryo lacks the morphological features of the fully differentiated spinal cord. Yet, like the cord is related to its morphological precursor, thought is related to gestaltperception as its functional primordium. More accurately, thinking involves an element of comparing and, hence, of perception. The comparison of objects requires no creative effort, except for the concentration of attention on more or less plainly visible salient features. The awareness of identical or different relationships in thought on the other hand is a more complicated process. Lastly, in creative thought, the relations generated in its inaugural phase must be compared with another relation produced in the concluding phase, the second relation having been generated by an act of transfer based on association by similarity. To reiterate, in perception, the items to be compared are immediately given. In thought, one of them (the "guide-structure") must be produced by transfer mechanisms. What the gestaltpsychologist calls the restructuring of the field is in actual fact the experience produced by the activity of these mechanisms, especially if they go into operation in a sudden, unexpected fashion. It is only then that there is initiated, or should be initiated, the process of verification, which eventuates in the awareness of "congruence" or of "incongruence," as the case may be.

It is intriguing to speculate about the historical roots of the gestaltpsychological doctrine. Conceivably, it goes back to Faraday's and Maxwell's concept of electromagnetism and the related notion of field forces as properties of the space or, in the words of Lenard (187), "quantitative connections between the states of the ether in space," that is, the ether then presumed to exist. The idea

of gestalt might well have been induced in Wertheimer's mind by a transfer mechanism or the association by similarity between psychological and physical phenomena. Be this as it may, it has been overplayed and met with considerable opposition, culminating in Spearman's (308) remark about "the confusion that is gestaltpsychology." We have gone to considerable length in assigning gestaltpsychological phenomena their proper place within the framework of higher cerebral functions, indeed we have correlated the configurational stage of reality recording with a developmental stage of the cerebral cortex. (Moreover, we have attempted to resolve the apparent discrepancy between associational psychology and gestaltpsychology by demonstrating that association mechanisms connect configurated elements.) Freud's physicalistic model of the libido was no doubt suggested by the idea of electric charge existing on the surface of a condensor. Physicalistic concepts will probably always suggest themselves in the process (be it successful or unsuccessful) of reducing unknown relations to known relations. In fact, Faraday himself "allowed innumerable analogies with the known, of the nearest and the most distant description, to arrive at his mind" (187). The analogy between the nervous system and an analog computer is another case in point, the crucial similarity being that the nervous system determines the response with which a given stimulus should be answered, that is, finds the value of x, especially if the situation in question involves a great many variables. I can hardly claim originality for this idea but, to the best of my knowledge, I may do so for the emphasis on analog mechanisms. Wiener (355), McCulloch (201) and other electronic engineers have thought in terms of computer mechanisms in general.

In concluding, after this digression, the critical comments on the gestaltpsychological school, it is pertinent to point out that, in spite of the derivative relationship between perception and thought, the function of the individual planes of "sensation" are not necessarily evenly developed. It is a truism that, e.g., visual and auditory perception does not of itself establish gestaltperception; neither does the latter fully account for the power of concept formation. By the same token, superior intelligence may be associated with poor gestaltperception and, within limits, superior gestaltperception with poor concept formation. It is not unreasonable to assume that the resources of the higher levels, that is, their ability to cope with an increasing number of variables, compensate for the poor performance of the lower grades and, although to a lesser degree, the lower strata for that of the higher. The diversity of sensory organization (of all three planes of the intellective level) is still further augmented by the factor of *modality-preponderance* which, in combination with *level-preponderance*, produces a great many different types, e.g., visual, auditory etc. types of organization. (Motor types and the problem of skill do not concern us here.) Lastly, the factors under consideration determine in large measure an individual's *gratification preference* which plays a more or less important part in personality organization.

Connectionistic theories of thought

In the current section, we propose to comment on the position of those writers who were concerned with the *directionality of thought processes*, the *relationship between perception and thought*, the *role of reasoning by analogy and generalization*, and lastly, the *relationship between conscious and nonconscious mental processes*.

THE DIRECTIONALITY OF THOUGHT

According to Humphrey (*137*), "the history of the directionality of thought in the last 50 years has largely consisted in a rebellion against the associational theory but a rebellion which has never quite succeeded." There are two connectionistic or associational schools of thought, namely, an *anti-mechanistic* and a *mechanistic*. The adherents of the anti-mechanistic school contend that thought processes conform to the general laws of life which, by their very nature, defy a mechanistic interpretation. Associations of ideas are instrumentalities comparable, say, to the propulsive power of the heart and the mechanical properties of the blood vessels which, once they have come to be, explain the circulation of the blood but which fail to account either for the origin of the integration of propulsion and conduction or the integration of the blood flow with the remaining activities of the organism. We shall discuss the views of the antimechanists first.

Russel (*280*), clearly under the influence of Schopenhauer's philosophy of voluntarism (1819), writes in an already quoted passage "that human directiveness inherent in life, that purposive activity issuing from purposive behaviour is to be regarded as a specialization of vital activity and that the common ground of both organic and psychologic activity lies in the directiveness of drive which is characteristic of both." Bumcke (*35*), in opposition to Liepmann (*189*), Ach (*1*) and, implicitly, also to Watt (*342*), Wahle (*334*), Moskiewitz (*237*), Selz (*290, 291*) and others contend that there is no known theory which accounts for the adaptive framework of operation into which, under the influence of the goal, the stream of thought processes is directed. Liepmann believed that the notion of the task ("Zielvorstellung") produces the frame into which all emerging ideas must fit and that, owing to the influence of the *task notion*, all thoughts are being suppressed which might emerge because of previous associations but which do not conform to the general frame. The task notion, then, is believed to be the factor which endows thought with appropriate direction. Bumcke, in explaining Liepmann's views to his students, hastens to add that we do not know anything whatsoever about the mechanism of selection operating in associational processes. "If," he said, "in daily life all thoughts would tend to form, which because of the factor of contiguity and other laws of association might be able to do so and if, with the exception of one, all these thoughts would first have to be suppressed, the most simple decision and the shortest answer would take altogether too long."

There are, actually, two mechanistic schools of thought, a *moderate* school and a *radical* school. The former, represented by Liepmann, Ach, Watt, Selz, Claparéde (*49, 50*) Woodsworth and Sells (*289*), holds that *the laws of association do not of themselves account for the orderliness of thought processes*, (hence the introduction of the term task notion, etc.) while Binet, E. G. Mueller (*238*) and others maintain that the laws in question do account either for the directionality of reasoning or the attainment of the goals of thought.

Both Ach and Watt rightly called attention to the fact that, in the presence of a stimulus, the consciousness of the task or of spontaneously emerging targets determines the train of thought even though at the moment the stimulus appears the goal may have ceased to be a conscious mental process. Ach refers to the persisting trends in association as *determining tendencies* which, he insists, must be sharply set apart from the elementary and reproductive processes. (See Chapter II.) Selz (*290, 291*), discussing Ach's thesis and similar ideas promulgated by Watt, stresses the necessity of elucidating (a) the mechanism of the action of the determining tendencies as a result of which intellectual processes proceed in a "determinate" or coordinated fashion and (b) the way of interaction of the determining tendencies with the laws controlling the association of ideas. Wahle (*334*) invokes the factor of *constellation* of a prevailing psychic state which determines the trend of reproduction of material and the mutual facilitation and inhibition of the reproductive processes. Selz, in turn, believes that the above notions need to be supplemented by what. he termed the "anticipatory scheme" of thought while N. R. F. Maier (*215*), in his criticism of Selz' theory, points out that it may be possible to grasp the unfolding of associative chains once the scheme has been put into operation but that the origin of the scheme itself remains obscure.

Thus, the thread of the historic argument was resumed by Maier who, like his predecessors, stipulated a special factor coordinating the selection and interaction of engrams and other psychisms. "What is the process," he asked, "which serves to select the elements of past experiences which are appropriate in test situations?" The concept of *direction* has been conceived as an "integrating function and it is through the integration of certain elements of past experiences that selection is achieved. . . . Selection of itself does not however explain coordination of thought. There must be a coordinating and organizing principle, a dynamic process having to do with selection and integration. . . . Different neural stressed are essential features in the various kinds of reorganization of experiences. The process of direction is rather specific in nature in that it makes for specific kinds of reorganization. but it is not an element in the sense that a past experience is an element. One direction in thinking may cause a dime to be an equivalent with a piece of metal, or a screw driver, or it may make the dime equivalent with two nickels . . . direction is a specific dynamic state which is set up in a problem situation and which acts upon the background of memories determining which will become organized into the figure or the solution and which

will remain in the background; in other words, which will determine the interaction of specific engrams." (Why, then, invoke figure-background relationships in addition to connectionist concepts?) Maier maintains that dynamic field forces are entirely established in the organism by the problem situation but, in opposition to Duncker's interpretation of creative thought, recognizes that direction is codetermined by the goal. He makes much of the fact that directions may be either helpful or confusing and that they are, to a certain extent, controlled by the experimenter. In studying Maier's views one gains the impression that some directions function as clues, or *actuating events* while misleading directions may derail the process of association. In either instance, directions, in the sense of Maier, are *extrinsic factors* which do not account for the self-directing properties of thought under the influence of a goal.

Maier's position is of interest from various angles and can be best understood in its historical setting. He recognizes a coordinating principle of thought but is reluctant to evaluate it in gestaltpsychologic terms alone. He vacillates between the gestaltprinciple and the connectionist camp, and tends to "regress" to the former whenever the necessity to explain an organizing principle becomes pressing—perhaps because of the seductive flavour of the term "gestalt" which, somehow, seems to encompass the concept of organization. However, in spite of his strong gestalt-theoretic leanings, he is willing to make important concessions to the associationists.

It is the same unknown factor with which the right wing of the mechanistic school is concerned and which, depending on the particular aspect of the coordinating process with which the individual worker happens to be impressed, is christened *constellation, task-notion, determining tendency, atmosphere effect, explanatory scheme, hypothesis* (Claparède), *Aufgabe* (*Watt*) and *direction*. Each writer has a keen eye for the weakness of the position of his colleagues and insists at the same time on the validity of his own hypothesis. Ultimately, however, they all refer to the laws of association. And these laws conform to the very same self-equilibrating event patterns that characterize all biological phenomena. About the goal leading mechanism itself nobody knows anything, like the plain foot soldier, although acquainted with the mechanism of his own weapons, is ignorant of the scheme of grand strategy.

The *radical exponents of the mechanistic view*, of which Binet (*21*) is perhaps the foremost representative, sidesteps rather than ignores the paramount issue of directionality. Binet holds that the fundamental element of the mind is the image and that reasoning is determined by the properties of the images themselves. The images have only to be brought together or become oriented and reasoning follows with the inevitability of a reflex. Each image is linked with the preceding one by those points which are common. (In other words, Binet implies, at least he does not disclaim, that the pattern of war is explained by the properties of the weapons with which it is fought,* which is true but not the whole truth.) We have already reminded the reader of the long known fact that images have both relevant and irrelevant aspects and that associations, which are guided simply by common points rather than by relevancy factors, are apt to result in flightiness and incoherence of thought. Selz holds that such associations are characteristic of states of confusion and of dreams. This notion however, is not entirely correct for dreams may have a rational content.

Our own position may be summarized as follows. We accept both the principle of directionality of thought and the existence of cause-effect relationships in thinking, as manifested in the laws of association. On the other hand, we deny the possibility of a mechanistic explanation of the appropriacy of thought processes that operate as links in causal chains. What can be explained on mechanistic grounds is the effect once the cause has been initiated. What cannot be explained on mechanistic grounds is the initiation of the appropriate cause at the appropriate time, or the "timed actuation of synergies." In this respect thought processes resemble other physiological processes. For example, the fact that the systemic blood pressure falls if the receptors in the carotid sinus are stimulated can be expressed in mechanistic terms. What cannot be grasped in mechanistic terms is the arrangement of appropriate instrumentalities which, having been seemingly predesighed, serve the biological equilibrium of the organism once they are actuated. Organizational

features cannot be understood in mechanistic terms in the somatic sphere, where both the causes and the effects are of a physical nature. Neither can they be accounted for on mechanistic grounds in the psychic sphere, where the instrumentalities assume the form of mental processes, both conscious and non-conscious. At this point, Pflügerss word, already quoted comes to mind: "The cause of every need of a living being is also the cause of the satisfaction of the need."

Perception and Thought

According to Binet (*21*), who was perhaps not aware of I. Kants contribution to the subject, Ampère was the first who recognized the intimate relationship between perception and thought. "The image is formed sensation," Binet writes, "because fusion which takes place between the present sensation of a sound and the image of the very same sound heard previously modified our actual sensations to the point of making us see more than we see and hear more than we hear. In the sphere of vision we conclude, say, from the appearance of a yellow spot that we are dealing with an orange." The importance of interpretive factors in perception is particularly striking in blind persons whose vision has been restored by operation, the patients being unable to identify objects until some time after light and form-perception has become possible (*292*). Binet, who generalized the role of what Ampère called *concretion* between old and new impressions, argued that fusion is the central factor not only in perception but also in productive thought. Like so many other writers in this field, he referred to Newton "who discerned an identity between the most remote phenomena such as the fall of a stone and the force which urges the moon toward the Earth." Now, it is true that perception and thought are interpretable as extremes of a continuous scale; it is likewise true that, "in perception, analysis reveals the essential parts of the syllogism and that perception is unconscious reasoning."* However, Binet ignored the specificity of thought as a higher product of the evolution of

---

* Interestingly enough, Napoleon Bonaparte expressed a similar view. (*178*)

* Cf., however, "the derivation of thought from perception" (point e), earlier in this chapter, and "the psychology of recognition," in Chapter II (see "Negative hallucinations under hypnosis") and in Chapter IV.

sensation and he overshot his goal by "fusing", on the one hand, *repetitive reasoning* involved in primitive recognition and, on the other, *productive thought*. In the former, no new awareness content is generated, at least not in an active (or productive) fashion. By contrast, productive thought is endowed with an additional dimension of operation. Binet's statement that the foundation of all reasoning is similitude, the transition from a known to an unknown fact by means of resemblance, is likewise too sweeping. It covers only the inaugural phase of thought which does not necessarily distinguish between genuine and superficial likeness. Binet's ideas are applicable to the early stages of mental development at which time the mind is a tabula rasa, many experiences are new, and are assimilated by the trial and error procedure involved in the primitive pattern of generalization. The potentially misleading effects of wholesale generalization are recognized only little by little and superseded by increasingly adaptive patterns of response.

REASONING BY GENERALIZATION AND ANALOGY

The important role of reasoning from the particular to the particular is rather generally accepted. According to Ribot (*270*), for example, the essential condition of creative imagination on its intellectual side is the power of thinking by analogy, that is to say, by partial and often accidental resemblance. Jevons (*145*) speaks of a "rare property of the mind which consists in permeating the disguise of variety and seizing the common elements of sameness, a property which furnishes the true measure of intellect."

Spearman (*308*) holds that "when an item and a relation to it are present to the mind then the mind can generate itself another item so related." Now, an item and a relation to it would be, for example, the expression a/b, where "a" is related to "b"; hence, as may be inferred from Spearman's argument, the mind could generate relations x/b, x'/b, x''/b, etc. As a result, x, x', x", etc., would be converted into known data and, since the data in question bear the same relationship to b, the mental operation would generalize the element "a"; in regard to their relationship to all items, regardless whether a, x, x', x", etc., they would be equivalent and, hence, the concept of "a" would be extended to include x, x', x", etc.

Clearly, Spearman's formula refers to reasoning by generalization rather than analogy and, moreover, covers only the inaugural phase of thought. Because of the kinship between analogy and generalization, the formula offered by Spearman might be acceptable, were it not for its failure to account for the item-generating mechanism which distinguishes thought from perception. He illustrates his concept of reasoning by generalization and analogy by two diagrams. Unfortunately, the drawings indicate merely the production of the relationship of generalization as such, that is, the production of a formal framework which fails to show how the new item (the produced relation) is generated.

Spencer (*313, 314*) resolved all processes of thought and perception into a classification of relations. "All modes and degrees of cognition are explained as intuition of equality and inequality, likeness and unlikeness between terms." He explained analogy as an "intuition or classification of relations differing from more precise forms by the much smaller degree of likeness which the terms of the referred relations bear to those of the known relation it is supposed to parallel. . . . Likeness of relations is enough to bring about the reproduction of terms similarly related. . . . To reason, we must have terms that are equal or similar. . . . The terms, though differing superficially, are the same in what appears to be new material." Spencer expressed the process of reasoning by analogy by the formula a/b equals A/B, *wherein, however, all four terms are known* and the new element is represented by the awareness of the identity of two proportions. His theory incited Binet to a lively attack. He claimed that Spencer's ideas are powerless to explain or to solve the problem of how an association between the terms can be formed by the medium of a former association. "What does Spencer tell us? That the mind, after having formed a relation between *a* and *b*, compares it to a beforehand known relation between A and B. What can follow from this intuition of a resemblance of the two relations? How can the comparison of the two add to the bond which already units the terms a and b?" The flavour of his concluding sentence is better brought out in his native tongue: "*Il y a là une question de mécanism a resoudre. M. Spencer ne le resoud pas, il ne s'en dout même pas*" (*21*). Let us illustrate Binet's legitimate criticism by an example. Suppose Darwin had been familiar with (a) the mechanism of the spontaneous transmutability of species and (b) the rationale of the deliberate production of animal species; further, that he appreciated not only (A), the survival value of innate inheritable qualities of animals living in freedom, but also (B), the breeding value of innate inheritable qualities of domestic animals; and, lastly, that the four known assertions (including the causal mechanism they involve) are related as expressed in the formula a/b equals A/B. It is certainly of significance that the four items fitted into the framework of a proportion but the point at issue is not the arrangement of known terms but, rather, *the generation of a new term*, namely, the cause of the spontaneous transmutability of the species. Darwin would have been in the position of, say, a stamp collector who discovers that small countries tend to issue large stamps while large countries prefer to print small stamps. It is true that his discovery is correct but it does not in the least increase the value of his collection.

In the concluding chapter of his eminently readable monograph, Binet outlines his position as follows. "Reasoning is the establishment of an association between two states of consciousness by an intermediate state of consciousness which resembles the first state, which is associated with the second and which, by fusing itself with the first, associates it with the second. (One is reminded of an amboceptor mechanism but the mechanism of fusion remains undefined.) Binet's notion of reasoning by analogy, which involves three elements rather than four, reduces, like Spearman's formula, analogy to generalization. Another shortcoming of Binet's theory is its limitation of the inaugural phase of thought to a more or less self validating mental act.

Conscious and Non-Conscious Mental Processes

Both Poincaré (*258*) and Hadamard (*100*) promulgated the theory that the mechanism of association or "combining of ideas", which they believe to be an unconscious mental process, is guided by a "sense of beauty" selecting all combinations which would be fruitful, and eliminating, at the same time, all other combinations. Poincaré believed that, within the unconscious, an "automatic combining and recombining takes place until certain combinations having a peculiar

affinity for our emotional consciousness occur and bring themselves to our attention." In other words, the dynamics of the "arousal reaction" underlying intuitive thought would be determined emotionally rather than relationally. Is it not paradoxical that the celebrated mathematician thought in terms of emotions and esthetic values rather than of relational alignment of terms and, as we shall see presently, in crude metaphors instead of notation systems of various inclusiveness? In parenthesis, we mention that Poincaré is not the only mathematician who makes reference to the beauty of mathematical reasoning (*302, 305*). Weierstrass (*345*) has been quoted as saying "that a mathematician who is not something of a poet will never be a perfect mathematician." Should there be a hidden charm in the very structure of algebra? In its logical and configurational elements which are appreciated by the discerning mind only? Or, indeed, by the discerning eye?

Although the phenomenon of consciousness must have some significance from the physiological point of view, Ribot claims that it merely "accompanies the physiological processes of reasoning, of sensation, of recollection, etc. . . . It does not constitute them; it is an epiphenomenon, and nothing more." If this were the case, consciousness would have no place in the economy of the organism. It is true that the subsidiary (non-conscious) sphere of mentation has item generating properties but the generation of an item without its subsequent translation into the dominant sphere of mentation (the overt system of notation that is) would be pointless.

Other authors discussed non-conscious activity without specific reference to its mechanism, and the element of depth appears to be merely implied. For example, Carmichael (*44*) wrote that "there seems to be a sort of subconscious activity which examines various possibilities, only a few of which, the more promising, appear in the field of consciousness, but that we are almost totally ignorant of the character and power of subconscious activity and have as yet no means of investigating the nature and operation of these subconscious processes of verifiably creative character." According to Rossman (*277*), the term "imagination refers to the mental activity which produces the new patterns from past experiences . . . many inventors attribute the formation of mental patterns to the unconscious mind . . . the formation of new patterns seems to be a matter of so called inspiration. . . invention is entirely based on the formation of complex patterns from simple patterns . . . it is wholly the subconscious reaction to past experiences, and imagination in invention consists in the arrangement of old material in new modes or organization." Ribot wrote that the process of imagining dissociates and associates mental items, while dissociation separates old configurations. It originates through interna- and external factors. Although in essential agreement with our own concept of productive reasoning, Ribot's and also Carmichael's and Rossman's ideas on the subject are too vague; in substance, they are as informative as the statement that an automobile moves by turning its wheels.

The naive wing of the depth-theorists makes us take a close look at the unconscious. Hadamard speaks of an antechamber and a main chamber of consciousness. There are several layers in the unconscious, some of which are quite near consciousness while some lie more and more remote; ideas meet at levels of various depth. In the intuitive mind, the zone where ideas are combined is deeper while in the logical mind that zone is rather superficial. It may be difficult for some minds to bring the result from the deeper to the superficial zones, while other minds bring ideas elaborated in the depth of the unconscious integrally to the light of consciousness. In another passage, Hadamard compares consciousness ideas with actors in the limelight of the stage; those existing in the fringe region of consciousness, to actors moving in the background. At the same time, he compares them to the "atoms of Democritos which, flying in space, get hooked up with one another."

Hutchison (*139, 140*) holds that "data are put into the well of the unconscious—a term borrowed from Coleridge—where there goes on the process of cerebration, organization, integration which results in insight if the situation is favourable. The potential organization of the major part of creative work must, as it were, be just under the surface volcanically ready to erupt when some slight tremor of the crust opens a vent." According to Jones (*148*), the unconscious "resembles conscious mentation in all respects except in the sole one of not being conscious." If this were true, the superior power of the unconscious would remain unexplained. One is curiously reminded of an object which, except for its invisibility, resembles another object in all respects but which, because of its invisibility, is assumed to acquire additional properties. On the other hand, it is quite possible that the dynamic or motivational factors underlying creative effort are not known to the creative mind. Hutchison, who rejects Lombroso's *genius-insanity theory*, but who is apparently disinclined to accept the theory of sublimation, offers a *genius-neurosis theory*. He stipulates that "insight constitutes an extreme of a continuum which joins it with partly logical thought as the other extreme, the degree of frustration being the varying factor . . . insight occurs after the person, in sheer desperation and defense of emotional balance, is forced to relax his effort for a time . . ."— whereupon he finds the solution.

Apparently, the author forgets that the core of the problem of productive thought is the explanation of a normal, or physiological, rather than a pathological process, for he invokes the mechanisms of "rising emotional tension, restlessness, feeling of inferiority, emotional excess, neurotic maladjustment, introversion, negativism, compulsion," etc., none of which is germane to the issue. He goes on to say that, "as the neurosis involved in creative effort is not really cured until the period of psychoanalytic re-education has built a whose system of acting and thinking, so, here, the act of creation is not entirely accomplished until the ideas contained in the insight are secured for consciousness . . . and made explicit in meaning." It remains obscure why the abreaction of a complex should be compared with the production of a truth, in turn considered a "repressed system," or a "creative complex." Moreover, if I correctly understand the theory of suppression in the Freudian sense (at least the original version of the theory), a complex represents previously experienced material, something that had existed in a person's mind at one time or another. Thus, suppression of something that does *not* as yet exist would be paramount to attempted abortion preceding conception. (We interpolate that the process of repression does not involve memories which are already unconscious but those which have become unconscious because of their having been repressed. To quote Freud: "Memory very often reproduces in dreams impressions from the dreamer's early childhood of which we can definitely assert not only that they have been forgotten but that they have become unconscious owing to repression.") The complex, Hutchison continues, gives rise to melancholy, anxiety, fatigue, sometimes inflation of the ego, indeed, to conversion of the repressed system into bodily symptoms, and mild hysterical and neurasthenic manifestations up to the most serious functional disorders. Fortunately, after the creative endeavour turns out satisfactorily, the patient, the creative mind that is, is cured. In contradiction to his previous statements (implying that psychopathological states are the result rather than the cause of creative effort), the author holds that mental tension "grows out of the fact that a balance cannot be effected between the intense and often overambitious creative drive and rate of integration and overaccomplishment."

Kris (174) theories that, "in the process of becoming conscious, the preconsciously prepared thought is sexualized, which accounts for the experience accompanying revelation. Id energies suddenly combine with ego energies, mobile cathexes with bound and neutralized cathexes to produce the unique experience of inspiration which is felt to reach consciousness from the outside. The feeling of triumph and release from tension remind the individual . . . on the period of nursing."

Our goal is to elucidate higher cerebral functions by tracing them to lower nervous system functions. Psychoanalysis reduces them to the function and motivational dynamics of bodily orifices.

TRANSITIONAL STATES BETWEEN NON-CONSCIOUS AND CONSCIOUS PROCESSES

Most of us have experienced states of nascent thought in which awareness contents appear fleetingly, in vague outlines, and which, in terms of the depth theory of consciousness, are sometimes referred to as the sphere of pre-consciousness. In terms of the notation theory, non-conscious processes are about to be transposed into the terms of the more inclusive system, that is, into lucid awareness. The transposition may however not be completed, or maturing thought, like a picture on tachistoscopic examination, may not sufficiently long persist to be recognized. Weininger (346), in his once sensational opus Geschlecht und Charakter, spoke of "henids", i.e., fleeting psychisms or mental states undergoing various grades of differentiation and distinctness. Among other experiences, he cited various shades of increasing

clarity through which the awareness of the meaning of difficult mathematical ideas must pass before they are fully understood, while the reverse process results in the disappearance of what the student was about to grasp at the very moment when the meaning escaped him. "Henids," Weininger writes, "is a term designating psychic data at the stages of their infancy . . . one is about to say something during a conversation, someone cuts in, and even the shadow of what one was beginning to think has disappeared. . . . The meaning may later return and be immediately recognized. . . . Henids cannot be precisely defined, all one can do is to take cognizance of their having been present." Henids, then, would be nascent "Bewusstheiten." (See Ach, Ref. 1.)

SCHOPENHAUER COMPARES HIS MIND WITH A CALCULATING MACHINE

A quotation from Schopenhauer's (285) writings will epitomize the role of non-conscious mental processes and, at the same time, help bridge the gap between two seemingly unrelated topics, namely, the psychologic and the machine theories of thought. "I might have familiarized myself," the philosopher wrote, "with the factual data of a matter, be it theoretical or practical in nature; often enough, after a few days, without having paid any more attention to it, the result, the way things are connected will be clearly before my mind . . . but the operation which achieved the result was just hidden as the workings of a calculating machine."

We can only speculate about the way the philosopher came to compare his own mind with a machine. Very likely, he knew about Pascal's (251) primitive adding device, and it is also quite possible that he saw Leibniz' expensive elaboration of Pascal's model, a weird contraption built by the French mechanic Olivier, in one of the remote galleries of the old Göttingen University. Leibniz' (185) machine had been successfully operated both in Paris and before the Royal Society in London. What's more, Schopenhauer, a voracious reader himself (although convinced that too much reading hampers the flow of original thought), may have come across the now famous article by Babbage, Synthetic and Analytic Engine, which appeared in the Edinburgh Review, in July 1834.

It is to be expected that the following comparison between certain principles of nervous system function and electronic equipment will contribute to the understanding of thought mechanisms. Originally a separate part of the "Critical Comments" just concluded, the "Electronic Theories of Thought" were examined after a critical evaluation of the gestaltpsychologic and associational theories. Moreover, it soon became apparent that, because of the positive aspects of the electronic theories, their separate study was in order. This does not mean that we have adopted them en bloc. They have been assimilated into the system here proposed rather than unreservedly accepted.

It will be necessary to concern ourselves with the following questions: What are the similarities, if any, between thought processes and certain mechanical phenomena? Are they any true similarities between electronic phenomena and *mnemonic functions* which, in turn, form an integral part of intellective processes? The *dynamic aspects* of memory were already discussed in conjunction with the phenomena of affectivity. However, there are good grounds for believing that mnemonic functions have, at the same time, *technical aspects* and that they may be profitably dealt with within the framework of the electronic theories of thought. Memory, in turn, is a crucial factor involved in *learning*. Are machines able to learn? Thus, an attempt will be made to clarify crucial psychopathological issues within the framework of certain modern physical concepts and, conversely, to study the "machine theories of thought" in the light of the insight into the unique nature of biological phenomena. For it is in this very field of mechanistic theories that the decisive battles are being fought and, hence, the opposing forces must be deployed. Thus far, it would seem, many issues have already been decided upon and the usefulness of certain psychological concepts depends on their applicability to the electronics of high speed computing machines. On the other hand, psychological processes, being organismic phenomena, can be thrown into sharp relief by contrasting them with certain mechanical events.

Since these lines were written, support for the author's views has come from several sources. Harlow (*113*) published an article entitled "Brain and Behaviour," in "Computers and Automa-tion," a journal devoted to cybernetics, automatic control and robot mechanisms; and Tustin, (*314*) an engineer, an illuminating essay on a related subject in the British Journal of Psychology. Hearnshaw (*118*), the psychologist, wrote that *"the attempt to reproduce mechanically some of the intellectual processes of organisms has necessitated a much more exacting analysis of these processes and this again brought to the fore some of the cardinal features of conceptual thinking."* At a recent meeting of the American Society of Electrical Engineers (a brief account of which may be found in one of the January issues of the New York Times, 1960) one of the speakers voiced the opinion that "the applicability of engineering principles to biology is helping to produce a better picture of the way the central nervous system works and that, conversely, applying a little 'bio-logic' to such engineering principles as computer design might increase the efficiency with which these so called mechanical brains work." Another speaker repeated what Hadamard (*100*) had suggested a long time ago, namely, that "the biologist should learn more physics and mathematics and get a training in engineering while some engineers should study biological science." Lastly, Ornstein (*238*) expressed the belief that "linguistics will be able to study a language in the way a physicist studied his material in physics, with very few human prejudices and preconceptions, because the language has to be reduced to operational characteristics in order to be handled electronically.

How did the electronic theories of thought come to be?

With the development of electronics and the replacement of the shafts, wheels and cranks of the early calculating machines by electromagnetic relays and, later, electronic tubes, and with the increasing versatility of the computing devices into which they were installed, there developed the notion that the workings of man-made systems of line connections and neuronal nets show significant similarities. To my knowledge, Wiener (*355*) was the first who elaborated on this idea. In his book on "Cybernetics, or Control of Communication in the Animal and the Machine" (which contains a brief history of communication research up to 1947) he suggested that switching devices operating in computation machines resemble nerve cell mechanisms, that the all-or-none character of neuronal discharge corresponds to what is known as "single choice" relays and electronic tubes, that significant parallelisms exist between animal and machine memory and that the human and animal nervous system is capable of the work of computation machines. (See also Wisdom (*359*) and Eisenhart (*78*.) McCulloch (*201, 202*) put the matter even more bluntly while Young (*364*) maintained a rather more cautious attitude. It is quite possible, he wrote, that the brain acts like an adding machine but proof is lacking thus far; it may use principles different from those of mechanical calculators. The "animistic fringe" of electronic engineers denies essential differences between brains and electronic switching equipment, indeed, they maintain that the schism between living beings and machines is artificial and that, in a hundred years or so, the very question of their diversity will have become meaningless (*18*). The problem of machine intelligence was taken up by Sir Geoffrey Jefferson (*143*) in his Lister Oration for which, ironically, he chose the name "The Mind of Mechanical Man." In spite of his close association with the "electrotechnical genius Williams" (I quote from one of Sir Geoffrey's letters addressed to me) he was quite outspoken in his criticism of the machine theory of thinking although, as demanded by the solemnity of the occasion, relatively polite. Referring to Wiener's treatise as an "entertaining book," he accuses the machine theorists of underestimating the complexity, extreme variety and flexibility of the nervous system, not to speak of their failure to distinguish between conscious and non-conscious processes. Lashley (*183a*), too, expressed the conviction that a comparison between brains and calculating machines has little value, if any.

I for one believe that the electronic theory of thought has its merits, that it is capable of further development, and that the new viewpoints it has to offer can be integrated into the concept of higher cerebral function here proposed. What, then, are the relationships between the workings of the brain and of machines? We cannot plunge into the discussion head on, as the nature of the problems involved demands a review of previously discussed subjects in a somewhat different context.

The adherents of the machine theory of life believe that thought can be fully expressed in terms of physicochemical mechanisms, and that the material processes underlying reasoning operate, if not in already existing, at least in machines feasible on the basis of known principles. This assumption raises the following general questions:

(a) How can the thinking machine theory be reconciled with the previously expounded nonmechanistic theory of life and thought?

(b) Can conscious mental activity be produced by machines?

General considerations

Organismic properties of thought

In the opening chapter, organisms were described in terms of systems which maintain a steady state by "controlled lability." In a diagrammatic fashion, the organization of living beings may be illustrated by a system of vectors having a common point of intersection. We chose the term vector rather than radius as vectors require that both magnitude and direction be given if quantities are to be completely specified. Let the individual vectors correspond to the various systems of the organism, including the nervous, cardio-vascular, resporatory, sceleto-muscular, etc. systems. They have the peculiar property that, beyond a certain range, every deflection of a vector from the common center is apt to be answered by a compensatory process in its own sphere and, since an inordinate deflection of one unit, because of the functional interrelations with others, may cause a generalized disturbance, by compensatory processes in other spheres. By the same token, every lengthening of a unit is compensated by shortening and vice versa. For example, hypoxemia is answered by hyperpnoe, and hypotension by pressure responses. Thus, compensatory events result in the reversal of disequilibrium and the restoration of the vector pattern. "Controlled lability" is the integrated total of homeo-static action stations rather than a state of rest, for stability there is only in death. (This statement, however, may be challenged, for death, rather than stability, is a revolution of the slaves.) Let us add that the suggested diagram is purely descriptive; it does not imply that a vital force or an entelechy maintains the orientation of the vectors. Within a limited range, it is true, fluctuations in the length and position of the individual units occur spontaneously and periodically; indeed, a certain degree of inconstancy belongs to the very dynamics of the pattern. Let us bear in mind that individual vectors do not express static units but, rather, the totality of integrative acts constituting the "function" of the sphere within which the individual acts take place; were the whole system self-illuminated, slow-motion photography would show a scintillating rather than a steadily glowing star of life.

Within every sphere, every spark and flicker is precipitated by a preceding event, or a concatenation of intra-vector and inter-vector changes in energy distribution by which the ensuing event is causally determined; conversely, every event requires energy derived from physico-chemical sources and expresses a change in energy gradients. In these respects, namely, causal determination of events and conservation and convertibility of energy, and in these respects only, do organisms resemble machines.

On the other hand, there are conspicuous differences which weigh heavily against a machine theory of thought. Organisms originate through highly complex processes of duplication of similar parent systems. From their very beginnings, they are systems that pass through the typical stages of birth, maturation and death. They are in a state of continuous fluxion as, within the individual vectors, although at different rates and in varying degrees, the integrated substrate is, (depending on both intrinsic and extrinsic factors,) built up by anabolic and broken down by katabolic processes—to be built up and broken down again. Within limits, loss of substrate can be repaired by regeneration, or integrative processes can be made to continue by adjustive redistribution and repatterning of activity as, for example, in the nervous system. The main difference between animate and inanimate matter is the self-regulatory property of the organism.

The term "thought" applies to certain integrative acts or, figuratively speaking, scintillations within the sphere of the vector "nervous system" which, like other biological processes, is self-regulating. If it is true that the process of thinking reflects the general properties of life processes it should also be true that it cannot be duplicated by machines. On the other hand, there is no valid

reason to deny that the individual acts are causally determined and that they depend on the metabolic generation of energy.

At this point, then, two alternatives remain open; either to drop the matter or to follow the line of reasoning and to defer judgement until such time as our thesis can be developed to a point where the relationship between thought and the activity of machines can be specified.

Thought is not only dependent on a material substrate and, as such, subjected to the laws of causality; thought is, at the same time, a psychic process. The question thus arises: Can conscious mental activity be produced by machines?

Further discussion of non-conscious thought

Let us resume the argument with respect to the previously offered concept of consciousness as the mode in which objective reality is recorded by the highest sensory levels the nervous system. That this is a justifiable assumption may be demonstrated by a ficticious experiment (a *Gedankenexperiment* as Ernst Mach would have called it) namely, by the assumption of having a person equipped with some miraculous device observe his own brain through a translucent calvarium. Theoretically at least, one feature of the experimental arrangement is entirely feasable, namely, the replacement of the natural coverings of the brain by the type of translucent skullcap used in animal experiments. The microscope used by the subject engaged in "exogenic introspection" should enable him to record the activity of every nerve cell involved in thinking. (It would have to be more "powerful" than an electron-microscope.) At the same time, we assume that the person is able to dissociate, from his other thought processes, the process of studying his cells concerned with the process of thought he observes in terms of structural changes. It stands to reason that the experimentalist would fail to "see" thoughts, perceptions and memory traces as such; he would see events involving a material substrate. And since modern physics stipulates that structure dissolves into processes and relations, the observer might not even see matter, but. somehow, become aware of actions and events only, Heisenberg (*122*) wrote that "the atom of modern physics can be symbolized only through partial differential equations in an abstract space of many dimensions. . . .All its qualities are inferential; no material properties can be directly attributed to it. That is to say, any picture of the atom that our imagination is able to invent is, for this very reason, defective. An understanding of the atomic world in that primary sensuous fashion is impossible.* Be this as it may, it is most likely that the hypothetical observer studying the substrate of his own thought would become aware of the concurrence of two sets of phenomena; on the one hand, he would see certain *measurable events* in an organ which, although his own, a part of his own body that is, has become a part of his extra-personal space or objective reality and, on the other, of certain *contents of his own consciousness*, that is, of subjective reality. Provided his instruments be capable of still further perfection, he might see even automatically recorded algebraic expressions which reflect ongoing thought processes. He would not by any means understand the co-activity and co-intensiveness of the perceiving subject and the perceived object—both himself— in terms of conventional cause-effect relationships.† Sooner or later, he would take the existence of typical correlations for granted. For another person, equipped with similar instruments, the exposed brain would be an object among other objects. In studying the organ of

consciousness and thought, the outside observer would fail to have any of the correlative, and "immediately meaningful" experiences which reflect the activity of the brain mechanisms under observation. In sharp contrast, the person studying his own brain would register the events underlying his own thoughts and think them at the same time; and again, the other person would see the very same cerebral events but would have to decode them to understand their meaning. For the "self-observer", the brain would be both subject and object; for the other person, a recording and computing instrument, or a "thing."

As far as we are able to see, the crucial experiment, although never to be carried out, can yield one result only. Machines, no matter how complicated their workings and how precise their performance, are as conscious as dolls. We take note of the fact that some authorities, including Turing (*329*) and Berkeley (*16*) hold the opposite view. The former claims that we have no criteria to decide whether calculating machines work consciously or not. The latter adapts the definition of the term consciousness to the particular needs of his thesis. We are not in a position to extend the discussion which followed the publication of Turing's article, neither do we wish to be drawn into a consideration of the particular circumstances that would justify (without compelling reason) the redefinition of the meaning of commonly accepted concepts. Jefferson (*143*) maintains that machines have no soul, one of the reasons being that they cannot write sonnets. Sir Geoffrey is perhaps too exacting; to try to bribe the contraption might be a much simpler way to find out whether they have a soul or not.

Thus, inasmuch as thinking implies problem solving, it does not seem to depend on conscious mental activity as problems can be solved in the absence of consciousness. And, although the results of non-conscious work are eventually translated into the notation system peculiar to the highest level of the brain, the generation of informative items at different physiological levels, including the subsidiary sphere of mentation, would suggest, at this point of the argument at least, that machines are able to think.

Following these preliminary considerations we propose to study the points of similarity between biological and mechanical brains, to be followed by an examination of their differences.

---

* Paradoxically, perception, if carried to "extremes", as in the above *Gedankenexperiment*, is converted into a conceptual process. For the reverse phenomenon, the perceptualization of thinking, see below.

† I discussed this *Gedankenexperiment* in 1950. (See Chapter I, ref. 64.) In 1953, H. Rohracher (*275a*) substituted an x-ray machine for the "super-electronmicroscope." However, neither he nor I expressed an entirely original thought. K. Kleist (*165a*) made reference to the following passage in Du Bois Raymond's lecture *Über die Grenzen des Naturerkennens* (*67a*): "A spirit equipped with superhuman intelligence and astronomical knowledge . . . watching the silent play of brain molecules, would survey their movements and twists and, with increasing experience, be able to correlate certain mental processes with certain movement patterns. Yet he would be unable to understand either the correlation between movement and thought nor, indeed, the production of conscious experience." For a detailed discussion see Du Bois Raymond, pp. 122–125. The superhuman spirit to which he made reference is a fictitious observer, referred to by Laplace (*179a*) but Du Bois Raymond suspects that Leibniz was the first who pondered the problem under consideration. (See also F. A. Lange, *Geschichte des Materialismus*, Kröner Verlag, Leipzig, 1907, vol. II, pp. 59–68).

Common properties of biological and electronic brains

In the first two chapters of the present monograph we mentioned the existence of recursive line connections or feedbacks (about which more will be said later) and we emphasized that thought involves, in the first place, the production of data generated by the relational alignment of terms. We learned that the inaugural phases of thought eventuates in the generation of relations and that, in the concluding phase (or tentatively concluding phase), the new data are matched along additional dimensions of operation. Potentially, the second phase of thought lasts as long as data that lend themselves to relational alignment emerge either through observation or through the ekphory of engrams. Ultimately, then, both phases can be expressed in terms of the comparison of relations which, after all feasable or at least available combinations have been exhausted, results either in the acceptance or the rejection of the original proposition.

Feedback mechanisms

At this point, it is necessary to establish the fact, already alluded to in various places, that certain phases of deductive reasoning are, essentially, feedback mechanisms operating at the highest sensory, that is to say, intellective level of brain function. Their nature may be best demonstrated by an analysis of recognitive thought that supplements our previous deliberations. Additional evidence will be adduced to show that reasoning is derivable from perception, in other words, that higher cerebral function can be reduced to lower functions of the nervous system.

What, precisely, is the meaning of the term feedback in the physical sphere? "By feedback is meant the activity of closed circuits such that some of the output returns and influences the subsequent activity in that circuit. . . . It is this error (the degree of failure) which determines the return input until the error becomes zero. . . . In any system displaying negative feedbacks some of the output of the system returns to limit and control its further input" (*30*). "All purposive behaviour is controlled by negative feedbacks from the goal; that is, there must be signals from the goal that are used to restrict outputs which would otherwise go beyond the goal. . . . Negative feed-

backs insure that the behaviour of an object is controlled by the margin of error at which the object stands at a given time with reference to a relatively specific goal" (*307*). Feedback is not an information from the goal but informative as to the magnitude of the discrepancy between the current state and the goal state (*208*). Wiener (*355*) might have been the first who suggested that certain performances of the nervous system are controlled by negative feedbacks. "In picking up an object," he wrote, "the movement of the extremity at each moment is regulated by the amount of which it has not yet reached it. This is accomplished by responding to informative impulses flowing from the proprioceptors to the effector organs. If the distance by which, at a given time, the hand has not yet reached the object is considered an error, its magnitude determines the return input until the error becomes zero. Feedback mechanisms serve the comparison of signals from the goal with those arising in the organs of movement."

The above quotations indicate that the concept of feedback, more especially of negative feedback, is not uniform. One group of writers consider feedbacks as *corrective;* others, as merely *informative.* Assuming the validity of either definition, it may be readily seen that both informative and corrective feedbacks operate in the nervous system, in fact, it is possible to identity a third variety which, for want of a better term, may be called *orienting* feedback. (See below.)

Feedbacks operating at the highest level of the nervous system would thus seem to fall into three main groups, namely, discriminative, corrective and orienting feedbacks.

(a) *Discriminative (comparing) feedbacks* indicate similarity or dissimilarity of or, for that matter, congruence or incongruence of perceptions or of perceptions and ekphorized engrams.

(b) *Corrective feedbacks*, by actuating appropriate engrams, initiate, in a more or less reflex like fashion, adequate reactions in response to preceding inadequate reactions.

(c) *Orienting feedbacks* are not immediately corrective processes, i.e., they do not initiate corrective transfer mechanisms. They connect, basically through association by similarity, the inaugural phase with the concluding phase of thought and, hence, are instrumental in establishing or, as the case may be, disproving the validity of the produced relation. However, the connection between the inaugural and the concluding phase of thought may be a complex process involving the combination of more elementary feedback processes in various combinations. It is this peculiar feature that establishes the role of transfer mechanisms as feedbacks of a higher order.

To *summarize*, feedback mechanisms operate at various levels of integrational complexity. The most complex varieties are orienting feedbacks which initiate the concluding phase of thought, and corrective feedbacks which operate between the appropriate components of the guide-structure on the one hand and the individual aspects or facets of a problem on the other. (See below.)

Feedbacks operate in the *recognition of objects*, in the *comparison* (the term being used in its widest sense) of *objects with class concepts*, the comparison between *relations and class concepts*, and in the *comparison* of relations, including *intrinsically generated relations*.

RECOGNITION OF OBJECTS (Fig. 21)

Let the complex of perceptions which represent the object to be identified (or "x-object") correspond to the individual surfaces of cube "a"; and, at the same time, the series of familiar perceptions representing the *guide structure* instrumental in recognition correspond to the surface of the half-cube* "A." A naive observer, looking at the two objects from an appropriate distance and direction, would notice the identity between surface a_1 of the cube, and surface A_1 of the half-cube. In so doing, he would however act like an infant who sees the similarity between a light within his reach and the moon. At a more advanced stage of experience, the observer learns that appropriacy of response to the object may depend on the evaluation of additional data. He realizes that a_1 may

---

* The sequential structure of recognition may be conveniently demonstrated by the process of identification (be it a process of perceptual matching or of matching from memory) of solids rather than by the identification of familiar objects. In the latter eventuality, recognition, for all practical purposes at least, is based on immediate gestaltperception acquired by experience, that is, gestaltperception that has become automatic. The procedure here followed will be readily appreciated by those who have difficulty in recognizing multifaceted solids, such as dodecahedrons, icosahedrons and other abstruse forms. For simplicity, we illustrate the principle of recognition by referring o a cube, or hexahedron.

be only a particular part of a complex having an unknown number of properties, or aspects, namely, $a_1 - a_2 - a_3 \ldots a_n$ and, to find the complete relation-structure of the unknown complex, assumes "a" to be merely one of its segments. Considering that, in the process of recognition, the components of either complex are experienced in succession rather than simultaneously, in other words, that the process of recognition involves a sequence of mental processes (see below), one may justifiably refer to the complex object to be recognized as *series a*, and to the guide-structure used in the process of recognition as *series A*. In both the present example and the following instances, the observer matches, tentatively, "a" with "A." Subsequently, the identification of the hypothetical facet a_2, which corresponds to "A_2, will help him to equate $a_1 - a_2$ with $A_1 - A_2$. In a similar fashion, he postulates a hypothetical facet a_3. However, as the diagram shows, he will not be able to match a_3 with A_3. Accordingly he cannot recognize or identify "cube a", at least not primarily.

Now, under ideal conditions of reasoning (of which the act of recognition is a particular instance) *series a* becomes the representative of a class of its own which bears a definite relationship to $A_1 - A_2 - A_3 \ldots A_n$ in that $2 (A_1 - A_2 - A_3 \ldots A_5)$, if put together in an appropriate fashion, equals $a_1 - a_2 - a_3 \ldots a_6$.

It is apparent that the process of comparison does not necessarily develop in the above described fashion; in other words, that series a might have been compared with series A in a different sequence. For example, the comparison between a_3 and A_3 could have been either the second or the fourth or the fifth step of thought. Unless previous experiences established a preferential sequence, or thinking set, the various possible combinations may be assumed to be equiprobable.

COMPARISON BETWEEN OBJECTS AND CLASS CONCEPTS (Fig. 22)

On a low abstractive level, only series a is represented by an object while series A is given by the class-concept "half cube"; accordingly, facet a_1 is compared with aspect A_1 of the concept "half cube" or engram A_1 which, in turn, actuates engram A_2 by contiguity; as a result of the activation of A_2, the reasoner scans the series a for the presence of facet a_3, etc.

PROBLEM SITUATION   GUIDE STRUCTURE

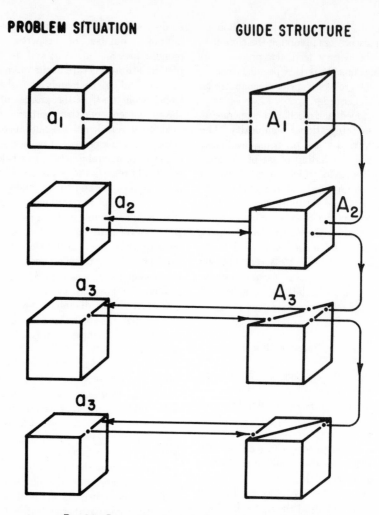

Fig. 21. Comparing circuits in the recognition of objects.

COMPARISON BETWEEN RELATIONS (a) AND
CLASS CONCEPTS (A) (Fig. 23)

The discussion, which up to this moment has been of a somewhat general nature, requires an example of actual reasoning to illustrate the principle in question. In the previously cited examples of diagnostic reasoning we emphasized the role of similarity and contiguity mechanisms. The following observations illustrates, in a similar fashion, how the process of recognition is guided by the structure of concepts and the systematic use of their individual constituents. It will carry us to an apparently different sphere of thought to be exemplified by a diagnostic problem. In the accompanying diagram (Fig. 23), illustrating the

appearance of normal ventricles and arteries, the guide structure is represented by a "visualized concept."

In a case of brain tumor suspect, both the ventricles and the blood vessels of the brain were made visible by the injection of contrast media. On the brow down view of the pneomoencephalogram, which disclosed the presence of air in the ventricles and the subarachnoid spaces, the superior surface of the corpus callosum appeared to be elevated while its inferior surface, i.e., the roof of the lateral ventricles, was depressed. The increased distance between the superior and the inferior surface of the corpus callosum suggested that it was enlarged by an infiltrating neoplasm. In other words, the perception of the abnormal

PROBLEM SITUATION   **GUIDE STRUCTURE**

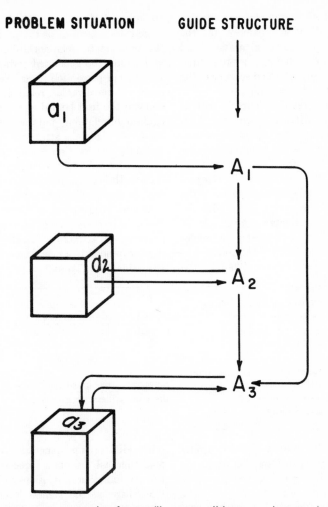

Fig. 22. Comparing circuits in identification ("comparison" between objects and class concepts).

configuration of a_1 recalled the concept "glioma of the corpus callosum," or, concept A. More specifically, it recalled its constituent A_1 which corresponds to the visual data a_1. Because of the characteristic appearance of callosal tumors at autopsy, a subsequently established contiguity-association recalled constituent A_2 of the concept "callosal tumor," that is, "nodular protrusion of a mass into the roof of the lateral ventricle as seen on profile views." The association of A_2 formed in the observer's mind helped him discover the roentgenological correlate a_2. The next constituent of the class concept A which guided the reasoner was A_3, that is, "upward displacement and forward shift of the anterior cerebral artery as seen on profile views of the skull." The abnormality A_3

could be verified in the roentgenogram as a_3. Subsequently, the remaining element of guide concept A, namely, A_4 or "downward displacement of the small vein of Galen" came to mind; it led to the discovery of a_4 in the phlebogram. The lesion was verified at postmortem examination.

COMPARISON BETWEEN TWO SETS OF RELATIONS

At the abstract level of reasoning, the various a-facets are no longer represented by percepts but by the awareness of relations. In other words, during the process of recognition, a_1 is not equated with A_2 but, rather, the relation a_1 to an item to the relation A_2 to an item. This point may be illustrated by some of the examples of creative thought previously discussed, namely, (a) the discovery of the law of universal gravitational attraction, (b) by the fact that light is propagated with a certain speed and, (c), the discovery of the chemical transmission of nerve impulses.

Newton equated the relation "circling path of the moon": terrestrial attraction with the (productive) relation "falling apple: terrestrial attraction." In this equation, the first term representing facet a_1, the second term facet A_1. In one of the preceding examples, the reasoner, while comparing a cube with a half-cube, became aware of the identity between the new perception a_1 with the familiar perception A_2; in the present example, he became aware of the identity between the problematic relation ("circling path of the moon": x) with a familiar relation, namely ("fall of the apple: gravitational attraction"). As a result, the fragmentary facet a_1 of the problem phase (i.e., the problematic relationship x/a) became converted into the generated term, or an assertion. In terms of perception it may be said that a_1 became a "perceivable" relationship at the very moment the fruit landed on the ground. The recognition of relations, and the substitution of x by the term "the globe attracts the moon", was initiated by observation b, i.e., the actuating element of facet A_1. In the course of further generalization, the newly generated item "gravitational pull of the Earth (previously corresponding to x) became an assertion, as epitomized by the term "solar attraction" and, eventually, "universal gravitational attraction." In other words, concept A was extended to a new class concept, formed by the elements A_1, A_2 and A_3.

$$\frac{\text{delayed message reaching Earth from Jupiter}}{\text{increasing distance Earth-Jupiter}} = \frac{\text{delayed receipt of a message}}{\text{increasing distance from sender}}$$

and

$$\frac{\text{accelerated message reaching Earth from Jupiter}}{\text{decreasing distance Earth-Jupiter}} = \frac{\text{accelerated receipt of a message}}{\text{decreasing distance from sender}}$$

Olaf Roemer saw the identity of the two relationstructures, as they appear on this page.

The left terms of the equations correspond to facet a_1; the right terms, to facet A_1.

Otto Loewi saw the identity between the relationstructure

(1) "Chemically active cellular products" to "chemical action from cell to cell", (A_1) and

(2) "Chemical products of nerve cells" to "chemical transmission of nerve impulses", (a_1).

Facet A_1 actuated A_2, that is, it suggested to Loewi an experiment built on anticipative analogy-relationships, whose rationale needs no comment.

COMPARISON OF INTRINSICALLY GENERATED RELATIONS

At a still higher level of abstraction, the production of the relation b of facet A_1 and, hence, the computation of the value of x becomes an intrinsically generated analogy-relation or some other kind of item-generating relation. Certain mathematical reasoning processes, for example the manipulation of relations in Boolean algebra, take shape at the highest level of abstraction, where the simultaneous surveying of relations made possible by the use of symbols re-introduces the element of perception and, in a great circle, leads the process of reasoning back to its very origin.

Thus far, we have studied largely classificatory or subsumptive thought processes. They were shown to be derivable from the association of the elements $A_1 - A_2 \ldots$ of class concepts, that is to say, the connection between the individual elements within the framework of concept A. Concepts, in turn, are products of preferential correlations of psychisms, that is, stimuli that categorize items in a usable fashion. Directed by the mutual affinity of the psychisms involved, the process of reasoning was, in a certain sense, repetitive in character, and it was kept going by the similarity and contiguity mechanisms that alternated with

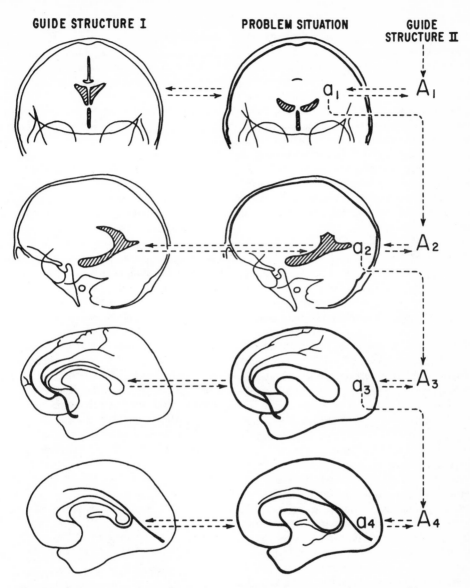

Fig. 23. Comparing circuits involving relations and class concepts in a diagnostic problem.

one another. However, if the succession A_1 – A_2 ... is called into being by analogy relations or by implication rather than by contiguity relationships, the over-all structure of thought becomes more and more variegated both in the direction of potential error and potential creativity.

In spite of the progressive complication of the process of reasoning, thought continues to be basically a process of sorting and comparing, wherein the guide material "A" is taken either from available data or, at appropriate stages of the reasoning process, created by the synthesis of complex data from primitive data, i.e., the initiation of transfer mechanisms. At the abstract plane of comparison, the utilization of test material is to a large extent influenced by the principle of *consistency*. At the concrete level on the other hand, the utilization of test material depends on the *shape* of the individual elements and their combinations. Rather like two geometrical structures cannot at the same time occupy different positions relatively to one another, so two terms, or assertions, cannot at the same time be true or false; not only thought is derivable from perception but also the law of contradiction. Recognitive, reconstructive and anticipative thinking are similar, the only difference being that, in the *recognition of patterns*, the reasoner is guided by known or, alternately, ad hoc recated "similarity sets", that is, thinking sets embodying, as crucial elements, the similarity of items. In *reconstructive* and *anticipatory* reasoning, the reasoner is guided either by known "contiguity sets" or "causality sets" whose leading element is the causal connection of items, and which were created in response to the demands of the moment.

To *summarize*: Recognitive thought is derivable from the perception of spatial relations. In comparing impressions, the process of perception is terminated by the experience of *similarity* or of *dissimilarity;* in comparing relations, individual phases of thought are concluded by the experience of *consistency* or *inconsistency*, briefly stated, by the propositions *true* or *false* at the abstract level. Under ideal conditions, the concluding phase of thought is guided by self-correcting and orienting processes which, in turn of the vector diagram of organization, indicate the existence of deviation or both the deviation and the means of correction. Lack of deviation on the other hand demonstrates that the original assumption is correct. Inadequate integrative acts of the nervous system which, in the realm of thought, represent incorrect assertions and implicitly the inadequate perception of relations, would appear as deflections of the vector "nervous system." On the other hand, the integrative processes underlying the concluding phase would indicate the degree of error although not necessarily its nature. To reiterate, deductive reasoning and its initiation is dependent on feedback mechanisms operating at the highest discriminative level. Although there is a far cry from the self-controlled adaptive reflex or movement control to the control of thought, both phenomena resemble self-correcting devices installed into various mechanical contrivances. This statement however is true only in part. Whenever the assertions produced in the concluding phase fail to provide corrective clues, they indicate merely the existence rather than the nature of deviations from the ideal position of the system. Neither does awareness of contradiction necessarily improve the adequacy of subsequent hypotheses. In fact, no further hypotheses may

be formed and the flow of thought may cease altogether.

Moreover, feedbacks would be merely instrumentalities within the framework of a more comprehensive mechanism since, to identify series *a* even at lower levels of recognitive reasoning, machines would have to initiate various other processes including the activation of engrams. In figure 21 the recursive connections representing feedback mechanisms were shown to play simply between corresponding elements, that is, facets or aspects of the two *objects* to be compared, with one another and thereby, during the successive phases of comparison, to indicate either congruence or incongruence of the surfaces a_1 and A_1, or a_2 and A_2, etc. On the other hand, in recognizing an object by its subsumption to the appropriate class concept and, likewise, in recognitive reasoning properly so called, the individual aspects of a problem series must be compared with appropriate *engrams* rather than *concrete guide structures*. Accordingly, during the process of recognition, feedbacks would have to operate *within* the machine. To put it in other words: both "congruence-indicating" (validating) and "incongruence-indicating" (invalidating) feedbacks, unless knowledge is based on perception and is therefore immediate, would have to originate *within* the machine itself. The feedbacks would have to alternate with the intrinsic components of a "self-sustaining process" involving engrams $A_1 - A_2$, etc., that is to say, with the constituents of the class concept A which is the guide used by the reasoner. More specifically, mechanical brains would have to be capable of performing the following steps in order to utilize engrams in the process of recognition. They would have to

1) initiate process a', representing the perception of facet a_1 of *series a*, (fig. 24).

2) actuate, as an act of recognition, the corresponding process A_1 (the ekphorized engram existing within the machine) and

3) to register a state of correspondence between the a' process and process A_1 by feedback mechanisms or self-checking devices, (*"sequence I"*). Machines would have to

4) actuate A_2 by contiguity, that is, as a result of A_1 going on in the machine,

5) scan *series a* for the presence of percept a_2,

6) initiate process a", the perception of facet a_2 of *series a*,

7) register a state of correspondence between a_2 and process A_2, (*"sequence II"*); they would have to

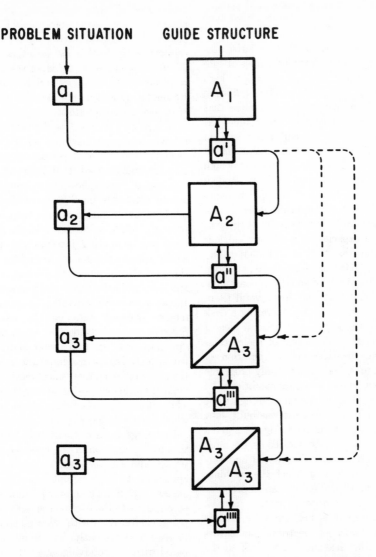

Fig. 24. Interaction of stimuli, perceptions and engrams in recognition.

8) actuate engram A_3 by contiguity, i.e., as a result of process A_2 going on in the machine,

9) scan the series a for the presence of percept a_3

10) institute process a''', the perception of facet a_3 of *series a*

11) register *non*-correspondence between process a''' and A_3 ("*sequence III*"); they would have to

12) combine 2 (A_3) prior to its comparison with facet a_3,

13) scan the a-series for the presence of a corresponding percept a_3,

14) reinstate the process a'''' and

15) register correspondence between a'''' and the intrinsically generated unit 2 (A_3). ("*sequence IV*").

To summarize, the machine would recognize the *series a* by using the guide-structure, or "*concept*" A.

For brevity, we omit the action sequences involved in the recognition of the remaining a-facets. At the same time, we remind ourselves that the sequence of steps thus far taken is only one of three possibilities, in other words, that the sequences indicated in Fig. 24 by dotted arrows are equiprobable. The point we wish to make is that *only a machine endowed with a certain degree of freedom would be comparable to a biological brain, especially if it had to find goal leading shortcuts.*

Structure and general performance of electronic information processing devices

At this point, it is necessary to familiarize ourselves in a general way with the principles of construction and the performance of modern high speed calculating machines. (The following account was written several years ago. Since that time, the performance of computing machines has been perfected but the principles involved in mechanical calculation have remained the same.)* The reader, having glanced over reports which appeared in the daily press or, perhaps, studied some of the articles published in popular magazines (*3, 4, 5, 17, 18*) and scientific journals (*19, 116, 117, 201, 293–299*), may be aware of the general performance capacity of electronic calculators. He may know that they are able to multiply 10 digit numbers 30,000 times a minute, to solve, all at one time, hundreds of equations containing many variables and that they are several thousand times faster than a person operating a desk adding machine. He may have a general idea of the usefulness of the calculators, of their versatility permitting the scientific computation of "optimum programs," including supply programs for the Air Force under changing conditions; he may have learned that the machine can figure out the flight of an airplane before it was built, how thick the cables supporting the bridge of a given weight and length have to be, etc. To us, the most remarkable features, rather than speed and versatility, is the principle upon which the machines work, the fact that their highly complex performance, like that of the nervous system, can be broken down into smallest uniform units. This is one of the peculiaries of electronic calculators which, among other features, gave birth to the electronic theory of thought.

The divisibility of complex functions into primitive functions applies more specifically to *digital* (or numerical) *computers* as opposed to *analog machines.*† Operations performed by the former include addition, substraction, division, multiplication, square root, etc., all of which can

be reduced to acts of counting, while those of analog machines, sometimes referred to as mathematical instruments, *involve the representation of variables of a problem by the physical quantities which are measured by them.* In this respect they resemble sliderules, where variables are expressed by lengths indicated on scales, and the equations to be solved have a term to term physical counterpart in the mechanism of the instruments. (See below.) In digital machines on the other hand, even such complicated performances as integration are arithmetized, that is to say, reduced to addition and multiplication or broken down into a great number of small steps. In other words, the machine carries out operations in *sequences;* in the process of addition, for example, the machine proceeds by computing intermediary products to which additional numbers are added and retains the partial products until needed, while analog machines solve the entire problem *simultaneously.* In order to solve equations, a computer must receive relevant data on the nature of the problem to be solved, i.e., machines must be "programmed" or "told" what to do by the data fed into it. Digital machines are more versatile than analog machines since most problems in applied mathematics can be solved by arithmetic while the latter solve only those problems for which they have been specifically designed.

Hughlings Jackson could have hardly foreseen that his subdivision of the cerebral cortex into a *sensory* and a *motor* segment would some day be applicable to high complexity calculating machines (Fig. 26). The motor portion of the cortex corresponds to the *output;* the sensory, to the *input* in combination with other machine organs to be described presently. The input may be compared with the receiving areas of a hypothetical unisensory brain which depends on artificially inserted data, in that the machine does not produce its own impressions but gets them pre-shaped. Further, in contrast to the cortical receiving areas, the input of computation machines receives instructions on how to deal with the data furnished to them from an extrinsic agency. The output unit is comparable to a combination of organs comprising (a) the motor speech center and (b) the effectors of written speech, the information computed being typed out by the machine and transmitted to the external world.

In the human brain, input and output are linked up with the *information generating mechan-*

---

* Cf., e.g., the "Special Science Report" in *Newsweek*, Oct. 24, 1960, p. 41, which is based on interviews with many authorities, including N. Wiener, Cl. Shannon, and many others.

† Except for the comparison between electronic and biological brains, the following account is based largely on the writings of Berkeley (*16–17a*) and Berkeley and Jensen (*19*).

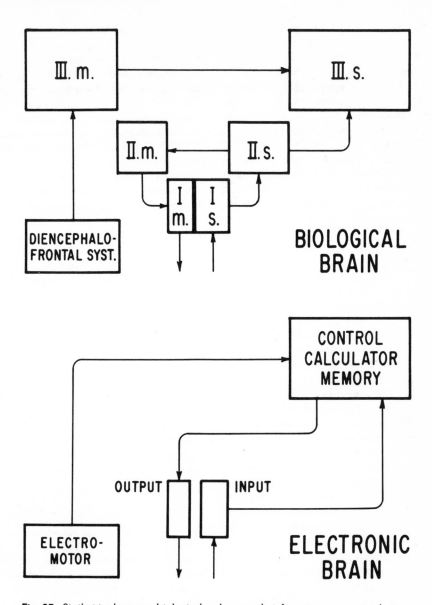

Fig. 25. Similarities between biological and man-made information processing devices.

ism vested in the posterior association fields. The posterior cortex of the brain, in turn, corresponds to the *memory unit,* the *calculator* and the *"control."* It is hardly necessary to point out that the machine does not do anything on its own initiative. However, after being started, its automatic sequence control enables it to work unattended until the problem is solved. The energy necessary to actuate its electromagnetic relays or electronic tubes is supplied by a motor.

The memory organ stores in its *registers* numbers and instructions transferred from the input while the performance of the computing organ corresponds to the purely technical aspects of calculation. The mathematical ability of the machine is vested in the control, an organ connected with the remaining parts of the machine by telegraph lines transmitting the plan of operation to the individual units in the form of signals. The execution of many operations is controlled by feedback mechanisms or self-checking devices. The control appears to be the "brain of the brain" as it were. It is this term control (perhaps a misnomer) which may convey the impression that the machine, like a gifted mathematician, autonomously determines the nature and course of the individual calculations. A passage quoted from Keister's (157) article on the logic of switching circuits will clarify this point. Referring to the habit of "circuit designers to use such words as tell, remember, know, and choose which, ordinarily, apply to rational mental operations and, at the same time, with surprising accuracy to the nature of the actions performed in automatic switching systems," the author tries to explain that the "actions are not the result of independent thinking on the part of the units but are more in the nature of automatic responses to the control signals. The designer has analyzed the situation which may occur, determined what shall be done for each and built into the control mechanism a means for reorganizing the situation and to act accordingly. The machine knows what to do for a definite set of circumstances and is able to analyze a combination of preconceived conditions and produce for each condition a result which agrees with the precise pattern of logic laid out by the designer. The preconception of the condition on the part of the latter enables the control to set up the proper paths at the proper time and to select subroutines or alternative procedures whenever the machine arrives at a choice point." Still, the question whether automatic computers are able to work creatively is a hotly debated issue among equally competent electronic engineers. We shall return to this aspect of the problem later

In a rather general way, the function of a digital computer may be described as follows. If, in the course of a computation, two numbers have to be added, the control operates in accordance with the instructions which have entered the memory unit from the input. The two numbers are stored in the memory registers as engrams and are deleted if not further wanted. Numbers, instructions, etc. are all given as *signals* constituting the language of the machine. The most primitive signals possible are "yes" and "no"; further, the sequence of operations of the machine or the choice of alternatives (built in by the designer) depends on the signals existing at that time. Not only directives but decimal numbers are converted into "yes-signals" and "no-signals." The

former are transmuted directly, into open or closed states of electromagnetic relays or electronic tubes; the latter indirectly, that is to say, by their conversion into the binary system which is based on the use of the two digits 0 and 1. In other words, all binary numbers must be written in the two digits 0 and 1. They report powers of two in the same way as, in the decimal system, digits report the power of ten (19). Any number can be represented by the state of two relays or tubes. For example, 01 can be represented by the state of two relays the first of which is open while the second is closed. Once uniformity between "information-signals" and "number-signals" has been established, the machine differentiates between the two categories of directives. (For details, see Ref. 19.) The salient points are that

(a) the function of the machine can be resolved into uniform physical processes, namely, responses to signals and that

(b) the variety of its performances can be reduced to structurally and temporally patterned positive and negative responses.

Preparatory to the discussion of the way in which mechanical brains would have to operate which are faced with the problem to ekphorize self-formed engrams and of the question of similarities of sequence control in biological and mechanical computers, it will be necessary to deal once more with the problems of recognition and memory, although from a different angle.

The nature of engrams. Mnemonic mechanisms in biological and mechanical brains

At all times, the speculation concerning the nature of memory traces was fashioned after new discoveries in various technical fields, including chemistry, physics and, lately, electronics. In substance, four theories have been promulgated, namely, a *resonance theory*, a *chemical* theory, a *synapse adaptation theory* and a *dynamic, or reverberating circuit theory*.

THE RESONANCE THEORY

Sir Robert Hooke (*133*), believed by some to have discovered the law of gravitational attraction before Newton, is reported by Jevons (*145*) "in seeking an analogy to mnestic processes, to have likened memory to those bells or vases which Vitruvius mentioned to have been placed in the ancients' theatre, which did receive and return the sound vigorously and strongly; and the unison tuned string bells or glasses which receive impressions from sounds and retain the impression for some time, answering the tone by the same tone of their own." Some of the modern theories of engram representation appear to be fashioned along the lines suggested by Hooke. (See below.)

CHEMICAL THEORIES

Another idea of historical interest is Goldscheider's (*92*) hypothesis of patterned changes produced by linear aggregations of stimulation effects in the neuronal nets of the sensory cortex. In a certain sense, Goldscheider anticipated both Katz and Halstead's *protein template theory* and Lashley's (*182*) *interference pattern theory*. (See below.) Goldscheider contended that material changes underlying engrams would have to satisfy any possible combination of discharge of a given group of ganglionic cells and, conversely, to be individually determined by any such combination. He believed that the changes analogous to those occurring in the side chains of highly complex and therefore labile protein molecules fulfill these conditions, and that the formation of sidechains, which he assumed to be the material basis of engrams, is encouraged by the repeated association of ideas; conversely, lack of repeated associations would reduce and, eventually, abolish the formation of sidechains. The mechanism of engram formation would resemble the formation of antitoxins (a special category of sidechains), the amount of which increases in proportion to the stimulation of the proteins upon which the toxins act. As is well known, Ehrlich stipulated that sidechains used in the process of dissimilation are built up in excess in response to their accelerated destruction. Goldscheider, reasoning by analogy, believed that the labile molecules regenerate whenever the associative processes whose material basis they form were repeated, in other words, that the engrams were potentially perpetuated. For example, during the perception of a circle, a certain number of cortical cells would be stimulated, their activity propagated through a feltwork of their processes and dissimilation of

protein molecules reach a maximum in sets of nodal points formed by interweaving lines of force; in other words, a figure, say, a circle, would be duplicated by a representative pattern of protein disintegration, and the repetition of the original experience would intensify the formation of engrams. He thought that the specificity of engrams corresponds to the configuration of the sets of nodal points of labile, regenerating molecules and that their breakdown would initiate secondary discharges. These discharges of energy in turn would form the basis of higher mental processes. Lastly, Goldscheider advanced the view that not only the cells would fire but, at the same time, the semipermeable aggregates of nodal points where chemical lability reaches a maximum. Katz and Halstead's (*155*) protein template theory stipulates that neurons, in spite of their fixed anatomical relationships, do not become functioning members of memory networks before certain structural changes take place. A condition of a neuron becoming operative is the formation of a new specifically oriented protein molecule, presumably a nucleoprotein, which acts as a template for the synthesis of protein replicas. As a result of the completion of the neural membrane, the neuron in question becomes a functioning member of the neuronal network to the extent only that it becomes capable of transmitting impulses. "A memory trace is distinguished by the chemical composition and geometrical orientation of the initial template molecule responsible for the initiation of the particular trace. Thus, each memory trace is differentiated by the composition and geometry of the repeating unit of the protein lattice and the relationship between the traces is determined by the various protein-repeating units to each other. The trace is initiated by the impingement of a stimulus upon a system of virgin molecules having a random structure and the imposition of a specific orientation upon it. A new template molecule arises in the neuron and protein replicas are synthetized. The trace is then transsynaptically propagated to other molecules. The rate of propagation of a trace, in turn, is believed to be related to the rate of protein synthesis and it may be anticipated that a relationship between the latter and the temporal requirements of learning exists. The process of organization originating from a given neuron will under certain conditions continue throughout the cortex and establish a long and complex net.

Thus, a given trace may spread over the entire cortex."

SYNAPTIC ADAPTATION THEORIES

At one time or another, both the structural and physiological properties of synapses were believed to be related to those of memory processes. For example, the *complexity of mental functions* was assumed to be enhanced by the richness of *synaptic arborizations*, perhaps by separate connections serving specific memories. The proponents (*93*) of this theory make the additional assumption that the *synapses* of the central nervous system can be *permanently modified* with regard to their readiness to transmit impulses; what's more, that *new synapses* cannot only be functionally activated but *literally created*. In any case, they suggest that, in response to the stimuli flowing through neural nets, terminal arborizations of neurons may be specifically adapted. Structural modification of synapses as a result of repetitive transmission of impulses was described by Carey (*43*) a. o., who advanced the theory that transmission of nerve impulses from one cell to another might be accompanied by decreased viscosity of the cell body membrane and of the terminal knobs; further, that, under repeated stimulation, as for example during the process of learning, the knobs stick to the surface of the postsynaptic neurons which, in turn, results in the formation of new synapses and new routes of transmission. Wiener (*355,356*) considered the possibility that information is stored over long periods of time by changes in permeability of each synapse to messages either by the opening of new paths or the closure of old ones. Moreover, he proposed that the chief changes of threshold in the memory processes are reciprocally increased in respect to processes other than those having produced synaptic adaptation. Whether or not identical cells participate in different working units is a lively debated issue. Both Wiener and Halstead assume cells to become conditioned while Goldscheider rejected the idea, prevalent at that time (1906), that associations become facilitated by ameboid movements of dendrites. He thought that the changes in question would interfere with the manifold combinations in which sets of ganglionic cells must operate, and that decreased resistance in one direction would only hamper cooperation whenever different groupings of cells became necessary. In a similar fashion, Lashley (*181*), perhaps under Goldscheider's influence, postulated that identical cells, because of the relative paucity of structural elements as compared to the practically unlimited number of individual performances, would have to discharge in various combinations. Lashley attempted to verify this assumption by his own anatomical observations which indicated that the number of neurones found in the visual area and the lateral geniculate body is relatively small. The various synapse adaptation theories will be critically evaluated later.

REVERBERATING CIRCUIT THEORIES

That electroneural impulses may travel in closed loops was first demonstrated by Forbes (*83*), and by Ranson a.ass. (*263*) in their work on certain reflex pathways of the spinal cord. Later, cyclic connections between ganglionic cells were demonstrated by Lorente de Nò (*196*) and Young (*364*) while Kubie (*175*) discussed some of the theoretical implications of the properties of excitational waves travelling in closed circuits. Young, having investigated the neuronal linkages in the brain of the octopus, amplified the circuit theory of memory and learning in considerable detail. Eventually, in one way or another, a representative group of neurophysiologists adopted the idea that *neuronal excitations including those underlying engrams may be perpetuated by self-reexciting neuron chains.* Some of these workers, for example McCulloch (*203*), believes that electroneural circuits are the basis of at least some categories of engrams while others, including Lashley (*182*), hold that they form the basis of practically all memory. Lashley's interference pattern theory includes elements of both Hooke's resonance and Ranson's circuit concept and, in some of its formulations at least, also Katz and Halstead's idea of semipermanent structural changes: "The various patterns of integrated activity in successive levels of the nervous system have the form of reverberating circuits. The principle of the establishment of interference patterns at successive levels in the nervous system is the modification of these patterns by superimposed patterns from earlier stages on the series of levels from the retina to the motor cells, and the reduplication of memory traces as a consequence of the properties of the interference patterns are, I believe, reasonable conclusions from the organization of behaviour and the structure of the nervous system" (1942). Adrian (2) criticized Lashley's theory on the ground that "memory can survive great changes in the overall activity of the brain during which the patterns in question would have been extinguished beyond recall". McCulloch (202) points out that reverberating memory could go unaltered neither through periods of complete explosions as during seizures, nor during sleep. Von Neuman (243) holds that closed and potentially reverberating neural pathways do not exist in the necessary large numbers. It is of interest that, at the present time, even the early proponents find fault with their own reverberating circuit theory. According to Lorente de Nò, the chief difficulty is to "maintain a steady state of any kind, for reverberating circuits, the closed chains of neurones, are arranged in such a way that we have either incremental or decremental activity". (196). And Young (364) writes that "it may be difficult to believe that such simple reverberating circuits continue in phase for anything like the necessary length of time. . . . It is still an open question whether any similar dynamic processes are involved, whether learning depends on more definite structrual changes and whether activity in the exceedingly plastic structures of nerve cells would be able to make memory traces appear in some form or other after a period of inactivity."

The Counterbalance (Inhibition) Theory

At about the same time, Lorente de Nò and Young began taking a more cautious attitude toward their own theories; structural changes were invoked to account for permanent memory. In 1950, I (283) proposed a supplementary hypothesis designed to eliminate the difficulty involved in the assumption that engram do not necessarily disappear after their reactivation. "If engrams were represented by reverberating circuits entering sidechains during the process of the utilization of engrams, their reinstatement would imply disappearance, and their reestablishment depend on new impressions. We are therefore inclined to believe that engrams are represented by circulating stimuli, which may be kept in abeyance by counter-currents in a fashion reminiscent of the de-gaussing process. (De-gaussing, in technical language, means to set up a magnetic field to counteract the magnetic effect, or to neutralize an electromagnetic current.) As necessity arises, engrams would be temporarily reinstated by breaking the silencing current without eliminating the primary circuit, in other words, without forgetting. However, a *reconsideration of the mechanical principles involved in the above process of engram fixation suggests that their reinstatement would seem to depend on the reinforcement of the primary current rather than the breaking of the secondary (de-gaussing) current as, once the latter would cease to flow, the former would be liberated.* In general, the phenomenon of forgetting would be comparable to the process of inhibition, while ekphory would be comparable to release by reinforcement. Reinforcement and, hence, ekphory might be thought of in terms of a positive balance. This positive balance, in turn, would be due to the intensification of the neurometabolic processes induced by those somatic events to which there correspond such psychic phenomena as association by identity, by similarity and other item generating mechanisms. Briefly stated, the *material basis of engrams would be represented by neurodynamic ecxitations kept in abeyance by counterbalancing influences while their ekphory would involve the temporary increase of the excitations.* The reinforcement of the metabolic processes supposed to underly the associative play of ekphory is a function of the posterior cortex, but ekphory, like engram fixtation, is set in motion and maintained by inflow of energy from the frontal lobes and their subcortical connections.

In other words, as long as a given mental process or synergy (or, for that matter, the neurodynamic basis of the engram), is counterbalanced by an opposing process (like the tension of a protagonist by its antagonist) the psychism in question is represented in the mnemonic system of notation. Conversely, if the balance of energy distribution is shifted in favour of the thus far neutralized, apparently inactivated process, which is accomplished by its reinforcement, e.g., by association by similarity, (a consonant stimulation so to speak) the mnemonic phychism is translated into the overt system of notation. Association by contiguity on the other hand would require a temporal linkage between neurodynamic processes having been established in the past, and synthetized to a stimulus of a higher order. Even assuming that engrams have a certain *fading rate* and *fading propensity* (although it is doubtful whether fading ever becomes absolute) it is not immediately apparent why the process underlying engraphy is not consistently reinforcable, in other words, why an experience which cannot be recalled at a given moment can be reproduced a moment later, or why memories may come back spontaneously, almost at any time after futile attempts to reactivate them. Apparently, the translation of a phychism from the mnemonic into the overt system of notation is an integrative act which materializes at a high level of sensory integration and whose confidence coefficient is accordingly of a low order. The above considerations make it extremely unlikely that the nature of engrams can be expressed in terms of any of the above discussed *structure-theories* and that *event-theories* of memory deserve preference.

Is there anything in the structure of machine memory that may have a bearing on the question of the fixation of engrams by inactivating currents? Recently, I came across an article by Berkeley and Jensen (*19*) on electrostatic storage and the use of dielectric screens in cathode ray tubes. (See also Eckert, *74*, and Haeff, *101*.) The authors explain how electric charges which have been recorded on the screen can be prevented from leaking away by a beam of electrons or "holding beam." Here, then, there appears to be an arrangement which, although static is a technical sense, has certain fundamental characteristics of dynamic storage, namely, fluency, lack of permanent structural change and a counterbalancing mechanism. We are inclined to consider temporary inactivation and spread of access (which permit the rapid incorporation of items into ongoing processes) as essential features of dynamic storage in both mechanical and biological systems. Disregarding for the time being that, fo lowing their reactivation, machine engrams disappear while biological engrams are preserved, indeed, if anything, reinforced, the fact that counterbalancing (engram inactivating) processes operate in electronic computers seems to give substance to the notion that a temporary inactivation of engrams may occur not only in mechanical but also in biological brains; in any case, the idea that neutralizing neurodynamic processes operate in the memory registers of

biological brains should not appear as far fetched, at least not as altogether fantastic.

Some applications of the process theory of memory

Unless otherwise stated, the theoretical considerations offered below are based on introspective experiences. Introspection, which, largely under the influence of the behaviouristic school of thought, has fallen into disrepute, has recently been salvaged from undeserved oblivion, As Sperry (*313a*) said in a symposon on the central nervous system and behaviour:" . . . one wonders if any physiological model of the conditioned response that fails to include the subjective properties is not bound to end up with some kind of gap in the chain of cerebral events. My point is merely that we may have gone a bit too far in the past several decades with our behaviouristic postulate that neurophysiological science can confidently assume that a full understanding of cerebral events is possible in theory from the purely objective approach and excludes and ignores the emergent properties of subjective awareness." Simon encouraged laboratory subjects to comment to themselves as they worked on problems and then compared the "taped-out loud" problem solving of human subjects with the traces made by machines solving the same problems. (New York Times, April 4, 1959, p. 17.) In other words, he regarded the experiences of his experimental subjects as reliable enough to be applied, as an evaluative baseline, to working patterns of computing machines.

PSYCHOLOGICAL DATA PERTAINING TO THE PROCESS THEORY OF MEMORY

Engrams may be ekphorized in a variety of contexts. While trying to think of the name of a French mathematician (Henry Poincaré) I recalled the names Richelieu and Curie as if the name Richelieu had been crossfiled in my memory registers under the heading "homophony", and the name Curie under the heading "French names." Yet the varieties of associative techniques are wider: had I been aware of the fact at the critical moment that the name searched for begins with the latter P, or that the scientist's first name was Henry, I had almost certainly recalled it through association by contiguity.

The following example illustrates the reflex-like reinstatement of experiences and, at the same time, the fact that the activation of psychisms may occur within a multitude of dimensions. While working on the present chapter, I remembered only the first part of a Latin sentence, namely, "nihil est in intellectu . . . " but could not think of the second part: "quid non fuerit antea in sensibus." Turning on the radio several hours later, I heard the tune "Gaudeamus igitur . . ." used by Brahms in one of his compositions. At this moment, the Latin core of the acoustic experience complex conveyed by the music brought back to my mind the entire sentence. Evidently, the episode was an act of subsumptive recall of an item guided by an ordering device, —the class concept "Latin."

The capacity to recall an item does not necessarily depend on previous experiences that are precisely identical. I had never tried to think of Poincaré's name, and I had never recalled the Latin sentence within the context of a melody. In fact, I had never heard Brahm's opus before. Hence, it may be concluded that *acts of subsumptive recall materialize within a multilinear system, that is, a "structure" providing for a multitude of dimensional contacts between the items involved. The items in question are thus potentially interconnected by a multitude of patterns rather than at random.* Does this structure already exist at the critical moment, or is it generated in response to actual demands? Because of its enormous complexity, and the rapidity with which it is being put to use, it appears more likely that it had already been built up by a process of *aspectual grouping* of items in the subsidiary sphere of mentation, perhaps even in the mnemonic system of stimulus representation (fig. 11); further, that a process of *aspectual grouping* had occurred along degrees and parameters of likeness, however remote, and of connection in time*. To the extent that the grouping activity in question increases the number of response patterns, it is a process of growth; in so far as grouping activity yields appropriacy of response, it is a biological process serving the equilibrium of the organism. As

expressed in conventional terms, concept formation is prepared, and may perhaps be accomplished, to a degree, by non-conscious integration (Carpenter's "unconscious cerebration", Ref. *153*), although, no doubt, the participating data derived from conscious activity are originally represented in the dominant sphere of mentation. It is an open question whether aspectual grouping (which, we might add, is instrumental in transfer mechanisms) goes on spontaneously or under the formative influence of stimulation extending from the dominant sphere of mentation into the subsidiary sphere either directly or by way of the mnemonic system. (Fig. 11).

Now, recall does not necessarily take place within the framework of those class concepts only which, like the former, are generated on the basis of similarity. Several years ago, I saw an interesting book in the library of one of my former patients who, having moved out of town some time after I was a guest in her house, could be reached by mail only. Having forgotten the author's name and also the title of the book, I sent her a note which contained the following passage: "It was a beautifully illustrated book, printed, I would guess, some twenty years ago. With the exception of the frontispiece, a photograph of the author, the illustrations were engravings. The book was standing on one of the shelves as you face the window. I looked at it for a little while only but I am almost certain that most illustrations showed plants and animals, that some diagrammatic drawings were of a more technical nature, and that they represent what I took to be common engineering principles in man made devices and organisms." The memory image (which, incidentally, was correct in part only) recalled the image of the shelf, the shelf—the library, the library—the living room, all more or less at the same time, that is, the original memory image brought back to my mind a certain *situational setting* by a process of association by contiguity.

The variety of access to a given engram is not the only peculiarity of remembering. For example, the access time to an engram may be inordinately prolonged and, then, surprisingly, the memory trace suddenly ekphorized after all attempts at its activation have been abandonned. The rapid reinstatement does not however insure equal speed of recall on subsequent occasions. Nevertheless, experiences have a general reduplication

---

* If this is true, the subsidiary sphere of mentation is not only part of a mnemic action mechanism, but also of a "concomitant action mechanism."

tendency in that re-percepts tend to evoke the original percepts or at least their representative residues preserved as engrams. For a fraction of a second, reduplication produces a state of mental diplopia.

REMEMBERING AS A PROCESS OF SYSTEMATIZED SEARCH

Rather than through reflex-like, immediate, association by similarity or contiguity, the engram may be reinstated by a searching process within the appropriate group of data as if in trying to reach a desired station of an automatic telephone exchange the appropriate number had been dialed. Expressed in terms of automatic switching equipment, the search takes place within a relay system, i.e., a group to which the item searched for belongs. On the other hand, if the information furnished by the pertinent experience was based on contiguity relationships, search takes place along temporally patterned parameters of grouping.

It is difficult to escape the conclusion that the ekphory of engrams resembles in certain significant aspects a successful search within *interrelated multilinear relay systems* or systems of channeled use patterns admitting of an almost unlimited correlation of psychisms. Although the intimate relationship between relay systems and neural nets is obscure, it stands to reason that the number of items that can be stored and, naturally, the possible number of their connections grows with the complexity and mass of the neural substrate concerned. No matter whether the reinstatement of the memory trace is more or less *reflex-like*, as in the process of immediate recognition or *context-determined*, as in productive thought, the engram containing relay pool appears to be run through until, under ideal conditions at least, the item searched for is located. Experiences with aphasic patients indicate that they may succeed in recalling the supra-ordinate group but are unable to differentiate in it with sufficient accuracy to reach the target. Similarly, paragnostic patients may not recognize an object but score at least a near miss, e.g., mistake a comb for a brush in the same way as I remembered Richelieu's instead of Poincaré's name. The acceptance or recognition of the selected item

appears to depend on the irreducible (though by no means infallible) experience of congruence or incongruence, of identity or difference. For example, I must have recognized as correct the name Poincaré because of its linkage with the concept mathematician, because the complex "Poincaré-Mathematics" was sufficiently consolidated to prevent its being confused with the names of either Richelieu or Curie and because names of other French mathematicians were not involved in the "ekphory contest."

In one of the above quoted episodes, the engram "Poincaré" was located by the activation of the concept "French names" and by differentiating within it, while the engram representing the Latin sentence emerged in the course of unintentional activation of the denotational dimension "Latin", either of which functioned in the fashion of a guiding chain. In either case, however, the relay system was actuated within a process unfolding, initially, in a variety of approximative steps and subjected to *secondary itemization*. The recall of my previous contact with the patient was made possible by the activation of the memory trace representing a certain book which, in turn, was reinstated in the course of thinking about the problem of similarity between organisms and machines. In all three instances, the pinpointing of the engram is reminiscent of the action of a relay computer searching in its registers either monophasically, or step by step, until the appropriate item is located.

Thus, the considerations leading to a "search theory" of remembering are based on the observation that the process of "finding the memory trace" appears to evolve within an organized group of items and according to certain principles, namely, association by similarity and contiguity rather than at random. Further, that the degree of approximation to the goal would seem to follow a preferential pattern reflecting the physiological organization of memory processes.

THE FRACTIONATION OF PSYCHIC PROCESSES. ITS RELATIONSHIP TO ERROR MECHANISMS.

The concept of secondary itenization is supported by additional psychological data. For example, the origin of goal directed acts as initially generalized (undifferentiated) responses is suggested by certain abnormalities of behaviour that are apt to occur under conditions of distraction. The itemization of the forerunning idea of a volitional act develops in steps separated by intervals. Slowed down itemizatiom, in turn, facilitates introspection, just like the study of quick movements is made easier by slow motion cinematography. To illustrate this particular point: I might have the vague feeling of having thought about a certain item a little while ago. This feeling is followed, step by step, by the following, increasingly specific ideas: That I want to take an article from the side pocket of my coat . . . that this article is a letter . . . that I received from a certain person . . . that I have to read it again and to answer it. Another example: I have the vague feeling to have to cross the street . . . to intend to go to the letter box . . . to intend to mail a letter . . . a letter to be sent to a certain person . . . and, ultimately, that it carries a certain message. (The inner experience described would thus seem to develop in steps of increasing specificity, which belong to the category of *Bewusstseinslagen* and *Bewusstheiten.*) In other instances, the process of itemization is, apart from its first step, derailed in its entirety. I intend to go to the letter box, but, distracted by some chance observation, find myself going to a nearby newstand. I intend to open the door to my apartment but find myself fumbling with the keys to my office. Interestingly enough, the "generalized" items are already categorized in a preferential fashion; it happens more often than not that I mistake the outside office keys for the outside apartment keys than I mistake an outside key for an inside key. Apparently, the categories "outside" and "inside" are supraordinate; the categories "apartment" and "office" subordinate. Other examples of erroneous itemization are typographical *miscorrections, misduplications,* and *confusions* of items. Having typed "3 weeks" instead of "three weeks", I miscorrected by typing "3 Weeks." Examples of misduplication are "insuuficiency" and "modd" (mood), in which case there was at fault the differentiation within a situational setting. It demanded that a specific letter be duplicated. Examples of confusion are the selection of "F" and "R" for "4" and "3" respectively. Very likely, the process of itemization is derailed by the intrusion of an auditory engram into the intended meaning of thought. (The psychology of

typing errors is in need of further investigation. Lashley, who kept a record of his typing errors, made an interesting contribution to the subject, *183.*) In a similar way erroneous itemization is to blame for such errors as to carry the wrong object into the right room, the right object into the wrong room or the wrong object into the wrong room. The relationship between these errors and states of outright confusion and ideational apraxia (see Chapter IV) are immediately apparent. The above given examples of misspelling illustrate the evolvement of mental processes from the general to the particular. Although the "matrix" of the process is normal, its development may be either slowed down or deflected. The first group of errors represents instances of *decelerated or fractionated differentiation;* the second group, of *erroneous differentiation* and of *misintegration.*

The fact that thinking and acting are subjected to differentiation within a general framework or scheme calls to mind the previously discussed processes of association by similarity and their correction by comparing feedbacks, which may well be the primordial process involved in secondary itemization. We have learned that reasoning by generalization and analogy encompasses elements some of which are represented in the dominant sphere of mentation; others, in the subsidiary sphere. In intuitive thought on the other hand (as far as can be determined from a study of both varieties of thinking and also of borderline cases of intuitive thought) the mental processes involved take shape within the subsidiary sphere or, to put it in another way, are represented in the mnemonic system of notation. The point we wish to make is that, owing to the preferential patterning of the processes in question, the subsidiary sphere of mentation appears to be channeled or, rather, as we have said, to have undergone a preferential organization and reorganization into certain groups. This organizational patterning is a precondition of the temporary arrest of mental processes. At the same time, it is a precondition of their deflection that may occur (at one or the other stage of their development) in a given situation. The abnormalities described bring to the fore the structure of mentation, just like the way a crystal breaks reveals its internal composition. No doubt the multi-linear relays are the functional basis of trial and error whereas, under ideal conditions at least, those channels are run through that are the most thoroughly tested.

THE STRUCTURE OF ASSOCIATIVE RELAYS

Is is possible to visualize, in some fashion, the relationship between concepts and multi-linear relays? Introspective experiences reveal the existance of associations by similarity and contiguity as reflex-like, irreducible, mental processes. The items connected by similarity form uni-linear relays, which, perhaps, correspond to *primitive class concepts*, that is, concepts of a complexity attainable by infants and animals, while items linked together by contiguity establish uni-linear relays which, one would assume, correspond to *primitive situational settings*. For brevity, we propose to call the former, which correlate similar objects, *object-lines* or *similarity-lines*, the latter *event-lines* or *contiguity-lines*. The multilinear relays are bound together by a common point of intersection of object-lines or event-lines or by both varieties of unilinear relays as indicated in figure 26. The composite systems may be regarded as use patterns which are the material basis of the integrative acts involved in mentation. It appears, then, that multilinear relays have in reality a more complex structure than class concepts proper and, accordingly, a wider range of operation. It is immediately apparent that chains of events, too, may be similar, that certain similarity-lines may be formed by the associative connection of events that have a similar relationstructure or of events that form comparable situational settings, in other words, that both principles of association may operate in a single train of thought. It is further to be noted that, ordinarily, the items lined up on the individual radii have gestaltcharacter, which throws new light on the point made previously that concepts embody gestalten. Lastly, to the extent that the experiences which form the lines of association are individualistic, they reflect the history of concept formation in a given person.

If the above considerations are valid, they illustrate the possibility of access from one item to another, more specifically, from any point of a line to the point of intersection and from the hub of the system to its periphery. At the same time, they illustrate the mechanism of *circumferential association*. In fact, more than one form of association of ideas may materialize concurrently. This happened for example in the episode that formed the point of departure for the present considerations: the ekphory of the name Richelieu (which if correctly pronounced is an acoustic image resembling the name Poincaré) indicated an intra-linear approach, that is, an approach along a similarity-line; the ekphory of the name Curie, which has no outward resemblance to the name Poincaré, illustrates the start from a nodal point, or a search within the general to find the particular. At the same time, the experiences reported under the heading "secondary itemization" indicate that the initiation of a mental process, as an antecedent of action, reflects a general principle involved in the selection of response. The specification of an item within a multi-linear relay (like, within the sphere of language functions, "Poincaré" within the concept "mathematician"), would seem to be merely a particular instance of this general principle. To reiterate: with the aid of multi-linear relays, ekphory takes place either by *generalization* of an item, in which case the particular target concept is ekphorized or it takes place by *particularization*, in which case one of its constituents is "pinpointed." In the latter eventuality, the class concept serves as a point of departure of the associative process which aims at the ekphory of a particular target within a general area. In the sphere of non-language functions, the processes described have their counterpart (a) in the phenomenon of secondary itemization of an initially poorly differentiated antecedent or forerunning idea of action, and (b) in the structure of certain error mechanisms. No doubt the above discussed psychological observations favour the process theory of memory versus the structure theories.

It will be convenient to base the following considerations on the study of a simple geometrical concept. In fig. 26, the point of intersection of the uni-linear relays represents the core of the concept "triangle" while the fringe character of any included item grows with its distance from the core of the concept. For example, the figure at the top of line I, which represents an inverted triangle, may produce the idea of a man standing on his head, while the elongated triangle on the extreme right of line II may give rise to the idea of an arrow. In either case, the fringe-oriented idea is formed by centrifugal associations by similarity. In a dream or, for that matter, in hypnagogic states, or under the influence of a hallucinogen, a person may see a triangle to turn around, to stand on one of its tips and, eventually, to assume the shape of a person standing on his head. The

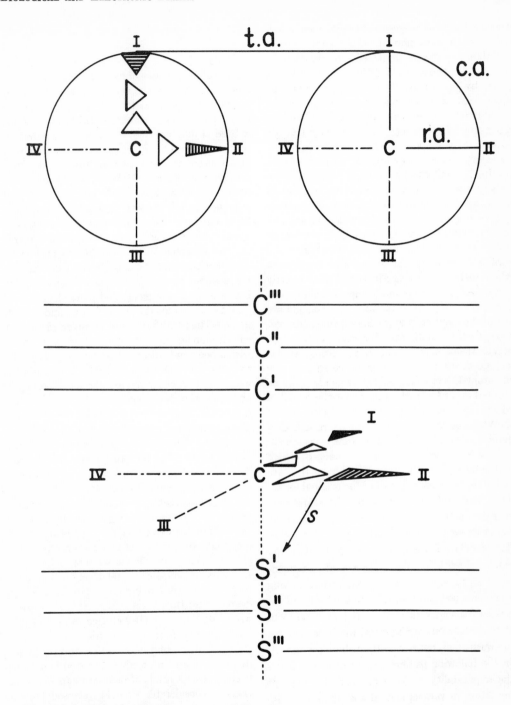

Fig. 26. Concepts and symbols.

I, II: configurations (objects) connected via association by similarity; III: events connected via association by contiguity; IV: similar events connected via association by similarity; I, II, III, IV: uni-linear relays; c.: core of concept; shaded triangles: fringes of concepts; r.a.: radial associations; c.a.: circumferential associations; t.a.: tangential associations; C', C", C'": levels of increasing abstraction; S', S", S'": symbolic representations of levels of increasing abstraction; s.: derivation of a symbol from a concrete element of a concept.

same sequence of images might have been experienced by a schizophrenic whose para-personal self thinks in images projected into the realistic world of his personal self. (See, e.g., the account given by one of Kronfeld's patients, and the description of experimental subjects after the administration of mescaline and LSD.) Similarly, a person might have seen, in his dream, a triangle to assume the shape of an arrow flying off a bow— an example of a circumferential association connecting a similarity-line with a contiguity-line. In any case, the above described associations of ideas, which conform to the pattern of spontaneous of drug induced oneroid experiences, are low-order intellective functions while high-order intellective processes depend on the utilization of the core of concepts as that part of their framework where their categorizing capacity is most heavily concentrated. The second group of mental processes that may evoke the idea of a triangle are the above mentioned event-lines formed through association by contiguity. For example, the sight of a textbook on trigonometry may bring to mind an examination in geometry whose subject was the properties of triangles. The same idea may be aroused in a person who walks past the school in which the examination took place, especially if the recollections connected with it are not altogether pleasant. Event-lines that develop in dreams are usually more or less changed, which makes them virtually unrecognizable, or they are elaborations or paraphrases of the original experience that initiated the dream. The following episode illustrates a line of association combining similarity-with contiguity-elements. The other day, a pillow I was carrying slipped out of my hand and fell to the floor. I immediately remembered (a) to have seen a nurse who, while making a patient's bed, put his pillow on the floor and (b) several years later, to have entered my hotel room at the very moment the maid, who was cleaning the washstand, put my toothbrush on the carpet. In the following paragraphs, we propose to test the applicability of the relay-model of concept formation to various normal and abnormal phenomena, some of which have already been dealt with in various contexts, while others, e.g., the relationship between thought and language, of hemispheric dominance etc. will be disussed in more detail in the following chapter.

CATEGORIES OF MENTAL CONFUSION

The model here proposed suggests a simple classification of states of mental confusion or misidentification of items. (a) The misidentification of individual items within one and the same line leads to *intra-linear* confusion, (b) between items located at different lines to *inter-linear* confusion, (c) the substitution of fringe elements for the core of a concept to *fringe-core* confusion and lastly, the misidentification of two or more multilinear relays to *inter-system* confusion. With special reference to the concept "triangle", intra-linear confusion may arise by overlooking the different spatial orientations of the triangles on line I, or their different shapes as indicated on line II. This particular variety of confusion patterns may be regarded as the prototype of the confusion between the above mentioned pairs of categories "inside" and "outside", and "office" and "apartment." The identification of an inverted triangle with a man standing on his head, with an arrow, with a book and with a school building, gives rise to fringe-core confusion. Mental confusion is the more likely to occur the greater the superimposability of the items concerned. Given a certain degree of congruence, confusion is a natural phenomenon and, moreover, a typical occurrence in learning. Under normal conditions, misidentifications that occur as a result of radial, *circumferential* and *tangential* associations, are corrected by comparing feedbacks (figs. 42, 43). The following are more "realistic" examples of confusion. A person who knows (or should know) that a certain chain store carries a particular type of stationery, may make the mistake of going to another chainstore that happens to lie on the same subway line. Inter-linear confusion is a relatively remote possibility because the two items overlap to a moderate degree only: the person is less likely to go to the wrong store if the store happens to lie on a busline. The two forms of confusion may occur in states of distraction of attention and in fatigue, in which comparing feedbacks are apt to be deflected, or as a result of defective ekphory, especially if considerable time has elapsed between engraphy and attempted ekphory. Core-fringe confusion on the other hand is frankly pathological: the person, under the influence of a drug, or in a fever-induced delirium, happens to see the stationary in his home and, therefore, thinks he is in the store were he used to buy it. Assuming, for the sake of the argument, the existence of entirely different relay systems, examples of inter-system confusion by tangential associations are the mis-identification of a musical score with a table, and of a melody with a brain operation mentioned in the course of the discussion of hypnagogic states. Fringe-core confusion and inter-system confusion occurs also in incomprehensible (non-interpretable dreams) and in schizophrenic thought, and they may well be related to the "meaning spells" occurring in schizophrenia. It is worthwhile repeating that it is only the schizophrenic's para-personal self that is "dreaming" while his co-existing personal self maintains contact with reality.

The proposed identity of relationstructures between concepts and multi-linear relays makes it necessary to comment on certain differences between *abstract* and *concrete* concepts. Any concept is abstract in so far as it has been derived by a process of abstraction; other concepts, although derived by the same process, are concrete to the extent that they refer to concrete entities. If this is accepted, concrete concepts, such as the concept "triangle", are interpretable as abstractive generalizations from object-lines while abstract concepts are interpretable as abstractive generalizations from event-lines. For example, the concept "inappropriacy" may be regarded as a situational generalization from the above described "pillow-episode" and "toothbrush episode". Another source of abstract concepts are affective states, e.g., the angry surprise aroused at the sight of the two objects being put on the floor.

The difference between the terms "abstract" and "concrete" on the one hand and "palpable" and "impalpable" on the other is significant. The term "palpable" refers not only to anything that can be touched or felt (palpare means, in Latin, "to touch softly") but, in a wider sense, to everything that can be perceived by the senses. The expression "impalpable" on the other hand refers to phychisms which, although experiental in nature, are devoid of any sensuous quality. (Cf. the experimental work of Külpe and his school on imageless thought, *167*). In other words, a reasoner who "manipulates" impalpable psychisms has no picturable experiences, regardless whether the impalpably represented psychisms are concrete or abstract concepts. He may think or talk about a triangle without necessarily having the corresponding mental image of a triangle just as he may use such terms as "appropriacy", "improvement", and the like without having any mental image whatsoever.

LEVELS OF ABSTRACTION

The above considerations lead to a further point. Like the concept "triangle," the concept "circle" or, for that matter, of any geometrical figure, may be represented by multi-linear relays. Further, the individual points of intersection or core-regions of each concept may be projected upon a plane which "lies" above the plane of reflex-like associations (fig. 26) which, in turn, is the functional primordium of the higher planes. It may be readily seen that the individual cores (which, for convenience, have been moved to a supradjacent plane and are thereby separated as it were from the remaining constituents of the individual concepts) may in turn be connected by association by similarity. These associations are of a higher order, in other words, the concept "geometrical figure" is formed at a higher level of abstraction. A still higher plane of abstraction would be necessary to represent various shapes, including non-geometrical figures. How many supra-ordinate planes or, for that matter, class concepts of increasing inclusiveness there are depends on the particular item involved. However, it is fair to assume that the highest level of abstraction is occupied by the incorporative symbols of algebra which, in turn, represent level of increasing inclusiveness up to the highest. Appropriate connections at higher levels of abstraction are generated by associations by similarity, contiguity or both form thinking sets. The most abstract thinking sets are the laws governing algebraic operations.

PRELIMINARY REMARKS ON THE RELATIONSHIP BETWEEN THOUGHT AND LANGUAGE

It is a matter of experience that the manipulation of concepts grows more difficult in proportion to their degree of abstraction; further, that the difficulty is lessened by the representation of concepts by *palpable psychisms* of a second order —*symbols* or *names*. The symbols S', S'', S''' etc. arranged on infradjacent planes, are the mirror images as it were of the corresponding concepts C', C'', C''' etc. arranged on supradjacent planes.

(Fig. 26) Just as the cores of concepts (c) *embody* their individual constituents, their *symbolic analogs* (S) refer to them in a general way. Thus, the expression "triangle" refers to any triangle, the expression "circle" to any circle and so on. On the other hand, expressions that have no referent are "empty." The symbolic analogs, be they verbalized or non-verbalized, are means of associative access to the constituents of the concepts to which they correspond. It was the class concept *Latin*, actuated by the title of a song (Brahm's "Academical Festival Overture") that brought an entire Latin sentence back to my mind.

There correspond, to the psychisms indicated in the accompanying diagram, neurodynamic processes of various complexity which may be brought into appropriate (synergic) relationships through *intra-plane association, inter-plane association* or a combination of both processes. The most primitive connections of items occur, as we have said, within the uni-linear relays, or the plane of reflex-like associations. The greater the "distance" of the plane of mentation from the plane of reflex-like associations, the more abstract the process of thought. However, horizontal and vertical associations, initiated by actuating events, may occur concomitantly and, in productive thought, operate as actuating events, which, in turn, organize psychisms represented in the overt and in the mnemonic system of notation. Vertical associations directed toward the lowest plane of concept formation (Fig. 26) (C→c) lead to *itemization* and *specification* while those evolving in the opposite direction (c→C) operate in *generalization* and *transfer mechanisms*. Because of the numberless variety of combinations in which associative processes interact, the most trivial observations may have the most far reaching effects. Descartes, seeing a fly crawling toward the corner of a room, conceived the system of analytic geometry. Shannon (*298*) made reference to the "remarkable memory classification and access features and the ability to rapidly locate stored data via numerous coordinate systems which characterize the human brain and, to a degree, distinguish it from machine memory." And Mephistopheles said to the bewildered student in Goethe's "Faust":

> Zwar ists mit der Gedanken-Fabrik
> Wie mit einem Weber-Meisterstück,
> Wo ein Tritt tausend Fäden regt,
> Die Schifflein herüber hinüber schiessen,

> Die Fäden ungesehen fliessen
> Ein Schlag tausend Verbindungen schlägt.

Or, in Taylor's (*91a*) translation:

> Truly, the fabric of mental fleece
> Resembles a weaver's masterpiece,
> Where a thousand threads one needle throws,
> Where fly the shuttles hither and thither,
> Unseen the threads are knit together,
> And an infinite combination grows.*

Names are psychisms representing relays systems in their entirety, including all possible avenues of approach to any of their constituents (although not to any consitituent at any time) so that, in this particular respect, names are comparable to algebraic symbols. For example, the name "triangle" refers to any triangle, just as in algebra, the letter n refers to any number. Furthermore, verbalized psychisms are brought into appropriate relationships by operative laws that conform, in a sense, to those which control algorithmic operations. In other words, language, apart from its function as a communicative skill, introduces an element of automaticity into the play of associations at the abstract level. Briefly stated, *language imparts, it to the conceptual plane of association, the technique of automatic or reflex-like association that operates at the configurational plane* (Fig. 26 C) *and, thereby, enhances the operational dimensions of thought. Conversely, the flexibility of mentation enhances the scope of symbol formation at the configurational level.* (See "reciprocal potentiation of level specific resources," Chaps. I; IV). Yet, although symbols have gestalt-character, and the configurational level (II.s.) is a precursor of the conceptual level (III.s.), the relationship between thought and language is a reversal of the original relationship between concepts and configurations—language, both from a phylogenetic and an ontogenetic viewpoint, is a later acquisition than thought. Subhuman brains lack the structural provisions for symbolic formulation and expression, although

---

* The following (verbatim) translation of the last four lines, which fails to maintain the spirit of the original, reads as follows:
> Where a step stirs a thousand threads
> The shuttles shoot from side to side
> The fibers flow unseen
> And one shock strikes a thousand combinations

(E. Atkinson's translation. See H. v. Helmholtz, "Popular Lectures on Scientific Subjects", Chapter II, Ref. *366*.)

it is claimed by some that they exist, in a nascent stage, in the brain of subhuman primates.

Since certain disturbances in the sensory sphere of language functions may be read off from the accompanying diagram, we may mention in passing that *amnestic aphasia* (an ideo-symbolic disorder) is the inability to link a specific item of the non-symbolic system (c) with the corresponding item of the symbolic system (s); *receptive aphasia*, the inability to connect a specific item of the symbolic system with its counterpart in the non-symbolic, conceptual, system of reference. Receptive aphasia, which is the inability to understand, although not necessarily to perceive, words as gestalten, (for the patient may be able to repeat the word he is unable to understand) is a disorder of recognition which may be tentatively defined as the inability to detect the place value of an item in a habitual gridwork of relations, and to verify it by comparing feedbacks (Figs. 42, 43). It would be intriguing to compare the difficulties in understanding, and especially the various forms of paraphasia, with the disorganization patterns of intra-linear and inter-linear confusion, and of inter-system and core-fringe confusion. The full blown syndrome of *sensory aphasia* is a composite form of language disturbance which includes agnosia for word gestalten. Thus, in Fig. 26, the lesion producing sensory aphasia would involve a plane of integration that corresponds to plane R (the plane of visual gestaltperception) while a lesion implicating pathway C-c-S would produce amnestic aphasia; and a block along the line S-c-C receptive aphasia. On the other hand, it must be borne in mind that the diagram represents a functional system in spatial terms, that the processes of impulse conduction along the lines indicated must not be mechanically projected upon the brain map, in other words, that the disorders in question reflect the inability on the part of the brain to combine, in disease, relatively simple integrative acts to those of a higher order.

REMARKS ON THE DERIVATION OF THE SYMBOLS OF SPEECH

What determines the choice of a particular symbol or expression? Although the roots of most words are unknown, it is fair to say that they were, originally, the audible products of articulatory movements that came to be linked up with specific experiences so that, eventually, the movement effects acquired denotational properties. Further, that the referent of a given expression is not necessarily the core of the concept concerned but, more often than not, one of its conspicuous attributes. In fact, the expression may refer to a one of its fringe elements. Interestingly enough, the choice of the expression-generating attribute is more or less group-specific in other words, in representing the entire concept, different attributes may be chosen. For example, the German expression for triangle is "Drei-*eck*", a three-sided gestalt (Fig. 26 s), but the term "Drei-*seit*" would have the same meaning. In the above quoted passage, Goethe speaks of a "thought-factory" and of "boats" that shuttle back and forth; and Taylor of a "fleece" of associations, while both writers speak of mental threads of *Fäden*, all of which are expressions derived from fringe regions. It is probably correct to say that most nouns and adjectives can be traced to the components of object-lines, while most verbs are derived from the elements of event-lines. The statement that, in the course of the development of thought and language, the core of the concepts is projected upon a higher plane needs, however, to be qualified. There is, according to Heidbreder (*121*), "between more perceptual and more conceptual performances a state of activity in which conceptualization regularly takes off from the directly perceptible by means of a process which resembles as closely as possible those involved in the perception of concrete objects and which maintain, as long as possible, some direct perceptual anchorage in the perceptible material." As regards the above proposed model of concept formation, the core of the concept would not lie precisely at the point of intersection of the unilinear relays but slightly "off center", reminiscent of the relationship between the magnetic and the geographical pole of the earth. In general, the perceptual anchorage of concepts is rather loose although less so in the *modality-related* concepts, such as triangle, harmony, etc., than in other concepts. Modality-related concepts are more likely to be represented by onomatopoetic expressions than neutral concepts. They develop in relationship to the corresponding sensory inflows into the posterior cortex, especially in relationship to the sensory areas of vision and hearing.

THINKING, HEMISPHERIC DOMINANCE AND
VARIATIONS OF ORGANIZATIONAL PATTERNS

In the great majority of individuals, concept formation and symbolization is concentrated in the left or major hemisphere, that is, the hemisphere opposite the preferred hand, while a certain measure of ambilaterality (which is more or less identical with left-handedness) develops only in a small proportion of the population. It appears likely that, within the limitations imposed upon by the booster elements of symbolization and verbalization, thought processes mediated by the subordinate hemisphere parallel those mediated by its more highly developed fellow. Thought processes mediated by the minor hemisphere are comparable to a wide-meshed gridwork while those put together in the major hemisphere form a close-meshed pattern. The components of the former are duplicated by some of the components of the close-meshed grid but certain elements elaborated by the major hemisphere are unique products of its activity that have no counterpart in the function of the minor hemisphere. On the other hand, clinical experiences indicate that the relationship between the two hemispheres may in some respect be reversed so that the minor hemisphere is dominant for some functions for which, accordingly, the major hemisphere is subordinate. This functional arrangement introduces a considerable measure of variability into the integration of higher brain functions. (See Chapter IV) The representation, by multilinear relays, of categorizing use patterns that are instrumental in thinking makes possible to express, in unifying language, various organizational patterns or *thematic variations* to which reference has been made in the opening chapter. Physiologically considered, the elements arranged along the various uni-linear systems are stimuli of a configurational order that have already attained a considerable measure of integrational complexity. Further thematic variations develop either in the direction of *gestalt-preponderance* or of *concept-preponderance*. The former is a supra-standard abnormality which, given a concomitant development of the apparatus of execution, induces artistic activity while concept preponderance favours practical and scientific pursuits. (It hardly needs to be added that both traits may exist in one and the same individual.) It is further to be noted that certain persons are inclined to think in *space-oriented* associations while others are apt to think in *time-oriented associations*, that is, either along object-lines or event-lines. Linguistic ability is a special type of supra-standard abnormality in the sphere of symbolic fornulation and expression based on time-oriented associations at higher levels of abstraction, and also of the ability to unify concepts and symbols in the course of expression.

In *conclusion*, we wish to re-emphasize that the relay-model of concept formation and of its role in mentation and language has been designed in spatial terms, but that concepts are *sensory stimuli* and, as such, integrative acts or processes mediated by a neural substrate. Thus, the phsiological correlate of the psychic element "concept" is a process rather than a structure* although, needless to say, events without material substrate do not occur. Now, concepts are experiental psychisms only if represented in an appropriate system of notation, that is, in the very same system in which we experience the psychisms that constitute the marginal and the axial stream of thought, especially the impressions emanating from the inner and the outer world of the organism. Now, engrams too, are, basically, stimuli or processes, although processes represented in a different system of notation than impressions and other elements of conscious experience. We suggested that they are central nervous system events that are temporarily inhibited or neutralized by opposing processes which, in physics, have their counterpart in "de-gaussing currents" and, in certain computing machines, in "holding-beam" devices. In other works, we spoke of engrams or imprints only as a matter of linguistic convenience. Given a state of biological disequilibrium, (or, to use a different metaphor, a positive scotoma at the conceptual or highest sensory level), appropriate psychisms are transmuted from one notation system into another i.e., the appropriate neurodynamic processes which are kept in a state of latency are reinforced just as, in response to the need of maintaining the equilibrium of the body, the tone of those muscles is increased which maintain it by their contraction. The reinforcing process actuated by similarity or contiguity-associations is not necessarily adequate (as is, in fact, the equilibrium maintaining process in the somatic sphere), in which case the

---

* Cf. the table of synergies in Chapter II, esp. point 9.

engram-representing biochemical process continues to operate in the mnemonic system of notation.* Whatever ekphory occurs is, under conditions of inadequacy, merely an approximate substitute as, for example, the name Richelieu is an approximate substitute for the name Poincaré. This substitute is generated by the synthesis of related processes, producing an inadequate "regeneration" of the engram searched for rather than the disinhibition of the original "memory trace." Depending on the competency of comparing and corrective feedbacks, the substitute process is recognized as incorrect, or it is accepted. (Figs. 42, 43) Every day experience demonstrates that engrams have a certain *fading propensity* and *fading rate*. On the other hand, "irreminiscence" is not necessarily due to the exhaustion of a neurodynamic process, that is, of an ongoing, self-reexciting circuit, the so called "erosion of the memory trace"; in dreams, in hypnosis and other, spontaneous, hypnoid states, the apparently obliterated memory trace may reappear with astonishing vividness.

Naive as the relay model of concept formation and related phenomena may appear to some—it may well be some day perfected or, perhaps, replaced by a more sophisticated scheme, preferably one devised by an electronic engineer working in association with a psychologist—it has proved to be of some value in the interpretation of higher brain functions. The discussion of mental processes will always require, as referent, a physical model of some sort. A hypothetical observer, who "literally sees" his own brain cells working would still not "understand" the mechanism of thought. Other than *correspondance*, which, in the fictitious experiment described earlier in this chapter, was converted into *identity*, there is no bridge between the physical and the mental sphere, between the object and the subject. Thus, we end up with what Kuhlenbeck (*1776*) called the "brain paradox" based on Schopenhauer's formulation: "Our phenomenal world of consciousness is a brain phenomenon, but the brain itself, as we know it, is a

phenomenon of consciousness; or, in other form: consciousness is a brain phenomenon but the brain itself is a brain phenomenon."

It is in order at this point to call attention to some other, recently developed theories of mnemonic functions and, implicitly, their relationship to concepts. McCulloch (*203*) differentiates between three types of memory, namely (a) temporary memory, which he believes is a reverberating process, (b) mechanisms subserving skilled movements and (c) memory which is "not immediately accessible and important in neurosis." Kubie (*175*) holds that engrams constituting McCulloch's third type of memory "faces a dynamic barrier which holds it down." In any event, the interpretation of mnemonic processes, that is, of processes existing in a state of potentially reversible inactivation (conterbalance theory) would seem to establish a unifying basis of conscious psychisms and non-conscious data—awareness depends on the algebraic sum of the inactivating and reinforcing processes involved in the physiological dynamics of mnemonic functions. If this notion is sound, it is not necessary to stipulate a separate memory organ as proposed, for example' by von Neumann (*243*) who suggested that the accessibility of engrams may be reduced or temporarily cancelled" as if a filing cabinet had been removed into the cellar"; nor can the "search for the engram" discussed by Lashley (*183a*) detect the memory trace—a mode of representation of a stimulus depending on the state of the recording function of the sensory level.

Hearnshaw (*118*), in an article devoted to the psychology of conceptual thinking, considers, among other topics, the following as a primary task for the psychologist. "To map, in greatest detail, the whole evolutionary process of conceptual thinking; to distinguish between levels of complexity; to tie these mechanisms to neurophysiological facts, to specify the role of morphological factors and to map the course of conceptual thinking." To a degree at least, the above discussion would seem to have realized the goal set forth by the psychologist.

---

* A the highest level of brain function, minute amounts of psychotropic drugs disorganize the train of thought. A the most elementary level of organization, the experimentally produced loss of a single electron as described by Jordan (*149*) produces extensive mutations of the cell. Identical mechanisms operate in the extreme ranges of life and, implicitly, in the intermediate stages of organization.

Activity patterns in biological and in electronic brains

A review of representative theories concerned with the neural basis of memory has shown that a variety of structures (particularly the synapses) have been credited with the ability to store engrams, or to subserve memory processes in some other fashion. Ultimately, the *structure theories* of memory postulated a state of co-extensiveness between micro-structures and the phenomenon of memory; the *event-theories*, a state of coextensiveness between mnestic functions and physiological processes, particularly electro-neural microcircuits. Already indicated, we assume that actual and dormant awareness contents are basically identical, and may be thought of in dynamic rather than structural terms. More especially, in terms of algebraic sums of opposing forces. The unifying theory here offered stipulates the interconvertibility of the phenomena under study into different systems of notation.

SIMILARITIES BETWEEN BIOLOGICAL BRAINS AND DIGITAL COMPUTERS.

ANDRIAN'S "SMALLEST UNIFORM UNITS."

The interaction between engrams and overt awareness contents could perhaps be more readily appreciated if both were fractionable into quantifiable and interacting units and the products of thought, which are derived from this interaction, were reducible to mathematically definable events. As the early workers in this field asserted, the electric properties of neural impulses flowing through the nervous system may be suggestive evidence of the quantifiability of psychic processes. It is common knowledge that elementary sensuous impressions, as for example qualitatively different colors, correspond to physical quantities. Adrian (2), in referring to an "universal agreement between impulse messages and sensations" explains how "neural communications are based on basically identical impulses which can be electrically recorded and that all the different qualities of sensation must be evoked by a simple type of material change."

The adherents of the electronic theory of thought see significant analogies between electronic equipment and neurons. Many electronic theorists, referring to the open or closed (either non-conducting or conducting) state of telegraph type relays, claim that neurons either respond to a stimulus transmitted to them or that they are refractory. They consider the electro-chemical processes flowing through neuronal nets as the ultimate units whose interaction determines the responses of the nervous system, like the impulses flowing through digital computers determine the results of the operations they carry out. It would be difficult to minimize these similarities. On the other hand, it may be argued that the chemical processes underlying action potentials are of enormous complexity and that they may be merely a general framework within which the postulated unitary events materialize rather than the ultimate units referred to by Adrian. The complexity of the processes underlying impulse transmission in the nervous system was described, among others, by Bremer (*31*), Katz (*154*), Eccles (*72*), Rushton (*278*), Nachmanshon (*241*), Hodgkin (*131*), Loewi (*195*), Bonhoeffer (*28*) and Taylor and Straube (*324*).

The problem in question has been recently discussed by Tustin (*314*). He holds that the "assertion of similarity between a high speed digital computer and a brain is usually based on the fact that both nerve fibers and the circuits of a calculating machine carry trains of impulses. However, the significance of these pulses is quite different. The calculating machine works by counting pulses while there is no action of this kind available in the usual response of the neurons." Tustin admits that the action of the neurons is well suited to provide for mechanisms of the indexing, sorting and recognition type, yet that the "detailed process characteristics of digital computers are not likely to be enlightening in respect of the working of the brain."

The similarities between digital computers and neuronal networks having response determinating capacity should not be taken literally. In the absence of definite knowledge of the mechanism operating in neural nets, it would be pointless to maintain that neurons work by counting pulses; still, it might be possible to establish common properties between neurons, electromagnetic relays and electronic tubes. For example, weight bearing structures, be they mechanical or biological in nature, may be adapted to changing conditions of stress and strain. Thus, a scaffold may be reinforced by removing certain parts while others are reinforced. Similarly, under conditions of changed weight bearing, the trabeculae of cancellous bone are thinned out by ostoclasts while appropriate places are reinforced by osteoblasts. Moreover, the trabeculae are laid down are entirely new and, jointly with the reinforced trabeculae, adapted to cope with the changed dynamic and static conditions. Both in the process of adaptation of the trabeculae of osseous tissue, and the adaptation of some other weight bearing structures, biological and mechanical units work in a comparable fashion although the behaviour of the "workers" or units in removing and installing material does not throw light upon the intimate mechanism of either osteoblastic or ostoclastic activity. (See also Welty, *349*.) By the same token, the performance of neurons may be comparable to those of relays and other electronic equipment and, in spite of the (apparent or real) difference between the workings of digital computers and neural nets, significant analogies may exist between, on the one hand, the way the nervous system works out appropriate responses, and, on the other hand, the way calculating machines produce data on the basis of informative stimuli fed into them. The general idea underlying the function of either variety of net may be the same although no claim is advanced that biological nets operate by counting pulses.

How do these viewpoints apply to neurodynamic processes of different complexity? As seen from the perspective of response determination on the part of the organism, thoughts and reflexes are basically identical; either variety of processes involves the attainment (or, for that matter, the computation) of target effects from baselines. Even reflex responses are not stereotyped (*73*) but may be influenced by a variety of conditions. For example, certain spinal reflexes depend on the position of the animal in space, (*261*) and cortical reflexes on previous stimulation. In the autonomic sphere, responses are governed by what is known as the "Original Value Rule." At higher integrative levels, the difference between response determination in the mathematical fields as opposed to the non-mathematical fields of thought is reducible to the elimination of non-quantifiable elements in the former. Hence, computations may be regarded as limit cases of response determination in the conceptual sphere; reflexes, instinctual functions, etc. as limiting cases of response determination in the non-conceptual sphere. The analysis of algorithmic operations disclosed that responses at the highest evel of abstraction re-acquire some of the characteristics of automaticity; at the same time, the study of perceptualization in mathematical thought revealed that abstract mental processes involving complicated algebraic operations fall back upon visual data, which still further narrows the gulf between the sphere of abstraction and perception, that is, low level processes ordinarily referred to as biological. At any rate, *the vast reaches, thus far uncharted, between stimulus and response, between baselines and target effects, would be filled in by processes corresponding, in the mathematical fields, to acts of computation.*

We know that algebraic expressions involve the introduction of algebraic symbols to which different values may be assigned so that, in contrast to the results of arithmetical expressions, those of algebraic expressions are generalizations of particular instances. In a way, algebraic expressions are comparable to a plot which does not change no matter who the actors are or, if you wish, identical with a pattern of action that remains the same no matter what the effectors are. Similarly, response patterns may remain identical irrespective of the receptors and effectors involved. For example, rats, which have been deprived of the normal use of their extremities by surgical means, will roll through a maze to reach their goal (*192*). In certain extrapyramidal disorders, pathological movement patterns or kinetic formulas will be transmitted to whatever muscles have escaped surgical denervation with the result that, sooner or later, the original disturbance is likely to reappear. Gray and Lissman (*97*) found that, in the toad, coordinated walking movements cease if the whole body and the limbs are de-afferentiated but that they can be elicited if the afferent supply to one spinal segment is intact. In other words, if a crucial minimum of informative data is fed into a response determinating device, goal leading responses are computed by the appropriate manipulation of data. Lastly, in the sphere of autonomic functions, fixated, non-corrected patterns of response give rise to disorders of homeostasis by vitiating regulatory mechanisms or for that matter, data processing (computing) mechanisms. The main conclusion to be drawn is that *biological computers generalize individual perceptions regardless of the sensing organs by which they are produced, and that they proceed from the generalization of perceptions to the generalization of transmission into the motor shpere.* For instance, an individual having translated, into written language, meanings conveyed to him by means of sounds, is able to express the same meaning by "writing" with his foot.

What are the implications of the ideas expressed in the preceeding paragraphs? The higher organism records reality in a subjective system of notation whose most complex symbols are concepts. Mathematical concepts are derivatives, or subcategories, of non-mathematical concepts. Thoughts are the computations carried out at the highest level of the nervous system; conversely, computations, regardless whether performed by biological or mechanical brains, are limiting cases of non-mathematical thought processes. At the reflex level, the target effects obtained from identical baselines are, for all practical purposes at least, identical; they are somewhat diversified and modifiable in the sphere of instinctual activity. At the intellective level, target effects, depending on the computations performed, may be vastly different even though the baselines may be identical. Nevertheless, reflexes, instinctive functions and thought processes are interdefinable. Physiologically, organisms are systems which maintain stability by controlled liablity in initiating, at least under ideal conditions, appropriate responses at the appropriate time, and it is these responses that produce selfequilibrating effects. This capacity of living beings is particularly striking in new and unaccostumed situations. At the lower levels of the neuraxis, the initiation of causes is stereotyped by comparison; at increasingly higher levels, there emerge more and more degrees of freedom. An increasing number of alternative responses and the detection of methods of computation is substituted for the relative stereotypy of responses at lower levels. Ultimately, at the highest level of brain function, causes operate as reasons.

It would thus appear that the lower and the higher functions of the brain can be interpreted on a uniform basis. To us, the proposed concept appears to be preferable to the creation of a schism between engrams and other psychisms, and to the virtual identification of memory functions with the morphological properties of synapses. It is true that the processes underlying response determination must have a material basis and, implicity, that mnemonic processes, a special group of integrative acts, must be mediated by use patterns of some kind. However, mental processes, especially the determination of responses on the part of the nervous system have a "process character" far beyond the range of synaptic morphology. This holds true although synaptic contacts may be structurally as well as functionally reinforced with use and reduced with disuse, and it is established that mental processes, both under natural and under experimental conditions, can be influenced by chemical factors. The inadequacy of the above discussed theories, (in particular the synapse adaptation theory and the chemical theory) lies in their failure to correlate mnestic and other mental processes with synaptic patterns. The co-extensiveness between the phenomena in question can be grasped on a functional, or coordinative, level only. By the same token, the interference pattern theory falls short of an explanation of the mechanism of interaction between engrams and overt psychisms, and also of the mechanism of response determination based upon them. It is precisely the nature of the processes intervening between stimulus and response that has plagued generations of psychologists and physiologists. Adrian, who wrote that, "for the most part, we have to be content with studying what goes in and trying to relate it to what comes out", called attention to the fact that the nature of the processes intervening between stimulus and response remains obscure. Lashley's elaboration of Goldscheider's interference pattern theory of memory, which correlates the qualities and spatial properties of visual stimuli with the consonance between percepts and engrams, fails to elucidate the coordinating, or computational, character of the processes in question.

In the course of the analysis of thought, we followed two seemingly different lines of investigation. On the one hand, we studied the psychological mechanism of thought; on the other, we attempted to establish the fact that thought is based on the interplay of what Adrian called the smallest uniform units, which, because of their very uniformity, and the fact that they represent the neuronal line connections, resemble the impulse mediations in electronic computing devices. How can the two ideas be unified? Both phenomena, namely, thought mechanisms in biological and mechanical computers, have the following in common: Like a calculating machine computes new data by the manipulation of data which are fed into it (that is, acts in the fashion of a data processing device) so the nervous system selects appropriate responses on the basis of informative stimuli or, for that matter, *determines with what particular responses a given set of stimuli should be answered*. Thus, Husserl's (*138*) definition of calculation as a "procedure . . . whereby figures and relations between them can be arrived at by known figures and their relations" would seem to apply to the workings of both mechanical and biological brains. Thought is nothing more than the representation of the interplay of the "small uniform units" at the highest integrative level of the nervous system. Whether the units in question count or operate in some other fashion is of secondary importance. The existence of significant similarities between the workings of mechanical and biological brain can hardly be denied. Mathematics, as a science, appears to be the rebirth of an organizational principle in the mind of man. (See Chapt. I.)

SIMILARITIES BETWEEN BIOLOGICAL BRAINS AND ANALOG COMPUTERS

From the foregoing, it would appear that the nervous system operates with uniform, discontinuous, units somewhat in the fashion of a digital computer. On the other hand, the psychological analysis of thought disclosed the existence of "generating terms", "generated terms", "produced relations", etc. which, ultimately, are representative of events occurring in the orbit of the organism. By the appropriate manipulation of data, sequences of events may not only be recorded as analogs but also reconstructed or, for that matter, predicted with a reasonable degree of probability. The contents of our consciousness do correspond to the data of the physical world not merely like a map corresponds to the geographical region it portrays but, at the same time, to the relations that exist between the cartographic symbols, just like geometrical figures embody, by their very existance, certain relations between points, lines and angles. Furthermore, we spoke of the ability of the mirror "nervous system" to form not only images but also more or less permanent records. Lastly, we said that the organ that produces the subjective world compares, to inner states, the data of reality it has absorbed.

What are the characteristic of analog machines? Operations performed by analog computers involve the representation (or simulation) of the variables of a problem by the physical quantities which are measured by them. The equations solved by them have a physical counterpart in

the mechanism of the instruments. The analog machines solves problems by analogy, "the similarity of proportions of relations without identity" (307), in that certain parameters in the machine, be they shaft rotations, currents of voltages, etc. vary continuously in proportion to the real parameters which they simulate. "The representations give a continuous correspondance to the problems being studied" (145). In the words of Samuel (281) the machine must be able to relate various parameters according to the same mathematical rules which determine the parameter in the real situation" although the parameters in the machine are not necessarily proportional to the simulated parameters but are related to them in some functional way." Craik (57) suggested that the organism carries a small scale model of external reality and of its own possible actions within his head. In this respect it would seem to act like the fully automatic pilot recently devised by Draper a.ass. (66), a combination of an analog computer and a feedback actuating robot in which the analog principle is carried to extremes. The technical dictionary defines an automatic pilot as a device which keeps an aircraft in a desired position and which basically consists of two gyroscopes. If the plane deviates from the course set on the automatic pilot the gyroscope axis and the aircraft axis is displaced. A signal is sent to an amplifier which in turn relays it to a servo. The servo mechanism in turn puts in the necessary corrections to return the plane to its desired course. (68). "Fully automatic flight is that type of flight in which all flight control functions, including stabilization, flight path, etc. are accomplished by automatic means. The term automatic is applied to all systems or functions which are, or are designed to be, self-regulating." (9) To underscore the analogy between electronic and biological analog computers still further, it is of interest to review other definitions pertaining to the field of automatic control. "*Sensors* are the part of the system which perceive deviations from a reference and convert these deviations into signals. *Actuators* are that portion of a system which, on the basis of signals from selectors or sensors, furnishes motor forces. A *selector* is a device by which an equipment may be adjusted to perform a desired effect" (9).

Another (although not fully automatic) analog device is the so called automatic gunsight, whose sense organ is a search radar. Within three seconds, the computer, which has a high degree of hit-probability, calculates the "lead angle of the gun's aim at an oncoming plane. It considers such factors as range, angular position, own speed, enemy's speed, air temperature, altitude, roll and pitch of own plane, trajectory characteristics and others. The gunner is then notified to squeeze the trigger." (New York Times, August 13, 1956.) Similarly, many factors have to be taken into account on the part of a person in deciding what to do in a given situation.

Tustin (330), in pursuing a line of thought suggested by Craik (57) deserves credit for having called attention to significant similarities between the nervous system and analog machines. He spoke of the essential elements of analog devices" which constitute, or embody, a kind of image or simulacrum of the relevant features of the external situation; of the building up of an identical analog, or simulacrum of the external world on the part of the organism, and its nature as a permanently growing structure constantly elaborated and stored as our ideas of the external world; lastly, of its independent activity corresponding with the subjective experience of thinking which occurs in terms of simplified representational elements, symbols, concepts and names that are not only the substance of immediate awareness but are related to the classification and recognition of mechanisms of memory and recall."

In all fairness, it should be said that the line of thought followed by Craig and Tustin was inaugurated by Heinrich Hertz (1857-1894), if not already suggested by J. Locke, and that Müller (239) and Mach (200) entertained similar ideas. "We produce internal images or symbols of external objects," Hertz (128) wrote in the Introduction to his Prinzipien der Mechanik "so that the logical consequences of the images are always the natural consequences of the objects represented as images. Yet, to enable us to form such images, there must be a certain correspondance between nature and our mind. Experience demonstrates that this stipulation is legitimate and that such concordance does in fact exist. Once we have succeeded in deducing from our accumulated experience images of the stipulated quality, we are able, by using these images as models, to develop shortly the consequences, both immediate and remote, that will occur in the external world as the result of our own actions. The images referred to are our own ideas of objects. They share with

the latter the essential quality which makes possible the fulfillment of the postulate of which we have spoken, and which make it unnecessary to know other common features of things and our ideas of things. In fact, we do not know nor, indeed, do we have the means of ascertaining whether our ideas of things and their qualities are otherwise identical, except for that one all relation" (of correspondence.)*

In conclusion, then, the analysis of function of the computer "nervous system" shows that it combines features of both digital and analog machines. The experience of thinking is nothing other than the mode in which there is recorded, at the highest level of brain function, the interaction of Adrian's "smallest, uniform units." (See above) At the same time, thought is the way in which the analog-function of the nervous system manifests itself at the very same level. As far as we can see, either statement is tenable; at the highest neuraxial level, patterned complexes of discontinuous nerve impulses are represented as psychisms that interact in the process of thinking. They are mentalized, i.e., translated from the notation system operating at lower level to that operating at the highest level and, at the same time, compounded from neural processes occurring at lower strata of the neuraxis. This is not to say that, at lower levels, relevant parameters of the external and the internal milieu of the organism are not represented in an analog fashion, in other words, that analog values are not established by the functions of Adrian's "smallest uniform units." Rather, the viewpoint here taken is that, at lower levels of the nervous system, the representative inner states or simulated parameters have no consciousness value. Simulacra may be assumed to interact with each other at every level of the nervous system. For example retinal processes, cochlear processes, etc., are analog values given in the simplest system of notation; the corresponding cortical processes on the other hand are analog values given in the most complex system. (One is reminded of Jackson's dictum that "each grade of the nervous system represents over again and coordinates in a more elaborate combination the parts represented and coordinated by the grade below.") The stimuli impinging upon the receptors of the carotid sinus are analogs of the rise in systemic blood pressure, those impinging on the

---

* Author's translation. See also Weyl (333a).

cerebellum are analogs of changing gravitational forces. At the cerebellar level, there are computed certain basic responses to the action of gravitational forces upon the organism; at the cerebral level, more elaborate responses that depend on a greater variety of data. At either level and, we may assume, also at the intervening grades of the neuraxis, the reactions in question are codetermined by the analog data which flow in from the sceleto-muscular system and which help regulate the tone of the striated muscles. Lastly, at the intellective level, certain analog values, such as perceptions, engrams, concepts and other psychisms of a still higher order form generating terms which, by interacting with other data of awareness (the symbols of the notation system "consciousness," and also with non-conscious material, form generated terms, and thereby establish analogy relationships between items. In other words, the derived relations generated in productive thought are the analogs of the known relations and they are instrumental in determining the reactions of the organism at the intellective level.

It is a far cry from the analog values, or "pictures" of the external world, formed by the sensing organs, to the creation of analogies, or metaphors, of which Aristotle (638) said in his *Poetics* that "they are the mark of the genius for they imply an eye for resemblance." Nevertheless, there exists a continual series of analog factors of increasing complexity. In addition to those already specified, the following analog processes may be recognized. At the lowest level of sensation, perceptions are the analogs of physical processes in the external and internal world. At the configurational level, perceptions are assembled to gestalten wherein identical gestalten, although they may be composed of different elements, are identical analogs. In the motor sphere, the identical, or "iso-effective" movement patterns, i.e., those executed by different groups of muscles have identical relation-structures and, hence, identical analog values. (See chapter IV).

To reiterate: in the human brain, there are realized, and combined in some peculiar way, certain principles involved in the construction of both digital machines and of analog machines. Admittedly, both principles can be recognized in dim outlines only and the nature of their combination is utterly obscure. It should be noted that the nervous system does not work in the fashion of an "analog to digital converter", that is, a machine that converts analog values into electrical pulses, as described by Burke (36) and Gray and Lissman (97). In the nervous system, the analog values established at the peripheray are maintained, although not preserved in their original form, up to the highest levels, where they form the elements of consciousness.

Thus, the previously offered definition of consciousness as the mode in which rality is recorded at the highest sensory or intellective level of the brain is another way of saying that the contents of consciousness are the analogs, represented at this level, of the states and events occurring in the physical world. The analog theory of stimulus representation and the correspondance theory of consciousness are basically identical formulation of the same principle of organization.

Differences between biological brains and electronic brains

Differences between biological memory and machine memory

On a previous occasion we have mentioned that, in mechanical brains, engrams disappear after each run of the machine if they are not further needed. In biological computers on the hand, the physiological processes underlying the engram are apt to be reinforced after the memory trace has been reinstated. Furthermore, if our concept of mnemonic mechanism is valid, the activation of biological engrams would depend on the reinforcement of the corresponding neurometabolic processes which, during the latency of the memory trace, are kept in abeyance as it were by inactivating currents.

In brain disease, the line connections subserving memory are overloaded and the data of memory unreliable. Indeed, attempts at reactivation of engrams are potentially unsuccessful even under standard conditions, and lack of absolute reliability of recall is a daily experience. Biological computers either do not need or cannot achieve the precision performance of machines; even vital functions of the organisms are "safeguarded" by relative rather than absolute levels of efficiency. Thus, given certain biological conditions as baselines, the searching mechanism will more likely than not reinstate an engram; and, although, in the sphere of thought, prediction cannot be made about individual events, it is a fact that, by and large, biopositive mechanisms are more likely to operate than bionegative mechanisms. As in other spheres of physiological functions, we reach statistical determinacy while an individual leeway remains, especially so in the realm of Jackson's "least highly organized" functions.

I do not agree with Shannon (298) who maintains that the operations of mechanical equipment are unreliable as compared with the performance of biological brains. "The brain", he wrote, "operates reliably for decades without really serious malfunctioning while the performance of an electronic computer in trouble is hopeless." I admit that electronic equipment works with absolute reliability under ideal conditions only. However, if the reliability of electronic computers would not far exceed the reliability of biological brains, the effort spent in their construction would have been utterly wasted.* It is difficult to see what useful purpose a calculating machine would serve that was guilty of even a fraction of the error and oversights that, at any moment, may be committed even by a genius. (Cf. Napoleon Bonaparte's and Leonardo da Vinci's errors). Interestingly enough, even the mathematical progidy Dase who, more than anyone else deserved the name of a human calculating machine, was on occasion "reliably unreliable." At least this might be inferred from a passage in the Gauss-Schumacher (89) correspondance where we read that the lightening calculator "at a test which he was to undergo reckoned wrongly every time."

In many respects, reproductive memory is a thought process, more accurately a process of reconstructive thought. There is no sharp dividing line between thinking and repetitive reasoning which, for its part, merges with unintentional fabrication, a borderline state of memory where its basically healthy core tapers off. For example, a number of statements contained in the previously quoted letter sent to one of my patients were "inventions", which accords well with Bartlett's (12) idea that, in remembering, quantitative alterations, importation, conventionalization, etc., of the remembered material plays a part. Having obtained the long desired

copy of Blossfeld's "Art Forms in Nature" (27), I found, to my astonishment, neither a frontspiece nor diagrams illustrating "common engineering principles in machines and organisms." The illustrations were all photographs of plants and flowers resembling works of art. In spite of the fact that the information communicated to the patient was considerably distorted, she had no difficulty in remembering the book, for the available data pointed to a concept equipped with a multitude of potent fringes. It is true that code-breaking machines exist but it is doubtful whether a man made mechanism would have recognized an object on the basis of a fragmentary description which, moreover, was by no means accurate.

The unwarranted assumption that every memory trace is permanent is one of the reasons that prevented the general acceptance of the dynamic theory of memory, at least if the expression permanency is taken to mean the preservation of a process in its original form. It has been disputed that even the human brain with its estimated 10^{10} neurons would possess the necessary storage capacity, especially since only a fraction of these neurons could be concerned with retention and recall. It is quite likely that a substantial proportion of engrams is, in actual fact, the product of reconstruction which, in turn, utilizes whatever fragments of genuine mnemonic material exist. Within the framework of a given experience supposed to be a true recollection, the "re-construct" may be far in excess of the "re-percept."

Under ideal conditions, it is true, machines store everything and, at least until such time as an item is needed, forget nothing. Furthermore, machine memory does not depend on the reinforcement of engrams while the amount of energy used by a biological computer to attain a comparable performance level would be prohibitive. Paradoxically, other memory traces, having a minimal fading rate, may be recalled even after many decades, without the least effort and without detectable associative clues.

Depending on the speed with engrams can be reactivated, machine memory is sometimes divided into a fast and a slow memory. This might have induced certain writers (203, 243) to assume that the same applies to biological computers but the elaboration of the reverberating circuit theory as proposed earlier in this chapter makes it unnecessary to invoke a multitude of biological memory mechanisms.

---

* Cf. G. Truxal in the above quoted "Science Report" (*Newsweek*, 1960).

The access time to engrams stored in electronic computers is minimal in comparison to the ekphory time in man. On the other hand, biological computers compensate for the relative slowness of ekphory by a multilinear technique of association. The fact that, by actuating a dialing mechanism, a called number can be reached through a great variety of lines must not be misapprehended for the variety of possible approaches to engrams in one or more categories which, in the brain of man, form a deversified though closely knit mental system. Nor should the above mentioned collateralily be confused with the capacity on the part of biological computers to shunt engrams into the stream of thought in almost any combination. In mechanical switching equipment on the other hand, both searching and shunt occur in one dimension only. Computers, dependent on whether they are digital or analog machines, can evaluate only one variety of information, namely, either information furnished in the machine language of numbers or information represented by physical states. Biological brains on the other hand draw information from a great variety of sources.

Performance limits of mechanical brains

The performance range of mechanical as compared to biological brains is a hotly disputed issue. Among the various problems which machines are "as yet" unable to solve, Berkeley (18) mentions the following: forming ideas out of sensations and recollections, expressing ideas in words, taking words in and getting ideas from them, listening to tone sequences, recognizing them as questions and answering them appropriately, using mathematical symbols other than numbers, to solve problems in algebra and calculus, etc.

The above problems are reminiscent of those previously mentioned. They would require

(1) the formation and utilization of engrams on the part of machines,
(2) the recognition of perceptual analogy relations,
(3) the generation of analogy relations as intermediate steps in thought and
(4) the solution of verbalized problems.

Although we do not share Berkeley's optimism, we consider as useful a discussion of the above questions in terms of machine intelligence. Firstly,

it may deepen our understanding of the psychology of thought. Secondly, we may learn whether certain performance patterns of mechanical computers are realized in those of biological response determinating equipment, and vice versa. For example, in studying the question of ekphory mechanisms operating in the memory registers of biological brains, we found some evidence that an item searched for is found by a process of differentiation within the framework of class concepts. A somewhat similar process of systematic searching appears to be realized in translating machines. Reduced to its simplest terms, the machine translates by searching the list of possible words. Each initial letter in the foreign language is represented by as many memory units as there are words starting with this letter. In a certain sense, the totality of memory units which starts with an identical letter forms a class concept. Each following letter is again represented as often as there are words having the first two letters, that is, by a "subcategory", and so on. In biological equipment, it is true, the class concepts have a multitude of accessibility parameters while the operational sequences of the machine are "uni-dimensional." It is only because the memory units can be set to respond in one way or another that the machine gains additional dimensions of freedom which, however, do not enable it to translate sentences of any complexity, let alone idiomatic expressions. (248, 268).

At this point, we turn to a consideration of the way machines would have to operate to duplicate the thought mechanisms of human brains (as far as they are known) rather than to call attention to similarities of performance.

PROBLEMS NECESSITATING THE UTILIZATION OF SELF-FORMED ENGRAMS

In order to form and to utilize engrams in the way biological computers do, machines would have to be able to carry out the following steps:

1) They would have to "perpetuate" either the percepts or their representative residues, or their conventionalized equivalents as expressed by various symbols. Presumably, the preservation of impressions would have to be achieved by the temporary inactivation of the physical processes by which percepts are represented within the machine.

2) Machines would have
   (a) to reactivate engrams either as the result

of the impingement of stimuli through *association by similarity*, or they would have to reinstate engrams in the presence of percepts having a *contiguity-valence*.

(b) They would have to identify engrams by the "fusion" of the two processes, namely, those underlying engram fixation and those forming the physical basis of percepts. (See above.)

(c) They would have to reactivate appropriate engrams in problem situations in which responses are dependent on a certain context.

3) Since the evaluation of data may depend on the ability to tap a multitude of sources, the machine would have to establish a common system of relays to insure that engrams are accessible from various directions. In other words, the machine would have to actuate appropriate engrams by differentiating within systems of multilinear relays. This may have to be done by a searching process which, although perhaps basically similar to that operating in dialing mechanisms, would require additional degrees of freedom.

PROBLEMS INVOLVED IN THE PRIMARY PERCEPTION OF ANALOGY-RELATIONS

To simplify matters, we regard thinking by analogy as a limiting case of thinking by generalization. In recognitive reasoning, the formation of *producing relations* and, implicitly, or *produced relations* is based either on the utilization of those concepts, or of those ekphorized engrams, which are instrumental in establishing the relations in question. In the inaugural phase of thought, the primary perception of analogy relations may materialize either by reflective or by intuitive generalization.

In the first eventuality (Fig. 27) machines would have to initiate a *process b'* in response to an *observation* (or actuating event) b_1 and produce a new item (that is, a process going on in the machine) by utilizing *engram a*.

In the second eventuality (Fig. 28) the machine would have to reinforce process b' spontaneously, and utilize it as above.

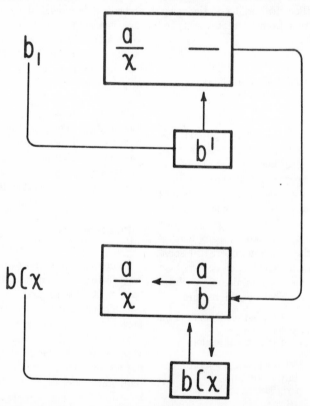

Fig. 27. Primary perception of analogy relations in reflective thinking. In the inaugural phase of thought, the relation a/b = a/x is established by the actuating event b_1. In the concluding phase of thought, the relation b⌊x is verified. Double arrows at bottom of diagram represent comparing feedbacks.

In the concluding phase of thought, the machine would have scan *series b* to ascertain whether the generalization of relation a/b is valid, that is, it would have to match the validity of the generalization by feedback mechanisms. Moreover, the machine would have to disprove hypotheses by deductive reasoning whenever the primary assumption, as ascertained by the machine, does not accord with the observed facts.

Problems Involved In The Intrinsic Formation Of Analogy-Relationships And Other Item-Generating Relations

If, within the guide concept "A," element A_1 evokes element A_2 by analogy (Figs. 27 and 28) rather than by contiguity (Fig. 22), the process of reasoning ceases to be recognitive, or a mere retracing of steps. It becomes the "slow and painful discovery of new paths" so vividly described by Helmholtz. (*123*) The reasoner, having discovered a relationship, uses it as a point of departure in producing a generating term, and he proceeds from A_1 to A_2 by reflective generalization and analogy or by intuitive generalization and analogy. A machine, which, in the process of recognition has reached station A_1, would have to

1) derive A_1 from A_2 by the relational aligment of terms similar to that described under the heading "Primary (reflective or intuitive) perception of analogy relations",

2) "scan" *series a* for the presence of an a_2 facet in order to confirm or disprove hypotheses A_2. In doing so, it would act in the same way as for example the astronomer Galle who, after Adams and Leverrier had stipulated the existence of a new satellite of the Sun from the perturbations of the orbit of the Uranus, scanned the sky for the existence of the planet to which, later, the name Neptune was given. (Fig. 29 illustrates an essentially similar situation.)

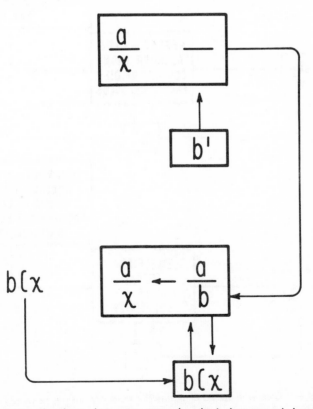

Fig. 28. Primary perception of analogy relations in intuitive thought. In the inaugural phase of thought, the actuating event is represented by the spontaneously ekphorized engram b_1, which generates the relation a/b and, indirectly, the relation a/x, that is, determines the value of x. In the concluding phase of thought, the relation b|x is verified. Double arrows at bottom of diagram represent comparing feedbacks.

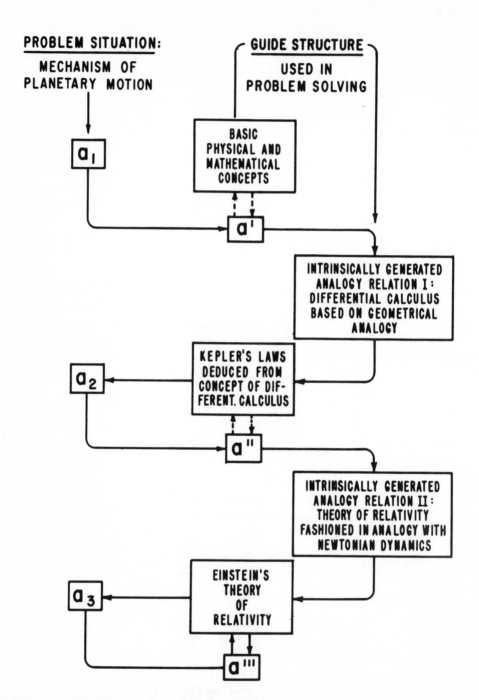

Fig. 29. Solution of a problem with the aid of intrinsically generated analogy relations of increasing complexity. The guide structure used in the process of problem solving (the "explanation" of the laws of planetary motion) are represented by theories (Kepler, Einstein) which were formed by the application of analogy relations. The total guide structure is the result of a process of "polymerization" whose elements are shown in the two preceding diagrams.

The function of a machine capable of analysing and recognizing relationships would depend on the stage of its maturation. In other words, the preference accorded to certain sequences would reflect its history, or the way it has learned to operate.

Are Machines Able To Learn?

Because of the intimate relationship between learning and thinking, the question whether machines are able to learn is more or less identical with the problem whether they are able to think. In the opening section of the current chapter, we stated that lower functions of learning are *repetitive* in character while higher forms of learning involve *transfer operations*. In so far as problem solving involves the utilization of pertinent segments of past experiences, learning is *applicatory* rather than repetitive. In other words, higher forms of learning involve reflective and, perhaps, even intuitive thinking.

A detailed discussion of the problem of learning is impractical chiefly because of the failure on the part of the various writers (*213, 214, 216, 217, 218, 220, 223, 224, 267, 310, 311, 312, 340, 341*) to agree on a definition of learning and thinking and, implicitly, on the difference between learning and thinking and also on the value of the various experiments designed to elucidate the nature of learning mechanisms in experimental animals and in man. For a detailed coverage of the subject the interested reader may be referred Hilgard's (*129*), McGeoch's (*207*) and especially to Kingsley's and Garry's (*162*) monograph who discuss the problem of learning in terms of the *continuity* and the *discontinuity theory* with special reference to Guthrie's *contiguity theory*, Thorndyke's and Hull's *reinforcement theory*, Tolman's *signgestalt theory* and Lewin's *topological theory*. In general, the continuity theory is favoured by the associationists, the discontinuity theory by the gestaltpsycholgists. The former maintain that "learning consists in the cumulative development of an association between the cue stimulus and the response, regardless of the presence of systematic response tendencies to other aspects of the stimulus situation." The discontinuity-theorists on the other hand insist that soluble problems are solved by insight which, in turn, is initiated by the awareness of the structure of the problem situation. They do not deny that the solution of a problem is "continuous with the past history of the individual (since the experience to be combined must have been present in that history) but that the particular temporal relationships between the experience that is necessary to solve the problem has not been present." (*102a*) We have been at pains to explain that the term "structure of a problem" is a metaphorical expression which prejudges the issuee in favour of the gestaltheory of learning and that the phenomena of insight may be accounted for in terms of the associational or contiguity theory and, implicitly, by transfer or transposition. At the same time, we made reference to Harlow's (*108, 113*) concept of "learning sets" and Birch's (*22*) experiences with stick using in chimpanzees which, no doubt, speak in favour of the continuity theory of learning.

In the introductory paragraphs to the present chapter, we defined learning as the acquisition of knowledge and skill by means of observation, instruction and participation. The acquisitive process, (largely identical with repetitive learning) may materialize at various levels of integrational complexity, in other words, it involves the adaptive modification of both instinctive and intellective functions. As a response to stimuli, learning has both sensory and motor aspects. Briefly stated, the sensory component of learning involves the formation of forerunning ideas of action, while the motor component involves the acquisition of eupractic coordination of muscles which are under volitional control. The relative importance of the sensory component grows with the knowledge necessary to guide action; that of the motor component increases with the complexity of the synergies necessary to translate thought into movement. For example, playing chess requires a maximum of knowledge and a minimum of skill whereas hitting a moving target requires by comparison a minimum of knowledge and a maximum of skill. In the *sensory sphere*, the adaptive modification of behaviour which develops in the course of learning is guided by the ekphory of corroborative engrams that operate under gratification producing conditions and by the ekphory of corrective engrams which operate when seeking reactions and avoidance reactions lead to frustration. Thus, an animal may learn to resist the impulse of attacking a stronger animal in order to avoid pain, and to overcome the fear to attack its prey to avoid hunger. The terms acquisitive and applicatory learning apply to the sensory component of the learning process. In the former, the crucial elements are transmittive activity (on the part of the teacher), repetitive thinking, and corrective feedbacks; in the latter, spontaneous activity, productive thinking, and orienting feedbacks, including transfer mechanisms. Acquisitive learning is based on the recognition of configurational data (including symbols, as in reading) and of the recognition of situational settings. It is apparent that transmittive activity in acquisitive learning facilitates the familiarization with hitherto unknown data and that it keeps trial and error behaviour at a minimum. Applicatory learning on the other hand, is based on the productive appreciation and the classification of situational settings, including the discovery of suitable principles of classification. However, acquisitive and applicatory learning merge with one another as do, in fact, learning sets and thinking sets. In the *motor sphere*, adaptive modification of behaviour is achieved by the eupractic refinement of motor coordination which, in turn, involves, in accordance with the principle of ecomony of effort, elimination of random movements, serialization and simplification of motor sequences, selective grouping of impulse formation, regulation of speed, and appropriate distribution of the tone of those striated muscles which produce the anticipated movement effects by patterned contraction and relaxation.

Although far from being a formal theory of learning, the above considerations would seem to apply to most, if not to all, learning situations. Take, for instance, the procedures involved in *surgical training*. The first steps include the acquisition of various skills by observation, instruction, and participation, which cover the motor aspects of learning. In the further course of his training, the surgeon becomes acquainted with typical and atypical situational settings. As experience broadens, he realizes that the exceptions fall into certain groups or, for that matter, represent certain settings, each of which requires the adaptive modification of basic procedures or the use of "subroutines." The more experienced the surgeon, the more subroutines he has learned to master. With the detection and classification of situational settings, he has reached the stage of applicatory learning, that is, he has developed surgical judgement. His reasoning has, to a large extent, become applicatory and anticipative

(which is now combined with repetitive and apperceptive thought) as preoperative clues suggest the possibility of certain conditions that may be encountered at operation and, with it, the appropriate surgical procedure, be it one already tested in the past or one yet to be tried. Needless to say, anticipative reasoning depends to a very large extent on repetitive thought. In other words, the calibre of a surgeon depends, among other factors, on the formation and the availability of corrective engrams. He is a poor surgeon who, in spite of great manual skill, keeps on making the same mistakes; who, on entering an operating room and seeing the nurse who will assist him, does not immediately remember what instruments she forgot to sterilize when he most needed them, or anything else that may have gone wrong under conditions similar to those anticipated. Of no less importance is the ability to improvise, i.e., to discover various unorthodox ways in which an instrument may be put to use. This capacity is based on transfer mechanisms and, in my experience, cannot be acquired but depends on innate intelligence. Apperceptive and anticipative thought that takes shape in the course of an operation covers a multitude of "event-lines" which must be evaluated simultaneously. In other words, the surgeon must learn to appreciate and, if possible to control, several interrelated situations by a combination of repetitive, apperceptive and productive thinking.

Although no one expects that the surgeon's task will ever be taken over by a machine, his activities illustrate the scope of human learning and provide a suitable background for the criteria of learning in man-made devices. The following discussion is based on Wilkes' (358) studies and other publications which will be cited below. Wilkes, who dealt with the general aspects of the problem under consideration, asserts that learning on the part of electronic equipment would depend on the ability of the designer to make the machine coordinate past "experiences with a present problem and that the machine would not coordinate any processes whose synthesis had not been specified and put into its program." To equip a machine with a self-modifying and self-extending program does not appear feasable at present. However, it "such program could be made it would be possible to teach the machine in much the same way as a child is taught." According to Shannon, (284) an organism or machine adapts to its environment while learning in that, with the passage of time, its local measure of success to a "specific class of environment" tends to improve. This would apply for example to a chess playing machine whose frequency of wins increases during its operative life.

DEVICES IMITATING REPETITIVE LEARNING

Shannon's "Mechanical Mouse" is a representative of the class of *machines imitating repetitive learning* of the organism. It is a maze solving device described in detail by its designer (298), and, in more or less popular articles, by various science writers. I had occasion to watch the performance of the mouse (and of other most baffling types of electronic equipment) in Shannon's own laboratory. Limiting the description to its actually visible performance, the mouse may be said to operate as follows. If placed into the center of one of the 25 squares out of which the maze is composed, it moves forward. If it strikes one of the partitions it happens to face, it turns around as often as necessary (each time at an angle of 90 degrees) to find an opening through which it enters one of the adjoining compartments. By a process of repetition, the mouse eventually finds its way out of the maze. To put it in other words, the mouse makes certain experiences, some of which were "frustrating" while others were "gratifying." Placed into the same maze again, although not necessarily into the square where it started its run, the mouse repeats the sequence of gratifying movements only. If the maze is changed, it resumes its old path, but, on striking partitions where previously were none, changes its course of action, that is, it eliminates movements which have now become frustrating. For a detailed description of the mechanism which consists essentially of an electromagnet beneath the maze, and a circuit system containing about 110 relays, the interested reader may be referred to the above quoted article.

Since the mouse, when put again into the original maze, finds its way out without blundering, its performance may well be superior to that of a live, blindfolded, mouse. On the other hand, the mechanical mouse would literally "get stuck" if the configuration of the maze be changed in an appropriate fashion, for example, if the squares were replaced by polygons. In the opinion of its

inventor, the behaviour of the mouse is not merely duplicative for it is able to (a) solve problems by trial and error, (b) to repeat the solution without error, (c) to add and to correlate new information and (d) to forget a solution when it is no longer applicable. Yet if one insisted on a comparison of the behaviour of the contrivance with the performance of a live mouse under similar circumstances, one would miss signs of applicatory behaviour; the mechanical mouse would continue to explore the maze as if it had never escaped through a hole. Its behaviour would remain as redundant as before.

On the other hand, certain similarities between the behaviour of the mechanical mouse and that of a "biological computer" are unmistakable. In fact, the behaviour of the contrivance is a classic example of originally generalized reactions modified by feedbacks or corrective engrams.

DEVICES IMITATING APPLICATORY LEARNING

Devices imitating applicatory learning are those described by Shannon under the heading (1) machines using rigorously playing formulas, (2) machines applying general principles of approximate validity, (3) learning machines (properly so called), (4) matching machines, (5) homeostatic machines and (6) conditioned reflex imitating machines. The first named variety are game playing devices, some of which compute a suitable winning move in any position that can be won. Others, for example those designed by Shannon (296) and Shannon and Moore (299) and by Strachey (320) apply general principles which insure a win in the majority of instances to the position at hand. Chess playing machines belong to the category of learning machines proper. Hagelbarger's (102) machine, which matches pennies against an opponent, is so designed as to "analyze certain patterns in the opponent's sequence of choices and to attempt to capitalize on these patterns. In other words, the machine has the ability to record certain tendencies favoured by its opponent and to initiate appropriate sequences of moves which counteract these trends recorded. However, a human opponent may lead on the machine to suspect patterns and then to reverse them abruptly." Presumably, the opponent may repeat this an indefinite number of times; the machine, for its part, (unless programmed to counteract this particular ruse), would not learn by its mistakes but play the game as naively as before. In spite of their ingenious construction based on Shannon's superb knowledge of the psychology of chess, chess playing machines display the same rigidity as the mechanical mouse whereas, as mentioned by Shannon in his article, a human player would examine only a few selected variations. One would suppose that, at some higher response determinating level, these variations are integrated into common principles, or thinking sets, and applied to individual instances. It is further to be noted that, because of the inability to create response modifiers, the chess playing machine would not literally learn by its mistakes even though its program may be improved. In short, the machine has neither self-analyzing nor self-correcting capacity.

Ashby's (7, 8) "Homeostat" is meant to be a mathematical model simulating the brain, in turn conceived as a "dynamic system of variables whose values are constantly changing so that the system moves from one state to another." Homeostasis is maintained by a feedback system that enables the machine to adapt to its environment by stabilization. The interested reader who, for one reason or another, is unable to study Ashby's remarkable monograph "Design for a Brain" may be referred to MacKays' (209) thorough review and to Shannon's article on learning machines. In Ashby's own words, which we here quote, his book is an attempt to solve the problem of the origin of the nervous system's unique ability to produce adaptive behaviour, including learning. Although the nervous system behaves adaptively, it is essentially mechanistic. The assertions that the nervous system behaves adaptively and mechanistically are not irreconcilable. What are the properties the nervous system must have to behave in this way?"

Let us disregard Ashby's somewhat vague statement that the nervous system operates in an "essentially" mechanistic fashion. Other weak points of his thesis are the alleged identity of adaptibility and stability and his misconception of the nature of consciousness. "The fact of consciousness is not used in this book because science deals, and can deal, only with what one man can demonstrate to another." Yet, at the same time, the author is aware of the fact that knowledge of personal awareness is prior to all other forms of knowledge—and, for this very reason, we might add, impossible to demonstrate. That man can demonstrate data *within* the medium of consciousness only rather than the medium of experience *itself* (as if it were an object or an event) is a corollary to the interpretation of consciousness as the irreducible mode in which events are experienced. Ashby, although quoting relevant passages from Cannon's work, does not seem to be aware of the relationship between homeostasis on the one hand, and, on the other, activities of the organism grafted upon it. Earlier in this volume, we compared homeostasis with the state of a bow which is kept under optimal tension and which, after an arrow has been dispatched, returns to its resting equilibrium. Homeostasis corresponds to the optimal tension of an otherwise inactive bow, it is a principle involved in the vital functions of the organism, and the minimum of these vital functions is the precondition of higher biological activities just as, in action, the state of increased tension of the bow is added to its state of apparent rest. The simile of the bow being in a state of resting equilibrium, that is, one permitting superimposition of *action strain* upon *resting strain*, admits of further elaboration: The goals of the organism are comparable to individual targets which cause the initiation of temporarily increased tension, in other words, of temporary disequilibrium. In fact, if it is granted that the awareness of a target, the pursuit of an aim that is, corresponds to a state of disequilibrium, the organism may be thought of as a phasically self-disequilibrating system which, however, tends to re-establish a certain balance of forces after its state of rest has been altered; the equilibrium is merely a fundamental condition, i.e., the basis of other activities rather than an end in itself. Even the periodical fluctuations in the responsiveness of the organism may be conveniently expressed in terms of spontaneous changes of "resting-strain" values. The needs of the organism on the other hand would correspond to the manifold forms in which spontaneous disequilibration is experienced. The term "gratification" would refer to the re-establishment of equilibrium, that is, the attainment of self-instituted goals which as has already been mentioned in the opening chapter, constitute the "aspirational world of the organism"; and the term "frustration" to the failure to find desired states of rest. Ashby's cardinal error, however, appears to be (a) the restriction of the term "adaptibility" to the maintenance of the "resting-strain", more accurately, the return of the system to a state of stability whenever its resting strain is disturbed and, (b) the concomitant extension of the term in question to cover practically every form of vital activity. "Every stable system", he writes, "has the property that, if displaced from a resting state and released, the subsequent movement is so matched to the initial displacement that the nervous system is brought back to the resting state." And he goes on to say that "this pairing of the line of return to the initial displacement has sometimes been regarded as "intelligent" and peculiar to living things. But a simple refutation is given by the ordinary pendulum; if we displace it to the right, it develops a force which tends to move it to the left; if we displace it to the left, it develops a force which tends to place it to the right. The pendulum shows a goal seeking behaviour. Another device, which works on the negative feedback principle, is the radar controlled searchlight." Now, it is very simple to prove that the pendulum shows goal seeking behaviour and that the function of a radar controlled apparatus can be fully explained by feedback arrangements; all that is needed is the combination of an animistic approach to physics with a mechanistic approach to biology. In actual fact, the equilibrium of the pendulum at rest is an imposed one, while that of the organism is a state of lability—"actively controlled"; and the radar controlled contrapiton nothing more than an instrument installed after its purpose has been established by an extraneous agency. Self instituted goals do not operate in either case. The pendulm does not develop a force on its own accord as its force is an induced one. Lastly, Ashby argues, adaptive behavious is equivalent to the behaviour of a stable system. Adaptibility and learning are coterminous; hence, the homeostat (which, in the opinion of its inventor, is not only a stable but an ultra-stable system, that is, one which keeps its essential variables constant) is able to learn ipso facto. The living organism uses the principle of ultrastability as an automatic means of ensuring the adaptiveness of its learned behaviour. The behaviour of the animal in training may be identified with that of an unstable system adapting to another system of fixed characteristics. The homeostat, after the experience of instability, changes its pattern of behaviour at a certain point, and the new field produced by the "step function change" is better adapted than the previous field for an unstable

field has been replaced by a stable field. In terms of the above proposed analogy the bow would return to its state of optimal tension in whatever way it might have been altered. On the other hand, in the presence of a suitable target, it would fail to acquire the technic of increasing its tension, of learning to differentiate between targets which are worthwhile and those which are not and, lastly, to dispatch its arrows. The following passage taken from MacKay's review of Ashby's book deserves to be quoted in full. "Finally, the multistable system appears to be weakest in achieving the author's principle aim—an explanation of learning and memory. It is less than obvious how an ideal multistable system constructed after the fashion of the author's homeostat or even the projected "dispersive and multistable system" machine could adapt more readily to a new situation for having previously adapted to a similar one or, upon repeated trials, reach stability with increasing directness and speed. The learning process, as described for such machines, seems to refer to the changed interaction of variables after failures to reach stability rather than changes wrought in a reaction by a previous trial." Gray Walter (*336, 337a*) epitomized the problem under study by comparing the homeostat to an animal which adapts to its invironment"; it stirs and finds a comfortable position when disturbed in its sleep but does not otherwise behave like a living being."

Wykoff (*363*) described an electronic model constructed to test whether a mathematical postulate system would yield plausible predictions of "observed response learning." The device consists of a robot which operates according to the postulates of the mathematical model. The electronic model, a specialized analog computer, was confronted with a discriminating problem in which it was required to select, by means of "observing responses", those aspects of the stimulus situation which were relevant. In the opinion of its inventor, the machine demonstrates that the theory will yield "observing response learning" and that the model can account for some kind of learning sets, concept formation and stimulus generalization. The evaluation of the performance of the Wykoff machine in terms of learning, concept formation, etc., will depend on the illustration of its performance capacity by concrete examples.

Deutsch (*64, 65*) built a machine which he

claims "rests on a new principle and is capable of insight and learning." It learns any two short and modified rat mazes and, as far as can be gathered from the designer's description, resembles Shannon's Mechanical Mouse in that it no longer enters blind alleys after having completed a learning run. The machine, which consists of a trolley, a memory unit and photocells attached to the walls of the maze and acting as receptors, appears to be superior to the Mechanical Mouse for no further trial and error will occur if the two mazes it has learned to share a common point. Rather, "it will then integrate its past experiences in accordance with its aim, like a rat which suddenly integrates its past experiences in accordance with its aim in the latent learning situation if a goal is introduced." Furthermore, the machine can "transfer or generalize its knowledge to mazes of completely different shape and similar only in a highly abstract degree." This is accomplished by marking each alley in the maze by a different signal which is supplied to the machine and, if the sequential order of the signals down the alley with respect to each other is kept the same even though the shape of the maze is quite altered, the machine can still find its way. The installment into the mechanism of "supraordinate" and "subordinate" relays, which form a hierarchy, appears to be of particular interest. The subordinate relays do not operate in a stereotyped fashion for their circuits can be broken. For example, the energizing of a preceding (supraordinate) relay causes the closure of its (subordinate) predecessor, and the switching of a predecessor leads to the opening of a relay whose closure it previously caused. Thus, the behaviour of the machine is conditional inasmuch as it is determined by the states of the supraordinate relays and, in this respect, resembles the behaviour of organism where higher response determining agencies of the the nervous system may or may not cancel the response patterns of the lower. On the other hand, I am unable to accept the designer's statements that the machine has insight in the true sense of the term, or the capacity to learn in the fashion of a higher organism. On the surface, the machine would seem not only to learn but to have the ability to reason for "it would form a spontaneous combination of parts of separate experiences," according to Maier (215, 221) a fundamental process in the formation of new patterns of behaviour. However, a comparison of the relatively simple "two-maze-combination-behaviour" of the Deutsch machine with Maier's rather complicated experimental arrangement designed to test the learning and the reasoning ability of rats makes it extremely doubtful whether the behaviour of the machine is insightful in the generally accepted sense of the term. If the two mazes through which the trolley has run share a common point, a situation is created which *automatically* determines the run of the contraption to the goal, while Maier's rats solved the problem of finding the food box in a variety of ways. In other words, rats, in response to a demand, *synthetized* (or computed) one of several circuit combinations. With regard to the alleged ability on the part of the machine to generalize, it should be pointed out that it does not find its way through different mazes of a different shape by discovering their common properties. Rather, it finds its way by automatically following a sequential pattern of light signals which actuate a system of repetitive circuits formed in the course of the original run. Significantly, Deutsch notes that the sequential order of the signals down the alley with respect to each other is kept the same. In other words, the machine is not guided by a self-created concept, or response scheme applicable to a situation that has in common significant parameters with the learning situation. It does not detect and classify situational settings. It is actuated by a rigid sequence of signals to which it was exposed and which, in turn, produce an equally rigid sequence of maneuvers.

Conditioned reflex machines were designed by Oettinger (246) and Walter (336, 337a). A description of the former may be found in Shannon's article. According to Wilkes (341) the action of the Oettinger machine may be influenced by signals given to it. Moreover, "it can produce a graded modification of the information held inside the device" so that the machine would become conditional. Walter's "Machina docilis" achieves connection between different stimuli requiring seven distinct operations. The details of its wiring pattern may be found in Walter's original article (337a) and in his book (337).

To *summarize*: The behaviour of machines may become increasingly adaptive in that they evaluate corroborative and corrective engrams and initiate corroborative and corrective feedbacks but *they are unable to produce orienting feedbacks, especially those operating at various levels of abstraction.*

PROBLEMS INVOLVED IN VERBALIZATION

At a certain level of abstraction, reasoning is facilitated by the representation of concepts by incorporative symbols, be they mathematical or non-mathematical. It is a common experience that a large and readily available vocabulatory enhances the dimensions of thought while amnestic and other forms of sensory aphasia deprive the reasoner of verbal tools. Just as in algebra the letter n represents any munber, for example 6 or, for the convenience of computation, any relation between quantities, so, a word, say "improvement", is an incorporative symbol representing a certain process no matter what was improved, will be improved or is being improved. Regardless whether or not symbols pertain to quantities, the use of symbolic expressions is instrumental in the experience and in the establishment (or computation) of relationships. It is not surprising that the symbolizing and generalizing character of thought is reflected in the organization of the more highly developed languages which are by comparison conceptual, inclusive and concentrated while primitive languages are "object-bound" and "event-bound", and expression proceeds from point to point in a hyperitemizing rather than a comprehensive fashion.

Both words and mathematical symbols reduce, to the level of sound and sight perception, the recognition of abstract relations. Thus, Whitehead's (352) remark that "by the aid of mathematical symbols we can make transitions in reasoning almost mechanically by the eye which would otherwise call into play the highest faculties of the mind" may be applied, with almost equal justification, to many non-mathematical symbols. We express verbalized relations by making the sequence of conventionalized sights and sounds, the syntactic context, conform to the relationships to be communicated; specific sequences of sound and sights parallel the specificity of relations and hence, convey their meaning.

To recognize verbalized relations, that is, to understand words, or to apprehend "a-facets" presented in the form of optic and acoustic symbols, a machine would have to be endowed with dimensions of operation exceeding those sufficient to recognize non-symbolized "a-facets." For example, in order to recognize, or understand the word "improvement," (i) the machine would have

(1) to convert the impression "i" into a perceptual process i'

(2) to activate the corresponding engram I_1 and

(3) to initiate a process underlying the appropriate concept.

The latter is a psychism devoid of any except, perhaps, rudimentary sensuous properties. By contrast, the recognition of symbols necessitates the activation of engrams having perceptual cores.

At this point, it may be well to remember that, in the course of the discussion, as a variety of aspects of the notion "concept" was brought to light, the "concept of concept" underwent a gradual evolution. Originally thought of in *static* terms, concepts were represented by aggregates formed by their partially superimposable constituents, and the probability of their associative connections was primarily determined either by degrees of superimposability or by their contiguity valences. Later on, we came to replace the notion of a static condition by that of a dynamic state determined, in turn, by probability bounds which direct associative processes. Subsequently, to account for certain peculiarities of ekphory, particularly the step-like differentiation within conceptual spheres, we entertained the idea that the material processes underlying concepts have the relation-structure of multilinear relays.

Now, if concepts be regarded as multilinear relays whose structure is determined by sliding rather than rigid priority relations, that is to say, priority relations operating between elements A_1 —$A_2 \ldots A_n$, then incorporative symbols or words should play the role of master switches that activate class concepts. Conversely, symbols or words would be ekphorizable by any element of the relay embodied in symbolic representation. Again we encounter, at least believe to see, an arrangement that permits, like a flexible algebraic notation system, both the specification of inclusive items and the generalization of individual items. The individuation of concepts and the incorporation of elements into the framework of concepts and collective symbols are interrelated.

Thus, in addition to the performance discussed under points 1, 2 and 3, machines would have to

(4) break down and to specify the incorporative symbol "improvement," that is to say, to initiate a number of itemizing processes. The term in question would represent a key process which

actuates and, if need be, specifies, by means of contiguity mechanisms of association, the awareness contents it represents. In other words, the appreciation of the meaning of a *generalizing symbol* would involve the potential production of *concrete instances* of the processes or relations to which the symbol refers. Furthermore, words connect or, as the case may be, relay condensed awareness contents to other concepts. In biological brains, priority relations are context-determined and, accordingly, fluid. The probability of an association ranges from zero to a maximum regardless whether the elements involved are represented by symbols. Nearly identical awareness contents may remain unassociated with one another. On the other hand, associations of any content of awareness with any other psychism may occur irrespective of the sphere to which they belong and irrespective of their level of abstraction.

The machine would have to be able to

(5) initiate processes produced by sights whenever processes produced by sounds are actuated and vice versa; it would have to convert auditory symbols into visual symbols, or visual symbols into auditory symbols. At the same time, the machine would have to

(6) actuate process 3 whenever either of the aforementioned processes takes shape.

Yet, the production of specific responses on the part of the machine confronted with sights and sounds could hardly be regarded as either understanding or recognition. "Machines", Descartes (*603, 103*) wrote early in the 17th century, "could never use words or other signals arranged in such a manner as is competent to us in order to declare our thoughts to others; for we may easily conceive of a machine to be so constructed that it emits vocables and even that it emits some correspondance to the action upon it of external objects which cause a change in its organs; for example, if touched in a particular place it may demand what we wish to say to it. If another, it may cry out that it hurts and such like but not that it should arrange them variously as appositely to reply to what is said in its presence, as men of the lowest degree of intelligence can do."

Lastly, to deal with problems formulated in written language, the machine would have to differentiate between pluri-dimensional systems of signs, recently summarized by Grewel (*98*) as a system of (a) distinct sound elements, (b) of

words, i.e., phonetic-semantic units, (c) of word formations, (d) of possibilities of sentence formation, (e) and of accents. This task would become even more complicated if the meaning of a symbol dependent on the particular context within which it is used.*

Yet, to approach the performance level of their biological fellows, electronic brains would have to be even more versatile. Not only would they have to register identical data furnished in different physical terms, such as light and sound waves, tactile impressions, etc., and to interconvert them but, at the same time, to differentiate between directive and non-directive data and to side-channel the latter. Nevertheless, machines would have to keep a record of both categories of information since, depending on the general context of events, irrelevant data may become pertinent, i.e., fringe experiences shifted into the core region. Thus, machines, in order to approach the performance of capacity of biological brains, would have to have at least vestiges of what is known as incidental (as opposed to pertinent) memory. They would have to reconstruct and anticipate events; they would have to evaluate indefinite data as expressed for example by such terms as "soon," "approximately", "at one time or another," "perhaps", etc., they would have to be able to trace the source of incorrect informations and to eliminate them. Certain modern computation machines are able to detect errors by means of "redundancy-circuits" but, needless to say, lack the other above mentioned properties.

INTERPRETATION OF MACHINE INTELLIGENCE

A full discussion of the problem of machine intelligence—a controversial subject—would require liberal quotations and has therefore been omitted for considerations of space. The interested reader may be referred to the writings of Berkeley (*17*), Turing (*329*, Wilkes (*363*), Hartree (*114*), Babbage (*10*), Lady Lovelac, Lord Bryon's daughter (*197*), Descartes (*63*), Keister (*157*), McCulloch and Pitts (*204*), and Bell (*14*).

The very existence of the controversy indicates that there is no sharp dividing line between the performance of electronic and biological computers. However, this holds true only in the sense

---

* Cf. the "Science Report" in *Newsweek*, October, 1960.

that there is no unbridgeable gulf between the image-forming eye of the higher vertebrates and a camera, between the heart and a pressure pump, between nerve fibers and cables; between, on the one hand, radar and sonar equipment and, on the other, the principle of echolocation in certain animals. Important differences nothwithstanding, common principles operate in both varieties of response-selecting mechanisms. If, to aid the brain, we make machines do what the brain does; if, to aid the eye, we make optical instruments do what the eye does, and other instruments do what the ear does; if, unwittingly, we employ technical principles realized in nature, it is evident that organizing forces do not manifest themselves around us only, but also within us. *Having given the human brain similar powers, they have made* *it both a product and a collateral pathway of evolution. Man creates his tools in his own image.*

In fact, since these lines were written, man no longer employs, unwittingly, technical devices realized in nature. He has come to appreciate their value and attempts to imitate them. "Studies of the beetle's eye . . . have provided a wiring diagram for a radical new type of airspeed indicator . . . The model of a computer has been made whose capacity to perceive and to remember shapes approaches that of the octopus . . . which, a member of Professor J. Z. Young's research team believes, uses a system for recognizing patterns that is simpler and more economical in components than the system hitherto proposed for airborne computers." (*New York Times*, April 19, 1959, p. 19).

Differential ranges of intellective ability

At this juncture, we propose to test the applicability to the dissolution and the growth patterns of thinking, of the theory of thought developed in the preceding sections of this chapter. The term *"dissolution"* is self explanatory; the term *"growth"*, as used in the present context, refers to patterns of thought believed to operate in the genius as the highest representative of the species.

Both dimensions and freedom of response are enhanced by abstraction. Abstract thinking, in turn, is predictated upon the existence of a certain system of notation in which the nervous system records experiences and brings them into relationship with one another. Hence, other factors being equal, appropriacy of response should be determined by the degree of perfection of the system of notation in which responses are computed. Furthermore, since organisms in a certain respect at least are comparable to machines operating on a probability principle, the likelihood of success of response should fluctuate around a mean level of efficiency. Obviously, constancy or near-constancy of performance at a hypothetical top level of efficiency will tend to maximize the confidence coefficient of adequate response determination, the opposite extreme being inconstancy and unreliability of performance even at habitually low levels. Temporal dissociation of function, the inordinately low reliability of integrative action in brain disease, is nothing more than a confidence coefficient lying well below the average considered normal.

However, versatility of notation and standard reliability of response as mediated by the highest levels of the nervous system are not the only variables which determine the quality of thought. Other, equally important factors will be discussed below.

DISSOLUTION PATTERNS OF THOUGHT

Disorders of thinking may be classified from various angles. According to their scope, they may be divided into *generalized* and *partial* disorders. For example, the inability to think in terms of concepts derived from visual or auditory experiences may be due to certain localized brain lesion. According to their etiology, the abnormalties under study may be grouped into a *primary* and a *secondary* variety. However, because of the close relationship between thought and language there may be recognized a third group, caused by the incongruity between concepts and their symbolic expression. It will be convenient to discuss the secondary thinking disorders first.

Secondary thinking disorders may be due to impairment (1) of consciousness, (2) of affectivity, (3) of perception and (4) of memory.

Primary thinking disorders comprise (1) the oligophrenias and (2) the dysphrenias.

The discussion of dysphrenic thought is here resumed (a) in order to contrast it with the growth patterns of thought, (b) to examine more closely than heretofore possible its relationship to dream experiences, (c) and, implicitly, of either phenomenon to creative thought. One of the questions to be answered is the following: what particular factor operating in dreams makes them potentially creative processes? And what particular factor establishes a link between the schizophrenic and the genius?

Any nervous system function, including intellective activity, can be expressed in terms of integrative processes dependent, in turn, on anatomical structures. Intellective functions represent the integrated total of many partial performances mediated by various cortical and subcortical provinces of the brain. We remind ourselves that the posterior associational fields are the "thought centers" proper, the most versatile "computation machine" that is, which corresponds to Bastian's elaborative cortex, or Broadbent's center of concepts and ideation. However, the performance of the highest selector mechanism is dependent on the functions of other parts of the brain. For example, an abnormal responsiveness level caused by lesions of the diencephalo-frontal system interferes with the performance of the organ of computation even if the latter is structurally intact. Moreover, the relationship between partial functions is reciprocal rather than unidirectional. Both inter-group and intra-group repercussions may occur which makes it difficult to unravel the pathogenic mechanism operating in an individual case. Not only are the higher, conceptual, and "contextual" disturbances dependent on the lower but, to a certain extent, elementary dysfunctions on those of a composite nature. For example, severe mental confusion may cause not only disturbances of consciousness; it may give rise to emotional disorders and vitiate both mnestic and perceptual data. Disorders of affect may produce disorders of memory. Furthermore, the organism may regress to more primitive, mnestic, functions where the goal of thought can be reached by productive thinking only. Conversely, a person may make futile efforts to solve a problem by a process of reasoning, where success depends on the ekphory of engrams rather than on originality of thought.

For the reasons given above any classification of thinking disorders is bound to be somewhat arbitrary.

Secondary thought disorders

Thought disorders incident to changes in consciousness

Man's awareness of his own self and of his environment may be *reduced, heightened,* or *warped.* Primary reduction of awarness is comparable to various degrees of somnolence while secondary depression of awareness may be due to inattention, distraction, inability to concentrate, indecision and preoccupation with various matters. However, awareness may also be heightened as in states of abnormal lucidity and sharpness of the senses; for example, it may be increased if the body temperature is inordinately high. In the absence of delusions and hallucinations, fever may interfere not only with the quality of thought but, at the same time, increase the intensity of perception. Warping of the state of awareness involves either de-realization or depersonalization. In the former, the experience of self is altered; in the latter, the experience of environment. In either form of disorder, the feeling of strangeness is not due to delusions but, rather, to a primary alteration of the notation system in which reality is recorded. Just like the circles of latitude and longitude on a map are not necessarily noticed by those using it, so the organizational stability of the environment (and at the same time of the body scheme) is taken for granted. However, in states of derealization (and depersonalization) the system of coordinates and implicitly the entire map is distorted. The feeling of strangeness may be associated with terrifying fear and is apt to force delusional interpretations of various complexity on the patient (*288*). Similarly, paranoid interpretations may be produced by drug intoxications.

Thought disorders incident to changes in affectivity

Both heightened and lowered affects may be either *primary* or *secondary* in origin. The former tend to accelerate intellectual productivity and to increase its volume although, as a rule, at the expense of its quality; lowered affects are apt to retard the rate of productivity, to reduce its volume and depress its quality. That the contents of thought are influenced by the quality of the prevailing affect or mood is an every day experience. In states of depression, the tenacity of psychisms is inordinately increased; in states of excitement, reduced. In the former, associations of ideas are rigid and their flow is retarded; in the latter, they are unduly fluid and speeded up.

A significant subgroup of thought disturbances, which resemble certain behaviour disorders in experimental animals, is caused by secondary depression of mood due to frustration. R. N. F. Maier's (224) experiments referred to in the preceding chapter demonstrate that, in the rat, motivated behaviour is constructive while frustrated behaviour may be destructive and lead to stereotypy in problem situations. The abnormality in question may be still further increased by punishment.

The role of responsiveness to stimuli upon thought was described by Beringer (15) a.o. In one of Beringer's patients, mental processes appeared to be practically non-existent. There was, as he put it, no activity whatsoever on the "stage of consciousness" and whenever signs of mental activity appeared to be present the mental processes remained isolated and failed to initiate new thoughts of any kind. Neither recognizable threads nor trends of thought could be detected. Whatever psychic processes might have been going on disappeared without leaving a trace. However, when spoken to, the patient would answer promptly. In Beringer's case the disturbance in spontaneity was caused by a bilateral frontal lobe tumor. I found similar patterns of thought disturbances both in a series of 216 verified cases of newgrowths involving the frontal lobes and in non-neoplastic lesions of identical location (283). Another schizophrenic patient described by Beringer stated that even the slightest mental exertion was associated with enormous effort. He found thought disturbances to be more prominent the greater the demand made on active thought, including speed, clarity, distinctness and availability of engrams and on what he called the adequate staying capacity of thought contents.

Thought disorders incident to perceptual deficit

Inadequacy of thought due to impairment of perception, causing in turn, misinterpretation of sights and sounds, is a trivial phenomenon here mentioned for the sake of completeness only. At a higher level, derailment of associations may be caused by hallucinations and delusions.

Thought disturbances incident to defective memory

They include the inability to form engrams, impaired ekphory, difficulty in responding to similarity and contiguity elements, either prolonged or unduly shortened access time to engrams, mass ekphory with resulting inability to differentiate between mnemonic material, inability to relate perceptions to engrams and vice versa with resulting disturbances of recognition, and, lastly, fusion of percepts and "re-percepts" with the ensuing inability to keep them apart.

Intrinsic thought disturbances

Oligophrenia

Thought disturbances representing pre-eminently quantitative defects of mentation are illustrated by various degrees and types of feeblemindedness. (The term dissolution of thought does not exactly apply, as intelligence may never have attained normal levels.) The disturbance in question, which represents a minus function involving primarily the conceptual sphere, may be further complicated by poor memory and emotional imbalance. On the other hand, a moderate degree of oligophrenia may be partly compensated by increased interest and drive, in fact, at least in certain performance fields, rather severe degrees of imbecility may be combined with excellent memory. Language functions may or may not be involved. There may be rather marked verbal fluency and an increased drive to talk, the intact speech melody giving rise to the impression that the speaker is not only talking but saying something. ("Salonschwätzer"). Oligophrenias may be partial or global, innate or acquired. In regard to special aptitudes, and applying a somewhat arbitrary standard, the mental level of not a few otherwise normal persons would seem to fall within the range of mild oligophrenia.

Kleist (*164*) developed the concept of "alogic" and "paralogic" thought disturbance. Buseman (*37*), who studied the former in brain injured persons, considers the following as characteristic of the first named disorder: lack of drive, retardation of thought processes, lack of understanding of written material of any length and some disturbances of calculating ability. (Paralogic thought disturbances will be discussed below.) The tachistoscopic recognition of objects and figures is likewise retarded. The most conspicuous abnormality however, he goes on to say, is a dearth of spontaneously emerging ideas, or underproductivity. The clinical picture may be complicated by frontal akinesia and poor mimic innervation. The majority of Buseman's patients showed damage to the frontal lobes, in particular their lower surface.

It is pertinent to define the relationship between alogic thought disturbances and oligophrenia. According to Kleist, the former involve what he considers to be the "motor component of thought." During certain reasoning processes, we experience ourselves as being active and to make a more or less definite effort to reach the goal of thought. Active thought has its own motor elements comprising mimetic and attitudinizing movements subserved by the posterior portion of the second frontal convolution. Loss of "mnestic formulas" used in routine reasoning operations interferes with thought in a similar fashion as loss of verbal and syntactic instrumentalities with motor speech. The mnestic (motor) formulas are under the influence of the sensory component of thought whose involvement gives rise to paralogic thought disturbances. (They correspond, by and large, to the dysphrenic disorders.) Briefly stated, Kleist applies the spinal reflex arc scheme, which he supplemented by a cortico-extrapyramidal component, to the physiology of thought processes. I for one believe that the frontal component of thought is furnished primarily by hoemostatic mechanisms which, in accordance with biological demands, impart to the posterior association fields various degrees of responsiveness while extrapyramidal mechanisms play a facilitatory role (Fig. 8). Hence, the clinical and physiological relationships of the frontal lobes to the phenomena of wakefulness, attention, affectivity and drive. Clinical observations suggest that thought disturbances caused by frontal lobe lesions resemble those due to the generally inadequate mobilization of intellectual resources. The relationship between oligophrenic and alogic thought disturbances are very close because of the common factor of non-connection rather than misconnection of ideas. The combination of alogic and paralogic thought disturbances in schizophrenia and the relatively rare occurrence of pure forms is emphasized in the more recent publications of the Kleist school (*161*).

In the above summary, which covers some theoretical aspects of thought and its disorders, we have re-emphasized the different role played in mentation by the posterior association fields and the diencephalo-frontal system. We are however disinclined to recognize either significant analogies between thought and speech mechanisms, at least the analogies suggested by Kleist, or the existence of a motor component of thought processes. In particular, we do not believe that the establishment of separate motor thinking disturbances analogous to those of motor speech is warranted. In the sphere of thought, it is difficult to detect a motor factor operating under the influence of the sensory, or computational element. Once a response is determined by the biological computing mechanism, appropriate signals are sent to the "biological robot" into which it is installed and whose effects operate on a lower level than thought mechanisms (Figs. 1 and 8).

In oligophrenia, the awareness and generation of relationships is generally reduced. This is due to the failure of what would otherwise be actuating events to generate producing relations and, hence, produced relations. Few class concepts are formed, and thinking sets remain primitive. More complicated relations are not likely to be grasped; if apprehended, they are apt to be forgotten. Generalizations are unwarranted and remain unsubstantiated, analogies faulty; intuitions, if any, are absurd. There is little tendency to check the validity of relations by deductive reasoning. In other words, there is relative lack of awareness of incompatibilities and inconsistencies. Errors are either not seen or not evaluated and therefore not corrected. Existing cause-effect relationships are overlooked unless quite primitive, while those which the average person would expect to occur are not anticipated.

Dysphrenias

DISORDERS OF CONCEPT FORMATION

Disorders of concept formation may be expressed in terms of *fringe-dominance, core-atrophy, fragmentation, condensation, blurring, abnormal perceptualization* and *abnormal symbolization*. The following account of schizophrenic thought disturbances is based largely on clinical and experimental observations published by Beringer (B), Cameron (C), Hanfman and Kasanin (HK) and Kleist (K), Schneider (Sch), Wegrocky (W), Zaslow (Z) and others.* (See, e.g., Vigotzky, *332*.) While the conceptions of the above enumerated workers will be given the prominence they deserve, it is our ultimate aim to integrate the ideas of the psychiatrists with those ideas which have been promulgated in the foregoing paragraphs.

One of Kleist's patients, showing her finger, said: "This is the Holy Trinity." Thus, she connected a fringe of the concept "finger" with the fringe of the concept "Trinity." Another patient who said that "she has laid America" connected a fringe of the concept "egg" with a fringe of the concept "Columbus." Fringe-dominance and core-atrophy of concepts is responsible for the reduction of their core to insignificant residues. For instance, a student, asked to think of the University where he had studied prior to his illness, produced merely the idea of having put his gown into a wardrobe (B). In other cases, concepts are inordinately perceptualized, which renders them altogether too unwieldy and too rigid to be manipulated in thought (B). Condensation of concepts can perhaps be reduced to fringe dominance, for "mixing" of conceptual material (Z) implies that the psychisms under study articulate intimately (and mostly at random) in the fringe-sphere, and that their meanings become amalgamated. Any fragment of a concept may thereby carry its meaning, and since fringes stray about as it were and may participate in a variety of other concepts, meanings may be transferred or substituted by others. In other words, fringes may become more or less fixated symbols which, in a highly individualistic fashion, represent cores of concepts. Accordingly, the selection of

* Ref. *15, 41, 42, 106, 153, 164, 165, 166, 284, 343, 365.*

a particular fringe element is dependent on the patient's personal experiences; conversely, the apparently fortuitous selection of fringes to be "hooked" up with others may determine the trend of subsequent thought contents.

DISORDERS OF THE DIRECTIONALITY OF THOUGHT

Generalizations are too broad, too involved, inapplicable and may include personal material (C). The range of similarity which the schizophrenic treats as equivalent tends to be either constricted to an abnormal degree or, due to the overinclusion of essentially dissimilar objects, diffusely expanded (Z). Schizophrenics have difficulties in grasping and applying principles of classification (HK). Expanded conceptual grouping tends to contaminate a concept and to rob it of its essential meaning (Z). One of Beringer's patients stated that his thought became hazy, and that he became incapable of directing it the way he wanted. Wegrocky (*343*) noted a difficulty in apprehending the directions given so that, under experimental conditions, constant repetition was necessary; thought is apt to be derailed and to lose itself in irrelevant channels. The author speaks of the "crossing of the main lines of thought" and the almost inevitable switching over to subordinate lines. Associations may take place rapidly beyond the patient's control. There is a constant stream of interfering awareness contents forcing themselves upon the patient; his own thoughts do not seem to belong to him any longer, which is apt to give rise to the delusion that someone else thinks for him, or to make him think the way he does. In addition, there are gaps in the stream of thought which, at any moment, may cease to flow altogether. Cameron aptly speaks of the "inability on the part of the patient to circumscribe a problem and to maintain the spatial and temporal limits of the experimental situation which therefore fuses with other environmental and imaginal material into a poorly organized whole of great complexity and instability." Fragments of their life problems may be included into the experimental situation. At the same time, the subjects show reduced sensitivity to incongruities, and they deny the existence and validity even of frank perceptual patterns. In trying to amplify an explanation, they make statements apt to increase the vagueness rather than to clarify the issue. The theme of the problem with which the patient is concerned and his pre-occupation may interpenetrate. There may be gross misinterpretations of cause-effect relationships resulting in bizarre actions. One of Kleist's patients poured hot oil into his ears to destroy his hearing and to become a great musician, "because" v. Beethoven had been deaf!

ON MENTATION IN DREAMS

The relationship between thought in schizophrenia and the contents of dreams were commented upon, among others, by Kraepelin (*172*) by Bleuler (*26*) Jung (*151*) and Schneider (*284*). In classifying those of my dreams which I more or less distinctly remember (and I believe that many observers would agree to a somewhat similar classification of their own dream experiences) I encountered the following varieties:

(a) *Repetitive* and *anticipatory* dreams
(b) *Realistic* and *constructive* dreams
(c) *Unrealistic* and *fantastic* dreams
(d) *Emotionally colored* and *indifferent* dreams
(e) Dreams in which the affect is *apposite* to the situation, and those in which the affect is *inapposite*.
(f) *Exogenous* dreams, for example those caused by noise and *endogenous* dreams, caused by visceral sensations.
(g) *Tenacious* and *evanescent* dreams.
(h) Dreams in which the dreamer is an *observer* and those in which he is a *participant*.
(i) *Paraphrasing* dreams which, I believe, are related to scientific and artistic inspiration and productivity.

The above suggested classification does not exclude the existence of other categories of dreams, especially those which patently express seeking attitudes or wishes, or attitudes of avoidance. Moreover, combinations of the individual categories are common. The doctrine that every dream expresses a wish is entirely too one-sided. In fact Freud (*85a*) himself qualified his original thesis in his last contribution to the psychoanalytic literature. No doubt fringe dominance plays an important part in certain experiences of the dreamer. Hence, their ambiguity, their vagueness, and the leeway in interpretation. Below, I shall report some of my own dreams in which fringe dominance was a prominent factor. It is unfortunate that only very few of them were immediately recorded;

otherwise I would have illustrated the above listed and, perhaps, other categories of dreams by many more examples. In retrospect, I believe I have been dreaming more often than usual at the time I was speculating about the nature of dreams.

Dream 1. While about to fall asleep, but continuing to think about the relationship between thought processes as they take shape in the waking state and as they occur in dreams, I suddenly saw the transition between the two varieties of thought to be symbolized by changing from one bus to another, handing the driver a transfer ticket and continuing my ride.

Dream 2. Again, while falling asleep and thinking about the same problem, I saw "falling asleep" symbolized by a large sheet of blotting paper moving slowly, like a curtain, over a manuscript page.

Both dreams are of interest because of the awareness on the part of the dreamer that fringe material has been substituted for core-material of a symbolic character, and that the nature of the symbols could later be readily be interpreted. No doubt dreams can bring to light the otherwise hidden constituents of concepts just as the process of hydrolysis yields amino acids which are the building blocks of proteins. Joseph's dream, in which the seven lean years were symbolized by as many decrepit cows, could have been dreamed anywhere and at any time in any cattle breeding society; the laws of concept formation have general validity.

Dream 3 was plainly anticipative in character. Anxious to read again an article published by one of my former teachers, I ordered the issue of the art journal in which it had appeared while I was still a youngster. Upon notification of the New York Public Library that the requested issue was available, I dreamed to have gone over the appropriate page of the Authors' Index and to have moved my finger down the page until I found my teacher's name. I distinctly remember that it was printed in bold face. To me, it may well have symbolized the importance of the matter or, perhaps, an attitude of deference toward the author.

While discussing the mathematical fields of thought, we argued that mathematical concepts are devoid of fringe elements. This should however not be taken to mean that numbers, if not used as mathematical tools, may not evoke associations that involve the marginal elements of concepts.

Dream 4. In one of my dreams I saw three boys, evidently triplets. One of them answered my question, "How many tongues have you all together?" as follows: "One brother, one tongue, two brothers, two tongues, three brothers, three tongues." They looked into a mirror and opened their mouths. The first triplet had one tongue, the second a bifid tongue, which looked like the tongue of a snake, and the third a tongue which was divided into three parts. For some reason, they laughed heartily.

Thus, the concept of one-ness was illustrated by one tongue, the concept of duality by a bifid tongue and the concept of three-ness of a tripartite tongue. Symbolization of concepts or, for that matter, of thought, was produced by a peculiar technique in which some sort of clang association obliterating the difference between the concepts of cardinal and ordinal numbers played a part. In parenthesis, I mention that the loosening of concept-word relationships, which I experienced in some of my own dreams may produce verbal paraphasias as documented for example by the following sentences: (a) "The house of months has produced ever new sciences." (b) "In Leoncavallo plays free Greek," and, (c) "They lost him a streetblock in Pelikan."

Dream 5. After seeing the picture of the two Dachshund puppies a breeder had sent to Queen Elizabeth of England, I dreamed I was playing with one of them. I turned on the switch of a gooseneck lamp whose light flooded the puppy's head. The glare of the lamp made him close his eyes and his face assumed a surprised expression. Turning around to discover the reason for his amazement, I saw another gooseneck lamp which, however, was not lighted. It occurs to me that a few days prior to the above dream episode, I had been a guest at the home of one of my colleagues. While sitting at the table, I caught sight of a two-branched gooseneck lamp standing in a corner. It seemed to me that only one of the two lights was turned. More or less automatically, I turned around for a brief moment to see whether this was actually so. I paid no further attention to this unimportant detail which, apparently, was immediately forgotten. The dream represents an odd combination of experiences brought about by the articulation of fringe elements, namely, the picture of the two puppies and the recollection of the twin lamp. Each experience symbolized the substitution of "twin-ness" by "one-ness." The identification of the dreamer with one of the two puppies was likewise caused by the association of marginal elements of concepts.

Dream 6. A calendar watch has to be advanced a full 24 hours on the last day of every month that has fewer than 31 days. On November 30, 1959, I forgot to set my watch, probably because I had a late unexpected visitor, who long overstayed his time and, since I had other plans for this evening, upset my schedule. For the same reason, I forgot to use the handcream that I usually apply before retiring. That night I dreamed that I looked at my watch but all I saw was a white blank disk surrounded by a metal frame, that is, the empty face of a watch, a watch without markings, figures, and hands to indicate the time. I turned it around I saw that its under surface was covered with yellow dust. I consider this dream a paraphrase of two situations of which I was not conscious before retiring; it is difficult to imagine that I would have had the dream had I not forgotten to set my watch and to use the handcream. I might add that the handcream is the same color as the dust, but the blank disk I saw in my dream was white while the face of the watch is black. Evidently, this indicated in symbolic dream language that a watch which is not set is useless. The yellow color of the dust, on the other hand, served the purpose of "identification in the guise of concealment. The dream conformed to several Freudian criteria: the representation of certain elements by their opposites, and the feature of condensation. Furthermore, it dealt with *Tagereste* not consciously experienced. On the other hand, I can see no trace of wishfulfilment. In my opinion, the dream experience reflects the pattern of a delayed action mechanism, paraphrasing, or, if you wish, resolving an unfinished situation, somewhat in the nature of a posthypnotic suggestion.

THOUGHT DISORDERS DUE TO CONCEPT-WORD INCONGRUITY

No doubt the difficulties inherent in verbalization increase the complexity of thought disturbances (C). Words, regardless whether spoken, read or heard, may change their meaning and they may become points of departure of new "determing tendencies" (B). Words may no longer evoke the appropriate concept but, rather, ideas which may be but vaguely reminiscent of the particular expression used—if not entirely unrelated to it. The correspondence between thought and speech is vitiated, indeed, words may be produced to which no thought corresponds (Sch.). The syntax may or may not be intact. In other cases, there are distinct difficulties both in verbalization and in grasping the import of sentences read or spoken by others. The inability on the part of the schizophrenic to express his thoughts precisely has been appropriately referred to as *elusive flavor* or *tangentiality* (*41*). Kleist and Schwab (*165*) found true *aphasic* disturbances. They were mostly of sensory character, including *misnaming, neologisms* and *verbal paraphasias, faulty determination, derivation and composition of words and both agrammatic and paragrammatic mutilation of sentences*; further, they found parts of sentences, words, syllables and letters contaminated and mixed and then arbitrarily *recombined* and *condensed.* Neologisms referring to relations produced by fringe dominance are formed by the interpolation and mixing of words. New synthetic concepts emerge out of which symbolic expressions are made up. Wegrocky called attention to the fact that texts read by the patients may suddenly assume the character of a foreign language, which is evidently a de-realization phenomenon in the sphere of speech. Similar experiences were made by patients on listening to music.

In *conclusion*, it may be stated that, in dysphrenia, an element of error is introduced into reasoning by analogy, by generalization and, it may be surmised, also by intuition. Inductive thought processes are misapplied and deductive processes deflected. Repetitive, recognitive, reconstructive and anticipative reasoning is inhibited or perverted, and the formation of similarity-, contiguity- and causality sets is disorganized. Reasoning sets may be twisted or broken down and thrown together in heaps, or taken apart and recombined into astonishing monstrosities. Similarity and dissimilarity perceptions may be blunted and the experience of consistency, compatibility and applicability may be empty and meaningless. In other words, the laws of contradiction and identity are abolished. Context forming mental processes, having become

either equiprobable, or their logical criteria having been "reevaluated," lose their directionality, or the very goal of thought is mischosen. Symbols, both verbal and non-verbal, are used, at the same time, as a means of communication and of concealment.

GROWTH PATTERNS OF THOUGHT. THE MIND OF THE GENIUS

At this stage, it is our task to specify the differences between the genius and the schizophrenic on the one hand, and between the former and average man on the other. Broadly speaking, the genius realizes superior goals while the schizophrenic satisfies perverted aims. Eventually, he ceases to will altogether. The self of the genius is one of life's supreme expressions; the self of the schizophrenic has become devoid of life at a time he may still go through the motions of living. The genius' creative work reflects the intensification of the *correspondence function of the brain.* He thereby extends the sphere of concordance between the subjective and the objective sphere of reality, and he resolves apparent homogeneity into diversity. In the world so created, which is richer in dimensions than the one he found, the frontiers of his own self widen. Freedom of choice between a variety of responses becomes multiplied as, whatever freedom of reaction there may be, flows from knowledge.

Not only the genius' power of mentation is superior but even his power of *awareness.* Goethe (*91*) mentions peculiar experiences in which the feeling of the past, the present and the future seemed to merge, which were associated with productive ecstasy and which, he believed, endowed some of his poems with their singular spell. That creativity may be enhanced in states of dream-consciousness was already noted in the course of the discussion concerned with the mathematical fields of thought.

The dynamic bipolarity of affects may engender productive drive. At least it is reported in the biography of many eminent men, especially artists, that, unlike in the average person, not only heightened but also lowered affects may stimulate rather than inhibit creative work.

However the mind of the genius is a realm difficult to map out even by what the mathematician would call *"inversion"** of data arrived at from the study of pathological material or by *extrapolation* of data falling within normal ranges. In order to illustrate our thesis that the genius, as the representative of a group, is the opposite of the schizophrenic as a group and, without being abnormal in the conventional sense of the term, is relatively free from the limitations inherent in the organization of the normal brain, we must look for examples of superior endowment which can be readily compared with the mind of average man and, at the same time, conveniently contrasted with the mind of the schizophrenic. Goethe, *(334)* in spite of his many philosophical and scientific interests, was essentially a poet, and most of the mathematicians who reportedly solved problems in their sleep, as for instance Inaudi, were relatively onesided. The same applies, in a sense, to Newton *(245)* and to Laplace, *(179)* both of whom were, basically, mathematical thinkers.

The bipolar patterning of superior mental ability

Cattell *(47),*† in a statistical study on what he believed to be the 1000 most eminent men in history, lists the ten most outstanding persons in the following order; Napoleon, Shakespeare, Mahomed, Voltaire, Bacon, Aristotle, Goethe, Caesar, Luther and Plato. Bowerman *(29)*, in a similar study, considers Leonardo da Vinci the greatest, in any case the most versatile genius in recorded history. Strangely enough, Cattell did not include Leonardo into the small elite of ten. What were Cattell's criteria in compiling his list? Apparently, they were very simple, for he used the aggregate length of their respective "write-ups" in various biographical dictionaries as a yardstick with which to measure the gift of genius. His quantitative method puts the Emperor of the French well ahead of his competitors in the Hall of Fame for we gather that, up to 1910, the *Bibliographie Napoléonienne (163)* had grown to the almost unbelievable

number of 20,000 entries, including books, pamphlets, articles, letters, diplomatic dossiers and various other biographical documents, and that some 5000 of his portraits, of cartoons (chiefly of British origin) and other material has been identified.

It may be a suitable point of departure to adopt Cattell's choice, although not necessarily his method of research; indeed, it would be preposterous to deny Bonaparte's outstanding intellectual ability. The scope of Leonardo's genius is unquestioned. Still, we must select the sources of information carefully, for a good part of history is conventionalized gossip or self-aggrandizement in the guise of hero-worship. Let us be mindful of Napoleon's own saying: "Believe me, we are a little duped by our faith in writers who have fashioned history for us to their own liking, according to the natural bends of their mind" *(276)*.

The mind of Napoleon Bonaparte

The following account is based chiefly on Napoleon's *Memoirs*, edited by Somerset de Chair *(306)*; the writings of Metternich *(233)*, Rémusat *(269)* and Roederer *(274)*, all of whom knew Napoleon personally, and those of his biographers Taine *(322)*, Sloane *(303)*, Rose *(276)*, and Masson *(220)*.* Count Metternich (M), the Austrian Ambassador in Paris (1805–1809) claimed to have known Napoleon more intimately than anyone else except, perhaps, a few of Bonaparte's own compatriots. A perusal of his work, prefaced one year before the exiled Emperor's death (1821) reveals an ambivalent attitude. While admiring Napoleon's great gifts, he evidently enjoyed jabbing at him and claimed that his, Metternich's, judgment had proved to be superior on many important occasions. Napoleon, in his own way, had spoken highly of the diplomatist: "Metternich," he said, "approaches being a great statesman; he lies very well" *(263)*. But the wily Metternich who, with Talleyrand, the French Foreign Minister, plotted Napoleon's overthrow, no doubt drew an essen-

---

* The term *inversion* designates, e.g., the substitution of root extraction for raising to a higher power. The process of inversion is a powerful tool of mathematical investigation. (See, e.g., ref. *173*.)

† Cattel, Professor of Psychology in the University of Philadelphia and, later, Columbia University, was the founder of the American Psychological Association.

* See also Fischer *(81)*, Lanza, U. S. War Department *(178)* and Reibmayr *(264)*. Somerset de Chair, a member of the British parliament, is a contemporary writer.

tially correct picture of the Emperor's mind, for his description accords well with Claire de Rémusat's (Rt) biographical notes and also those published by Roederer (Rd). The former was the wife of Napoleon's Prefet de Palace, the latter one of the Deputies of the National Assembly during the period of the Consulate. An intimate of the First Consul during his rise to power, he was later banished from Paris and requested to live in Naples. Taine (T), the noted historian, needs no introduction. Rose (R) was professor of history at Amherst College, Massachusetts, and Masson (M) a well known historical essayist. The three sets of Memoirs, written, respectively, by Metternich, Rémusat and Roederer, and comprising some twenty (fortunately well indexed) volumes, appeared some time after the Emperor's abdication in 1815, at a time Europe enjoyed the blessings of legitimacy again. Obviously, none of the writers could have expected any favors from Napoleon, nor could anyone have felt any particular gratitude toward him. Their statement must be accepted to be as reliable as any historical document can be. Among the many biographies, Rose's and Sloane's works, as far as I am able to judge as a layman, are probably among the most complete, scholarly and critical and, although any biographer loves his hero, their attitude appears to be as unbiased as is humanly possible. Hendrik van Loon's Preface does not add anything of value to Sloane's work. He depicts Napoleon as an individual hopelessly struggling with a mother complex and, by implication, cautions the reader to quench any Napoleonic ambitions he may harbor.

We do not intend to lose ourselves in an analysis of Napoleon's character, to expose his egotism and other anti-social stigmata. (These traits, however, it should be said in all honesty, were mitigated by his administrative gifts which, under different circumstances, might have been eminently beneficial, by his abolishment of the infamous Inquisition in Spain and other acts of broadmindedness.) On the other hand, it will be necessary to present certain biographical data in order to supplement the study of his intellectual qualities; for it is a truism that the achievements of man, although in the last analysis determined by innate traits, are, at the same time, shaped by environmental influences. Among these, psychologic factors are given much weight at present;

their potential significance demands close scrutiny (*55, 87, 361*).

As a boy, Napoleon would roam the woods of Ajaccio and then take his books to a little grotto, his favourite retreat, to learn his lessons. As a cadet, he was of a somber and brooding mood, shut in, tempestuous and combative. While his classmates in the Military Academy where he was educated would spend their free time with games and other diversions, he would keep aloof and stay in a small plot of the Academy Gardens he had fenced off for himself and his two neighbours. He would read voraciously, chiefly books on geography, history and mathematics. In his (still preserved) notes, he commented on many subjects he had read. He soon became familiar with the life histories of the great heroes of the past, into which he appeared to withdraw. The present, in the way of gratification, had little to offer to the foreigner, worse than that, the native of an Island conquered by France, a boy born of poor nobility, of a proud caste hating the conqueror. ("I was born when my country was perishing.")[1] One wonders what modern psychologic tests would have shown; most likely, he would have been labelled a schizoid or paranoid personality. But even at the age of fifteen—he was to command the French Armies operating in Italy only twelve years later—Napoleon was a psychologist of some stature. "Joseph would make a good garrison officer but a poor soldier," was his verdict based on the methodical evaluation of his elder brother's aptitudes. Even as an adolescent, Napoleon might have developed the notion that men are essentially tools, useful for some purposes, useless for others, or useless altogether. He was thinking in terms of objectives and the means of achieving them, carefully eliminating anything that might have appeared as poor technic and, thereby, debased him in his own eyes. Apparently, everything that would put him ahead of others fascinated him. He must have become aware of his intellectual superiority at an early age. The gulf between himself and his fellowmen widened steadily. Later in his life, "he would look upon himself as being isolated from the rest of the world, destined to govern it and to direct everyone according to his will[2]." The following is one of his frequently quoted

---

[1] R. p. 1.
[2] M. p. 277.

remarks: "I am not a man like others and laws of convention and morality cannot be made for me." He repeatedly expressed his conviction that, by and large, human needs are guided by selfish motives and he treated his coworkers accordingly. His heroes were Julius Caesar and Alexander the Great with whose feats he would often compare his own achievements. As he himself stated, he played with the idea to conquer India, there to impose his own reign and the ways of the Western World as he wanted them to be. (His account of his Egyptian Campaign, unknowingly perhaps, is patterned after the business-like description Caesar gave of the wars he had conducted in the barbarous North.) In his mature years, having become a more realistic dreamer and ruling over some 80 million people, Napoleon saw himself in the role of Charlamagne, as the head of a united Europe. "Peace will never return to Europe as long as it is not united under one head, one Emperor!"

What were the outstanding traits of Napoleon's mind? Both the authenticity of the above cited historical sources and his insight into the workings of his own intellect justify liberal quotations from original sources.

All biographers emphasize Napoleon's mental and physical endurance and his almost limitless power of concentration. His fiery energy, it cannot too often be repeated, was the man's distinctive character[3]. The First Consul manifested these remarkable powers of precise analysis which enabled him for ten hours at a stretch to devote himself to one subject or to several without ever allowing himself to be distracted by memory or aberrant thoughts[4]. He would awake from profound slumber and rouse his mind instantaneously to the highest pitch so that he then composed as incisively as in the midsts of active ratiocination[5]. He had the quality of laborious, untiring, self-initiated, self-contained industry[6]. What distinguished him from all of us was above all the speed, force and perseverance of his power of attention. He never lost energy and could never be distracted[7]. Napoleon said to Roederer: "I think much, I am always working, when dining, when at the theater. I waken at night in order to work. I never have found the limit of my capacity to work[5]." "I have no interest outside my work[8]."

In many respects, his memory was above average. His topographical knowledge of various localities, be it towns, villages or whole sceneries resembled inner visions which he could conjure up at will even after many years[9]. His memory for names and dates was quite poor but astonishingly accurate for events and places[10]. He himself said about his memory: "Various matters and affairs are arranged in my head like in a chest of drawers. Whenever I want to interrupt a train of thought I close that particular drawer and open another one. I never confuse them and the game does not tire me at all. Whenever I wish to finish it I close all the drawers and instantly fall asleep (T). The amount of facts he accumulated in his memory staggered the imagination[11]. He was always the man who knew more about anything than anyone else[12].

He was able to evaluate complex situations and details at a glance. He immediately grasped the essential aspects of a matter. In all questions and discussions, he always differentiated essentials from non-essentials. He very quickly saw what even people of great intelligence would have seen only after studying the matter thoroughly, and he arrived at conclusions by intuition rather than logic. One idea gave rise immediately to a thousand others. Yet there was a peculiar order in his mind, where everything had its proper place.[13] His intellectual capacity seemed to be vast from the number of subjects he could take in and classify without fatigue. He hated everything disorderly and problematical. He had a mania for order.[14]

Metternich wrote: "What first struck me was the remarkable perspicuity and great simplicity of his mind and his processes. Conversation with him had always a charm for me difficult to define. Seizing the essential points of subjects, stripping them of useless accessories, he developed his thoughts and never ceased to elaborate them till he made them perfectly clear and conclusive. He

---

[3] Sl. IV. p. 248.
[4] Rd.
[5] Sl. IV. p. 225.
[6] Ibid. p. 247.
[7] Sl. III p. 210.

---

[8] R. p. 585.
[9] Bourienne, quoted by Taine. (See also Roederer.)
[10] Rt.
[11] T. p. 18.
[12] Sl. IV. p. 249.
[13] Rt. p. 10.
[14] Rt. p. 363. (See also Fischer, p. 23.)

always found the fitting word for the thing or invented one where the usage of language had not created it.[15] Of insatiable curiosity, he took a great interest in every detail of administration[16]. He was an expert in military matters other than those directly concerned with war. He constantly studied the history of the great generals. What he thus learned he applied to his own problems[17].

The following passages refer largely to Napoleon's ways of doing things. In his conclusions all was clear and precise and in what required action he knew neither difficulties nor uncertainty. Ordinary rules did not embarrass him at all[18]. In practice as in discussion he went straight to the end in view without being delayed by considerations which he considered secondary . . . The most direct line of approach to the object he desired to reach was that which he chose by preference and which he followed to the end while nothing could entice him to deviate from it. But, then, being no slave to his plan, he knew how to give it up or modify if the moment his point of view changed, or new combinations gave him the means of attaining it by a different path[19]. The flexibility of Napoleon's mind will clarify the apparent contradiction involved in the following passages.

"If I appear always ready to meet any emergency, to confront every problem, it is because before undertaking any enterprise I have long considered it and I have foreseen what would possibly occur. It is no genius which suddenly and secretly reveals to me what I have to say or to do in some circumstances unforseen by others. It is my own mediation and reflection[20]." As Metternich remarked: *"He displayed an extreme sagacity in appreciating causes and foreseeing circumstances[21]."*

In another connection, Napoleon said about his "First Principles:" "In all the science necessary to war, theory is useful for giving general ideas which form the mind; but then strict execution is always dangerous; they are only axes by which curves are to be traced. Besides, *rules themselves compel one to reason in order to*

discover *whether they ought to be departed from[22].* Military science consists in the first place in calculating to a nicety every chance and then in endeavoring exactly, almost mathematically, make allowance for it. It is upon this point that a general must not deceive himself, a decimal more or less may change all. Now, the distribution of science and risk can only find place in the head of a genius, for that is necessary whenever there is creation and *surely the greatest invention of the human spirit is that which gives existence to what apparently has none.* Hazards remain a mystery to mediocre minds and only become a reality to superior man[23].

No doubt Napoleon's power of *reproductive, reflective,* (especially *anticipatory*) and *intuitive reasoning* was extraordinary. His words about the conditional applicability of rules brings to mind the role of evaluative circuits of the nervous system which discharge under the control of supraordinate circuits of greater evaluative potency, and which have lately been "duplicated" by mechanical contrivances. And the process of "giving existence to what apparently has none" bears an intimate relationship to the *correspondence function* of the brain which expands the sphere of subjective reality along the dimensions inherent in the structure of the external world.

Earlier in this chapter, we discussed the relationship between concepts and multilinear relays encompassing in turn, a multiplicity of psychisms. A moment's reflexion shows that the number and complexity of relay systems having potentially fertile relationships grows much more steeply than the number of individual items. Conventionalized thought which is basically repetitive in nature, may be expressed in terms of more or less stereotyped actuation of relays ("beaten paths") while productive thought requires that potentially fertile fringes of concepts be utilized and incorporated into use patterns which, owing to the great number of relations between fringes, become not only more or less closely knit but also more complexly arranged. Given a large number of concepts, the number of potentially fertile fringes by far exceeds the number of explicit data. (We know that Napoleon amassed a wealth of knowledge and, moreover, was a master of improvisation.) Ingenuity,

[15] M. I. p. 271.
[16] T.
[17] M.
[18] M. II. p. 272.
[19] M. I. p. 272.
[20] Rd.
[21] M. I. p. 272.

[22] Memoirs, p. 290.
[23] Rt. p. 363.

inventiveness and the ability of improvising depends on the fluidity with which apparently unrelated items are utilized in forming novel combinations. They are the operational background of transfer mechanisms, the technique of mastering new and unaccustomed situations.

His own words appear to support the contention that the genius senses alternative ways of thought and action and sees his way clear to choose where, for the mind of plain man, the capacity to choose has reached its limits. It matters little that the necessity to make use of the freedom of choice may be an imposed one. Napoleon believed in an optimum rather than a maximum of planning, knowing full well that, beyond a certain point, planning would be pure speculation. In many battles he fought foresight was of no avail, as events moved so swiftly that his carefully worked out schemes became useless. It is under these conditions of danger that he would display the utmost readiness in seeing just what needed to be done and in discovering the means of doing it. He would act as if equipped with an additional dimension of thought. The effects of this readiness were obvious but its nature remained hidden. It is probably this wizardry in which, ultimately, the Napoleonic myth is rooted.

He was often quoted as saying that genius is nothing but industry. To drive his point home, he no doubt exaggerated his importance of diligence. A perpetual student, he cultivated the style of thinking he had acquired in his formative years. His mind became a piece of machine-like equipment. It absorbed and categorized every item likely to increase its efficiency. One would imagine that, in the ever growing registers of this brainmachine, errors were conspicuously marked, potential ramifications of events worked out and gaps in knowledge indicated to facilitate their elimination; that, to integrate the various data, an ingenious crossfiling and searching system was designed; that a steady stream of readiness—growing in action to a torrent—enlivened it.

The very organization of the human brain which, far from being a precision instrument, operates on a probability principle, involves inconstancy and hence a certain measure of unreliability of performance. It is established that some of Napoleon's errors were foreseen by men of relatively modest intellectual calibre, as was the ruin of Leonardo da Vinci's "The Last Supper" predicted by painters who, while mediocrities by comparison, had warned him that the painting would flake off the wall.* Napoleon committed errors in judgement the psychology of which, as for example his idling at Waterloo, will perhaps never be clarified. A similar state of indecision was also noted by his aids at Leipzig. "A certain carelessness on the part of Napoleon which is impossible to explain and difficult to describe filled the cup of our sorrows," Marshal Marmont (*225*) wrote[24]. Both the Spanish War—he himself spoke of the "Spanish cancer"—and the invasion of Russia were ill conceived adventures. In trying to convince himself that the Russians would not dare to burn their capitol he misjudged their mood; and he misjudged the temper of the British at Mont St. Jean in assuming (or believing to see) that they were about to withdraw when, on the second day of battle, the day before his final defeat, the fortunes of war had turned against them. In his "Memoirs," he made no attempt to conceal his error; on the contrary, he admitted to having been confident of victory.

Here, then, was a man whose chief aim was conquest, and who, in spite of the imperfections inherent in the human brain—imperfections which are the faults of its virtues—came almost within reach of his goal, the complete conquest of Europe. Is it possible to account for his lust for power and his efforts to seize it by motivation alone? Did his ambitions flow from a feeling of humiliation, the resentment of France's conquest of his native Corsica? A childhood reminiscence he was unable to live down? Or from the identification with the greatest of the ancients he had chosen as his heroes? No indeed. Did he by any chance overcompensate a complex rooted in the awareness of organ inferiority? To judge by the scope of alleged overcompensation, his organs

---

* In other instances too, superior intelligence did not protect against a peculiar mental block and lack of insight. In other words, superior intelligence is compatible with a considerable error-potential. Ernst Mach (*200a*), considered by some as a forerunner of Einstein, proposed a continuity theory of matter, in fact, he decried the atomic theory as a "naive and crude notion." And Goethe considered his theory of colors, which was based on faulty experimentation, and which has by common consent no merit, as his outstanding scientific achievement (*224a*).

[24] Sl. IV. p. 31.

must have been so inferior as to make the very viability of his organism a mystery. Was he merely a successful gambler as H. G. Wells would make us believe? No one could have successfully gambled over a period of two decades. Did his success result from his utter disregard of the lives of his fellow men? Evidently not. Without his intellectual ability, his achievements would have been those of a first rate criminal or a second rate clown. It was a unique combination of circumstances that enabled him to rise to the height of power. Under different conditions, he would have become a brilliant administrator, an outstanding physician, an eminent person in any field where perseverance, long term planning and rapid integration of thought and action is essential. Napoleon said about himself (as quoted by E. Schneider (284a) and here translated from the German): "I would have cultivated the study of exact science, and followed Galilei's and Newton's path ... I would have won great fame through scientific research. I would have made important discoveries. No other kind of fame would have aroused my ambition."

In discussing the problem of intelligence, we have taken the view that intellectual endowment is determined by the "intrinsic" function of the posterior cortex (more accurately, its highest sensory level), which is basically a *selector mechanism* of response, while the anterior cortex furnishes an "extrinsic" factor, i.e., it determines the *receptivity* to stimuli and, indirectly, their *externalization*. The responsiveness to stimuli, in turn, is intimately related to their affective loading. The relationship in question may be specified as follows. Responsiveness is under the control of the autonomic nervous system whose role in homeostasis is established. Further, the functional primordium of affective states is the homeostatic element inherent in impelling and aversive responses (Fig. 10). It is the responsiveness to stimuli and the affective loading associated with them which is the background of *motivation*. Expressed in dynamic terms, powerful personalities are those which are strongly motivated, indeed, are capable of imparting similar motives to others. As applied to Bonaparte's personality, the main motivating stimuli were undoubtedly of a higher, conceptual, order. The source of the strength of motivation that determined his life

goals is unknown. It might have been innate or, may be, a complex which, however, was neither an inferiority complex nor an unresolved Oedipus complex as Jekels (141) seems to believe but, more likely, an identification complex with the great of the past (introjection), acquired as a reaction to certain experiences of youth and adolescence. The phenomenon of Napoleonic grandeur, incomprehensible without taking into account his extraordinary intelligence, should be given more serious thought than the diverse depth-psychological schools have thus far cared to display.

Let us now examine some of the more general aspects of the biology of the genius. Is there any proof that Napoleon's brain or, for that matter, the brain of any other person endowed with supreme intelligence—for there is no doubt that Napoleon Bonaparte was merely the "Napoleon best known" and that every nation has its great sons (and of course, daughters, (46)—is there any proof that his brain was as different from the thought organs of average man as were their respective achievements? Napoleon's brain weighed only 56 ounces (20). Much has been written about the weight and the convolution pattern of the brains of eminent men, but thus far no relevant data have crystallized. Whatever statements have been made (20, 56, 168, 180, 230, 249, 250, 256, 272, 382, 317) are so beset with ifs and whens as to make them practically useless. In studying normal brains, it is impossible to be certain whether they belonged to a genius or to one of the legions of workhorses of human society who trod beaten paths efficiently and with an exaggerated sense of their own importance, or, indeed, to individuals of very low intelligence (328). Weidenreich (330) called attention to the difference between the convolutional patterns of the right and the left hemisphere which may be so marked as to make the individual to which they belonged a member of two seemingly different classes of man. There is no clear cut diversity between the convolutional pattern and the weight of the dominant and the subordinate hemisphere. Every zoologist knows that richly gyrated brains do not reflect superior intelligence. Whales have the most richly gyrated brains of all mammals, including man. One wonders whether the gyrational pattern may not be essentially a species characteristic lacking the significance that is attributed to it; and whether it may not be as unwarranted to draw conclusions from the convolutional pattern of the brain surface to mental qualities, as it is impossible to infer, from the elaborate surface ornaments covering some of the old buildings in which, in various capitals, diplomatic business is transacted, to the calibre of the diplomatists working in their offices. It is established that a minimum of brain substance and of nerve cells and a certain pattern of cortical lamination is a prerequisite of normal functioning. Beyond that, nothing is known at present. I do not know whether, in examining the brains of eminent men, sufficient attention has been paid to the relative number of small richly ramified ganglionic cells which Ramon y Cajal (*196*), McIntyre (*73*) a.o. claimed to be significantly related to intellectual ability. Conceivably, it may be a process of a more subtle nature, perhaps, a concatenation of metabolic factors, which accounts for intellectual endowment. Unfortunately, we know relatively little about the metabolism of the normal brain in spite of the fact that we know more and more about the chemical influences which upset it (*130*). Hence, it would be unwise to stipulate a causative relationship between certain metabolic processes and superior mental ability. Yet since certain drugs, although only temporarily, improve the quality of mentation, the possibility of a different type of metabolism should not be dismissed as altogether fantastic. Shall we, then, postulate different metabolic processes as the basis of the innumerable traits the genius may display? Perhaps, specific metabolic elements responsible for mathematical ability? Or for partial aptitudes within the wide realm of mathematics? This idea has little to recommend itself. On the other hand, we know that, at least in animals in which genetic phenomena can be studied under controlled conditions, events at the molecular level resulting in a different constitution of genes determine without any doubt different somatic and physiologic traits incomparably more complicated than their submicroscopic determinants. Certain abilities of man, too, follow the law of heredity. It is thus legitimate to conclude that both somatic and psychic properties in man and animals are rooted in genic properties of some kind, wherein the increase in complexity of structure by no means precludes the operation of a unifying principle. That is as far as we can go at present in tracing the mechanism underlying the gift of genius (or, to be more truthful, in suspecting its nature) and there the problem must rest—at least for the present.

As already noted, Cattell listed the names of what he believed to be the 1000 most outstanding personalities of all times. It is of minor importance whether list is accurate, indeed, whether a correct list can be compiled at all. We cannot here tackle the problem of mental endowment by evaluating the life histories of a representative number of eminent men and women. Cox (*57*) and her collaborators employed the inductive method but her study, based largely on the evaluation of the IQ, strikes one as rather onesided. Bowerman's (*29*) monograph is of interest chiefly from a statistical point of view; however, statistical studies like those compiled by himself (and, it appears, undertaken for their own sake), yield little insight into the intimate nature of the material evaluated. (See also Terman, *325*.) The inductive method resembles a fisherman's net; if its meshes are too wide, the fisherman's efforts will be in vain even though the net is thrown out in the right place. Although our approach may be attacked as attempting to prove precisely that which has been put into the premises—i.e., to catch the fish with which we have stuck the stream—it will be necessary to search for a different method based on a rather definite idea of what one will find.

Is it possible to think of a representative of the class "genius" who, though seemingly his exact opposite, resembles Napoleon Bonaparte in all essential points? If, then, a common core is detectable in different varieties of eminent men, crucial similarities should be even more readily demonstrable in the absence, at least the relative absence, of glaring outward differences that are likely to detract from the salient traits of the probands. In other words, Napoleon and his antipode—and mate in spirit—should indicate the poles between which the world of the genius extends, although not necessarily the poles around which it revolves, for, indeed, in studying different personalities, a great many polar differences are found.

At this point, Leonardo da Vinci's name comes to mind. I am referring to Leonardo chiefly as a scientist rather than an artist although the Florentine's achievements were promoted by his scientific insight, as were his scientific feats aided by his artistic abilities, which makes it difficult to separate the two aspects of his genius.

The mind of Leonardo da Vinci

The main sources of information are the two Vasari biographies (*315*), and Leonardo's pictorial and literary work as collected in his Notebooks, edited by Richter (*258*) and McCurdy (*197*).* The original notes are scattered over various collections of artistic and literary treasures in England, France, Italy and perhaps Austria, the "Codex Atlanticus," so christened because of its large size, being displayed in a magnificent crystal shrine in the Ambrosian Library of Milan. The aggregate page number of the individual notes is usually given as 5000 but it appears likely that not all of Leonardo's writings were preserved and that the full extent of his contributions to science will never be known. He himself spoke of 120 books. That he always kept one chained to his belt, sketching and making notes whenever he found something worthy of recording may be mentioned for what it is worth.

The outer circumstances of his life (as far as they are known) are quickly told. Born five centuries ago (1452), as the illegitimate child of a wealthy Florentine lawyer and a peasant girl, he was brought up in his father's house after his mother's marriage, several years after his birth, to a man of her own class. His eminent artistic abilities were discovered while he was still a child and he is reported to have learned so rapidly whatever was taught to him that he appeared to remember rather than apprehend things—to the philosophically inclined reader a belated confirmation may be of Plato's creed that the soul, having been reborn, remembers the eternal Ideas. Leonardo became a member of the Florentine Guild of Painters at the age of twenty; four years later he opened a workshop of his own. The records of the Guild, incorporated for some reason into that of the Physicians and Apothecaries (for which, incidentally, he harbored an aversion) showed that he failed to pay his dues, that he was neglectful in his religious duties and that he worked on high festival days. Various sponsors, among them Cesare Borgio and

---

* For biographical data, see also the following sources: *11, 13, 48, 119, 125, 126, 156, 158, 199, 227, 236.*

Lodovico Sforza, Duke of Milan, employed his services as an artist and engineer. The master lived in various Italian cities, mostly in Florence and Milan. Unless called upon to inspect fortifications, to map out the country side and to study the problem of rerouting the river Arno, he seemed to have travelled little. (His description of an earthquake in Asia Minor is pretty generally regarded as a capricious fantasy.) His chief contacts were the mathematician Luca de Pacioli, a monk, the youthful and witty Marc Antonio della Torre, (*227*) believed to have been the leading anatomist of his time, and Leone Battista Alberti, reportedly his equal in many respects. Leonardo studied the writings of Galen and Archimedes and the famous Roman builder Vitruvius but showed little interest in the poetry and the philosophical writings of the ancients; having never been taught either Greek or Latin, he was, from a purely literary viewpoint, not a true representative of the Renaissance spirit. He wanted to be "a son rather than a grandson of Nature" and to "read by the light of experience." His later years were clouded by a conflict with the Pope who ordered him to discontinue his anatomical studies. At the age of 64, he went to France where he spent his last few years in the King's services.

The legend spun around Leonardo's name fills but a short moment that vanished long ago in the infinite void of time; moreover, the fact that, several hundred years after his death, the lead coffins found in the crypt of the chapel of St. Cloux where he was buried were melted down, seems to acquire symbolic significance. The physical destruction of his remains deepens the illusion, created by his dreamlike drawings and the terse, detached language in which many of his thoughts are phrased, that Leonardo da Vinci lived in the past as an unearthly spirit rather than as a human being. Yet he was depicted as a good natured lad, amiable, charming, extremely handsome and of unusual physical strength, a famous dancer, an accomplished lute player, and involved in love affairs with the fair maidens of Florence. He was fond of colorful, gorgeous clothes, of which a short coat of his own design, tailored of pink silk, seems to have been much talked about by the gay crowd. He enjoyed whatever life had to offer. At one time or another, a widening gulf began to separate him from his fellow men. It is not established whether sexual abnormalities which came to the fore, or unhappy experiences he found difficult to forget or mounting preoccupation with his manifold work were responsible for his aloofness. This interpretation may justifiably be attacked as superficial. Various charges were levelled against him. That he chose his pupils according to their comeliness was interpreted as a sign of homosexuality; that he had no true personal friends, as a sign of withdrawal. He was suspected of having selfishly sought the company of men of distinction from whose experiences he could profit, or taking without giving anything in return. Leonardo, on the other hand, complained about the ungratefulness of his pupils, of which Francesco Melzi, who accompanied him to France and later became his heir, was a notable exception. As a man of intensely aristocratic taste, having more dislikes than likes as far as people were concerned, Leonardo preferred to live in the cold yet clear and clean air of solitude*. The following passages found scattered over various periods of his writings are here collected. "Only by being alone can you belong completely to yourself. If you have only one companion, you are only half your own. Strength is in solitude. I have come to the conclusion that it is bad if men are hostile and worse if they are friendly. Man has a great power of speech but the greater part thereof is empty and deceitful. Coarse people with bad habits do not deserve such beautiful instruments, such a complex anatomical equipment as the human body. They should merely have a sack for taking in food and letting it out again for they are nothing but an alimentary canal." (He anticipated, so to speak, the discovery of the coelenterates.) His famous caricatures mirror this attitude perhaps even more eloquently. Drawn with sadistic delight, they feature dwarfs, ugly people of all kinds and freaks which he picked up in the street and induced to come to his studio to serve as models. He was certainly not consistent in saying—unless of course his drawings should be shrewdly reinterpreted—that, "in the final analysis, the painter paints himself."

His Notebooks, kept under double lock for most of the time, the story has it, are the most authentic and elaborate guide to Leonardo da Vinci's mind. It was suggested by some that the notes were merely laboratory diaries; yet it would appear more likely that they were a means of recording ideas as they blossomed in his mind in overwhelming abundance. Some remarks he must have jotted down in great haste for fear of forgetting them, for they run into drawings to which they bear no relationship. He would crowd many drawings covering in turn a wide variety of subjects into one page, which made future editing a practically hopeless task. Several features were widely commented upon, namely, the fact that the notes are written from right to left (which is of little interest in the present context) that they are penned in code letters and that they do not pertain to the writer's private life, more particularly its sexual aspects. It is true that there are merely a few terse statements touching upon personal affairs as, for example, the money spent for his mother's funeral and the military defeat and moral ruin of the Regent of Milan, a remark which, because of a close association of many years, is noteworthy for its dryness: "This day the Duke lost his state, his possessions and his liberty, and none of his works is completed." It was suggested that he wrote in private code for fear of antagonizing the church—did he not write, in capital letters: "THE SUN DOES NOT MOVE?" On the other hand, would not the use of code letters have aroused the very suspicion he tried to avoid? To us, it would seem that the peculiarity in question reflects his retiring nature, that it symbolizes the writer's covenant with himself, a compensation for the loss of communion with his fellowmen. His notes, we feel, were a means of communication with a unique audience the sole member of which was the man who wrote them. It cannot be very well known whether his failure to refer to personal sex-experiences indicates perversion, or the fact that an outlet, be it natural or abnormal, had been found elsewhere. The following note leaves room for almost any interpretation: "Intellectual passion drives out sensuality; he who does not curb lustful desires puts himself on the level with the beasts." Is this rationalized asceticism or a confession of guilt? What, then, may be the key to Leonardo's personality? What was the fountainhead and the nature of his genius? Is it not absurd to compare such different persons as Napoleon and Leonardo?

In a way, Leonardo da Vinci's childhood seems

---

* "For the most part I do the thing which my own nature drives me to do ... I live in that solitude which is painful in youth, but delicious in the years of maturity." (A. Einstein, 77a.)

to have been perpetual. Nature, his laboratory, was at the same time his nursery; his toys were canvas, brushes, colors, chemicals, pencils, pens, compass, ruler, scalpels, optical, measuring, mechanical and musical instruments. Like Napoleon, he thought in terms of objectives and their attainment. Unlike the latter's way to come to terms with reality, however, his own attitude was contemplative and self-contained; the steady growth of knowledge carried its own reward. "The truth of things," he wrote, "is the chief food of all finer intellects." Anything that would arouse his insatiable curiosity was his goal. Thus, he remained in a certain sense a child who finds his happiness in "playing," but who at the same time learns and creates, rather as Napoleon remained in a certain sense a perpetual student who, while studying, became a creative thinker. Changeable like a child, Leonardo would drop a "toy" the moment another object caught his imagination. Playing, he became a painter, sculptor, musician, physicist, engineer, mathematician, anatomist, physiologist, geologist, geographer, philosopher, designer of costumes, and— maker of playtoys.*

The essays and books dealing with Leonardo's manifold activities fill many library shelfs†. To the physician, McMurrich's (211), Keele's (156) and O'Malley and de Saunder's (247) monographs, which are devoted to his anatomical and physiological studies, are the most interesting. The writer was a universal genius who accomplished (or might have accomplished) more than anyone else but rarely ever finished anything he had begun. Even some of his very first commissions remained uncompleted. His famous "Treatise on Painting" was edited by literary

executors. Temporizing on his part would give rise to conflicts with his patrons and involve him in litigation. Yet in spite of this basically child-like trait he was unable to overcome (one does not really know whether he tried) he remarked: "No amount of work is sufficient to weary me. Obstacles cannot bend me. Every obstacle yields to effort." (Centuries later, Napoleon said: "When one wills strongly, one succeeds"). It is reported that he would stand for hours, absorbed in thought, although many a truth must have come to him readily. One day peasants brought him incrustated shells they had found in the mountains. At that time, the opinion prevailed that what we now know to be fossils were produced by the light of the stars, a striking illumination of the mystic trends warping the mind of medieval man. Much later, even the keen Voltaire thought that the shells had been lost by pilgrims carrying them on their hats. Leonardo's interpretation, which is too long to be summarized here, is, in substance, identical with that of present day geologists. It may well be one of the most remarkable instances of reconstructive reasoning in science (125, 126).

Leonardo, whose mind absorbed everything that happened to catch his fancy, set out to make his own discoveries. Being a predominantly visual type he felt that, through observation, Nature would eventually yield her secrets. What more accurate way or recording could there be for this "seer" but to draw what he was seeing? To him, seeing meant intellectual absorption of reality—"saper vedere" . . . "the eye which is the window of the soul is the chief means whereby the understanding may fully and abundantly appreciate the intimate works of nature."

The variety of things he studied—drew, that is—and the variety of other, sometimes fantastic, objects to which he gave life for his own amusement are almost limitless. In turning the pages of the volumes in which his drawings are reproduced we find leaves and flowers, the play and interaction of shadows cast by geometrical bodies to bring out the eternal laws of projection, the "tenderness and charm of faces of men and women as they pass along the shadowed streets between dark walls of houses at twilight on clouded days." We see gowns and draperies falling into a maze of folds; the dissected tendons and claws of a bear's paw, the flight patterns of birds, a flying machine, the measurements of a

---

* A. Valentin (314a) writes: "How many plans he might have carried to completion if they had not been too vast and too amazingly bold; how many discoveries he might have passed on to humanity if he had not always been wrestling with flawless and absolutely complete demonstration; how many masterpieces he might have finished if he had not striven for absolute perfection:" Valentin's interpretation would suggest a compulsive rather than a childlike element in Leonardo's character. However, the two traits are by no means incompatible.

† According to a recently published article in the AMA News (December 29, 1958) the Elmer Belt Library of Vinciana in Los Angeles consists of 950 items and answers each year more than 2000 queries from all over the world.

horse's leg, the intestinal blood vessels of an old man to whom he had spoken shortly before his death and whose corpse "being a heretic and cynical dissector of human bodies" he had cut into right afterwards; the unborn child curled up in its mother's womb, portraits, playing and fighting animals, weird monsters, winged dragons, allegories, designs of buildings, streets intersecting at different levels, the plan of a canal ascending a hill by means of locks, fortresses and weapons to destroy them, towering rocks, the confusingly intermingling streams of whirlpools, which only the eye of the genius could unravel, and the eddies formed by blood flowing around the aortic cusps. We see soft light falling from friendly skies, caressing sleepy Tuscan valleys. We see cloudbursts, raging floods, the mad, triumphant waters of the deluge, and the smile, brightening the faces of saints and angels—a smile that might have enlivened the master's countenance, a thinking mask.

Is it possible to bring Leonardo's artistic and scientific genius upon a common denominator? Perhaps, his word that the eye is the window of the soul, or the chief means whereby we fully and abundantly appreciate the intimate works of nature, provides a clue to the workings of his mind. As a thinker, he translated configurational data into abstract relational, terms; he *thought where others would merely see*. As an artist, he expressed abstract relations in configurations and patterns. His power of visualization, of depicting graphically what he thought out, and of "reasoning" with the aid of pencil, brush and tool were unique assets; *he produced visible worlds where others would merely think*. "The discerning power of his eye overtook the swiftness of motion and penetrated the complexity of rapidly changing forms. His analysis of a bird's wing in flight and of the movements of water in a whirlpool were confirmed by slow motion cinematography." (125) His inventions demonstrate his gift of anticipative reasoning. His countless discoveries prove his equally stupendous power of apperception and mental reconstruction. Leonardo's life was short in proportion to the wealth of his accomplishments. It is likely that he reasoned more often intuitively than reflectively, taking rapid shortcuts. Relying on his own, inexhaustible mental power, he might have considered discursive reasoning a waste of time.

Apart from his artistic ability, then, the sig-nificant traits of Leonardo's genius appear to be his insatiable thirst for knowledge, or exploratory instinct, his universality and ingenuity. Peculiar features were his changefulness, and distractibility by whatever fields of science and art happened to arouse his interest, a certain shyness, sensitivity and mysanthropy which, particularly in the presence of his great physical strength, cannot be readily accounted for. That his sexual life was abnormal or eventually became abnormal was suspected by many; that his alleged sexual abnormalities, whatever their nature, and his abnormal character traits were causally related is possible; that they explain his intellectual achievements and artistic eminence appears unlikely. Freud (85), in his well known psychosexual study on an infantile reminiscence of Leonardo, conjectured that a dream of a vulture having thrust his tail several times into the child's mouth betrays Leonardo's early feminization, homosexuality, his ensuing disgust and repression and especially the sublimation of sexual inquisitiveness to scientific curiosity. Leonardo's saying that of the "artist's work having been born of the union between the sense with what it loves as if a lover would unite with the object of his own desire" would seem to lend color to Freud's belief that the Florentine's intellectual curiosity and his passion for work were substitutes. On the other hand, a similar analogy might perhaps have been used by any artist who found it natural to compare creative drive and lust for work with sexual pleasure. Yet Leonardo's passion for knowledge is only part of the story. It may well be that the genius, a child of love, was brought up in the company of women, but does this necessarily mean that his experiences were different from those of other illegitimate children of his time? In the warm Italian nights, scores of bastards must have been sired. And many of these infants born out of wedlock no doubt were very dearly loved by their mothers with whom they lived. What became of these peasant children? Probably hill billies who, in due course, did as their progenitors had done. I cannot see how Leonardo's thirst for knowledge can be accounted for by his early childhood experiences; neither am I able to understand how his extraordinary achievements, even if his intellectual curiosity flowed from unresolved and therefore perpetuated sex curiosity, can possibly be explained by this trait alone. It seems difficult to believe that Freud should have explained Leonardo's accomplishments on the basis of sexual curiosity. Nevertheless, the curiosity-theory seems to be the very core of Freud's argument. In composing his essay, he acted as if unconsciously repressing the role of innate traits; and the concluding paragraph of his work leaves no doubt that he considered his own argument as far from conclusive.

Stripped to its bare essentials, the structure of superior mental endowment as illustrated by the personalities of Napoleon Bonaparte and Leonardo da Vinci shows two crucial determiners, namely, *strength of motivation* and, within the limits of human nature, *technical perfection of thought*. While both men saw their ultimate goal in the growth of their personality, they were different in many other respects—although, perhaps, not as different as one might be led to believe. Bonaparte's chief aim was the expansion of personal power; military science was an instrument wielded with virtuosity, although, in spite of the gratification its mastery afforded, it was a tool used for ulterior purposes rather than for its own sake. Leonardo was an artist-scientist who devoted his life to many endeavours, to activities which, seemingly, were ends in themselves. Yet the Florentine, too, might have (unknowingly perhaps) striven for power in whatever form he could embrace it. Hence, the common center of gravity representing the core of the genius' world might well unite, as we have surmised from the beginning, apparently unreconcilable diversities.* Both Napoleon and Leonardo, each in his own way, experienced growth through creation, the extension of the subjective world, and the corresponding extension of objective reality. The ever growing extension of subjective reality along the innumerable dimensions of the objective world may well be the highest function of the human intellect. Yet, by the very nature of things, it is bound to fall short of its goal; objective reality is the supreme paradox—an unending manifold which, the more intensely it is explored, the more unscrutable it becomes, and whose boundaries seem to recede into a great void.

The study of Leonardo's genius brings up the

---

* In other words, their *gratification preference* and *saturation potential* had much in common. (See Chapt. II, "Gratification and Frustration"

question of the relationship between science and art that exists within the wider framework of creativity. The common root of the two fields of human striving which, however, is not everywhere apparent as in the Florentine master's life, is the correspondence function of the human mind, which serves the concordant extension, just mentioned, of subjective and objective reality—the growth of the experiental world. Yet the two offshoots of the root are rarely equally developed, in fact, more often than not, only one will sprout. The scientist, be he a discoverer or inventor, by *"giving existence to what apparently has none,"* transforms objective reality or pre-existing truth into insight, which is a subjective state; the creative artist, on the other hand, translates subjective states into objective reality or to "works born of the union of the sense with what it loves." The nature of the subjective states involved and the significance of the phrase "the union between the sense and what it loves," will occupy us later. It provides a clue to the interpretation of art. In spite of the unending manifold of artistic and scientific creation, and of the different directions of growth, the correspondence function of the brain emerges as a basic, uniform, entity.

A proposed mechanism of superior mental aptitude

Thus far, we have studied supra-standard thought mechanisms in three ways. They were (a) the analysis of the mental traits of two eminent men who were polar opposites (b) the extrapolation of data arrived at from the investigation of normal thought processes and (c) the "inversion" of dysphrenic thought patterns. On the surface, it may appear safer, and therefore preferable, to employ purely inductive methods in examining superior mental endowment. However, the results of the investigation carried out along these lines by various psychologists proved to be meagre in proportion to the great number of data upon which they were based, and we feel that they need to be supplemented by other, somewhat unorthodox methods.

The following is a sketchy description and, to a degree, an interpretation of the mental processes in question. Owing to the possibility of cross-correlating not only marginal elements of concepts but also concepts with other data, goal leading associations are more likely to form in the mind of the genius than in the mind of average man. In fact, productivity seems to be exponentially related to the wealth of knowledge acquired on the part of the reasoner in various fields, rather than related in a linear fashion only. At the same time, the sources of error which, ordinarily, would be augmented by the large number of data, and also by the readiness and speed with which ideas emerge in a person's mind, are, the error-potential of the genius not-withstanding, counterbalanced by the intensified directionality of thought. (At this point, we remind ourselves that increased directiveness of thinking is nothing other than increased equi-libratory capacity of the organism at the intel-lective level of integration, that is, ultimately, a biological function.) In the mind of the genius, a vast number of associations of ideas is called into being. The increased associative power of fringe material favours bold generalizations and the discovery of analogies. The products of the associative processes described match the as-sertions generated in the inaugural phase of thought against the individual facets of class concepts or, alternately, the combinations of known data rapidly synthetized to guide struc-tures at crucial points of the reasoning process. Both the number of concepts and the complexity of thought material grows sharply, as does the potency and flexibility of psychisms involved in thought. It is chiefly the reconstructive and anticipative varieties of thinking—be it reflective or intuitive—that are brought to near perfection.

Is it possible to identify "technical" aspects of superior mental power which, conceivably, underly some of the above discussed phenomena? We suspect that, as in the course of algorithmic operations, incorporative symbols are invented and introduced into the process of thinking to represent complicated relations, indeed, whole sets of relations, so in non-mathematical thought, the tendency to symbolize psychisms is enhanced in line with the increasing complexity of thinking sets involved and, at the same time, in proportion to the tremendously multiplied possibilities of their interaction. Once accomplished, symboliza-tion of thought material should facilitate the manipulation of complex mental systems. Inter-estingly enough, these symbolic devices presumed to operate in superior intelligence are not necessarily verbalized. Rather, some of them seem to be embodied in non-verbalized and non-

picturable or only vaguely picturable mental experiences. We have explained how mathe-matical symbols span vast reaches of thought at heights from which details are no longer visible, indeed, that they appear to bridge an apparent void. At the same time, we have made it clear how the operational dimensions of the intellective level acquired by the use of symbols seem to re-introduce elements of automaticity prevailing at lower strata of the nervous system. We have called attention to the rapid attainment of results, for which, on the part of mathematicians, no immediate proof could be furnished, and which suggests that whole reasoning sets may be represented and manipulated by non-picturable psychisms. Similar algorithmic-like mechanisms may well operate in non-mathematical thought.

Certain observations appear to give substance to the notion that algorithmic-like operations play a more frequent role in thought than is commonly recognized. As described by Cleveland (51) highly gifted chess players make goal leading moves for which they are unable to give im-mediate reasons and which, we surmise, represent perhaps only a small segment of a variety of other, "intuitively" performed acts. Einstein's introspective experiences, described in his already cited letter to Hadamard (100), are likewise suggestive evidence of a "non-mathematical algorithm." In this communication, the physicist describes "psychical conditions" which seem to serve the elements of thought. They can be more or less voluntarily reproduced; they have, in Einstein's words, a certain connection with relevant biological concepts—"the play with these elements is aimed to be analogous to certain logical connections one is searching for"— and they are represented by more or less clear visual images or kinesthetic experiences. "Con-ventional words or other signs have to be sought for laboriously to express them in secondary stages of thought."

The above account of productive thinking seems to substantiate the theory that the psychisms ("psychical conditions") in question are not verbalized, but that, nevertheless, their relationstructure corresponds to that of the nascent logical connections. At the same time, it is evident that the psychisms are not mathe-matical symbols; they are elements representing relations that are only secondarily expressible in mathematical language. Perhaps, in Einstein's mind, the translation of (non-mathematical) algorithmic elements into the notation system consciousness took shape at the level of primitive visual sensations (his *Bewusstseinslagen* and *Bewusstheiten* were visually colored) and the kinesthetic sensations marked the appearance of impulses designed to convert the emerging data into the written symbols of language.

As regards the question of verbalization, Einstein's experiences, especially if supplemented by Francis Galton's (*86*) records based on introspection and also Kainz' (*151a*) studies (who quotes Roentgen and other scientists), adduce further evidence that verbal fluency is not necessarily a prerequisite of superior intellectual ability. On the other hand, the establishment of concept-word relationships adds more, oftentimes self-created tools of thought to the genius' armamentarium in that meanings become fixated. By the interaction of verbal symbols which, too, acquire an element of automaticity inherent in the structure of language, new meanings emerge and, thereby, are given both existence and expression.

The thought patterns and thought mechanisms of the genius and those of the dysphrenic are extremities of a unitary scale. To reiterate: the patterns operating in superior intelligence are the very inversion of those involved in dysphrenic thought. In the genius, the directionality of thought and, with it, the state of equilibrium at the intellective level reaches a maximum. In dysphrenic thinking, the cores of concepts, let alone their fringes, lack goal leading properties. At the opposite extremity of the scale, fringes are shifted as it were into the widening center of concepts. Granted that this is merely a metaphorical expression which may be challenged by some as verbal explanation, it nevertheless indicates that even the fringes operate in the fashion of core-elements and that the apparent tangentiality of thought thus produced results in peak productivity. In fact, the utilization of fringes as relation generating devices comes to the fore even in the genius' dreams, as the symbols of dream language are pictorialized fringes of concepts. It may be well to recall renewed attention to Kekulé's experience who, in a dream-like state, saw a snake biting his own tail, and immediately grasped the meaning of the picture he saw before him—the ring-like constitution of the benzene molecule. Thus, the fringes of concepts operate as core-elements even in the

dream of the genius and, likewise, in the dream-like restructuring of the waking state that occurs in certain forms of artistic inspiration. In other words, the core-area of concepts is widened. At the dysphrenic extremity of the scale on the other hand, the core-fringe relationship is reversed in line with the core-atrophy of concepts. In the dream-like life of the schizophrenic, fringe dominance is carried to extremes, disrupting both concept formation and thinking. The pseudo-productivity of the schizophrenic reflects the tendency of associations by similarity to develop along tangential paths, of associations by contiguity to emerge in a mechanical fashion and, at the same time, the absence of corrective feedbacks.

The role of *modality-related* and of *mathematical concepts* deserves special consideration. Goethe, "whether in the throes of creation or engaged in research always dealt with visual concepts and it is readily seen that such method must have benefited his scientific work as it enhanced the perceptual values of his creative work" (*224a*). In a certain sense, the use of modality-related concepts establishes a close link between the thought technique prevailing in dreams and in dysphrenic thought. Nevertheless, the products of the apparently identical techniques differ widely. One can hardly imagine a more profound difference than that between the "Faust" tragedy, a "dream" spun over a period of some six decades, and the schizophrenic's dream-like visions and creations. On the other hand, superior thought techniques would seem to make use of conceptual elements whose formal properties resemble *mathematical concepts*, that is, mental ordering devices from which, in the course of concept formation, every trace of sense modality has been extracted, which lack fringes altogether and which are the direct opposite of modality related concepts. And since, as we have said, relationships between mathematical concepts exist of necessity, the genius, as a thinker, is apt to discover eternal truths*.

————

* The question arises why not every genius is, at the same time, a gifted mathematician, in fact, why superior mental endowment may be associated with almost complete lack of mathematical aptitude. (Cf., e.g., Goethe and Freud.) The answer to this question may be provided by the law of variability operating in biological systems, and of dissociation of function under normal and abnormal conditions.

To *summarize*: To the extent that the mechanism of thinking in the genius is at all accessible to psychological interpretation and understanding, superior intellectual endowment is a state of *supra-standard abnormality*, that is, one exceeding the normal performance range, while dysphrenic thought is a *substandard abnormality*. (The expression abnormal and pathological are not necessarily coterminous as has already been hinted at in the introductory chapter.) The correspondence function of the brain of the genius is geared to the highest pitch, and both abstract and concrete ordering devices ranging from the most impalpable psychisms to the most vivid mental images are used to structure reality along significant parameters. In dysphrenic thought on the other hand, the correspondence function of the brain is distorted at the perceptual level, and "inverted" at the intellective level. Paradoxically, the extremes of the scale may turn toward each other in a wide circle as it were and, eventually, overlap. As a result, supra-standard and sub-standard abnormalities may create either mixed—and sometimes puzzling—patterns of productive thinking in one and the same individual or they may become segregated in the course of hereditary transmission of traits. In the first eventuality, they may well account for many peculiar features in the genealogy of the man of genius, and for seemingly inconsistent traits of his personality.

It hardly needs to be mentioned that abnormal thought patterns may be produced not only by dysphrenic but also by dysphoric states. Gauss, by common consent one of the greatest mathematicians who ever lived, confessed that he was given to states of depression during which his power of reasoning waned and his productivity was at a low ebb.

IV

Skill

The hand is man's external brain

KANT

Broadly defined, skill is the translation of thought into action mediated by a special mechanism which, in turn, integrates the intellective level with the sceleto-muscular effectors of the organism. Although many skilled movements are dependent on the coordinated activity of both cerebral hemispheres, it is convenient, for now, at least, to disregard the factor of cerebral dominance. Hence, we propose to study the phenomena of mono-hemispheric integration first.

─────────Mono-hemispheric integration of skilled movements

General considerations

Thought and movement

In the following pages, we shall develop a general concept of the neuropsychology of skilled movements, touch briefly upon some of their comparative anatomical and physiological aspects, review representative rival theories and offer a conceptual analysis of the terms *function*, *dissociation of function* and *symptom* with special reference to the disorders of skill and recognition. Recognition has thus far been studied in connection with the process of thinking. The reason for reopening the discussion on a subject already dealt with is the twofold function of the cerebral provinces concerned with recognitive thought, that is to say, their position at a crossroad of the integration of higher cerebral functions, one of which is thinking, the other skilled action. The student, working his way through the territory he set out to explore, will find himself sooner or later at a strategic junction already encountered which, however, presents itself, as he continues his journey, from a different angle.

Although many parts of the nervous system are in one way or another concerned with the integration of skilled movements, the crucial role of the psycho-neural level (Figs. 1, 2, 8), which is compounded of a *sensory division* (II.s.) and a *motor division* (II.m.) requires a study of its own. The term psycho-neural refers to the dual function of certain cortical localities, more precisely, as has been explained in the opening chapter, their pathophysiology rather than their physiology. Nevertheless, it will be necessary to define the function of both II.s. and II.m. not only in pathophysiological terms but also in physiological terms, that is, to assign, to either group of centers, a specific quota of action. It will bear repetition that lesions of the centers under study (some of which prove to be quite small) may involve cerebral functions that embody *psychic elements*, for example those involved in reading and writing. A person may become aphasic as a result of a small lesion in Broca's center but a patient cannot be *globally demented* incident to a small lesion anywhere in the cortex of either hemisphere of the brain. In fact, the distinction between sensory-motor and conceptual provinces of the cortex on the one hand and psycho-neural centers on the other is based largely on the observation that (a) small, optimal lesions of II.m. may temporarily or permanently abolish skilled movements without paralyzing the muscles by means of which they are carried out and (b) on the parallel observation that lesions of II.s. may abolish the ability to recognize objects, to read, etc., without damage to the cortical end stations of vision. (In certain instances, there may be some concomitant weakness or impairment of elementary sensory functions which, however, is of minor degree, and the same applies to potentially coexisting intellective impairment whenever present.) In other words, in the sensory sphere, the appreciation of visual, auditory etc patterns rather than elementary perceptions is apt to be impaired by appropriately placed lesions in the poterior cortex and, in the motor sphere, the ability to perform skilled movements (rather than motility as such) by strategically located lesions in the anterior cortex. The idea, then, that certain parts of the posterior cortex that represent the sensory division of the psycho-neural level are concerned with pattern perception and, by the same token, that specific parts of the anterior cortex representing the motor division of the psycho-neural level mediate skilled movements, is an inference based in clinical observations. Now since, as we have pointed out in various contexts, the idea of a psycho-neural level of integration is based on the existence of specific disorders, it would be logical to stipulate *centers of disorders* rather than *centers of function*. On the other hand, there is much to be said for the concept of *cortical centers as localities which control the totality of integrative acts on which a given performance depends*. Obviously, this point needs to be clarified especially since the performances in question, namely, reading, writing, etc., have been acquired during life, and it is difficult to understand how the centers of recognition and skill have come into being in the first instance while the existence of, say, respiratory, cardio-vascular and other centers of a similar category is a foregone conclusion.

Thus, if the concept of centers of recognition and skill is to be maintained, we have to find *positive criteria* to justify the continued use of the terms in question. Such criteria, one would assume, might be certain physiological properties common to all *motor* psycho-neural centers, and other properties common to their *sensory* counterparts, if not, indeed, properties common to all psycho-neural centers, both sensory and motor. The presence of common features will validate the concept of a psycho-neural level of function and, hence, of dysfunction. At the same time, it will justify the segregation of an intermediate level thus established from a sensory-motor level proper (I.) and an intellective level (III.).

THE ROLE OF CENTER II.s. AS AN ASSOCIATIVE BRAIN ORGAN

It is of the utmost importance to realize that the execution of skilled movements may be made impossible not only as the result of a lesion involving localities designated as II.m. but also of their sensory counterparts II.s. The reverse does not necessarily hold true and, moreover, the symptoms referable to lesions of II.s. differ in some respects from those caused by damage to II.m. The impairment of skilled movements incident to lesions involving the sensory sphere is a peculiar feature whose mechanism is not immediately apparent.

The following explanation may be offered as the most likely solution of the problem of the physiology of skilled movements, including the role of the sensory elements in their integration.

Certain *motor use patterns* which are neural substrates of the corresponding *synergies* are innate while others develop in the course of the maturation of the nervous system and the concomitant individuation of early mass movements. For example, grasping movements become manipulative movements; the babbling of the infant differentiates to oro-articulatory movements; and, after many trials, its crawling to erect gait. It is not unreasonable to assume that, out of the vast number of random movements performed by the infant, those movements which, little by little, through association by contiguity, become linked up with certain anticipated effects, are selected with increasing frequency and deliberation and, further, that some of them form the early *seeking reactions* or preferentially initiated synergies. More specifically, the following categories of movements representing increasingly effective means of reality control may be recognized:

(a) those elicited, rather than volitionally performed, by *instinctive needs* and by the *releasers of consummatory reactions*,

(b) *primitive expressive movements*, and

(c) *repetitive, seemingly self-perpetuating movements* which, although initiated in an automatic fashion, are kept going by the gratification they provide. Earlier in this volume, we made reference to the fact that gratification or pleasure, in the widest sense of the term, is a potentially self-perpetuating stimulus producing a "closed loop response" (Fig. 10), and that it has the properties of an impelling, positive affect which re-initiates the seeking reaction after it has run its course. We are referring especially to certain repetitive movements which, gradually, become associated with predictable changes or conditions. Some of these movements occupy, because of their gratifying effects, a preferred position within the early kinetic repertoire of the organism. The predictable effects are tested out on an inductive basis as it were as long as they provide pleasure, that is, continued to the point of saturation. Not only are they related to early seeking reactions, but to nascent playing activity which, sooner or later, develops to higher forms of play. As movements effects come to depend more and more on the resources of the still orimentary conceptual level, thought begins to shape the kinetic repertoire of the child.

Now, the conceptual level of the mature

organism is a superstructure erected upon the configurational level (Fig. 7). The latter, for its part, is nothing other than the sensory division of the psycho-neural level, at which there are formed the precurrent sensory correlates of volitional movements. The above described trial and error phase of sensory-motor integration is superseded by the increasing concordance between, on the one hand, sensory use patterns or "blueprints" of movements elaborated by II.s. and the motor use patterns elaborated by II.m., in other words, the *somatization of sensory patterns by motor patterns*. Clearly, there must be concordance between the sensory and the motor activity although concordance is manifest only in those instances in which the organs of execution literally duplicate sensory patterns in the external world. In the visual sphere, the precurrent sensory patterns may be anticipatory visualizations of specific movements performed in the past; in the auditory sphere, it may be the inner experience of a sound, or of a sequence of sounds that has been heard. That this is actually the case is brought out by self-observation in the course of the acquisition of diverse skills, which corresponds to the state of universal inexperience at early ontogenetic stages. In other instances, kinesthetic feedbacks are instrumental in the execution of the movements in question but it would be a mistake to assume that, in the early stages at least, the duplicated patterns are purely kinesthetic in character. Somatization, as previously defined, is the production of motor effects which conform to, and thereby realize, corresponding sensory (visual and auditory) patterns. True, the somatization of sensory elements is manifest only whenever sensory patterns, the "blueprints" or forerunning ideas of motor processes, are literally translated into corresponding motor patterns (as, for example, the mental image of a triangle into its pictorial representation) but somatization mechanisms are instrumental in the realization of forerunning ideas even in those instances in which, at least at an advanced stage of training and experience, the replicating character of the movement concerned is inconspicuous. And, in so far as countless gradations exist between replicating movements and those in which the element of pattern duplication is at a minimum, the sensory division of the psycho-neural level is the connecting link between the conceptual level as the highest

selector mechanism and the motor division of the psycho-neural level. Indirectly, then, *II.s. is the connecting link between III.s. and the effector organs*, or, for that matter, *between thought and movement*. The formation of sensory-motor use patterns so established serves as a baseline for any form of integration at the configurational and, implicitly, at the conceptual level. This is only natural; the former is the functional primordium of the latter and, in the course of development, both phylogenetically and ontogenetically, the configurational level is relegated to a subordinate although still active agency. It is fair to say that replicating movements, i.e., movements which literally repeat or, more accurately, give reality to configurational patterns, are limiting cases of movements shaped in accordance with conceptualized schemes. The schemes, in turn are the mental designs of motor acts.

THE ROLE OF CENTER II.s. AS A PROJECTIVE BRAIN ORGAN

The understanding of the relationships between II.s. and II.m. as we see them is further dependent on the determination of the quota of action contributed

(a) by II.s. to the performance complex mediated by the entire sensory division of the brain and

(b) by II.m. to the performance complex mediated by its entire motor division.

The infant's experiental world is poorly structured as compared to the world of the mature organism. As a result of the grouping activity of the highest levels of the nervous system, which elaborates the stimuli furnished by the receptor apparatus to several experiental modalities, significant aggregates of perceptions are gradually assembled into structured stimuli, the aforementioned configurations or gestalten. Accordingly, the creation of gestaltqualities in what would otherwise remain mere aggregates of perceptual experiences is a function of the sensory psychoneural apparatus. Gestalten, for their part, are *concrete categorizing* psychisms or the functional primordia of concepts, which are *abstract categorizing psychisms*. Now, once configurationals timuli or gestalten have been formed, they can be generalized, that is, their analog value kept constant although they may be built up out of different elementary stimuli; their relation structure remains the same in spite of the fact that their individual components (perceptual constituents) may vary within a wide range. It is this property of the brain that enables a person to read numbers "written" on his skin, and to recognize letters out of cardboard and put into the palm of his hand. Thus, another function of the sensory segment of the psychoneural level is the *configurational generalization* of stimuli and their incorporation into higher (concrete or palpable) *iso-morphic units*. Configurational generalization is a precursor of *conceptual generalization* or concept formation which, for its part, is the generalization of stimuli accomplished by their incorporation into higher *invariant units*. To put it in another way, II.s. is concerned with the appreciation of sensory relationstructures in the course of the elaboration of thought from perception. *The "centers of recognition" have a generalizing function in that they are able to pattern, to equivalent units, any combination of perceptions having identical relations in space or time.* For example, a child that has learned to recognize a chair will ordinarily recognize any chair no matter how oddly it may be shaped or, having learned to recognize the letter A, will recognize it even though it may be written as V or ▷ or ◁. The very same principle operates in the auditory sphere. Once one has learned to recognize a tune played in a certain key one will have little difficulty in recognizing it if it is played in a different key. Small, appropriately placed lesion interfere with the ability to appreciate gestalten in the sphere of the diverse sensory modalities. For example, diseases processes involving Wernicke's center, a specialized part of II.s., involve, in spite of adequate auditory acuity, the appreciation of certain auditory gestalten. Other lesions of II.s., although primitive visual and tactile functions may be entirely intact, interfere with the appreciation of visual or, as the case may be, tactile gestalten. The resulting disorders are known, respectively, as *visual, auditory,* and *tactile* agnosias.

The Role of the Center II.m. as an Associative Brain Organ; Its Interaction with Center II.s.

The motor division (II.m.) of the psychoneural level is concerned with the somatization of configurational stimuli, or the execution of movements that duplicate the configurational data elaborated by II.s. Thus, II.m. is concerned with the *somatization* of conceptual stimuli, that is to say, the realization, in the external world, or objective sphere of reality, of relations conceived in the internal world, or subjective sphere of reality. In other words, *II.m. is concerned with the conversion of sensory analogs into motor analogs.* Broadly defined, *constructional apraxia* is the inability to convert sensory analogs into motor analogs, *ideo-kinetic apraxia* the inability to integrate sensory analogs with the appropriate motor analogs, *motor apraxia* the inability to form motor analogs, *ideatory apraxia* the inability to form the mental designs of motor acts in their proper sequence; and lastly, *amnestic apraxia* the inability to initiate appropriate sensory analogs. Combining the propositions formulated in the foregoing paragraphs, we realize that the functions of the conceptual level or III.s. as a superstructure of the configurational level accounts for the strategic position and the dual role of the latter in the elaborate reflec arc scheme illustrating the integration of higher cerebral functions, more especially the fact that II.s. is instrumental (a) in linking II.s. with III.m., that is, implicitly, in *recognition* and *thought* and (b) in linking III.s. with I.m., in other words, in *skilled action*.

The Role of Center II.m. as a Projective Brain Organ

The somatization of configurational use patterns and their conceptual derivatives is not the only function of the motor division of the psychoneural level. *It structures the motor output in a similar way as II.s. structures the sensory input.* Within natural limits, the somatization of sensory patterns may be accomplished by any effector. For example, movements which are habitually executed with the right hand may, in a crude way, it is true, be performed by the right leg. For example, Lashley (*287*) observed that monkeys shift readily from one hand to another when one side has been paralyzed by neural injury. If the animals were taught manipulative skills in which they used only one hand and the motor cortex responsible for that limb was then removed, the animals promptly used the other hand to solve the problem. To the extent that different movements embody identical elements, that is, that they are *iso-effective movements*, the motor division of the psycho-neural level selects not only the sceleto-muscular mechanism most suitable for their realization but, whenever necessity arises, mediates iso-effective movements by means of second line effectors. The performance patterns of second line effectors are crude analogs of those produced by first line effectors. It is fair to say that motor psycho-neural centers form use patterns of movements having in common the production of similar motor effects. In a certain sense, the *motor psycho-neural centers are able to generalize a given movement pattern kinetically, rather as the sensory psycho-neural centers generalize a stimulus complex configurationally*. Optimal lesions abolish certain skilled movements irrespective of the effectors used. For example, an agraphic patient is unable to use any (otherwise normal) limb for the purpose of writing. By contrast, a right handed person suffering from a paralysis of his right arm is able to perform writing movements with his limbs other than his right upper extremity although, it is true, the movements are crude by comparison. *The sensory and the motor psycho-neural centers are not only centers of dysfunction but, at the same time, centers of function*. It is not true that only dysfunctions can be localized while functions are unlocalizable. It is not true that, in a complex machinery, only damage is a reality while the concept of the function of its individual parts is a phantom of the mind. Whether or not a function can be localized depends, as has already been said in the opening chapter, entirely on what is considered a function. Functions related to or mediated by certain provinces of the brain are, for example, the ability to differentiate between likeness and difference at various levels of complexity, that is to say, between congruence and incongruence on the one hand, and consistency and inconsistency on the other.

Now, the sensory use patterns underlying configurational relations are incorporated into abstract categorizing stimuli, just like perceptions are incorporated into configurational stimuli. With increasing maturation of the sensory division of the nervous system, stimuli of a conceptual order take the lead in response determination. Concepts, (embodying configurations and, implicitly, perceptions), are comparable to the incorporative symbols of algebra that embody primitive symbols. Failure to incorporate elementary impressions into the configurational reference system established by II.s. produces *perceptual agnosia*; to incorporate configurational data into the highest, conceptual system of reference established by III.s., *conceptual* (amnestic or associative) agnosia. Either form may be *visual, auditory* or *tactile* in character.

The Element of Volition in Skilled Movements

With increasing conceptual preponderance, there grows the repertory of forerunning ideas and, potentially at least, the variety of skilled movements. The more extensive the activity of the conceptual sphere of mentation, that is to say, the greater the repertory of *intellective antecedents* of motor responses, and the possibility to create and to multiply them by the initiation of *transfer mechanisms*, to generate new relations by the "alignment" (Figs. 16, 17) of known relations that is, the stronger the element of *volition* in skilled movements and, implicitly, the experience of self. On the other hand, the stronger the *innate element* in skilled movements, i.e., the greater the participation of archaic motor mechanisms, the less volitional the movement, the less prominent, accordingly, the experience of self and, at the same time, of the intentional character of the movement. The term *self*, we remind ourselves, refers to the *mode* in which there are experienced the interaction and interdependence relationships of the psychisms operating in the dominant sphere of mentation or the highest *sensory* agency of the neuraxis. The term *will* is a shorthand expression applied to the experience of the *sensory-motor* dependence relationships at the highest level of response-determination, namely, the dependence of movements on precurrent evaluative processes, in other words, the anticipation and the actual performance of movements in conformity with precurrent ideas. The delusion of the will being free is referable to the possibility of imagining the reality of decisions other than those having been made, and to visualize the reality of actions other than those having been taken. It is not the self that thinks but the mode in which intellective activity is experienced at the highest sensory (intellective) level *is* the self. And it is not the will that moves the effector organs but the mode in which their actuation is experienced *is* the will. The terms self and will are reification artifacts or products of language structure. The more prominent the role of response determining processes, the stronger the volitional element in the execution of skilled movements; the less prominent the response determining component in high level sensory-motor sequence, the weaker the volitional element. For example, a choreatic patient studied by Bostroem (*60*) declared that the abnormal movements occur automatically and cannot be suppressed. Other patients formulated their experiences somewhat as follows. "I cannot do anything about these movements. I cannot hold my arm still. I feel the urge to move and I have to give in." A third group of patients having been obviously confused by the disorganization of the sensory-motor apparatus expressed themselves as follows: "My arm moves by itself. Besides, I have the desire to fall in with the movement and to move the arm deliberately." Although the movement is induced by a pathological mechanism, the choreatic patient may to a degree experience himself as active or to a degree believe to act spontaneously. By contrast, patients having Jacksonian seizures feel that the movements are forced upon them, the reason being that the excitory process sparked by the epileptogenic focus plays directly upon the neurons constituting I.m., or, depending on the integrational complexity of the movements elicited by the abnormal stimulus, on II.m. or lastly, on the extrapyramidal centers of contraversion or other mass movements. I happened to observe a patient who, several times in succession, bared his thigh and, after scratching his skin, replaced the blanket with which he was covered. Originally, these movements were in no way conspicuous except perhaps for a certain measure of stereotypy. Their nature as inaugural movements of an epileptic seizure became manifest only after they had quickened and became frankly stereotyped, at which time the patient, pulling his blanket abruptly up and down, and alternatingly scratching his thigh, was found to be unresponsive. Similar pseudo-spontaneous movements may be observed when post-seizure unconsciousness subsides.

Likewise, the experience of self is dependent on the participation of the *axial stream of thought* in volitional movements. The more prominent the role of the axial stream of thought, the more vivid the experience of the self; the more prominent the role of the *marginal stream of thought*, the weaker the experience of the self. The other day, I removed a burned-out electric bulb from its socket. As I was about to replace it with a new one, I noticed that the corner in which the lamp was standing was quite dark and, in order better to see what I was doing, but still holding the new bulb in my hand, I "turned the light on." At that moment, the experience of self had vanished; in fact, it almost seemed as though the switch had been turned on by someone else. In the process of learning various skills, fore-running ideas are formed in the axial stream of thought, and the same applies to other, more complicated stimulus-response situations. An absent minded musician may play a melody in perfect coordination although, it is true, he is likely to play it with poor expression. As a result of training and experience, intended movements reach a high degree of automatization and, in this respect, are "less volitional and more automatic" (to use a phrase coined by Jackson) than they were at the stage of learning. With increasing experience, precurrent ideas emerge, seemingly of themselves, in the marginal stream of thought, freeing the axial current for the acquisition of novel synergies and of new skills. And since, in the course of training, skilled movements tend to become less volitional or, for that matter, increasingly automatic, the peculiar quality of awareness attending the execution of skilled movements is apt to fade in proportion to the automatization of the movements performed. Ultimately, the apparent automaticity with which skilled movements take shape approaches the automatism of primitive, somatic functions.

AUTOMATIZATION OF SKILLED MOVEMENTS

In *thought*, automatization is inaugurated by the introduction of symbols, that is to say, configurational stimuli representative of meanings, the specificity of relations. In a certain sense, then, the principles governing the integration of lower cerebral functions are substituted for those controlling higher functions of the neuraxis. With increasing automaticity, higher functions of the brain would seem to follow the laws controlling functions mediated by lower levels of integration. Discussing, in the preceding chapter, the comparison of "intrinsically generated relations" with one another, we found that, at the highest level of abstraction, where the simultaneous surveying of relations is made possible by the institution of symbols, the element of perception was re-introduced and that it lead, in a great circle as it were, the process of reasoning back to its very origin, perception. Apparently, *the automaticity of low level functions is put into the service of high level functions. Conversely, the superior relation generating capacity of higher levels enhances the performance range of lower levels.* The exemplification of this principle however must await the discussion of language functions later in this chapter. We see, in mere outlines it is true, a trend toward the *combination of level specific resources*, perhaps an expression of the principle of economy of effort that governs the functions of the organism.

In *conclusion*, then, the acquisition and, later, the execution of willed movements under the control of the conceptual level is merely a transitory stage of integration, to be superseded by a form of integration in which the resources of "adjacent" levels potentiate each other. (See "language mechanisms" and the "relationships between language and thought.") Just as the appreciation of abstract relations becomes perceptualized in the sensory sphere, so volitional movements become automatic in the motor sphere. Higher cerebral functions are derivatives of lower central nervous system functions. Yet, once the former attain a certain level of complexity, the performance pattern of the lower levels is re-introduced, and, by a synthesis of operational dimensions, the functional capacity of the highest level enhanced.

Motor pathways of skilled movements

In one of the foregoing paragraphs we made reference to the correspondence between mental design and motor act. Clinical experiences indicate that the cortico-spinal efferents constituting the pyramidal tract of the classics (the cortico-spinal neurons issuing from area 4) represent the structural elements involved in the realization of precurrent ideas into motor acts or, for that matter, of the translation of sensory analogs into motor analogs. How is I.m., the origin of the pyramidal tract, connected with II.m., a part of the anterior cortex and, indirectly, with the selector mechanism located in the posterior cortex?

Area 4, the motor strip, lies between (a) that part of the parietal cortex where the entire surface of the body is represented (the postcentral gyrus and the adjacent parts of the parietal lobe, more especially the superior parietal lobule), and (b) that part of the frontal cortex which receives, via numerous relay stations, the cerebello-vestibular afferents from the opposite part of the body. Thus, the pyramidal tract may be regarded as the cortico-spinal system most intimately related to the representation, in the cortex, of the two sensory systems that are concerned with the regulation of volitional movements, namely, of somesthetic and vestibulocerebellar systems. (Other vestibular afferents terminate in the temporal cortex and it may be surmised that they are parts of the supravestibular system concerned with mass movements.) Lassek (*291*) raised the following question: "What are the possible anatomical connections which make the pyramidal tracts work? There must be some that are concerned with initiating, directing, and breaking the impulses coming over the pyramidal tract. By braking, I mean inhibiting or dissipating the efferent flow, signaling accomplishment . . . Sherrington (1895) was the first who advanced the view that the pyramidal tract is composed of internuncial neurons which conduct under the influence of afferent nervous impulses acting upon their cells of origin. Bartlett, Bastian, Gooddy and Adrian felt that it is the afferent system, in association with its different receptors which is concerned with this particular phase of pyramidal activity." Now, there are good grounds for believing that the breaking mechanisms are the somesthetic and vestibulocerebellar afferents which function as intra-axial feedbacks while the initiating and directing mechanisms are nothing other than the selector apparatus consisting of II.s. and III.s., and its auxiliary, II.m. (At the present state of our knowledge, it would be idle to speculate about the technical aspects of the connections between the "biological computer" in the posterior cortex and the "biological robot" in the anterior cortex.)

Relationships Between the Pyramidal and the Extrapyramidal System

Other cortical efferents which, like the pyramidal tract, are related to the cortical representation of the somesthetic and the vestibulo-cerebellar systems, are *cortico-subcortico-spinal* efferents which form the *extra-pyramidal tracts* of the frontal lobe. As we have already explained in Chapter II, there exist basically identical sensory-motor arrangements or "sensory-motor units of constitution" in other sensory modalities, as both pyramidal and extrapyramidal efferents (or cortico-spinal and cortico-subcortico-spinal efferents) issue from the cortical fields contiguous with the primary receiving areas of vision, hearing, etc. (Fig. 5). In other words, since cortico-spinal (pyramidal) and cortico-subcortico-spinal (extrapyramidal) efferents take origin in the vicinity of other sensory provinces of the cortex, every sensory modality may be assumed to have access to the anterior horns of the spinal cord or Sherrington's *common final path*. Nevertheless, the diverse sensory-motor units of constitution are not coordinated units. They are neural systems subordinated to the pyramidal tract, or the cortico-spinal efferents of area 4; only the neural system that issues from the motor strip and controls the totality of striated muscles is structurally equipped to establish correspondence between mental design and motor act, while the remaining cortico-spinal tracts function in response to local stimulation of the adjacent primary sensory areas. (See below.) To express the matter differently, the precentrospinal tract subserves isolated and more detailed movements which are sufficiently differentiated to realize mental designs or to establish sensory-motor conformity at the highest level of cerebral function while the remaining efferents subserve less specific synergic movements.

Bucy (77) has recently challenged the concept (believed by many to be firmly established) of the pyramidal tract in the sense of the classics largely on the ground that surgical section of the midportion of the cerebral peduncle carried out for the alleviation of involuntary movements in extrapyramidal disease failed to produce complete paralysis. He maintained that the patients "were not necessarily paralyzed and that they had extensive, well coordinated, finely controlled movements even of their most distal parts." At the same time, he minimized the compensatory role of the cortico-spinal tracts arising in the ipsilateral hemisphere and also the fact that the patients were paralyzed at least for some time after the operation. The discrepancy, involved in Bucy's observations, between the traditional

concept and the rather revolutionary views expressed by himself and some other workers in this field (328) may perhaps be resolved by assuming that the function of the precentrospinal tract (the pyramidal tract of the classics) in previously healthy individuals and in those with long standing extrapyramidal disease is not necessarily the same, especially if the disease responsible for its modification has been acquired early in life. Bucy himself, referring to the complexity of neural arrangements, states that "in this intricately coordinated maze the results of activity of any one part may be vastly different from what it may have been under other circumstances." Thus far, the aggregate evidence, especially clinical evidence (for the possibilities of experimental verification advocated by Bucy in the healthy human are limited) would seem to support the theory that finely coordinated movements are maximally represented in the precentro-spinal tract. This is not necessarily the case in dystonia and other extrapyramidal diseases in which, in the course of attempted restitution on the part of the nervous system, the original patterns of function may have been restructured. Since only about one half of the fibers running through the pyramids on their way to the spinal cord issue from the motor strip, the terms precentro-spinal tract and pyramidal tract should not be used as synonymes. The origin of the term extra-pyramidal tract is worthy of note. Foerster (145), continuing the work of the Vogts (497), demonstrated that postcentral stimulation evoked finely coordinated movements only when the precentro-spinal tract was intact. Accordingly, he concluded that the less specific movements which could still be obtained following precentral injury are mediated by cortical areas other than the pyramidal, i.e., extrapyramidal areas. It is a widely held belief that the cortico-extrapyramidal and the subcortico-extrapyramidal tracts facilitate volitional movements and provide, at the same time, their postural background. In infancy and childhood, the specialization of the individual pyramidal and extrapyramidal tracts is less clear cut than later in life, as may be inferred from the observation that, in the monkey and in man, lesions of the pyramidal tract proper (precentro-spinal tract) are more readily compensated than later in life (252, 254). It should also be noted that the pyramidal tract is not fully myelinated until the second year after birth (415). No doubt its maturation proceeds concurrently with the individuation of early mass movements and the acquisition of skilled movements. The large size of the pyramidal tract in ungulates is an apparent exception to the rule that the system under study becomes increasingly prominent with rise in the phylogenetic scale. In this particular species, the somesthetic area, especially the area corresponding to the oral and circumoral receptors is particularly extensive (152).

The above considerations may be supplemented by data indicating that extrapyramidal movement patterns are the functional primordium of the highly adaptive movements mediated by the phylogenetically younger pyramidal tract.

Extrapyramidal Centers Located in the Anterior Cortex

The extrapyramidal centers located in the anterior cortex participate in the integration of manipulative, static, locomotor, equilibratory, attitudinal, oculogyric, expressive and alimentary synergies controlled by the pyramidal system. As explained in the foregoing paragraphs these synergies form integral parts of volitional movements. According to Foerster (143), abnormal activity of the premotor extrapyramidal cortex (area 6 a) gives rise to spasms of all muscles of the contralateral half of the body and, hence, generalized contraversion associated with a corresponding deviation of the eyeballs. Concomitant spasm of the spinal muscles may cause violent spinning movements of the body at the onset of the seizure. The arm is thrown into a spastic flexor synergy including elevation of the upper arm, flexion and pronation of the forearm and flexion and tension of the muscles controlling the finger joints. Extensor synergies in the upper extremities occur less frequently than flexor synergies. The lower extremities exhibiting, like the upper limbs, gross tonic and clonic movements, are thrown more often into extensor synergies than into flexion. Stimulation of area 6b in the lower part of the precentral gyrus produces rhythmic chewing, licking, swallowing, smacking, grunting, croaking sounds and singultus. Stimulation of area 8 in the midportion of the second frontal convolution turns the eyes to the opposite side.

Extrapyramidal Centers Located in the Posterior Cortex

The extrapyramidal centers located in the posterior cortex subserve predominantly oculogyric movements and attitudinal movements of the head, neck, extremities and trunk that occur in response to stimuli impinging upon the sensory foci with which the motor centers are integrated. It may be assumed that the individual cortico-fugal pathways are intra-axial feedbacks (Fig. 5). They mediate adaptive reflexes to increase or, as the case may be, to reduce the intensity of the sensory stimuli. In other words, they are the cortico-subcortical substrates of primitive seeking and avoidance reflexes.

Abnormal impulse formation including artificial stimulation of the post-rolandic centers yield irritative phenomena, namely, of

(a) the *inferior parietal lobule*, (areas 7), a sensory aura followed by contraction of the contralateral limbs and associated with phenomena in the ipsilateral limbs, particularly the leg; of

(b) the *midtemporal convolution*, an acoustic aura with turning of the eyes to the opposite side; of

(c) the *uncus gyri hippocampi*, an olfactory and/or gustatory aura followed by licking, smacking, and chewing movements and/or dreamy states; and

(d) of the *convexity of the occipital lobes* (area 19), turning of the eyes to the opposite side and complex visual hallucinations. Stimulation of area 18, the optico-motor reflex center of the visual area (area 17), produces conjugate movements of the eyes to the opposite side and elementary visual hallucinations.

The synergies listed in Chapter I, which are integrated by *somatic* (pyramidal, and by cortico- and subcortico-extrapyramidal) centers, operating in association with *viscero-cortical* and *viscero-subcortical* cell stations, subserve autonomic (e.g., cardiovascular, respiratory, etc.) adjustments. The composite neural systems are units of constitution each of which, comprising and coordinating various categories of neurons, may be regarded an "elementary brain" in its own right. In the white matter, cortico-fugal extrapyramidal and pyramidal fibers are intermingled, as a large number of direct cortico-spinal neurons (to which reference has already been made) issue from cortical fields outside area 4. A similar relationship prevails between somatic and autonomic neurons.

SUBCORTICAL DIVISION OF THE EXTRAPYRAMIDAL SYSTEM

The subcortical division of the extrapyramidal system is compounded of closely knit superimposed reflex arcs. Their afferent limbs are represented largely by the vestibulo-cerebellar systems of centers and pathways, especially the dentate nucleus and the nucleus ruber and, indirectly, connections of the former with the nucleus ventralis anterior of the thalamus and the rolandic and premotor cortex. Additional elements are the corpus Luysii, the globus pallidus, the corpus striatum, and the substantia nigra.

To put in another way, the *pyramidal system* proper excludes (a) the fibers arising in the cortical centers which mediate conjugate eye movements, fibers subserving, respectively, contraversion of the body and mass movements of the limbs, and pathways arising in certain subcortical centers, (b) all fibers, whatever their origin, which do not course through the bulbar pyramid and (c) all corticospinal fibers terminating by way of internuncial neurons which do not issue from the somatotopically organized areas of the pre-rolandic cortex. Cerebro-spinal fibers which originate in any other part of the cortex and the subcortex, which reach the spinal cord by whatever route and which terminate on the anterior horn cells in whatever fashion are eo ipso *extrapyramidal* in origin.

The above data are here presented to illustrate the application, to the sphere of psychomotor functions, of the concept of *functional primordium* and *representation of function*. It may be readily seen that the above motor and, by the same token, sensory phenomena attain higher forms of adaptability by their integration with more elaborate patterns of response, that is, responses mediated by agencies which are structurally equipped to deal with an increasing number of

variables. By and large, the movements elicited by electrical stimulation correspond to those seen in epileptiform states, which makes it extremely unlikely that they are stimulation artifacts, no more. To say that oculogyric, attitudinal etc. functions are represented in specific parts of the cortex of the cerebral hemispheres means that certain cortical provinces, although perhaps not exclusively so, are concerned with certain functions, or fractions of functions; to put it in another way, that they add their quota of action to those already inherent in the lower centers of the same system. The cortical provinces do not necessarily correspond to cytoarchitectonic areas, the delineation of which (if at all possible) has yet to be determined. The highest centers are not the only cell stations concerned with a specific function, say, reading or writing; they are ultimately responsible for their integration just like certain higher brainstem centers are ultimately responsible for the integration of righting reflexes, the functional components of which are mediated by a chain of lower centers. In other words, certain localities of the brain act as the highest centers or "the" center of a given performance only in combination with subordinate centers. The entire performance, which depends on the integration of a chain of centers, remains fragmentary unless the highest cell stations add their quota of action to that of the subordinate strata. This will happen if, as a result of appropriately placed lesions, the level specific resources of the highest echelons are unable to interact with those of the lower. The smaller the lesion, the more precise the localization of the centers which, in different brains, do not necessarily occupy the same locality but cluster around an identical place of the cortical map. If, at the site of the lesion, a sufficient amount of cortical tissue is preserved, cortical stimulation will produce irritative symptoms. In the absence of a sufficient mass of cortical tissue on the other hand, the symptoms will be the negative of those produced by stimulation, e.g., weakness or sensory deficit. In addition, there may be what Jackson called positive symptoms due to release of lower centers.

The concept of representation of function in the nervous system has recently been challenged by Gooddy (*178*) who has somewhat overplayed

Jackson's idea of release. He claimed that the above suggested correlation of structure and function is inadmissible on the ground that dysfunction following destruction of the part involved by disease precludes the localization of the corresponding function in the part involved by disease, and that the observed function must be a release phenomenon on the part of the lower centers. Although Gooddy's approach has some merits on theoretical grounds, actual experience proves that, with certain exceptions, effects of destructive lesions may be satisfactorily correlated with those of irritative phenomena involving the same locality of the nervous system, be they caused by disease or by experimental stimulation, that is, under conditions in which the views advanced by Gooddy are generally inapplicable (See also Bailey, *19*). Besides, the consistent application of Gooddy's principle would interminably shift, from one center to another, the legitimate question concerning the quota of action contributed by an individual nerve center to the total process of integration. It would be equally uninformative to express the function of a denervated muscle in terms of the function of those muscles with which it works in coordination. In *conclusion*, definitions of normal functions in terms of the uninvolved parts of the brain are inadequate from the viewpoint of brain pathology. The highest centers are agencies which, although they may be actuated by extraneous stimuli, (e.g., II.m. by II.s. and III.s. in combination) control the totality of factors on which determine a given performance.

It is attested by innumerable clinical observations that, in spite of the unquestioned existence of negative cases, all higher motor functions are represented in the cortical segment lying in front of the rolandic fissure while all higher sensory functions are represented in the posterior cortex. Paraphrasing Bastian's (*27*) famous dictum, one has yet to find a case of motor aphasia caused by a lesion adjacent to the visual area, and one of visual agnosia by a lesion of Broca's center. This is not to say that, apart from mechanical factors, gross organic lesions may not disrupt the unity of interrelated performances, as is not at all uncommon owing to the extensive *disturbance-range* of highly sensitive foci subjected to unphysiological stimulation. Since, in general, motor centers operate under the guidance of sensory centers, disturbances of the motor sphere may be either primary or secondary. Contrairwise, primary disturbances of the motor sphere may have *repercussions* in the sensory sphere. For example, a lesion involving Broca's center may interfere with reading if the patient happens to be a motor type, that is, an individual which, be it audibly or inaudibly, moved his lips while learning to read. It does not depend on the localization of a lesion only whether or not a specific function is involved but also on its *integrational history* which may vary with different individuals.

To *summarize*: under normal conditions, the precentro-spinal tract would seem to be the most versatile instrumentality of the cortical organ of skill while the remaining contingents of pyramidal fibers mediate generalized movements occurring largely in response to stimulation of those primary cortical receiving areas of the sense organs to which their cells of origin (generally, like the Betz cells, large pyramids) are topographically related. The extrapyramidal tracts provide the postural background for isolated, finely differentiated movements. At the same time, they serve as amplifiers of the "kinetic melody" composed by the conceptual level and "played" by the pyramidal tract. The kinetic melody in turn, is represented in that (overt) system of notation in which, at the highest sensory and response determinating agency of the neuraxis, the data of the senses are recorded and to which, conventionally, the term consciousness is applied. With increasing training and experience, the axial stream of thought is freed for new impressions, and response determination is taken over by the marginal stream of thought, if not the subsidiary sphere of mentation. Within the natural limits fixated by the distribution in the brain of sensory and motor centers and their connections, the patterning of higher cerebral functions is preferential rather than rigid and fixated. To that extent, functional organization is flexible and disorders of function are to a degree at least, compensible. A certain measure of functional interdependence of sensory and motor provinces accounts for the relative frequency of mixed syndromes, e.g., mixed forms of aphasia and combinations of apraxia and agnosia, but the existence of composite forms does not militate against the concept of the sensory-motor nature of higher cerebral functions, more especially skilled movements.

Where will it lead us when we attempt to verify the principles of anatomical and functional differentiation in the human in the brain of animals, including subhuman primates? We shall find ourselves in the position of a stranger who tries to find his way through a city but is using an obsolete map. Sooner or later, he will realize that some parts of the city have remained virtually unchanged but that, since the map went into print, new sections have been added to its historical core.

Comparative physiological aspects of skill

Skilled movements in animals

Lashley studied the integration of the more highly organized movements in the rat and the monkey.

In a series of experiments (274) involving bilateral removal of the electrostimulable areas, he tested the animals for retention of acquired motor habits which, surprisingly, he found preserved. He therefore denied that the motor areas have the function commonly ascribed to them. In another series (277), he tested the visuomotor ability of his experimental animals after removal of various parts of the visual cortex. Provided the destruction of the striate areas was not excessive, visuo-motor habits were likewise retained. He therefore considered the visual areas autonomous. However, while visuo-motor autonomy may exist in the rat, Lashley's experiments do not necessarily imply that a similar organizational principle applies either to the monkey or the human. In the former, retention of visuo-motor habits depends on the integrity of the temporal lobes, as already shown by Bucy and Klüver (78). Besides, loss of the habits occurred also following combined removal of the parietal, pre-striate and temporal areas (281).

Taking the different organization of the cortex in the human into account, the discrepancies can probably be eliminated: The brain of man is by no means a proportionally enlarged brain of a mammal (Fig. 7); it is a brain equipped with specifically human organs. In fact, a discussion of Lashley's experiments should permit to grasp the organization of volitional movements in man in their historic perspective, both ontogenetically and phylogenetically.

In terms of the previously developed concept of a hierarchy of functional levels, the following concept suggests itself. With rise in the mammalian scale, the connection of the psycho-neural centers with the pyramidal tract (complex II.s. → II.m. → I.m.) acquire, increasing importance in that skilled movements come to depend chiefly on the pyramidal system. In other words, the center of manipulative activity has gravitated frontward, to the precentral cortex, where an innervational apparatus serving the control of specialized movements was elaborated. In the monkey and in the rat, both acquired and innate motor responses to visual stimuli are mediated preponderantly by extrapyramidal efferents; however, as regards both perception and motor functions that occur in response to visual stimuli, the visual sphere is autonomous in the rat only. This may be conceded for the sake of the argument, although Lashley was contradicted in this point by Hunter (229) and by Morgan and Woods (341a). Granted, then, that, in this animal, the visual sphere has retained its functional homogeneity. This is but another way of saying that the three levels are present in a larval fashion, that the neuron-complex II.s. → II.m. → I.m. exists in a nascent stage only and, lastly, that it comprises cortico-cortical neurons which connect the sensory with the intrinsic motor elements of the visual sphere. In regard to the complexity of its cortical organization, the monkey occupies a somewhat intermediate position. Ohrbach (365a) found that the "occipital cortex seems to participate in non-visual orientation, probably more in the rat than in the monkey," which, to us, indicates a lesser degree of "equipotentiality" in the monkey and a still lesser degree in man. In man, who acquired a more independent and more versatile (and, at the same time, more vulnerable) instrument with which to perform volitional movements, the visuo-fugal extrapyramidal pathways are relegated to cortical reflex fibers which retain little if anything of their original functional capacities. Similar considerations would seem to apply to the functional relationship between the remaining sensory areas on the one hand and the motor area on the other.

Mental organization, for instance the attainment of concepts, appears to proceed concomitantly with the development of the innervational apparatus mediating skilled movements. As we ascend the mammalian scale, the differentiation into the three sublevels becomes increasingly clear cut and both skill and thought, being correlative phylogenetic acquisitions, are raised to a higher power. We are unable to accept Lashley's statement (280) that "the chimpanzee's hand is capable of the elementary movements of the human hand, yet is used scarcely more effectively than the rat's paw." The emergenc of the motor areas, (I.m.), the posterior association fields (III.s.) and their intervening apparatus (II.) are interrelated events. Making allowance for individual (intraspecies) variations determined by hereditary and environmental factors, it is probably fair to say *that, in the course of evolution, the thought elaborating mechanism is being linked up with that type of motor agency it is competent to control, and that the motor area is subjected to those directives it is able to follow.* In other words, the hand has become the "external brain of man" and, to paraphrase Kant's dictum (which we put at the head of this chapter), the paw has "remained" the external brain of the rat. In spite of wide individual variations, inter-level dysharmony, as a general biologic principle at least, is unthinkable.

Lashley (274) concludes from his experiments that the motor areas have no concern with voluntary movements which, he believes, are mediated by the primary cortical receiving areas; rather, the motor areas appear to be "part of a vast reflex postural system which includes the basal nuclei, the cerebellar and vestibular systems." Clearly, this theory is applicable neither to the face area of the rat nor of the monkey (in which the cortical fields in question are extensively represented in the motor cortex) nor to the arm area in man. At least in the bipedal organism, the areas in question are developed in practically the reverse proportion to their possible significance for postural mass reflexes. The detailed representation of individual units in the motor area, be it of muscles or movements, (73, 94, 143, 293, 379) suggests that what used to be group performances have become fractionable into units which can be combined to specialized and highly adaptive motor activities.

This ability by no means excludes the concurrent importance of some of these performances, for instance movements of the lower limbs, as regards reflexly operating mechanisms concerned with posture and gait.

Coghill (95) showed that motor performances serving specialized functions emerge, ontogenetically, within a framework of more crude and generalized movements, comparable to the differentiation of tissue from a relatively homogenous matrix. For instance, the first elbow flexion occurs with action of the arm as a whole, and the same holds true for the movements of the hands and digits. Now, the biological principle of the *"progress from the general to the special in function and from the simple to the complex in structure"* formulated by K. E. v. Baer (16) applies exactly to the gradual emergence of specialized movements (which are mediated by the pyramidal tract) from the pool of extrapyramidal, i.e., "not yet" pyramidal cortical activity. Even so, intentional movements embody both extrapyramidal and pyramidal elements. (Structurally, as may be inferred from Lassek's work, who demonstrated that pyramidal fibers issue also from cortical fields other than area 4, the gradual emergence and condensation of the pyramidal system to an individual pathway is still evident in man.) Furthermore, it accords well with this general concept of cerebral organization that, even in the human, skilled movements are of a composite nature. In this respect, they resemble the locomotor effect achieved by a man walking on an escalator, for his motion depends on both his own effort and the motion of the moving belt. This holds true although an individual controls, though merely indirectly and to a limited extent, the extrapyramidal component of motor activity in addition to the pyramidal.

From a phylogenetic point of view it appears likely that, in the rat and the monkey, particularly the former, the emancipation of individual movements has become "arrested" at a nascent stage and that the motor areas, in which both the upper and lower extremities are represented, remain to a large extent concerned with postural and locomotor functions. In the human on the other hand, where postural functions are for all practical purposes limited to the legs, the extrapyramidal components may become manifest under pathological conditions only; for example as forced grasping which represents a normally suppressed postural reflex (*152*).

It is apparent that Lashley, in his discussion of the role of the motor and visual areas in mammals, failed to take into account the phylogenetic trends involved in the organization of movements. It is likewise apparent that Lashley, in spite of his broad biologic approach to problems of physiology which makes his studies so valuable, considers the animal scale as a static system where certain morphological elements subserve identical functions, and where the variable of evolution is lacking. This impression is further deepened by his statements that "there is constancy of perceptual organization throughout the mammalian series," and that "the rat exhibits the same principles of visual organization as does man" (*277*). Yet ideas which may valid with regard to the organization of the cortex in subhuman mammals are anachronistic when applied to the human cortex, where the less differentiated, relatively uniform organization has become superseded by a heterogenous organization of function. As Herbert Spencer wrote in a passage already quoted: "Evolution is the progress from indefinite incoherent homogeneity to definite coherent heterogeneity." Evidently, the nervous system of man, at least as regards the interrelated factors of intelligence and skill, is more coherent and more heterogenous than the nervous system of animals.

Some of the more recent publications dealing with the question of cortical localization in animals contradict Lashley's views while others, on the surface at least, seem to support them. Pribram and Barry (*397*) found that, in the monkey, circumscribed lesions within the parieto-temporo-occipital sector produce performance decrements which are modality specific and that the primate parieoto-temporo-occipital cortex may be subdivided into areas serving separate functions. Monkeys with infero-temporal lesions consistently failed in visual and showed no impairment in the somesthetic discriminations. Conversely, monkeys with parieto-occipital resections showed a decrement in retention in the somesthetic tasks initially administered, but no impairment in the visual discrimination. Chow (*89*) exstirpated various portions of the posterior

associative cortex in seven monkeys. Batteries of tests administered both preoperatively and postoperatively to each animal provided separate indices of primary visual abilities, visual integrative capacities and general intellectual status. He found that the deficits produced were not exclusively those of integration. . . . The pattern of disturbance conformed neither to the clinical syndrome of "visual agnosia" nor to a derived experimental definition of the term. He arrived at the conclusion that the postulate of separate cortical foci for receptive and integrative functions is untenable. (Chow's definition of agnosia deserves to be quoted in full: A failure in tasks requiring reaction to combinations of sensory elements in a given modality without accompanying sensory and general intellectual impairment sufficient to account for this specific arrangement. See also Semmes, *442*. After what has been said about the phylogenetic difference between the brain of the monkey and the brain of man, the above summarized results of experimental investigations are only to be expected. Results obtained in lower forms do not disprove the existence of organizational pattern in higher forms, inferred to exist in clinical grounds, especially with respect to higher cerebral functions in more advanced forms of biological organization. Harlow (*192*) concluded from experiments extending over many years, and eventuating in the production of chronic preparations in whom only islands of associative cortex remained, that the associative areas should be renamed. Further, that "the results provide striking suggestive support to Lashley's brilliant hypothesis that sensory and motor areas also mediate associative functions." However, Harlow hastens to add that the associative areas have generally evolved from the sensory motor areas. . . ."* Implicitly, after the segregation of areas has reached a certain degree, appropriately placed lesions in the higher forms will cause deficit which differs from that of "corresponding" lesions in lower forms.

---

* According to Lindley (*307a*), the alpha rhythm appears first (in the third month of life) over the sensory-motor area and only later over the remaining parts of the cerebral hemisphere.

Phylogenetic trends governing the organization of skilled movements

With the above qualifications, a comprehensive analysis of the organization of skilled movements in various species, including man, would seem to suggest the following evolutionary trend.

The entire cortex which, at an arbitrarily chosen phase of development, displays infragranular, granular and supragranular (that is, motor, sensory and associational areas) has advanced from the "stage of the neuropil" (the primitive neural net) to the stage of elementary differentiation. In the region of the cortical terminals of the thalamic radiations, both the perceptive and associative layers become reinforced and, in the *posterior parts* of the cerebral hemispheres, the cell layers subserving correlative functions more and more prominent; they form the posterior association fields, which are the common coordinating centers of both the cortical terminals of most of the lateral thalamic radiations. In the *anterior part* of the cerebral hemisphere, concomitantly with the formation of the posterior fields, those motor elements form the motor strip in which the entire musculature is about to become individually represented. The degree of development of the posterior fields and of the motor strip are reciprocally related events as, in the motor sphere, the principle of mass action (which is perhaps most conspicuous in the rat) becomes modified by the principle of progressive individuation. In the sensory sphere, the connecting mechanism becomes specialized in a similar fashion. Eventually, in the human, the representation of motor functions grows most conspicuous in the prerolandic segment of the cerebral hemispheres but regional motor (cortico-extrapyramidal) representations remain distributed over the entire cortex in a seemingly scattered fashion. In spite of this trend toward specialization, the cortex, having differentiated into an increasing number of areal sectors, retains in principle its original architectural pattern as sensory, motor and associational elements remain present throughout. In the words of Lorente de Nò, already quoted, the sensory-motor arrangement of even the smallest elements expresses a general principle of organization. The cortex maintains to a large extent the basic structure of the neuropil even at its most advanced state of evolution, and the principles of bipolarity and unipolarity of conduction seemingly coexist. By the same token, there appears to be no inherent difference between the associational pathways of various order, as intracortical, subcortical and long tracts express the general trend to connect any point with any other point, no matter how close or how distant these points may be. At the same time, preferential connections coursing through the subcortical white matter become increasingly prominent.

The archaic type of nervous system integration is perhaps never entirely abandoned. Thus, the at least partial persistence of the most primitive pattern of organization, as represented by extensive synaptic fields, should facilitate the establishment of morphologic and functional collaterality and, hence, at least partial restitution following injury. Except for the shift of visual functions from the superior colliculi to the striate areas, and that of the highest auditory functions from the inferior quadrigemina to the transverse convolutions of the temporal lobe, new functions may indicate a rostral extension of neural substrates. This, in turn, leads to higher degrees of integrational complexity of function rather than global cephalad shift.

The term "increasing, or progressive, integrational complexity" refers to the apparently paradoxical combination between the increasing freedom and the increasing dependence of nerve centers. At successively higher levels, the individual performances controlled by local centers become increasingly free in that they are no longer dependent on a relatively small number of neural circuits; they become increasingly dependent in that they are now potentially codetermined by events which, for the lower levels, do not "exist." In the more highly organized brains, overall integrational complexity reaches a maximum. Within the individual phyla, integration develops along different organizational parameters.

The phylogenetic aspects of organization of skilled movements may thus be summarized as follows.

(a) Owing to the different though genetically related organization of intentional movements in man as compared to mammals, conclusions based on animal experiments cannot be applied to man in a wholesale fashion. One must recognize existing differences in organization and interpret them as events guided by evolutionary trends.

(b) The gradual emergence of pyramidal from extrapyramidal functions, that is to say, the individuation of pyramidal within the extra-pyramidal centers, is entirely consistent with the postural functions of the motor area in the quadruped and, inasmuch as it includes the representation of the lower extremities, also its functions in the human. In the main, the motor area in man serves skilled movements rather than posture.

(c) The development of the sensory centers proceeds pari passu with that of the motor centers, and the complexity of thought with the complexity of manual skill. In this respect, how-ever, the existence of great intra-species varia-tions is evident in spite of a seemingly identical morphologic organization.

From all this, it appears that skill, the transla-tion of thought into the innervation of muscles subject to volitional control, comprises, of necessity, the preparatory stage of action even though action may be kept in abeyance. In other words volitional movements, unless "short-circuiting," as a result of recognition, at the psycho-neural plane, are initiated as the result of planning at the intellective level.

Comment and criticism

The problem of high level sensory-motor integration, which is inseparable from the concept of general central nervous system function, was, and still is, discussed within the framework of (1) *totalistic theories*, including the *field-theories*, *organismic theories* and *perceptionist* theories, (2) *behaviouristic theories*, (3) *localistic theories* and (4) *eclectic theories*.* By and large, the totalis-tic theories stipulate that the workings of the nervous system can be expressed in holistic terms and that its individual parts are, in a way, artifacts. For example, the *gestaltpsychologists* operate on the assumption (at least implicitly so) that the configurational rather than the intellec-

_____
* The terms *organismic* and *perceptionist* are not used uniformly in the literature. Their meaning will become clear in the course of the discussion.

tive level is the highest agency of the brain and that the higher cerebral functions follow gestalt-laws. The *organismic theorists*, carrying the same principle to extremes, project the laws of gestalt-perception into the workings of the entire organism while the *perceptionists* relegate the functions of the brain to those of the receptor organs. To the extent that they have no eclectic leanings, the *reflexologists* and *behaviourists* regard even the highest provinces of the brain as reflex centers and they study higher brain functions as if neither the configurational nor the intellective level existed. The *localists*, or localistic theorists, at least their extreme right wing, have phren-ologic leanings. The *eclectic schools of thought* combine the errors inherent in the parent con-cepts of their own theory. With the exception of the eclectic approach, the above theories are generally exclusivistic and extremistic.

Holistic field and perceptionist theories

FIELD THEORIES

The basic principles of gestaltpsychology

According to v. Ehrenfels (*123*), Wertheimer (*514, 515, 516*), Koffka (*268*), Köhler (*265, 266*) and others, *gestalten are structured sensory ex-periences which form segregated wholes and which stand out against their loosely shaped or amorphous environment*. Rubin (*417*) showed that visual gestalten lie on a more or less homogenous plane like figures on their background, and seemingly protrude somewhat against their surroundings. In the auditory sphere, elements separated by short intervals tend to form wholes, just as simultaneously given dots appear to be arranged in groups on a surface or in space. Within the circumscribed whole the individual parts which aggregate spontaneously appear to belong to-gether yet, although determining one another, nevertheless derive their character from the total experience complex. Lewin (*294*) contends that gestalten are systems whose parts are dynamically connected in such a way that a change in one part is a change in all other parts. On that particular point however opinions appear to be divided. According to Wertheimer, gestalten are configurations whose behaviour is not determined by the individual elements; rather, the partial processes are determined by the intrinsic nature of the whole complex. This he contends is suggested by the experience that both visual and auditory gestalten are more than the sum-total of their parts or a mere juxtaposition of sensory impressions. A picture is more than the sum of lines and colors and a melody more than the sum of its sounds.

The *grouping of the individual constituents is determined by likeness, proximity, equality, common directional properties, etc.* According to Wertheimer, who established the law of "good gestalt," we tend to perceive certain patterns because of the proximity or similarity of their parts and the continuity and inclusiveness of their structure. Another determining factor is an empirical one but the concession of the gestalttheorists that both external and internal organizing factors operate, in other words, that the self plays a part in gestaltgenesis, is considerably diluted by the stipulation that the self is included into the total field.

Another essential feature of gestalten is their *transposability*. For example, the shape of a figure or an object remains an invariant even though its brightness and size and location be changed provided the relations between its parts remain approximately the same. By the same token, melodies can be transposed to a different pitch without altering their basic structure.

Gestalten tend to appear as circumscribed or "*prägnant*" as possible; and simple and regular wholes, and also closed areas are more readily formed than irregular and open wholes, which are apt to be seen as closed. Since sensuous material of any kind constitutes a mere mosaic in which no particular area is functionally segregated and shaped, it is reasonable to assume that, in the process of gestaltperception, the material in question undergoes some sort of transformation.

At this point we wish to supplement our own concept, proposed at various places of the present monograph, by the following remarks. *We regard gestalten as products of grouping of relatively complex and extended stimuli into concentrated and schematized patterns which take shape in response to the needs of orientation and of appropriate reaction on the part of the subject; to gain a "sensory foothold" in the external world, the receptive apparatus concentrates upon the most conspicuous elements.* In other words, gestalten are "ordering devices" operating at the sensory segment of the psychoneural level. We are inclined to interpret the phenomenon of gestaltformation from the viewpoint of the level hierarchy of the nervous system, that is, as the performance of agencies controlling a greater variety of operational dimension than those which record amorphous impressions only. If *higher functional levels* take the lead, the resulting experience becomes potentially significant in terms of the reaction patterns of the "configurational" and, indirectly, of the highest, or conceptual agencies. If, on the other hand, the *lower levels* take the lead whenever the higher are expected to assert themselves, confusion and, in extreme cases, panic reactions may ensue. (If, unexpectedly, the higher levels assume a leading role in perception, the subject may have the experience of artistic inspiration as, for example, Leonardo da Vinci, who, seeing a wall torn by rents and cracks, visualized a landscape.) Although we agree with the fieldtheorists in recognizing spontaneous grouping tendencies on the part of the sensuous material, and share Köhler's view that experience is based on gestaltperception, we believe that empirical factors are more important than the fieldtheorists admit. *Spontaneous grouping tendencies come to depend more and more on empirical factors which exert a corrective influence and which assume an ever increasing role in recognition.* Eventually, recognition, more especially "learning to recognize" is made possible because irrelevant grouping patterns are gradually crowded out by relevant memory images. Clearly, the "segregated shapes" perceived do not necessarily coincide with the images of objects. (The art of camouflage is the substitution of misleading groupings for realistic groupings.) In the course of roentgenological teaching sessions, I am not infrequently asked about the significance of certain shadows, or configurations, which suggest the existence of anatomical structures. At this point, I spread the fingers of my hand to point out the interdigital spaces and to explain to the students that they were mislead by conspicuous shapes that to them looked like "figures" on a "background" rather than guided by structures that have a meaning in anatomical terms. No doubt spontaneous grouping tendencies or those imposed upon by conspicuous stimuli may produce pseudofigures and, unless held in check by the concentration of attention on essential configurations, interfere with the correspondence function of the brain which, under normal conditions, furnishes us with a picture of the physical world.

As a result of processes which are essentially acts of association by similarity, *gestalten are primarily experienced as "object-equivalents" or "quasi-objects" seen against their background, somewhat in the manner true objects are seen in space.* In a sense, then, *gestalten are subcategories of objects* and, paradoxically, at least one of the basic mechanisms underlying gestaltexperience namely, Hume's association of "ideas" is a connectionist one. The gestaltheorists have revived the old experience that the background may assume figure character but that, after some time, the original figure may re-emerge. This may be explained by the fact that gestalten are not true objects but that they have phantom character, that they are in part intrinsically generated stimuli and that an alternative type of categorization is possible. In other words, that the figure is unstable, in sharp contrast to the relation between a true object and the space in which it is seen. While the perception of gestalten as "apparent objects" is imposed upon the observer through a natural process of association by similarity, their role as symbols is evidently conventionalized. However, either form of experience "makes it possible for the sensory world to appear so utterly imbued with meaning to the adult," an admission on Köhler's part that empirical factors play an important role if not in the formation at least in the utilization of gestalten. They are eminently suitable instruments of communication; in fact, communication would be impossible without gestalt-perception and, of course, gestaltproduction. In the present context, it is of interest to note that certain devices used in communication as for example hieroglyphs and also some Chinese characters are ideograms which combine the properties of objects, gestalten and symbols.

The transposability of gestalten depends on the awareness on the part of the subject of the similarity of their essential relationstructures; *in other words, like the very perception of gestalten, their transposability is based on the association by similarity with objects.* This is denied by the field-theorists who insist on the primacy of gestalt-experience. But it is precisely this awareness of similarity which makes possible recognition of objects, figures and symbols as individual items and as members of a class. At the very least, it produces the feeling of familiarity. It is probably more correct to say that objects seen from different angles do not appear identical but more or less similar. For example, the full face view and the profile view of a person may be so different that their correlation is impossible unless one is slowly "rotated" into the other. The same applies to a line which, seen on edge, appears as a point.

The ability to see one's environment gestaltet is of the utmost importance for the very reason that sensory experiences having identical relation-structures are apt to elicit similar responses. *However, similarity or identity may be merely an apparent one and it is the function of thought, which is a more versatile tool of discrimination, to discover parameters of difference within apparently similar or identical data.* It is a far cry from the dissolving power of the retina to that of the mind; from pattern blindness to problem dullness and from the ability to separate a figure from its background to the ability to discriminate between essentials and non-essentials. As far as thought processes are concerned, the ability to perceive gestalten is merely a basic prerequisite or base-line of appropriate reaction. (It should also be noted that, although similar gestalten have identical relationstructures, not all entities having identical relationstructures have necessarily gestaltcharacter. For example the thought processes of two people thinking along similar lines are by no means gestalten.) In the following pages we do not intend to criticize the valuable core of the fieldtheory but, rather, its outgrowths, including the interpretation of gestalt-phenomena, and the application of gestalt-mechanisms to neural and general organismic processes. We object not only to the doctrine of *isomorphism* (see below), but also to the incorporation of the perceiving subject into the perceptual field; and particularly to the totalitarian aspirations of the field-psychologists who claim that the laws of perception are applicable to the processes of learning, recall, striving, feeling, thinking, acting and other cerebral functions of a higher order. Eventually, the aspirations of the fieldtheorists approached madness: A German student, I have it on good authority, wrote in an examination paper that Germany tends to round herself out in order to become a *"gute Gestalt"* and, in so doing, engulfs her neighbours.

The theory of isomorphism

Köhler contended that not only psychic processes but also the corresponding physiologic processes have gestaltcharacter and that there are purely physical events which follow gestaltprinciples; hence, he concluded, the study of "physical gestalten" should enable us to gain insight into the mechanism of psychic phenomena. Physical gestalten taking shape in the brain, he goes on to say, are in no way different from those operating in the inanimate world. The term "gestalt" has acquired a twofold meaning. It is not only applicable to shapes as segregated wholes but the concept as the meaning of a concrete entity per se which does not necessarily have a shape as one of its characteristics. The emphasis has thus shifted to the fact of organization. Whenever a process dynamically regulates and distributes itself determined by the actual situation in the whole field, this process is said to follow the principles of gestalttheory. "The problem of gestalt-attributes has become a special problem among many with which the fieldtheorists have to deal. The wider concept of gestalt, that is, of extended events which regulate themselves as functional wholes, may be applied far beyond the limits of sensory experience. In the meaning of shape it is no longer the center of the gestaltpsychologist's attention, for to some of the facts in which he is interested the term gestalt in the meaning of shape does not apply at all."

In substance, then, Köhler contends that our knowledge of physical gestalten makes it possible to grasp the nature of physiologic gestalten as they form in the central nervous system and, hence, of the correlated psychic processes. For example, "a physical gestalt is oil which has been poured into a fluid with which it does not mix, and which assumes a certain shape owing to the action of dynamic field forces operating in the boundary region. Notwithstanding the

general dynamic interdependence throughout the field there are boundaries in it, at which dynamic factors operate toward a measure of segregation rather than uniform continuity; and the boundaries of the two fluids remain sharply defined by the action of the very same dynamic factors which operate there. Just like surface tension tends to reduce the area of liquid surfaces so, in the sensory field, grouping tends to establish units of a certain kind rather than others. The order of sensory fields in this sense shows a strange predilection for particular kinds of organization, just like the pull of surface forces in physics operates in a specific direction. The orderly distribution of the oil is the result of forces which act at each point and which constitute a continuous pattern of stress and it is the sum total of local changes which brings the total system nearer the balance of forces. . . . Undisturbed interaction operating in the direction of balance promotes, at the same time, the orderly distribution of material. In this sense dynamic self-equilibrium is the kind of function which gestaltpsychologists regard essential in neurologic and psychologic theory. More especially, they assume that the order of facts in a visual field is to a high degree the outcome of such self-distribution of processes. From this point of view a stationary visual field corresponds to a balanced distribution of underlying processes."

Another frequently cited physical phenomenon which, supposedly, explains the transposability of psychic gestalten, is the behaviour of fluids in a communicating system and the distribution of electricity upon an isolated conductor having a certain shape. "There, not only every individual element is dependent on every other, but the reduction of the electric charge is followed by a redistribution which conforms to the same pattern; and so is the diminution and the increase in the size of the conductors which (supposedly) illustrates the transposability of physical gestalten. Structuring follows dynamic principles by which it is completely determined; and rather like in an electromagnetic field every partial process depends on any other that may occur, so every neural event depends on the totality of processes with which it is connected." (Cf. Goldstein, *175*). "Within the psychophysical field there is a spontaneous self-regulation and self-distribution of forces owing to the peculiar physical and chemical forces on which it depends. The laws operating in the inorganic and the biophysical world are identical." The principle of gestalt is applicable not only to psychic processes but to nature as a whole. Organisms are gestalten.

The self as part of the total field

The gestaltpsychologists extend the field concept to include the subject which thereby becomes a part of the total field in which the forces of stress operate. Nevertheless, it retains a certain measure of independence. According to Köhler (266) the "peripheral order" of visual stimuli is maintained up to the point where they reach the striate area beyond which the forces of dynamic self-distribution begin to act. We are thus expected to accept the three following theses: (a) Only the functions of the cortical provinces beyond the primary sensory receiving stations are subject to gestaltprinciples. (b) The entire organism is a gestalt. (c) The organism and the sensory data with which it is confronted form a total dynamic field within which all events are governed by the principles of gestalttheory.

To *summarize*, Köhler contends that gestaltphenomena exist wherever events arrange themselves according to dynamic conditions of the field. If this is conceded it makes no particular difference whether we deal with a perceptual process, or the formation of the organism, or of a cloud, or an avalanche. The theory of isomorphism is perhaps the weakest point of the fieldtheory which, needless to say, has been criticized by psychologists (235, 365, 459) and biologists (39, 40) alike. How can the behaviour of a drop of water in oil or, for that matter, the distribution of electricity on a conductor, account for the principles of sensuous organization and of higher cerebral functions, including thought processes and human striving? Evidently, the Gestaltpsychologists are convinced they can do just that, for Wertheimer (514, 515) attempted an explanation of the reasoning processes that led Einstein to his theory of relativity by the action of field forces, and Rees (401) tried to account in a similar fashion for the phenomenon of artistic endeavour. It is likewise difficult to see why fieldforces should act as organizational

factors in the neural sphere only, more particularly in that part of the cerebral cortex "beyond" the striate area; and why they should not regulate other physiological phenomena which depend on physicochemical forces as, for example, to mention only two, the secretion of bile and the growth of bone? As far as I am aware the gestaltpsychologists have, thus far at least, failed to account for the processes in question in terms of their own theory; some day, perhaps, they will surprise us with a new approach to anatomy and physiology.

Lashley and his associates (283) took the theory of isomorphism seriously enough (or did they?) to subject it to experimental testing by implanting bands of metal into the cortex of monkeys. The behaviour of the animals did not indicate that electrical forces or vectors had been introduced which would influence their actions.

ORGANISMIC THEORIES

Goldstein, in his magnum opus "The Organism" (172) and also in some of his later writings (175) professes to have thrown out gestaltpsychology altogether—which however sneaked in through the backdoor. "*Ihr naht Euch wieder, schwankende Gestalten.*" Positive symptoms no longer reflect the release of lower mechanisms from the control of the higher as Jackson taught; rather, the pathological manifestations are due to a new type of energy distribution interpretable in terms of abnormal figure background formation. The field concept becomes dominant. The principle of level hierarchy according to performance fields, organs and organ systems is scrapped. The basically gestaltpsychologic core of the "organismic" approach is given away, again and again, by the terms figure, background and dedifferentiation. In the same monograph Goldstein devotes considerable space to the discussion of the differences between the gestaltpsychologic school and his own approach but his terminology fails to bear him out.

In his work on "Language and Language Disturbances" (174) he recognizes (a) direct symptoms, (b) indirect symptoms, (c) those due to catastrophic reactions and (d) those caused by fatigue and perseveration. The first named group comprises in turn two subdivisions, namely, those due to *dedifferentiation* and those due to the separation of an undamaged substrate from a damaged one. Dedifferentiation involves rise and lability of threshold, abnormal extend and duration of excitation (cf. v. Weizsaecker), undue determination by external factors and modification of the patient's performance as revealed by blurring of the sharp boundaries between figure and background. "A performance, or combination of neural excitations, or figure, must be seen against the background of general excitation. In either performance the cortex is in activity but the excitation of the cortex is not the same all over. It has a definite configuration, in which one part of the cortex is in a peculiar state of excitation, corresponding to the figure, while the rest is in that excitation which corresponds to the background. Localization means a definite configuration of excitation in the cortex. A particular localization in the brain matter is characterized by the influence which the structure of this locality exercises in the total processes. (Cf. v. Monakow.) Figure background performances have their counterpart in processes of the nervous system. *The processes which take place in a circumscribed area and which correspond to the physiologic performance are designated by the term figure. The processes in the rest of the nervous system are the background, or ground. Damage to the nervous system, especially the cortex, disturbs the normal figure background relationship. The sharp differentiation of figure from background suffers, indicating a general leveling or intermingling of figure from background"* (174).

Although these examples could be multiplied almost at will, further citations are hardly necessary. It must be amply evident that the figure-background concept, as employed by Goldstein, has become unduly extended. The concept of figure-background relationships as applied to the physiological sphere has no explanatory value. In fact, it is not even a suitable metaphor with which to illustrate the process of impulse generation and other neurophysiological processes. The resemblance between abnormal functions and the blurring between figure and background is superficial. The term dedifferentiation does not apply to pathological processes; it designates a hypothetical process of retrograde evolution along normal stages of descreasing heterogeneity. For

instance, the dedifferentiation of a tree could be demonstrated by a moving picture run backward while the fate of a tree attacked by some disease process would have to be illustrated in an entirely different fashion. Goldstein's fundamental errors are the equation of pathological conditions with dedifferentiated gestalten and, at the same time, of organisms with differentiated entities of the same category. This may be gathered both from his above epitomized analysis of dysfunctions and from Riese's (412) review article where we read that Goldstein, seeing the close relationship between progressive differentiation and therefore dedifferentiation, or dissolution, became Jackson's heir. This heritage stems solely from an equivocation for Goldstein writes that "positive symptoms are due to a new type of energy distribution in the total nervous system, comparable to the dedifferentiation of a figure on a background." Clearly, his thesis amounts to a rejection of the concept of release of low level activity under pathological conditions. Another interesting parallelism between the gestalt-psychologic and the organismic approach, which can hardly be coincidental, is Goldstein's emphasis on the universality of a disturbance in whatever performance field it may primarily appear. For example, a dysfunction in the visual sphere, supposedly, influences the functional structure of all other spheres, that is to say, it is believed to manifest itself in the patient's total behaviour.

On the surface, Goldstein accepts the view that organismic activity cannot be expressed in gestaltpsychologic terms; in fact, he devotes considerable space to the discussion of the difference between his own approach and the fieldtheory. For example he quotes Driesch (118) who remarked that, in sharp contrast to organisms, the topography of physical gestalten is determined by extraneous conditions; yet, in substance, his own and Köhler's approach are identical.

The problem of organization has occupied us in a variety of contexts. Organisms are self-regulating, self-checking and self-gearing systems, but it scarcely needs to be emphasized that the self-regulation of the organism is different from that of fluid levels in communicating vessels or any other "physical gestalt," no matter how complicated it may be. Although the concept of homeostasis has thus far escaped the gestaltpsychologists attention, I am not at all sure that, some day, homeostasis will be regarded as a figure background relationship. What then, is the difference between organisms and gestalten? Organisms, to the extent that we are able to grasp their nature, are open systems which, in spite of their chemical lability, maintain physical constancy. The energy they draw from suitable sources is only partially used up while the balance is stored until such time as needed. Although, within the organism, work may have to be performed against gradients, the chemical processes take place in such a way as to maintain an active energy balance and to prevent an increase in entropy*. Apart from the phenomenon of birth, growth, aging and death, self-regulation and, within limits, self-restitution, are cardinal properties of organisms. (Are we perhaps to hear that growth is a limiting case of transposability?) Every unit of the mani-celled whole expresses a common principle. The function of the entire system represents the activity of any of its elements raised to a higher power. Von Bertalanffy (39, 40), one of the ablest critics of the fieldtheory and its application to biological phenomena, emphatically denies that life is nothing other than a borderline case of gestalt-formation in the inorganic sphere. The determining factors of organization lie within the organism, while inorganic systems, as for example, electric fields, depend on external conditions. (Radioactivity, generated by intrinsic conditions, and life processes have nothing in common; in fact, the former is the mortal enemy of the latter). Both metabolism and change of form is autonomous. Koehler's physical gestalten are entirely powerless to explain either the phenomenon of development or the progressive differentiation of form; neither do they account for the recapitulation of phylogenenis on the part of the developing organism. The specific gestalt-factor inherent in the organism is not reducible to, or derivable from, the formation of gestalten

---

* *Entropy* is a measure of that amount of heat in a closed system that can no longer perform work, i.e., of heat that has become "lost." In other words, entropy may either remain constant or it may increase but it cannot decrease. The increase in entropy in a closed system is a probable development. As expressed in mathematical language, entropy is "a measure of thermodynamic probability, more precisely, its logarithm"(*503a*).

in the inorganic field even though gestalten display a special aspect of organization of sensory stimuli. In *summary*, then, the concepts *gestalten* and *organism* are not coterminous, unless one chooses to extend the gestaltconcept still further, in which case its very generality would render it meaningless.

PERCEPTIONIST THEORIES

Weizsaecker's and Stein's interpretation of psychoneural functions

The approach of the modern perceptionist school is based on Head's (*198*) studies. As is well known, Head recognized two sensory systems, a physiologically older, protopathic, and a younger, epicritic system. Supposedly, the younger (cortical), system serves cognitive functions and exerts a restraining influence on the protopathic system which mediates the more crude sensations. If the epicritic, or *cortical*, qualities are eliminated there come to the fore the protopathic, or *thalamic* qualities. More specifically, the epicritic system mediates light touch, intermediate grades of temperature and the capacity to localize single and simultaneous two point stimuli. It serves a low threshold mode of sensation. The protopathic sensory system responds only to painful cutaneous stimuli and to extreme heat and cold. It has a high threshold, and the sensory response is maximal, ungraded and erroneously referred. As regards the anatomical representation of this dual mechanism Head's description is somewhat confusing; at one time he states that the two systems are a purely peripheral apparatus; at other times he refers, as already indicated, to the epicritic as cortical and to the protopathic as thalamic qualities. In passing through the central nervous system, he goes on to say, the stimuli are "resorted, regrouped, combined, inhibited, facilitated and repressed." Yet, in spite of their "specific combination" and "selective inhibition" (the net result of reshuffling) the epicritic and protopathic qualities are preserved. From a functional viewpoint the relationship between the two systems is the following. "Removal of epicritic sensibility exposes the activity of the protopathic in all its nakedness. In the same way, when removal of the influence of the cortex sets free the optic thalamus from control, sensation assumes an overwhelmingly thalamic character. In each case a more primitive organization is kept under the control by the activity of the higher sensory system. But removal of the dominant mechanism does not reveal the function of the physiologically older organs in all their primitive simplicity. A lesion which sets free the human thalamus produces a highly specialized series of phenomena which never existed in this form in phylogenetic history."

According to v. Weizsaecker (504, 505, 506, 507) and his pupils (116, 117, 377, 458, 459, 460, 461) normal sensation represents the coordinated action of the total sensory system or "Gesamtsystem," that is, the epicritic and protopathic mechanisms which are integrated to a unit of a higher order. Disturbances of sensation, even those of the seemingly most primitive sensory performances, are the result of disintegration or "Abbau" of the performance complex mediated by the total system. Von Weizsaecker makes only passing reference to the simple disturbances referable to the interruption of impulse conduction. By contrast, he stresses the significance of the multifarious modulations of the complex physiological structure of stimulus conduction in disease, including paraesthesias, alloparesthesias, synaesthesias, etc. He coined the term "Gestaltwandel," which designates the pathological alteration of gestaltperception, and contends that the modification in question occurs as a result of dysfunction of the underlying neural substrate which fails to keep the threshold constant. Gestaltwandel is due to the alteration of a sensation by one which preceded it, that is to say, to "Funktionswandel." To reiterate; according to the perceptionists, disintegration of function, far from being the result of elimination of one or the other elementary quality out of a "bundle of sensations," is the alteration of the gestaltquality inherent in normal experiences, somewhat, one would assume, like the substitution of a sound by one of different pitch. The inability on the part of the nervous system to keep the threshold constant, originally found in the visual sphere, was described by Helmholtz (209) as "Umstimmung," or "re-tuning." The perceptionists, however, might have overlooked that it is the very absence of an individual

element from a whole which may radically alter a given gestalt-experience, just like the absence of a wavelength alters the composition of colorless light.

More recently, the role of threshold lability was studied by Stein (458, 459) who demonstrated that the stimulation of cutaneous receptors causes a temporary change in irritability. In the sphere of vision similar phenomena were investigated by Stein and Bürger-Prinz (463) Cibis and Bay (93) and by Bay and Lauenstein (28). The authors found that, in the tactile sphere, the threshold may be increased in lesions involving the posterior columns, the thalamus and the cortex, the spinothalamic tracts, in the course of regeneration of peripheral nerves and in neuritis. In the visual sphere, threshold lability was encountered not only in lesions of the visual centers but also of those involving the optic tracts and the retina. The perceptionists assert that *one and the same receptor serves different qualities and that it can be thrown out of function in different ways.* For example, not only visual acuity depends on the very same factors which convert peripheral stimuli into gestalt-phenomena, but also the ability to localize stimuli. Cortical lesions, in turn, modify what appears to be the elementary qualities within the individual sensory spheres. Perseveration, iteration and apparent disturbances of attention may be present not only in cortical lesions but also in disease of the posterior columns, in other words, the pathophysiology of peripheral and central lesions is substantially identical. In most cases, cortical lesions produce both blunting and local irritation or loss of irritability and modification of the spatial, temporal and qualitative properties of sensation. The duration of sensory experiences is prolonged, the precision of localization suffers and the spatial gestaltquality becomes distorted and more primitive. What's more, the quality which has undergone the above described alteration is combined with the unpleasant affective experiences accompanying protopathic sensations. Contrary to the classic concept the posterior columns do not conduct individual qualities of sensation; they control the order of their spatial and temporal properties and, together with the secondary and tertiary neurons, maintain threshold constancy. Conventional methods of examination of sensation fail to detect the vitiating influence of threshold lability on the appreciation of cutaneous stimuli and the *Gestaltwandel* resulting therefrom. Hence, the negative result of a conventional clinical examination does not justify the conclusion that tactile agnosia is a disturbance of a higher cerebral function. In fact, no such disturbances exist, nor, for that matter, higher cerebral functions. Each sensation, even the so called elementary sensation is a composite phenomenon, the result of a certain spatio-temporal organization of neural processes. It is pointless to distinguish between gestaltfunctions properly so called and elementary sensory functions for the very concept of sensation is merely a logical abstraction from a perceptual whole having gestaltcharacter. The total performance cannot be broken down into elementary functions or building blocks of experience and, since the concept of elementary function is merely an abstraction formed from more comprehensive yet unitary data, sensory examinations test recognition rather than sensation. According to Vogel (*496*) such examination represents a task as far as the patient is concerned, and every statement on the part of the patient that he has been touched "now," "here" and "there," or that a simulus is felt as hot or cold or painful is an act of judgement. Conversely, every gnostic act is in turn mediated by a sensory process. In the course of performance tests each seemingly elementary perception is in reality a problem solution. The formal analysis of functions consists in the systematic variation of conditions whereby the statements of the subject are evaluated in measuring and detecting both threshold and phenomena of sensation and, at the same time, the general character of sensory experiences. By the same token, the examination of so called elementary motor functions is one of action, that is, of eupraxia.

Involvement of a performance reduces its range and renders it stereotyped. The more sharply a stimulus is to be spatially and temporally defined the more neural substance is needed. Loss of substance has a dedifferentiating influence. Involvement of the various performances manifests itself in the impoverishment of their relationship to other performances, of their adaptability, their differentiation and their availability under different conditions. *Funktionswandel*, which results from the different way

of reacting of the total sensory system, does not necessarily eliminate gestaltperception altogether but may give rise to experiences having new configurational properties. In contrast to Head, v. Weizsaecker stipulates that the performances replacing those lost correspond to earlier ontogenetic and phylogenetic stages of the normal performances (Cf. Conrad). There is no difference between sensory and motor functions, which are inextricably interwoven. *"Each motion occurs within the framework of an action and hence is indissolubly linked with a perception. And each perception is a turning-to reaction ("Zuwendungs-reaktion"), that is, one involving an act which is in most cases a motor one, or an action."*

To *summarize*, Weizsaecker believes that disturbances of function are not positive, analyzable entities; they are merely abstractions. The pathological realities are abnormal performances which substitute the normal ones and which have protopathic properties. They are qualitatively different from the normal, in other words, they are not derivable by mere subtraction or the elimination of a functional component from a total performance complex. Diminution of neural substrate leads to threshold lability which gives rise to *Funktionswandel* and *Gestaltwandel*. Rather than isolating and eliminating pre-existing fractions of functions, anatomical lesions change the entire character of a performance. There is no essential difference between lower and higher functions, both of which have gestalt-qualities, nor between their *disturbances* which are *dedifferentiated gestalten*. In other words, abnormalities of seemingly primitive sensations and also of seemingly elementary motor functions, that is to say, of agnosias and apraxias, are manifestations of identical *Abbau*-mechanisms. The concept of higher cerebral functions, including those of agnosia and apraxia, are altogether superfluous. To round off the epitome of v. Weizsaecker's theory, we add that "in no single case can disease be understood by a localized destruction of tissue and that it is unwarranted to differentiate between purely organic and purely psychic functions." It would take us too far afield to follow this line of thought in all its ramifications.

I am not sure whether I have succeeded in presenting the above theory adequately; Weizsaecker's writings, which are couched in complex and highly individualistic language, make difficult reading and are not at all easy to translate into English. In any event, I am not responsible for any contradictions the reader may discover. Some of the basic tenets of the theory under discussion were gathered from the recent work of Bay and of Conrad, writers of some stature. The matter may become somewhat clearer later on, in the course of the discussion of their own views. However, before dealing with contemporaneous developments of Head's and Weizsaecker's doctrines, it will be necessary to comment on some of the latter's theses summarized above.

The question of motor elements in sensation

It is obvious that, in the process of perception, the receptors must be brought into contact with sensory stimuli. On the other hand, the fact that the sensing organs are equipped with contact mediating devices does not establish unity between sensory and motor performances. Gestaltperception is possible without the aid of motor activity. Man does not use his external auricular muscles in perceiving auditory gestalten and he is able to appreciate visual pattern even though his eyes are kept immobilized.* Furthermore, motor and sensory functions can be separately involved. Perception does not necessarily depend on a "turning-to" reaction. The subject may feel stimuli and appreciate gestalten without seeking them, indeed, while trying to avoid them.

The question of the basic identity of lower and higher cerebral functions

It is true that even elementary perceptions are recorded by the highest level, which is concerned with the elaboration of thought, and that they include an element of judgment. This element may however be infinitesmal. The recognition of elementary sensory qualities is not identical with the appreciation of objects, of situations and of events, although, according to the perceptionists, the difference is an artificial one. This is a

* Concerning the appreciation of visual patterns, this statement holds true only with certain reservations.

palpable fallacy; gnosis involves conceptual elements, at least in man, while the mere awareness of such stimuli as hot, cold, sharp, blunt, etc., is for all intents and purposes perceptual. This is evidenced by the reactions of animals and infants which are identical with those of adults. If it were true that any ordinary sensory examination is in reality one for gnosis, and any motor examination one for eupraxia, the examination of elementary auditory functions would be an examination of speech and language and sounds would be merely logical abstractions.

The question of epicritic vs protopathic qualities

As regards the existence of a dual sensory apparatus, Walshe (492) maintains that no subsequent observer, including Woolard and his associates (525), Trotter and Davis (479) and others have confirmed Head's findings in essential details and that the explanatory value of Head's theory of sensation is limited. Somewhat acrimoniously he refers to the "sway exerted upon the imagination of neurologists and physiologists by the words epicritic and protopathic which may have little to do with the continued currency of the hypothesis which was their setting." How true this is will become apparent later on, when we subject the fruits of von Weizsaecker's theory to closer scrutiny.

The so called organismic and the perceptionist approach, then, is a direct descendant of the fieldtheory. Either subjugates the parts to the whole; and either reduces abnormal phenomena to changes of the whole which, allegedly, retains whole character in spite of the blurring of the boundaries between figure and background.

Bay's interpretation of agnosia

In general, Bay's work (26) is based on v. Weizsaecker's philosophy. At the same time it amplifies Siemerling's (446), Poppelreuter's (396), Stein and Bürger-Prinz' (463) and Beringer and Stein's (38) studies on the disturbances of higher visual functions. Siemerling attempted to produce visual agnosia by the artificial reduction of visual acuity, by the constriction of the visual fields and the diminution of illumination. Poppelreuter, who examined a large number of soldiers injured during World War I, greatly refined the technique of perimetry, of the determination of form and color perception, of visual attention and other visual performances. Although his studies let him to appreciate the importance of the various components of vision in recognition, he never questioned the existence of visual agnosias in the sense of classic neurology. For example, in referring to Gelb and Goldstein's (159) now legendary case Schn., he accused the authors of having confused a primary visual defect with visual agnosia. Bürger-Prinz examined a hemianopic patient who had difficulty in recognition. Although there was evidence of *Funktionswandel*, he doubts that the abnormality in question played a cardinal role. Beringer and Stein, to whose case of pure alexia we shall make reference below, took a similar view.

Bay's position is a fundamentally different one. He holds that disturbances in recognition are attributable to a *combination of Funktionswandel with disturbances of intelligence or of consciousness*, as the case may be. In this respect, his approach is reminiscent of Pierre Marie's (320) theory of aphasia for, as is well known, Broca's (71) opponent attempted to reduce language disturbances to a combination of dysarthria and impairment of intelligence. Bay reported four cases of tactile agnosia in which the position sense was impaired but the cutaneous qualities appeared to be intact. Yet, a more detailed examination revealed that the threshold for the seemingly unimpaired functions was increased, that it rose sharply in the course of the examination and that many after sensations appeared. Together with Lauenstein (28) and Cibis (93) Bay examined five cases of injury to the occipital lobes which presented the classic syndrome of object agnosia as described by Lissauer (308). They showed lability of temporal and chromatic threshold which, allegedly, ran parallel to the agnostic disturbance.

Bay's conclusions, which were refuted point by point by Scheller (422), Jung (255), Faust (138, 139), Dünsing (109) and Best (41), are at the same time at variance with the results of Cohen's (96) and Gans' (156) investigations. The first named group of authors had occasion to examine many war injured persons, and they make reference to other well authenticated cases, while Cohen's and Gans' work epitomizes

older but nevertheless pertinent experiences in this field. It is convenient to base the discussion primarily on the work of the modern writers. Scheller pointed out that the visual inattention as seen in hemiamblyopic persons and the impairment of attention in cases of general paresis are incommensurate, and the same applies to the relation between the loss of topographical memory in local disease processes and to the general disturbances of retentive memory in senile individuals. Beringer and Stein's (38) patient had no difficulties in recognizing colors and objects. Not only was she able to copy letters but she readily recognized foreign alphabets. Instead of the word "Reichstag" she read "Berlin," instead of "Elephant" the word "India" and instead of "Fox" the word "Hare." She was unable to read the word "Goethe" but recognized it after the examiner had dropped the hint that it represented the name of a poet. Since, in the particular setting of this examination, any number of persons might have produced the name Goethe, the patient's performance was perhaps a word association. However, the verbal paralexia in the first three tests is quite inexplicable in terms of *Funktionswandel; the consistent selection of names of members of the appropriate class on the part of the patient is beyond the bounds of probability. Funktionswandel would have produced blurring of printed material but would not have operated along conceptual parameters.* In this connection, it is of interest that the patient never complained about indistinct vision as one would have expected in a case of hemiamblyopia. Evidently, she was unable to differentiate within the sphere of the class concept. In conformity with his general conception of agnosia, Bay contended that disturbances of auditory recognition are referable to poor hearing. This theory however, cannot be harmonized with Scheller's observations made on a patient suffering from sensory aphasia who had no difficulty in recognizing various noises. Furthermore, Scheller points out that *Funktionswandel* does not account for cases of transcortical aphasia in which the patient repeats correctly what he hears but can neither speak spontaneously nor understand what he himself has said. In support of his view that disturbances of peripheral type do not necessarily explain difficulties in recognition, he quotes the case of a patient with bilateral hemianopsia and a residual field defect of 5 degrees who was able to read both small print and numerals, to recognize pictures and to appreciate gestalten formed by groups of dots. Only the topographical orientation and the revisualization of spatial relationships was impaired. The patient had an excellent memory and was highly intelligent. Pallis (372) reported the case of a patient with impaired identification of faces and places but denied that the difficulty experienced by the patient was due primarily to impairment of the visual analysis or to intellectual loss. The patient had a visual acuity of 6/6 in each eye and there was no hint of dementia. Moreover, whatever abnormalities of local adaptation time, flicker-fusion and tachistoscopic performance might have existed, could hardly be responsible for the highly specific disability displayed by the patient. Ettlinger (131), in a recent study on sensory deficits in visual agnosia, writes that (a) sensory deficits of the type adduced by Bay as responsible for visual agnosia do not play a significant role in the genesis of the disorder, (b) impairment of visual discrimination, while present in many cases with disturbances in visual perception, is not in itself adequate to provoke the symptoms of agnosia, (c) no consistent relationship between any one pattern of sensory deficit and visual-spatial agnosia can be detected, (d) global intellectual loss as the cause of higher disorders of perception is unlikely and (e) defects in visual discrimination are commonly encountered in cases of cerebral lesions and may be elicited in perimetrically normal areas of the visual field—in summary, that *no evidence was found to support the thesis that agnostic conditions are secondary to deficits of visual sensory discrimination.* Haidenhain's (190) patient could read numerals only when told in advance that the test material was composed of both numerals and letters. He was unable to read most letters which however he could distinguish from one another. The author concluded that the agnostic difficulties could not be attributed to reduced visual acuity.

It is common knowledge that the recognition of objects, letters, numerals, etc. is possible even though only a fraction of the visual data which constitute the whole are given. A person passing a street corner, where he is accustomed to see a sign reading "INTERNATIONAL BUSINESS MACHINES," will get practically the same information by reading the two letters "L...B" or "S...M" in case the sign is not in full view, that is, under conditions of virtual duplication of tubular vision. Martin (322) emphasized the role of a minimal number of data ("Erinnerungspunkte") as the irreducible minimum of stimuli on which there depends the process of recognition. It appears, then, that objects can be recognized by their characteristic fragments. We recognize a button or a match from tiny parts; and a person from its shadow, cast in a fleeting second, upon the periphery of our retina. An efficient roentgenologist may diagnose certain diseases by catching a glimpse of not more than a square inch of a film. In conformity with the classic concept these observations would seem to indicate that agnosias, at least a certain variety for which the term *perceptual agnosia* may be suggested, is caused by lesions of those agencies which serve the appreciation of the relation-structure of visual *gestalten*, while amnestic (asscoiative of conceptual) agnosia may occur in spite of the intactness of gestaltperception. (The two forms correspond, respectively, to Lissauer's apperceptive and associative visual agnosia.) That the ability to appreciate relations varies even with normal persons and that it is relatively independent of visual acuity is an everyday experience indicating that, in "peripherally" handicapped individuals, the higher agencies may compensate for the shortcomings of the lower. That this is the function of the higher level, holds true even for animals, at least I am inclined to interpret Lashley's experiments in this way. Lashley (278) found that cutting of the posterior radiations (or the transcortical connections) along the margins of the striate area have no more effect upon maze habits of rats than peripheral blinding while removal of the striate areas produced severe loss and difficulty in relearning maze habits regardless whether they were formed with or without vision. In all likelihood the level specific resources of the "cortical retina" are more variegated than those of its peripheral counterpart. (The importance of the striate area as regards performances which have been learned without vision appear to support the view that, in the rat, the higher and the lower sensory level form a relatively undifferentiated unit.) Blum, Chow and Pribram (54), after removing large segments of the posterior associative cortex in the monkey, found that the observed deficit cannot be ascribed to primary sensory impairment. According to Blum (*53*), the pattern of affected and unaffected functions following large lesions of posterior association fields is similar in some respects to the astereognosis or tactile agnosia described in man. However, Blum rejects the concept of agnosia as a pure deficit of associative function in a given modality unrelated to sensory impairment. In his opinion, "the sensory associative dichotomy as applied to the cortical substrate does not permit adequate description of experimental results nor of many phenomena observed in clinical practice." Evidently, Blum refers to the perceptual type of agnosia.

Dünsing's approach conforms, on the whole, to the classification of the disturbance into a perceptual and an amnestic form. He concurs with the opinion that recognition depends on gestaltperception but denies that agnosia is consistently caused by "protopathic *Gestaltwandel*." On the other hand, intact gestaltperception does not preclude agnosia. Accordingly, he differentiates between gestaltperception and gestaltrecognition. In his opinion the latter is due to the inability to associate gestalten with their corresponding engrams. Best (*41*) expresses the belief that constriction of the visual fields does not necessarily give rise to difficulties in recognition. Jung (*255*), who criticized Bay for disregarding cases of pure alexia, congenital word blindness and visuospatial disturbances, vigorously opposes the view that *Funktionswandel* accounts for every form of visual agnosia. In opposition to Cibis and Bay, he showed that occipital lobe lesions do not produce agnosia by increased local adaptation (a rise in threshold) even though the abnormality in question (which causes undue fatigue of vision) may be combined with lack of intelligence. At the same time, Jung stresses the frequent occurrence of isolated disturbances of visual memory, or the revisualization of objects, which, in the presence of adequate vision, cannot be attributed to *Funktionswandel*. He tachistoscoped 60 patients suffering from occipital lobe injuries. Of these, 30 showed disturbances of recognition of pictures, linear drawings, letters and numerals, as evidenced by retardation of the perceptual processes. The

deficit observed did not in any way account for the lack of recognition; some of the patients were able to read numerals, but could not read letters. At the same time, Jung found that, in the presence of gestaltwandel, difficulties in recognition grew with the exposure of objects whereas, in visual agnosia, the performance was apt to be improved. (This holds true for those cases only where gestaltwandel can be excluded.) Faust examined a brain injured soldier whose visual acuity had dropped to 5/50 c.u. On tachistoscopic examination, the patient was able to see practically nothing below 100 sigma, yet, nevertheless, was able to grasp every essential detail of a moving picture. Thus, *high level performances do not depend on the competency of the receptors only and agnosias are not necessarily due to disturbances of "peripheral" type.* Brain (*62*), in a study devoted to visual object agnosia with reference to gestaltheory, came to the conclusion that the visual object agnosia was not the result of a disorder of visual gestaltfunction. In his opinion, the division of visual perception into the two phases of awareness of sense data and their secondary association, as suggested by the older writers, (including Lissauer (*308*) and Stauffenberg (*457*)) is an oversimplification; in the first phase, both synthetic and discriminative processes occur which are an essential preliminary to perception, and the activities of the sensory phase enhance sensory awareness. Nevertheless, disease may disrupt the "unitary activity" involved in the process of perception, as evidenced by the reaction of his own patient who scored high in matching tests while he failed in object recognition. Brain's theory would seem to be difficult to reconcile with his own data.

In regard to *tactile agnosia* Cohen distinguishes between two forms, a *primary* and a *secondary*. Only the former is due to *Funktionswandel*, while the latter reflects the inability on the part of the patient to recognize objects in spite of the capacity to appreciate tactile gestalten. In analogy with the corresponding visual disturbances discussed in the preceding paragraphs, tactile disturbances in recognition may be regarded as either perceptual or amnestic in character. Gans (*156*) recognizes a tactile agnosia for forms and one for objects, neither of which he asserts can occur as a result of motor dysfunction or a moderately increased threshold for touch. Although tactile agnosia for forms does not in his experience occur without disturbances of spatial perception, minor disturbances of perception do not give rise to difficulty in recognition. On the contrary, he found, in cortical lesions, a striking disparity between the preservation of tactile sense and complete loss of the ability to recognize objects, which contradicts v. Weizsaecker's contention that differences between central and peripheral lesions are imaginary. *The various observations should disprove the idea, hastily adopted in some quarters, that the classic concept of agnosia is an empty construction and that the inability to recognize objects and symbols is due to an elementary sensory deficit combined with intellectual loss.* Even Conrad (*97*), Bay's cousin in spirit, to whose work we shall refer presently, doubts that Bay has proven his point. "Bay made it quite clear," he wrote, "that there is no agnosia without *Funktionswandel*. So far he failed to demonstrate convincingly that *Funktionswandel* and agnosia are inherently identical. This however, he himself hardly expects, as evidenced by his stipulating mental changes as a contributory factor." Whatever can be said in support of Bay's view is very little. It is true that poor visual acuity and lack of intelligence may interfere with the recognition of objects and visual gestalten and that a combination of peripheral and central disturbances may have catastrophic results. Similar concessions to Bay's view may of course be made in regard to auditory and tactile agnosia.

In *summary*, low level disorders do not necessarily give rise to those of higher functions as the former may be partly compensated by the resources of the higher echelons. Global disturbances of thought must be set apart from modality related dysfunctions as, for example, disturbances of visual attention, of visual memory and the ability to think in visual terms. Concomitant low level disorders fail to account for the impairment of higher cerebral functions whenever high level functions are involved in a dissociated rather than a global fashion.

Conrad's interpretation of higher cerebral functions

Among v. Weizsaecker's pupils, Conrad (*97*) follows a somewhat different line of investigation. He contends that, in the course of *Abbau*,

("disintegration") of sensory functions in diseases, the various elements of the functions concerned are eliminated in the very same sequence in which the functions were built up. Further, that the individual phases of disintegration can be tachistoscopically reproduced by the diminution of illumination, of the size of testobjects and the exposition of stimuli in the periphery of the visual fields. He claims that disturbances in reading experimentally produced in normal persons by too short an explosion of words or letters indicate a state of *"Vorgestalt"* or preconfiguration, which is nothing other than a *state of immaturity of perception.* Such immature states appear also in the course of *Abbau* of other performances, for example, of the understanding of sounds, words and sentences. *Abbau* leads to poor differentiation and to disintegration in the process of gestaltperception as exemplified, respectively, by the inability on the part of the patient to analyze a word into its component sounds and letters and, conversely, to synthetize a word from separate letters or sounds. By a series of sweeping generalizations, Conrad jumps to the conclusion that the law governing the development of perception as discovered by experimental means apply to any higher cerebral functions, and that normal gestalten have epicritic properties, while abnormal gestalten have protopathic properties. "We designate the primarily lost component of the performance as the epicritic performance and the remaining, altered, that is, de-differentiated and disintegrated performance as the protopathic gestaltwandel of the performance." The meaning of this passage is somewhat obscure; firstly, because the author identifies an already disintegrated performance with *Gestaltwandel*, which is a process rather than a condition, and secondly, because the terms *Abbau* and disintegration are not synonymous. As we have already explained, the former signifies a systematized, layer by layer reduction; the latter the process of breakdown or decomposition. (The correct translation of the term "disintegration" would be *"Zersetzung."*) Evidently, we encounter the same difficulty with which both Goldstein's and Weizsaecker's ideas are burdened. At the same time, we are reminded of Head's (*198*) "protopathic animal," a hypothetical creature which existed at some arbitrary stage of evolution. Supposedly, the characteristic mode of movement of this animal was the mass reflex, wherein, in conformity with the idea that the response of the protopathic nervous system is ungraded, diffuse and erroneously referred, the stimulus fails to determine the distribution of response. Although, as Walshe (492) pointed out, such poorly equipped creatures could not have survived, it is worthy of note that the mode of function of its nervous system resembles Coghill's animals prior to the stage of individuation of movements. However, Coghill (95) studied embryonal animals while Head referred to mature forms. In any event, Conrad claims that, as a result of cortical lesions, the configurational processes are arrested at the pre-configurational or protopathic stage, while epicritic performances are characterized by the preservation of the integrating and the differentiating component of gestaltfunction. Cortical lesions reduce the size of the energy potential, which interferes with the completion of gestalten. The location of the cortical lesion determines the particular category of the involved performance, while the type of disturbance is always the same, namely, the impairment of configuration which, lacking analyzing and synthetizing components, assumes protopathic qualities. Even the tension exhibited by the patient on examination is a protopathic manifestation. Psychic functions are the result of configurational processes which proceed in a steady stream. The center of the stream reaches completion, while the periphery remains in the pre-configurational state. Even the relationship between conscious and unconscious mental processes corresponds to that between figure and background. The unconscious in the sense of Freud is a *Vorgestalt*!

The "way from thought to speech" (See this Chapter, *Disorders of recognition and skill*), is a configurational process or a so-called *"Gestaltkreis"* (von Weizsaecker). Pathological movements, including those involved in motor aphasia, are protopathic *Vorgestalten*. Disturbances of word finding follow the same general principle in that the underlying performances fail to attain full maturity. Confusional states (amentias) are due to the impairment of the integrational *Gestaltfunktion* exerted by the total field of consciousness while delirious states are caused by the impairment of the analyzing or dedifferentiating *Gestaltfunktion* which arrests mental

processes at the stage of pre-configuration. Sensory performances are sensory gestalten, while motor performances are motor gestalten. Apraxia is the result of dedifferentiation of motor gestaten which leads to protopathic configurations.

Although, supposedly, sensory and motor performances are merely different aspects of one and the same entity, or *Gestaltkreis*, Conrad and especially Mutschler (347) studied them in terms of independent phenomena. Mutschler investigated motor *Gestalten* ("*Bewegungsgestalten*") and tactile perceptual gestalten ("*taktile Wahrnehmungsgestalten*") in two cases of fronto-parietal lesions involving the opposite cerebral hemisphere. Allegedly, the lesion, besides causing sensory disturbances, had produced the clinical picture of "hand-finger-apraxia" (Kleist, 260) but a perusal of Mutschler's protocols makes it doubtful whether the disturbances of volitional movements corresponded to those described by Kleist. Apart from their paretic character, they involved essentially the appearance of associated movements in the muscles controlling the fingers, in the remaining muscles of the arm, and also in the face. By contrast, Kleist's patients, on being asked to move the terminal phalanx of his thumb and index finger (to make the movement of counting money) would press them against each other and, then, alternately, flex and extend his thumb and index finger. Clearly, he would perform volitional movements other than those requested by the examiner while the associated movements were inconspicuous by comparison. Mutschler's patients, apart from a few isolated movements of their index finger, were unable to use the fingers of their paretic hand individually, the movements having been limited to stereotyped flexions and extensions. Allegedly, the finger movements were dedifferentiated while the epicritic qualities, i.e., the play of the individual fingers had become lost or an epicritic performance replaced by a protopathic performances. The fact that the patients were still able to make a fist and to open it indicated that the "contour" of the motor gestalt was preserved while the inability to move the fingers meant that its finer, intrinsic details, or its *"Binnenstruktur,"* had become obliterated. Mutschler's conclusions drawn from the study of perceptual *Wahrnehmungsgestalten* are equally unconvincing. The distorted tactile experiences of his patients, as reproduced by drawings made by their sound hand, showed evidence of both transformation and falsification of the test figures, i.e., a circle, a cross and a "B." To me, granting of course that the patients were able to reproduce their experiences adequately, the figures indicate, if anything, distortion rather than simplification; and the testfigures reproduced in a like fashion by young children reveal that they were either correctly reproduced or that they represented a playful elaboration of the testpatterns. Neither the mutilated nor the elaborated testfigures displayed protopathic qualities nor did they prove that *Vorgestalten* are the ontogenetic precursors of *Gestalten*.

The reflexologists and behaviourists

The reflexologists (15, 29, 365) and behaviourists (496), who found the phenomenon of consciousness a stumbling block, wasted no time in pushing it aside. As someone expressed the matter in academic language, "the behaviourists avoid the difficulty by the simple expedient of omitting from their account all mention of a stream of thought, feeling and sensation." Thus, they are left with a decapitated hierarchy of nervous system levels which, in spite of the absence of its leading stratum, masters every trick under the sun. In the opinion of the behaviourists, the most important if not the only role of consciousness appears to be the denial of its own importance, perhaps the denial of its own existence. We cannot waste time in discussing this mental aberration.—For a detailed criticism of the Pavlovian school, we refer the reader to Ekehorn (127) and E. Strauss (466) and, for a critical evaluation of behaviourism, to McDougall's (316) lecture series "Man or Robot." The latter recognizes three behaviouristic schools including "(a) the strict behaviourists of the Watson group, (b) the Tolman group which ignores consciousness but accepts the view that behaviour is a goal seeking process, and, (c) the Alport group which neither denies nor totally ignores the facts of conscious-activity but neglects to make use of the introspection of observable facts." In their opinion, every instance of human conduct or animal behaviour is merely a mechanical reflex response to a sensory stimu-

lus. For a more extensive discussion of behaviourism, the reader may be referred to Woodworth (524).

Localistic theories

C. and O. Vogt, (498) in a tribute paid to Meynert's (329) pioneer work on the histology of the cortex, first published in 1869, expound the view that the cortex of man comprises at least 200 areas which may be recognized by their cyto- and myeloarchitecture and, frequently, their glio- and angioarchitectonic features. (The authors note, however, that a complete map which, they hope, some day will be standardized, has as yet not been worked out.) Kornmüller (269), having supplemented the work of the Vogts in the physiologic field, claims that the individual areas can be differentiated not only on morphological grounds but also electroencephalographically. The Vogts, who regard the individual areas (grisea) as the "cortical organs" postulated by Meynert, believe that cortical functions including the highest are the products of the activity of the individual areas operating in appropriate combination. They deny that either vision of hearing can be localized in the cells of the primary receptive areas of the cortex. Significantly, they object to their localization not on epistemologic grounds; in their opinion, it is the lack of discernible intracellular structures which renders "premature" the correlation between morphological and functional data.

Lashley and Clark (284), Bailey (19, 20) and Bailey and v. Bonin (21, 22) question the physiologic significance of the traditional detailed subdivision of the cortex as proposed by Meynert and elaborated by many other workers in this field; furthermore, they doubt the validity of the morphologic criteria permitting such subdivision. Kleist (262), on the other hand, holds that Vogt's areas are autonomous, at least a study of his brain maps appears to preclude any other interpretation. One is faced with one of the perplexities in the history of human thought, considering that, from a practical viewpoint, Kleist's ideas have been largely vindicated, indeed that some of them, for example his views on the significance of the orbito-cingulate region as regards personality traits and emotional processes have been truly prophetic (331a). It is my impression that it is merely the oversimplification of Kleist's ideas which makes them appear as falsehoods. Still, the seemingly strict correlation between higher cerebral functions and morphologically determinable areas stipulated by Kleist goes far beyond the teachings of the Vogts' which, he noted, form the basis of his own theories (*263*). Unfortunately, the value of Kleist's theses is not generally appreciated. See, e.g., his *Bericht über die Hirnpathologie* (1936).

The same objections that may be raised against Meynert's (*329*) and the Vogt's conception of localization of function in the nervous system apply to the work of Flechsig (*142*) with the notable expetion it is true of his concept of the virtual identity of the organ of thought and the posterior part of the cerebral hemispheres. They apply, likewise, to Henschen (*203, 204, 205*), Jendrassik (*239*) and, to a certain extent, to Nielsen's (*356*) theories. However, a careful perusal of Nielsen's work (which popularized the ideas of Liepmann and other classic in this country) renders doubtful Nielsen's position as a strict localizer. For example, we read, in his article on visual agnosia (*358*), that "no memory images can be deposited in the occipital lobe but images cannot be evoked without the function of this area."

Eclectic schools

Although the term "eclectic" might be applied to many contributions, it is especially appropriate to the teachings of v. Monakow and his followers. This celebrated neurologist published numerous studies devoted to the problem of structure function relationship but his ideas on the subject, which became permeated with increasing scepticism, are apt now to promote current trends favoring decentralization of function. This has been a deplorable development because the relation of a seemingly unitary performance to a variety of centers, no doubt a fundamental truth, is likely to be mistaken for the equivalence of the centers concerned. Von Monakow's overemphasis on *diaschisis* as a symptom producing mechanism of a rather general nature has further focused attention on totalizing factors and has created a psychological atmosphere in which the very concept of localization, perhaps contrary to his own intentions, has fallen into disrepute. In short, the valuable part of v. Monakow's work has been widely misinterpreted, and his conception of apraxia has been accepted by many without much criticism. On the whole, his work is apt to promote a reversal of what A. Pick called the "neurologic approach to psychiatry" (*388*). Because of the danger involved in this trend, namely, the psychopathological approach to neurology, v. Monakow's writings deserve particular attention from the critic.

His theories on central nervous system organization and its disturbances are an application of Semon's (*238, 443*) ideas on the mneme (an expanded concept of memory covering many biological phenomena) to the integration of intentional movements and their disturbances. At the same time, his theories were a reaction to the claims of those who, deservedly or not, created the impression that what were naively considered functions but, in reality, are abstract concepts, could be localized in individual provinces of the brain map. Von Monakow was influenced by the philosophical system of Henry Bergson (*37*). His concept of the *horme*, an instinctual, organizing force, resembles what Bergson called *élan vital*. On the other hand, v. Monakow's thesis that volitional movements may be interpreted in terms of chronologically established (and fixated) engrams which, on appropriate stimulation become self-ekphorizing, and which might be adapted to the demands of the moment by attention and concentration, is a disguised concession to the reflexologists—whom Bergson detested. In v. Monakow's opinion, the representation of engrams in *"tectonic layers"* determined by the sequence of their acquisition and their *"phasogenic ekphory"* is the cardinal principle of localization. He claimed that organic brain disease typically caused a reduction of the total performance complex of the brain from layer to layer and, by way of example, in apraxia, older movements were substituted for those more recently acquired. On the surface, his ideas on dissolution of the nervous system resembled those propounded by Jackson. From all this it may be seen that one is indeed justified in classifying v. Monakow as an eclectic. This impression will be deepened when we learn that he shared, unwittingly, certain fundamental views with his great opponent, Hugo Liepmann.

The basic tenets of v. Monakow's theories may

be illustrated by passages taken from his own writings, from v. Monakow and Mourgue's (342) monograph and a series of articles published by his pupil Brun (74). *On the localization of movements and the role of chronogenicity.* (a) the term localization of function designates the relationship (*Verteilung*) of the various components of a performance to all structures concerned with its integration. The structures in question may be widely distributed in the brain and the spinal cord. Localization in my [v. Monakow's] opinion must be chronogenic. In analysing functions, their temporal structure has to be taken into account. (b) Developmental, phylogenetic and particularly ontogenetic elements operating in the integration of functions out of their components, which develop in succession and which are differently organized, are elaborated in the form of a principle of *chronogenic localization*. This principle is consistently developed not only in regard to the organization of movements but also to the function of the sense organs and also to higher functions including speech. From this point of view disturbances caused by cerebral lesions have to be thought of as phenomena of dissolution (*Abbau*). (c) Each type of movement includes phylogenetically as well as ontogenetically old tectonic components and, for this reason, factors of different functional value. *Mnestic layers of engrams.* (a) The stimuli originating in the primary cortical areas are distributed over the entire cortex; and a differentiation of these ever growing engram sets is possible only if they are viewed as chronologically determined layers of *kinetic melodies*, some functional fragments of which may become manifest by diaschisis. Diaschisis, in turn, is produced by focal lesions in the nervous system. (b) The child acquires skill by trial and error. The underlying kinetic melodies become fixated and those that are associated with success are more readily ekphorized than the others. The automatic mastering of the kinetic melodies to the degree of perfection and complete secondary automatization is obviously the result of the innumerable superimposed layers of engrams which, in the course of countless repetition of movements, are acquired during each motor sequence. *Dissolution of function.* Disturbances caused by cerebral lesions manifest themselves as developmentally determined, at least as genetically influenced

processes of dissolution and disorganization. *Diaschisis and reorganization of function.* (a) The reemergence of function can be explained neither by a process of new acquisition nor by the formation of new centers but solely by temporary inhibition. (b) Diaschisis, which exerts its influence beyond the boundaries of the anatomically destroyed tissue, involves those parts of the grey matter which are connected with the involved region by fiber tracts. *Apraxia.* (a) Apractic disturbances are nothing more than a dissolution of volitional movements which are subject to definite biological laws, that is to say, a regression of eupraxia to a more or less earlier ontogenetic and phylogenetic level. Dissolution depends essentially on time factors. (b) Neither apraxia nor aphasia nor agnosia are caused by the lack of one or the other psychic elements. They are brought about by gaps in the successive ekphory of the normal sequence of the kinetic melody. (c) Apraxia represents a complicated syndrome which includes characteristically other related symptoms as essential ingredients. Unilateral apraxia is always associated with gross central disturbances of innervation, disturbances of deep sensibility and hemiparesis. Bilateral (sensory) or ideational apraxia is combined with agnosia. Nevertheless, the concomitant symptoms cannot be interpreted as the cause of apraxia. (d) Apraxia occurs as a result of *diaschisis commissuralis* which is temporary in character and conditioned by certain definitely localized lesions in the left hemisphere. (e) In apraxia, we are dealing with wrong ways in the realm of volition and appetitive attitudes (*Begehren*). (f) The roots of apraxia must be looked for in our vital needs and drives and the mobilization of the mechanical factors and kinetic melodies which are subordinated to the former. (g) We do not know anything whatever about the way the individual components of intended movements are integrated. The ideational plan believed by Liepmann to precede the execution of volitional movements (*Praxie*) is an empty psychological construction which has nothing to do with the actual psychobiological events involved. To execute movements we do not need such ideational plan; the various kinetic melodies have been fixated in early youth and they follow each other automatically in the fashion of conditioned reflexes. (h) Apraxia belongs to those general cerebral dysfunctions which assume a focal character because of the presence of a lesion, that is, a main lesion having a definite localization. (i) The mechanisms superimposed upon the individual kinetic melodies regulates and co-ordinates the latter by virtue of their longer loading time.—(*längere Ladungsdauer.*)

Considerable doubt may be expressed about Von Monakow's concept concerning the acquisition of skilled movements, the significance of chronogenic localization, the relationship of deterioration of function to time factors, the dependence of the ekphory of engrams on the entire cortex, and the role of instincts as regards the integration of skill. *Skilled movements.* If, as implied by v. Monakow, the pathophysiology of apraxia, agnosia and aphasia are similar, not only intentional movements but also gnosis and skill should be dependant on mnemonic mechanisms (1.b). If this is conceded, there should exist "records" of both kinetic and perceptive melodies. Yet, because of the changing demands made on the organism in various life situations, the mere storage of records to be "played" in response to familiar stimuli would be of only limited use. Not only are perceptual records stored for future reference but it is evident that relevant information is digested, to be stored as engrams of a higher order. Other patterns may be instantaneously created in response to the demands of the moment and in turn preserved as engrams. The digests, or abstracts, which constitute the conceptual sphere of the mind are used whenever experiences are generalized and transferred from one problem situation to another to insure adaptive behavior. Neither the performance of the child learning new skills nor working under unfamiliar conditions is merely repetitive nor is the behavior of the adult facing new tasks mere repetition. The child perceives new objects as new experiences, thinks new thoughts and deliberately performs for the first time intentional movements, the effects of which it foresees clearly. In a similar fashion the adult transfers experiences acquired in one performance field to other spheres of activity. As already pointed out in an earlier section of this chapter, the thought elaborating mechanism shapes the kinetic play of the child by reducing trial and error performances to a reasonable minimum. The individual builds up the idea of what it is about to

do, whereupon, during the phase of translation of thought into action, the motor effectors follow suit. The same holds true for adults learning new skills. Without an anticipatory mechanism keeping ideo-motor detours at a minimum, the individual would make no progress and the kinetic play would lead to exhaustion. It may be true that the higher, superimposed mechanism regulating movements has a longer loading time but sustained ekphory of engram chains does not explain the adaptability of behavior based on the awareness or the anticipation of relationships between mnemonically fixated movements on the one hand and new tasks on the other. It is not the time factor as such that matters but rather, the way the time is utilized. *Chronogenic localization of function.* In taking the theory of chronogenic localization literally, and it is difficult to see how else it could be interpreted, one would have to assume that (a) each neuro-dynamic process underlying an individual movement leaves traces in individual systems of neurons which, after its repeated execution, produces large numbers of functionally related though morphologically distinct neuron sets and, as a corollary, that (b) each so established unit represents a structurally preserved and, at the same time, independent event in the history of the function concerned.

It appears more likely that sequences of uniform movements tend to utilize identical substrates and that neuron teams become knit together by both functional and structural individuation. Once an individual movement comes to depend on specialized sets of neurons, the individual chronogenic layers (the layers laid down by the kinetic events as they succeed each other in time) would become telescoped into identical tectonic layers. They would lose their temporo-spatial individuality and the principle of chronogenicity would loose its dominance, in fact the concept of chronogenicity of function would be deprived of its very meaning. Whatever is chronologically conditioned must be located somewhere in the nervous system; and whatever is represented in space, although not necessarily in a circumscribed fashion, must exist somewhere. The notion of chronogenic localization would become superfluous whenever, in the course of the repetition of previously performed movements, the ontogenetically acquired movement patterns were to be synchronously reactivated in sets.

Movement patterns, once they have come to be, are, of course, "hooked up" with the thought elaborating mechanism in different ways. No doubt the establishment of such connections may be years perhaps decades apart. A boy who learned how to tie a sailor's knot may use practically identical innervational sequences at the operating table many years later. Although both sailors and surgeons use quite similar movement patterns in entirely different situations, only the contexts in which the patterns are activated rather than the patterns themselves belong to distinctly different historical periods. The integrational history of the total performance involves, therefore, the elements of concentration of function on the one hand and of its adaptation on the other. It cannot be fully expressed in terms of chronogenicity. *Dissolution of function.* In previous communications (*429, 431, 432*) we showed that dissolution of skilled movements may involve whole complexes within which no single movement can be considered either ontogenetically older or younger from any viewpoint whatsoever. This may be demonstrated by the observation that, particularly as regards mnestic and intellectual performances, dissociation may proceed either from stratum to stratum or that it may single out individual (receptor-linked) systems or lastly, that it may take place in a combined fashion. Even granting some measure of chronogenic localization, deterioration of function is not necessarily time-related.

Not only could the dominance of time-relatedness of neurologic disturbances not be verified on clinical grounds but it appears that it cannot be established for quite another reason. Assuming the most recently acquired performances to be the most vulnerable, general lowering of the cerebral metabolism may well account for general depression of function. On the other hand, it is difficult to see how circumscribed lesions destroying any parts of the cortex could single out the most recent functions with which the region in question happens to be concerned. If chronogenic localization is the dominant mechanism, the chronogenic layers of engrams would be spatially interwoven and their selective impairment impossible.

The implications of the theory of time-related dissolution patterns may be brought out by the following example. Two persons may have learned to select a certain object on hearing the sound of a bell and, say, six months later, a different object upon the flash of a light. Let us suppose that after continuing to practice these performances for some time, each person develops a brain lesion involving, respectively, the temporal and the occipital lobe. It is evident that, in the former eventuality, the ontogenetically younger performance is jeopardized; in the latter, the ontogenetically older. This hypothetical situation would not support the theory of the dominance of the chronogenicity but, rather, demonstrate the dominant role of localization. It is only under conditions of general depression of awareness or in states of severe fatigue that reactions to visual stimuli would be affected.

The significance of instincts. According to v. Monakow and Mourgue (*341*) the role of the psychic elements, which according to Liepmann (*304*) operate in certain forms of apraxia, is purely imaginary. At the same time, they stress the importance of a "defect in the ekphory of the normal sequence of the kinetic melody set in motion by instincts." This may well apply to arthropodes whose behavior lacks flexibility rather than to higher organisms. And, strangely, it is the motor patterns governing insect behavior which Brun (*74*), an authority on the subject, invokes in support of v. Monakow's theory of integration of skilled movements in man. The reference to insects, which are notorious for their inability to cope with relatively simple problem situations, appears to be of dubious value, for their responses, no matter how intricate, are highly stimulus bound.

If the acts of man were determined by instincts and the innervational sequences by means of which they are materialized were likewise activated by instincts alone, "contre coeur" volitional movements would be impossible. This is brought out by everyday experience which tells us that normal persons and even animals are able to act against strong instinctual impulses. Moreover, apractic and aphasic patients are usually very eager to cooperate on examination. Man's actions, except for primitive goal seeking and consummative performances, do not depend chiefly on inherited or acquired kinetic melodies set in motion by instincts. They are governed by thought which may cancel instinctual factors. In fact, if necessity arises, thought may instantaneously create kinetic melodies where none existed. In other words, without Liepmann's ideational plan, which v. Monakow regards as an empty psychological construction, the whole concept of apraxia would lose its meaning and the skilled movements of man would be relegated to motor performances controlled mainly by preoprioception. Were it not for the role of proprioceptive stimuli and the clues furnished by other senses, man would be a Cartesian automation rather than a living being who, within the natural limits of his organization, is the master of his own actions.

Von Monakow and his pupils overemphasized the subcortico-extrapyramidal components of volitional movements, which in essence provided their postural and tonic background and which make for eutaxia rather than eupraxia. At the same time, they minimize the role of the thought elaborating mechanism which is responsible for flexibility and creativity in human behavior. They assign, whatever role is left for thought, to play to the "entire" cortex as an apparently equipotential jumping off ground for self-ekphorizing, or phasogenic, movement chains; and they minimize the significance of the sensory sector of the highest level, which is responsible for the elaboration of thought. They confuse the more or less conscious preparatory phase of mentation, that is, the intellective antecedents of movement, with the conversion of thought into action. They emphasize the association of apraxia with other disturbances, e.g., agnosia, but this throws no light on its nature, and they ignore the specific qualities of the highest strata of the nervous system.

Because of the great volume of v. Monakow's writings, it is difficult to give an adequate account of his theories within the framework of a brief abstract. The above quotations refer to those parts of v. Monakow's theory which were most emphatically stressed throughout his own and his pupils' work. However, these theses were interspersed with occasional remarks approaching more nearly the ideas of the classics than those of an iconoclast. For example, v. Monakow speaks of prefocal and perifocal cortical agencies which govern the aggregates of foci in the lower

prerolandic region and which are evidently identical with Broca's center. Further, he distinguishes between a simultaneous and a successive phase of volitional movements and speaks of the localization of the former in fairly circumscribed cortical provinces. In spite of the fact that he places undue emphasis on the chronogenic localization of movements (the successive phase), his article on the structure and localization of movements in man (336) has always impressed me as an outstanding piece of neurological writing. Although disinclined to think in terms of heterogeneity of the cerebral cortex, he was, of course, aware of the relationship between gnostic disturbances and perceptual disorders following lesions of the sensory areas, or sensory terminals, and also of the peri-focal and parafocal points to the primary motor foci. In fact, his classification of apraxia, except for the terms employed to designate the individual varieties of the disorder, would seem to suggest that, ultimately, his own ideas and Liepmann's views on the subject are not too far apart.

Structure, function and symptom

By and large, the proponents of the totalistic, reflexologic, localistic and gestaltpsychologic theories were concerned with the nature of functions and dysfunctions, and with their relationships to the data of neuroanatomy. It is not intended at this juncture to summarize the points at issue. Suffice to say that the above discussed theories have been found wanting either because of basic misconceptions on the part of their protagonists, or the misapplication of basically sound principles. The present approach to the interpretation of higher brain functions is based, although with some modifications, on the Jacksonian concept of *systematization*, *stratification* and *sensory-motor dualism* of the nervous system, and its elaboration by Sherrington (445) and Kleist (259). Another basic concept is that of *integrative function* of the nervous system. To quote Sherrington: "Integrative action ... is nervous reaction par excellence which welds the organism together from its components and constitutes from a mere collection of organs an animal individual." (See Chapter I.)

As a corollary to the idea of integrative action we offered the concept of *integrative acts or processes mediated by the nervous system and its auxiliary organs*. Since the individual nerve centers are concerned with the production of integrative processes which, aiming at physiological "target effects," may either succeed or fail, it may be said that they subserve the maintenance of a reasonable balance between failure and success; clearly, the nervous system is not a precision machine, at least not as regards its higher, or "least highly organized" functions while it operates with remarkable accuracy in the sphere of the lower, "most highly organized" functions.

Structural dissociation of function

We propose to use a personal case (*430*) of head trauma as a point of departure. The patient, a middle-aged right handed man, developed, following a closed head injury, agraphia, deviation of the tongue to the right, a lower facial weakness, motor aphasia and apraxia of the face and tongue. He made futile attempts to protrude his tongue on command and produced, at the same time, distortions of his facial muscles. The neurological examination was otherwise negative. In particular, it failed to reveal any abnormalities in the right upper and lower extremity. Mentally, the patient was normal. He was very anxious to overcome his speech difficulties. He tried to talk to his roommates and practiced writing eagerly. Certainly, the speech defect could not be attributed to any form of "embarrassment and feeling of insecurity" (which are doubtless present) resulting from the "brain lesions as such," as recently stipulated by Alford (*8*) for agnostic, aphasic and similar disorders. Neither did the patient's behavior indicate that the abnormalities of higher cerebral functions could be interpreted in the light of the "psychopathological approach in neurology" nor that they were merely a part of a massive disturbance of brain function. As far as could be determined, reading was less severely involved than speaking and writing because the patient immediately noted whether a newspaper page was handed to him upside down or in a correct fashion. The aphasic and agraphic symptoms showed marked fluctuation.

Although the loss of the ability to write was not isolated, experiences with similar cases prove that agraphia is not necessarily part of a global organic brain deficit which, in the opinion of v. Monakow (*340*), Goldstein (*176*), and others, is only artificially separable into fractions. Furthermore, motor aphasia and agraphia may occur independently. In motor aphasia not associated with agraphia the disturbance may be so severe that, as one of the early students of aphasia remarked, "the patient had to transact business in writing" (*179, 180*).

The "global organic brain syndrome" can be broken down into still smaller fragments. Agraphia may be limited to the inability to write certain letters only, and alexia to the inability to read them. One of Rieger's (*409*) patients was unable to read the Gothic letters p, x, a, d, y, and the Latin letters p, a, y, d, h, k, and v. He was unable to recognize capital letters P, X and H either in Gothic or Latin print and, in addition, unable to read B, F, M, N, R, T and W in Latin. He was able to read all other letters of the alphabet. (See also Haidenhain, *190*.)

Gerstmann (*165*) observed impairment of calculation with practically complete inability to add, to subtract or divide, while the ability to multiply was preserved to a striking degree. When the patient was asked "How much is 6 + 5?" She repeated 6 and 5 to it and said: "I don't know; I cannot even make a guess." On being asked "6 − 3," she declared: "There is no such thing." (Why not?) "Because it couldn't be, wouldn't be possible." ("What did I ask you?") "6 − 3; it isn't possible, absolutely not. You can't take away 3 from 6; I know what I am talking about and you can't fool me either." When told that the result is 3, she said: "Guess so, I guess it is." Presented with the problem 8:2, she remarked, "There is no such crazy number like that; you get me all twisted up." ("What did I ask you?") "8 divided by 2: I do not know it; honestly, I don't." But if given multiplication problems, such as 6 × 5, 3 × 9, 4 × 6, and the like, answers were prompt and correct.

These observations prove the point made previously, that *seemingly unitary functions are nothing more than aggregates of smallest integrative acts which, moreover, in disease, may be selectively involved while other, similar, processes remain intact.* We may put this in another way by saying that a state of *structural dissociation of function* indicates that a seemingly unitary performance is compounded of individual physiological entities. (It does not concern us here that these fractions may be further broken down into smaller innervatory patterns.) The same applies to the writing of musical notes, of numerals, to the recognition of figures and, in a certain sense, also to elementary sensory functions. Von Weizsaecker described various dissociation patterns of sensation, for example disturbances of discrimination, of the perception of posture and movements and of spatial disturbances while the ability to localize stimuli was unimpaired. In other cases, he noted that dissociation may lead to exactly the opposite combination of symptoms, indeed, any possible grouping of abnormalities. Similar experiences were reported by other observers who studied the clinical symptomatology of lesions of the centro-parietal cortex (*201*).

One may be tempted to explain the structural dissociation of function by stipulating that, in the cerebral cortex, the pertinent centers are arranged in a mosaic-like fashion and that they may be involved in various combinations. However, neither anatomical data nor clinical observations (see below) favor such an assumption. For example, Henschen (*202*) collected 122 cases of patients suffering from word blindness. Of these, seventy-one were able to read numbers while the remaining 51 were unable to read either numerals or words. It is highly questionable whether, in the second group, the lesions showed a different pattern of distribution in the cortex which could be correlated with the clinical manifestations.

Temporal dissociation of function

Fluctuations of the ability to read certain letters was described by Haidenhain (*190*) and, of identifying large letters cut from cardboard and placed in the patient's hand, by Gordon Holmes (*219*). Instability of the performance level could be readily demonstrated in a personal case of a patient with virtually unilateral construction apraxia (*429*). During one and the same session, normal and abnormal responses alternated quite irregularly and unpredictably.

We have already made reference to Beringer and Stein's experiences and also to those of other writers who pointed out that fluctuations of the ability to read, although they may be conditioned by abnormalities in perception, cannot be fully explained on the basis of *Funktionswandel*. In our own case, the role of abnormal perception was excluded by the virtual unilaterality of the disturbance. Paterson and Zangwill (*373*) observed fluctuation in the degree of spatial orientation following cranio-cerebral injuries. In aphasia, the phenomenon of temporal dissociation is generally considered as trivial and, from a theoretical viewpoint, hardly worthy of note, in fact, it is so common that it is taken for granted. In the process of temporal disorganization of any function, failure and success may follow each other with such conspicuous irregularity that the influence of inattention, fatigue, etc., as causative factors can be excluded.

Conrad (*97*) advanced the view that the above mentioned disorder conforms to a definite pattern indicative of *Gestaltwandel*, and that it may involve not only perception but also disturbances of recognition and action. Allegedly, the laws governing disintegration of higher cerebral functions are the same as those of *Gestaltwandel* which determine the pathology of sensory functions. Regardless of the function involved, the general performance level of the brain injured shows, according to Conrad, typically four phases, namely, (a) an initial phase in which the performance is still possible, (b) an inter-ferential phase, in which typical errors occur, (c) a refractory phase, in which the number of errors reaches a maximum, and (d) a phase of restitution. The performances tested by Conrad include reading, writing, word finding, calculating, the execution of various tasks, auto-toporientation, building with blocks and the finding of subcategories of general concepts. Allegedly, the disturbance patterns can be accounted for by two mechanisms, namely, the abnormal persistence of stimulation and the refractoriness due to threshold lability which, he claims, is analogous to that encountered in sensory dysfunction.

Since the fluctuations in question have long been known, it is difficult to see how the above described fluctuations patterns should have escaped the attention of the individual examiners. For example, Franz (147) wrote that, in a case of his observation, three series of tests he employed showed the same condition, namely, a variation from day to day in the ability to name certain objects, etc., instead of a gradual increase with minor variations such as is to be expected in a normal training series. At the same time, these variations run to extremes of full accuracy to no ability or the reverse. "It is to be noted that these variations do not correspond by days, for there may be a loss one day for one name and on another day when that name is suddenly picked up, there is a loss for another name. Nor do the losses occur only once in a series with each object. In a few cases there is an apparent high ability followed by a loss of this ability, and after some days with a reacquisition a second less or great decrease." (Franz attributed the fluctuations described to "variations in the permeability of neuronic connections or in the degree of smoothening out of the paths.") Schuell (437, 438, 439) referred to the fluctuations described above as "inconsistent responses." See also Jackson (1866) and Goldstein (174). Our own data, published in 1928 and 1940, indicate that, in the behaviour of the brain injured, failure and success follow each other in an unpredictable fashion. These data have been recently confirmed by Critchley (104) whose observations deserve to be quoted in full. "... One of the most striking clinical features of the patient with a parietal lesion is the variability of his performance. He may make a gross error at one moment, and give a successful response the next ... these very irregularities, variabilities, repetitions, hesitancies, changes of mind, evasions and so on, are, I submit, important. As Head and Holmes have noted in their sensory testing of parietal lesions, answers may be quite correct one moment and quite erroneous the next, and later still correct again. Gnostic defects show the same paradoxes and vagaries in all spheres."

The abnormalities in question, thus far at least, have not been regarded as a clue to the interpretation of cerebral mechanisms. They are by no means confined to parietal lesions. They indicate that the *instability of performance levels may involve any activity, that "elementary" integrative processes operate throughout the nervous system and that they are the individual entities of nervous system functions. In disease, the individual dynamic fractions fail to materialize within the normal range of accuracy and dependability.* The phenomenon of temporal dissociation, suggestively present even in the normal individual, is of crucial importance in interpretating brain mechanisms, both in disease and in health. Under normal conditions, functions have a reliability coefficient, or "confidence coefficient" which, in disease, falls below standard levels. The low coefficient is the result of lesions involving localities where the site-relationship or both the side- and site-relationship of integrative acts reaches a maximum. It may be inferred from the various ways in which, for example, the function of writing may become dissociated, that the individual letters are "events" which, in disease, do not readily materialize, or which are abolished altogether. The resulting defect may be attributable to one or more of the following: destruction of brain tissue, distraction of attention, disturbances in affect, and various other neurologic and psychologic factors. The above considerations would seem to apply also to other cerebral functions, including those involved in finding appropriate words for objects or symbols, in verbalizing complicated thought processes, in understanding of what we see or hear or perceive in any other fashion; in recalling, in revisualizing and, of course, in performing intentional movements. *Whenever the execution of a movement is intended, appropriate integrative acts must be built up; and whenever, in any sphere of behaviour, individual target effects are to be achieved, separate neurodynamic processes must take place. Temporal dissociation is due to the irregular sequence or failure or success of individual processes.* It is evident that the central nervous system produces sequences of integrative acts like, say, the heart muscle which, by a succession of contractions, produces sequences of pressure gradients. With every integrative act of the nervous system, innumerable neurons discharge in teams as, with every heart beat, innumerable fibers contract.

Electric potentials obtained from certain parts of the cerebral cortex on concentration of attention, from the rolandic region on intended muscular innervation (376), from the brainstem on exposure of experimental animals to variously pitched sounds (153, 481) and from peripheral nerves on direct stimulation (345), to give only a few examples selected at random, prove the phasic nature of central nervous system activity at various levels.

Temporal and structural dissociation of function are closely related since, whenever the confidence coefficient of an integrative act reaches zero, temporal dissociation is intensified to the degree of structural dissociation*.

While the frequent repetition of a performance tends to establish, and to deepen, a beaten path for every individual "beat," experimental and clinical evidence suggests that, in addition to the main stream of fibers and the corresponding cell stations, collateral pathways play an important part. As long as a critical amount of suitable substrate is available, the integrative action of the nervous system is seemingly unimpaired although "misintegration" is more likely to occur than under normal conditions. We are inclined to believe that paraphasia, paralexia and similar disorders are the products of inadequate integration on the part of the centers involved.

In our already quoted study on dissociation and reorganization of cerebral function (1940) we expressed the opinion that there is a "scattered arrangement of the neural substrate underlying the various performances in extrafocal regions" and that the (limited) equipotentiality and collateral organization of the cortex is the structural basis of reintegration. Chow (*89*) and his associates, who investigated the effects of combined destruction of the frontal and posterior associative areas in the monkey (1951), found that the "neural substrate which is critical for retention and ready acquisition of certain habits is organized into discrete centers specific for the functional category. These areas of concentration are supplemented by the overlapping fringes of secondary significance and the "greatest disturbance of a given function is produced by damage to its critical focus although deficits of larger magnitude follow lesions of the fringes." Förster (*143*) demonstrated that the principle of collaterality operates even in the apparently rigidly organized rolandic cortex. Glees and Cole (*165*) found that, in the monkey, lesions of area 4, although they eliminate certain movements completely, had no permanent effect as neighbor-

hood areas developed their latent ability to control the functions of the previously removed cortical part of area 4. Lidell and Phillips (*296*) interpret this phenomenon to express "emergent functioning of cortical fields surrounding the classical areas." According to Kennard (*252, 254*), "the highly developed and coordinated motor performances which are present in the monkey deprived of motor and premotor tissue in infancy are due to the integration from other cortical regions, namely, the frontal association areas and the postcentral gyrus." Thus, our early observations were amply confirmed.

The activities of the nervous system of which we are accustomed to think in terms of unitary entities, or functions, are not mediated by autonomous, more or less sharply circumscribed centers. They are subserved by more or less diffuse neural nets although, with rise in the phylogenetic scale and with the increasing versatility of cortical circuits, those processes assume a leading role in recognition and skill which are spatially related either to the primary sensory areas, or to the motor area, where the muscles subserving volitional movements are represented. The concept of center, as here proposed, is not inconsistent with the previously offered definition of centers as localities that control the totality of integrative acts on which a given performance depends; in fact, the definition supplements what has been said before. (See Ch. I.) It may be assumed that, in central nervous system disease, functional individuation, perhaps similar to that operating in the growing organism, occurs as long as critical amounts of "matrix" endowed with specific potencies remain intact. In health, the individual cortical centers or neural arrangements subserving recognition and skill are apt to develop in close spatial relationship to the cortical terminals of the individual senses and to the motor area. With the reduction of nerve substance in disease the "fringes" assume added significance but the degree to which they are able to compensate for the loss of the "areas of concentration" varies from individual to individual and, in one and the same person, from moment to moment. Not only has the performance range of the individual centers been reduced but they tend to gravitate toward different parts of the nervous system, that is, toward the former fringes. In animals,

---

* Although the antonym of the term *temporal* is *permanent* rather than *structural*, I have avoided using this term because of potential restitution in apparently permanent lesions.

the fringe-core relationship is shifted in favour of the former even under normal conditions and, since the functional potencies of the animal cortex as compared to those of the human cortex are small, it is not surprising that the animal cortex is believed by some to be either equipotential throughout or that, within a specialized area, functional equivalence prevails. The question to what extent the subordinate hemisphere may be regarded the fringe-region or collateral agency of the dominant hemisphere will be discussed later.

Performances of similar integrational structure are apt to be represented in adjacent parts of the cortex and, in cases of cortical damage, to be jointly affected. This rule, however, has exceptions as evidenced by the *dissociability of syndromes* which is a natural consequence to the dissociability of functions. For instance, the particular performance complex whose involvement is known under the name of Gerstmann's syndrome, may be dissociated in different combinations. In one of Meyer-Gross' cases (*324*), and in Conrad's (*98*) case, finger-agnosia was combined with agraphia and acalculia; in another of Meyer-Gross' cases and in Zutt's (*534*) case, the two symptoms were associated with left-right disorientation while finger agnosia was absent. In Meyer-Gross' third case, finger agnosia was combined with acalculia and right-left disturbance. In Ehrenwald's (*124*) case, only agraphia and acalculia were preserved. In Meyer-Gross' (*324*) case IV, finger agnosia was associated with constructional apraxia. In one of Gerstmann's (*161*) cases, there was originally an isolated arithmetical deficit while constructional apraxia appeared only later. In Lange's (*272*) case of Gerstmann's syndrome there was little or no acalculia. Several additional cases of dissociation of Gerstmann's syndrome were cited by Benton and his associates (*35*) and by Nielsen and Sult (*360*). J. Lange advanced the theory that his patient had lost the capacity to organize space both conceptually and creatively and that he had lost the category "direction in space." Such basic (fundamental or categorical) functions are of course, nothing more than logical abstractions. Lange himself must have been aware to have substantialized an abstract concept for he spoke of "*Herantragung fremder Gesichtspunkte an das Hirngeschehen*," which means (in free translation) the application of viewpoints to the physiology of the brain which, in the last analysis, are utterly inapplicable to "what goes on there."*

Strictly speaking, there is no function of either writing or reading or speaking or, for that matter, any other function as understood in the conventional or psychological sense of the term. One might say there is no such thing as rain; there are merely drops falling from the clouds. Neither is there any such function as memory, but the reinstatement of individual experiences. Occasionally, attempts at remembering a name made in groping approximations to the target may result in a near miss, or the engram searched for may prove to be temporarily or permanently unekphorizable. That the reification of psychological terms is bound to lead to confusion may be illustrated by various examples. It is inconsistent with the notion of the loss of a basic function (on which, allegedly, the individual performances of copying depend) that a person, who lost the category "direction in space" should, on occasion at least, be able to copy patterns. Curiously enough, Alajouanine appeared to be vexed by the problem whether the diagnosis agraphia is at all justified if the patient is able to write his own name. "Le term agraphie est-il justifié dans ce cas? Comment parler d'agraphie chez un suject qui a perdu l'usage de l'écriture mais reste cependant capable d'écrire correctement son nom?" Contrarily, it is not illogical to assume that individual integrative acts in, e.g., the visual or motor sphere and, likewise, those underlying mnemonic functions may fail not only in disease but, on occasion, in health as well. Even the best marksman may miss his objective. The nervous system, unlike an ideal machine or an ideal marksman, operates on the principle of probability.

Negative and atypical cases

Certain observations, particularly the existence of what is known in brain pathology as *negative cases* would seem to suggest that the correlation between structure and symptom may be loose rather than rigid. In other words, that, given certain lesions, the presence of certain symptoms is probable rather than necessary because (among other reasons) of the increasing looseness between structure and function at progressively higher levels of the nervous system.

How, then, shall we account for the existence of negative cases and also for the relative absence of *pure cases*, the diversity of clinical syndromes associated with grossly similar lesions, and lastly, the existence of systematized disorders, which comprise, at the same time, disturbances of related lower and higher cerebral dysfunction? And how is it possible to reconcile the occurrence of systematized and non-systematized syndromes? What is the role of psychological factors? Some of the above problems have already been touched upon in the preceding paragraphs. That the patterns of original integration utilized available systems in a preferential fashion, in other words, that there prevails, within the natural limits imposed upon by morphological destination, a certain leeway in structure-function relationship, is consistent with the conception that an archaic, diffuse, and a recent, more concentrated, type of integration coexist and that the latter, as experimental work indicates, emerges from the former. By the same token, the evolution of the recent type of organization of the nervous system implies some variability of structure-function relationship. While the statistical evaluation of large series of cases proves the general validity of localisatory principles, atypical cases are by no means rare, even when distant effects of a lesion upon primarily uninvolved parts at the brain can be excluded. In clinical usage, the site of cortical lesions is expressed in terms of their relationship to individual convolutions and to conventionalized cytoarchitectonic maps, although, with certain exceptions (122) the relationship between areas and surface patterns is far from constant. According to Lashley and Clark (284) "there is scarcely a qualitative histologic character which does not vary by 25 to 100 percent in local regions" and "the brain is extremely variable in every character that has been subject to measurement." Since the variability of the ramifications of nerves and blood vessels, or of the size and the shape of the human face and hand are taken for granted, one should not be surprised by the variability of the even more complicated convolutional pattern of the brain (see, e.g., Beck, 30) and also of the areal arrangement and intra-areal differences. In a sense, the term center has

not only a morphologic and a physiologic meaning but also a statistical connotation. It can hardly be expected that localities of maximal concentration of function (and hence of maximal vulnerability) should exist in topographically identical places of the idealized brain map.

The relatively frequent occurrence of atypical cases does not militate against the principle of structure-function relationship. Although pure cases are rare (for the involvement of maximal concentration of function by minimal foci is improbable) the former are of greater theoretical significance than the more numerous lesions which, because of the chance vulnerability of the nerve substance, cause massive aggregates of neurological abnormalities. Such extensive lesions may be caused by interference with a common vascular supply, which is notoriously variable, or the haphazard configuration of extensive brain injuries.

If the main pathways and their collaterals subserving a given performance were concentrated into linear, neatly isolated, tracts and the functional levels were separated from each other (as indicated for simplicity in the various diagrams illustrating the concept here proposed), pure cases should be the rule rather than the exception. However, unlike hypothetical lesions of a diagram, most brain lesions are apt to involve densely crowded fibers and centers which may or may not belong to identical or functionally related systems. Thus, it can hardly be a matter of surprise that hemianopsia is apt to be associated with visual agnosia, motor weakness with motor apraxia, and sensory impairment with sensory aphasia (498, 499), that the latter may be combined with ideational apraxia and, frequently, the inability to draw from memory (58). On the other hand, the association between word blindness and color agnosia is fortuitous. It will bear repetition that the impairment of higher cerebral functions is not necessarily the result of involvement of the lower functions in the sense of von Weizsaecker and its pupils, and that they do not represent an inseparable aggregate as stipulated by von Monakow and the field theorists. To a large extent, the composite character of many clinical pictures is due to the proximity of low level and high level nervous arrangements of the same functional category. On the other hand, we do not mean to imply that lesions of similar location will consistently produce identical clinical pictures. Owing to the variability of the areal organization as regards the convolutional pattern, this can hardly be expected. Taking into account individual variations, the existence of "absolute congruent" lesions is doubtful.

It stands to reason that damage to identical points of macroscopically identical cortices of two hypothetical individuals would not necessarily produce identical effects unless the two cortices were also histologically identical. In fact, one might go further and assume that, even under those "ideal" conditions, the effects of the lesions may be different because of the potentially different functional history of the two cortices or the fact that the way in which seemingly identical performances are integrated may vary with different individuals. For example, of two drivers, one will watch out for the green light and the red light; the other, for the appearance of the lower and the upper light—if he should happen to be color blind. The observation that "identical" lesions may produce different effects does not invalidate the doctrine of localization of functions in the cerebral cortex.

Since, within the sphere of seemingly *unitary* performances as, for example, reading and writing, dissociation of function may occur in various combinations, the segregation of a performance complex may yield an even wider variety of syndromes. Moreover, the clinical manifestations may be different at different times and, during the stage of recovery, may be present in a residual fashion only. In principle, it is immaterial whether a given clinical syndrome be regarded an independent entity or, like various types of aphasia, "merely" as residual stages, or subordinate types, of what is known as cortical aphasia. Difficulties arise only if individual performances are interpreted as manifestation of basic functions. For example, alexia may or may not be associated with the inability to draw—either syndrome is equally comprehensible.

The clinical manifestations are no doubt influenced by the general mental organization which may vary from case to case, for instance by the various ways in which the ability to read (58) has been acquired, in other words, by the *integrational history* of the performance already referred to, the dominance of vision, hearing,

motor and kinaesthetic factors and also by the various *psychological repercussions* and the *interactions* and *cumulative effects* of organic lesions in the brain. Schiller, (429) who studied the reciprocal relationship between language function and arithmetical ability, found that "when a patient is laboring with the task of relating figures to each other, his expression will suffer and that, conversely, the difficulty in saying and finding words will interfere with the process of calculation." Weinstein and Kahn (540) have shown that certain symptoms are likely to appear in certain personality types. On the whole, however, clinical syndromes associated with organic lesions, particularly focal lesions, are basically determined by the site of the lesions while their variability is due to the structural and temporal dissociation of functions which permits their involvement in various combinations. At the same time, we would assume that lesions involving different sites of the brain may cause identical clinical symptoms because of the identity of the ultimate effect upon a "target organ," say, the diencephalon.

In *summary*, individual performances may in nervous system disease be involved regardless of the time of their acquisition and degree of automatization and in almost any combination. Apart from the site and size of a lesion, structural dissociation may be due to the scattered arrangement of the neural substrate mediating the various performances in the extrafocal regions and to the different functional value of the various intrafocal fields as regards the common integrational structure of related performances. Other dissociation promoting factors may be the different development of compensating collaterals and different types of psychic organization. The fluctuation of performance levels is largely due to the fact that the performance involved takes place in individual attemp s which may fail or succeed at different times. In the light of the above advanced concept of cerebral function, it should be possible to appreciate the following peculiarities of abnormal performances; (a) their *structural and temporal dissociability*, (b) *transitory symptoms* produced by permanent lesions, (c) *incongruent symptoms* produced by congruent lesions, and, (d), *dissimilarity of symptoms* produced by one and the same lesion at different times (432).

The nature of symptoms considered in the light of neuropsychology

The "brain-rest theory," which stipulate that neurological abnormalities represent the activity of that part of the brain which is still capable of functioning, is self-defeating by its very wisdom. It is true that, following section of a nerve supplying an extremity, the residual functions represent the activity of the remaining nerves. On the other hand, a consistent application of this principle would shift the problem of structure-function relationship from one province of the nervous system to another. The function of an individual nerve may be readily determined by severing the remaining nerves of the extremity. In studying brain functions, on the other hand, the method of exclusion is not always feasable; apart from the fact that some of the lesions produced may be fatal, the functions observed "in isolation" are not necessarily those of the corresponding structures as they exist in the normal nervous system. Furthermore, they may be too highly integrated to be defined in the same simple terms as residues of cutaneous sensation as may follow peripheral nerve section.

It is evident that the problems of structure-function relationship cannot be divorced from that of structure-dysfunction relationship. If "function" is a generic term referring to closely related or identical integrative acts (such as those involved in producing similar or identical letters or sounds), symptoms must be thought of as the expression of *misintegration*. More especially, the type of faulty integration in nervous system disease depends on the absence of one or more component parts which fail to contribute specific quotas of action. The central problem of localization is the specification of the contribution of a given element to the total process. It is certainly not solved by the idea, advanced by v. Monakow and his followers, that a given abnormality is an answer of the uninvolved part of the brain to the effect of a lesion in a certain locality. Von Monakow was impressed by the bewildering complexity of clinical pictures, the seemingly inexhaustible variations in which they occur, and the apparent hopelessness of assigning the various disturbances, let alone the underlying functions, to specific structures in the brain. Jackson stressed especially the significance of the level relationship of pathological performances. "When disease attacks the nervous system," he wrote, "there are always two sets of manifestations, negative and positive—loss of function and excess of function. The functions lost are those of the centers diseased; the functions that are excessive are those of centers subordinate to the centers diseased and permitted to act excessively by the removal of control normally exercised by the centers now diseased. The centers whose function is abolished may belong to the lowest, to the middle or the highest division, affording examples of local dissolution. On the other hand, there may be uniform dissolution the whole of the highest grade of all being first lost and successive grades being pared off as it were in layers" (233). To forestall misapprehension, it will be necessary to supplement the above passage by Head's (200) comment. He maintained that "release does not reveal functional properties of the lower centers but their modification by the formation of recent centers which utilize and develop certain functions previously subserved by the older. In a similar vein, Walshe (492) wrote that "Jackson nowhere suggests that the lower planes of evolution exposed by disease or injury necessarily represent physiological states and that they were the normal endowments of a primitive nervous system in earlier stages of phylogenetic evolution. Nor did Jackson suggest that dissolution of function was associated with the release of primitive anatomical systems to resume their original activities in their pristine form." Parenthetically, we note that Gamper (155), who had occasion to study the behavior of an anencephalic monster, very wisely cautioned against the identification of performances of the preserved interbrain and midbrain of the abnormal infant with functions mediated by corresponding structures in the brains of normal children of the same age. Evidently, he assumed that, in the brain of the anencephalus, the existing highest centers play a relatively higher role than in the normal, where they are subordinated to other, higher, centers. (See Chapter I.)

Broadbent's (69) summary of Jackson's ideas on the dissolution of the nervous system is most elucidating. The functions of a center in which a lesion has occurred are suspended, he wrote, and corresponding symptoms may be called negative.

There are however not the only symptoms; others, usually more obtrusive and infinitely more important, are produced by the activities of other centers, either (a) unbalanced in consequence of the absence of normally opposing activities, or (b) liberated from the control of the higher level centers; or (c) intensified by attempts to compensate for the missing function.

Symptoms are not necessarily be breakdown products but, potentially, attempts at reintegration which utilize whatever anatomical and physiological fragments are available. If this is granted, the symptoms in question are attempts at self-realization of the organism so eloquently described by Goldstein (172). In disease, self-equilibrating mechanisms continue to operate. Certain somatic and also some psychopathological, including neurotic and psychotic phenomena may be products of opposing forces.

It was convenient to develop the concept of structurally and temporally fractionable mechanisms in conjunction with a critical review of v. Monakow's theory which emphasized the composite nature of the variously combined complexes into which the total function of the brain can be broken down rather than the elementary character of the integrative acts out of which both normal and abnormal performances are built up. This approach was not entirely fruitful, for neither normal nor abnormal performances can be satisfactorily explained by the true but unconstructive statement that the brain works as a whole; that, in disease, cerebral functions become dedifferentiated; that lack of precision of function expresses blurring of figure background formation; and that there remain, as a result of brain disease, only amorphous aggregates of performances which fail to show intelligible relationships between structure and function other than those dependent on time factors. Such attitude is bound to misdirect the analysis of both normal and pathological phenomena into the blind alley of holistic philosophy, for what good can possibly come from the notion that a specific defect in the workings of the organism is due to dedifferentiation? What would people think of an engineer who, called upon to repair a machine, declares that it has become dedifferentiated and that its performance is the expression of the "rest," or the still functioning part? We attempted to demonstrate that neural functions are compounded of individual integrative processes which utilize appropriate substrates; and that functionally related performances, because of the basically similar arrangement of the substrate concerned, are apt to be involved in more or less typical combinations. We advanced the theory that structures which mediate functionally related performances are apt to be arranged in contiguity or that they may interpenetrate. We suggested that, whenever functionally related acts are called into play, the structures concerned are either jointly actuated or were utilized at earlier stages of their integrational history. This concept should enable us to avoid the pitfalls involved in the concretization of abstract concepts. And they make unnecessary the invention of a separate psychological theory for nearly each syndrome encountered and lastly, to speculate about the nature of nonexisting basic functions.

The totalistic schools give a one-sided version of nervous system function because they place undue emphasis on the primacy of the whole over its parts. The holists fail to appreciate the role of the individual parts which make up the whole. The localistic schools on the other hand, do not place due weight on the fact that the role of the individual parts can be understood within the context of the whole only. The field theory, as applied to the organism, is the overextension of a basically sound concept and the same may be said about perceptionism and behaviorism. We cannot gain insight into the nature of the organism unless striking a balance between the totalistic and the localistic views, for "integration is the very essence of the organism." One must recognize both the primacy of the whole and the specificity of its parts, without which the concept of the whole is meaningless.

As applied to the brain, the largest and most conspicuous parts which form the whole are the cerebral hemispheres—one seemingly the replica of the other. The role of the two parts will be dealt with presently, the discussion of the functional organization of the nervous system having thus far been based on that of a hypothetical and much simpler *mono-hemispheric brain*. Hughlings Jackson wrote: "That the nervous system is double physically is evident enough. This is a very striking fact but one so well known that we are in danger of ceasing to think of its significance—of ceasing to think of it." It is this striking fact to which we now turn.

The functional inequality of the two hemispheres of the brain enormously complicates the organizational plan of the nervous system in that the minor hemisphere, because of its morphological characteristics seemingly the equal of the dominant, is merely a collateral agency from the viewpoint of functional competence.

Bi-hemispheric integration of the motor components of skill

Unilateral vs. bilateral integration of skill

We have already indicated that the centers of eupraxia tend to develop as closely as possible to the primary motor centers, that the existence of a unilateral center of eupraxia of speech and other complex performances appears to be preferable to that of a bilateral center and lastly, that the centers in question develop almost typically on the side opposite the preferred hand.

These more or less theoretical considerations appear to be supported by clinical and electroencephalographic data. According to Orton (368), the physiological optimum is dominance rather than equicompetence. He found that lack of laterality is associated with motor incoordination of muscle systems arranged near the midline of the body where the structural and functional antitropy is poorly developed or difficult to maintain, Oates (361) observed that lack of lateral dominance is definitely associated with greater difficulties in learning school subjects, that mixed dominance may accompany defective development or instability of the nervous system and represents a handicap to the equilibrium of the more highly integrated functions. Kerr (255), Burt (821), Durost (123), Eustin (136) and many other authorities pointed out that children in whom decisive handedness failed to develop are more likely to have reading disabilities than those who are definitely left handed. They are apt to show difficulties in writing, including slowness, mirror writing, reversal of figures, speech deficiencies, including slow utterances, stammering, unclear speech, late development of speech, reading and spelling disability, typical maladjustment owing to difficulties in muscular coordination, and lastly, heightened fatigability. Other abnormalities associated with lack of dominance include emotional unrest, feelings of inadequacy and of inferiority. Dextrals are less apt to be mixed eyehanded, that is dominant in the eye opposite the preferred hand, and less apt to have difficulties in reading, speech and spatial disorientation.

It is of considerable interest that a person who is left-dominant is by no means the equivalent of a subject who is right-dominant though reversed. Smith (449), who tested 120 persons to ascertain the normal spread and degree of laterality in different activities, found that the group of right sided subjects showed a higher percentage of laterality than did the group of left handed subjects in every type of activity with the exception of eyedness. Conrad (97), who studied speech disturbances in 47 war injured soldiers, came to the conclusion that left-handedness is not simply the opposite of right handedness, but that it indicates a certain degree of mixed dominance. In the opinion of Lindsley (307), the analysis of the brain potentials simultaneously obtained from the right and left occipital regions demonstrates that the alpha rhythms in the two hemispheres are out of phase a greater percentage of time in ambidextrous and left handed subjects than in right handed persons. Asynchronism of the alpha rhythm was also described by Greenblatt (183) and his associates. Aird and Garoutte (3) hold that the consistent bilateral synchrony of the two cerebral hemispheres suggests the presence of a subcortical pacemaker.

In *summary*, it may be said that (a) right handedness appears to be an organizational state superior to left handedness and (b) that pure left handedness is less common than ambilaterality. It scarcely needs to be emphasized that these rules have exceptions and that left handed individuals may be endowed with exceptional manual "dexterity."

Hemispheric disconnection

It is chiefly the ideomotor or idiokinetic variety of apraxia which is intimately related to, and complicated by, the problems involved in the bi-lateral integration of skill. In retrospect, a satisfactory explanation of the mechanism of ideokinetic apraxia as suggested by the early writers might not appear too difficult. It now seems only logical, at least on the surface, that the corpus callosum should have been credited with the function of interhemispheric and there-fore bimanual coordination. It establishes by far the most extensive connection between the two hemispheres, i.e., a twin system in which the left upper extremity is connected with the right motor area and the right upper extremity with the left motor area. The centers on the left side of the brain must cooperate with those on the right in all activities which require either simultaneous or alternating use of both hands.

Apractic phenomena were first mentioned by Jackson in 1888. In a series of brilliant essays, the disturbances under inquiry were more fully discussed by A. Pick (*383*), Liepmann (*298, 299, 300, 302, 303, 304*) and Liepmann and Maas (*305*). The early writers were able to demonstrate that ideokinetic apraxia (also called sympathetic apraxia of the left hand) may occur in callosal lesions which, they believed, deprive the sub-ordinate hand of the directive impulses from the dominant hemisphere. These observations were corroborated and amplified by van Vleuten (*489*), Hartmann (*195*), Goldstein (*167, 168, 169*) and more recently by Critchley (*104*) and Sweet (*474*). (A more comprehensive presentation of the subject from a historical viewpoint may be found later in this chapter.)

Before proceeding with the discussion, it will be profitable to review briefly the anatomical connections between the two hemispheres, and the effects of experimental lesions in the monkey. As already indicated, the most extensive inter-hemispheric connection is the corpus callosum. The corpus callosum and the anterior com-missure are derivatives of the commissural plate of the embryo. The corpus callosum is both a commissure and a decussation but the fibers connecting symmetrical areas are more numerous than the crossing fibers. According to Curtis (*108*) and Sunderland (*473*), those areas which control the movements of synergistically func-tioning muscles in the Rhesus monkey have the most abundant callosal connections. The anterior commissure is composed by an olfactory or palaeoencephalic portion which connects the olfactory bulbs with each other, and a hemi-spheric or neencephalic portion which links the left with the right basitemporal cortex and vice versa. The (archipallial) hippocampal commissure connects the hippocampal cortices, Meynert's (or anterior hypothalamic) commissure, the lenticular nuclei. The hippocampal commissure is an interhemispheric commissure while Forel's (supramamillary or posterior hypothalamic com-missure) is composed of a hemispheric contingent and a brainstem contingent of fibers. The former is in reality a projection system rather than a commissure for it joins the lenticular nucleus with the contralateral subthalamic region while the latter connects the mammillary bodies and the corpora Luysii. Another, minute, bundle is Ganser's commissure which lies dorsal and rostral to Meynert's commissure. Thus, the posterior, the habenular and Gudden's intergeniculate commissure are fiber tracts connecting sym-metrical centers of the upper brainstem. It appears necessary to mention these details for some writers claim, in all earnest, that the commissures running in the floor of the third ventricle may compensate corpus callosum deficit. In parenthesis, we add that the corpus callosum is believed by some to serve the purely mechanical purpose to hold the two hemispheres together. However since the hemispheres do not fall apart if the corpus callosum has failed to develop this hypothesis can hardly be taken seriously.

Harlow and ass. found (*193*) that section of the corpus callosum in the Rhesus monkey results in failure of coordination of the two sides in motor activity. This is manifest in postural rigidity, extreme hesitancy of reaction and relative immobility. The defects are more pro-nounced in the absence of area 4 but in either case compensation is rapid. The authors believe that the rostral half is the only portion involved since the effects of total section are not greater than those of the section of the anterior half. Section of the anterior commissure of an other-wise intact monkey has no appreciable effect on motor behaviour. However, in "callosal" animals who have functionally recovered, anterior com-missural section brings about a return of the callosal syndrome. If, in addition area 4 has been destroyed bilaterally, there is no appreciable recovery although, if the premotor cortex is intact, some recovery does take place. I myself (*429*) have split the corpus callosum in monkeys with the exception of the rostrum and few fibers coursing in the splenium and sectioned the fornix and the hippocampal commissure to expose the veins running in the roof of the third ventricle. The animals showed a certain slowness in climbing which lasted only a few days.

The transitory character of most apractic disturbances in man has thus far remained unaccounted for, Monakow's concept of diaschisis having been rejected by Henschen (*203*) and others as a wholesale concept explaining, at the same time, too little and too much.

According to Von Monakow (*204*), diaschisis represents a shock like inhibition of function in more or less distant parts of the brain, which is mediated by nerve fibers connecting the region of the primary anatomical damage with those of secondary or functional damage. Diaschisis commissuralis is a transmission of inhibitory impulses via corpus callosum from one hemisphere to the other. Hence, Liepmann (*303*) contended that interruption of callosal fibers should protect the primary uninvolved hemisphere rather than cause dysfunction.

Subsequent observations by Foerster (*146*), Dandy (*109*), Van Wagenen and Herren (*490*) and Maspes (*323*) seemingly failed to confirm the above mentioned observations. Foerster, Dandy and Maspes cut the corpus callosum to expose tumors of the third ventricle; and Van Wagenen, to prevent the spread of epileptic seizures from one hemisphere to the other. The latter reported 10 cases of corpus callosum section, five of which were complete, in which apractic phenomena failed to appear. Akelaitis and his associates (*6*) working on Van Wagenen's material did not find apractic disturbances in a series of 16 cases, except in three patients who had concomitant lesions in other parts of the cerebral hemispheres. Only in ambidextrous and left handed persons who had been subject to callosal section there was noted temporary impairment of bimanual coordination of ideomotor acts and unilateral handling of tools. (Smith's findings will be discussed later.) Speech disturbances were absent in all cases. Several patients were able to perform bimanual skills, such as typewriting and piano-playing, which require a high degree of motor

integration. Patient 2, who had been an accomplished typist, was able to type German passages two months postoperatively; patient 5, with complete section of the corpus callosum, had no difficulties in typing German passages by the touch system soon after the operation. She regained in a year her ability to play the piano as well as before.

These observations make the existence of an alternative system mediating interhemispheric coordination a seemingly inevitable conclusion. Akelaitis (*5*) believes that bimanual activities can be mediated by Forel's commissure. We have already rejected this contention, pointing out the small size of the fiber system in question; besides, there may be extreme thinning of both the floor of the third ventricle and of the corpus callosum, as seen in cases of advanced hydrocephalus, yet signs of apraxia are absent.

How, then, can the contradictory statements of the neurologists and the surgeons be harmonized?

The role of the corpus callosum

From a phylogenetic viewpoint, the prominent development of the corpus callosum is a relatively recent achievement. Is it not possible that bilateral coordination does not come to depend on the callosal system until a relatively advanced state of ontogenetic development?

Learning of more complicated performances, including skilled movements which necessitates bimanual coordination, is subserved by mechanism III.s. → II.s. → II.m. → I.m., which translates mental designs into motor acts (Fig. 8).

As everyone who learns new skills may readily notice by introspection, a succession of purposive movements is preceded by an appropriate sequence of thought processes. We submit (a) that thought is a twin event, occurring simultaneously in both hemispheres, and (b) that the activities of the two halfs of the forebrain, for the time being at least, may be compared with those of two synchronized and synergized mechanisms. (In attempting to clarify in my own mind the relationship between the two hemispheres I "tested" all sorts of analogies including a comparison of the two hemispheres

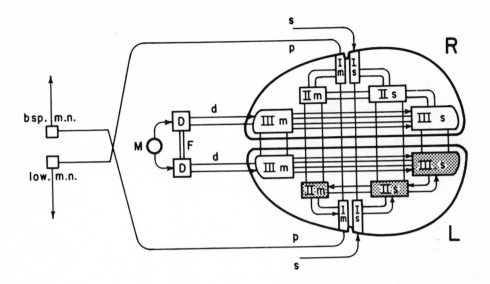

Fig. 30. Circuits mediating skilled movements under conditions of hemispheric equipotentiality. (Synchrony established by brainstem pacemaker).

L.: left hemisphere; R.: right hemisphere; M.: midline pacemaker; D.: diencephalon; d.: diencephalo-cortical connections; p.: pyramidal tract; s.: somato-sensory tracts; Bsp. m.n.: bulbo-spinal motor neurons; Low. m.n.: lower motor neurons.

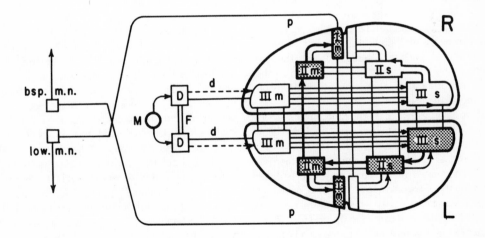

Fig. 31. Circuits mediating skilled movements under conditions of hemispheric dominance (synchronomy established by brainstem pacemaker and reinforced by corpus callosum).

L: Left (dominant) hemisphere.

with synchronized fly-wheels* and with synchronized identical twins. In their respective spheres of function, the parallel performances of the two as yet equipotential cerebral hemispheres (Fig. 30) resemble those of the two lungs, and the surprisingly mild effects of cerebral hemispherectomy, if performed on the subordinate side, those of pneumonectomy (33, 84, 157, 249, 362, 528).

Now the bilateral representation of thought does not necessarily imply synchrony of identical impulse transmission within the left hemi-system to the left motor area and of the right hemi-system to the right motor area. On the contrary, there are good grounds for believing that the different activities of the two hands are made possible by the transmission, to the motor cortices, of different phases of the two ideational processes which, in turn, occur simultaneously at both conceptual levels (III.s.). The different components would be transmitted at different times, and in a sequence corresponding to the anticipated effect. More especially, the left posterior associative cortex would discharge into the left motor area while the right posterior associative cortex, alternating with its fellow, would discharge into the right motor area. This sequence pattern would be established, e.g., in typewriting while simultaneous but different innervational patterns would control the two hands in bi-manual piano playing and in other skills requiring the production of simultaneous but incongruous effects.

If it is granted that thought processes are events that occur synchronously in both hemispheres, the activities of the two posterior associational fields could conceivably be performed by one of them. They may well be taken over by the associative cortex which developed the psycho-neural and sensory-motor systems controlling the preferred hand, provided interhemispheric transmission of impulses via corpus callosum is possible (Fig. 31).

The original process of impulse transmission

from the highest intellectual to the motor centers within either hemisphere would not necessarily become obsolete. It may well be that higher, potentially response determinating processes may continue to operate in the subordinate hemisphere without any overt motor manifestations. Conceivably, the functions of the minor hemisphere may go on to a limited extent and at least in some performance fields while their motor effects would be left in abeyance. That latent neurodynamic processes take place which, perhaps, are mediated by closed neuronal circuits and ready to be utilized by tapping a "closed loop" excitational process is suggested by the ability of a person to "write" with his foot more effectively than a person who is learning to write with his hand, although writing with the foot might have been performed for the first time. (Closed loop excitations, postulated by Forbes (145), were verified by Ranson and Hinsey (399). There is not only clinical but also some experimental evidence that the centers mediating skilled movements transmit identical innervational patterns to "isoeffective" sets of muscles, that is to say, to motor effectors which, although inferior as compared to the preferred organs of execution, are able to translate the basic dimensions of innervational patterns into similar actions. Earlier in this chapter, we mentioned that monkeys shift readily from one hand to another when one side was paralyzed by neural injury. If the animals were taught manipulative problems in which they used only one hand and the motor cortex responsible for that limb was then removed the animals promptly used the other unparalyzed hand to solve the problem. Rats who have been taught to run a maze are still able to roll through it after they have been mutilated by surgical means. Apparently, the executive apparatus selects suitable kinetic parameters by a process to which, in the intellectual sphere, the term abstraction would be applicable. In animals, isokinesis is a more primitive process than in the human where the capacity to translate thought into muscular innervation becomes more or less concentrated in the psycho-neural centers. In speculating about the technical aspects of impulse transmission we remind ourselves that, in the course of individuation of early mass movements, neuronal group connections of the nervous system are

---

* J. P. Cordeau and M. Marcia (199a) who studied electroencephalographic synchronization patterns in cats, consider the results of their investigations as "valid evidence in favour of the existence of a 'synchronizing mechanism' originating in the caudal part of the brainstem." Their findings would seem to support the above contention. (Cf. p. 380, Ref. 3.)

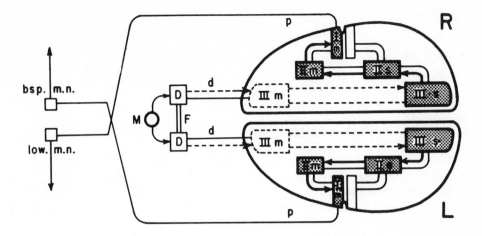

Fig. 32. Circuits mediating skilled movements following section, or absence of, corpus callosum.

replaced by individual connections. At the same time, inappropriate effectors are gradually excluded. The reader may be familiar with the principle of "preference lockout", (241) an electronic switching device which permits service to only one of a plurality of switching linkages and which, incidentally, is reminiscent of the physiological mechanism of reciprocal innervation. Clearly, the motor patterns which most closely resemble those to be actuated are mirror movements that is, patterns that depend on the excitation of symmetrical cortical localities. It is therefore not unreasonable to assume that mirror movements are apt to occur if the biological lockout mechanisms here postulated are inadequate, and that, under normal conditions, lockout impulses are transmitted by the corpus callosum. We do not know whether mirror movements occurred in van Wagenen's series of cases but it may be significant that they are more common in children, in left handed persons and in congenital agenesis of the corpus callosum which is frequently a heredofamilial disorder (59, 81, 107, 242, 217, 148, 482).

Since, following disconnection of the cerebral hemispheres, bimanual coordination is not necessarily affected, or, if this should be the case, sooner or later compensated, we assume that the callosal system is a collateral pathway whose destruction may be compensated by the reinstatement of the ontogenetically older route from the higher to the lower level of the minor

hemisphere, that is, by the regression to a state of hemispheric equicompetence. Following section of the corpus callosum (Fig. 32) the older route may be rapidly reopened for the integration of any skilled movement. (This quick adjustment contradicts, apart from Liepmann's above mentioned objections, the role of diaschisis, as the surgical interruption of callosal fibers takes place much more rapidly and is more complete than the disconnection of the two hemispheres in disease. In either eventuality, the effects of diaschisis as postulated by Monakow should be profound and prolonged.) Hence, if the ideas advanced above are valid, permanent or progressive apraxia due to various disease processes of the corpus callosum is most probably interpretable by invoking a concomitant involvement of the original (intrahemispheric) pathways of impulse transmission.

Following the interruption of impulse transmission from one hemisphere to the other, the unity of response determination would be reestablished through the synchronization of thought processes by coordinating cell stations located in the brainstem (Fig. 32). Contrariwise, if the brainstem should fail to maintain a state of bi-hemispheric synergy, the surgical section of the corpus callosum should give rise to interference phenomena in the psychomotor sphere of function. Later on, we shall have to test the hypothesis that psychomotor difficulties which, in left handed or ambidextrous persons, appear after the interruption of the callosal fibers, are attributable to poor synchronization. The hypothesis is based on the experience that, following callosal section, the already existing dysfunctions are apt to be increased.

Admittedly, it is difficult to visualize a process of unified response determination in the absence of direct anatomical connections between the two hemispheres even under conditions of synchronization mediated by a brainstem pacemaker. One would have to assume that there operates, in each hemisphere, a choice determining mechanism consisting of two agencies which, although separated and forming different excitational patterns, operate in perfect coordination. Conceivably, the separation of the two hemispheres may be compensated for by the establishment of an auditory-motor feedback system, or by the intensification of such feedbacks that had already functioned in association with the pacemaker system prior to the separation of the two hemispheres. Since auditory stimuli reach both hemispheres synchronously, they produce, in either half of the brain, an identical sequence of impressions which, in turn, may function as a "single" baseline in the development of corrective feedbacks. More specifically, it may serve as the basis for the formation of intra-hemispheric preference lockouts or timing patterns which, although separated from each other and different in each hemisphere, operate in coordination. Visual and kinesthetic data would play a similar role in the acquisition or re-learning of other bimanual skills, especially if functioning in combination with auditory impressions.

Yet, a moment's reflection shows that, following callosal section, the formation of a common baseline of response is at most one of the conditions of bihemispheric integration, and that the preservation of some skills and the relearning of others would require additional regulatory stimulation of the effectors on the part of the response determining mechanism. This co-ordinative factor, we submit, is the formation, at both conceptual levels, of the forerunning idea of the appropriate movement. The anticipatory idea, for its part, would introduce a differential since, under certain conditions, including e.g., bi-manual piano playing, the appropriacy of a movement initiated by one hemisphere implies inappropriacy of the *same* movement initiated by the *opposite* hemisphere or, to put it in another way, appropriacy of a movement initiated by one hemisphere implies appropriacy of a *different* movement initiated by the opposite hemisphere. Further, since the appropriacy of a movement is, as we have said, determined by its conformity with a forerunning idea of action (the anticipation of the suitable movement in thought), appropriacy would have to be individually and differentially "enforced" in either hemisphere. We would imagine that this crucial phase of coordination is mediated by corrective feedbacks which, in each hemisphere, develop "independently" and in response to the degree of non-conformity between the fore-running idea of a movement synchronously and identically experienced in both hemispheres. The two sets of feedbacks, being differentially patterned on the two sides, eliminate or "lock out" (perhaps only after many trials and errors), inappropriate movements and, at the same time, favour those which translate thought into anticipated action. By and large, the innervational process here envisaged would resemble what is known as *reciprocal inhibition*. In *summary*, then, the integration of the two disconnected hemispheres into a functionally unified response determinating system would be made possible by (a) the synchronous inflow of informative data into both hemispheres, (b) the idea of the anticipated effect, which, likewise, forms bilaterally at the same time, and (c) the formation of differentially patterned corrective feedbacks which play, on either side of the brain, between the conceptual level and the psycho-neural level.

Having grappled with the problem at hand up to the stage at which we have just presented it, we were fortunate to come upon a passage in Sherrington's epic "Integrative Action of the Nervous System" (*445*) where the author analyzed the results of his experiments with flickered light. Sherrington concluded that "the cerebral seats of right eye left eye images are separate ... that conductive paths no doubt interconnect them but are unnecessary for visual unification of the two images." In referring to the role of the corpus callosum, he said that "contemporaneity of itself explains sensual synthesis without necessarily any spatial fusion of the neural processes ... that is, without spatial confluence of a unit apparatus." He disagreed with E. v. Hartmann (*199*) who wrote that "only because of one part of one's brain has a direct communication with the other is consciousness of the two parts justified." A perusal of von Hartmann's work shows that the philosopher no doubt referred to the connection of the left with the right hemisphere by the great cerebral commissure. "Assuming the brain of two individuals to be connected by a bridge of the same conductive capacity as that linking the two hemispheres of one brain—a common consciousness would at once unify the as yet separate consciousness of two persons. Neither would be able to distinguish his own thoughts from those of his fellow. They would experience each other as one ego rather than two, just as the two hemispheres of the brain would know each other as one individual."*

Little could v. Hartmann know that some day section of the corpus callosum, rather than disrupting the unity of the mind, would interfere only with the unity of action in a small minority of the subjects concerned. To a certain extent however, his speculations appear to be vindicated for, as brought out by Sherrington, unity of perception is established by extrinsic stimulation of a duality of corresponding centers while unity of mentation is mediated by coordinating cell stations with which both hemispheres are linked together in the absence of any direct communication between the former. This accords well with the experiences of Heine (*206*) and of Chusid and his associates (*92*) who failed to find evidence of electroencephalographic asynchrony in cases of absence of the corpus callosum.

Reference to the possible role of the brainstem had already been made by Smith (*449–452*) who, working on Van Wagenen's and Herren's patients, studied the function of the intercortical (callosal) neurons in sensory-motor integration and thinking. He came to the conclusion that the underlying patterns of neural activity "evidently include the subcortical centers, at which level integration between the two sides of the brain can be made even when the cortical commissural paths are destroyed." However, he did not elaborate on how the integration of

cortical by subcortical activities might be achieved. As to the associative mechanism of the cortex, he expressed the belief that it acts, in accordance with Lashley's general concept of engram formation (*282*), "in terms of general patterns of excitation rather than a system of specific pathways between sensory and motor centers." He took it for granted that if "specific neural pathways underlying motor learning and association existed, some of them would be included in the extensive connection of the cerebral hemispheres." The author did not take into account the possibility that the sensory-motor mechanisms represented by the two hemispheres could be synchronized by a subcortical apparatus, and that the postoperative performance of the patients be explained by the ontogenetically earlier state of interhemispheric equipotentiality. He believes that "between the different parts of the subcortical centers there exists an integration of activity and unification of function providing for organization of postural activity and transient moment to moment response."

However, Smith disregarded the fact that subcortical centers (which lack the level specific resources of the cortical centers), would be unable to compensate for the loss of callosal connections. (What thalamic, hypothalamic and still lower centers in man can do is to set cortical activity off, keep the cortex going and shut it off.) It is not without interest that Lashley (*277*), in his study on the autonomous function of the visual areas in the rat, excluded the possible significance of the thalamus in visual perception. Clearly, since the thalamus plays no role in this relatively low function in the rat, it can scarcely be expected to do so in man.

Penfield's (*377*) concept of the centrencephalic nervous system is rather more explicit than Smith's notion. The centrencephalic nervous system, he writes, is a functional complex that is not isolated from the cortex or other anatomical areas. It seems likely that the major portion of the mechanism is located in part of the diencephalon, midbrain and pons and the higher brainstem which includes the two thalami. The centrencephalic nervous system initiates a stream of willed impulses capable of producing the action that is appropriate at all previously received information. Its afferents are fibers from

* Author's translation from the *"Philosophie des Unbewussten,"* vol. II, p. 64.

the "elaborative" and sensory cortex including the postcentral gyrus of either side; its efferents, fibers terminating in both precentral gyri and the subcortical motor ganglia. The motor cortex discharges into the bulbo-spinal mechanism and into the subcortico-motor apparatus. Transcortical connections must serve some useful information but at all events the function is not essential for voluntary action. Specific movements and skills do not depend on the origination of nerve impulses in the cortical motor gyrus. The motive power of its activities comes from elsewhere. Consciousness is made possible by integration of the mechanism of the cortex with those of the centrencephalic nervous system but the mechanism of consciousness is unknown. All that can be said is that nerve impulses are translated into the phenomenon of the mind and conscious decision can express itself in a patterned stream of afferent nerve impulses.

Penfield's ideas on the mechanism of volitional movements is based on electroencephalographic and neurophysiological observations. On rest, a practically pure beta rhythm can be picked up from the pre-central gyrus with regular waves at about 25 per second and 100 to 250 microvolts in amplitude, considered by Penfield and Jasper (378) to be the resting rhythm of the sensory-motor strip. On volitional innervation, the beta rhythm vanishes in the sensory-motor strip, somewhat reminiscent of the disappearance of the alpha rhythm from the occipital lobes when impulses reach the visual cortex. Penfield concludes that the impulses which abolish the resting rhythm of the motor hand area reach the pre-central gyrus from some subcortical region rather than across the cortex from the auditory and visual areas in the same hemisphere, and he adds that they are probably the impulses which produce voluntary action "although one must admit that such observations alone do not finally prove it." Another reason, he goes on to say, for assuming that impulses do not reach the pre-central gyri across transcortical fiber tracts is the preservation of volitional movements in the contralateral extremities, following excision of the premotor and postcentral cortex. These observations would seem to indicate that the highest level of integration is that area of the central nervous system "in which the final integration of nerve impulses takes place and the

efferent stream of voluntary motor impulses is generated." Briefly stated, he believes that the precentral gyrus is, in many respects, the target organ of the brainstem.

Penfield's concept of centrencephalic function may be challenged on the following grounds.

(a) The disappearance of beta rhythm on volitional innervation proves neither the centrencephalic origin of motor cortex activity nor the kinetic function of centrencephalic impulses even though, on volitional innervation, the impulses in question should actually play on the precentral cortex. Conceivably, the centrencephalic system may provide a locally increased or adaptive tone as the background of kinetic function proper, just like the autonomic nervous system increases the tone of the striatal muscles on volitional innervation which is a function of the somatic nervous system.

(b) Disturbances of the centrencephalic nervous system (which, it may be noted in parenthesis, comprises a great many structures of quite different functional value) should give rise to akinesia and apraxia, the reason being that the system in question comprises in Penfield's opinion not only energizing neurons but, at the same time, skill-mediating complexes of neurons. Clinical experiences demonstrate that this is not the case.

(c) The extensive repertory of movements in the higher primates including man should be associated with an increase in the size of the anatomical structures representing the centrencephalic nervous system. In actual fact, it is the organization of the subcortex in man, which, at least relatively, becomes more primitive with rise in the phylogenetic scale while the mass of transcortical association fibers and, implicitly, of the cortex itself is increased.

(d) If it is true that the sensory and elaborative cortex sends informative stimuli to the centrencephalic nervous system, the number of cortico-subcortical projection fibers should grow somewhat in proportion to the number of messages allegedly delivered to the center of motive power and coordination. In reality, the elaborative cortex is characterized by the relative paucity of projection systems.

(e) The increased number of cortico-cortical association fibers which make their appearance with rise in the mammalian scale remains un-accounted for.

(f) Messages from the extra-motor cortex are not delivered to the motor cortex by way of the postcentral gyrus. The latter would have to be much larger were it a way station collecting the messages whose ultimate destination is the premotor cortex.

(g) Penfield does not attempt to clarify the concept "consciousness" and "will." From his reference to the will one gains the impression that it is an entity in its own right having its seat in the centrencephalic nervous system—somewhat in the fashion of an executive who receives informations from the entire sensory cortex and, by sending patterned impulses to the motor cortex, initiates appropriate reactions. Similar considerations apply to the way he uses the term consciousness.

(h) "The bilaterality of the centrencephalic relations, in the cat at least, is not sufficient to effect interhemispheric transfer of learned information" (456a).

Kuhlenbeck (1957), Walshe (1957) and Spiegel (1958) have joined Lashley (1952) in his criticism of the concept of the centrencephalic nervous system. Penfield's (377) recent answer to Walshe, in my opinion at least, amounts to a retreat from his original position outlined in the fore-going paragraphs. What remains of the functions of the centrencephalic nervous system are those of the bulbo-thalamic and thalamo-cortical activating and alerting systems.

Our own ideas on the role of the corpus callosum may be *summarized* as follows. In rough analogy to the function of a line connection system the corpus callosum may be regarded as a (preferred) impulse transmitter linking the dominant hemisphere with the subordinate hemisphere of the brain. Dysfunction will there-fore produce apraxia, at least temporarily, until such time as the originally utilized connections between the intellective and the motor level within the subordinate hemisphere are reestab-lished. In the absence of pathological processes involving the minor hemisphere, "switching over" may take place within a short period of time. Failure on the part of the patient to improve may be due to any of the following:
(a) Bilaterality of the pathological process,
(b) compression of the minor hemisphere by a

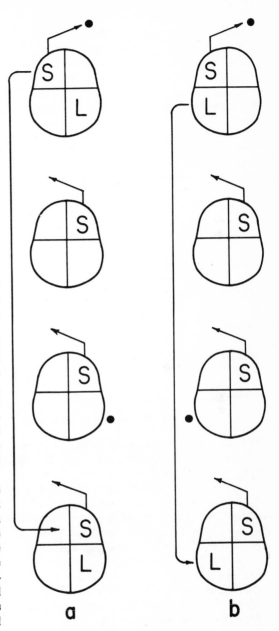

Fig. 33. Needles' series of cases.
S.: skill centers (level II.m.) in anterior (left and right) quadrants of the cerebral hemispheres; L.: language centers (level II.s.) in posterior (left and right) quadrants of cerebral hemisphere; dots: sites of lesions; kinked arrows: control of opposite upper extremity; curved arrows: shift of language centers.

neoplasm of the dominant hemisphere or (c) pronounced laterality with concomitant lack of adaptibility on the part of the minor hemisphere. These conditions, however, are but rarely realized, and apraxia is therefore almost typically a transitory phenomenon. In the average case, the adaptive capacity of the minor hemisphere appears to be quite remarkable even under conditions of generalized intracranial hypertension, increased local pressure and more or less diffuse vascular degeneration. Sympathetic dyspraxia of the left hand is of the ideokinetic variety. Movements are no longer guided by thought, with resulting dissociation between intended and achieved effects. There is no ideational apraxia as thought processes are not dependent on interhemispheric connection only. Motor apraxia fails to develop as there is no interference with the organization of the individual movements out of their elementary innervational components. Lastly, interruption of the fibers of the corpus callosum fails to give rise to anarthria, since the activities of the dominant speech formulating center are not dependent on unilateral impulse conduction but are transmitted through bilateral pathways to the nuclei of the lower brainstem, or lower cranial nerves.

Brainedness and handedness

In the preceding paragraphs we made reference to the apparently trivial observation that the centers serving skill and speech are located almost typically on the side of the preferred hand. This statement however appears to me merely a rule of the thumb, and the exceptions to the rule, although by no means frequent, are of theoretical interest and practical significance.

Needles (*352*), in an article on the transfer of cerebral dominance, cites four cases which had the following features in common: (1) loss of function in the *right hand*, (2) adoption of function by the *left hand* and, (3) three years later, the onset of aphasia. The *variable factor* was that in two cases the aphasia was provoked by a lesion in the *right hemisphere* (Fig. 33a) and in two by a lesion in the *left hemisphere* (Fig. 33b). In two cases in which the function of the right hand had been lost and the function assumed by the left hand, a lesion in the speech area of the *right hemisphere* produced the aphasia,

which suggested to Needles a corresponding shift in the function of speech; in two other cases in which the loss of function of the right hand had occurred at a much earlier phase in life and in which the author believed the factors making for shift of dominance in the cerebral hemisphere should have presumably been set in motion more strongly, a lesion in the *left hemisphere* provoked the aphasia, indicating retention of the speech function by that hemisphere.

Among the theories offered to explain the various atypical cases, Needles enumerates the following. (a) The theory of representation of speech in both hemispheres, (b) of shift in language function without any antecedent shift in handedness, (c) of the establishment of a speech zone dependent solely on the prior functioning of the hand, (d) of the predestination of dominance (e) of crossed representation of skill centers and language centers, (f) of stockbrainedness and (g) of preferred conventionalization of handedness. After a brief discussion of the respective merits of the various hypotheses Needles expresses doubt that any one is able to account for the various exceptions encountered thus far. He himself is inclined to believe that in his own four cases the function of speech was not relinquished by one hemisphere and taken up by the other but continued rather to be participated in by both; more especially, that the speech area of one hemisphere was newly activated while the other still retained its function. As will be seen below, however, he gives some validity to an alternative explanation, namely, that a secondary speech center can be set up by training of the hitherto non-preferred hand. Chesher (*88*) studied two groups of cases of converted sinistrals, all of whom, with one exception, employed the right hand in writing. All cases developed aphasia due to lesions in the language zone of one hemisphere and since, in five cases, the disturbances was caused by a lesion in the left, in four cases by a lesion in the right hemisphere, he concluded that the language mechanism is unlateralized and that, accordingly, a lesion in either hemisphere is capable of producing a disturbance of speech. Oppenheim (*367*) believed that, in children, both hemispheres are originally much more equal in function and that either right or left sided lesions can provoke aphasia. Dejerine (*110*) postulated a bilateral representa-

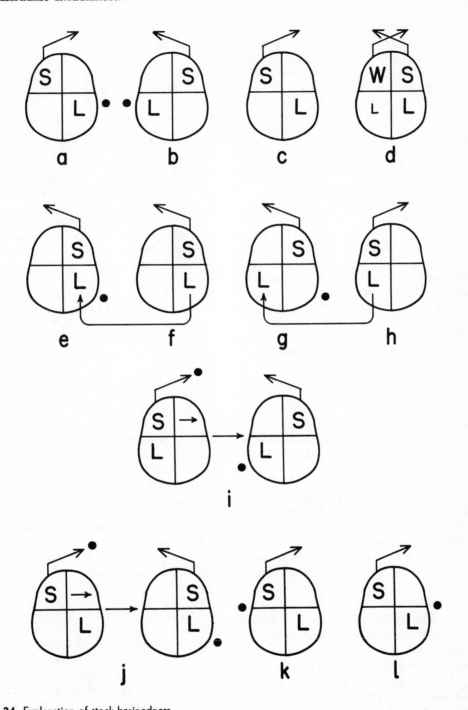

Fig. 34. Explanation of stock-brainedness.

a.: purely right handed individuals sustaining left hemiplegia with aphasia; b.: left handed person sustaining right hemiplegia with aphasia; c, d: Bramwell's theory of stockbrainedness; e f, g, h,.: Kennedy's explanation; i: Needles second group of cases (cf. fig. 33b); j: Needles' first group of cases and Kennedy's third case (Cf. fig. 33a); k: Wechsler's case; l: Riese's and Kennedy's right handed patients.

tion of the function of speech; aphasia, he thought, might be of brief duration because of the activity of the other hemisphere or might fail to appear at all. Bastian (*25*) reported the case of an ambidextrous patient who developed complete motor aphasia in association with a right sided hemiplegia but whose speech recovered suddenly 24 hours after the onset of the attack. Bramwell (*65*) and Kennedy (*255*) proposed the theory of *stockbrainedness* to explain cases of arossed aphasia, a speech disturbance associated with a lesion of the hemisphere ipsilateral to the preferred hand and indicating the location of skill centers and speech centers on opposite sides. For instance, a purely *right handed individual* may sustain a *left hemiplegia with aphasia* (Fig. 34a), or a *left handed* person a *right hemiplegia with aphasia* (Fig. 34b). Bramwell suggested that in most cases the patient's *ancestors* were all *right handed* (Fig. 34c), and that the patient himself had been taught to write with the right hand and/or is ambidextrous (Fig. 34d). At the same time he thought that in certain individuals corresponding areas of the minor hemisphere play a definite though subordinate part in speech and that, accordingly, appropriate lesions would give rise to minor transitory dysphasic symptoms. Kennedy tried to explain the occurrence of left hemiplegia *and* aphasia in a *left handed individual* (Fig. 34e) by the fact that several members of the family were left handed and that the patient, like his ancestors, was really right brained (Fig. 34f). On the other hand, if *in a left handed individual a left hemiplegia without aphasia develops* (Fig. 34g) *despite the evident involvement of the speech zone the family stock was uniformly right handed* (left brained, Fig. 34h). Needles challenged the validity of Kennedy's interpretation on the ground that we are not justified to draw conclusions from the handedness to the brainedness of the stock if handedness is not a true indication of brainedness and that, if brainedness of the stock does determine the brainedness of the individual for speech, it should also determine the brainedness for the hand.

In the following paragraphs we shall offer a unifying scheme which, it is to be hoped, will yield some insight into the mechanism of the various abnormalities including the patho-

physiology of atypical cases. This scheme is based on the following points.

(a) The *sinistrality of both speech centers and skill centers* which according to Chesher and others occurs in 95% of the cases.

(b) The occurrence of *spatial segregation of speech and skill centers* as evidenced by cases of crossed aphasia, or dissociation of dominance as regards skill and language, and

(c) The *gradual development of dominance* with respect to both handedness and language irrespective of their representation either unilaterally or bilaterally or on opposite sides.

As regards speech, specialization would involve the gradual *loss of competence* of one of the two language centers presumed to exist in childhood; as regards skilled acts, specialization would consist in the *increasing competence* of the skill centers on the side of the brain opposite the preferred hand and, to a minor degree, the skill centers on the ipsilateral side. The latter would subserve acts of relatively minor integrational complexity which are mastered by both unequivocal dextrals and sinistrals and without which the non-dominant hand would be practically useless.

It is not unreasonable to assume that mixed dominance in regard to language and mixed manual preference are *developmental phases intervening between a stage of minimal and one of maximal differentiation* regardless whether

(a) absolute differentiation is ever attained and regardless whether

(b) skill centers and speech centers exist in one hemisphere or in both hemispheres.

It is conceivable that, as in other spheres of function, for example, in reading and spelling, specialization may be arrested at an early stage.

In classifying the diverse patterns of organization, including their developmental phases, it will be convenient to differentiate between two main groups, namely, (a) *right handed individuals* and (b) *left handed individuals* although, in either eventuality, lateralization of function may not necessarily be complete. The following possibilities should be taken into consideration.

RIGHT HANDED INDIVIDUALS

1) In subgroup I (Fig. 35, AI) both skill and language functions are gradually taken over by

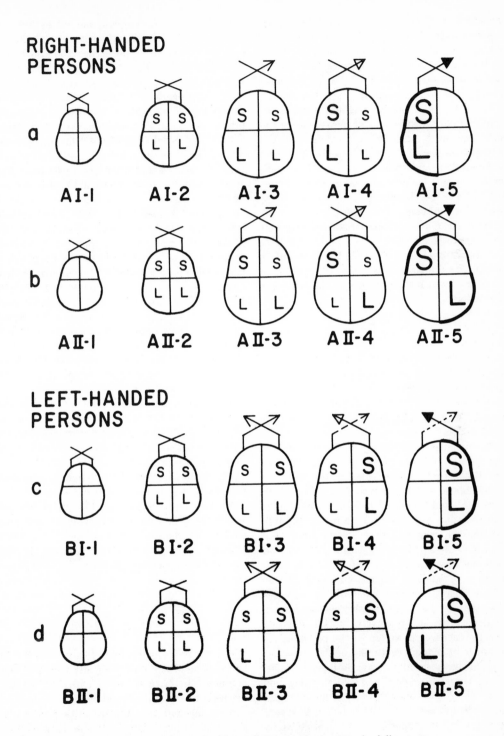

Fig. 35. Early equipotentiality of the cerebral hemispheres developing into the following:
a: pure dextrality; b: mixed dextrality; c: pure sinistrality; d: mixed sinistrality.

the left hemisphere. With respect to language functions, the development is punctuated by (1) *early, physiologic aphasia,* (2) *equicompetence,* (3) *beginning unilateral incompetence,* (4) *advanced unilateral incompetence* and (5) *absolute incompetence* on the part of what has now become the subordinate, or minor, (right) hemisphere. Concomitantly with the loss of competence of the minor language area the competence of the major hemispheres would increase by a process of maturation and training. In regard to *skill,* on the other hand, the development would proceed in the following phases: (1) *early, physiologic apraxia,* (2) *equicompetence,* (3) *incipient dominance,* (4) *advanced dominance* and (5) *unequivocal dextrality.*

In subgroup II (Fig. 35, A II) the skill centers develop in a similar fashion in the left hemisphere while the speech centers develop in the right hemisphere.

LEFT HANDED INDIVIDUALS

In subgroup I (Fig. 35, B I) both skill centers and speech centers develop in the right hemisphere.

In subgroup II (Fig. 35, B II) the skill centers develop in the right hemisphere, the speech centers in the left hemisphere.

For simplicity, we disregard the possibilities that (a) the diverse centers of recognition and also the various sensory and motor language centers develop on opposite sides, for which Riese (*411*) and Nielsen (*356*) have adduced some evidence, and (b) an even more complicated combination, namely, that some motor and sensory centers subserving either manual and communicative skills (both of which are compounded of spatially segregated partial skills) form exclusively or predominantly on one side while the other motor and sensory centers develop predominantly or exclusively on the opposite side; in other words, we ignore the possibility of an apparent random scattering of the numerous "partial aptitude centers" over both hemispheres. That a considerable degree of spatial segregation is "feasible," for example, that, in ambidexters, the centers subserving written and oral speech may develop on opposite sides, is attested by Bastian's case; the patient who, prior to his illness had been able to use both his hands equally

well, developed a complete motora phasia but continued to write fluently with his left hand. Segregation of lateral preference was also found by Smith (*449, 450, 451, 452*) in v. Wagenen's series of patients. For example, shift in manual or pedal sideness did not change the ocular dominance at all while a cortical lesion which brings out a shift in eyedness does not change manual and pedal laterality. At this juncture we remind ourselves that there is a marked difference between dextrals and sinistrals. In terms of the concept here proposed, the trend toward specialization in sinistrals appears to be terminated before phase 5 is reached, so that, in left handed individuals, unequivocal dominance and absolute sinistrality is rare, and the same may hold true as regards Group A II. In Bramwell's experience persistent crossed aphasia is confined to left handed individuals and Humphrey and Zangwill (*228*) failed to find what they considered convincing evidence of crossed aphasia in overtly right handed persons. In their series of ten left handed patients with unilateral brain lesions (Fig. 38, f, g, h, i) only one was free from dysphasic symptoms (Fig. 38, j) which, they claim, lends support to the hypothesis that cerebral dominance occurs rarely if at all in left handed persons and, if it does occur, tends to be less well developed than in the general run of right handed individuals. In spite of these experiences we propose to consider, as limiting cases, the possibility of absolute right-brainedness for speech and of absolute left handedness.

In the following paragraphs we shall list various atypical cases of aphasia associated with motor disturbances and, at the same time, attempt their interpretation in terms of the concept here proposed.

RIGHT HANDED INDIVIDUALS

Group A. I

In Needles' second group of cases, comprising two patients, there was as already indicated loss of function in the right hand, adoption of function by the left hand and, several years later, onset of aphasia incident to a disease process involving the left hemisphere. Originally both patients were left brained for both speech and skill, i.e., right handed (Fig. 39 b). Following injury and con-

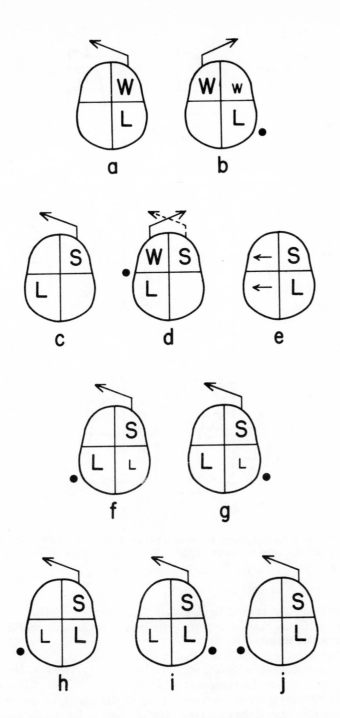

Fig. 36. a, b: Chesher's group of four converted sinistrals; c, d: Tilney; e: Needles's explanation; f, g, h, i: Humphrey and Zangwill's left handed patients with unilateral brain lesions and dysphasic symptoms; j: without dysphasic symptoms.

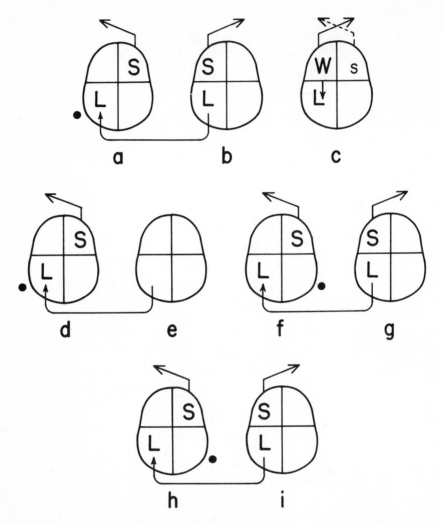

Fig. 37. a: Kennedy's first left handed patient; b: Kennedy's explanation; c: Bramwell's explanation; d: Kennedy's second left handed patient with unknown ancestry (e); f, g: Kennedy's fourth left handed patient; h, i: Kennedy's fifth left handed patient.

comitantly with the training of the left hand, a skill center was set up in the right hemisphere while the language center remained on the left side (Fig. 34 i). Thus, aphasia was produced by a left sided lesion. (According to Needles the left hemisphere continued to mediate the function of speech even though the right hand had become functionless at a very early age. If the establishment of a special zone depended solely on the prior functioning of the hand, he argued, the hemisphere should have remained inactivated

so that the assumption of a predestined dominance appears unescapable.)

Group A. II

(a) In Needles' first group of cases there was loss of function by the right hand, adoption of function by the left hand, and onset of aphasia several years later, following a lesion of the right hemisphere (Fig. 34 j). Both patients were originally right brained as regards speech and left brained as regards skill. Following injury, the skill centers were shifted to the right side, where the speech centers were located (Arrow). (Needles believed that there occurred, in contrast to his cases 3 and 4, (which make up his second group referred to in the preceding paragraphs), shift of the function of speech from the left to the right side.)

(b) Wechsler's case (499). In a 26 year old right handed man who at the age of 11 had sustained a fracture of the left side of the skull, Jacksonian seizures occurred at the age of 20. Removal of what appeared to be the sensory speech center on the left side, left the function of speech entirely unimpaired (Fig. 34 k). The patient's speech centers were on the right side, his skill center on the left side. (Wechsler, who had anticipated that, because of the absence of aphasia, excision could be hazarded, concluded that the patient was either right brained for the speech function or that the right hemisphere had assumed the function of speech following traumatization of the left.)

(c) In the three right handed aphasic patients reported by Riese (413) the lesions were found on the right side. The skill centers were located on the left side, the speech centers on the right side (Fig. 34 l).

(d) The three right handed patients of Kennedy's series developed aphasia as a result of a right sided brain lesions.—The location of the skill centers and the speech centers was identical with that in Riese's cases. In the first case the mother was left handed. In the second case two brothers, and in the third, both parents were left handed. It may be surmised that, if in a left handed stock, dissociation of dominance occurs with regard to laterality, either the speech centers tend to remain on the right side or the stock was right brained for skill, left brained for speech.

(e) Kennedy's third case was one of acquired left handedness and aphasia that developed in a woman of 59 who had been found to use her left hand for all purposes owing to injury to the right hand at the age of seventeen. The skill centers, originally located on the left side, were gradually transferred to the side of the speech centers on the right side (Fig. 34 j).

Left Handed Individuals

Group B. I

Chesher's group of 4 converted sinistrals who employed the right hand in writing developed aphasia due to lesions in the language zone of the right hemisphere. Originally, the skill centers and the speech centers were in the right hemisphere (Fig. 36 a). A skill center in the left hemisphere was secondarily set up for writing, while the center for spoken language remained on the right (Fig. 36 b). (See Bramwell's case. Chesher explained the aphasia by the non-lateralization of the speech centers.)

Group B. II

(a) Tilney (477), who was born left handed (Fig. 36 c) was taught to write with his right hand but did everything else with his left hand. Later in life he developed a right-sided hemiplegia with aphasia.—In spite of his right brained stock, (four of his relatives were left handed), Tilney's speech center was on the left side (Fig. 36 c). Later on, as the result of training, he formed a writing center on the side of his speech center. (Needles contended that Tilney, concomitantly with his skill center, had set up a speech center in the left hemisphere. Fig. 36 d.)

(b) Chesher's second group comprised five left handed persons who had been taught to write with the right hand and in whom a lesion in the left language area produced aphasia.—Like in the preceding case, the skill centers were originally in the right hemisphere. A skill center for writing was secondarily set up on the left side. Thus, eventually, both writing centers and speech centers existed on the left, and aphasia was produced by a lesion on that side. (Chesher's explanation is the same as that given for his first group of cases.)

Kennedy discussed the cases of five left handed individuals, two of which developed aphasia and right hemiplegia as a result of a lesion to the left hemisphere.

In the first case (Fig. 37 a), none of the relatives was left handed and a twin brother was right handed. In the two patients, skill centers were on the right, the speech centers on the left side. (Bramwell argued that in spite of the patient's

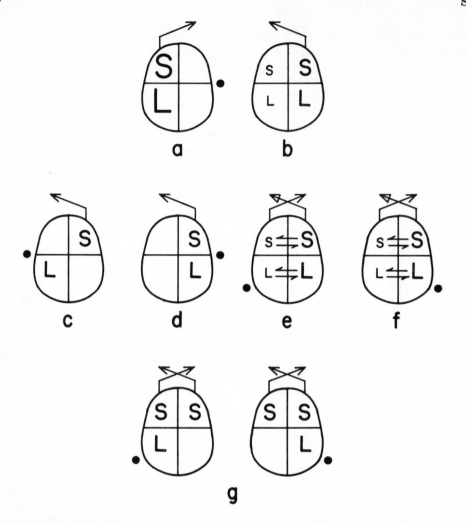

Fig. 38. a: Chesher's cases with unequivocal dextrality; b: Chesher's cases with decreasing sinistrality; c: Conrad's series of sinistrals with left sided brain injury and dysphasia; d: Conrad's series of sinistrals with right handed brain lesions and dysphasia; e, f: Cases with near-equicompetence of the cerebral hemispheres; g: Bramwell's case.

left-handedness the left brain was educated as a speech area by reason of his having been taught to write with his right hand (Fig. 37 c). According to Kennedy, the patient was isolated as a left handed person in a stock entirely right handed (Fig. 37 b).

The second case concerned a left handed woman (Fig. 37 d) about whose stock brainedness nothing is known (Fig. 37 e) and who had a right sided hemiplegia with aphasia. At autopsy, a widespread destruction of left Broca's area and its annectant gyri was found.—The skill centers

were on the right, the speech centers on the left side of the brain.

The third case was discussed under heading A. II.

Kennedy's fourth and fifth case (Fig. 37 f and h) failed to develop aphasia following lesions of the right hemisphere. In the first case the father was right handed (Fig. 37 g) while in the second case there was no left handed relatives in the family. (Fig. 37 i)—In the two patients, skill centers and speech centers were located on opposite sides. *From Fig. 37, the interesting fact*

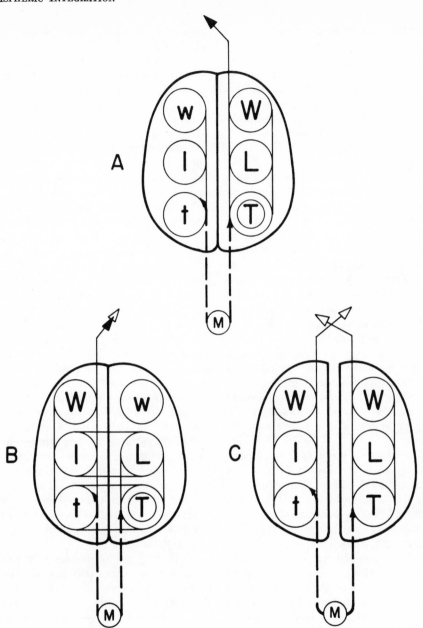

Fig. 39. Relationship between thought (T), spoken language (L), and written language (W) in sinistrals, (A), under conditions of forced dextralisation (B), and following callosal section (C). Note asynchrony in A and B.

may be read that, very likely, the ancestry determines the side of the speech centers rather than the skill centers or, perhaps, that the stock plays a more important role in the determination of the side of the speech centers than of the skill centers. (Thus,

Needles' criticism would not necessarily invalidate the Bramwell-Kennedy theory.)

Thus far, we have tested the "four-type concept" of handedness and brainedness with regard to both *individual* cases, and to *groups* of cases. The following is an attempt to apply the same theory to observations of a more general character.

(a) It is well established that damage to any one part of the minor hemisphere may cause no language disturbances whatsoever. Hence, we may assume that the sound, major hemisphere monopolizes the function of speech and that, whatever pathological changes and clinical disturbances are produced by the lesion on the minor side, have no repercussions on the sound, dominant, side. In other words, the dominant hemisphere is a completely independent unit.

(b) The fact that Chesher encountered only three purely left handed persons in a group of 166 cases may be explained on the supposition that, in left handed persons, the trend toward inequality between the left and the right hemisphere is more likely to be arrested before the state of full specialization has been reached. In other words, in contrast to unequivocal dextrality (Fig. 38 a) maximal inequality fails to develop so that residual language functions, to a certain extent at least, continue to be represented on the side of decreasing competence (Fig. 38 b). The fact that, ordinarily, bilateral representation of speech is associated with mixed preference is a corollary to the statement that pure sinistrality is uncommon.

(c) In Conrad's (97) series of brain injured sinistrals there was severe lasting dysphasia in five cases of left sided injuries (Fig. 38 c), and an equal number of right sides injuries (Fig. 38 d). The majority of left handed patients showed only slight and transitory dysphasia where the nature of the injury was such as would have expected to cause a more profound loss of speech. The first ten patients, (five of whom belonged to group B. I., and an equal number to group B. II.) represented cases of more advanced specialization (like the three purely left handed patients mentioned by Chesher) while the remaining cases which showed relatively mild symptoms represented a state of near equicompetence (Fig. 38, e, f). In other words if, in left handed persons, injury to the language area occurs, it is less likely to involve the rare, fully or almost completely, differentiated stage. And if, in cases of cerebral inequality (as in not fully unilateralized left handedness) damage to any one hemisphere occurs, there is bound to be some degree of

aphasia as manifested by repercussions of left sided lesions in the right hemisphere and of right sided lesions in the left hemisphere. Apparently, in contrast to those persons in whom laterality has progressed to the stage of absolute dominance (which is associated with functional independence) the two hemispheres maintain some kind of cooperation. This may be the reason why (a) appropriately placed lesions, no matter on which side they may be located, are apt to cause aphasia in children in whom, however, the chances of recovery are excellent, and (b) why ambidextrous persons are apt to recover. This appears to have occurred in Bramwell's case (Fig. 38 g, h), the favourable course of aphasia in children having been emphasized by Isserlin (231) and other authorities (110, 135, 187).

(d) The various atypical cases including those reported by Bramwell and Kennedy dispose of the necessity to stipulate a transfer of the enormously complicated speech mechanism from the dominant to the subordinate hemisphere. It would seem more likely that, with regard to speech, *the choice of the dominant side seems to depend on hereditary factors and that a shift of the speech mechanisms fron one side to the other does not occur*. If a left handed person is taught to write with his right hand, a writing center is secondarily set up in the left hemisphere but the speech center (in any case the major speech center) remains on that side. However, that a writing center may exist in the hemisphere opposite to that in which speech is represented is suggested by Bastian's case in which ambidextrous aphasiacs regained his ability to write in a very short time.

(e) If, in a case of damage to the dominant hemisphere, the minor (still partially competent) hemisphere takes over, great fatigability is noted. This may be due to the fact that the less competent hemisphere behaves in the fashion of an apparatus having undergone structural and temporal dissociation of function.

(f) If it is true that, in left handed persons (Fig. 39), the synchronization of hemispheric functions via the brainstem is inadequate, left handed subjects should be even more dependent on auxiliary synchronizing agencies, such as the corpus callosum and the anterior commissure, that is, on pathways which transmit impulses from the dominant to the subordinate hemi-

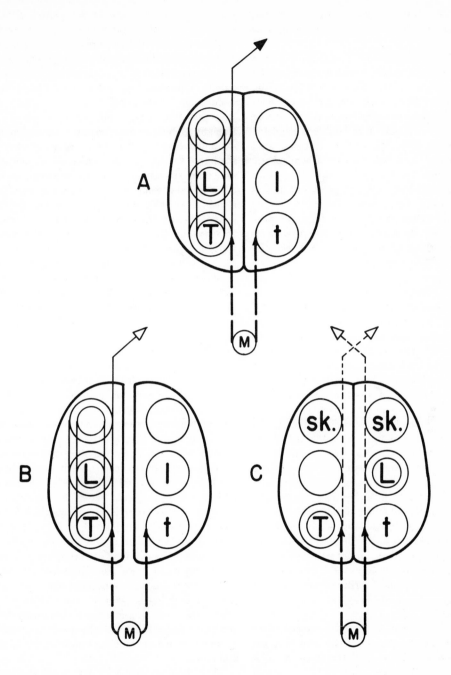

Fig. 40. Impracticability of representation of thought and language mechanisms on opposite sides of the brain. L: major language center; l: minor language center; T: major thought center; t: minor thought center; sk: skill centers.

sphere. (That the corpus callosum does not increase the degree of the already existing poor synchronization may be inferred from the fact that, as shown by Smith (*449, 450*) for sinistrals and ambilaterals, the disturbances following callosal section are increased rather than decreased.) In other words, in sinistrals, poor synchronization of higher centers by lower centers is, to some extent at least, compensated by interhemispheric impulse transmission and, hence, becomes manifest in cases of hemispheric disconnection.

The high incidence of postoperative changes including postoperative shift in laterality accords well with the assumption that sinistrals are "poor synchronizers." It may be assumed that, pre-operatively, the lack of synchrony between the left and the right hemisphere is latent since, on the subordinate side, the connections between the centers of spoken language (l) with those of written language (w) are inoperative (Fig. 39 A). If, however, the formation of left sided writing center (W) is imposed upon a sinistral, a connection between the newly formed writing center and the minor (left sided) speech center (l) is likely to be established because of the intimate connection between speaking and writing (Fig. 39 B). Coordination between the writing center (W) with both the minor speech center (l) and the major speech center (L) is maintained by the secondary synchronizer (T), which corrects the poor synchronization mediated by the midline pacemaker (M). Following callosal section and the separation of T from the left hemisphere, there develops the tendency to revert to the pre-operative state of integration, in other words, "W" is "shifted back" to the right side (Fig. 39 C). Implicitly, prior to callosal section, the training of the left writing center increases the competency of the right writing center so that the training or the left hemisphere produces a state of partial ambidextry.

(g) The neurodynamic processes occurring at the highest integrative level are synchronized and, in spite of their spatial segregation, dynamically unified. However, in so far as certain thought processes depend on verbalization, and the two language centers are not equicompetent, one would assume that only those segments of thought are synchronized which either do not depend on verbalization or only on as much

verbalization as the minor hemisphere is able to furnish (Fig. 40 A). If this concept is sound, certain thought processes would be mediated exclusively by the hemisphere subserving speech and, to the extent to which thinking depends on symbolic formulation, lesions of the dominant hemisphere would cause disturbances of intelligence. If the corpus callosum is intact, either thought elaborating mechanism can utilize the dominant speech center (Fig. 40 A). Following section of the corpus callosum on the other hand, only the thought mechanism existing on the dominant side would have access to the dominant speech area (Fig. 40 B). (The absence of intellectual disturbances in van Wagenen's series of cases would seem to indicate that the major thought elaborating mechanism and the major speech center were ipsilaterally located.) The peculiar relationship between the two synchronized thought mechanisms (T and t) and the language zone (L) may be one of the reasons why, in disease processes causing aphasias, apart from the difficulties involved in a rapid shift of highly complex neurodynamic patterns, transfer of the speech mechanism (L) from the dominant to the subordinate hemisphere is impractical, at least in cases of unequivocal dominance. It may be readily seen that, following transfer of dominance, i.e., of language patterns from the left to the right side, the highest response determining agency (T) would now operate on the side at which integration between thought and language has broken down (that is, on the left side) and, hence, where response determination, to the extent that it is dependent on language function would be inadequate (Fig. 40 C). The technical difficulties involved in a shift of function would not apply to non-verbal performances, at least not to the same degree, as either thought elaborating mechanism is still connected with its ipsilateral skill centers (sk) and, furthermore, within the natural limits imposed upon by their unequal competency, skilled action has reached a higher degree of emancipation from verbalized thought.

These deliberations accord well with the data furnished by Needles, and particularly with Nielsen's (*356, 359*) statement based on a large personal experience and an exhaustive knowledge of the literature, namely, that handedness can be shifted by training in early life but that brainedness as regards language does not shift with it.

The above suggested theory would seem to account for a number of hitherto unexplained facts, including, among others,

(1) the different effects of brain lesions involving identical localities in those instances in which, as a result of injury to the preferred hand, shift of handedness occurred,

(2) the nature of left-handedness (ambi-"dextry") as a manifestation of arrested specialization and, hence, the bilateral although unequal representation of speech,

(3) the decreased vulnerability of the speech mechanism in left handed individuals which, however, is associated with a greater incidence of speech disorders following lesions to either hemisphere,

(4) the role of stock-brainedness as regards the representation of speech centers,

(5) the non-transfer, in disease, of the speech centers from one hemisphere to the other and,

(6) the more severe disorders following complete section of the corpus callosum in left handed individuals.

On the other hand, several questions remain open as, for example, the reason for the absence of mirror movements and of stammering following callosal section in left handed individuals. Perhaps, to keep inter-hemispheric cortico-subcortical asynchrony at a minimum, feedbacks are postoperatively reinforced.

The publications dealing with the problem of cerebral dominance in sinistrals (especially of the bilateral representation of speech in left handed individuals) which appeared after the completion of our own studies on brainedness and handedness were ably summarized by Ettlinger a.ass. (*132*) with special reference to the work of Hecaen and de Ajuriaguerra (1952), Critchley (1953, 1954), Goodglass and Quadfasel (1954), Bauer and Wepman (1955) and Roberts (1956). See also Anastasopoulos (*8a*). Seemingly conflicting data furnished by the above named authors may be readily reconciled if interpreted in terms of individual developmental phases outlined in the above suggested scheme (Fig. 35).

It can hardly be a matter of surprise that attempts have been made to explain abnormalities of the skill-language-complex on *psychopathological* grounds rather than neuro-psychologically. Blau (*49*) stipulated that emotional negativism

Fig. 41. Visual agnosia following callosal section.

is probably the most common type of sinistrality and that it accounts for its greater incidence among individuals with antisocial disorders. Sinistrality, Blau goes on to say, is one of the symptoms that point to negativism and is caused by an unsatisfactory relationship between the child and its mother. Other causes are imitation of left handed parents, nurses and other children and injury to the right hand. Stuttering, specific reading disability and developmental motor awkwardness are developmental language disorders which have a type of psycho-neurotic origin that is similar to that of negativistic sinistrality.

It is abundantly clear that Blau's theory fails to account for the diverse disorders of skill and language functions dealt with in the foregoing paragraphs, with the exception perhaps of certain types of acquired sinistrality. His concluding statement that "people are left brained because they are right handed, and the reverse is true for sinistrals" is the least assailable although it was qualified by the stipulation that the choice of left or right is decided by experience and learning.

In the course of the discussion, it was brought out that dextrality exists in 95% of the population and that it appears to be associated with a left sided representation of the various skill centers while, in the remaining 5%, there occurs dissociation of laterality. Considering the great number of a priori existing possibilities of the cerebral representation of skill and language, the pattern of organization involving the representation of the functions under study in the left hemisphere is only one of many. (Language is, to a large extent, a communicative skill.) Fig. 35 would seem to indicate that, theoretically, at least, 13 organizational patterns are possible provided that skill be regarded a unitary ability rather than a generic term referring to a variety of special aptitudes which may be "scattered" over both hemispheres, in which case the pattern of organization would be even more variegated. Now, if the organization of the skill-language pattern should be left to chance, pattern A I-5 (which is realized in 95% of the cases) should not be more frequent than any other possible type. Yet the non-applicability of chance values to biological phenomena holds true not only for the individual, but also for the species. If, then, a given organizational pattern (which neurological observations have shown to be superior) is realized in the great majority of cases, it may be thought of in terms of a "target-effect" attained within the realm of the species. In this respect, it resembles the performance of physiological function, say, the successful performance of purposeful movement, which is a target effect attained by an individual. This is all the more likely as the term "species" is merely an abstraction referring to a wide variety of biological events involving individual units. It may well be that the organization of skill-language mechanisms follows the principle of *biological probability*. The term, which was explained in the opening chapter, implies that one *useful combination of factors if favoured beyond chance expectancy*—in other words that nature, having achieved the almost universal institution of pattern AI-5, has shown remarkable "skill." If this is granted, the distribution pattern of the skill-language complex should be definable in terms of a steep Gauss-curve, the vertex of which is represented by pattern AI-5. On the other hand, AI-1 and its equivalents, together with BI-5 and BII-5, would occupy the bottom of the curve, while the patterns representing

intermediate stages of organization, (ambidextry of Type A and B) would occupy its slanting, intermediate segments. Lastly, the more mature stages of ambidextry should approach AI-5 more closely than the immature stages.

In *conclusion*, then, any of the above patterns would represent a stage of approximation to a biological target. Biological phenomena should be explained in their own right rather than as a side-show of psychopathological mechanism, a trend which, for some time, has infested their interpretation. More specifically, abnormalities of the skill language mechanism should be accounted for by invoking mathematical principles. They are altogether too complicated to be blamed on an unhappy family situation which, moreover, might have never existed.

Bi-hemispheric integration of skill determining factors in the sensory sphere

Gnostic functions

Trescher and Ford (*478*) and Maspes (*323*) divided the splenium of the corpus callosum in order to expose tumors of the posterior portion of the third ventricle. In neither case was the operation followed by apraxia, which confirmed the observations of other writers. In some cases, however, the operation produced alexia and agnosia for objects in the left visual fields (Fig. 40). Maspes' patients were unable to read letters in the extrafoveolar parts of the left visual fields and they could not "read" wooden letters placed in the palm of their hands. Trescher and Ford's patients were unable to recognize objects in the left visual fields. The authors concluded that section of the splenium in their case interrupted the pathway from the right calcarine fissure to the center of object recognition in the left hemisphere, and that the test letters and objects could therefore be seen, but not identified. Maspes, whose patients could recognize objects but were unable either to read the letters or to identify them by touch, concluded that a center for the recognition of objects existed in both the dominant and the subordinate hemisphere but that a reading center developed only in the former. At the same time, he expressed the belief that, as regards cerebral dominance, the centers concerned may be arranged in different combinations.

Intellective functions

Assuming that lateralization of intellectual functions and unilateral preponderance of the intermediate cortical plane conform to similar principles, we may expect complicated thought processes, particularly those depending on verbalization and symbolization, to be more readily elaborated by the posterior association fields of the dominant side, while the functions of the minor hemisphere would be limited to more primitive performances. It is known for instance that disease processes involving the left temporo-parieto-occipital region in right handed persons produce more marked mental disturbances than right sided lesions. A number of writers hold that certain language functions, the general predominance of one hemisphere notwithstanding, may be the domain of the minor side, and the same may hold true for certain intellectual functions. On the assumption that the activities of the right and the left associational fields are not superimposable throughout, the callosal system may conceivably be thrown into action whenever, (to furnish material for the synthetizing activities of the dominant side), the resources of both the right and the left hemisphere of the brain would have to be mobilized. However, since the functions in question, to the extent that they are vested in the posterior associational fields of either side, are for all practical purposes identical, interruption of the callosal fibers, under ordinary conditions at least, would fail to produce obvious defects.

Unlike the posterior association fields, their anterior "counterparts" do not (with the exception of the motor speech center) consist of a dominant and a subordinate component. Accordingly, effects of disease processes of the right frontal lobe do not significantly differ from those of the left as far as higher mental functions are concerned. With regard to the activities in question, the frontal lobes appear to be merely a regulatory mechanisms determining the degree of receptivity and reactivity of the posterior fields which, as previously discussed, subserve not only mnestic functions, but also the selection of appropriate reactions. Should intense mental effort require shunting of additional activating impulses to the dominant side, the fibers of the forceps anterior of the corpus callosum would represent suitable pathways for its optimal distribution (Fig. 25). However, section of its fibers would leave intact the ipsi-lateral pathway from the anterior to the posterior fields and the effects of hemispheric disconnection should therefore not become apparent except under conditions of stress.

Bi-hemispheric integration in animals

Bremer and Terzuolo (66) observed that stimulation of the medial geniculate body in cats produced electrocortical potentials not only in the ipsilateral but also in the contralateral auditory area. He obtained similar responses in the °visual area on stimulation of the lateral geniculate body, and in the somesthetic area I on stimulation of the nucleus ventralis posterior of the thalamus. Strychninization of any of the three cortical areas on the stimulated side intensified the response on the opposite side while section of the corpus callosum or exstirpation of the areas in question on the side of the stimulation considerably weakened the response on the non-stimulated side. The authors concluded that the duplication of sensory impressions and also of engrams of skilled movements (*acquisitions praxiques*) may be of considerable significance from a physiological viewpoint.

Myers (348) found that monocularly learned discrimination transferred readily to what they called the untrained eye in cats in whom the crossed fibers of the optic chiasm were severed but that, following section of the corpus callosum, the animals were unable to recognize the patterns with the untrained eye, that is to say, under experimentally produced conditions of impulse conduction limited to one side of the brain. More specifically, the afferent connections from each eye were restricted to the ipsilateral brain half by section of the optic chiasm in the midsagittal plane, and the animals were trained to perform pattern discrimination with a mask covering one eye. When the mask was later shifted to the opposite eye, it was found that the discrimination could be performed correctly with the untrained eye, that is, with the eye connected with the opposite hemisphere whose visual areas received impulses from the trained eye. According to Myers, the results indicate a "type of functional equivalence of an integration of considerable complexity between the visual mechanisms of the two sides of the brain." If, on the other hand, the posterior half of the corpus callosum was also sectioned, the animals were unable to recognize the test patterns with the untrained eye and they could only relearn the discrimination at rates similar to the original training with the first eye. The function of the corpus callosum proved to be similar in contralateral transfer of somesthetic discrimination. "If the cats in whom both the optic chiasm and the corpus callosum were severed were taught completely conflicting discriminations with the two eyes, the learning occurred with relative ease and without indication of interference. This implied independent functioning of the two hemispheres in visual learning and recall and was in contrast with the performance of cats with intact corpus callosum" (*349*).

In a subsequent series of experiments, Myers and Sperry (*350*) severed the corpus callosum in chiasma-sectioned cats following (rather than preceding) the monocular visual training. They found (a) that section of the corpus callosum did not noticeably affect levels of performance with the "trained" or "experienced" hemisphere, (b) that it resulted in complete or near complete loss of memory for the more difficult discriminations on the part of the "untrained" or "naive" hemisphere but did not destroy recall of the simple discriminations and (c) that, as regards simple tasks, the results of extensive destruction of the cortex of the "trained" hemisphere were similar to those of callosal section. The authors concluded that one hemisphere seemed to have the capacity "to establish well marked and lasting memory traces in the opposite hemisphere through the corpus callosum if the communica-

tion handled is of simpler dimensions" and that "the cortex removed from the trained hemisphere normally must contribute actively and substantially to performances with the untrained hemisphere at the time of responding." Further, that the "contribution of brainstem mechanisms to high level activity has as yet to be fully explored but that, apparently, the brainsteam prepares and maintains levels of activity of the cortex."

A moment's reflection shows that Myers and Sperry produced a *dominant* (trained or experienced) hemisphere and a *subordinate* (untrained or naive) hemisphere, that is, a state of functional diversity which, in the human, develops spontaneously. Although, in man, (apart from the projection to monocular fields) the very same perceptions reach both hemispheres, the increasing complexity of psychic functions comes to depend on the lateralization or, for that matter, on unilateral concentration, resulting in turn in the establishment of a "highest center" or, alternately, a "highest level of the highest functional order" rather than two highest levels of the same rank. In man, certain components of higher psychic functions are mediated by both hemispheres and, to the extent that their integration is a bilateral process, synchronized by a brainstem mechanism, while other components (especially in dextrals) are mediated by the dominant hemisphere only. Considered in the light of experiences with humans, Myers' and Sperry's ingenious experiments indicate that the quotas of action underlying the simple task are bilaterally represented while those underlying the more difficult tasks are represented in the trained hemisphere.

--------------- Disorders of recognition and skill

DISORDERS OF HIGHER SENSORY FUNCTIONS

In studying higher sensory functions and their clinical disorders, the following points should be kept in mind. The expression *higher sensory functions* is a generic term referring to integrative acts mediated by (a) the *configurational level*, i.e., the sensory division (II.s.) of the psycho-neural plane, and (b) by the conceptual level III.s. In

disease, integrative acts are apt to undergo dissociation along *temporal* and *structural* parameters. From what we have learned from the analysis of handedness and its relationships to brainedness, it is reasonable to suppose that the functions of II.s. and III.s. are the products of interaction of the dominant and the subordinate hemisphere. Moreover, the mutual proportion of the activities of the two hemispheres is not necessarily identical. From the very beginning, the generally dominant hemisphere may be subordinate with respect to some functions; with regard to other performances, the generally subordinate hemisphere dominant. In childhood, the two hemispheres are more nearly equipotential and defects, other factors being equal, more readily compensated. In disease, the subordinate hemisphere may, to a varying degree it is true, contribute quotas of action previously furnished by the dominant hemisphere and vice versa. In other words, in response to abnormal conditions of stimulation, potential collaterality is converted into actual collaterality of integration.

There are as many higher sensory functions as there are higher senses. Accordingly, the functions under study are preeminently *visual, auditory* and *somesthetic* in character. In each sensory system, the configurational level adds its quota of action to that of the perceptual level; and the conceptual plane its quota to that of the former. Thus, as applied to sensory levels of integration, the higher forms of grouping activity build, out of elementary impressions, the conceptual world of man. The resources of the visual configurational level make possible the appreciation of aggregates of stimuli as visual gestalten; and those of the conceptual level the formation of concepts and their interrelation in thought. The enhancement of operational dimensions at levels of increasing integrational complexity (which reflects the parallelism of phylogenetic and ontogenetic development) enables the individual grades of the neuraxis to deal with an increasing number of variables and it yields a wider range of reality control. This property, in turn, is commensurate with the extension of the correspondence between subjective reality and objective reality.

Under otherwise identical conditions, the competency of the higher sensory levels is dependent on that of the lower or, for that matter, on the quality of the sensory raw material furnished by the former. On the other hand, substandard function of I.s., may within limits be compensated for by the level specific resources of II.s.; and substandard function of II.s., to a degree, by those of III.s. To a certain extent, poor perception may be compensated for by superior gestaltperception and, by the same token, poor gestaltperception by superior concept formation. In spite of this dependency relation-

ship which, as brought out by experiences of daily life, is not entirely unipolar, suprastandard and infrastandard performances may at each sensory way station occur independently. It is truism that suprastandard perception of elementary and of gestaltdata is not necessarily combined with superior intelligence and vice versa although, conversely, normal mental power would seem to presuppose a certain minimum of low level activity. It is well known that mental development may be handicapped by the infrastandard performance of the higher senses, if not indeed of the sense organ serving vision and hearing. Individual variations in perceptual organization, that is, the existence of the diverse visual, auditory and other types may be readily expressed in terms of preponderance of a given sensory level within an individual system. (Like gratification preference, level predominance is a factor although, by comparison, a secondary factor in personality organization.)

Within each sensory system, the recording of data, ultimately, takes place at the conceptual level of sensation. To put it in another way, objective reality is experienced "knowingly" in spite of the relative independence of the individual levels out of which each sensory system is composed*. Conceptual data embody configurational elements and the latter perceptual elements. Since perceptions are perceptual analogs, configurations or gestalten are configurational analogs, and concepts conceptual analogs of the data of the senses, conceptual analogs embody configurational analogs and the latter perceptual analogs. Nevertheless, within each system, appropriately placed brain lesions may involve individual levels separately. The involvement of a given perceptual level, e.g., of the area striata, produces diverse perceptual disorders; of the configurational level, elementary disorders of recognition even though levels I.s. and III.s. function normally; and damage to the conceptual level gives rise to complex (conceptual, amnestic or associative) disorders of recognition and of visual or, as the case may be, of auditory thought even though the remaining two levels function in a normal fashion. More often than not, how-

---

* "By means of sense objects are given to us and sense alone provides us with perceptions; by means of the understanding objects are thought and from it there arise concepts" (Kant, *247a*).

ever, disorders of various complexity exist in combination.

The representation of engrams of different complexity at successive levels of a given sensory system (Fig. 8) introduces a certain difficulty which, however is more apparent than real. The "closed loop" represented at level III.s., indicating an engram of a conceptual order, embodies engrams of a configurational order, i.e., the "closed loop" represented at level II.s. This is another way of saying that, from a *developmental* viewpoint, the conceptual engram is related to the configurational engram which, however, still operates in the former or that, from a *physiological* viewpoint, one and the same stimulus is carried over to successively higher recording stations of the neuraxis, to be embodied there into more complex units of experience. Thus, the diagram shows the still existing, and still active, traces of individual developmental stages of experience wherein the anatomical substrates serving successive phases of one and the same process have retained a certain measure of independence. (By the same token, a similar relationship obtains between perceptual engrams and configurational engrams.) In principle, the functional relationship between the individual grades is the same as that prevailing at lower levels of the nervous system; at successively higher strata, the individual centers are able to cope with an increasing number of variables. That the individual planes of the sensory, e.g., visual systems have retained a certain measure of independence may be inferred from the fact that bilateral damage to I.s. which, if complete, causes cortical blindness, does not necessarily interfere with the function of either III.s. or II.s., that is, that the patient, in pure cases at least, may still be able to visualize and to think in visual terms. Damage to II.s. on the other hand, may interfere only with recall at the configurational level, for example, with the re-visualization of gestalten. Damage to level III.s. may reduce only the ability to form and to manipulate *modality related concepts* (see below) or may involve both functions in combination.

One may suppose that, at level II.s., the recorded stimuli become elements of a more adaptively organized form of subjective reality, and that they are combined with other, configurationally related engrams generated by the

same system. At level III.s., the stimuli in question are represented in a still more versatile experiental setting, and in combination with conceptually related engrams some of which can be traced to the same sensory modality while others are related to other modalities. Experiences with the process of recognition under normal and abnormal conditions (which will be discussed in detail below) indicate that the process of recording unfolds in successive stages, and that it may be arrested at the stage of configurational awareness, in which case it yields a feeling of familiarity. In principle, the same relationship exists not only between *engrams* and levels of increasing integrational complexity but also between *stimuli* of increasing complexity on the one hand, and, on the other, the levels at which they are registered. Ordinarily, objective reality is recorded at the most elaborate and adaptive, i.e., conceptual system so that subjective reality is dominated by conceptual data. The latter exist however in combination with those of a configurational and perceptual order; under certain conditions, conceptual data may be relegated to a mere background of experience which is dominated by the appreciation of forms. In fact, the contents of awareness may be dominated by elementary perceptions especially those mediated by the lower senses. Thus, at the individual planes of the nervous system, the anatomical substrates concerned with the recording of objective reality for the purpose of immediate or delayed reaction are not identical although, as at increasingly higher sensory levels, identical elements are re-represented as different, more adaptive, forms of experience. Progressively more adaptive modes of experience are acquired in phases, both ontogenetically and phylogenetically and, in the animal series, can be shown to depend on the proportion between the recording and the elaborative cortex. The subjective reality of the infant is, by adult standards at least, chaotic (*483*) and the experiental world of animals as far as can be inferred from their behaviour, perceptually and configurationally organized. In sharp contrast, their conceptual sphere has been arrested at an orimentary state of complexity. To express the same matter in a different way: In the course of ontogenetic and phylogenetic development, the data of objective reality are at successively higher sensory levels of the nervous system recorded as analogs of an increasingly higher order. Lastly, in the course of the translation of thought into action, analogs of a configurational order are converted into motor analogs. The above considerations should be understood in terms of the laws of neuropsychology which stipulate, among others, that a given performance is to be expressed (a) in terms of its *functional primordium* and (b) the specific quota of action which, at the higher level, is generated to increase its *operational dimensions*. Further, that the more adaptive functions mediated by a higher level of integration supersedes the more primitive function of the lower plane but maintains the general pattern of organization of its precursor. To quote from the opening chapter: "This principle applies ... to the relationship between conceptual, configurational and perceptual stimuli."

Although concepts are representative of abstract relations between data, certain concepts embody *modality specific thought material*, that is to say, visual, auditory and, in the blind, probably somesthetic psychisms. According to Heidbreder (*204*), "conceptualization readily takes off from the directly perceptible by means of processes which resemble as closely as possible those involved in the perception of concrete objects and which maintain, as long as possible, some directly perceptual anchorage in perceptible material." In certain intellectual tasks, for instance in descriptive geometry, the utilization of visual elements is essential. Visually "minded" persons (the aforementioned visual types) are virtually forced to think in visual terms; they may fail whenever the nature of a problem does not permit its translation into the visual sphere of experience. Auditory types on the other hand are apt to think in words and, when disturbed, complain that they cannot "hear" themselves think. Critchley (*103*) has recently studied the phenomenon of tactile thought in the blind. As we have already pointed out, the organization of a particular sensory sphere depends not only on the technical perfection of the elementary recording processes but rather on the elaboration of the recorded data at the conceptual level. From what has gone before, it follows that the intellectual ability of animals fails to keep pace with the acuity of their senses, notably the sense of smell. On the other hand, it may be difficult

to disprove that the memory of some animals equals that of man. For a more detailed discussion of the subject the interested reader may be referred to Bierens de Haans (*45*) *Animal Psychology* where the author raises the question if a dog's "smell recollections" of persons and objects his "smell dreams" and the "smell physiognomies" to which he responds.

To the extent that the above considerations refer to pathological phenomena they no doubt oversimplify matters and do not do full justice to the disturbance patterns of higher cerebral functions. Clearly, it would be a mistake to equate "damage to a diagram" with damage to the complexly integrated substrate of the functions under study. On the other hand, elementary considerations based on simple drawings, which are a map of reality, no more, represent certain selective aspects, and no doubt facilitate the interpretation of brain functions under normal and pathological conditions. Thus, it may be stated that *visuo-perceptual disorders* are by and large abnormal patterns of sensory functions referable to a defective perceptual component which, under normal conditions is an essential constituent of the entire fabric of higher visual functions. By the same token, *visuo-configurational disorders* are caused by a defective configurational component which interferes with responses based on gestaltdata, and the same applies to *visuo-conceptual disorders* with regard to a conceptual factor. In any eventuality, the integrative acts mediated by the individual level involved may be disorganized or they do not materialize at all as, for example, in cases of bilateral complete destruction of the area striata. The *clinical syndromes* referable to the partial or complete elimination of one or the other sensory component represent at any given moment the integrated response of the still available use patterns, i.e., *ideal cross sectional representations through a flow of events which, in their totality, are attempts at restitution based on whatever substrate is still available, including the actual or potential resources of the subordinate hemisphere if the dominant side is involved and vice versa.* In line with what has been said before it is virtually certain that the cooperation of the two hemispheres varies from case to case. Thus one will hardly expect to find a one to one correspondence between individual syndromes on the one hand

and anatomical lesions on the other although, eventually, the correlation between a sufficiently large number of carefully investigated syndromes and equally well studied anatomical data may yield patterns of topical predilection. The matter will be further considered below.

No doubt it would simplify matters if one could set apart syndromes caused by a defective perceptual component from those referable to configurational disability and the latter from purely intellective deficit. However, because of the complex interrelationship between the three factors on the one hand and, on the other, the vagaries of, e.g., traumatic lesions, the variability of vascular supply and other factors, pure forms will be the exception rather than the rule; in other words, the fortuitous pathology of brain lesions will rarely if ever implicate the substrate of any functional level in isolation. The approach here offered combines the localistic viewpoint with the valid elements of the already discussed "brain rest theory" and, to a degree, also the theory of "chronogenic localization." It is preferable to the theory of "disintegration of function" (*Abbau*), a metaphorical expression based on the idea that a functional whole breaks down into fragments whose bizarre "shapes" are not determined by lines of construction (at which the whole structure is naturally more vulnerable) but, rather, that it breaks down in a haphazard and unrevealing fashion unrelated to the composition of the now fragmented whole. At the same time, the neuropsychological approach here proposed, that is, the analysis of the more complex performances of the brain under conditions of partial or complete absence of specific quotas of action (or operational dimensions related to specific localities of the brain) eliminates the still existing, almost phrenologically simple "box-concept" of localization, upheld by some, i.e., the rigid correlation of the (so called) entities of traditional psychology with certain localities of the brain map.

For completeness, the following survey of disorders of higher sensory functions, which is arranged in terms of psychopathological mechanisms, embodies also disorders of *modality specific attention* (point I.) and certain *disorders of lower sensory functions* (point II.). To reiterate, the individual syndromes, indicated below by small letters of the alphabet, may reflect the involve-

ment of more than one pathophysiological mechanism. Conversely, one and the same pathophysiological mechanism may operate in different clinical syndromes. We reiterate that the latter are nothing more than *semi-stable cross sectional representations of dissociated functions*, i.e., dissociated either singly or in combination with others. However, since, in one and the same case, different syndromes may be present at the same time, the underlying mechanisms may interact and attempted compensation may occur by utilizing the remaining resources not only of the same (involved) system but also of other systems. (Cf. e.g., Gelb and Goldstein's case Schn. *159*.) In a certain sense, the clinical pictures represent, provided restitution, however limited, takes place, different stages of a process of healing.

I. Disorders of *receptivity and reactivity* related to sensory modalities.
   1. *Visual* inattention syndromes.
      a. Active and passive (general or hemianopic) inattention (*394a, 396*)
      b. Dyslexia. Disorders of visual counting (Best, *41*)
      c. Psychic paralysis of visual fixation. (Balint's syndrome)
   2. *Auditory* inattention syndrome (See "subcortical sensory aphasia")
   3. *Somesthetic* inattention syndromes (See "anosognosia")

II. Disorders of the *analog function* of the CNS at the *perceptual* level of sensation.
   1. Disorders of the perceptual analog function of the CNS in the *visual* sphere.
      a. Field defects. Disorders of the appreciation of light and darkness, of color, of space, of movement and direction
      b. Disorders of the visual coordinates (*34, 290*)
      c. Disorders of the visual localization of objects in space (*44, 62, 63, 259*)
      d. Disorders of distance perception (*63, 416, 419, 483*)
      e. Disorders of the appreciation of movements (*63, 219*)
      f. Defective appreciation of the spatial properties of objects
   2. Disorders of the perceptual analog function of the CNS in the *auditory* sphere
      a. Partial anakusia
   3. Disorders of the perceptual analog function of the CNS in the *somesthetic* sphere
      a. Non-productive anosognosia

III. Disorders of the *analog function* of the CNS at the *configurational* level of sensation.
   1. Disorders of the configurational analog function of the CNS in the *visual* sphere.
      a. Charcot's mindblindness

b. Configurational components of object agnosis. (Lissauer's mindblindness)
c. Agnostic alexia
2. Disorders of the configurational analog function of the CNS in the *auditory* sphere
a. Perceptual agnostic auditory agnosia. Gestaltdeafness.
b. Auditory agnosia for symbols
c. Auditory agnosia for musical qualities. (Rhythm, pitch, modulation, melody and harmony)
3. Disorders of the configurational analog function of the CNS in the *somesthetic* sphere
a. Gestaltanaesthesia. (Wernicke's apperceptive mind blindness, apperceptive form of tactile agnosia, "perceptual" astereognosis, disorders of primary identification.)
b. Somatotopagnosia. (Global somatotopagnosia, partial somatotopagnosia, Finger-agnosia Gerstmann. Body-scheme disorders.)
c. Productive form of anosognosia
IV. Disorders of the *analog function* of the CNS at the *conceptual* level of sensation.
1. Disorders of the conceptual analog function of the CNS in the *visual* sphere.
a. Conceptual (amnestic or associative) components of object agnosis (Lissauer's mindblindness)
b. Conceptual forms of left right disorientation
c. Disorders of topographical orientation. (Route finding, map drawing, dressing)
d. Disorders of visual cognition. (Wolpert's simultanagnosia, Pick's apperceptive mind blindness, disturbance of visual comprehension in the senile.)
2. Disorders of the conceptual analog function of the CNS in the *auditory* sphere.
a. Amnestic agnostic auditory agnosia. (Conceptual or apperceptive form.)
3. Disorders of the conceptual analog function of the CNS in the *somesthetic* sphere.
a. Amnestic (conceptual or associative) variety of tactile agnosia. (Disorders of secondary identification.)

Disorders of higher visual functions

Visuo-perceptual disorders

By definition, visuo-perceptual disability including the disorders listed under point I does not of itself constitute a disorder of a higher visual function. The term "higher" applies only to visuo-configurational and visuo-conceptual defects but the latter are, as we have said, rarely found in isolation, in fact, they are likely to interact with low level dysfunctions. Moreover, visuo-perceptual disorders may elicit the reaction- and restitution patterns that are found in visual dysfunction at higher levels of integration. For example, in cases of hemianopsia, certain parts of the uninvolved fields may function as a pseudofovea as described by Fuchs (151), Gelb and Goldstein (159) and others. Polyak (394a), taking a strictly localistic view, challenged the validity of the concept of reorganization of the visual fields but his position would appear to be a rather isolated one. Although visuo-perceptual disorders are apt to occur in association with those at higher levels of the visual system, their study is a field in its own right, as is, of course, the investigation of their psychophysiological background, *visual perception*. (See, e.g., Vernon's monograph, 483.) Renewed attention may be called to the perceptionist school of thought which maintains that higher forms of visual deficit, e.g., visual agnosia, are referable to *Funktionswandel*, and also to Siemerling's (446) experiments, who claimed to have produced visual agnosia by artificial reduction of visual acuity, constriction of the visual fields and the diminution of illumination. However, as we have pointed out earlier in this chapter, poor peripheral function does not necessarily give rise to poor central function.

The discussion of the visuo-perceptual disorders will be limited to those of visual attention and dyslexia. For this reason, references to the literature on visuo-perceptual disorders are given in the accompanying table.

Visual inattention may be either general or limited to one of the two halffields. Global disturbances include those of passive and active attention. *Passive inattention* manifests itself in defective receptivity and reactivity to visual stimuli while *active inattention* which, like reactivity, involves a motor factor, is responsible for defective scanning. The disturbances in question are practically always combined. As described by Kleist (259) a.o., the patient has difficulty in directing his gaze from one object to another, the eye movements being slowed down or even impossible at times. If an object held in front of the patient's eyes is moved he is apt to lose sight of it although his visual field may be normal and his visual acuity adequate. The semi-automatic eye movements, which ordinarily serve to fixate an object, are scarce, or they appear to be frozen. At other times the patient's visual distractibility appears to be increased. The condition is not necessarily associated with the inability to recognize objects. Poppelreuter describes the eye movements as unsystematic; the patient may fixate an object but fails to take note of it at all, or only fleetingly so and may then direct his gaze toward another object. The eye movements are ill directed with resulting loss of the fixation point and difficulty in shifting attention. Hartmann, (195, 196), supplementing Wernicke's (510) and Anton's (9) description of the condition, called attention to the poor eye-hand coordination. Balint's (23) patient, who was unable to see more than one object at one time, entirely excluded the peripheral part of the visual field. Space seemed to fall apart into disarticulated segments. Once he had fixated an object he could no longer direct his gaze to certain parts of the field although there was no weakness of the individual eye muscles and the visual fields were not really constricted. Whatever systematic exploratory visual activity the patient displayed was limited to a small part of the field to the left of the fixation point but his performance could be somewhat improved by calling his attention to the position of objects, letters, etc., which he would fail to see or, rather, to find spontaneously. Whether or not he saw an object did not depend on its size; on the other hand, whatever he did see he would perceive correctly. For instance, he would see a person standing in front of him, or a pin, but once he had fixated it he could not see a candle only a few centimeters away from the fixated object. The moment he tried to indicate the center of a circle its outline would disappear. As Lange (272) put it, his visual world appeared to end at the periphery of the object he happened to fixate. There was no true agnosia, alexia, etc. Balint called the condition "Seelenlähmung des Schauens" or "psychic paralysis of gaze."

In unilateral neglect of the visual space which, as a rule, involves the left side, the patient may lose his way in neglecting to make left turns. He may fail to perceive the left side of his body and, in spite of the absence of hemianopsia, the left side of objects, persons and pictures. What's more, he may in space transpose visual images from the involved part of the field to the opposite

half (visual allaesthesia). Occasionally, transposition from the lower to the upper quadrant occurs.

The disturbance of reading known as dyslexia is closely related to the general disturbances of attention. Eye movements are unsystematized and ill coordinated; the patient frequently loses the place he fixates and has difficulty in shifting fixation from one end of the line to the beginning of the next. Hence, the patient is apt to lose his place as a result of missing one or two lines. However, if he is shown an isolated word or a brief sentence, he reads it promptly. According to Jossman (243), defective coordination of the eye movements manifests itself in the inability on the part of the patient to coordinate the successive movements of the eye from left to right according to the sequence demanded by the individual arrangement of the words. At the same time, the patient has difficulty in avoiding recursive movements of his eyes. The same disorders may be responsible for the disturbances of optical counting described by Best (41).

Visuo-mnemonic disorders

The psychology and psychopathology of recognition

The process of recognition is dependent on the interaction of the dominant sphere of mentation with the mnemonic system, that is, on the identification of the stimulus to be recognized (or x-stimulus) with the appropriate engram. In the preceding chapter, we defined recognition as the detection of the place value of an item (the x-stimulus) and its verification, by means of comparing feedbacks, in a gridwork of relations established by experience. (As will be shown presently, the two definitions supplement each other.) In the above suggested classification of sensory disorders, intended to bring out the relationship between psychopathological mechanisms and clinical syndromes, the disorders of higher sensory functions were arranged in terms of inadequate analog functions mediated by the individual levels of sensory integration, including the highest, which is concerned with the elaboration of thought from perception. It follows that the individual syndromes may in an alternative fashion be expressed as disorders of thinking, which is more convenient for our present con-

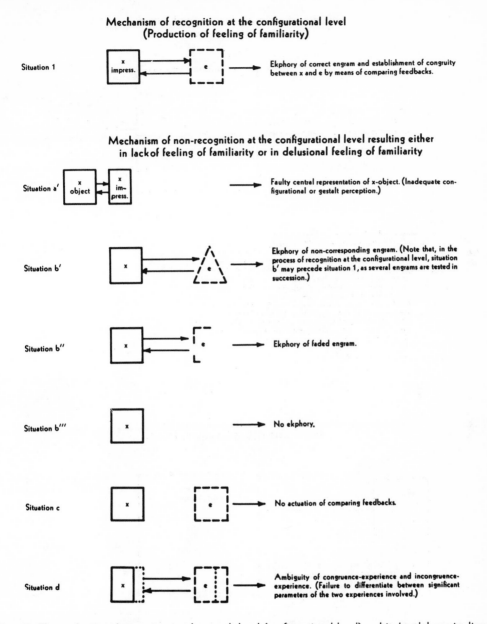

Fig. 42. The mechanism of recognition at the gestalt-level (configurational level) and its breakdown in disease (Perceptual agnosia, defective primary identification, Charcot's mindblindness).

siderations. As explained in the opening pages of Chapter III, thought processes fall into three broad groups, namely,

I. Reproductive thinking
  1. Repetitive thinking
  2. *Recognitive thinking*

II. Reflective thinking
  1. Apperceptive thinking
  2. Reconstructive thinking
  3. Anticipative thinking

III. Intuitive thinking

In the following paragraphs, we shall concern

Mechanism of non-recognition or misidentification at the conceptual level

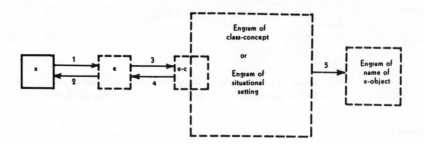

x: stimulus to be recognized at the conceptual level.

e: engram of stimulus at the configurational level.

e-c: engram of stimulus at the conceptual level, i.e., engram of the appropriate class concept or concept of situational setting (see text).

Sources of error: non-ekphory of engram of stimulus formed at the configurational level; non-ekphory of engram of class concept or engram of situational setting; ekphory of inappropriate class concept or concept of situational setting; inadequate appreciation of relations between stimulus and engram of class concept or inadequate appreciation of relations between stimulus and engram of situational setting (This particular defect corresponds to the ambiguity situation referred to under point 1(d) illustrated in the previous diagram).

1, 2, 3, 4, 5: phase sequences.

Mechanism of recognition of an object if its name is given (roundabout-recognition)

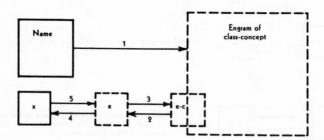

Fig. 43. The mechanism of recognition at the conceptual level and its breakdown in disease (Associative or amnestic agnosia, defective secondary identification, Lissauer's mindblindness).

ourselves with the mechanism of recognitive thinking and its disorders. Disorders of *re-visualization* and the corresponding disorders in the auditory sphere belong to those of repetitive thought; disorders of *recognition* at the configurational and the conceptual level to those of recognitive thought, and disorders of *visual cognition* (e.g., simultanagnosia) chiefly to those of apperceptive thought.

Now, if recognition is in reality a process of thinking, it should be compounded of an inaugural phase and a concluding phase. In the *inaugural phase of recognition*, the x-object is recognized at the configurational level, that is, its perception produces a state or mode of awareness known as *feeling of familiarity*.

(1) *Recognition at the configurational level* (Fig. 42) would thus depend on

(a) adequate configurational perception of the x-object,

(b) the ekphory of the corresponding engram which, in turn, is actuated by a process of association by similarity,

(c) the initiation of comparing feedbacks between the x-object and its reinstated memory image and

(d) on adequate congruence indicating or, as the case may be, incongruene indicating (discriminatory) capacity. Either process, in turn, is dependent on adequate gestaltperception.

The process of recognition at the configurational level of awareness may, at stages a, b, c and d, fail because of the following:

(a′) inadequate configurational perception (which can be brought out by sorting or matching tests),

(b′) ekphory of a non-corresponding engram

(b″) ekphory of a faded engram

(b‴) failure of association by similarity to materialize, with resulting non-ekphory

(c) failure to actuate comparing feedbacks and

(d′) lack of discriminatory capacity secondary to inadequate gestaltperception which, in turn, causes uncertainty as to the congruence or incongruence of the compared items. Failure or derangement of the inaugural phase of recognition will result either in the *absence of the feeling of familiarity*, or a *delusional feeling of familiarity*. However, within limits, defective configurational perception of the x-object may be compensated for at the conceptual level.

In the *concluding phase of recognition*, the x-object is recognized at the conceptual level as the ultimate framework of reference.

(2) *Recognition at the conceptual level* (Fig. 43) would depend on

(a) the above discussed recognition at the configurational level,

(b) the ekphory, through association by contiguity, of the setting of which the x-object is a part (especially of its habitual setting) or of the class to which it belongs,

(c) the actuation of comparing feedbacks between the configurationally identified object and the mnemonic image of its situational setting or, alternately, of the appropriate class concept, and

(d) adequate sensitivity to inconsistencies brought out by the correlation of the configurationally identified object with either framework of reference mentioned under the heading "Recognition at the configurational level" (Fig. 42).

For example, one may or may nor recognize a familiar looking person one happens to meet outside its costumary setting, say, the store in which the person has been seen to work. The individual will be recognized at the moment the mnemonic image of the store is reactivated and the x-person and the activated engram of the store are correlated for consistency (or, rather, tested for contiguity), by invoking the engram of the total situation. In a general way, it may be said that the relationship between the configurationally identified object and the habitual setting of which it is a part, or with which it is contiguous, forming an experiental unit, corresponds to the relationship between an item and the appropriate class concept. In fact, *class concepts* and *concepts of a setting* are equivalent to the extent that both are ordering devices or grouping schemes. Within the framework of a class concept, the constituting items are arranged according to their similarity; in "situational setting concepts," according to contiguity. Similar "contiguity units," in turn, may be arranged to class concepts of a higher order. An object is fully, or conceptually, recognized by the ekphory of the appropriate class concept or its equivalent, and the fitting of the x-item into its framework. (Subsumption.) In fact, it is fair to say that an organized system of class concepts, situational or otherwise, represents the stock of an individual's knowledge and experience.

Now, the structure of the class concept makes possible the awareness of a maximum of relations of which the item concerned is a constituent (see Chapter III, "multilinear relays" as models of class concepts) and since, ordinarily, class concepts are represented by the appropriate *name*, in a symbolic fashion that is, the object is fully recognized at the moment of the ekhpry of its name, which is the "masterkey" to the

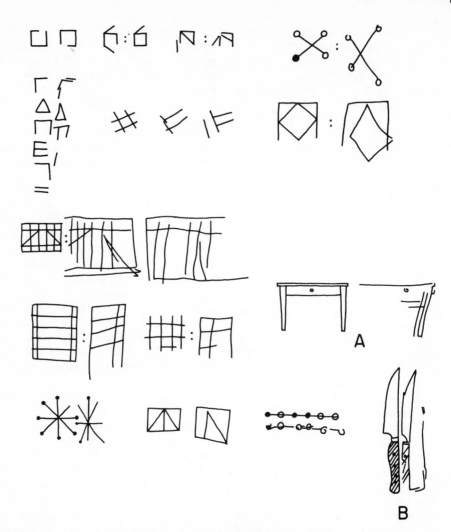

Fig. 44. Drawings of a patient with left homonymous hemianopia and a mixed agnostic and apractic syndrome. A: Attempt to copy the outline drawing of a table (hemianopic error); B: Attempt to copy the outline drawing of a knife (configurational error).

The remaining drawings show omissions and distortions of proportions referable to defective gestalt-perception. The patient was unable to copy other simple test figures with her apractic left hand, but could do it immediately afterwards with her relatively eupractic right hand, thereby excluding the agnostic deficit as the only source of her inability to copy.

relay system concerned. On the other hand, it may be the class concept which facilitates the recognition of an item. For example, a patient who is unable to understand a word he has just read, may become aware of its meaning after being told it is the name of a poet. In other instances, the patient may operate within the class concept but fail to pinpoint an item in the

gridwork of relations, or the framework of the relay. In an already quoted example, a near miss occurred in three instances, the patient having read the work Berlin instead of Reichstag, the word elephant instead of India, and the word hare instead of fox.

It is important at this point to keep in mind what has been said on a previous occasion about

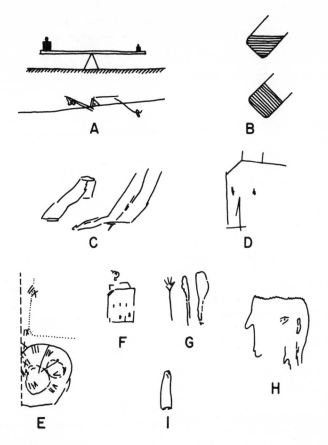

Fig. 45. Drawings of the same patient.
A and B: see text; C: shoes; D and F: house; E: watch; G: fork, knife and spoon; H: human profile; and I: egg drawn from memory with the right, relatively eupractic hand (defective revisualization independent of hemianopic defect).

the relationships between *primary generalization, recognition* and *association by similarity as a sort of mental diplopia*. Under point (b), attention was called to the fact that the original pattern of primary generalization may be permanently although not overtly maintained in the process of recognition and that it may in turn be followed by *secondary differentiation*. Primary (tentative) generalization may result in temporary mis-identification of the stimulus, that is, its equation with one or more non-corresponding engrams (situation b′) which are tested out until, ulti-mately, the correct engram is ekphorized. At advanced stages of experience, at which the confidence coefficient of recognition reaches higher values, misidentification and its immediate correction are fused to a unitary process but the individual phases may become re-segregated under conditions of fatigue and distraction.

Lastly, it is worthy of note that, in animals, situational "class concepts" are apt to be formed at the configurational level and that they act in the fashion of stimuli in conditioned response situations. Let me cite an incident from my own experience. A dog that developed the habit of nestling down on my lap as I sat in a hotel lobby in the evening would furiously bark at me (and only at me) when I walked across the lawn in broad daylight. In the animal, then, the two concepts are merely different reaction patterns (Mach's *Reaktionsidentitäten*) which are not resolved, that is, tested for consistency at higher conceptual planes.

General behaviour under conditions of gestalt-
blindness or configurational blindness
(Fig. 44, 45)

The ability on the part of a patient to appreciate shapes, more especially geometrical figures, is sometimes confused with true recognition although objects, to be sorted according to shape and size, do not have to be recognized at the conceptual level. A patient may be able to sort objects with which he is entirely unfamiliar. Sorting depends on gestaltperception rather than the knowledge of the use of an object, or the determination of its place with one or several conceptual systems of reference. Similarly, a person may be able to sort various colors which he has never seen and which, of course, he is unable to name. One of my patients (A. Berl.), on being asked to sort out circles, triangles and squares spread out in front of her indicated corresponding figures promptly but experienced difficulty in differentiating five-cornered from six-cornered stars and also at other, more complicated figures (*428a*). However, she was able to distinguish between quadrangles of various shapes and various types of triangles. It is important to note that a different orientation in space of similar or identical (meaningless) figures interfered with the process of gestaltperception. By contrast, the patient succeeded in identifying differently oriented symbols, which supports the idea that an intellectual factor operates in the perception of symbolic gestalten. For example, she failed to appreciate the similarities between differently oriented (non-symbolic) shapes. On the other hand, she could read capital letters but did not recognize whether they were correctly oriented or upside down; in other words, she experienced their gestalten as identical. She could not specify differences between more complicated figures although she was aware of the fact that such differences existed "somewhere." Likewise, she was unable to copy closely crowded (meaningless) test figures, probably because her drawings (the first of which was correct) inordinately increased the complexity of the field which sooner or later, overtaxed her power of gestaltperception. At this stage of testing, she could no longer differentiate between the figures drawn by the examiner and those produced by herself but this task could be made easier by drawing the test figures farther apart.

Disorders of revisualization, of visual recall and
of reproduction

Reproductive visual recall includes visual imagery which may be tested either by having the patient describe or draw familiar objects. Although the information derived in this fashion is an indirect one, and the ability to draw varies from person to person, it may reflect the power of reproductive memory with a fair degree of accuracy. The patient referred to in the preceding paragraph was asked to look, as long as she wished, at a series of objects lined up in front of her, and told that she will be asked to name them with her eyes closed. She failed almost completely although her general intelligence and memory were adequate and she could name the objects without difficulty while looking at them. Her recollection for the route from the ward to the examining room was fragmentary and the description of simple objects from memory rather incomplete. On being asked to enumerate the differences between a chair and a table she maintained that both have backs. On the other hand, her description of animals, for example, a hippopotamus and an elephant was surprisingly accurate and, in my opinion at least, could not be accounted for by the verbal association between "elephant" and "trunk" and between "hippopotamus" and "horn." Reference to Fig. 45 will illustrate the patient's inability to draw from memory.

CONFIGURATIONAL MINDBLINDNESS (CHARCOT)

One of the most dramatic cases of defective revisualization is the case of a patient reported by Charcot (*87*). The patient, who had previously been an outspoken visual type, lost his power of visual recall after an emotional upset. Familiar objects and persons assumed a strange appearance and, on looking into a mirror, he believed he saw himself for the first time. Initially, the patient's difficulty in visual recall was combined with difficulty in recognition, for he failed to identify members of his own family and also streets and places with which he was well acquainted. Charcot's variety of mind-blindness must be differentiated from the Lissauer type, especially its amnestic component.

Conceptual (Associative or Amnestic) Mind-Blindness (Lissauer)

Object agnosia, which is identical with Lissauer's mind blindness, is a form of amnestic agnosia; as can be demonstrated by sorting tests, the patient is aware of the basic properties of objects which he is unable to recognize at the conceptual level, that is, to fit into the highest relational framework. The objects to be identified look either somewhat unfamiliar or, although the patient is able to identify them as something he has seen before, fails to name them, or to indicate their use. The disorder cannot be accounted for by defective sensation, intellectual deficit or aphasia, with which, however, it may be associated.

In Lissauer's case, the patient could recognize objects by sounds and touch but not by sight. She mistook a dog for a physician and a brush for a cat; in fact, she pointed to what she thought were the animal's legs and tail. It is important to note that the very same objects which cannot be recognized visually can be identified through some other sensory channel. Moreover, the independence of visual agnosia from general intelligence is evidenced by the fact that concomitant intellectual disturbances, if any, are apt to improve in the course of the disease while the agnostic disturbances become more and more marked. Neither is there any consistent relationship between non-recognition and field defects; out of 34 cases collected by Stauffenberg (457), only 20 showed one or the other form of hemianopsia. In 21 cases in which color vision was tested it proved to be intact in six cases. Initially, visual object agnosia is apt to be combined with disturbances of orientation which, however, are apt to subside while the object agnosia may persist for years. In the case of severe disorder of topographical orientation reported by Scheller and Seidemann (423) the recognition of objects was unaffected as we had already occasion to mention. Depth perception is as a rule normal. Visual agnosia is not pure but may be combined with tactile agnosia and transitory amnestic aphasia. Object agnosia is frequently associated with alexia but either disturbance may exist independently, and writing is apt to be normal. Curiously enough, the very same patient may be able to draw a fairly good picture of an object he is unable to recognize. In other cases he may be able to recognize objects but unable to recognize their pictorial representation.

Agnostic Alexia

In the present context, we shall deal with those disturbances of reading only, which represent a special form of visual agnosia rather than of aphasia. In the more severe forms of agnostic alexia the patient may be unaware of the fact that he is looking at letters; he may be under the impression to see some sort of objects and may even try to pick them up. In less severe cases he can recognize individual letters or words and, although he may not be able to differentiate between them, at least realizes that they are some sort of symbols. In a given case, the impression that alexia is a visual disturbance may be verified by writing letters on the patient's skin, or by putting letters cut out of cardboard in the palm of his hand. If he can read them tactually, the inability to recognize letters by sight is in all likelihood a visual disorder unrelated to aphasia. In the absence of speech defects, the association of alexia with other gnostic disturbances corroborates the impression that the disorder is agnostic rather than the aphasic in nature. On the other hand, the dissociation between the patient's ability to read and his helplessness if confronted with objects and pictures of objects may be striking. In Lissauer's (308) patient, for example, the ability to read was preserved. Neither can the disorders be consistently attributed to visual spatial agnosia (which makes it impossible for the patient to recognize the true relations of the various lines within the individual letters) and to the letters and words to one another. Scheller and Seidemann's (423) patient showed gross disturbances in route finding while reading was unaffected. It is unlikely that agnostic alexia is always a component of general agnosia. In so far as the disturbance in question occurs frequently in association with agnosia for colors and with right sided hemianopsia, it appears to be primarily determined by the localization of the lesion. In other words, the lesions involves performances represented in adjacent parts of the cerebral cortex. By contrast, agraphia and paragraphia associated with agnostic alexia is probably a secondary disturbance, as the patient is confused by his own writing. However, the very same patient may be able to ekphorize the appropriate engrams of letters and words; he can write spontaneously but fails if he tries to read what he himself has written. (Cf. "Subcortical alexia.")

Visuo-conceptual disorders

The existence of intellective factors in vision comes to the fore whenever a person, faced with the task of evaluating visual data, i.e., perceptions and engrams, does not know "how to go about" to combine them spontaneously to a meaningful whole. Because of the importance of reproductive and recognitive thought, there are transitions between disorders of visual imagery and of visuo-conceptual performances properly so called. For example, the above mentioned patient (A.Berl.), was unable to indicate the orientation of a fluid level if the vessel in which water was contained was tilted; when presented with two alternative drawings, she believed Fig. 45A to be correct. Fig. 45B illustrates one of her futile attempts to indicate the impossibility of two unequal weights balancing each other, although she insisted that the side of the board upon which the heavier weight was placed would move downward. She did not know how to draw the shadow cast by a stick when both the stick and the source of light were indicated. With the exception of the first test, the tests described are examples of her inability to "compute visually," that is, to arrive at *data inherent in, but not directly furnished by, those given.*

Visual tasks whose solution is dependent on intellective factors are left-right-orientation, topographical orientation, map drawing and dressing which, however, may be made difficult by apraxia. Lastly, visuo-intellective factors play an important role in what, for want of a better term, may be called visual cognition. Many examples illustrating defective visual thinking may be found in Wertheimer's (*515*) postumous monograph.

DEFECTIVE LEFT-RIGHT DISCRIMINATION

While taking his first dancing lessons, a child may be surprised to learn that he has to revise his concept of "right" and "left." At least it had to be pointed out to me that, whenever we stood face to face, my partner's right side was on the side of my left arm and her left side on the side of my right arm. A student, learning the various positions of the fetus may resort to the trick of projecting himself into a giant womb. Benton and his associates (*35*) found that mentally defective children may make five times as many errors in the recognition or, for that matter, cognition, of laterality than any number of normal controls.

DISORDERS OF TOPOGRAPHICAL ORIENTATION

Spatial orientation plays a very important part *in route finding, map drawing, and dressing.* True topographical orientation, which involves knowledge of one's position within a spatial whole, is, however, not a prerequisite of route finding; a person may find his way by the moment to moment evaluation of clues. It is common knowledge that an individual, no matter how good a draftsman he may be, may be unable to draw a plan of a building through which he finds his way without difficulty. Map drawing depends on the ability to visualize and to duplicate the significant details of a spatially organized whole in the form of a graphic reconstruction or model. Thus, attempts at map drawing may fail owing to the impairment of general reproductive memory, because of geometrical agnosia, "repercussive" confusion resulting from the perception of a distorted pattern, and, lastly, by constructional apraxia. Moreover, in drawing a map, a person must exert conceptual control over the visual task with which he is confronted. The ability to draw a map depends on recognition and anticipative thought, and ultimately on panoramic vision.

As far as introspection serves me, the acquisition of spatial orientation may be said to develop somewhat as follows. Originally, visual clues are recognized as data that have been useful in one way or another. Proceeding from a positive clue, additional data are found to have positive or negative values. At a more advanced stage, one or more positive clues are anticipated and verified; ultimately, the whole sequence of clues is anticipatively visaulized. At this stage orientation depends on a person's ability to translate into a spatially organized whole the sequence of clues he "knows."

I do not deny altogether the role of kinesthetic data, as, particularly at advanced stages of experience, one's route appears to be influenced by associatively evoked tendencies, acting in the nature of "pulls," to walk in certain directions or to make certain turns. However, these impulses play a subordinate role; they are of no value unless checked by visual data. A map may or may not be helpful. A person confronted with the task of finding his way through a building with the aid of a floor plan may become confused and may prefer to use a sequence of clues. Moreover, poor visualizers are handicapped by a "psychomotor perseveration tendency." For example, a person, having reached his goal by a sequence of right turns, may have difficulty in finding his way back from where he started unless the motor automatisms established by repetition are reversed by orienting factors of a visual nature. Auditory types may be aided by memorizing cues verbally.

It is believed in some quarters that topographical orientation depends on a topographical sense, that is, a primary sense of direction, but there appears to be little if any evidence for his position. Apparently, even the most proficient pathfinders would do no better in pea-soup fog than one who, depending on whatever landmarks he is able to discover and to recognize, habitually gropes his way through a "system" of poorly articulating fragments. Kinesthetic clues can hardly play a decisive role. It is difficult to believe that a person is able to "unwind" his kinesthetic engrams in the reverse direction and to use them like a guiding rope. That a man is capable of blind navigation in a dense fog would prove that he has a primary sense of direction, if the term "sense" is meant to indicate information furnished by a sense organ. The fact that a man gets lost for want of landmarks proves that he lacks an organ that tells him of his position relative to a goal.

It would take us too far afield to discuss at length the related problem of orientation in animals. Griffin (186), who recently devoted a comprehensive article to the problem of spatial orientation in birds, ants, bees, and other animals, denies the existence of a special sense of direction. He mentions, for example, that ants maintain direction because of their ability to perceive polarized light, that water beetles generate surface waves that are reflected from solid objects and detected by means of special sense organs. Bats which emit intense sounds and hear the echo reflected back from obstacles lying ahead orient themselves by means of "echo-location," comparable to our sonar devices.

In the absence of special sense organs, route finding in man depends on both visual and general memory, particularly on recognition, and on reasoning processes, which enable him to align the coordinates of his own body with the main coordinates of his environment. It should also be noted that finding one's way back depends to a greater extent on *visuo-intellective* data than finding a goal from a habitual point of departure.

These preliminary considerations should enable us to discuss representative views on man's orientation in space. Brain (62) states that a patient may be able accurately to describe routes familiar to him in spite of defective visualization of objects in space, of loss of stereoscopic vision, of agnosia for the left half of space and, lastly, visual allesthesia. Hence, Brain concludes, loss of topographical memory is a disorder independent of other forms of visual discrimination and loss of memory for objects. In the following pages of his article, however, he refers to the well known fact that patients with visual object agnosia have difficulty in finding their way about. Paterson and Zangwill (373), who studied the relation of topographical defects to concomitant disturbances of visual perception, general memory, and the body scheme, concluded that their patients sustained a specific topographical memory deficit and, further, that certain features suggested that the causes of the topographical derangement went beyond visual perception in the narrow sense of the term. They believe that their patient's errors of place recognition suggested a special derangement of those "cerebral mechanisms or schemata built up through past experiences which must be assumed to underly the recognition of topographical data, and thereby mediate orientation." Unfortunately, they say nothing about the nature of those schemata. In fact, their own case demonstrates the crucial importance of topographical clues, for the authors describe in considerable detail how their own patient failed to identify a well-known landmark in spite of the fact that he recognized it as a hill, "which clearly proved that he actually perceived it."

However, perception in itself is a poor guide. The patient could not even initiate the process of route finding because of his inability to visualize the place of the hill in a mental map. Not only did the patient suffer from amnestic agnosia for particular landmarks, but he was unable to visualize their place in a spatial framework and to correlate them with a topographical whole, or model. Besides, he recognized neither his own home, nor a church nor other objects which no doubt would have directed a normal person. (Obviously, it did not help him that he recognized familiar objects that lacked topographical value.) Furthermore, in the stage of recovery, the patient himself stated that he utilized various landmarks as he used to do prior to his illness.

The ability to describe a route and actual route finding are not always associated performances. A person who cannot describe a familiar route will not necessarily get lost as long as he is able to recognize landmarks. On the other hand, a patient who has just described the layout of his own home accurately may be unable to represent it on a ground plan (315). This defect may be regarded as an exaggeration of the "physiological" inability to draw a map. Moreover, the description of familiar surroundings involves merely the ekphory of engrams, while the translation of the visualized layout into a system of linear, quasi-abstract terms requires the manipulation of spatial relationships, and the ability to organize the fragments constructively. (See, especially, refs. 219–224 and 467.)

The term "dressing apraxia" is probably a misnomer for, at least in the cases reported by Brain (63), Paterson and Zangwill (373) and Hecaen and Ajuriaguerra (202), severe visuospatial disability was present. At most, the apraxia was of the ideational type, if not a secondary or "optic apraxia" in the sense of Poppelreuter (396). The patient reported by McFie and his associates (315) showed neglect of the left half of the space, impairment of visuo-

spatial judgment, inability to differentiate between left and right, of top and of bottom; in other words, a "disorganization of discriminative spatial judgment." In the normal adult, dressing consists of a definite sequence of acts in which spatial relationships between objects and of one's own body must be reproduced on the basis of relationships existing at a given time. Eventually, in the course of time, dressing becomes a near automatic performance as do many other performances which, originally, depend on intellective factors. Among others, the regression from automaticity to thought was displayed by one of Brain's (63) patients who said that it was "quite hopeless for him to put his clothes on in an automatic fashion. He could put on his pajama coat only if he put it in front on his bed. He had learned that the handkerchief picked was on the left side and the button on the right side; by utilizing these landmarks he was able to put them on. If he tried otherwise he got into a hopeless muddle."

DISTURBANCES OF VISUAL COGNITION

Disorders of visual thought were described by Wolpert (522) under the name of "Simultanagnosia" and by Pick (384) as "apperceptive mind blindness" or "disturbance of visual comprehension in the senile." Wolpert's patient could recognize individual objects without appreciable difficulty but failed to discover their meaningful relationship in pictorially or cinematographically represented scenes. The disturbance was probably not a pure one but very likely complicated by a deficiency of scanning. Pick's patient, a presbiophrenic, was unable to recognize large objects, for example the large picture of a man; he recognized only its individual parts. When shown the picture of a horse, he recognized his hindlegs which, however, failed to suggest to him the nature of the whole figure. Briefly stated, he failed to synthetize parts into a comprehensive, interrelated, whole.

Brain lesions causing disorders of higher visual functions

The complexity of the problem of localization of higher visual functions, already alluded to in the discussion of the composite nature of normal performances, is brought to the fore by seemingly conflicting pathological findings. The following data refer to the attempted correlation between certain syndromes and cerebral lesions. A more comprehensive account would serve no useful purpose other than to show what can be epitomozed by a limited number of observations, namely, that there is no consistently uniform correlation between symptom and lesion. The presumptive reasons for this discrepancy were discussed earlier in this chapter under the heading "Structure, Function and Symptom." For a more detailed account the interested reader may be referred to Lange (273), Hecaen and Ajuriaguerra (202) and Critchley (104, 105).

Distortion of visual coordinates. McFie and his associates (315) stress the role of right sided parieto-occipital lesions in the causation of space distortion. *Disorders of visual localization in space.* Kleist (259) found area 18 of Brodmann and the subjacent fibers of the stratum sagittale to be implicated in combination with the fibers connecting the peristriate area with the parietal and occipital lobes; Best (41), area 18, the precuneus and the superior parietal lobule; and Hecaen and his associates (202), the precuneus and the dorsal portion of the occipital lobes. In their own cases, disorders of spatial localization were combined with disorientation. Other authors stressed the importance of the bilateral involvement of the occipital lobes. Patterson and Zangwill (373) disagree with Lange (273), who laid stress on the importance of the parietal lobe for the appreciation of space.

Visual agnosia. According to Kleist (259), mindblindness is caused by cortical and subcortical lesions of the second occipital convolution, especially of the left side of the brain. Stauffenberg (457) emphasizes the bilateral location of the lesion between the posterior portion of the lateral ventricle and the convexity of the occipital lobes. The lesions are however not necessarily symmetrical. Hecaen and de Ajuriaguerra (202) found cortical blindness especially in large left sided lesions including the external occipital convolutions and the splenium of the corpus callosum, Nielsen (356) in lesions of the second and third occipital convolution.

Disorders of orientation in space. Riddoch (407), in his study on spatial disorientation in hemianopic fields, found the opposite parietal cortex to be involved, and he blames the interruption of the fibers which connect the calcarine cortex with other parts of the brain, the nodal point being the supramarginal and angular gyrus. McFie and his associates (315) found visuo-spatial disabilities, including mild spatial agnosia, topographical disorientation, loss of topographical memory and right-left disorientation to be frequently caused by unilateral lesions of the posterior portion of a hemisphere.

Disturbances of higher somato-sensory functions

Perceptual astereognosis

Somesthesis comprises, in addition to the diverse cutaneous qualities (including touch, pain, temperature, and spatial discrimination), the sense of pressure and weight, of position, of vibration and the associated ability to localize stimuli originating in the deep structures including muscles, joints and tendons. Tactile recognition depends on a critical minimum of sensuous data. Primary tactile identification (or perceptual stereognosis), which involves the ability to perceive the crucial figural properties of an object by the appreciation of its somaesthetic qualities, may be thought of as a process of gestaltperception, or tactile gestaltexperience; loss of this ability, as "gestaltanaesthesia." The latter is analogous to gestaltblindness or perceptual visual agnosia and, at the same time, to gestaltdeafness, or perceptual auditory agnosia. (See below.) If a "gestaltanaesthetic" patient is asked to identify an object, say, a pencil, by touch, he will be *unaware of the fact that he is dealing with a thin, long and pointed object, or a short blunt object*, just like a patient suffering from a severe form of perceptual visual agnosia fails to distinguish a triangle from a circle. Wernicke, who described the disorder in 1895, called it *"apperzeptive Seelenblindheit,"* or *apperceptive mind blindness (apperceptive form of tactile agnosia)*. He emphasized that the disturbance is relatively independent on sensory disturbances, as evidenced by the fact that, in tabes dorsalis associated with severe sensory disturbances, primary identification may be essentially intact, and vice versa. (Similarly, visual gestaltperception may be intact in spite of astigmatism, nearsidedness, etc.)

Amnestic astereognosis

If the tactile recognition of objects is affected in spite of the absence of gestaltanaesthesia (tactile gestaltblindness or perceptual astereognsois), we are dealing with the amnestic type of tactile agnosia or disorders of secondary identification. The patient has a rather clear idea of the object he is asked to identify; *for example, he will describe the pencil as a long, thin and pointed object* but will be unable to recognize it. (It is this particular disorder of recognition which is conventionally referred to as astereognosis.) Needless to say, we are not dealing with a disturbance of speech, for the patient is unable to indicate how the object is used and, when allowed to look at it, will find its name instantly On the other hand, the performance is not necessarily improved by manipulating the object bimanually. (See, especially, refs. *96*, *156*, and *330*.)

Astereognosis due to intellective deficit

Under ordinary conditions, tactile recognition is the highest form of mentation based on somesthetic data. The object manipulated is brought into relationship with a conceptual reference system which, however, is not solely of unisensory (tactile) derivation. Awareness contents to which, with some justification, the term "tactile concepts" may be applied, develop, however, in the blind, where the somesthetic sphere of awareness appears to be enhanced by an additional dimension. We have already referred to Critchley's article on tactile thought with special reference to the blind. (Perhaps, animals can think in visual and in auditory terms to the limited extent only that man "thinks" tactually, which would mean that they cannot form concepts* in spite of their unquestioned discriminatory capacity for sights and sounds.) Critchley believes that, in sighted persons, tactile imagery must be most rare and that is probably uncommon even in the blind with the possible exception of the congenitally blind. Perhaps, sightless persons who have

* See, however, the *Reaktionsidentitäten*, and orimentary concept formation in animals discussed elsewhere in this monograph.

learned geography by studying embossed maps may develop a mental picture of geographical regions in the form of tactile impressions but it is noteworthy that even blind persons may try to transpose haptic impressions into visual impressions by a process of "optification." Sculptures made by congenitally blind children, to some degree at least, allow one to appreciate their "baseline" of tactile mentation for they greatly exaggerate bodily parts which assume special importance, e.g., hands and fingers. The space concept of the blind is a manual, brachial and ambulatory one. And the "touch horizon" delimits remote space, within which orientation depends on acoustic stimuli (*103*).

Disorders of the body scheme

The term body scheme (Head, *198*) designates the three-dimensional map of one's own body to which there are referred events in the personal space and, indirectly, those occurring in extrapersonal space. It is a plastic sort of map which is moulded by postural, visual and cutaneous data, and which records postural changes and those involving the body surface. Inasmuch as it records movements, it depends at the same time on messages from the interior of the body (particularly from the muscles), which are integrated with visual data. Cutaneous stimuli produced by touching the surface of one's own body are a special category of impressions for they yield information derived from both the organs of touch and the touched parts of the skin. Thus, they are of particular value in providing the body scheme with supplementary details. The "body scheme is a kind of inner diagram representing one's own body as a whole as well as in its single parts according to their location, size, shape, structure and functional differences and spatial interrelations" (*182*).

Somatotopagnosia

Inasmuch as the various stimuli are recorded by the cortex of the brain in the same way as stimuli from other sources, one's own body becomes an object among others as it were, and it is recognized in a similar fashion. And just as lesions of the occipital lobe produce visual agnosia, and those of the temporal lobe auditory agnosia, those of the parietal lobe are apt to produce agnosis of one's own body or "somatotopagnosia." In either case, disturbances of the higher, gnostic, functions may or may not be associated with those of the more primitive, perceptual, functions. Gerstamnn (162) prefers the term somatotopagnosia to the term autotopagnosia coined by Pick (1908), the reason being that disturbances of the awareness of one's own body are typically associated with the inability to appreciate the somatotopic relations in the patient's surroundings. Under pathological conditions, visual spatial agnosia and somatotopagnosia may "disintegrate" into their tactile, kinesthetic and visual constituents. Another type of dissociation involves the two halfs and the individual parts of the body, particularly the fingers. Hemi-somatotopagnosia and fingeragnosia are examples of dissociation of seemingly "unitary" functions.

GLOBAL SOMATOTOPAGNOSIA

The patient is agnostic although his whole body is not necessarily aware of his defect. He cannot differentiate or indicate the individual parts of the body on command. He is helpless when asked to point specifically to his chin, mouth, ears, eyes, shoulders, etc., and commits striking errors in appropriate tests. Usually, there is defective left-right discrimination. Orientation may be intact in respect to objects outside the body, in spite of the fact that most patients show signs of diffuse mental impairment.

HEMI-SOMATOTOPAGNOSIA

Among six of Brain's (63) patients with visual spatial agnosia, three experienced some positive disorder of awareness of the half of the body corresponding to the side on which visual disorientation was disturbed, and all showed defective postural sensibility on this side. Pineas' (392) patient failed to perceive the left half of his own body and, though there was no hemianopsia, one half of objects, pictures and persons.

FINGERAGNOSIA (GERSTMANN)

The disturbance in question will be best described in Gerstmann's (161) own words. It involves the primary selective disturbance, or loss of ability to recognize, identify, differentiate, name, select and indicate the individual fingers of either hand, the patient's own as well as those of other persons. It is characteristically associated with disorientation for right and left in respect to the patient's own body as well as that of other persons with special reference to the hands and fingers. It is often combined with agraphia and acalculia. There are no concomitant psychic (particularly intellectual) disorders, aphasia and apraxia; neither are there other manifestations of agnosia or of motor or sensory changes to which fingeragnosia could be ascribed. It occurs in spite of the patient's adequate theoretical knowledge of his hands and fingers, in spite of the absence of disturbances of general optic and tactile comprehension and in spite of sufficient vision to guide him. Lastly, it occurs in spite of normal sensitivity. It is a circumscribed disturbance of the capacity for recognition and orientation in one section of the body. As far as the limbs, including the toes, and other parts of the body are concerned, the ability to recognize them and to orient with reference to them remains essentially intact. The syndrome occurs with lesions of the transitional area of the angular gyrus and the second occipital convolution of the major hemisphere.

BRAIN LESIONS CAUSING DISORDERS OF THE BODY SCHEME

According to Hecaen a. ass. (202) lesions involving the parietal area of the dominant hemisphere produce bilateral body scheme disorders which may be either limited to the fingers, or which may produce global somatotopagnosia. Lesions of the subordinate parietal lobe on the other hand give rise to unilateral disturbances of the body scheme. In the few instances in which right anosognosia was encountered in the presence of a left sided lesion the patient was probably ambi-dextrous. In the experience of Nielsen (356) lesions of the minor (subordinate) side produce loss of the body image, i.e., loss of the image of the body of the patient; of the major side, loss of the concept of the body image in general.

How are these findings to be interpreted? In terms of the concept here proposed, the body image is indeed a mere diagram, that is, built up to the configurational level, by the resources of the minor hemisphere. On the major side, on the other hand, the diagram is conceptualized. And since, as previously explained, concepts embody configurations, the body image would seem to be configurationally represented on both sides, conceptually represented on the dominant side. This is also in accord with our deliberations concerning the presence of synchronous, partially identical thought processes mediated by the two hemispheres as, on the minor side, thought presumably matures only to the configurational stage of mentalization.

Anosognosia

Early in the 18th century, French physicians noted that patients may be unaware of what, we know now, were receptive paralytic, paraphasic and syntactic disorders. Unawareness of cortical blindness was described by v. Monakow in 1885, Rieger and Wolf (1882) and Dejerine and Vialet (1893). Pick (1889) reported the case of a patient who was unaware of his left-sided hemiplegia. Anton (9, 10) was the first who recognized unawareness of disease as a pathological entity and who correlated the defect with cerebral lesions causing hemiplegia, blindness or deafness. Other observers found non-perception of blindness in tumors of the sellar region in optic atrophy of peripheral origin and other peripheral disease processes. At the present time, unawareness of hemiplegia (which almost invariably involves the left side) is usually referred to as *anosognosia* (*Babinski 14*), and unawareness of cortical blindness as *Anton's syndrome*.

The difference between somatotopagnosia and anosognosia is obvious. In the former, the patient fails to recognize parts of his own body; in the latter, he denies their defective performance. He may insist that he can move his paralyzed arm or leg, that he can walk, see, hear and talk correctly. On being ordered to move his paralyzed arm he may move the healthy one but will maintain that it is the diseased arm. The patient who is apt to neglect his paralyzed side may turn away from it and, when his attention is directed upon the extremity he is unable to use, declare

it belongs to someone else. At the same time he may produce various illusions, distortions, confabulations, hallucinations and delusional states.

Gerstmann found anosognosia to be almost typically associated with homolateral loss of sensation of different degree and impairment of perception in the left half fields. In his experience, the patients do not necessarily show lowering or impairment of general cortical or mental function; their sensorium, mentation, memory and judgment are adequate, and the amnestic agnostic disturbances in the sphere of body awareness and body recognition represent relatively isolated defects. Gerstmann voiced the opinion that anosognosia is related to the localization of the lesion (which is apt to involve the thalamoparietal radiation) and that mere sensory loss does not account for it. Roth (*416*) described the case of a patient whose attitude toward her paralyzed left side, although not grossly deluded, was distinctly pathological at a time when she had no clouding of consciousness or other intellectual defect beyond some apathy, drowsiness and mental retardation. He felt that no complete explanation of the phenomenon is possible because the patient retains adequate sensory and intellectual means for discovering his defect, because agnosia is seen only in a small proportion of cases with massive hemiplegia and hemianesthesia, and because even confused and demented persons do not always deny painless paralysis. Apart from the possibility of effective pressure against the acceptance of disease, he weighs the possibility of a specific agnostic factor in consequence of which the patient's orientation with regard to his own body is disturbed in a specific way, and he is no longer able to relate himself to it correctly. Apparently, a specific focal disorder of cognition arising from a disorganization of the body scheme makes its contribution to the genesis of the disorder in all cases. According to Sandifer (*419*), definite intellectual disturbances seem always to be present in those cases in which fixed delusions occur that parts of the body or an entire half is missing. Freiman and his associates (*198*) studied the syndrome in question in a series of 25 patients, including patients with right hemiplegia, left hemiplegia, blindness and unilateral sensory and motor disorders of cerebral origin with minimal or no hemiplegia. In one case blindness was due to bilateral retinal detachment. Unawareness of illness which was apt to occur in association with unilateral sensory impairment was usually transitory, and it appeared at a time when the patient showed some degree of confusion. Conversely, when the patient's general mental condition improved, anosognosia was uncommon. The authors insist that the disturbance is not due to a focal lesion producing the physical illness and that, whenever it did occur in association with extra-cerebral lesions, an organic mental syndrome was noted. They feel that the underlying and essential factor is the impairment of brain function associated with an organic mental syndrome and that the personality structure alone does not account for it. Weinstein and Kahn (500) observed anosognosia in 22 cases, in 17 of which intracranial pressure was increased. The disease process involved various parts of the brain. The syndrome appeared in the setting of spatial and temporal disorientation, disturbances of psychomotor activity, changes in affect and personality organization, alteration in the use of language, mainly in the paraphasic type and, in some cases, in the presence of hallucinations. In three cases in which it was transitory it could be provoked by intravenous administration of sodium amytal. The aspects of illness which were denied included left hemiplegia, involuntary movements, blindness, loss of memory, incontinence, impotence, vomiting and the fact that the patient had been operated upon or that he was ill. The authors concluded that the phenomenon in question is not wholly explicable on the basis of a localized defect or as a manifestation of the disruption of the body scheme. In their opinion it expresses the patient's desire to be well, which appears in the particular pattern of organization prevailing in the damaged brain.

Gerstmann (162) classified anosognosia as follows. (a) Complete forms, involving total unawareness of disease. (b) Incomplete forms, with ignorance of the nature of the disease; for example, paralysis or the accompanying sensory impairment with vague realization of some sort of disablement. (c) Anosognosia with amnesia or imperception of the affected side, from simple forgetting or non-recognition to obstinate denial of their existence. (d) Anosognosia associated either with delusions or distortions centering around the perception of stimuli and of con-fabulations or delusions referring to the affected side.

I propose to differentiate between two varieties of anosognosia, namely, a *non-productive* and a *productive* variety. It is not unreasonable to assume that, in the first eventuality, the patient is unaware of the deficit, just like a normal person is unaware of sounds and sights beyond the physiological range of perception. In the second eventuality on the other hand, he is aware of the deficit, but this awareness is conveyed by a diseased perceptive mechanism, more especially its central components. What may be the patient's reaction to distorted stimulus patterns?

Ehrenwald (124), who called attention to the similarity between the delusions of anosognosia and dream-like states, reported an observation which may provide a clue to the nature of the disorder. A 59 year old man sustained a paralysis of his left upper and lower extremity while stooping over to tie his shoelaces. He was only slightly dazed but became delirious the same night. He complained that there was a full nest of hands in his bed and demanded that they be amputated. Even after the delirium had subsided he asked that the hands may be put in a sack, together with the other hands. He subsequently claimed that there was a dead arm and a dead leg in his bed which should be thrown out. On being asked to describe the condition of his paralyzed arm he looked for it in his bed and then called it a new hand. Asked about the old hand he said he was unable to find it; it had become much smaller while the new one was more voluminous. He could not find his arm, he asserted, probably because he had left it at home. Nevertheless, he failed to realize that the paralyzed arm had been put in front of him and continued looking for it below his bed covers. Later on, he stated that he had several hands right around his knee but that the arm was missing. He theorized that the hands had been produced by the disease; nevertheless, he declared a moment later that he had only three hands, two left hands and one right hand.

The similarity between productive anosognosia and certain experimentally produced dreams is unmistakable. Vold (489), who studied experimentally produced dreams, reported the case of a lady who had a minor injury on the second phalanx of her left index finger. On awakening in the morning she found that three fingers of the injured hand were flexed around the terminal phalanx of the injured finger. She had been dreaming that the phalanx had been cut off, that she saw it lying about and that she had attempted to re-attach it. Vold, himself, dreamed that one of his fingers of the right hand had become shorter, that worms were crawling out from it and that a physician wanted to cut it off. On awakening he found that the right hand was closed and the finger pressed against the hand. His experiments consisted in tying off the fingers of his subjects with a ribbon. The author distinguishes between the following delusional patterns. (a) The dreaming subject feels and imagines the ribbon. (b) The subject does not dream of the fingers tied together but of situations which are related to it in one way or another or he dreams of persons who find themselves in a similar situation. (c) The ribbon is substituted by some other object, for example a snake. (d) The person experiences peculiar sensations which, however, fail to produce the imagination of the ribbon. (e) The person dreams of moving his or her hand or fingers or sees others performing such movements. The movements may spread to the remaining muscles of the upper and lower extremities. (f) The subject reports imaginal experiences which have a peculiar relationship to the fingers or it dreams of objects having a similar shape.

Apparently, a true kernel is elaborated to a "story" in both the delusional form of anosognosia and in dreams. Gamper (158a) held that the delusions and confabulations of the anosognosic patient are reminiscent of Korasakoff's syndrome and the delirious states of alcoholics. All three conditions are characterized by the production of delusions that are apt to occur in states of clouded consciousness. In the present context, it matters little that anosognosia differs from both Korasakoff's psychosis and dream like states by the relative stereotypy of the patient's personal material, which is typically represented by a somatic defect and which may be a contributing factor owing to the inadequacy of the highest recording mechanism of the brain. In spite of these and other differences, (for example the production of delusions and hallucinations by verbal suggestions in the last named

condition) the three disorders in question have certain peculiarities in common, notably the absence of the awareness of obvious incompatibilities and inconsistencies, and the production of delusions. In senile individuals, delusions are more frequent during the night, at a time when transitional states between sleep and wakefulness are apt to occur. In Freiman's case the syndrome of anosognosia appeared characteristically in association with generalized confusion, and Weinstein and Kahn could provoke the abnormality under study by the administration of a barbiturate. While on vacation, I met an elderly lady who, at lunchtime, would mention that thieves had "again" broken into her hotel room at night and stolen all her jewels. She was not in the least disconcerted by the fact that her jewels, which were never replaced, could have been stolen only once. Weinstein and Kahn emphasize that their patients denied their illness in spite of all the evidence to the contrary and that their drive for self-realization came to the fore. Evidently, their patients, like Vold's subjects, ignored the laws of logic. Senile individuals behave in a similar fashion. These observations are not inconsistent with the concept of anosognosia here proposed for the desire to be well may be expressed in dreams in which, the law of contradiction having been cancelled, unlimited possibilities exist. We are not in accord with the view that the drive for self-realization accounts of itself for the symptomatology of productive anosognosia. For what kind of self-realization could possibly manifest itself by the desire to have three arms, or a lot of hands? Only the elementary mechanism of denial is rooted in human nature. To quote Spinoza: "The mind is disinclined to think of whatever weakens the power of the body." The positive symptoms of anosognosia must thus be accounted for by a separate mechanism.

In *conclusion*, then, a certain constellation of factors appears to be essential to call forth the symptoms of productive anosognosia. These factors include:

(a) the presence of abnormal sensations arising from an organic defect, e.g., the paralysis of a limb,

(b) the recording of the sensation by an abnormally functioning "gnostic cortex," producing in turn a partial, or modality-related disturbance of consciousness and

(c) a state of generally reduced awareness which favours the production of dream like thoughts and experiences.

Apparently, more or less severe productive symptoms will occur in the presence of severe abnormalities of gnosis even though the patient's mental state is essentially intact; on the other hand, depression of awareness in spite of relatively normal gnosis may of itself give rise to productive anosognosia. *Productive symptoms are the result of rationalization on the part of a mechanism which operates in an irrational fashion; denial of illness on the other hand, is the product of derationalization on the part of a mechanism which operates essentially in a rational fashion.*

Phantom limb

Patients who have undergone amputations of an arm or a leg may suffer from the delusion that the extremity, although in a more or less altered form, is still a part of their own body. (Ambroise Paré, *545*, Weir Mitchell, 1872.) The awareness of the phantom limb differs from anosognosia in that it involves the *nonrealization of the actual absence of a part of one's own body* while anosognosia concerns an existent though diseased part (*162*). Anosognosia is apt to be associated with brain damage. In cases of phantom limb, on the other hand, the brain is intact; indeed, in one of Head's (*198*) cases the phantom disappeared as a result of a cortical lesion.

Phantom limb sensations follow more frequently sudden loss of an extremity. The severed limb may continue to be represented in the body scheme in the form in which it was last experienced, the impression being most vivid immediately after the amputation. In this respect, Ehrenwald's case of anosognosia is of particular interest because the patient, having become paralyzed while putting on his shoes, believed that he saw his hands somewhere around his knees. Initially, then, the phantom or, for that matter, the involved extremity may be recorded in the body scheme in the very same place where it last functioned. (One is curiously reminded of the hands of a watch which are arrested at the moment of a catastrophy.) Gradually, the limb appears shorter or the hand seems to approach the stump. In other cases it appears to shrink or the intervening parts of the extremity disappeared and the phantom seems to be suspended in midair. It may be motionless, or appear to move either spontaneously or under volitional control, particularly if postural control of the stump has remained unaffected, or movements of the other extremities appear to induce associated passive movements of the phantom. An extremity has to be represented in the body scheme for some time in order to produce the abnormality described; as mentioned by Pick, the phantom limb sensations fail to appear in children.

Riddoch (*408*) found that phantom impressions may occur with lesions of the nervous system at different anatomical levels from the peripheral nerves to the cortex, in which case the phantom may either coincide with the real limb or exist concomitantly, and the patient may have the impression that he has a duplicate limb. Riddoch raises the question of why the posture and surface models remain in many cases unchanged when a limb is amputated. He believes that the sensation of the limb is kept alive by the "continued bombardment of the body scheme by stimuli originating from the severed nerve stumps and that the impression of the hand or foot predomiates owing to their more extensive representation in the cortex." In the course of uncomplicated healing the phantom is apt to disappear while continued irritation of the nerve stumps may perpetuate the phantom which, moreover, may be associated with intolerable pain. He believes that the phenomenon of phantom is combined with central pain of various etiology.

Disorders of higher auditory functions (Auditory agnosia)

Agnosia for non-language gestalten is of little clinical significance and, hence, its discussion at any length is hardly warranted. Depending on the extent of the lesion, auditory agnosia may be combined with other forms of agnosia and with disturbances of various other cerebral functions.

Agnosia for non-symbolic auditory stimuli

Although noises may have referential properties, for example street noises may symbolize a busy city, while the noise of the wind in the trees may make us think of a wood, the auditory experiences in question, unlike words or signals, are not intended to have symbolic value. Like other forms of agnosia the non-symbolic forms of auditory non-recognition comprise two varieties, a perceptual and an amnestic.

PERCEPTUAL AGNOSTIC AUDITORY AGNOSIA

The disturbance in question involves the appreciation of auditory gestalten which may be represented either by simple rhythms or by more complex noises. For example, Gelb and Goldstein's (159) patient Schn., (who had sustained a gunshot wound to his left temporo-occipital lobes), was unable to recognize simple rhythms. Neither could he indicate whether one of two tones was longer or shorter than the other, nor whether the intervals between a series of noises were shorter or longer as compared to another series. Thus, he showed the classical features of gestalt-deafness. Interestingly enough the patient had no difficulty in understanding spoken language. (Cf. the paragraphs on "dissociation of function.") Similar observations were made by Woerkom (521) on four patients.

AMNESTIC AGNOSTIC AUDITORY AGNOSIA

Cases of non-recognition of noises, for example those made by keys, etc., are rare. According to Kleist (259) "Geräuschsinntaubheit," that is, nonrecognition of the meaning of noises is, a theoretical construction, but since Reinhold (403) reported the case of a patient who failed to recognize familiar noises of various kinds, the actual existence of the disturbance in question has been proven. Like Gelb and Goldstein's patient, Reinhold's patient did not show sensory aphasic disturbances.

Auditory agnosia, both perceptual and amnestic, should be differentiated from partial *anakusia*, just like visual agnosia should be differentiated from field defects and scotomas. Partial anakusia occurs as a result of bilateral

lesions of the auditory radiation. According to Feuchtwanger (139) *Funktionswandel* in the auditory sphere causes anakusia rather than agnosia for sounds, noises, etc. The anakusias are apt to involve circumscribed segments of the "sound-field", while the appreciation of crude noises is apt to be relatively intact. The disorder in question is not necessarily associated with those of speech and auditory imagery. The differentiation of the two disorders, if combined with subcortical sensory aphasia, may however be difficult. The attention to auditory stimuli is diminished in either condition.

Auditory agnosia for symbols

The second variety of auditory agnosia, which is incomparably more important from both a theoretical and practical viewpoint, plays a crucial part in the disturbances of language to which the last section of this chapter will be devoted. Agnosia for the "symbols" of music and its elements, including rhythm, pitch, modulation, melody and harmony will be dealt with in Chapter V.

DISTURBANCES OF HIGHER MOTOR FUNCTIONS (APRAXIA)

Apraxia has been variously defined as the inability to move the limbs purposively, to move a certain part of the body in accordance with a proposed purpose, the motility of this part being otherwise preserved, or the inability to perform certain purposive movement complexes with preservation of motility, sensation, and of coordination (491). Later on we shall explain in more detail why apraxia may be accompanied by any of the above mentioned disturbances from which, however, it can be differentiated by appropriate tests.

The first observations were recorded by Jackson in 1866, as may be gathered from the following passage: "In some cases of defect of speech the patient seems to have lost much of his power to do anything he is told to do, even with those muscles which are not paralyzed. Thus, a patient will be unable to put out his tongue when we ask him, although he will use it well in semi-involuntary actions—for example, eating and swallowing.

He will not make the particular grimace he is told to do, even when we make one for him to imitate. There is power in his muscles and in the centers for coordination of muscular groups, but he—the whole man, or the will—cannot set them agoing. Such a patient may do a thing well at one time and not at another. In a few cases patients do not do things so simple as moving the hand (i.e., the non-paralyzed hand) when they are told. . . . A speechless patient who cannot put out his tongue when told will sometimes actually put his fingers in his mouth as if to help to get it out; and yet not infrequently when we are tired of urging him he will lick his lips with it. . . ." In the pre-Liepmann era apractic phenomena were mentioned by Spamer (454), v. Monakow (337), Kussmaul (271), Griesinger (185), Wernicke (510), Bruns (75), and Meynert (335). The latter spoke of the loss of "*Innervationsbilder*" while Wernicke thought in terms of "transcortical disturbances of motility". The term apraxia, which was coined by Steinthal, (465) a linguist, was unknown at that time. In 1899, Buck (76) published a paper entitled "Les Parakinésies". The patient was "suffering from spasms and associated movements". She could imagine the movement carried out but was unable to actuate the corresponding kinetic images. "The patient, when asked to lift her right arm, crossing it over her body, putting her left in her left axilla and making various energetic but hopeless efforts said plaintively: "Je comprends bien que vous voulez mais je ne parviens pas à la faire." As far as I am able to judge from my personal observations, the reactions of the apractic seem to be rather stereotyped for one of my patients, on being asked to imitate a movement of the examiner's arm, declared, greatly embarrassed, "Es geht nicht, man sollte es nicht für möglich halten, dass es nicht geht, aber es geht nicht." De Buck stipulated an "interruption between the centers of kinetic images and the sphere of ideation due to lesions in the parietooccipital lobes." In 1900, Liepmann (304) established the syndrome of apraxia as a distinct entity. Twenty years later, he wrote, not without pride, "Prior to 1900, the brief notes of the various workers in this field which have a bearing upon the problem of apraxia were either not discovered or ignored. The few who paid attention to the matter failed to recognize its tre-

mendous importance. Neither was the subject grasped nor was it analyzed from the clinical, physiological, or psychological viewpoint. What's more, no attempt was made to study apractic phenomena from the point of view of cerebral localization. Of the various comprehensive reviews, those of d'Hollander, Rose and Wilson are to a large extent verbatim translations of my own writings; unfortunately, the two first named reviewers have failed to understand my work completely." Thus, the great discoveries concerning the integration and the dissociation of thought and movement were made at the turn of the century. In addition to Liepmann, it was chiefly Pick (383), Kleist (260, 262), van Vleuten (484), Hartmann (195), Forster (196), Goldstein (167, 169) and, somewhat later, Foix and Hillemand (144), who made the most important contributions to the subject. Subsequent studies were more or less confirmatory and elaborative.

Although Liepmann's position has not remained unchallenged, v. Monakow's (346), Bruns' (75), Sittig's (448) and, recently, Nathan's (351) and Ethelberg's (130) articles have not made any worthwhile contributions to the theory of apraxia; they attempted to demolish it, without offering anything worthwhile in return (Comment and Criticism). This statement is no reflection on the value of Sittig's observations which were recorded in the great traditions of the Pick school. Nielsen's (356) work which is based on Liepmann's ideas and many clinical as well as pathological data brings the literature on the subject rather up to date.

Symptomatology

It is convenient to distinguish between the following basic types of apraxia.

(1) *Ideatory apraxia.* (The pattern of composite movements is distorted as a whole.)

(2) *Amnestic apraxia.* (The movement pattern has been forgotten, but can be recognized and imitated.)

(3) *Ideo-kinetic apraxia.* (A movement other than the one intended is performed.) See also "constructional apraxia."

(4) *Motor apraxia.* (The intended movement is executed in a crude fashion.)

(5) *Apractic agraphia*. (The agraphia is secondary to apraxia.)

In any type of apraxia, then, the patient is unable to perform certain purposive movements or movement complexes. Liepmann a.o. postulated that the causative role of paralysis, paresis, sensory disturbances, ataxia, motor irritation, aphasia and tactile agnosia must be excluded. This may be a difficult undertaking for apraxia is apt to be complicated by disturbances of sensation, weakness, and disturbances of various high level functions. On the other hand, the diagnosis rests on firm ground if a patient is unilaterally ideo-kinetic apractic, or his inability to execute purposive movements is out of proportion to the degree of ataxia, aphasia, dementia, etc. Because of the frequent association of apraxia with other abnormalities, it was suggested that it is their direct result rather than an accompaniment. Liepmann, answering von Monakow's criticism, expressed his views on the subject as follows. "If apraxia is in some cases accompanied by motor aphasia; in others, by sensory aphasia or visual agnosia or tactile agnosia or hypaesthesia or hemiparesis or ataxia, if ataxia may be present either in the apractic or the non-apractic extremity; lastly, if any of these symptoms may be very severe or only slight or absent—then I would be inclined to think that none of them is a necessary condition of apraxia. On the contrary, I would assume that they represent independent variables and that apraxia is a disorder in its own right."

Ideatory apraxia

It hardly needs to be emphasized that we cannot perform purposive movements unless we have some sort of "forerunning idea" of what we intend to do. It is true that the necessity of a plan is manifest during the stage of learning only, at which time every step requires close attention. However, in a less explicit fashion, an ideational plan or *"Bewegungsentwurf"* operates even at advanced stages of experience, as evidenced by the fact that movements, especially composite movements, may go astray when we are distracted. Thus, ideational apraxia appears to be due to defective mentation although not every type of intellectual deterioration necessarily leads to apraxia. Moreover the "motor" defect

does not necessarily parallel existing intellectual deficit. Kleist contends that a patient has a poor memory for those movements which he is unable to perform. However, a patient who has just described a sequence of movements correctly may get confused if he has to execute them. According to Pick, the complex mechanism of ideatory apraxia can be reduced to the following errors: (a) Disturbances of the temporal sequence of the individual movements, for example the anticipation of a movement which should be carried out later, (b) premature termination of the entire sequence of movements, (c) condensation of two movements into one, (d) derailments of a movement due to faulty association and (e) perseveration and the use of wrong objects. In certain instances, the wrong use of an object may be conditioned by what appears to be poor differentiation within appropriate conceptual spheres. For example, the patient may use a toothbrush in the fashion of a spoon, the use of either object requiring that it be put into his mouth. Certain faulty movements are open to more than one interpretation. For example, if a patient tries to write with a pen he has failed to dip into ink, he may have forgotten to make one movement, or failed to differentiate (at least behaved as if he had failed to differentiate) within the sphere of the concept "writing implements." The interpretation of ideatory apraxia is more difficult if the patient tries to write with a pair of scissors. Does he not recognize the instrument at all or does he get confused when using it? Morlääs (*343*), who made reference to this particular difficulty, speaks of *"apraxie d'utilization."* The following examples are illustrative. Liepmann's original patient, the famous *"Regierungsrat,"* was asked to pour water out of a carafe into a tumbler; his left hand grasped the handle of the carafe to pour out the water but his right hand seized the empty glass and brought it at the same time in the direction of his mouth. Nielsen's and Fitzgibbon's (*356*) patient tried to light a safety match by striking on the sole of his bare foot. Other patients strike matches but forget what they are lit for and hold them between the fingers until they burn themselves. One of Pick's (*383*) patients was supplied with a cigar and a matchbox. He opened the latter, stuck the cigar in and tried to shut the box, apparently as though it were a cigar cutter.

Then, taking the cigar out, he rubbed it on the side of the box as if to light a match. On another occasion, when all the necessaries for striking were laid before him, he took the matchbox and, putting it between his teeth, tried to smoke it.

Amnestic apraxia

Marcuse (*321*) ascribed defective movements observed in his senile patients to disturbances of mentation and of memory. Goldstein (*169*) recognized the identity between amnestic aphasia and amnestic apraxia. Like the amnestic aphasic patient is unable to recall certain words but recognizes the right word out of a series and is able to repeat it, the amnestic apractic patient has forgotten how to perform a certain movement; yet, he distinguishes it from wrong movements and is able to imitate it.

Ideo-kinetic apraxia

Ideo-kinetic apraxia may involve the muscles in the region of the head and neck, of the upper extremity, the trunk and the lower extremity. Accordingly, the following movements should be tested (*491*).

(a) Looking in various directions, performing lateral movement of the jaw, protruding the jaw, making a wry face, whistling, showing the teeth, raising the eyebrow, blowing out the cheek, wrinkling up the nose, smiling on command, coughing, swallowing, taking a deep breath, sighing, yawning, protruding the tongue and licking the lips.

(b) Taking hold of objects, imitating movements performed in front of the patient, separating the fingers, making a fist, throwing a kiss, saluting and clasping the hands as in prayer, making movements for definite objects (the material not being at hand), for example, pretending to knock at the door, to catch a fly, to play a piano, to ring a bell, to count out money, to turn a barrel organ, to turn a key in a keyhole, to draw a cork, to thread a needle, to sew, etc.; performing true purposive movements by manipulating objects, for example lighting a match, pouring out water, tying a knot in a string etc.; executing "reflexive" movements, including touching various parts of the body (both those which the patient can see and which he cannot

see), for example brushing the hair, brushing the teeth, blowing the nose and, lastly, imitating movements from right to left and left to right. (See constructional apraxia.) For reasons already explained, it is imperative to test both upper extremities separately. Other movements to be tested include the following.

(c) Getting up from a chair, sitting down, lying down, turning over from one side to the other, from the prone to the supine position, getting up, bending the trunk to the left and the right side, forward and backward, etc.

(d) Walking, putting the heel to the opposite knee, crossing the legs, kicking an object away, putting the foot into a slipper, etc.

Some of the above movements are, of course, tested in the course of routine neurological examination. However, the faulty reactions of the patient are usually obscured because of the frequent occurrence of bizarre movements which are not accounted for by ataxia, weakness, agnosia or lack of understanding. On occasion, apractic movements are carried out with undue force, even though the limb employed be paretic.

Ideokinetic apraxia of the muscles of the face, hand and neck. Liepmann's patient, on being ordered to show his tongue, threw his head back, turned his eyes up, opened his mouth and made snapping movements with his jaw. When asked to smile, he made hissing noises through his teeth. On several occasions, when ordered to perform certain movements he would direct his gaze to one or the other side. Bechterew (*40*) reported the case of a hemiparetic patient who, when food was put into his mouth declared he had forgotten how to swallow it. He would keep the food in his mouth until it was taken out or pushed back behind the root of his tongue. At that moment, the patient (or, rather, his deglutory mechanism) would gulp it down. Puussep and Levin (*398*) described a patient who suffered from a disturbance of speech, a paresis of the right side of his face and a bizarre type of apraxia. He made chewing movements and moved the food from one side to the other but would not move the bolus backward. During these maneuvers he made gestures indicating that he could not swallow but did so promptly when the food was manipulated into his pharynx. At autopsy two relatively small softenings were found; one in Broca's area, the other in the anteroinferior portion of the left supramarginal gyrus. The authors called attention to the fact that, in both bulbar and pseudobulbar palsy, not only swallowing but the movements of the masticatory muscles and those of the tongue and lips were involved, and that apraxia of swallowing can be experimentally produced in dogs.

Ideo-kinetic apraxia involving the trunk and the lower extremities. The patient (behaving somewhat like an awkward dancer) does not seem to know what to do with his legs. He may not move them alternately, he may try to put both of them to the right or the left side at the same time, or he may perform walking movements on one and the same place, he may not move them at all, declaring that he had forgotten what to do. When put on the edge of a bed and ordered to lie down, he will not pull his legs up, support the weight of his trunk with his arms and swing his body and legs around. When put to bed he may not be able to sit up but move helplessly from one side to the other. Apraxia of station and gait may be combined with disturbances referable to the fronto-cerebellar and fronto-extrapyramidal systems. For example, Gerstmann and Schilder's (*163*) patient showed the following abnormalities of movement. He flexed his legs in all joints from the hips downward but his toes appeared to be literally glued to the floor which he kept on tapping with his heels. At the same time, he showed evidence of *asynergie cérébelleuse* which, when occurring as a separate disorder, does not give rise to the bizarre abnormalities described. Autopsy disclosed a baso-medial glioma exerting pressure upon the opposite frontal lobe but infiltrating the rostrum of the corpus callosum to a minor degree only.

Ideo-kinetic apraxia involving the upper extremity. Ferrier's (*141*) patient, when asked to make movements of cutting with a pair of scissors, made indefinite movements of his left forefinger and his thumb; to make the movement of striking a match, he struck forefinger and thumb vertically on to bed; to count pennies out of his hand, he touched thumb and tip of each finger. Liepmann's patient (in addition to the already described apraxia of his face, head and neck muscles) showed ideo-kinetic apraxia of his right upper and lower extremity and a mild dyspraxia of his left upper extremity. When first seen, he appeared to be either agnostic or aphasic

for he could not select objects and manipulated them in an absurd fashion with his right hand. However, it soon became manifest that he was able to carry out commands which did not necessitate the use of either arm; for example, he would get up from a chair and walk to the window or the door of the examining room. Besides, the movements of his right arm had a bizarre character which aroused the examiner's suspicion that the patient's abnormal behavior was due to some sort of defective motility. This suspicion became a certainty when the patient, after much prodding, used his left arm in a normal fashion for almost any movement. When asked to put his right forefinger to his nose he said yes and, with his stretched forefinger, executed wide circling movements in the air. He made the correct movement at once with his left hand. Asked to close his right hand into a fist he performed various absurd movements of his arm and body but attained the required goal at once with his left hand. On being asked to give the examiner a certain object with his right hand, he frequently picked up the wrong thing and, still holding it in his hand, used the left to take up the required object and present it to the physician. He was asked to brush the examiner's coat. Accordingly, he took the lower corner of it correctly with his left hand and held it out while, with his right, he picked up the brush but made rhythmical movements with the latter in the air above his right ear. With his right hand, he was unable to perform reflexive movements, that is, to touch parts of his own body even if the movements were shown to him or he tried in front of a mirror. He could point with his left hand to his right hand but, when asked to execute the reverse movement lifted up an inkstand. He was unable to perform gestures with his right upper extremity only and, instead of making a fist, made movements with his trunk. He could not perform simple movements with his right lower extremity, point toward a sound source or touch his ear when it was tickled with a piece of cotton. In addition, he displayed *dressing apraxia* and *constructional apraxia.* On trying to put on his left stocking, he eventually pulled it over his right hand and arm. Embarrassed, he laid aside the stocking and, then, although he had already put on his left stocking, tried to pull the right stocking over his left foot. With his right hand he used a toothbrush as if it were a pen. At other times he put the handle into his mouth or manipulated it as if it were a spoon. Only occasionally did he succeed in using it the right way. He was able to write individual letters but not the one he was asked to write. With his left hand, he would write letters correctly but oriented them in a wrong fashion.

It should be noted that the patient displayed "*secondary ideatory reactions*" in addition to the ideo-kinetic reactions. For example, when asked to tie a knot in his handkerchief, he put his hand into his pocket, pulled out his handkerchief and blew his nose. (Perhaps, the term "associative parapraxia" would be more fitting to denote shortcircuiting reactions of this particular type.) What's more, he performed certain movements with his right upper extremity correctly; for example, when his right hand was brought into contact with a button he could close and open it. Apparently, this is one of the movements which had become "semi-involuntary."

Pondering over the nature of the disorder, Liepmann argued as follows. The patient's defective responses could be due neither to agnosia nor aphasia for he performed correctly with his *left* upper extremity. That they could not be explained by sensory disturbances in his *right* upper extremity was proven by the fact that he could button and unbutton his coat and perform other movements which, although they did not depend on more or less explicit "planning," required a considerable measure of sensory control.

Although the localization of apractic disturbances will be discussed later, it will be profitable to describe the *localization of the lesions in Liepmann's original case* in connection with the clinical findings. The autopsy disclosed a softening involving the entire corpus callosum with the exception of the splenium, one destroying a large part of the left parietal lobe and a small lesion in the right frontal lobe which, however, was too recent to have played a part in the production of the syndrome. In addition, there were numerous small lesions scattered over both hemispheres. Due to the peculiar localization of the two lesions, the *left rolandic region was almost completely isolated from the opposite hemisphere and, at the same time, deprived of the inflow of impulses originating in the ipsilateral occipital and*

temporal lobes. Furthermore, the parietal lesion which blocked the fibers skirting the Sylvian fissure deprived the left "sensomotorium" of impulses arising in a large part of the parietal lobe itself. Liepmann theorized that, whatever the patient had been able to accomplish with his right upper extremity, required the resources of the left sensory-motor area only, while movements requiring the evaluation of visual and acoustic data were inadequate because of the virtually complete interruption of impulse transmission from either hemisphere to the left rolandic region.

Motor apraxia

Kleist (*260*) describes motor (or "innervatory") apraxia as a slowing and stiffening of movements, a difficulty in performing isolated movements, a tendency for associated movements to occur and, noticeably, a loss of fine and complex movements and their serial coordination. The more complicated the innervation of skilled movements of the hands and fingers, the more outstanding the disorder. Kennard and Fulton (*254*) called attention to the increasing awkwardness, stiffness and clumsiness of the hands and fingers rendering them unfit or partly so for tasks previously performed without difficulty, although most often the gross power of the hand remains unaffected. The more rapid or complex the movements required, the poorer the results. Movements patterns composed of delicate, smoothly coordinated movements are most severely involved while their gross spatio-temporal relationship is preserved. Motor apraxia is also known under the terms *cortical apraxia* (Heilbronner) or *limb-kinetic apraxia* (Liepmann).

Apractic agraphia

In 1884, Pitres (*394*) reported the case of a right-handed patient who, without being aphasic, could write with his left hand only. Today one would classify the disorder as ideokinetic agraphia. On the other hand, if agraphia develops within the setting of aphasia, the patient is suffering from a disturbance of written speech, that is, he cannot write with any extremity for want of "directives" from his writing center.

Sittig (*448*) who discussed the problem of apractic agraphia at some length pointed out that the disorder in question may be limited to either the right or the left upper extremity. However, in emphasizing that it may occur without apraxia and vice versa, "although writing represents a more refined type of movement," he weakened his own claim that central nervous system disease involves the most complex movements first. He was therefore justly criticized by Nielsen (*356*) for "crowding the subject of apraxia into the law of Jackson." In agraphia secondary to aphasia the patient is able to copy slavishly but cannot convert print into script; he cannot "write", but merely delineate letters. In (complete) apractic agraphia, on the other hand, the patient cannot even delineate letters. Goldstein (*169*) described in detail a case of *amnestic agraphia*. The patient recognized any letter while reading. He indicated wrong letters and was able to select those named by the examiner but could not recall the shape of a letter at the moment he intended to write it. Goldstein noted that the patient could write the same letters at other times, but he did not dwell on the subject of "temporal dissociation" of function.

Pathophysiology

Apractic mechanisms, although already discussed at several appropriate places, merit a consideration within the general theory of higher cerebral functions and their disturbances. It is convenient at this place to recapitulate briefly what has been said about the relationship between volitional movements and consciousness mental processes.

Volitional movements and consciousness. Mentalization is the technical setting which makes possible the evaluation of various stimuli and the selection of responses on the part of the highest levels of the nervous system. Mentalization is perception raised to a higher power, rather as the concept "cross" is a pattern of retinal excitation raised to a higher power. Stimuli are mentalized whenever the evaluation of data and the selection of responses is based on the utilization of concepts, however primitive they may be. As applied to the problem of volitional movements, the biological significance of consciousness and thought involves the capacity of acquiring movement patterns which, eventually, become semi-involuntary, that is, borderline states of conscious mental activity. After these patterns have been built up and integrated into the repertory of biologically significant kinetic effects, new movement patterns are created which enhance the range of activity of the organism still further, and which enable it to accumulate stockpiles of motor responses. The acquisition of flexible response patterns, then, appears to depend on a specific mode not only of the representation but, at the same time, of the manipulation of data. These relationships exist although, strictly speaking, the reactions in question are no longer represented in the form of true conscious processes but, like other physiological processes, in a fashion which is inaccessible to direct experience.

These somewhat abstract and, being in the nature of a summary, necessarily brief considerations may be illustrated by the following examples. In the absence of consciousness, biologically significant target effects may be attained by low level integrative acts. For instance, injury to a blood vessel will produce a spasm of its muscular layer; and, if the tear is not too extensive, bleeding will cease. The contraction of the muscular wall of the vessel, the inversion of the endothelium, the clotting of the blood, etc., are, by definition, integrative acts for they help maintain the biological equilibrium of the organism. The potentialities of the reflex mechanism are of course limited; if the hemorrhage is profuse and the muscular coat too weak in proportion to the size of the tear, local physiological mechanisms will be unable to control the hemorrhage. In this contingency, the initiation of appropriate integrative acts, which aim at the control of bleeding, depends on the resources of the highest level of the brain, namely, intellective functions and skill, both of which presuppose conscious mentation. In essence, however, the local reaction to injury and the integrative processes mediated by the highest level of the brain are identical biological phenomena. In the full light of consciousness, tying of a surgical knot is carried out at the stage of learning only. With increasing experience, the surgeon's movements become semi-automatic, although they remain volitional in respect to the selection of the movement out of an almost inexhaustible variety of kinetic patterns. Thus, *consciousness serves, ultimately, the attainment of automatization* —a pattern of biological activity resembling the behavior of the injured wall of the blood vessel, the inversion of the endothelium, the clotting of the blood, etc.

The mechanism of *ideo-kinetic* apraxia is more difficult to grasp than that of the remaining varieties of apraxia. *Amnestic* and *ideatory* apraxia are pathological phenomena involving essentially the psychic sphere of the organism while *motor* apraxia affects the somatic sphere. Amnestic and ideatory apraxia involve the "soul;" motor apraxia, the "body." Amnestic apraxia may be expressed in conventional psychiatric terms; motor apraxia, in equally familiar neurological terms. In ideokinetic apraxia on the other hand, the "soul" has lost its ability to control the body. This is remarkable in itself but that the soul may be unable to control one, otherwise normal, half of the body—indeed only one otherwise normal limb—appears to be almost incomprehensible.

Now, in *ideo-kinetic eupraxia*, the neurodynamic processes underlying *thought*, i.e., the selection of the goal, are integrated to a higher functional unit with the processes underlying the *movements* i.e., the production of the desired effects, in other words, sensory analogs are translated into motor analogs. If ideo-kinetic functions were merely chain reflexes (as stipulated by v. Monakow for every eupractic movement) ideation would be a non-conscious process. The application of a special name to ideatory processes would be pointless; indeed, for want of ideation, impossible. In the preceding paragraphs we have reiterated that the pre-innervatory (ideational) phase of the ideo-kinetic performance complex must be mentalized in order to select goal leading movements out of a practically unlimited number: it must become the forerunning idea of the intended action. In other words, the pre-innervatory phase must be represented in a specific fashion, or as an immediate experience, which, in turn, is the mode of representation of stimuli at the highest sensory level. This representation is at the same time the technical setting in which the reactions of the organism are determined inasmuch as they depend on the formation of concepts. It is true that both the pre-innervatory phase of volitional movements

and the innervatory phase are physiological processes but the former is of necessity a more or less conscious act of mentation occurring at the stage of acquisition of skilled movements, while the action of the discharging cells in the motor area and the "supradjacent" skill centers lacks the attributes of consciousness. In other words, the determination of responses is a conscious process while their realization occurs outside the sphere of consciousness. Only the movements of the innervated limbs set in motion by high level activity are recorded by the very same level which is concerned with their selection and initiation. Thus, ideomotor apraxia is the manifestation of "dis-unity" of the two integrative acts, the *ideatory* and the *motor*. Yet, insight into the nature of symptoms, to which a special section of the current chapter was devoted, suggests that ideo-kinetic apraxia is not only the manifestation of the shattered unity of physiological processes but, at the same time, an attempt at reintegration based on the use of whatever suitable fragments of the original substrate are still available.

The history of the problem of ideo-motor apraxia is of sufficient interest to warrant a brief summary. Munk (*344*), who regarded the cerebral cortex a sensory organ, believed that a volitional movement is nothing other than the "revitalization" of a kinaesthetic engram, and that the very same ekphorized engram actuates the movement that initiated it. Munk's idea was elaborated by Wernicke (*512*) who stipulated that, prior to the performance of a willed movement, its goal is imaginatively anticipated and that the anticipation of the movement produces the desired kinetic effect by evoking the kinaesthetic engram. By contrast, Liepmann relegated the kinaesthetic engrams in question to a "neurodynamic process devoid of any except, perhaps, the faintest conscious quality." (See also the controversy between Alexander Bain and Bastian, *25*.) According to Liepmann, any intended movement is visualized prior to its execution; and the visualization of the movement actuates a purely physiological process which is the mnestic residue of the previously performed movement now intended. As a result, the movement itself is re-actuated. Goldstein (*167*) went even farther than Liepmann. He completely eliminated the kinaesthetic factor and stressed, at the same time, the importance of visual or "stereopsychic" elements. He contended that the function of the "apparatus of transmission" manifests itself in visual experiences, but that its function may be so modified as to lack conscious qualities. At the same time, Goldstein voiced the opinion that the role of kinaesthetic elements involves the proprioceptive regulation rather than the anticipation of movements. It is worthy of note that Liepmann had expressed the same idea, namely, that the repeated coexistence of innervations and kinaesthetic experiences is apt to promote their linkage whereas kinaesthetic engrams bear no relationship to volitional innervations. It was only his "desire to express himself in conventional terms" which made him refer to kinaesthetic elements. Martin (322) concluded from her experimental studies that the various movement patterns of daily life lack "pre-innervatory" elements, be they visual or kinaesthetic, and that, in her subjects, imaginal processes take place only if the movement to be performed is complicated. S. Meyer (326) expressed the belief that, given the intention to move, the mere visual anticipation of the movement will produce it. In his later years, Liepmann stressed unequivocally the purely physiological character of kinetic engrams. In a previous study (428a) I arrived at the conclusion that the movements of daily life do not require their anticipation in the kinaesthetic or the visual sphere; rather, that, given the intention to move, the movements sooner or later materialize automatically in response to the more or less abstract idea of the goal. (Cf. the definition of the will in Chapter II.) Only the reproduction of gestalten depends on visual or auditory elements. (Unfortunately, Lange, in his article on apraxia in Bumcke-Forster's "Handbuch der Neurologie" (273) has misunderstood the term "automatic," and imputed that I endorse v. Monakow's views.)

The above sketch of the history of the pathophysiology of apraxia might well have been omitted were it not for the misrepresentation of Liepmann's ideas by various writers, notably Nathan (351) and Ethelberg (130). The attacks on Liepmann's theory were made in recent years, at a time one would think that the subject (having been brought up by Munk some 70 years ago) was at long last closed.

Within the intended scope of the discussion it is difficult to do justice to Denny Brown's (115) recent article on the nature of apraxia. Among many correct observations, e.g., that loss of the sense of position is not necessarily associated with apraxia, the paper contains a number of sweeping statements which are patently unacceptable as, for example, the notion that "what we called willed movements is in fact the learned ability of the organism to utilize movements that are primarily reflex for purposes that involve a more tenuous stimulus situation." Does this also apply to writing and other highly complicated skilled movements?

Brain lesions causing apraxia

We have learned that a patient may be able to describe movements he is asked to perform but that he may get confused in attempting to execute them. Other patients may have forgotten how a sequence of movements is carried out. Additional varieties of apraxia, already described, include the faulty anticipation of individual components of complex movements, the premature termination of movement sequences, the use of wrong objects, the derailment of movements due to faulty association or to perseveration, the condensation of two movements into one, the substitution of one movement by another, the substitution of a correct by an incorrect movement which strikes us (and sometimes the patient) as inapposite or bizarre and, lastly, the substitution of a correct by an awkward or clumsy movement which, however, displays at least the general structure of the intended movement; we still recognize a correct movement pattern even though it is incorrectly performed.

Thus, the arrangement of apractic movements in a certain order helps establish differential ranges of the disturbance complex known as apraxia. The first named disorders, listed on the "sensory" side of the scale, are difficult to distinguish from mental confusion (which, however, may not become manifest until the patient acts) while the performances listed on the "motor" side of the scale may be difficult or impossible to differentiate from ataxia. Moreover, the individual disturbances occupying the "intermediate" ranges of the scale may be difficult to classify.

The scale of apractic movements resembles a spectrum wherein only the basic colors stand out.

How can this pathophysiological scale be brought into relationship with the "cortical map?" We have learned that, roughly speaking, the cortex is composed of a posterior, response determinating, and an anterior, response effectuating division. On the whole, the *response determinating* division occupies the cortex lying behind the rolandic fissure; the *response effectuating* division, the cortex lying in front of it. The oganization of the former depends on the location of the primary sensory centers; the organization of the latter, on the somatotopic organization of the motor area in which the entire striated musculature is represented. More especially, response determination to acoustic stimuli is mediated by cortical areas adjacent to the primary acoustic centers; the determination of response to visual stimuli, by cortical areas adjacent to the primary visual centers; and to tactile stimuli, by cortical areas contiguous with the somato-sensory areas. Response determination to groups of stimuli of both tactile and visual elements depends on neurones which occupy an intermediate position in the region of the inferior parietal lobule, i.e., between the somato-sensory and the primary sensory area; by the same token, response determination to groups of stimuli of *auditory, tactile* and *visual* elements is dependent on the activity of cell stations which occupy an intermediate position between the acoustic, somato-sensory and visual areas. Now, at the highest level, response determination depends not only on perceptual but, at the same time, on configurational and conceptual data which are represented in the cortex in a more diffuse fashion. Yet even the diffuseness of the representation in the posterior cortex of the response determiners in question is not an absolute one. *The more intimate the functional relationship between a given category of movements and a specific category of sensory data, the closer is the spatial relationships between, on the one hand, the cortical representation of the sensory quality concerned, that is, of level I.s., and, on the other, the representation of the configurational and conceptual factors which codetermine the movements in question, i.e., of level II s. and III.s. for that particular sensory modality.* For example, spoken language depends on auditory data, configurational and conceptual

auditory factors; written language, on visual data, configurational and conceptual *visual* factors. (To call attention to an already quoted passage: "conceptualization readily takes off from the directly perceptible by means of processes which resemble as closely as possible those involved in the perception of concrete objects and which maintain, as long as possible, some directly perceptual anchorage in perceptible material," *204.*) Accordingly, the cortical agencies controlling spoken language "gravitate" in the direction of the primary *auditory* area while those controlling written language are shifted in the direction of the primary *visual* areas. In other words, within the highest level, both Wernicke's center and the angular gyrus occupy an "excentric" position.

Thus, one might reformulate the notion of a concept center or elaborative cortex and its location in the brain as follows. Evaluative behaviour, the sum total of responses which, ultimately, are based on the utilization of concepts, is under the control of the posterior cortex. Within this extensive part of the cortex, certain segments have become specialized in that they mediate responses based on specific sensory modalities of stimuli and, within the diverse categories, the specific stimulus dimensions. The concept center of Broadbent comprises the entire "sensory cortex (or "postrolandic cortex in the wider sense") *minus* (a) the primary sensory areas and (b) the specialized segments (or sensory psychoneural centers) which develop in close topographical relationship to the former. The concept center is the youngest both phylogenetically and ontogenetically, the complex of primary sensory areas the oldest. The skill centers develop before the concept center although, with increasing maturity, skill depends more and more on the resources of the conceptual level. On a previous occasion, we have spoken of visual thought and its disorders, and we mentioned the possibility of tactile thought as conceived by Critchley (*103*). It is a plausible assumption that, within the concept center, as here defined, the cortical provinces contiguous with the visual psychoneural centers are chiefly concerned with visual thought; those contiguous with somesthetic psycho-neural centers chiefly with tactile thought. An even more intimate topographical relationship may exist between the auditory psycho-neural centers and auditory thought, that is, *verbalized thought* or *inner language*.

To repeat my previous point, the *response effectuating* area occupies the precentral gyrus and the premotor cortex. The agencies co-ordinating cranial nerve synergies lie in front of the lower rolandic region, while those controlling the lower extremities and the trunk occupy the remaining part of the pre-rolandic cortices. Movements of the trunk and the lower extremities depend to a larger extent on extra-pyramidal centers than those of the upper extremities and of the cranial nerves. The long associational fibers connecting the sensory and the motor provinces of the cortex are most densely massed in the vicinity of the sylvian fissure and the Island of Reil, while those subserving the movements of the trunk and the lower extremities are most extensively connected with the brain stem. The so-called frontal or "fronto-callosal" apraxia of gait appears to be due to the involvement of brain stem centers and their connections with certain fronto-extrapyramidal cell stations. Severance of the corpus callosum in otherwise healthy brains fails to produce apraxia of gait, and anterior callosal disease produces locomotor apraxia only if associated with basal ganglia lesions.

The more posteriorly the apraxia producing lesion is located the more conspicuous the involvement of the sensory components of response; the more anteriorly, the more prominent is the involvement of its motor components. Lesions located at the opposite poles of the "apraxia spectrum" implicate, respectively, performances depending on "pure ideation" and "pure effectuation." By contrast, disease processes involving the intermediate segments of the scale of apractic movements involve both ideatory and motor elements. Lastly, diffuse lesions are apt to be associated with agnostic and intellectual disorders.

Liepmann's own views on the localization of apractic phenomena which cover both the mono-hemispheric and the bi-hemispheric integration of skill may be summarized as follows. (a) Parieto-occipital lesions on the dominant side cause ideatory apraxia, most often in the presence of diffuse atrophy of the brain. (b) Severe, sometimes permanent ideo-kinetic apraxia is apt to occur in massive, deep lying lesions of the white matter of the dominant parietal lobe, particularly of the portion lying behind the arm center, while cortical lesions cause relatively minor disturbances. (c) Superficial lesions of the rolandic region and the adjacent portion of the first and second frontal convolution cause motor (limb-kinetic) apraxia. The boundaries between the three territories overlap. (d) Lesions blocking the transmission of impulses from the dominant to the subordinate hemisphere via the corpus callosum deprive the minor hemisphere of directives, thereby causing dyspraxia chiefly of the left upper extremity. To a minor degree, the kinetic engrams of the subordinate hemisphere are of importance for the integration of skilled movements in the right (dominant) hand. (e) In right-handed individuals, (chiefly as a result of appropriately located lesions in the left hemisphere) apraxia occurs not only in the right extremities but, for the above explained reasons, also in the left extremities. Dyspraxia of the left hand in the right-sided lesions is rare, whereas, in ambidexters, bilateral apraxia has been observed to occur as a result of lesions on the right side. In the few cases in which right-sided lesions occurring in right-handed individuals caused dyspraxia of the left hand, large neoplasms were exerting pressure upon the left hemisphere were found. (f) Severe damage to the left rolandic region masks right-sided apraxia by causing paralysis but produces dyspraxia in the left upper extremity. (g) "The eupraxia region combines the sum total of cortical provinces, damage to which seriously interferes with the function of the entire apparatus and which *therefore* (italics mine) mediates the most crucial and indispensable substrate of the physiological processes concerned." The above definition of the eupraxia region, which has repeatedly been misinterpreted, leaves no doubt in my mind that Liepmann considers the eupraxia region as a cortical center, that is, an aggregation of neurons that control the totality of integrative acts concerned with a given performance.

How can Liepmann's concept (which should be interpreted in the light of the experiences with callosal section) be expressed in terms developed in the current chapter? And what is the relationship of the centers of eupraxia to the speech centers?

The sensory psycho-neural centers are spe-

cialized organs of the posterior (response determining cortex) chiefly of the dominant side.
By the same token, the motor psychoneural
centers are organs of the anterior or response
effectuating area. The motor speech centers, in
turn, are a product of differentiation of the
centers of eupraxia. Thus, the speech area is in a
sense a more "concentrated" center than the
eupraxia area. The *motor* segments of the eupraxia
area are contiguous with the motor segments of
the speech area, the sounds of language being
merely movements or gestures rendered audible;
the *sensory* segments of the eupraxia area are
contiguous with the sensory segments of the
speech area. Owing to this contiguity relationship
both the two *motor* segments, i.e., subcenter
II.m. (which is concerned with willed movements)
and sub-center II.m., (which subserves articulatory movements) are apt to be involved in
combination. By the same token, the corresponding *sensory* segments of level II.s. are apt to be
concomitantly affected. What's more, I.s. is
contiguous with II.s., the sensory psycho-neural
centers subserving movements and speech; and
I.m. with II.m., the motor psycho-neural centers
subserving movements and speech. Hence,
ideatory and amnestic apraxia and sensory
aphasia are apt to be combined with disturbances
of the *sensory* control of *any* willed movement
while motor apraxia is apt to be associated with
disturbances of *motor* control of *any* willed movement. In the following section of this chapter the
relationship between various forms of disturbances will be made more explicit.

Recent work on the localization of apractic
disturbances is concerned, among other questions, with a comparison of the effects of lesions
to the dominant and the subordinate parietal
lobe. Hecaen a.ass. (*202*) found that ideatory
and ideo-motor apraxia are part of the clinical
picture following lesions to the left side, dressing
apraxia to be due to right sided lesions, while
visuo-constructive disabilities are integral parts
of both the right and the left parietal syndrome.
Critchley (*104*) on the other hand disputes that
dressing dyspraxia is of necessity a minor parietal
sign and he regards as non-proven the concept of
dualism in lesions of the right hemisphere in
sinistrals although, when the right parietal lobe
(in dextrals) is involved certain other clinical
phenomena appear which are rarely seen with
left sided parietal lobe disease.

Comment and criticism

The difficulties involved in defining the mechanism of ideokinetic apraxia in terms which have,
at the same time, a psychological and a physiological connotation stems from the inability on
the part of the diverse writers to appreciate that
consciousness is the mode of representation of
sensory data at the highest integrative level of
the nervous system, in other words, an attribute
of certain physiological processes. Nathan, (*351*)
after devoting some five pages to a "presentation
and critique" of Liepmann's views, blames him
for (a) having allegedly ascribed psychic qualities
to the motor areas, (b) having used the metaphorical expression "kinetic engram" and (c)
having been aware [!] of using a simile for the
purpose of illustration, that is, of having seen—
and escaped—the snare of language. In support of
Liepmann's views it should be stated that, because of the palpable role of mnestic processes
in skilled movements, his choice of the above
metaphor was a particularly fortunate one.
Nathan's criticism would have been justified only
if Liepmann had suffered from the delusion that
kinetic engrams are memories in the commonly
used sense of the term. What's more, Nathan,
himself, quotes Liepmann as saying that innervatory kinaesthetic engrams are physiological rather
than psychological processes. After having accused Liepmann of introducing psychological
concepts into brain mechanisms, the critic,
throwing up his hands in despair, asserts that a
"psychological being makes the decision to move
and that a physiological being carries it out."
Sittig, who (*448*) was equally unfortunate in his
search for an acceptable theory of sensory-motor
integration, relegated eupractic movements to
most highly developed automatisms. Thus,
Nathan, having tried in vain to find a common
denominator of psychic and physiological phenomena, gave up altogether, while Sittig committed the error of false categorization. Ethelberg
was puzzled by the phenomenon of psychophysical integration, as were many others before him.
The behaviorists had attempted to get rid of the
problem by minimizing it, if not ignoring it.
Ethelberg attempted to eliminate the difficulty

in question by invoking the concepts of objective psychology, a somewhat less offensive form of behaviourism. The passage here commemorated is taken from Ethelberg's monograph on anterior cerebral artery occlusion. "Frequently, the disorder (i.e., ideo-kinetic apraxia) is read in terms of the older psychology as the inability to perform 'willed' or 'voluntary' movements—a disorder of volition or willing as distinct from 'knowledge' in the sense of 'cognition' or 'gnosis'. *On the other hand, from an introspective point of view only movements explicitly associated with verbalization, meaning 'I will' have to be considered as 'voluntary.'*" (I wonder if Ethelberg said to himself, "I am going to write a book on arterial occlusion," or whether he did not, in which case, on the strength of the criteria set forth by himself, the composition of his valuable monograph would have been an involuntary phenomenon.) "Under actual circumstances," Ethelberg continues, "I regard such 'voluntary movements' as rare. And, further, from the point of view of an 'objective psychology', 'knowing' in the sense of perception, ideation, or gnosis, 'volition,' in the sense of the initial mental stage of action or reaction may be removed from the realm of guesswork when they are considered merely aspects of one entire cycle, from stimulus to bodily movements, so that 'knowing' becomes something active and not something contemplative." At this point, Ethelberg invokes the authority of Bertrand Russell (*454, 463*) who argued along similar lines. In parenthesis, we call renewed attention to the fact that Russell had a forerunner, the little known Viennese psychologist Stöhr who, thinking in the tradition of the Mach school, contended that a concept comprises the sum total of experiences which are responded to in a similar fashion. ("Begriffe sind Reaktionsidentitäten.") In other words that the "concept" of concept is rooted in common reaction patterns. The contention that knowledge is something active rather than contemplative can be readily refuted. Suppose a mischievous maid had stolen Ethelberg's records on which his monograph was based and that the author, suspecting her of theft had had her interrogated by the police. Would he not have proceeded on the assumption that the suspected culprit knew about the theft all along, i.e., not only at the moment of confession at which contemplation became action? Yet

Ethelberg attacks, from still another angle, the concept of knowledge as applied to the problem of apraxia. "I believe", he writes, "that increased adaptability and integration of motor performances must count as increase of knowledge or, conversely, a decrease in integration and adaptability must count as a "lack of knowledge" although, from a clinical point of view, paralysis —or paresis—a simple loss of power—is usually not regarded as a lack of knowledge." The redefinition of the concept of knowledge, as suggested by Ethelberg, would obliterate the difference between determination of response on the one hand and its execution on the other.* Thus, it is bound to lead to confusion because the motor centers do not *know* anything; they simply *perform* while knowledge is the mode of perception prevailing at the highest sensory level. At long last, Liepmann's critic arrives at the conclusion that, in practice, this definition, although arbitrary, may hold. Should his (volitional) criticism have ended on a note of harmony? No indeed. Ethelberg questions another of Liepmann's theses, namely, the distinction between the terms "purposive" and "purposeful." According to Liepmann, the term purposeful (*zweckmässig*), denotes a category of appropriacy which is commonly accepted. Purposeful movements are "publicly purposive movements" while the other category of purposive movements (zweckgemässe Bewegungen) are "purposive according to the actually experienced purpose" only. Obviously, it is the second variety in which the clinician and, for that matter, the patient is interested. Although Ethelberg questions the patient's authority to decide "whether the means chosen are the right ones," it is established that the patient may not only know that he had performed an inapposite movement but he may demonstrate his knowledge (and thereby satisfy the most rigid standards of objective psychology) by performing correctly with the non-apractic extremity, which is still under the control of the "soul."

---

* According to Vasari (*482a*), Leonardo da Vinci, defending himself against the charge of inactivity, remarked: "Men of genius are sometimes producing more when they seem least to labor, for their minds are then occupied in the shaping of those conceptions to which they afterwards give form."

DISORDERS OF LANGUAGE

The nervous system is a mechanism that determines with what particular response a given stimulus should be answered. The language mechanism, being a specialized part of the nervous system, determines the nature of responses to symbolized stimuli. At the same time, the language mechanism determines in what particular symbolic form a given stimulus is represented at the conceptual level both for the purpose of manipulation in thought and of communication. Lastly, since communication is a two-way process, disorders of language fall into two broad groups, a *sensory* or *agnostic* variety, and a *motor* or *apractic* variety.

REMARKS ON THE ONTOGENESIS OF LANGUAGE

We have mentioned earlier in this volume that language is a *communicative skill* and, at the same time, a *technique of thought*. To the extent that language is a particular skill, it is a function of the psycho-neural level; a technique of thought, of the intellective level. On a previous occasion, we have demonstrated that, in the course of evolution of thought from perception, thinking, by an apparent reversal of the general trend of evolution of higher from lower cerebral functions, falls back as it were on its functional primordium, perception. This occurs at a stage of development at which thinking has attained levels of abstraction where the simultaneous surveying of relationships necessitates their representation by symbols, which are palpable data of awareness, or data of the senses. We have further indicated that high level functions utilize the element of automaticity inherent in low order functions and that, conversely, the flexibility of the higher levels enhances that of the lower echelons. At high levels of abstraction, the awareness and generation of relationships is made possible by symbols, i.e., configurational data (which are representative of meanings) generated concurrently with the manipulation of relations in thought. At the same time, the formation of symbols is diversified by the wealth of relations generated at the intellective level. (See "reciprocal potentiation of level-specific resources," Chapter I.)

The following statements regarding the development of language in the child (which will be resumed, in a different context below), are based on everyday observations. They may be corroborated by a perusal of the literature, especially the work of Arens (*12*), Buehler (*79*), Bloomfield (*52*), Jesperson (*240*), Pillsbury and Meadows (*391*), Kainz (*248*), Revesz (*405*) and other authorities. The interpretation of the empirical data on the other hand is an integral part of our own concept of high order brain functions. The fact that language is a communicative skill accounts for the pattern of early development of language functions in stages which correspond, by and large, to the evolvement of non-language skills. The latter comprise (a) movements elicited by instinctive needs and the releasers of consummatory reactions, (b) primitive expressive movements and (c) repetitive, seemingly self-perpetuating movements which are continued to the point of saturation, (*Funktionslust*). The crying of the hungry infant corresponds to the *generalized movements elicited by instinctive needs* etc.; the mimetic expressions of pleasure and pain to *early, poorly differentiated expressive movements*; and the sound producing movements of the oro-labial and oro-lingual effector organs are the counterpart of the *repetitive activity* in the general somatic sphere.* In the third phase of the development of language, the articulatory play of the infant acquires an increasingly volitonal character concurrently with the experience that certain movements and the sound effects that accompany them yield a certain measure of environmental control. In other words, the babbling of the infant is the functional primordium of articulate sounds which acquire denotational properties. They are the infant's personal vocabulary which reflects, in a sense, its experiental world. The infant's and child's individualistic stock of words, which is the arbitrary representation of data of awareness by articulatory movements and the corresponding sounds of speech, is the tentative symbolic representation of existing, of desired and of rejected relations between the growing organism and its environment, in other words, the early vocabulary is the symbolic expression of acceptance, of seeking and of avoiding. The primordial vocabulary, "invented" to denote meaningful relations is generated largely by random vocalization, be it spontaneous, or imitated by the "replicating" movements of the organs of speech. Just like the repetitive testing of certain non-articulatory

* (See p. 336.)

skilled movements makes the child aware of its growing capacity to produce certain environmental changes, so the repetitive performance of certain articulatory movements makes it aware of the fact that desired and attained effects follow the production of certain sounds of speech. Conversely, the meaning of frequently repeated words produced by the persons in the infant's environment are expected to be understood by the infant. Some of these words are sooner or later repeated and, eventually, apprehended, that is, they acquire meaning as soon as words and their effects are linked together through association by contiguity. Little by little, the one-word sentence of the child develops to the two word sentence and, eventually, to the propositional speech of the adult.

One of Stumpf's (472) sons stubbornly stuck to his own private vocabulary over a period of two years. It consisted of two groups of words, namely, (a) personal expressions such as "aja," interpreted to mean beautiful, "a," interpreted to mean ugly, "sch-sch," meaning railroad and (b) some mutilated words of everyday language. At a time he already understood what was said to him, he combined the above expressions according to circumstances. He began to speak rather abruptly and quite fluently at the age of three years and three months. Steinthal's (462) son combined the few words he knew to two-word sentences as follows: "Papa hut" meant papa wears a hat, and "dat huhu" meant the soldier ("dat") is riding horseback. He formed his first sentence "nante singen" (asking his aunt to sing) at the age of one year and eight months. For further examples of early speech, see Clara's and William Stern's (465) monograph.

In *summary*, then, the *private, poorly structured, pre-configurational analogs of a symbolic order*, which are the denotational and depictive elements of the infant's language, are superseded by *conventionalized, well structured, configurational analogs of a symbolic order* which are the denotational and depictive elements used by the community. Languages are thematic variations of one and the same biological function, namely, the synthesis of the awareness and generation of relationships on the one hand, and their communication on the other, i.e., the transmission of meaning by the patterned production of auditory and, later, visual symbols. By a process of *reciprocal potentiation* of level specific resources of the nervous system, the awareness and generation of relationships is enhanced by their symbolic representation; at the same time, symbol formation is diversified by the abundance of relations created at the conceptual level. As Abailard (1079–1142) wrote: "Sermo generatur ab intellectu et intellectum generat."

INTERACTION OF CONCEPTS AND SYMBOLS

The formation of the symbols of language is, as we have said, an auxiliary mechanism operating at the configurational level which facilitates and, to a degree, makes possible the awareness and generation of relationships in thought. In a certain sense, non-numerical symbols resemble numbers; and the laws of operation of words conform to the pattern of stimulus manipulation known as algorithm, which involves an element of automaticity. Yet the pattern in question is neither fully automatic, like a reflex apparatus, nor fully autonomous but rather, an instrumentality of thought, and interwoven with the laws that control the manipulation of concepts. The element of automaticity operating at the configurational level exists in every language. As Schiller wrote in a little known verse: "Weil ein Vers Dir gelingt in einer gebildeten Sprache, die für Dich dichtet und denkt, glaubst Du ein Dichter zu sein." The word *gebildet* means *refined* but its original meaning is *formed* or *structured*. Combining both meanings, one may say that the very potentialities inherent in formed language will rhyme and think rather than the poet himself. The fact, we might add, that the configurational level maintains, in the process of expression, a certain measure of autonomy, links the esthetic framework of language to that of presentative art, which may well account for the different atmosphere effect produced by different languages. To name only two, Latin conjures up the idea of solid rocks embodying, by their very weight, a whole world of meaning, while French resembles more nearly molten rock which flows with great speed and, at any moment, may burst into a cascade. As Edith Hamilton wrote in a recent article: "They [the Romans] were able to put an idea into an astonishingly small number of words without losing a particle of intelligibility." (Saturday Evening Post, September 12, 1958.) There are virtually as many modes of thinking as there are languages to express them and, to a degree, to create the products of thought. In other words, the relationship among the cerebral agencies mediating the thought language complex is not only one of reciprocal potentiation but of reciprocal modification as well. Schopenhauer (*435*), the polyglot, gives several examples illustrating how modes of expression establish shades of meaning. Among others, he quotes the following sets of apparent synonymes, including "ingénieux, sinnreich, clever," "Geist, esprit, wit," and "malice, Bosheit, wickedness," and, to drive home his point, quotes Charles V as having said: "Quot linguas quis callet, tot homines valet," which means, in free translation: "As many languages a man can speak, so many persons is he worth." In a different context, he writes: "In learning a language, the chief difficulty consists in making acquaintance with every idea which it expresses, even though it should use words for which there is no exact equivalent in the mother tongue; and this often happens. In learning new languages a man has as it were to mark out in his mind the boundaries of quite new spheres of ideas, with the result that spheres of ideas arise where none were before. Thus he has not only learned words, he gains ideas too. . . . It follows from this that a man's thought varies according to the language in which he speaks. His ideas undergo a fresh modification, a different shading as it were, in the study of every new language. Hence an acquaintance with many languages is not only of much indirect advantage but it is also a direct means of mental culture in that it corrects and matures ideas by giving prominence to their many sided nature and their different varieties of meanings and also in that it increases dexterity of thought. . . . (This is precisely what went on in the anonymous's mind who produced this masterful translation and who was very likely bilingual. I was already thirty years old when I began studying English, and my poor teacher's admonitions, repeated over and over again, "You must think in English," naturally were for a long time quite fruitless.) Leibniz (*387*), who spoke several languages in addition to his native German, but who preferred to write in Latin or French, said in his "Nouveaux essais sur l'entendement humain" (1704, published in 1765) that words denoting entirely abstract concepts are derivable from those that originally were applied to concrete ideas (cf. Heidbrener, *204*) that the sounds of language were shaped in conformity with affects and with the activities of the mind, and that language facilitates thought in that it enables one to operate with general concepts as with figures, making it superfluous to define meanings in each instance in which the concepts in question are used. Lastly, he called attention to a point to which allusion has already been made, namely, to the fact that the very structure of language modifies, to a high degree, the scope of human knowledge as the instrumentalities of thinking are transmitted from generation to generation. To conclude these introductory remarks, it would seem that complete conformity between meaning and what is meant, or its referent, exists only at the two extremes of symbolic formulation and expression, one of which is the language of affects understood by all, the other the language of numbers understood, in comparison to the former, by only a few.

NEUROPSYCHOLOGICAL INTERPRETATION OF THE CLASSIC CONCEPT OF APHASIA

The classic concept of aphasia, inaugurated by Meynert (*239*), Wernicke (*508*) and Lichtheim (*295*) has been criticized, not without justification, on the ground that it involves a projection of psychological concepts on the brain map. (This projection has been done in pictorial language by means of diagrams, the first of which was composed by Baginski, *17*, in 1871.) On the other hand, the purely psychological approach to the problem of aphasia has gained little popularity largely because of the lack of correlation between psychological and anatomical data. The concept of aphasis offered in the present study is a compromise; the symbols of speech are regarded as a specific class of stimuli involved in skilled movements, more specifically as analogs of a second order whose formation is brought into relationship with the same divisions of cortex that are concerned with general psychoneural functions. In so far as language is a communicative skill, the pattern of central representation of language functions conforms to that of any skill, in other words, the sensory center of language corresponds to the sensory segment of the psycho-neural level, while the motor center of language corresponds to the motor segment of the psycho-neural level. In fact, the sensory center of language or Wernicke' center, is a specialized part of II.s. and, by the same token, the motor center of language a specialized part of II.m. (Fig. 46). The two centers form the sensory-motor core of the language mechanic which, however, does not operate in isolation but in conjunction with the conceptual level III.s. on the one hand, and the sensory-motor level (I.s. and I.m.) on the other. In other words, Wernicke's aphasia is essentially a disorder of the auditory system at the psycho-neural level and, because of the strategic position of the sensory psycho-neural center discussed early in this chapter, at the conceptual level. Broca's aphasia, on the other hand, is a disorder of the motor system at the psycho-neural level. The diagrams ridiculed by Head (200) lose their alleged absurdity if we tacitly substitute the term sensory-motor for subcortical, psycho-neural for cortical and intellective for trans-cortical. With certain reservations, the use of aphasia-diagrams is permissible; in fact, in discussing language and its disturbances, diagrams can hardly be dispensed with as they enable one to illustrate the development of language in the child, and to specify the terms "sensory," "motor" and "level" as applied to language functions. At the same time, they make it possible to visualize, although only in crude fashion, the mechanism of individual forms of aphasia, particularly the dissociated forms. The following outline of the development and the basic structure of language processes is based on Liepmann's (301) work. It should be followed by reference to Fig. 46 and studied in conjunction with the physiology of skilled movements in general.*

In the child, the hearing of words, including

---

* The present study makes no pretense to be exhaustive. For an extensive covering of the subject along conventional lines, including the long and involved history of aphasia, the interested reader may be referred to the monographs and articles by Binswanger (47), Bonvicini (58), Goldstein (174), Heilbronner (205), Isserlin (237), Liepmann (307), Lotmar (311), Nielsen (354, 355, 356), Nielsen and Friedmann (359), Riese (413, 414), Schiller (428), Thiele (476), Weisenburg (502) and Weisenburg and McBride (503). We are especially indebted to Bonvicini, to Weisenburg and McBride's monograph, and to Schiller's article which epitomizes the experiences with aphasic patients in World War II.

its own early pre-language utterances gives rise to the formation of auditory engrams in that part of the cortex of the temporal lobe which, in the course of maturation, develops to Wernicke's center. Subsequently, the child, using motor engrams or use patterns formed in what will later be Broca's center, learns to translate the auditory engrams, that is to say, sensory analogs of a symbolic order into the corresponding articulatory movements or motor analogs of a symbolic order. For the time being, we disregard the fact that the centers, as previously explained, develop bilaterally. The motor speech engrams, or the "motor word" are under the control of the sensory engrams, or "sensory word," the sensory-motor linkages being consolidated by the repeated actuation of the motor by the acoustic engrams. Sooner or later the child forms concepts, that is to say, it becomes aware of the meaning of words including those it has learned to form. The neurodynamic processes underlying the formation and the manipulation of concepts are mediated by the "concept center" of the classics, or the conceptual level. In the further course of mental development, which takes shape in close interdependence with the growth of speech, conceptual processes are closely linked with the appropriate motor and especially the sensory engrams of words. Reading is acquired by the association of the sensory engrams of speech with the visual engrams representing the symbols of written language which, according to Jackson, are "symbols of symbols." Writing is acquired by the association of engrams of spoken language with those of the movements necessary to produce the symbols of written language. The visual and the graphic (motor) engrams are associated, both functionally and anatomically, with each other and those of spoken language. More specifically, the (sensory) engrams of visual language become linked with the (sensory) engrams of acoustic language. In a similar fashion the motor (graphic) engrams of visual language are linked with those of acoustico-motor or spoken language. To put it in other words, sensory engrams become associated with sensory engrams and motor engrams with motor engrams of the corresponding category and, hence, are apt to be jointly actuated both in expressive and receptive language. The same holds true for reading and writing. The process of reading involves not only visual but also

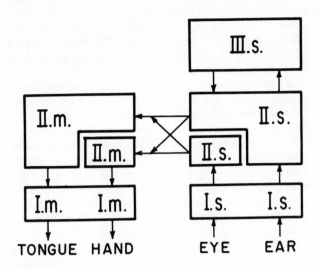

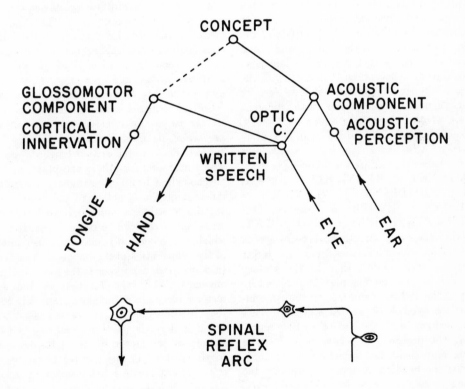

Fig. 46. Correlation between the three-level organization of the cerebral cortex and a conventional aphasia diagram.

II.m.: general motor psycho-neural level; II.m. (insert): Broca's center; II.s.: general sensory psycho-neural level; II.s. (insert): Wernicke's center.

auditory elements, and the process of writing not only cheiro-motor but also articulo-motor elements. At the same time, the sensory engrams of written language, which according to Dejerine (*110, 111*) form in the angular gyrus, are integrated with the neuro-dynamic processes underlying the function of the conceptual level. However, because of the chronological relationship between the more recent, written language and the previously acquired, spoken language (the integrational history of language functions) the associations between the reading center and the concept center is mediated by Wernicke's center and, hence, is an indirect one. It is only with increasing experience, Liepmann holds, that reading and writing become more or less emancipated from spoken language, and that both can be directly actuated by the conceptual sphere. On the other hand, it is common knowledge that inexperienced persons retain the habit of moving their lips while reading and writing. Inner speech is based on the integrated activity of the conceptual sphere and of the acoustic and visual centers of written and especially spoken language. It would seem to depend on the intimacy of the linkages between the intellectual level and its motor agencies, which varies with different persons, whether the writing center (or Exner's, *136*, center) is included into the chain of centers concerned with inner language. *Spontaneous speech* is believed to utilize the following centers: BROADBENT → WERNICKE → BROCA; *writing*, BROADBENT → WERNICKE → DEJERINE → EXNER; and *reading*, DEJERINE → WERNICKE → BROADBENT.

In the motor and kinesthetic type of speech organization, sensory activities depend to a larger extent on motor centers than in the sensory type. For example, reading may be involved by injury to the writing center if a person has committed the symbols of written speech to one's visual memory with the aid of writing movements. On occasion, a person may rely on writing movements for correctness of spelling, allowing the hand to "determine" whether the spelling is correct. More frequently, however, writing is dependent on the reading center because it is apt to be learned under the guidance of vision, i.e., by the reversed mechanism. Impairment of inner speech is caused by lesions of the conceptual sphere, of Wernicke's center

and their inter-connections. Yet inner and outer speech are not necessarily involved in combination, at least the former does not depend on the latter. The distinction between inner and outer speech was already made by Bouillaud (*61*), one of Gall's pupils. The French neurologist Lordat (*309*), himself a victim of aphasia, said after recovering his ability to talk, "Je possédais complétement la partie interne du langage. Je n'en avais perdue que le partie externe." If motor and visual elements cooperate in inner speech formation, language disturbances may be caused by lesions of Broca's center, the angular gyrus, the writing center and their interconnections.

How can the above interpretation of the speech mechanism and its disturbances be correlated with the concepts developed in the first section of this chapter? We defined *centers of higher cerebral functions as cortical agencies which control the totality of integrative acts on which a given performance depends*. The "center of concepts and ideation" which is the highest response determining agency of the nervous system controls a variety of psycho-neural instrumentalities. In a sense, then, *the integrative acts controlled by the sensory language centers are intellectual activities which have become specialized for the purpose of communication including the production, the transmission and the reception of symbols*. Spoken and written language are likewise integrated at the conceptual and the psycho-neural level, either agency contributing different quotas of action to the total process. Injuries to strategic points indicated in the diagram interfere with certain integrative acts which, in a general way, may be defined in terms of the contribution of the previously functioning (now involved) nerve cells to the total function of language. While the function of the architectonic elements is unknown, it is fair to say that the functional value of the neurones in question depends on their relationship to the sensory or the motor sphere of the brain at a particular level of the cortical hierarchy. The effects of any nervous system lesion of sufficient size may be expressed in terms of depression of the reliability coefficient (or "confidence-coefficient") of the particular performance involved. Moderate depression of reliability produces temporal dissociation of function, that is, inordinate fluctuation of the performance level;

total depression, the reduction of the reliability coefficient to zero and, accordingly, structural dissociation. (The fact that lesions interfere with the precision of performance no doubt induced certain writers to apply gestaltpsychological principles to neurological problems, and created the semantically convenient but clinically sterile phrase "blurring of a figure" against the background of central nervous system function.)

The diagrams of the classics, which are made up of circumscribed centers and their connections, are inadequate inasmuch as they create artificial differences between cortical, subcortical and "transcortical" lesions. In the last analysis, aphasia results from damage to a neural network which generates neurodynamic processes of different kind and complexity, and which has developed chiefly around the auditory cortex. Injury interferes not only with the physiologic constancy of performances but gives rise to the substitution of integrative acts by products of inadequate integration. The abnormal performances of the aphasic patient are the products of defective integration of neurodynamic processes which have "survived" the effects of the injury and which, under normal conditions, would have been organized to integrative acts with the processes now eliminated. Theoretically, damage may be caused by lesions of either the gray matter or the white matter; however, since most lesions are probably of a composite nature, the terms cortical and subcortical do not strictly apply, quite apart from the fact that transcortical varieties of aphasia are likewise produced by cortical or subcortical lesions or by their combination. Furthermore, the conventional schemes fail to account for what Goldstein (*174*) called the *plus symptoms* of aphasia as, for example, the abundance of speech impulses in Wernicke's aphasia.

In spite of these shortcomings the diagrams of classic neurology are useful maps of the functional organization of the speech mechanism; they illustrate at least the general interrelationship of the systems and levels involved in the elaboration of speech. It is freely admitted that they fail to explain every abnormality but their explanatory value is sufficiently high to place it well beyond the bounds of probability. By contrast, there is little to gain from a purely psychological approach, which disregards the fact that language is the function of an organ having a definite anatomical structure, and which ignores the fact that the construction of the language producing organ reflects language mechanisms fundamentally in the same way as the anatomy of the spinal segments reflects the presence of relatively simple reflex mechanisms.

THE CIRCUIT CONCEPT OF LANGUAGE MECHANISMS

Crudely defined, the line connections which mediate language functions are made up of a system of circuits of increasing versatility which serve the production, the transmission and the reception of signals. The control of the entire system is the conceptual level ("concept center" or elaborative cortex) which selects outgoing and deciphers or recognizes incoming signals. (See below.) Wernicke's center (II.s., auditory) serves the formation and ekphory of symbols both in expressive and receptive speech; and Broca's center (II.m., articulatory), the translation of the patterns or "sensory analogs" formed in II.s. into the corresponding movements, or "motor analogs." The patterns formed in Wernicke's center may be thought of as a kind of blueprint which, in the process of receptive speech, is analyzed by III.s. and, in expressive speech, transmitted to II.m. In other words, II.s. composes, out of incoming stimuli, auditory patterns of various complexity. They are recognized, that is, understood or brought into relationship with a conceptual reference system by III.s., while II.s. synthetizes outgoing stimuli to auditory patterns or blueprints to be converted into sounds by II.m. and I.m. Center I.s. comprises, among other sensory terminals, the primary auditory cortex; center I.m., the motor cortex subserving movements of the muscles which are concerned, among other functions, with the production of articulatory movements. To reiterate, with respect to expressive speech (and the same applies to any sphere of volitional movements) III.s. is a selector of response, II.s. is a synthetizer of acoustic patterns, II.m. a coordinator of movements, and I.m. a cortical effector. In receptive speech, I.s. is a cortical receptor, II.s. an analyzer in the configurational and III.s. an analyzer in the conceptual sphere. Center III.s. is the highest level subserving language functions as, indeed, any act of mentation. The neuro-dynamic processes, no matter at what level they take place, are to be thought of as integrative acts or processes serving the unity of the organism. It is suggested that the patterns formed (or integrative processes operating) at level II.s., the acoustic engrams of speech that is, are latent and, if actuated by temporally patterned aggregates of sounds, produce the physiological framework of word gestalten and of syntactic gestalten. The activity of I.s., the primary acoustic area, produces merely amorphous replicas of the events originating at the sound source, while II.s. records aggregates of sounds according to their relation-structure or gestaltqualities. A given word, mumbled or sung, transmitted directly or by means of instruments (which may alter its pitch and other acoustic qualities) is adequately recorded as long as there is preserved a minimum of sound elements, or characteristic details necessary to preserve the crucial relationships of the "blueprint." In the absence of a perceptual minimum, on the other hand, the sound-gestalt will be blurred, or garbled. The same applies to sentences, but only to the extent that they are sound gestalten of greater complexity than words, for III.s. may record an inflowing sentence with "high fidelity" without being able to analyze it. A sentence, which can be repeated is not necessarily understood. (Many people are able to pronounce, almost faultlessly, entirely unfamiliar words.) As in other spheres of nervous system functions, the higher and lower levels work in a reciprocal fashion. Other functions being equal, the quality of reception at the highest level is improved by an acute sense of hearing; conversely, the specific qualities or level specific resources of the higher strata produce effects which are more than the sum total of the data furnished by the lower. We have already mentioned that the sensory patterns of Wernicke's center actuate not only those of Broca's center but those of the reading center, and vice versa. A similar relationship prevails between the patterned processes depending on Broca's and Exner's center.

Because of the wide disturbance range of the speech centers, aphasia may occur in rapidly developing lesions located well outside Broca's and Wernicke's center. In a personal case (434) a solitary metastasis in the superior parietal lobule

of the dominant hemisphere produced massive aphasia. On the other hand, minimal lesions will give rise to speech disturbances only if they are well "centered" as, for example, in Gordiner's (179, 180) and in Scheincker and Kuhr's case (424). In the former, aphasia and agraphia was caused by a small tumor involving the posterior part of the second frontal convolution; in the latter, motor aphasia developed incident to a small softening of Broca's center and the adjacent portions of the frontal lobe.

Derangement of the entire system of circuits may occur in a systematized fashion, in which case one or the other of its component parts is thrown out of function. At this point, the "brainrest theory" comes to mind which stipulates that the symptoms of aphasia are merely the expression of what the rest of the brain can still do. (By the same token, the function of, say, an arm, may be expressed by that of the still functioning parts of the skeletal musculature, after the arm has been amputated.) If the entire circuit system is involved in a non-systematized fashion, fragments of any of its component parts are thrown out of function either singly or in combination. Pure cases of Wernicke's or Broca's aphasia, which are rare, are the result of systematized structural dissociation of the entire system caused, respectively, by injury to II.s. and II.m. Any type of structural dissociation will give rise to primary and secondary symptoms of aphasia. The former are due to the absence of the involved center; the latter, to the effects of its absence in the remaining parts of the circuit system with which the center now diseased used to form a functional unit. The primary symptoms of Wernicke's aphasia are the defective formation of acoustic patterns. As a result, III.s. is unable to analyze the symbols of speech (to bring it into relationship with its level specific, conceptual, reference system), and to have them translated into the articulatory movements by II.m. Defective formation of acoustic patterns gives rise to disturbances both of receptive and expressive language. We have repeatedly called attention to the dual nature of language, which is not only an instrument of thought but, in so far as the production of certain classes of relations is dependent on the manipulation of symbols, a method of thinking. The patient's difficulty in manipulating symbols is a twofold one; he cannot remember them with sufficient clarity nor can he synthetize them to auditory patterns to be analyzed by the conceptual level. As a result, the performance of the latter will be involved to the extent that it is concerned with expressive-semantic and receptive-semantic functions. Other intellective functions are secondarily involved. In certain instances, the inability to ekphorize symbols for the purpose of expressive speech may dominate the clinical picture and thereby gives rise to the notion that amnestic aphasia is an independent variety of sensory aphasia. In other cases, the reciprocally related centers III.s. and II.s. function normally but the total language function appears to be dissociated in a fashion suggesting that the transmission of impulses from II.s. to II.m. is interrupted. This form of speech disorder is known as *"aphasia of conduction."* The presumptive mechanism of the individual speech disturbances will be discussed after a description of their symptomatology.

Thus far, then, we have differentiated between the following varieties of language disturbances. (1) *Wernicke's aphasia*, including its varieties, *amnestic aphasia* and *conduction aphasia*, and (2) *Broca's aphasia*. The diagrams of the classics make possible the derivation of four additional forms of aphasia, namely, *subcortical sensory aphasia, transcortical sensory aphasia, subcortical motor aphasia*, and *transcortical motor aphasia*. It is worthy of note that some of these forms were postulated on clinical grounds prior to their clinical verification.

The above outline of the mechanism of language disturbances may be challenged for several reasons. First, as we have already had occasion to mention, it does not explain every symptom in every phase of aphasia. This is undoubtedly true but may be blamed on the causative lesion which fails to conform to the "architectonics of the diagram," in turn a much simplified representation of the language mechanism. Other difficulties arise from the reciprocal relationships of certain components of language, which makes it exceedingly difficult to distinguish between primary symptoms and their repercussions; and, lastly, they are referable to the fact that language functions have an integrational history which may be different in different persons and which determines preferential functional linkages and, hence, preferential and

highly variable patterns of dissociation. Nevertheless, the terms based on the classic concept of aphasia have not, thus far at least, been supplanted by other terms. For example, Goldstein (*174*) refused to abandon the anatomical term "transcortical aphasia," which designates a psychopathological entity, although the term in question is derived from a theoretical interpretation of aphasia which, in his own opinion, is no longer acceptable. He uses the expression "transcortical" on the ground that we have "as yet no better understanding of the underlying functional disturbances and because we are accustomed to bring a definite symptomcomplex in relation to it." Similar considerations would seem to apply to the subcortical forms of aphasia. In fact, whenever different (and, supposedly, more suitable) names have been suggested as for example by H. Head (*199, 200*), it was shown that the syndromes to which they were applied could be expressed in conventional, or connectionist terms.

Wernicke's aphasia (Cortical sensory aphasia)

The classic form of Wernicke's aphasia

The mechanism of the disorder can be broken down into two basic components, namely, ideo-symbolic and receptive disturbances. It should be noted that the term "cortical sensory aphasia," which is coterminous with Wernicke's aphasia, covers only the receptive aspect of the disturbance.

(a) *Ideo-symbolic disorders* involve the use of symbols, the structure of inner speech and, indirectly, of expression.

(b) *Receptive disorders*, commonly regarded as the cardinal symptom of Wernicke's aphasia, involve the process of comprehension. As already indicated, the difficulties of comprehension, both of spoken and written language, are essentially due to the inability to appreciate word-gestalten rather than the defective perception of speech sounds.

The nature of ideo-symbolic disorders would be difficult to understand without an examination of the relationships between ideas and symbols, or between thought and speech.

Ideo-Symbolic Disorders

The non-identity between ideation and verbalization—we deliberately speak of non-identity rather than disparity—may be demonstrated by the following examples.

(1) One and the same thought can be expressed in different ways without changing the meaning of what the speaker, or writer, wants to express. (For details, see Buyssens, *83*.)

(2) Many patients who can neither talk nor understand what is spoken to them can express themselves by gestures.

(3) Brobeil and Stallwitz (*70*) studied a patient suffering from total aphasia incident to left carotid artery ligation. The patient, a highly intelligent student who prior to his operation had spoken three languages, recovered his ability to speak them several months later. He declared that, for a time, his thoughts were entirely wordless and that he had no inner acoustic or motor experiences whatsoever. Interestingly enough, he was unaware of the inability to express himself, and his speechlessness appeared to him as a perfectly natural state. Unfortunately, we have no information on the degree of complexity of the wordless thought processes to which the patient made reference.

(4) It is generally appreciated that the expression of identical meanings in different languages may require entirely different sentence constructions. This applies not only to proverbs and various idioms but, more or less, also to ordinary language. Although the inner logic of what the speaker or writer intends to express remains the same, sentences cannot be translated word for word, but must be recast. Delacroix (*113, 114*), in referring to what W. v. Humboldt called the "inner speech form" wrote: "Il est très certain que les categories grammaticales ne correspond pas exactement aux categories logiques. Un certain disaccord apparait partout. L'example classique de ce discordance, c'est le genre . . . *les grammaires expriment des habitudes d'esprit et des niveaux de pensée très différents; elles reflètent les points de vu variés des divers groups sociaux sur le monde de relations* . . . un langage est toujours une mélange de convention et de logique, d'arbitraire et du raison." Boas (*55*) wrote in his Handbook of American Indian Languages: "In each language only a part of the complete concept that we have in mind is expressed . . . each language has a peculiar tendency to select this or that aspect of the mental image which is conveyed by the expression of the thought. In the Malayan languages passive sentence constructions are quite common. For example, a Malayan does not say, "I am going to beat up your brother," but "Your brother wants to be beaten up by me." We are all familiar with passive sentence constructions for, in years gone by, we have been plagued with the "deponentia"—according to Schopenhauer "the only illogical element in the Latin language." (To the Romans the sentence "Roma locuta, causa finita" did not appear illogical.)

(5) The emergence of thought processes does not necessarily coincide with their symbolic formulation. It is true that, in a flash, an idea may take shape in the form of a complete sentence. On the other hand, emergent thought processes may be represented in the form of vague meanings which do not crystallize into sentences until after some time, and after a good deal of effort has been spent to fixate them. Eventually, they are cast into words, that is, heard with one's inner ear or spoken with one's inner voice. For example, reluctance to accept a speaker's view may first be experienced by the listener as a general feeling of opposition, which undergoes a more or less rapid evolution into a more definite and specifiable awareness content. The latter is the immediate precursor, if not already the initial phase, of symbolic formulation of thought, while the intervening (as yet incompleted) ideatory phases do not admit of verbalization. Because of the twofold nature of language as an instrument of thought and as a method of thinking, the intervening phases occupy the twilight zone of consciousness which is difficult to penetrate. However, even in the absence of definite knowledge, it is evident that intellectual processes must be differentiated not only from semantic activity but also from semantic ability. Of two persons, one may express his counter-arguments with great fluency while the other may find it difficult to phrase his thoughts although he knows what he wants to express. The former is not necessarily more intelligent but his communicative skill is superior to that of his less fortunate colleague. He may elegantly express

a thought which, missing the main point entirely, is the product of a relentless "glossogenic" impetus. (As Lourié [313] wrote in his little known book, "La Verbomanie:" "Les savants et les philosophes le plus profonds ne disposent souvent que d'un vocabulaire restraint, tandis que les parleurs superficiels possèdent une provision inépuisable de mots" and Ombredane (366) makes reference to the "idiot bavard des salons.") On the other hand, a semantically handicapped person, if given time, may produce a wealth of constructive ideas. Needless to say, the semantically gifted person is not necessarily less intelligent. Not only are intellectual and semantic ability apt to be combined but the latter, like any aptitude, depends on a certain level of intellectual ability. At the pathological level, difficulties in phrasing were graphically described by Lordat to whose aphasia we have already made reference. He could not use words for, as he put it, "parce que je ne me souvénais pas de la manière dont il fallait les coordiner pour qu'ils exprimâssent ma pensée."

A historical sketch will illustrate the problem of thought-language relationship better than general statements. Aristotle believed that thought is silent speech. According to W. v. Humboldt (327), language is the perpetual struggle of the mind to adapt sound to the expression of thought. In another passage, however, he wrote that speech and thought are the same. Among the early writers, Bastian (25) asserted that speech and thought were inherently identical while Wernicke was well aware of the complicated nature of their relationship. Bühler (79), referring to his own experiences, wrote that, prior to the appearance of words in his mind, he is conscious of a framework, that is, something in which the individual words can be fitted. Külpe (270) believed that thought processes are independent of the signals that express them. They are a special class of awareness contents which, although they may be accompanied by perceptions and feelings, lack their sensuous properties. Messer (325) contended that thought may be guided by sensuous representations of words and objects which, however, do not of themselves form thought processes. According to Bühler (79), introspection reveals the existence of thought processes which completely lack sensuous

elements including optic, acoustic and motor images of words. In principle, every meaningful awareness content may exist without sensuous experiences. The opposite view was expressed by Steinthal (462) who "interdefined" silent thinking as speech which is being thought, and speech as thought which is being spoken loudly. Other advocates of the identity between speech and thought were Hoenigswald (218) and Binswanger (47). The lengthy and at times heated controversy between the latter and Lotmar was epitomized by Conrad (97) and Meyers (327). Erdmann (129) differentiated between non-formulated and formulated thought, which passes from a pre-verbalized to a verbalized stage, while Woerkom (521) distinguished un-structured from structured thought processes. The argument, which goes back to Plato, was resumed, although not resolved, in a recent sympsosium on "Thinking and Language" (406).

A. Pick, (385, 386, 387) who held the view that the process of grammatization can be differentiated from those of selection of words and the ekphory of word engrams, divided the "way from thought to speech" into four phases.

The *first phase* is a poorly differentiated and as yet non-explicit awareness quality which, he suggested, corresponds to Marbe's (319) *Bewusstseinslage*, that is to say, a state of awareness whose contents cannot be specified at all or, at most, in vague outlines only. ("Eine Bewusstseinslage ist eine Bewusstseinstatsache deren Inhalt sich einer näheren Charakterisierung entweder ganz entzieht oder schwer zugänglich ist.") Messer (33) believes that one variety of *Bewusstseinslage* is represented by a state of awareness associated with the diverse shades and degrees of comprehension. For example, reading and understanding a sentence are not necessarily identical processes; sometimes, the meaning of the sentence flashes into the reader's mind a fraction of a second *later*. Another form of *Bewusstseinslage precedes* the verbalization of an awareness content, whose full meaning, however, does not take shape unless one succeeds in casting it into words; one is already aware of the general outline of the meaning but mentation lacks verbal elements. Messer distinguishes between a Bewusstseinslage involving, e.g., the awareness of reality, of difference, of incompatibility, etc*. (Evidently, the previously mentioned elementary feeling of opposition belongs to the same category of wordless experience.) Messer, who feels that the awareness and production of relationships at the level of Bewusstseinslage is possible, regards thought processes proper as elaboration of the undifferentiated mental acts which mark the beginning of the preverbal phase.

The *second phase* corresponds to Ach's (*1*) "*Bewusstheit.*" General awareness qualities have become differentiated into individual elements of whose specific interrelationship the person is already conscious and which form the *general scheme of thought*. According to Ach, Bewusstheiten are "complex awareness contents whose structure is fully known to the subject although the semantic correlate of the entire complex has yet to materialize. Apparently, this is due to the fact that the entire complex *has not yet become sufficiently* explicit to permit verbal expression." ("Es gibt sehr komplizierte Inhalte bei denen die Teilinhalte bei mannigfachen äusseren Beziehungen bewusst vorliegen, ohne dass hierbei die einzelnen Inhalte durch ihre adäquaten sprachlichen Beziehungen und dergl. repräsentiert sind, *oder auch nur sein können.*" (Emphasis added.)) The above quoted (and somewhat freely translated) passage makes it doubtful whether Ach's notion of the preverbal phase is entirely free from contradictions since, on the one hand, verbalization is made to depend on the *maturation* of the preverbal phase, whereas, on the other hand, the very same process of maturation of meaning appears to depend on the *already completed* translation of thought into words.

The above difficulty reveals the unsettled stage of the problem under study. To my knowledge at least, no important contributions to its solution have been forthcoming since the work

* Another form of *Bewusstseinslage* involves what may be called, for want of a better term, the "feeling of imminence." While reading one of Lotmar's (*311*) articles for the second time, I came to the bottom of page 255 and was about to turn the page when I had the feeling that a certain unusual experience was about to happen again—and found on the following page, line 5, the expression "Logasthenie," an (obsolete?) term coined by Lichtheim, and referring to the mental impairment that may be associated with sensory aphasia.

of Pick and the Würzburg group of psychologists. Be this as it may, the very existence of phases intervening between thought and speech may have a bearing upon the interesting problem of the ontogenesis and, possibly, the phylogenesis of language. Disregarding the lack of precision of the above discussed concepts, but accepting their general validity, it is conceivable that, with increasing maturation of the language mechanism, both *receptive and expressive speech of the child passes successively through the stages of Bewusstseinslage, Bewusstheit and verbalization.* In other words, whatever primitive thought may take shape in the child's mind, would initially mature to the stage of Bewusstseinslage only; later on, to the stage of Bewusstheit and, eventually, to that of verbalization. To quote Delacroix: "Dans la mésure où nous pensons nous construisons les signes." As far as can be judged from the behaviour of higher animals the development of language has not kept pace with that of their intelligence. Yet, within their limited capacity to be aware of relationships of the kind man is capable of appreciating, *animals may be capable of mentation* approaching *the stage of Bewusstseinslage and, perhaps, of Bewusstheit.* However, even these primitive states of knowing, which are determiners of animal behaviour, can be but poorly exteriorized (at least by human standards) although they can no doubt be evoked by communicative activities of other animals and, to a limited extent, of human beings. According to K. Bühler, the most elaborate system of (non-symbolic) communication in the sub-human realm of the animal kingdom is used by ants, termites and bees.

In the *third phase*, the scheme of thought activates a *grammatical scheme*, which Pick compares with the linear pattern into which the stones of a mosaic are to be fitted, while the *fourth phase* involves the choice of appropriate words, the filling in of the design, in other words, the selection of symbols intended to convey the meaning the speaker wishes to produce in the listener or in the reader. On a subsequent occasion, Pick commented upon the process of translation of thought into speech as follows. Under *normal* circumstances, the speaker's attention is focused upon what he means to express while speech itself is an automatic performance. Under *pathological* conditions, attention is apt to be focused more upon the act of speaking than the thought to be expressed, the speaker being occupied with the connection of words rather than the contexts of ideas. Moreover, the close relationship between word and meaning becomes unstable, and incorrectly used words are apt to derail the train of thought by perseveration. The views of other authorities conform, essentially, to Pick's theory. Delacroix (*113, 114*) holds that, apart from the intention to talk, intelligent speech requires not only the actuation of the *thought* to be expressed, but also the composition of the *sentences*, and lastly, the close scrutiny of the *parallelism* between meaning and expression. Keeping Pick's ideas on the subject in mind, one would assume that the scrutiny operates in the fashion of (semi-automatic) feedback mechanism which, provided the speaker masters the language, does not distract his attention. Otherwise he finds his thought continuously blocked by the painful search for expressions and suitable sentence constructions. ("*Sprachnot.*") According to Goldstein (*174*), grammatical construction may be faulty because of the inadequacy of the intellectual antecedents of the syntactic process or the involvement of a specific linguistic difficulty. Klein (*258*) epitomized the problem under study as follows. Defective thought involves either the state preceding verbalization only, or there is a global defect of intelligence which gives rise to a secondary language difficulty. To be expressed in words, thought must fulfill the following conditions. Formal thought, which involves the establishment of relations and acts of comparison must be intact; furthermore, there must be "*thought material*" which can be translated into language processes. On the other hand, thought processes can only be expressed to the extent that "*speech material*" is available. Weisenburg and McBride (quoted by Meyers *327*) assert that "language symbols and verbal formulations permeate mental functions to a far greater extent in some persons than in others and that for this reason greater or smaller manifestations of general intellectual disorder may appear in different dysphasic persons." (See also Reitan, *404*.)

Whatever the intimate mechanism of the processes referred to by Pick's expression "the way from thought to speech," it involves a highly complex and exceedingly vulnerable chain of integrative acts. (The reverse way, from speech to thought, will be discussed under the heading "Receptive Disorders.") Brissaud (*68*) speaks of "un défaut de l'adaption de l'idée à mot et du mot à l'idée." In studying ideo-symbolic disorders, it may be well to take advantage of Pick's metaphor which he did not exploit to the full. If the patient finds the way from thought to speech blocked altogether, we are dealing with *amnestic* disturbances; if he is unable to execute the steps intended to lead him to the goal of thought, with *paraphasic* disturbances. The latter, in turn, include syntactic, verbal, and literal paraphasias. The process of verbalization may go astray for various reasons. The patient may not be able to find words or, without necessarily being aware of it, use wrong words. He may have difficulty in finding the words necessary to express whatever he is able to think. Whatever words he does find are apt to be connected in a faulty fashion and, moreover, to be intermingled not only with words which do not express what he intends to say but also with more or less severely mutilated words. They correspond to the bizarre and absurd movements of the apractic patient. If the patient is at all aware of the wrong choice of words, he may become confused, or, because of the lack of words with which to express his thoughts, his mentation may be inadequate from the beginning; the structure of language becomes disrupted by vicious circle mechanisms.

Metaphorically speaking, ideo-symbolic disorders are caused by obstacles encountered on the "way from thought to speech." (To repeat our point, the patient may find the way blocked altogether or he is unable to execute the steps which would lead him to the goal of thought.) The disorders in question comprise two categories, namely, *evocative* (or amnestic) and *paraphasic* disorders which, in turn, include *syntactic, verbal* and *literal* paraphasias.

Evocative disorders, which may be combined with other ideo-symbolic disturbances, (see "Amnestic Aphasia"), involve the inability to ekphorize symbols for the purpose of verbalization of meaning, while paraphasic disorders consist in the faulty composition of symbols.

(1) *Syntactic paraphasias.* They occur if the exact translation of the thought scheme into the grammatical scheme is impossible. One of

Schiller's patients, when asked what a gown is answered: "Gown is a thing on in the morning and up on a bed." The disturbances in question are better known under the term *expressive pseudo-agrammatism* (Pick, Goldstein), or *expressive paragrammatism* (Kleist), but their inclusion under the paraphasias is justifiable in view of the fact that sentences are symbols of a higher order. *Impressive pseudo-agrammatism (paragrammatism)* is the inability to distinguish correct from incorrect grammatical constructions. Pick believes that both impressive and expressive agrammatism is an intellectual deficit occurring within the general framework of aphasic disorders. In the opinion of Kussmaul (*271*) the ability to use grammatical forms, the formation of correct inflection, declination and conjugation and the syntactically correct construction of sentences, i.e., the ability to arrange the parts of a sentence according to established usage, is the product of education which has become an automatic performance of the speech mechanism. He held that syntactic paraphasias may occur (a) in normal persons as a result of lack of concentration and the sequence of words and (b) as a result of organic brain lesions as, for example, circulatory disturbances causing general depression of awareness. In Wernicke's aphasia, the general construction of sentences may be essentially correct but the inflection and declination of the individual words is faulty.

(2) *Verbal paraphasias* involve the use of wrong words. Interestingly enough, the mischosen expression may belong to the same conceptual sphere as the correct one, and the close relationship between thought and language (and, at the same time, their instability in disease) comes to the fore by the emergence of a symbol referring to the appropriate class concept. The sensory aphasic patient speaks rapidly and does not appear to lack words but his vocabulary is limited, and the paraphasic expressions are intermingled with numerous iterations, circumlocutions, circumstantialities and perseverations. In sharp contrast to the relative absence of substantives there are abundant interjections. Like the syntactic variety of paraphasia, verbal paraphasia may be due to inattention (in which case it may occur even in normal persons) or it may be caused by more or less diffuse cerebral lesions. (Cf. Kussmaul.) Similarly, Dejerine

(*110*) believes that verbal aphasia may occur in healthy persons under the influence of affects, fatigue and inattention. It is worthy of note that paraphasias may complicate not only sensory but also motor disturbances of speech.

Weinstein a.ass. (*501*) observed paraphasic misnaming in patients harboring brain tumors of various location. The defect is apt to appear within the framework of an organic mental syndrome including anosognosia and disturbances of consciousness. In their series of cases the choice of the misnaming words appeared to be related to Freudian mechanisms. It is understandable that personal material came to the fore as their patients were in a state of organically conditioned "over-relaxation" (a state of depressed consciousness), in which mental processes are apt to lose precision and to be influenced by complexes. Apparently, it matters little whether the states in question are conditioned by states of sleep, or whether they have an organic basis. (Cf. anosognosia.)

(3) *Literal paraphasia* is the term applied to the most severe mutilation of words which, eventually, are no longer understandable. There occur severe distortions of sounds and sound complexes and also omissions of sounds (jargonaphasia). The following frequently cited case was reported by Osborn (*369*) in 1883. His patient read, as follows, the sentence "It shall be in the power of the College to examine or not to examine the Licentiate previous to his admission to a Fellowship as they think fit," "An the be wat in the tmother of the trothotodoote majorum or that emodrete eni enikastrai mestreit to ketra totombredei to re framtreido as kekristest."

The paraphasic patient may or may not be aware of his speech defect. Lordat described his paraphasias as follows. "Ainsi quand j'avais intention de demander un livre, je prononçais le nom d'une mouchoir ... Un autre mode de paramnesie consistait a l'invertir les lettres des syllables d'un mot composé que je venais de retrouver; par example, pour raisin je demandais du sairin; pour dire muselman, j'avais du penchant a dire sumulman." The already mentioned patient studied by Brobeil and Stallwitz was unable to enunciate a word unless he heard it first with his inner ear. However, as the patient reported after having reacquired his ability to speak, the acoustic images (or "blue-prints" of language) were frequently incorrect, although they were similar to those he tried to recall. At times he would pronounce the very same word he knew was inappropriate but it was the only one which could be actuated; at other times, however, he would pronounce a word other than that he had heard with his inner ear. Again, the word he intended to pronounce would not necessarily resemble the actually produced word.

RECEPTIVE DISORDERS

Wernicke's aphasia is not merely a disorder of language formulation, that is, an *expressive asymbolia* but, first and foremost, a *receptive disorder of speech*. Expressive speech is affected although the motor speech centers are anatomically intact. This was explained by Wernicke (*509, 511*), Kleist (*261*) and others on the ground that the acoustic word traces control the motor speech process. Goldstein (*174*) contended that the sensory process would come too late to influence the motor processes. In support of Wernicke's and Kleist's view it may be said that the sensory process controls the motor acts at least during the phase of learning, and that the integration between the two may be a very intimate one as everyone knows only too well who tries to get rid of a foreign accent. In this respect, children are in a more fortunate position as, in the child, no firm bounds have as yet been established between sensory and motor processes. The sensory process may have come too late to improve similar attempts which are made in the future. It should be noted that sensory processes influence motor processes in the adult. In the deaf, intonation, volume, pitch and inflexion of voice are altered, although the "feedback mechanism" works in a different way.

A. Pick found the following stages (ranging from "zero" to "full understanding") in the *comprehension of language*. (1) Inattention to auditory stimuli is absolute. (2) Speech and noise can be differentiated. (3) Speech and parts of words are recognized. (4) Word gestalten are correctly perceived and words automatically repeated without however being understood. (5) Words are voluntarily repeated without being understood. (6) Words can be understood if repeated. (7) Words are understood if, at the same time, the corresponding object is shown. (8) Words are understood after a word belonging to the same conceptual sphere has been recalled. (9) Both words and sentences are comprehended. Broadly speaking, disturbances of understanding of language correspond to perceptual or amnestic agnosia. The former is essentially a disturbance of perception of auditory gestalten. Agnosia for words is the inability to associate words with the awareness contents to which they correspond. Piéron (*390*) distinguished between *acoustic paragnosia*, i.e., the inner *distortion* of what is heard, and the inability to comprehend the *correctly* perceived word. Thus, the process of understanding speech cannot be fully expressed in gestaltpsychologic terms; understanding is not completed at the level of gestaltperception but involves the grasp of meaning, which is an intellectual function. (Cf. the "psychology and psychopathology of recognition," Figs. 42 and 43.) As has been demonstrated by sorting tests, a patient may have sufficiently adequate impressions of an object without recognizing it; similarly, an individual suffering from receptive aphasis may be able to repeat a word correctly, indicating that he has no difficulty in appreciating word gestalten, at least of those words he is able to duplicate but he does not necessarily know what the repeated words mean. It is true that, in rapid speech, the word gestalt may be badly mutilated. However, if a minimum of "characteristic details" is preserved difficulty in understanding does not usually arise. At a still higher level of "recognition" of meaning, a sentence may be grasped even though it be phrased in telegram style; and the gist of a story may be gathered from certain key sentences. Either observation proves the role of intellective factors in recognition and comprehension, in other words, demonstrates that the level specific resources of the highest strata are able to compensate to a degree for the defects of the lower levels. (See also "subcortical sensory aphasia" and Chapter I.)

DISTURBANCES OF WRITTEN LANGUAGE. APHASIC ALEXIA AND APHASIC AGRAPHIA

In the classic type of Wernicke's aphasia, the patient has difficulty in reading and writing, the disturbances being of verbal, literal or mixed character. Nevertheless, he may be able to read correctly without comprehending anything. Sometimes understanding is facilitated by reading aloud; at other times, by silent reading. There is no parallelism between the degree of alexia, agraphia and aphasia. Reading may be involved out of proportion to writing or, under exceptional conditions, may remain intact. If the patient is asked to write, he has difficulty in remembering the symbols of written speech, or he produces paraphasic mutilations of written words. In brief, he produced spoken and written paraphasias. (See, especially, refs. *332* and *427*.)

Dissociated forms of Wernicke's aphasia

AMNESTIC APHASIA

The leading symptom is the difficulty in finding words, particularly nouns. Apart from the halting speech due to the omission of words, speech melody and sentence construction is intact. There are no primary disturbances of written language and no paraphasias. The patient himself is aware of the defect rather like an otherwise normal person who finds it difficult to remember names. Liepmann (*301*) who held that amnestic aphasia is identical with transcortical motor aphasia, was contradicted by both Isserlin (*231*) and Heilbronner (*205*) on the ground that the amnestic disturbance of word finding in the latter is both more severe and, moreover, not limited to the names of persons and objects. Kleist expressed the belief that amnestic aphasia is a stage in the recovery from cortical sensory aphasia, while Goldstein interpreted it as a disturbance of the *"categorical attitude."* He argued that speech is one of the characteristics of human nature inasmuch as it is tied to man's capacity of categorical, or abstract behaviour as opposed to concrete behavior. In taking the abstract attitude, man is concerned with classes of objects; in taking the concrete attitude, on the other hand, he is concerned with the "concrete aspects of individual objects in their particular uniqueness." In taking the abstract attitude, he uses words as representatives of classes; in taking the concrete attitude, he regards words as individual properties of objects. Hence, because of

the impairment of abstract behavior, the patient is no longer able to use words as symbols for classes but merely as symbols for individual experiences. He is unable to classify objects according to some higher category, for example their functions, or colors according to their hue. All performances based on the loss of concepts are involved. However, Hauptmann (*197*), Schafer (*421*) and Isserlin and his associates (*232*) showed that amnestic aphasic patients, although the language defect made their task more difficult, are able to solve complex problems which require the use of abstract concepts in spite of their inability to recall words, and that they are able to classify objects according to their function and other categories. At the same time, the authors pointed out that deaf mutes show no primary defects of intelligence. Lotmar (*311*) showed that the patients understand the nature of objects they see without being able to name them. In a case reported by Misch and Frankl (*332*) the patient who could not recall the names of the cards played the game well!

CONDUCTION APHASIA

The salient feature of this rare form of aphasia is the severe limitation of repeating spoken language. There is little impairment of understanding which makes it relatively easy to establish contact with the patient. In contrast to the severe impairment of repeating spontaneous speech, series speech and reading are more or less intact. There may or may not be amnestic and paraphasic disturbances.

SUBCORTICAL SENSORY APHASIA (LICHTHEIM'S DISEASE)

The cardinal symptom of subcortical sensory aphasia (*381*) is the inability to understand spoken language, which may or may not be associated with sound deafness and noise deafness. Impairment of auditory acuity, although frequent, is of minor degree and generally out of proportion to the severity of receptive language and auditory recognition. The patient pays little if any attention to the sound of speech. Because of his inability to understand words, he is unable to repeat spoken language and to write from dictation while spontaneous writing is commonly preserved. Intellectual functions, inner language, copying and reading are intact. Paraphasias, if present, are inconspicuous. The disorder may or may not be associated with the inability to appreciate rhythms and melodies. Nielsen and Sult's (360) Case V could understand language well but no other sounds. (See above, "Amnestic agnostic auditory agnosia.")

Subcortical sensory aphasia is of particular interest from various angles. With respect to the doctrine of the level hierarchy of the nervous system and the operational dimensions of its individual levels it is noteworthy that Henneberg's (201) patient who was unable to appreciate the word gestalt, or only fragments of it, nevertheless "understood" the meaning of the word "canary," as evidenced by his answer that the word meant "the ordinary yellow bird," and the meaning of the word "mosquito," indicating that the examiner had spoken about something that "stings and at the same time sings in a low voice." These and similar observations already quoted strongly contradict Bay's (26) and Conrad's (97) concepts of aphasia. Moreover, the symptomatology of subcortical sensory aphasia has a bearing on the notion of "multilinear relay systems as models of class concepts." (Chapter III.) The patient indicated by his reaction that he had "grasped" the meaning of the word by reacting with a word that would denote the appropriate class concept or some other related concept. For example, when asked to repeat the word "turtle" he said "crocodile." Although he was unable to "grasp" the meaning of longer words and of three digit numbers he could follow a conversation by "guessing with astonishing speed the essence of the matter."

In reality, the term subcortical sensory aphasia ("subcortical acoustic verbal agnosia" of Nielsen and Fitzgibbon, 356) is a misnomer; the disorder may be produced either by cortical lesions, namely, the auditory division of level I.s. of the dominant hemisphere (Heschl's gyrus) or, according to Nielsen and Fitzgibbon, the interruption of the fiber tracts from both primary hearing centers to Wernicke's center of the dominant hemisphere in which case they believe the defect is produced by the "imperfect functioning of the minor side." (See also Pfeifer 381, who attributes the first description of the disorder to Kussmaul.)

It may well be that the pathology of pure word deafness is not uniform in that, in one group of cases, the formation of word gestalten is inadequate secondary to inadequate perception at level I, be it incident to a local cortical lesion or a lesion of the auditory radiations. In another group of cases, on the other hand, the configurational processes mediated at level II.s. are inadequate in spite of the adequacy of sound perception. Lastly, level I.s. and II.s. may be involved in combination. The matter will be further considered in conjunction with the pathophysiology of the cortical forms of aphasia.

SUBCORTICAL ALEXIA
(DEJERINE'S DISEASE)

Subcortical alexia ("cécité verbale pure"), an isolated inability to read, resembles subcortical sensory aphasia in that inner speech is intact. The patient cannot read even what he himself has written, be it letters, musical notes or mathematical symbols.

It is one of the perplexities of the history of human thought that perhaps the most bizarre disorder of speech, Dejerine's cécité verbale pure, should have been described long before, to my knowledge at least, any written record of the more common forms of aphasia existed. J. Schmid's (434) "De Oblivione Lectionis, Ex apoplexia. Salva scriptionis" (1673) is a classic description of the disorder which deserves to be quoted somewhat in full. (A verbatim quotation may be found in Bonvicini's article.) To facilitate the understanding of the seemingly endless Latin sentences, they will be broken up, and the translation of their fragments added in parenthesis. Schmid describes the nature of the speech disturbance afflicting a 65 year old man, Nicolaus Cambier, a "primarimus apud nos civis," that is, a most worthy member of the community. Superatis tanden Dei beneficio hostibus ipse atrocissimus, non semel instantem mortem qui minati erant (Having, at long last, by the grace of God, conquered the enemies who more than once threatened to bring his life to an abrupt end) ultimum debelandum linquebatur malum (there remained for him to fight, as the last evil to be conquered) quod characteres legere (his inability to read letters) multominus combinare nullatenus posset (much less to combine them to words) neque enim unam ab alteram distinguebat (nor could he distinguish one from the other) sed quod mirum est (however, miraculously) si nomen ipsi aloquod vel dictio scribenda traderetur (if someone asked him to write a letter or a sentence) prompte illum et orthographice in quocunique ipsi antea noto ideomate scribere sciebat (*he did know how to write letters* and words in any language he had known) scriptum autem propria licet manu legere, vel characteres distinguere et diagnoscere non proterat; (*but he could not read either what he had written with his own hand or to indicate why he had combined the individual letters in the way he had done*) si enim quae haec vel esset littera, (However, on being asked to point out individual letters) vel qua retione literae combinatae fuerint ex eo quaereretur (or to explain why he had combined them in a certain way) casu tantum vel scribendi consuetudine, sine omni judicio scriptionem peractam fuisse apparebat, ne que informatio ulla locum hebebat. (one gained the impression that the words had been put together fortuitously or by force of habit. Effects to teach him how to read were entirely fruitless.)*

The peculiar disturbance of reading is not without parallel in normal psychology. For example, a person, having just started to study shorthand writing may be unable to read the symbols written by himself which however can be deciphered by a more experienced person. Apparently, reading is generally more difficult than writing, perhaps because the evocation of visual images is aided by their motor engrams. In the process of reading, on the other hand, the visual impressions must be translated into thought without the benefit of an intermediary process. Interestingly enough, Warrington and Zangwill's (*495*) patient, who was unable to read, improved his performance somewhat by following the outlines of large letters with his index finger. "I can see the words," the patient remarked, "but I do not get what I am looking at. I can see the various letters and that but while I am looking at them I do not know what they are." The authors call attention to the fact that alexia is almost invariably associated with other visual

defects, e.g., in their own case, but, referring to the work of Holmes, of R. W. Brain, and of Hecaen and de Ajuriaguerra, and David assert, that alexia may exist in a pure form and that the presence of any of other visual deficit does not account for the diverse forms of visuo-linguistic loss. In their own case, they claim, the deficit was materially increased, if not produced, by the combination of visual field defects and oculomotor disability, that is, difficulties in scanning. The term "subcortical alexia" is just as inappropriate as the term subcortical sensory aphasia. Dejerine attributed the disorder to the interruption of the subcortical connections between the calcarine fissure and the angular gyrus, and the resulting block of visual stimuli on their way to the higher centers subserving the recognition of symbols. In preangular lesions on the other hand the patient can read but cannot translate written into spoken language, supposedly because of the interruption of association fibers extending from the angular gyrus to Wernicke's center. More recent observers however found the basal parts of the occipital lobe to be involved, especially the gyri lingualis and fusiformis. It is possible that Dejerine's disease, like Lichtheim's disease, is a composite disorder and, that, eventually, three forms will be recognized, namely, (a) a subcortical form proper, (b) a cortical variety and (c) a combined form which may be complicated by the defective integration of the visual apparatus with auxiliary motor mechanisms. Be this as it may, the analysis of Dejerine's disease in neuropsychological terms suggests that the patient is able to convert (or somatize) visuo-symbolic analogs, that is, the visual signs of language, be they letters, syllables, words, numerals etc. into visuo-motor analogs, that is to say, that he is able to perform movements whereby visual gestalten are duplicated but, nevertheless, is unable to recognize the signs of written language, although he, himself, produced them. He is unable to recognize the symbols in question at the configurational level, at the conceptual level or at both levels. (See also ref. *470*.)

TRANSCORTICAL SENSORY APHASIA

The patient does not understand what is spoken to him, in fact, even what he himself says sounds to him like an idiom with which he is not

---

* I am indebted for this translation to Felix Cleve, Ph.D.

fully familiar. In other words, transcortical sensory aphasia is an amnestic agnostic disorder. Spontaneous speech may be mutilated by paraphasias. The patient is able to repeat spoken language although in a parrot-like fashion only. He can read and write both spontaneously and from dictation but does not understand what he himself has written (58).

Broca's aphasia
(Cortical motor aphasia)

The classic form of Broca's aphasia

The incompetency of Broca's center may be compared with the inability on the part of a conductor to read a score and, hence, to lead his orchestra. The score corresponds to the directives received from Wernicke's center; the orchestra, to the lower motor area where there are located the foci for the muscles of the tongue, lips, jaws, soft palate, larynx, diaphragm and other respiratory muscles. (In the process of swallowing and related functions, some of the very same muscles are lead by other conductors as may be inferred from the fact that, in Broca's aphasia, the functions in question are apt to be intact.) We have already mentioned that the writing center is formed under the guidance of Broca's center but, sooner or later, may function autonomously, at least this would appear from the preservation of writing in subcortical motor aphasia. (See below.) Translated into neurological terms, the crucial defect involved in Broca's aphasia is the lack of integration of Wernicke's center with Broca's center due to the incompetency of the latter. Broca's aphasia (cortical motor aphasia) involves the partial or complete inability to talk ("aphemia"), and to repeat spoken language. Because of the dependence of the engrams of written language on those of spoken language and, perhaps, of the visual speech engrams on motor speech engrams (the integrational history of writing), Broca's aphasia is complicated by the inability to read and to write. The difficulty in writing involves both spontaneous writing and writing from dictation. However, the patient understands most of what is said to him and is able to copy slavishly. The inability to talk spontaneously is rarely complete and, whatever

fragments of speech remain, permit a differentiation between two abnormalities, namely, (a) aphemia and (b) articulomotor akinesia and parakinesia.

APHEMIA

Both literal and syntactic paraphasias may occur. The former resemble the paraphasias produced by sensory aphasic patients while the latter are different from the pseudo-agrammatism (paragrammatism) previously described. The mechanism of sensory aphasia is roughly comparable to ataxia due to sensory deficit; of motor aphasia, to inadequate coordination caused by motor deficit. We remind ourselves that pseudoagrammatism is characterized by the dilution of sentence structure due to the abundance of relational and auxiliary words, the paucity of essential words, alterations of the word order and confusion of prefixes, suffixes and inflections. In true agrammatism on the other hand, sentences are skeletized, that is, reduced to key words put together in telegram style. (*Telegrammatism.*) Because of the different structure of the various languages, the syntactic disturbances are more obtrusive in French and in German than in English. The patient's repertory of words is greatly reduced. Jackson called attention to the "*recurrent*" and "*occasional utterances.*" Whatever phrases and words are available may or may not be appropriately employed, the patients using the residues of speech as a means of "expressing" almost anything. In a way, even the entirely speechless patient resembles an intelligent animal which, were it not for its inability to talk, might be regarded as being almost human, while a person suffering from Wernicke's aphasia appears to be helpless and confused. In fact, he may appear to be manic, friendly or submissive. Moreover, the motor asphasic patient who is aware of his defe ct may become impatient, excited, or depressed (58).

HYPOKINETIC AND APRACTIC DISORDERS

In contrast to Wernicke's aphasia, the patient lacks the initiative to talk which results in poverty and slowness of speech. His efforts to articulate may be associated with apractic movements of the facial muscles. The monotony and the abrupt changes of intonation and the long intervals between the various utterances cause characteristic changes of the speech melody. Lüers (*314*) is inclined to attribute the hypokinetic component of Broca's aphasia to the interruption of pathways linking Broca's cortex with the medial nucleus of the thalamus.

APHASIC AGRAPHIA

The disturbances of written language consist in slowing up of writing, and in fragmentation of the words into incorrectly connected components. At the same time, there may be perseveration and difficulty in recalling the symbols of written speech. We have already mentioned that reading and writing may be so intimately associated with the recognition and interpretation of the symbols of spoken language that alexia and agraphic disturbances occur in consequence of aphasia (*58*).

Dissociated forms of Broca's aphasia

SUBCORTICAL MOTOR APHASIA

The patient cannot speak but can express himself in writing, which proves that inner speech is more or less preserved. Ordinarily, the main difference between Wernicke's and Broca's aphasia is expressed by the phrases "ne pas *savoir* parler" and "ne pas *pouvoir* parler." However, Brissaud's (*69*) famous definition fails to specify the difference between the subcortical variety of Broca's aphasia on the one hand and the cortical variety on the other, for the patient cannot speak in either variety of language disturbance. Neither can the different behavior of the two groups of aphasic patients be accounted for by the loss of the "word-concept," or "perte de la parole," as contrasted with "la perte de souvenir de procéder qu'il faut suivre pur articuler les mots." By "perte de la parole," Broca meant what was later called the "word concept," according to the classics a "combination of the sensory word and the motor word."

At the risk of straining the above proposed analogy to its very limits, we suggest that, in subcortical motor aphasia, the "conductor" is unable to lead the orchestra because of a motor deficit rather than the inability to read musical scores. In Broca's aphasia, we are dealing with a disturbance of inner speech; in subcortical motor aphasia, with an innervatory apractic disturbance. Now, subcortical motor aphasia must be differentiated not only from motor aphasia, but also from *dysarthria*. In the latter, the members of the orchestra are incapacitated and, since the very same individuals are supposed to fulfill different functions, dysarthria is associated with dysphagia. In subcortical motor aphasia on the other hand, swallowing is intact. In contrast to cortical sensory aphasia, where the integration between Wernicke's and Broca's center is at fault, subcortical motor aphasia is caused by the incoordination between Broca's center and the foci in the lower motor region. The disturbance may of course be of a mixed character. Not only may the conductor have difficulty in reading musical scores but he may be handicapped by apractic disturbances; one or more of the players may be absent, or crippled, and moreover, the musical score defective. Like in many other cortical lesions pure syndromes are exceptions rather than the rule but they no doubt exist. They are reducible to the very same pathophysiological mechanisms which operate, in essentially the same fashion, in other spheres of the central nervous system.

TRANSCORTICAL MOTOR APHASIA

The most prominent symptom is the severe limitation of spontaneous speech, while understanding, repeating spoken language, reading and writing from dictation is intact. We have already mentioned that the difficulty in word finding is more severe than in amnestic aphasia.

The topological aspects of the various types of aphasia will be discussed following a summary of their pathophysiologic features (*58, 469*).

Some rare forms of language disturbances

Disturbances of sign language

INABILITY TO EXECUTE AND TO UNDERSTAND GESTURES

Gestures are movements which accompany spoken language for the purpose of emphasis.

Critchley (*101*) regards gestures a form of italicized speech, while "pantomime is a dumb-show which expresses an idea." In motor aphasia the language of gestures is relatively preserved. By contrast, the sensory aphasic patient may lack the ability to execute gestures. They can apparently be somewhat better executed by those patients who are aware of being aphasic than those who lack the awareness of their defect. Pierre Marie (*320*) distinguishes between *emotional, conventional* and *descriptive gestures.* On the other hand, some patients are unable to execute gestures and to understand them. (Cécité mimique.)

DISTURBANCES OF SIGNALLING

Critchley described disorders of signalling in naval signal men. In one of his patients the disability was associated with other language disturbances. The patient, who had difficulty with Morse signals, was probably suffering from word blindness. Another patient could not execute Morse signals. The third naval man was unable to interpret hoists and signal flags but could read Morse with accuracy and speed. However, he had obvious difficulties in reading print or script.

APHASIA IN THE DEAF MUTE

Critchley's (*104*) case concerns a partial deaf mute who, as a result of a stroke, sustained a right-sided paralysis and, for a number of days, was deprived of what little speech had previously been possible to him. He could no longer lip read and was unable to understand people who communicated with him by finger-spelling. Grasset's (*181, 182*) patient developed a right-sided weakness but the defect of motor power and coordination was insufficient in degree to account for the failure to write or to finger-spell. However, the patient was able to reply with the left hand finger-alphabetically. For recent data, see Tureen a. ass. (*480*).

Disturbances of Shorthand Writing

Leischner (*289*) described five cases of this rare disorder in four of which the symptoms were caused by injury to the right parietal lobe while the fifth case was one of encephalitis. In four cases, defective shorthand writing was an isolated disturbance. The most frequent errors involved the choice of symbols expressing articles and other auxiliary words, tenses, prefixes and suffixes and the use of different symbols for one and the same word. Furthermore, there were errors in position writing (high, low and middle position) which play an important part in German shorthand.

Congenital alexia

Schilder (*427*) found that congenital alexia involves the inability to differentiate the spoken words into sounds and letters, which he attributed to a failure of development of cortical discriminative function. Congenital alexia, which is almost always associated with difficulty in writing, may be hereditary. Hallgren (*171*) believes that, at least in certain forms, the mode of inheritance is "monohybrid, autosomal dominant." As a rule there are no concomitant disturbances in copying, reading and writing of either numbers or musical notes. The patients may not only be excellent mathematicians but of superior general intelligence. The defect is related to both gnostic and aphasic mechanisms. It is of a composite nature and isolated alexia for numbers and musical notes is rare. Congenital alexia is only one of the various developmental diseases of psycho-neural functions, including *aphasia, congenital auditory imperception (developmental word deafness), developmental agraphia, mirror writing (99),* and *congenital stuttering. Congenital apraxia* on the other hand, is a congenital defect which manifests itself in abnormal clumsiness. (See also refs. *297* and *556*.)

Aphasia in the polyglot

According to Leischner (*288*) who reviewed some 30 cases of this rare disorder, only those persons are *true polyglots* who master more than one language and who do not show any language preference except one imposed upon them by accidental conditions. In these persons, lesions of the speech area produced more or less diffuse impairment of symbolic formulation and ex-

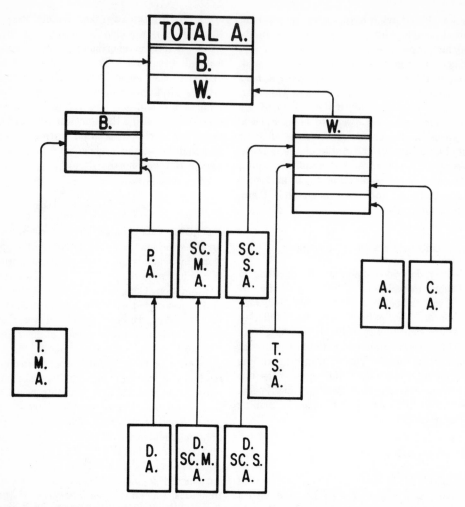

Fig. 47. Total aphasia as a combination of partial defects.

T.: total aphasia; W.: Wernicke's aphasia; B.: Broca's aphasia; P.A.: pure agraphia; S.C.M.A.: subcortical motor aphasia; S.S.C.A.: subcortical sensory aphasia; T.S.A.: transcortical sensory aphasia; A.A.: amnestic aphasia; C.A.: central aphasia; T.M.A.: transcortical motor aphasia; D.A.: dissociated forms of agraphia; D.SC.M.A.: dissociated forms of subcortical motor aphasia; D.SC.S.A.: dissociated forms of subcortical sensory aphasia.

pression. The patients are apt to mix words taken from several languages, to use *hybrid grammatical forms* (Pick) and to produce new words, for example those which are of partly German and partly of French derivation. *Polyglot agraphia* may occur in association with polyglot aphasia. The bizarre combinations of words produced by the patients are known as *"polyglot reactions."* Other patients are unable to switch from one language to another, at least on

certain days, when they will speak (or try to speak) one language while they speak a different language the next day. According to Leischner, the sensory speech centers of the polyglot extend into the second and the third temporal convolution and the adjacent portions of the inferior parietal lobule. He regards the above indicated parts of the temporal lobe as a reservoir of the enormous vocabulary of the polyglot while he attributes the selection of the appropriate elements of speech to the parietal lobe. Pitres (*394*) denied the existence of different centers for the different languages.

The *pseudo-polyglot* masters one language only. It is either the language which he has learned to speak first, or the one he has learned best, although he may speak and write several languages with remarkable facility. Pitres, who observed seven cases of aphasia in pseudo-polyglots, found relatively little involvement of the primary language in the presence of more or less severe impairment of the secondarily acquired language, or languages. Restitution of speech is apt to occur in the following order: (1) understanding of the primary language, (2) speaking of the primary language, (3) understanding of the secondary language and (4) speaking of the secondary language. Exceptions to Pitres' rule are attributed to the circumstances existing at the time of the onset of the aphasia. Kauders' (*251*) patient who sustained a cerebrovascular accident while talking to a French physician, produced French words whenever he talked to a nurse. The same patient, however, spoke German with his wife. Other exceptions to Pitres' rule have been attributed to emotional factors or to chance preference for one of the secondarily acquired languages, etc.

Pathophysiology of language

Figs. 47 and 48 indicate that the individual forms of aphasia are derivable from total aphasia (or, conversely, that total aphasia is made up of certain components), and that the language area whose involvement causes total aphasia is composed of individual speech centers, that is, cell stations which control the totality of integrative processes involved in symbolic formulation and expression. In general, it is true that the "localization of damage which destroys speech and the localization of speech are two different things." However, Jackson made the above quoted remark in reference to the then (1874) burning problem of localizing speech (le siège de la faculté du langage articulé") in Broca's center which, he contended, was too small to subserve the totality of speech functions. He believed that the causative lesion involves the corpus striatum, and that the extension of brain damage into the frontal lobes interferes with the

expressive components of speech, while its extension into the temporo-parietal lobes implicates its receptive components. To all intents and purposes, then, he regarded the corpus striatum and certain parts of the hemisphere as physiological centers rather than points of maximal vulnerability. (Cf. Liepmann's definition of the centers of eupraxia.) Not only did Jackson speak throughout his writings of higher and lower centers, but he attempted to explain the very principles of their function. His remark on the relationship between function and disturbance has been vastly overplayed, in fact, there appears to be a creeping tendency to assume that a given part of the central nervous system is unrelated to a given function—paradoxically, it appears—for the very reason that the "negative" of the function in question is associated with injury to the very same part of the nervous system to which, by certain schools of thought, the "positive" is attributed. Even if we disregard this extreme position, we feel that the relegation of the language area to an aphasia producing area serves no useful purpose. How could injury to the former produce aphasia unless the local nerve cells actually controlled and coordinated the crucial physiological processes involved in language functions? No doubt the basal ganglia cooperate with other cell stations in maintaining the coordination of volitional movements but no one in his right mind would call them a "tremor producing" complex of nerve cells.

It was H. Head, (*200*) one of the most eloquent opponents of the identification of functions with centers, who remarked that the knee is not a center of gait because injury to the knee interferes with walking. "The abnormal manifestations following severe lesions of the brain which give origin to the physiological processes underlying symbolic thinking and expression are not the primary elements out of which speech has evolved but the form assumed when the complete and highly complicated functions are broken up . . . when a man has received an injury to his foot, he is found to be walking after awhile in a particular manner according to whether the wound affected his toe or his heel. The gait he assumes is not an elementary component of his normal method of walking." In other words, Head contends that, although the functions in question are broken up, the breakdown products do not constitute primary functional elements. Still, the characteristic features of abnormal gait are referable to the abnormal functions of the injured parts which, in turn, can be expressed in terms of their specific quotas of action (now lacking or altered) that is to say, those quotas which they contribute to gait under normal conditions. The above metaphor is of value for two reasons. Disease, an experiment performed by nature, makes us realize that the total performance is the integrated whole of partial performances of many specialized parts. Further, that living systems react to damage with more or less successful attempts at reintegration so that the clinical picture is the resultant of opposing forces. It is essential to understand joint mechanisms (omitting, for simplicity, the role of muscles, nerves, and central nervous system connections) to appreciate arthrogenic disturbances of gait. By the same token, it is necessary to appreciate the nature of language mechanisms to determine the individual varieties of language disturbances. Not only joint surfaces articulate, but, in a certain sense, the centers of language. In fact, the analysis of joint mechanisms, absurd as such attempt may appear to be, may well throw light upon the disorders of symbolic formulation and expression. (See below.)

Dissociation of the language mechanism results in Wernicke's aphasia if the sensory components are thrown out of function; in Broca's aphasia, if the motor elements of speech are eliminated. However, since language is both a psychoneural and an intellectual performance rather than a reflex mechanism properly so called, the terms "sensory" and "motor" as applied to language acquire of necessity a somewhat different connotation. The sensory segment of the language mechanism mediates receptive functions, including comprehension of spoken and written language. At the same time, it subserves the ideatory and ideo-symbolic phase of response determination, that is, inner speech, which precedes the audible and visible movements involved in expression.

Global impairment of the sensory speech centers involves defective reception, understanding and recall of the elements of speech which, because of the interrelationship of language and mentation, are apt to have reper-

cussions at the conceptual level. Depending on the involvement of the particular components of the language mechanism, there develops one or the other form of dissociation. *Subcortical sensory aphasia* (perceptual agnosia for the symbols of speech), *transcortical sensory aphasia* (amnestic agnosia for the symbols of speech), *conduction aphasia* (inability to repeat spoken language) and *amnestic aphasia* (inability to ekphorize the symbols of speech). Damage to Broca's center yields either *subcortical* or Broca's *cortical motor aphasia*. In the former, the patient is not speechless but cannot perform articulatory movements with the very same muscles which he is able to use for other performances; in transcortical aphasia, he is unable to speak spontaneously but can repeat spoken language. However, the various forms of aphasia may undergo even further dissociation in that a patient may be unable to enunciate, or to write, or to read only certain words, in fact, even certain letters only. What's more, he may be unable to speak, red, and write them only at times. (See "structural and temporal dissociation of function.")

The existence of certain aphasic symptoms which cannot be explained either singly or in combination by the involvement of the individual speech centers is disconcerting. Perhaps, the "plus symptoms of aphasia" are referable to the fact that the speech centers and certain adjacent parts of the cortex have a partially overlapping vascular supply or are apt to be involved in combination. Kleist (*259, 261*) holds that, in injury, paucity of speech impulses, *logorrhoea, echolalia, iterations* and *stereotypies* may complicate any type of aphasia, that they are unrelated to injury to the speech centers but, rather, caused by concomitant damage to the basal ganglia. Furthermore, it should be kept in mind that speech is a biological activity, whose involvement may give rise to reactions on the part of mechanisms with which it was previously integrated and whose nature may not be immediately apparent. Head's classification of language disturbances admits of a correlation between clinical and pathological findings to the extent only that *verbal, nominal, syntactic* and *semantic aphasia* can be translated into terms created by the classics. Conrad's interpretation of aphasia has completely lost touch with reality; he regarded any defective performance in the

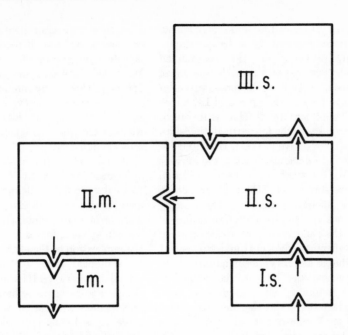

Fig. 48. Correlation of the individual types of aphasia with defective integration occurring at the "articulating surfaces" of the speech mediating mechanism.

sphere of language (indeed any nervous system function) either as a dedifferentiation of gestalten or as an arrest of differentiation at the stage of Vorgestalt. If this were true, the pathophysiology of the nervous system could be expressed in one single sentence.

In Fig. 48 the complex of speech centers is indicated by squares which correspond to the various levels of the cortical hierarchy indicated by the symbols I., II. and III. (It is hardly necessary to add that the figure is a "trick-drawing" and that the articulatory facets do not exist in fact.*) According to Herrick (206) and Lorente de Nò (310) the cortex is a synaptic field. Thus, it is not unreasonable to think of the speech area in terms of a neuron complex whose elements are reciprocally connected but whose organizational pattern, concurrently with the acquisition of language, is gradually superseded by predominantly unidirectional patterns of impulse conduction. Apart from feedback impulses, reciprocal connections would continue to operate only between the conceptual level (or

* They are merely pictorial symbols designed to permit a rapid "survey" of integrative processes.

"concept center") and Wernicke's center in the fashion III.s. ⇆ II.s. It is convenient to represent the speech centers as adjoining or "articulating" squares rather than as points. Their representation as squares facilitates the visualization of their mutual relationship and also of the potential effects of pathological processes. The contact between, or "articulation" of, two or more centers indicates their integration to higher units while the direction of the arrows marks the stream of the impulses which flow from one center to the other. In principle, apart from intra-central disturbances, defective integration may be due to the failure of a center to add its quota of action to the total process, or to utilize the inflow of impulses received from a neighboring center, or loss of mutual "contact." In terms of articulation, dysfunction is comparable to damage to one "facet," to both "facets" or to their failure to articulate.

(1) The different types of aphasia may be symbolized by the involvement of the various "articulating facets" singly or in combination. *Receptive speech* depends on the integrated activity of I.s. → II.s. → III.s; *expressive speech,*

on III.s. → II.s. II.m. → I.m; and *conversational language*, which requires immediate comprehension and response, on the coordinated activity of the entire speech area. In *subcortical sensory aphasia*, because of the preservation of inner language, the efferent surface of I.s. rather than the afferent surface of II.s. is involved. In *Wernicke's aphasia*, the four articulating sides of II.s., facing, respectively, III.s., II.m. and I.s. are implicated. In *amnestic aphasia*, the efferent surface of III.s.; in *transcortical sensory aphasia*, the receptive surface of III.s.; in *conduction aphasia*, the efferent surface of II.s., facing II.m; in *Broca's aphasia*, the receptive surface of II.m. facing II.s.; and, lastly, in *subcortical motor aphasia*, the efferent surface of II.m. Involvement of I.s. produces auditory deconfiguration. In amnestic aphasia, the item to be named is known; that is to say, represented as an integrated awareness content at the conceptual level (III.s.) but the "inter-center" integrative acts symbolized by the expression III.s. → II.s. fail to materialize. In other words, the item in question remains non-auditory or non-symbolized and, therefore, unnamed. In transcortical sensory aphasia on the other hand, the word designating an item is heard but remains a "mute" awareness content; it is not brought into relationship with the universal reference system operating at III.s, in other words, it is not comprehended, or "recognized."

(2) Contiguous elements are more likely to be implicated by appropriately localized lesions than by spatially unrelated lesions. Thus, the various types of aphasia represent more or less typical predilection patterns which depend primarily on factors of localization; secondarily, they depend on the dysfunction produced in the dependent centers and, at the same time, on repercussions in the primarily not involved parts of the language mechanism.

(3) Translated into neurological terms, subcortical sensory aphasia is due to defective integration of I.s. → II.s, while Wernicke's aphasia is due to inadequate integration of II.s. → III.s. → II.s. → II.m., etc. The integrative acts which unify the activities of contiguous centers may be involved in a twofold fashion and, thereby, produce different patterns of dissolution of function. For example, depending on the type of faulty integration of III.s. with

II.s., there will occur either conduction aphasia or amnest. aphasia; depending on the type of defective integration of II.s. with III.s., either Wernicke's aphasia or transcortical sensory aphasia. This is by no means a far fetched assumption; even the type of derangement of a simple reflex arc is different depending on whether the spinal ganglion of the anterior horn cells are damaged.

(4) Pure cases of aphasia may be interpreted in terms of involvement of individual or adjacent "articular facets," while mixed types of language disturbances are caused by the involvement of more or less odd combinations of damage. Conduction aphasia, for example, which is caused by the implication of the efferent facet of II.s., may be combined with the involvement of the articulation between III.s. and II.s, with resulting amnestic aphasia, paraphasia, and difficulties in understanding. In other words, the integrative processes involving both coordinated activity of II.s. and II.m. and of III.s. and II.s. have become defective.

(5) Although the above proposed concept of the organization of the speech mechanism is merely a crude analogy (unintentionally suggested by Head) it facilitates the comprehension of the more or less controversial entities of conduction aphasia, amnestic aphasia and transcortical sensory aphasia. Any of the three varieties may be understood either in terms of (a) a subordinate type of Wernicke's aphasia, (b) as incipient types or residual stages of Wernicke's aphasia or (c) as independent disease entities.

(a) If, within the framework of Wernicke's aphasia, the defect involves chiefly the integrative acts II.s. → II.m. one will be inclined to classify the resulting language disorder as conduction aphasia. This form, however, will not be pure but contaminated as it were by difficulty in understanding, paraphasias and paragrammatism due to the concomitant implication of II.s. → III.s. and III.s. → II.s. By the same token, if integrative acts II.s. → III.s. and, to some extent, III.s. → II.s. are involved, one will be justified to classify the disturbance as transcortical sensory aphasia (a difficulty in comprehension of spoken language) combined with some degree of amnestic aphasia, paraphasia and paragrammatism, and also with difficulty in repeating spoken language. Lastly, if, within the total disturbance complex of Wernicke's aphasia, the partial function III.s. → II.s. is more severely compromised than the others, the term amnestic aphasia will apply. Again, the disturbance will not necessarily be pure; rather, it will be combined with difficulty in understanding, paraphasia and paragrammatism in repeating spoken language.

(b) If, in the course of development of Wernicke's aphasia, the involvement of one or the other subgroup of integrative processes occurs early in the disease, the patient, depending on the involvement of a particular component of the total process, will temporarily display symptoms of amnestic aphasia, or of conduction aphasia, or of transcortical sensory aphasia. Similar disturbances are apt to occur if, in the course of recovery from Wernicke's aphasia, any of the three above named conditions disappears as the last one, or if they become permanent. Hence, any of the three above discussed language disorders may be regarded either as a *stage of recovery* from Wernicke's aphasia, or as an *early stage* of the same disorder.

(c) If the integrative processes underlying the individual subgroups are involved in isolation, there may develop conduction aphasia, amnestic aphasia and transcortical sensory aphasia as independent entities. This sequence of events occurs more often in amnestic aphasia than in the remaining disorders of language. The different ways in which language processes can be implicated may be readily recognized as instances of structural dissociation of function.

(6) Transcortical motor aphasia, the inability to speak spontaneously for lack of words, was interpreted by the classics as interruption of the association III.s. → II.m. They postulated functional links which, supposedly, developed as a result of the practically synchronous actuation of thought processes and the corresponding motor patterns of speech. However, since such association is difficult to accept on anatomical grounds, we propose, as an alternative theory, that the basic mechanism of transcortical motor aphasia consists in the difficulty of integrating process III.s. → II.s. with process II.s. → II.m. At the same time, we assume that III.s. → II.s. remains available for the purpose of inner language and II.s. → II.m. for the repetition of spoken lan-

guage. However, as in other speech disturbances, composite patterns of involvement may occur.

(7) Alexia is either an agnostic disturbance which develops within the framework of visual agnosia or a disorder of language, in which case it appears as a component part of an aphasic syndrome. By the same token, agraphia is either an apractic disorder which occurs within the setting of more or less generalized apraxia, or a disorder of written language, in which case it is apt to be combined with other aphasic disturbances. However, since the severity of agraphia may be out of proportion to the comparatively minor involvement of spoken language, it is doubtful whether the former can be attributed to the latter. Conceivably, this type of agraphia may be looked upon as a manifestation of structural dissociation of function. In disease, an apparently dependent fraction may behave like an independent one; on the other hand, as illustrated for example by the frequent association of alexia with color agnosia, two independent performances may appear to be interrelated as if a basic function were involved.

BRAIN LESIONS CAUSING APHASIA

Projected upon the cortex, square II.s. (Fig. (48) occupies the posterior portion of the first temporal convolution; II.m., the foot of the first frontal convolution. The two centers, which appear to extend into the cortex of the Island of Reil, are connected by intracortical and subcortical association fibers and, if the writing and reading centers are included, occupy the foot of the second frontal convolution and the angular gyrus. Center I.s., which occupies Heschl's gyri of the superior bank of the temporal lobe, is contiguous with II.s. while I.m., the lower rolandic region, is contiguous with the opercular portion of II.m. Segment III.s. occupies a large portion of the temporo-parieto-occipital cortex particularly of the dominant hemisphere.

The essential validity of the classic concept of aphasia is brought out by experiences with war injured persons and by the clinical data evaluated by Isserlin (*231*) and others. They show that motor disturbances of language are caused by lesions in the anterior part of the dominant hemisphere, sensory disturbances in those of the posterior portion and that, within either part, points of maximal vulnerability exist. It would take us too far afield to list the opinions of the various authorities in greater detail. Because of the exceptional importance of Schiller's (428) observations, we prefer to call the reader's attention to his already quoted article, and to quote his conclusions somewhat in full. He found that wounds affecting the lower part of the precentral gyrus produce disturbances in articulation, inflection and speech, poverty of speech, and telegrammatic style. Repercussions on other aspects of speech including impairment of word finding may also be noted. The more the lesion enroaches upon the temporal lobe, the more impaired is the auditory control of what the patient says and his understanding of word sounds. The nearer to the frontal lobe a temporal lesion is situated, the more will the involved performance be "tinged with frontal characteristics." Telegrammatic style will be prominent together with other syntactic shortcomings. Paraphasia and jargon are the outcome of most lesions of the first temporal convolution but, when the former are present, the parietal lobe is also affected. The further back the lesion in the right temporal convolution, the greater is the disturbance of reading and writing in addition to auditory incomprehension. In parietal lobe lesions all aspects of speech relative to orientation in space are affected. Writing, a translation of words into symbols of speech, is grossly impaired together with reading and calculating. In frontoparietal lesions, difficulty of recall of the symbols of speech occurs with characteristic frequency. The more widespread the lesion and the further back up and along the slant of the sylvian fissure, the more prominent is the patient's intellectual loss. (See also Brown and Simonson, 73.)

While the above suggested model of the speech mechanism may be criticized as mechanistic, it appears to be sufficiently flexible to categorize the various clinical types of language disorders. At the same time, it is not incompatible with the general principles of nervous system organization. The type of the "articulation" of the various components of the speech mechanism illustrates although in a crude fashion only the general pattern of integration underlying language processes. Complete chaos would result if one were to alter the relative position of the speech

centers or to reverse the direction of the arrows in diagram 48, that is to say, the mutual relation of speech centers. Motor aphasia would then be likely to occur in combination with homonymous hemianopsia, and Wernicke's aphasia with akinesia. And if one were to discard the diagrams altogether, the speech mechanism would be left hanging in mid-air. About the intimate mechanism of the integrative acts going on between and within the individual centers nothing is known, and Sigmund Freud's (149) remark that "within the speech area the individual associations and transmissions of energy occur with a complexity which defies comprehension" holds true as it did in 1891.

If hot and cold water flow into a basin, the two streams of fluid mix while the path of the individual particles remains unknown. It is intriguing to speculate about what might happen if one were to substitute the square in diagram 48 by tanks, and the arrow heads by valves and then to imagine that the tanks are filled with fluids of various colors. To integrate the individual tanks, the valves must work in certain combinations so that, depending on what has gone wrong with an individual valve or in certain sets of valves, one or the other type of aphasia will ensue. The movements of the valves and the mixing of the fluids is of course not a passive process but a process of response determination on the part of biological units.

THE LANGUAGE OF NUMBERS

Mathematics is a language which expresses meanings, and poduces meaningful relationships between quantities, by the manipulation of numbers. Numbers, in turn, are a special category of concepts. In discussing disorders of recognition and skill we have almost lost sight of the fact that deviations from an average level of efficiency may occur in either direction and, accordingly, depending on the direction in which it occurs, produce either patients or prodigies. No doubt there exist not only diverse forms of visual agnosia and diverse forms of apraxias but, contrarily, of "hyper-gnosias" and "hyperpraxias." It would take us too far afield to study the physiology of prodigies, for example the mental makeup of persons who are exceptionally gifted for languages, or which show astonishing motor skill. However, in a work devoted to higher cerebral functions, the question of exceptional ability cannot be entirely ignored. We have chosen the subject of mathematical, intellectual and artistic ability. Superior intellectual endowment was discussed in the preceding chapter. Artistic ability requires a study of its own, to which the following chapter will be devoted.

Akalkulia and dyscalculia

The terms akalkulia and dyscalculia designate different degrees of the difficulty to operate with numbers. In either case, *structural* and *temporal* dissociation may be encountered. The inability to name figures does not necessarily abolish the ability to operate with them whereas, in other cases, arithmetical disturbances can be quite definitely traced to figure anomia. Certain patients are able to read figures when written out in letters, but are unable to understand them when represented in numerals. There may be loss of the ability to count, or the patient has lost his capacity to understand the meaning of operational symbols. Nevertheless, they may succeed when asked to perform the corresponding mathematical operations. In certain cases, the patient is unable to indicate the positional value of individual numerals. In others, he may know the place value while reading but may fail when asked to write the figure. Specific arithmetical *counting disturbances* as well as *figure disturbances* such as *figure-aphasia*, *figure-agraphia* and *figure-deafness* do not necessarily cause (global) *acalculia* properly so called. Any mathematical operation such as subtraction, multiplication etc., may be separately involved. When asked which number, 7 or 3, is larger, the patient may have to count, beginning with 1, in order to arrive at the series meaning of 7, and to compare it with that of 3 (*380*).

These examples prove that there is for all practical purposes no limit to the "structural dissociability" of mathematical aptitude under the influence of disease. (For details, see Henschen, *202*, and Isserlin, *231*.) There are so many combinations in which the residual functions may be combined that the disturbance cannot be explained by the loss of a basic function, for example "direction in space" as attempted, among others, by Lange (*272*). To invoke basic functions to account for the various dissociation patterns would be self-defeating for one would have to stipulate almost as many if not more basic functions than there are elementary disturbances. What's more, the combination of structural with "temporal dissociation" confirms the concept that the various *functions must be interpreted in terms of individual integrative acts or of dynamic fractions.*

Brain lesions causing disorders of mathematical ability (*36, 56, 184, 202*). Like other cerebral functions of a higher order, mathematical ability is not localized in any circumscribed cortical territory. However, there appear to be "ultimately responsible" parts of the brain without which the smooth integration of the dynamic fractions (of which mathematical ability is composed) is impossible. Available evidence suggests that the sensory component of the language of mathematics may be involved by temporo-parieto-occipital lesions; the motor, in precentral lesions. Perhaps, the area of maximal vulnerability lies in the inferior parietal lobule or its vicinity, namely, the inferior portion of the superior. The aptitude to operate with mathematical concepts depends however largely on various sensory, more particularly optic and to a lesser extent acoustic instrumentalities; in other words, mathematical like non-mathematical concepts find and utilize various ways of integration and of symbolic formulation and expression. While direct evidence is lacking, it is not unreasonable to assume that the mathematical prodigies Whatley, Jungreis and Colburn (see below) would have been more severely handicapped by lesions in the optic sphere, Inaudi in the auditory sphere. That disturbances in the mathematical sphere are rarely isolated is only to be expected, and does not justify their interpretation as global depression of the whole-function of the brain for, if this were the case, dyscalculia and acalculia, either singly or in combination with other disturbances, should occur with equal frequency in brain lesions of *any* location. Of course, if the global performance of the brain be depressed, mathematical functions will not escape; in fact they may be involved in the very early stages of the disease. The integrational history of the various performances referred to as mathematical ability explains the preferential combination of acalculia with certain other disturbances constituting Gerstmann's syndrome, a group of mutually related though not necessarily interlinked dysfunctions (*11, 167, 432*).

No doubt the seemingly unitary realm of mathematical aptitude is composed of potentially associated individual factors. Haecker and Ziehen (*189*), who subjected mathematical ability to a detailed psychologic analysis, distinguished between a *spatial* and a *logical* factor which however are not necessarily combined. The spatial element includes the perception of gestalten, especially in regard to quantity-relationships, memory for spatial figures, spatial abstraction, including the appreciation of common traits and relations, spatial combinations, including grasping, recall, and discovering of intricate relations. The logical component includes the formation of picturable and especially non-picturable sharply defined concepts, for example triangle, sinus, logarithm, tensor etc., and also conceptual abstraction as well as comprehension, remembering and discovery of general and conceptual contexts, particularly of those of a quantitative nature and, further, the mental grasp, retention and power of independent reasoning both in single steps and contextual sequences of reasoning processes. Other essential components of mathematical ability include counting, memory for figures and, lastly, comprehension and retention of symbols and of course the ability to operate with them. Confirming Mitchell's (*339*) more general conclusions, the authors point out that the individual traits are relatively independent from one another and that they may occur in various combinations. All of them however appear to be related to the awareness of relationships between magnitudes and the ability to work with concepts that embody these relations. According to Blackwell (*50*), mathematical ability depends on four factors, namely, one similar to the factor *g* of Spearman, (a general factor, roughly corresponding to what is known as general intelligence), an imagery factor, and one involving the manipulation of verbal data; the fourth factor is hypothetical (*488a*). The *g* factor is described as the capacity for selective quantitative thinking and deductive reasoning, involving the ability to apply general principles to particular cases in number, symbolic

and geometrical work, and the power to abstract, generalize and to use the essential features of a given complex situation and to make deductions for the elucidation of other complex situations.

Mathematical prodigies

The capacity to operate with numbers is relatively independent of the general level of intelligence and, conversely, lack of mathematical ability consistent with supreme mental endowment. It has always been a source of comfort to poor mathematicians that both computational ability and mathematical reasoning power is compatible with general intellectual mediocrity, indeed, even with downright inferiority. Goethe is a classic example of lack of mathematical aptitude. Having been well aware of the importance of mathematics but conscious of his own limitations, he wrote: "I cannot boast of any culture in the realm of mathematical thought, and therefore keep aloof from sciences depending on exact measurements which, lately, have sprung up everywhere." On another occasion he said: "Nobody can possibly shy away from figures more than I do" (*170a*).

Mitchell (*333*), himself a mathematician of considerable ability, to whose paper we shall frequently have occasion to refer, distinguishes between three types of individuals endowed with superior mathematical faculties. The *calculating* prodigies think merely of the properties of numbers and of series; they show no mathematical insight properly so called, and the shortcuts used are of a relatively simple nature; in fact their viewpoint is never even arithmetical. The *arithmetical* prodigies, being interested in operations of calculation rather than the properties of numbers, show a fairly well developed knowledge of arithmetic and a distinctly arithmetical point of view. The *mathematical* prodigies know how to take a distinctly algebraic point of view, to generalize and to discover all sorts of ingenious shortcuts and symmetries.

As the various case reports demonstrate, the achievements of these individuals border on the miraculous irrespective of the group to which they belong. It is true that many of these prodigies were sensationalized in the lay press, but, fortunately, a large body of evidence exists which establishes historical truth. For instance,

Dase numbered among his friends many eminent mathematicians and was frequently mentioned in the Gauss-Schumacher letters. Bidder published his method of arithmetic and the procedure he devised for computing compound interests has been widely commented upon in the mathematical literature (65). He was a member of the Institute of Civil Engineers and frequently testified before Parliamentary Committees who had come to rely on his prodigious memory. Inaudi, at the age of 12, was presented before the Paris Anthropologic Society by Charcot (440). Relatively recently, the arithmetical prodigy Jungreis was studied by Brill (67), and an imbecile individual showing remarkable calculating ability by Scheerer and his associates (425). The material here presented is based to a large extent on publications by Moebius (334) and Mitchell (333), with the emphasis however on various abilities rather than on biographical data.

Peak Performances

Colburn found, mentally, by successive multiplications, the 16th power of a one-figure number, the square root of a 6 figure number and the cube root of a 9 figure number before the original number could be written down. He immediately identified 36,083 as a prime number and found, by mental calculation, the factors 641 and 6,700,417 of 4,294,976,297 to equal $2^{32} - 1$. Inaudi, in addition to solving algebraic expressions of the first and even those of a higher degree, solved such problems as the resolution of a 4 or 5 figure number into the sum of four squares. Dase multiplied mentally two 8-figure numbers in 54 seconds, two 20-figure numbers in six minutes, two 40-figure numbers in 40 minutes and two 100-figure numbers in 8¾ hours; he could extract the square root of a 60-figure number in 52 minutes. Buxton was able to calculate while working or talking. Mondeux, too, could solve a problem while attending to other things. On July 14, 1952, "Time" magazine devoted a short article to the mathematical prodigy Shakuntala Devi, an Indian girl, then 20 years old, who, like Gauss (see below) discovered her extraordinary arithmetical ability as a child. Without knowing how she did it, she

extracted the 20th root of a 42 digit and multiplied figures that yielded a 9 digit result.

Precocity

The "mathematical drive" may come to the fore with irresistible force and at an incredibly early age. Gauss (158), and Whatley (517), later Archbishop of Dublin, showed astonishing calculating ability at the age of three. When ten years old, Gauss was ready to begin with the study of higher analysis and, at the age of 14, could read the works of Euler, Lagrange and Newton. Inaudi showed great calculating ability at the age of four, Ampère between three and five, Stafford and Colburn at six, others between six and ten years of age. At the age of eleven, Blaise Pascal discovered, entirely without tutelage, many elementary geometrical theories, among them the theorem that the interior angles of a triangle equal two right angles. He constructed a geometry of his own and covered the ground as far as the 32 propositions of Euclid. At the age of sixteen, he wrote a paper on conic sections. Gall said that an advocate came to him complaining that his five year old son was occupied exclusively with numbers and calculations and that it was impossible for him to fix his attention on anything else. Inaudi, when a six year old boy, started to figure with the aid of pebbles and made rapid progress after his brother had told him the names of figures. (He did not learn to read or write before the age of twenty.) Dr. Ferrol said that figuring was a passion with him even when he was a child and that he greatly enjoyed performing algebraic operations. He learned them with such incredible speed that he thought he was merely repeating previous experiences and that he must have lived before. When alone, Ferrol, seemingly without effort, would continuously turn over the most involved mathematical problems in his mind. Bidder, by his eleventh year, was already in possession of a method by which he could solve compound interest problems mentally almost as rapidly as a good computer using a table of logarithms. The three following persons were all prodigies at the age of six. Stafford was able to calculate mentally the number of barley corns, 616,760, in 1040 rods, Colburn could extract square roots with little effort and Jungreis could instantly give the totals of formidable columns. Mitchell states that, of 24 prodigies studied, 18 were precocious.

HEREDITY

We have already mentioned that the Bernouilli family produced several famous mathematicians in three generations and that the mathematical genius was inheritable in the Bidder family (43). Diamandi's father had an excellent memory and one brother and one sister out of a family of fourteen people shared his ability for mental arithmetic. A maternal uncle of Gauss was a man of considerable mathematical and mechanical talent, and Jungreis' grandfather was considered a "mathematical wizard." The Cassinis were mathematicians from father to son and Euler and his children were all mathematicians of various proficiency.

MEMORY

Buxton could retain long numbers for weeks and even months and performed enormous calculations which would occupy him for a long time. Bidder could memorize 24 figures in ½ minute. Zamboni, while stationed in a railway depot, amused himself by memorizing a vast body of data related to time tables and distances between cities, populations, tariffs, etc. Jungreis, when six years old, was given numbers from 4 to 6 digits to remember. He could repeat them by heart up to 45 minutes later. Inaudi's mathematical memory was stupendous. He could remember 5 or 6 words only at one time, but had no difficulties in recalling figures from 25 to 30 digits and to cite them either forward or backward. At the conclusion of the meetings at which his mathematical ability was demonstrated, he was able to recall every single problem and, on one occasion, repeated 40 figures. Gauss had an unsurpassed memory for figures and used in his mental calculations the decimals of logarithms from memory. He remembered the divisor of any number once examined.

Visual memory-types

Bidder, who was able to repeat 24 figures with one mistake only, had a photographic memory.

Bidder's son had inherited the gift of visual imagery of "numberforms" (154, 453) and a grandchild has also inherited it, although to a lesser degree. Bidder Jr. said: "If I perform a sum mentally it always proceeds in a visible form in my mind. I cannot conceive of any other way possible of doing mental arithmetic." Colburn saw his calculations clearly before his mental eye. Diamandi had a numberform of a common variety which he saw localized within a grayish figure. It also served as a framework for any particular number or other visualized objects. Bidder preserved a numberform running from right to left, the numbers up to 12 being arranged in a circle as in a clock. Visual images appeared in some calculators in groups or dots; in others, as plain or colored numbers of various significance. Shortcuts or abbreviations in figuring may also be connected with numbers. The power of *gestaltperception* of some of the visual calculators is worthy of note. Dase was able to distinguish some 30 objects of a similar nature in a single moment as rapidly as other people can recognize 3 or 4, and Gauss could boast of similar abilities. On the other hand, Ferrol was a poor visual type as compared with Dase, and while learning to read had confused letters more often than other children.

Auditory memory-types

Inaudi's memory for figures was of the purely acoustic variety. He thought that the figures were whispered into his ear and, while calculating, almost always pronounced at least some of his words either with partial distinction and in a seemingly confused manner. Dr. Ferrol and Stafford, too, were acoustic types of calculators.

COMBINATION AND DISSOCIATION OF MATHEMATICAL APTITUDES

Prodigious calculating and mathematical ability may be combined either with outstanding intellectual endowment in a great many other fields or with average intelligence or a low average intelligence or, surprisingly, even with imbecillity, as we already had occasion to mention. On the other hand, a genius may have a scotoma for mathematics which in Goethe's case was a painfully positive one. Among the persons mentioned, Gauss, Whatley, Stafford and Ampère were men of wide interest. Ampère had a prodigious memory and Stafford, being at home in the fields of chemistry, botany, philosophy and history, an almost encyclopedic knowledge of the sciences. The same may be said about Leibniz and Newton to whom we owe some of the most important discoveries in the field of mathematics, and who excelled in so many other spheres of knowledge that their position is difficult to classify. At the opposite end of the scale we find individuals like Tom Fuller who came from Africa as a slave at the age of about 14 and Buxton who was of such limited intelligence that he could hardly understand anything. Elliot tells of "half an idiot" whose modes of abbreviation were ingenious. Midway between the extremes of the scale we may place, among others, Colburn who in general was of less mediocre intelligence. Nevertheless, he was not merely a human calculating machine but showed considerable reasoning capacity and invented processes ordinarily solved with the aid of algebra. Ferrol, while at the head of his class in mental arithmetic, was below average intelligence. I myself remember two of my classmates who excelled in mathematics but whose performance in other fields, except in physics, was not above average.

Elements of Mathematical Ability

High level performances in mathematics are not necessarily universal; rather, they may be broken down into a variety of individual aptitudes which may be combined in various ways, while other performances may be more or less undeveloped. Jungreis' ability for subtraction and multiplication for example was extremely poor. One of Bidder's brothers, while far from being a remarkable mathematician, possessed an excellent memory and showed the Bidder inclination for figures. Colburn showed no remarkable geometrical aptitude and, while able to extract roots of exact squares and cubes with little effort, found subtraction and division difficult. Dase who deserved more than anyone else the name of a human calculating machine was practically incapable of understanding the

principles of mathematics and, like Buxton, of very limited ability outside his "chosen" field. The distinguished mathematician Hadamard (*188*) wrote that he never felt at home in certain provinces of his science, more especially in what is known in technical terms as Sophus Lie's "continuous group theory." With this very same mathematical system some of his colleagues of equal scientific rank had familiarized themselves without apparent difficulty; what's more, they succeeded in developing the theory further.

A comparison of opposite ranges of mathematical aptitude

The contrast between acalculia and dyscalculia on the one hand and the achievements of mathematical prodigies on the other is of considerable theoretical interest. To a certain extent, opposite ranges of performance can be compared point by point. Some patients are unable to estimate the number of a few geometrical figures or objects while Dase and Gauss could determine the number of up to 30 objects at a glance. One of the patients described by Henschen (*202*) was unable to comprehend that the number 12 can be expressed in various ways, for instance, as 3 times 4 or 2 times 6, although he was able to perform the two multiplications correctly. Colburn, when asked to multiply 23 times 23, answered 529, or 33 times 16 plus 1. For him, numbers immediately displayed a relational meaning. Gauss, too, has a peculiar sense for the quick apprehension of complex relations of numbers. For example, when asked to add the figures from 1 to 100, (according to a different source from 1 to 60), Gauss, then a six year old child, immediately recognized the relationship between 99 and 1, between 98 and 2, between 97 and 3, which, like the other corresponding numbers of the series terminating with 50 and 50, add up to 100. The reader may decide for himself how many adult persons would have discovered this relationship, and, having become aware of them, recognized its significance.

Although the number of examples is not large they demonstrate I believe that, in principle, mathematical prodigies are preeminent in the very same performances in which brain injured persons are deficient. And while it would be difficult to find a representative number of mathematical prodigies each of which happens to excell in exactly the same categories in which brain injured persons have failed, the aptitude profile of the mathematical genius is no doubt the mirror image of depression of function produced by disease and leaves little room for psychologic speculation.

In spite of these data, various writers attempted to explain mathematical peak performances on psychologic grounds. For example, Scheerer and his associates (425) studied mathematical ability with particular reference to number manipulation and retention and to unusual features of memory in amented individuals. As to the former capacity, the authors hold that two groups of individuals exist, namely, those which use a concrete approach and never outgrow the state of concrete grouping and those who, using the abstract attitude, develop further toward a cognitive understanding of mathematics. As to the unusual features of memory the authors call attention to the fact that the retained material is not understood by the amented in a normal manner, that the individuals in question suffer from changes in figure-background organization as experienced during pathologic concreteness and that a defective organism will cling to those aspects of a situation and those features of the material which make concrete palpable sense to him. However, it is difficult to see how the selection of odd concrete material on the part of the amented can explain the superior way he deals with it. Likewise, it is difficult to understand why but a few aments should exhibit this superior mental capacity. Should not the existence of odd concrete material be a challenge to every demented person rather than a few only? Self-respecting morons usually indulge in different activities. Intensified concreteness of behavior and perversion of figure-background relationship do not explain superior mathematical ability either in the amented or the normal. As regards Brill's (67) ideas about the relations between the manipulation of pebbles by lightening calculators and events in the anal sphere the original article should be consulted, including the discussion which followed the presentation of Brill's paper. I for one do not believe that the riddle of the mathematical genius can be solved by psychological proctoscopy.

The truth of the matter is that supra-standard abnormality and sub-standard abnormality are opposite ranges of a continuum. In the former, normal traits are exaggerated whereas, in brain disease, the very same traits are entirely or partially lost.

Art

The work of art is the product of the union of the sense with what it loves.
LEONARDO DA VINCI

In studying artistic endeavour and realization, we shall continue our thesis along the lines followed thus far. In a certain sense, it may be said that the scientist translates objective reality into insight, a subjective state, while artists objectify subjective states. Yet, there are two varieties of subjective states; those experienced by the scientist are the result of investigative work which satisfies intellectual curiosity; those felt by the artist appeal primarily to the senses. Now, what is the nature of these inner states which, having been objectified, that is, having found expression in the work of art, appeal primarily to the senses? And how does the sense accomplish union with what it loves?

Introspective experiences of artists have been reported by many writers, including Bahle (4), Delacroix (20), Downey (23), Harding (37), Griswold (35), Hoffmann (44), Levey (64), Knowlson (56), Moebius (76), Patrick (86–88), Plaut (91), Reibmayr (103), Prescott (97) and others. These data will enable us to fall back upon the artists' personal experiences, to compare them with those of others and to interpret them in the light of brain mechanisms as we see them. The writers themselves think in terms of traditional psychology or their approach is purely esthetic, psychoanalytic or mystic. Take for instance the following passage from Maritain's "Creative Intuition in Art and Poetry": "What matters to us is the fact that there exists a common root of all the powers of the soul, which is hidden in the spiritual unconscious, and that there is in this spiritual unconscious a root activity in which the intellect and the imagination, as well as the powers of desire, love, and emotion, are engaged in common. The powers of the soul envelop one another, the universe of the sense perception is in the universe of the imagination, which is the universe of intelligence. And they are all, within the intellect, stirred and activated by the light of Illuminating Intellect." Unfortunately, problems of physiology are rarely if ever touched upon by the writers who speculate about the nature of art, indeed, no mention is made of the brain which happens to be the organ of art. Therefore, whatever common basis for discussion there is, is rather narrow. On the other hand, artistic endowment has in common significant features with mathematical aptitude which, as we have shown in the foregoing chapter, has "organic aspects",

that is, is rooted in cerebral organization. Let us, then, forget about the soul, the spiritual unconscious, the universe of sense perception and the like, and concentrate on biological data, chiefly the role of heredity, before we go any further.

NATURE AND NURTURE

The question of heredity versus environmental influences is a lively debated issue. That genius is a gift of the Gods has been claimed by the sages since the beginning of recorded history; and that it is handed down from generation to generation, although with favors to a chosen few only, is a widely held belief. A time honored subject of philosophical speculation, the question of inheritance of superior mental faculties has however been the subject of scientific inquiry since the time of Galton only.

On the whole, there have been two main lines of investigation centering around family pedigrees and identical twins reared apart. Primarily concerned with the question whether nature and nurture is of greater influence, Galton (30) found genius to run in families and environmental influences to play a minor role. Moebius (76), Kretschmer (57), Hoffman (44), Newman (82) and his associates (83, 106), Reinoehl (104), and many others arrived at quite similar conclusions. In studying their work, one finds frequent references to the Bach family which produced twelve outstanding musicians in six generations (and, incidentally, the Bidder and Bernouilli families with several generations of mathematicians), and to the Holbein, Titian and Granach families of painters. There were no less than 18 painters in three generations of the Tischbein family. Moebius lists well over 100 persons, among them sculptors, painters and musicians whom he classified according to their relationships into groups of father and son, uncle and nephew, brother and sister, etc.

Careful studies (82, 83, 129) revealed the existence of identical traits in remote sidelines and, within individuals of common descent, dormancy of talents over many generations. Among others, the Darwin-Galton and the Goethe-Haeckel-Feuerbach family (125) are cases in point. It may well be that the outstanding persons related by blood represent recessive phenotypes, which would explain the wide spacing and the apparently isolated appearance of the man of genius. Apparent exceptions to the rule that supernormal faculties are inheritable may be accounted for by the rarity of the appropriate genes; further, by the fact that outstanding ability in various fields depends on the concatenation of many individual traits which do not necessarily remain linked but, on the contrary, may be irretrievably lost in successive generations. To a certain extent, this trend may be compensated for by the intermarriage between artists, which, perhaps, is somewhat more frequent among musicians than among other artists.

Although the application of Mendelian laws in man as compared to its applicability in animals and plants is difficult, and instances of conspicuous aggregation of a particular faculty among individuals of common descent are rare, the individual groups in which such aggregations appear are too large to be explained away by coincidence; and the contact between individuals members, provided it has ever existed, is too loose to have been of any significance.

Those who favor the role of environmental factors would naturally claim that a son grown up in his father's workshop is bound to acquire his skill. There is of course no art without skill but skill is only part of the story, and nobody can possibly have learned how his father thinks creatively by watching him at work. Instances where open feud broke out when the son was unlike his progenitor and determined to follow his inner calling may seem to contradict the laws of heredity; actually, they cast doubt on the importance of environmental influences. Environmental and related psychologic factors may play a decisive role in influencing gifted persons in one way or another; they do not of themselves produce them.

GENIUS AND INSANITY

The following data which, too, speak in favour of a hereditary influences, will alert us, at the same time, as to the possible role of psychopathological factors. Juba (*50, 51*) made a tabulation of the life histories of 19,000 persons, 294 of whom were highly gifted individuals. She found "no significant relationships between highest mental capacity and psychic health and disease and no evidence to support the contention that the genesis of highest intellectual ability depends on psychic abnormalities . . . although milder psychotic traits within the limits of psychoneurosis, etc., exerted in some instances a stimulating influence." At the same time, Juba stated that the "geniuses and their families show a much higher incidence of psychosis and psychoneurosis and that, among the geniuses themselves, psychoses occurred in a frequency 10 times the incidence of the average population." Psychopathological, especially schizoid traits were more common in the group of 131 artists than in the group of 183 scientists. In the families of the probands, superior mental endowment was more frequent than in the average family.

————————— Sources of art

The subject matter of the present chapter may be conveniently subdivided into two main sections, dealing, respectively, with the *sources* of art and the *spheres* of art. The artist depends on skill to express inner states. Artistic endeavour embodies also affective and intellectual elements. Works of art are products of a creative urge the expression of which requires craftsmanship; and since, to produce works of art, skill must be guided by intelligence, the artists combine thought, skill and emotion which, to that extent, may be regarded as sources of art. They form a whole the parts of which can be only artificially divorced and which will be separately considered for the purpose of analysis only. The studies of the various spheres of art will be limited to the auditory and the visual arts, that is, *music* and the *fine arts*, omitting almost entirely composite arts such as poetry which involves both musical and intellective elements.

THE ROLE OF THOUGHT IN ART

It is a truism that there can be no artistic activity without an idea or inspiration that preceded it. In certain instances, the act of inspiration can be traced to core-oriented associations, in others, to fringe-oriented associations. In many instances, it is true, the origin of the creative idea is entirely obscure. Whatever mechanism may produce them, the ideas which take shape in the artist's mind are sooner or later elaborated, and it is therefore convenient for the purpose of presentation to subdivide artistic activity into two phases, namely, a phase of *artistic inspiration* and a phase of *creative work*.

The phase of artistic inspiration

The role of conceptual core material

Almost any scene or incident witnessed, any plot or any character studied may initiate thought sequences which, in their final form, may be only remotely related to the original observations. Zola and Balzac roamed the streets of Paris, observing incidents and making notes of scenes that aroused their interest and subsequently using them in one form or another. Even melodies, probably by awakening or reviving ideas conveying emotions of similar content, may inspire pieces of literary art (5).

In any case, inspiration appears to stem from the union of sensuous impressions and knowledge, feelings or other personal material. The associative process, initiated by diverse experiences and maintained by the extent of the artist's resources, may materialize with amazing speed. Patrick speaks of a flash coming without apparent reason. The moment Goethe learned of Lotte's death, he conceived the plan of his "Werther." "Like water which is about to freeze becomes a solid mass the moment the vessel is touched, the whole of the novel suddenly took form" (*32*).

The role of conceptual fringe-material

One of Bahle's (*4*) subjects, after reading a poem, experienced indefinite visual forms which evoked harmonies and melodies. Another composer, hearing words and phrases, had indefinite ideas of images or bridges, structures and colors which he called "fog-ideas" and which in turn gave rise to tonal forms passing through various stages of completion. Abstract texts were first translated into concrete images which led to certain emotional experiences. Mozart was inspired by beautiful scenery. Richard Wagner, fascinated by the panorama of the Swiss Alps, conceived the plan of his "Nibelungen." Mussorgsky's "Pictures at an Exhibition" was inspired by the paintings of his friend Hoffmann to whom he was deeply devoted. Van Beethoven remarked when asked how he derived his ideas: "Ideas come spontaneously; while walking through the woods; in the quiet of the night; more readily in the morning. They may be suggested by feelings and moods which I translate into tones and which poets would probably translate into words. The tones sound and ferment; they storm."

Judging from the following, Goethe (*32*) was aware of the role of fringe-elements: "I am rather of the opinion that the less comprehensible to the understanding a poetic production so much better is is." Undoubtedly, the beauty of Goethe's poems, as well as of other great poets, lies in the compelling consonance between the earthly melody and the cosmic depth of meaning.

The same long, seemingly endless span which separates experience, idea and expression, marks the thought of other artists, be it expressed in prose or poetry. Neither the artist nor the student attempting to analyze the artist's work will necessarily find immediate relationships between artistic production and the experiences that inspired them. Patrick (*87*) tells of poet who saw the moon coming out of a cloud, which reminded him of an owl. Another poet saw a nun leaning over a pool of flamingoes and imagined them to be in captivity. Hemmingway got the idea for a story while riding in a bus, apparently without any connection with what he happened to see—a department store in Paris.

Artistic inspiration may resemble delusional or hallucinatory experiences. Although it may be difficult to draw a line between true delusions and delusion-like states, and the same holds true for hallucinations, the terms "delusional" and "hallucinatory" as employed below should not be taken verbatim but, rather, understood to apply to borderline processes.

Delusional states

Leonardo da Vinci (*135*), having pondered over the motif of a landscape, visualized it in the chance patterns of a wall full of rents and cracks with the bricks sticking out. Turner thought he saw landscapes in random blots made by children who had dabbled with the containers in which his colors were mixed, and Menzel would imagine whole scenes in the texture of a blank canvas. Probably everyone has seen apparitions suggested by weird formations of clouds. My own teacher would turn paintings of some of his less gifted pupils upside down and point out "motifs" which he thought could be made use of. To Weber (*177*), seeing chairs and tables piled up on top of one another, the table tops and chairs suggested the head of notes, their legs the upward and downward sprawling tails of the notes, and the whole image, chords. Richard Wagner, who heard musical motifs in the noise made by the wheels of the train in which he was riding, composed part of his Meistersinger Ouverture on his trip from Venice to Vienna. Brahms heard melodies in the sounds of raindrops. Rimsky-Korsakoff, Schubert and a great many other composers heard melodies in the natural cadence of poems.

Hallucinatory states

Mozart and Schubert would imagine hearing melodies in their entirety (as if they were actually played) while other composers heard merely chords, phrases, motifs and themes on which they subsequently elaborated. Cowell (*16*) described "curious experiences of glorious sounds leaping unexpectedly into my mind, of original melodies, and complete harmonies which were of an exalted quality such as I had never heard before, nor imagined." Reznizek stated that his Donna Diana Ouverture sounded ready made and perfectly orchestrated before his ear and all he had to do was to write the musical notes. The "Creation" appeared with great vividness in Haydn's mind. A. W. Houseman would hear whole stanzas while to Neal musical ideas assumed a ghost-like quality. On occasion, however, musical thoughts appeared in a more abstract form, like a scheme to be completed in greater detail. In the visual arts, hallucinations have also been quite common. Thus, Corot saw in his studio "streams flowing, rivers charged with a thousand reflections of the sky and everything upon their banks." He imagined the sun rose and set for him in his home. Goethe experienced impressions of a "sensuous, animated, charming, varied hundredfold kind, just as a lively imagination produced them." The plot of "L'Arlésienne" came to Daudet as in a sudden hallucination on hearing two women call each other, one in a high shrill voice, the other in a deep tone at twilight. Blake admitted that he had written a poem as if someone had dictated it.

Dream-like states

Tartini saw and heard the devil playing the violin in a dream. On awakening, he wrote the "Devil's Sonata." Richard Wagner was in a hypnagogic state when he heard the opening passages of "Das Rheingold." Turner duplicated the contents of his dreams. Dürer saw in his sleep torrents of water fall from heaven. When he awoke in the morning he reproduced the scene on a canvas. Many poets and writers, as, for example, E. A. Poe, stated that ideas occurred to them while they were either dreaming or in a dream-like state of consciousness. Goethe said he wrote "Wilhelm Meister" while in a state reminiscent of somnambulism. Some verses of his poems which readily occurred to him and which simply demanded expression he composed as if in a dream. Many ideas were experienced at night while asleep. He arose from his bed and rushed to his desk to write them down as he heard them, preferably using a pencil rather than a pen for fear that scratching noises would awaken him. According to Moebius (*76*), the great poets composed "dreaming while awake" and Schopenhauer (*118*) remarked that "everybody is a poet while dreaming." Rachilde's works, with one exception, were all first conceived in dreams. The story of Dr. Jekyll and Mr. Hyde appeared to Stevenson in a dream. Max Brod sometimes conceived while dreaming verses and epigrams and, on one occasion, an entire novel. Likewise, several stanzas of his poem "Kubla Khan" appeared to Coleridge in his dream.

Many intuitive inspirations resemble dream-like experiences in that they are forgotten unless immediately recorded. Well aware of this possibility, Rosetti, Rimsky-Korsakoff and many other artists promptly made notes of their thoughts.

ozart's and Coleridge's prodigious memory permitted them to copy what they had dreamed. Conversely, Goethe elaborated some of his conscious experiences in his dreams: "What I see while awake," he wrote, "appears in my dreams, occurring with some regularity; and on opening my eyes, I see it like something new, complete, and altogether miraculous but forming but part of a whole."

Panoramic states

It is well known that experimental subjects may dream events of great complexity in an unbelievably short time, and it has often been reported that persons being in mortal danger "condense" a great many memories which makes their whole life appear to them to be concentrated in one single moment. "I walked off," Charles Darwin (18) wrote in an already quoted passage, and fell to the ground but the height was only seven or eight feet high. Nevertheless, the number of thoughts which passed through my mind during this short but sudden and wholly unexpected fall was astonishing and seems hardly compatible with what physiologists have, I believe, proved about each thought requiring quite an appreciable amount of time." Goethe described in his "Dichtung und Wahrheit" how the plan of a play in all its essential phases would suddenly flash into his mind. Mozart would dream or hear, in the waking state, entire compositions in a brief moment. Beethoven remarked that, in the process of composing, he would visualize and hear his instrumental music in its entirety and that there remained nothing for him but to write down the notes of the score which he quickly accomplished. On the other hand, a study of his notebooks show that, in some of his compositions at least, literally every bar was altered and that the way from the original version to the final version was long and arduous. ("I discard and try again until I am satisfied.") Arnold Bennet would conceive an entire play like a flash, and Felix Salten experienced the inspiration for his plays and novels in the single moment in which, he asserted, all events were literally visible and audible.

The phase of creative work

The phase of artistic creativity is characterized by a peculiar blending of tension, of deep satisfaction and of mental concentration inherent in absorbing, arranging, controlling and of selectively suppressing ideas which offer themselves.

The following is a composite picture of the mental state experienced and described by various artists. They speak of a feeling of restlessness, of pulsation and quivering, of fevered or rapturous states, of feverishness, of feverish excitation, of a volcanic fire, of the white heat of production, of furor, of intoxication, of madness, of a charming state, and of immeasurable sense of bliss and of ecstasy. While composing "The Creation," Haydn was in a state of almost intolerable excitement. "My body would feel like ice and, then, again, as if glowing in feverish heat. I was fearful of dying." The occurrence of feverish states of mind in association with creative effort must have been known throughout the ages, Plato, Aristotle and Seneca having compared the "frenzy" of the poet to the madness of the lunatic.

The feeling to be driven by an inscrutable force is depicted by the artists as an invincible impulse, an irresistible, compelling urge, the yoke of a mysterious power; as the feeling of complete passivity, of frank obsession, of an occult power holding the writer's pen, of words flowing spontaneously, against their will, of words coming so quickly as to make it almost impossible for the pen to follow, and of notes coming so fast that they seem to tumble over one another, of thousands of details chasing each other; and of the brain boiling over and throwing off images faster than they can be skimmed off.

Many artists refer to the *autonomy* of the products of their own minds. The characters created appear to assume an independent existence, and to lead the writer where they please. Goethe wrote that "the characters he created would not give him peace." They appeared in different scenes, he believed to hear fragments of their conversation, to be no longer thinking his own thought and to have only to look and to record what happened around him. Similarly, Hugh Walpole felt as if he were merely recording the actions and experiences of characters leading their own lives, and Hurst, that their characters made their own situations. At this point, I must quote Cowell's (26), the composer's, own words: "The experience of being in the throes of musical creation is distinctly an emotional one; there is a mere semblance of the intellectual in being able to steer and govern the meteors of sound that leap through the mind like volcanic fire in a glory of fullness unimaginable except perhaps by those who have heard them." Other artists, however, stress the importance of an intellectual factor. Thus, Leonardo da Vinci wrote in his *Trattato della Pittura*: "It is a poor master whose work runs ahead of his intellect; the one who strives for perfection in art is he whose intellect towers above his work." "What has been set down in an ardous moment," Tschaikowsky remarked, "must now be critically examined, extended or condensed as the form requires." According to Patrick (*87*), some poets compose in a cold, detached, objective manner and the vast majority of poems must be elaborated and revised. The ways and habits of many musicians, poets and sculptors are apparently quite similar. To quote Rodin (*108*): "Till the end of his task, it is necessary for the sculptor to maintain energetically, in the full light of his consciousness, his global idea, so as to reconduct to it and closely connect it with the smallest details of his work. And this cannot be done without a very severe strain of thought." Inasmuch as I know what I want, the fundamental idea never deserts me, it rises before me and grows," Beethoven said; and Richard Strauss (*130*) wrote that, in his own experience at least, musical ideas rarely extend over four measures and that the following passages are the result of concentrated mental effort. Richard Wagner's "Bacchanale and Venusberg Music" is so carefully thought out and so cunningly wrought that supreme intellectual mastery must have been at work to give it final form.

Not all artists are endowed with the power of mental concentration. Mozart, Schubert, and Berlioz were able to carry on a conversation and to compose at the same time. Kienzl was unable to write a letter in noisy surroundings but utterly undisturbed by noise while composing. Richard Wagner, on the other hand, was extremely distractible and removed all unnecessary objects from his studio. Reportedly he moved to Venice because it was the quietest town in Europe. The last lines of Coleridge's "Kubla Khan," about to take shape in the poet's mind, were irretrievably lost when a caller interrupted him.

The above data leave little doubt that artistic inspiration and creativity are phenomena that are apt to occur in the course of *dissociative states* which, in turn, are productive of a personal self and a coexisting para-personal self. The dissociative states differ however from the previously discussed, psychopathological dissociative reactions in two respects, namely, (a) *the activity of the personal self which organizes the oneroid elements produced in the trance-like condition of the para-personal self and* (b) *the nature of the motivational factors* (to be discussed below) *that produced the seeking reactions operating in the process of dissociation.* It hardly needs to be said that the two types of dissociative reactions are the two extremes of a scale, and that many transitional forms exist which make it difficult to sift the normal from the pathological.

THE ROLE OF SKILL IN ART

No doubt the exercise of skill on the part of the artist affords gratification which, perhaps, in the extreme case, may be pursued for its own sake but the relationships between skill and art are of a more complex nature than those between stimulus and response at high levels of sensory-motor integration. Levey (*64*), in a lucidly written article, takes issue with the art theories of his fellow-psychoanalysts Freud, Rank, Sachs and Sharpe, who describe as typical for the artist certain unconscious conflicts very commonly found among neurotics and ordinarily eventuating in daydreams and symptoms. Levey found that "none of these writers demonstrated why the artist's daydreams do not stop simply with being daydreams, how and under what circumstances special features of creativeness occur, and why only some of the artist's daydreams become inventions which he is then compelled to translate into artistic creation." It is precisely the translation of ideas into action that requires skill.

None of the above mentioned writers do justice to the role of skill; they take its existence for granted. Obviously, not every daydreamer masters the skill to translate phantasy into reality; not every daydreamer, even if he should happen to be endowed with manual skill, becomes an artist if he lacks drive; and not every daydreamer having the drive to do things becomes an artist, a great artist that is, if he lacks the necessary intelligence.

The role of skill in art was emphasized by many artists. Rodin (*108*) said that "the artist who neglects the technique will never attain his end, which is the interpretation of feelings and ideas, and that it is only too evident that if drawing is lacking and color is false, the most powerful emotion cannot find expression." And Hindemith (*43*) wrote: "Technical skill can never be great enough. No one is too able or too accomplished to learn more than he knows. Technique must be learned as a child learns to move his limbs; what was difficult first must become easy; it must be at one's instantaneous disposal; it must function so perfectly that its action is no longer noticed; it must sink to the level of subconscious activity."

The element of skill is apparent whenever tasks requiring great manual dexterity are carried out smoothly, speedily and, seemingly, without effort. As Michelangelo said: "Do the thing with a great amount of labor, so it seems to have been done almost without any" (*72*).

In evaluating the role of skill in art, we must however preserve an open mind; it is true that great skill is needed to paint so naturalistically as to induce the birds to pick on the grapes, as in Zeuxis' painting. On the other hand, a primitive still-life may have greater esthetic qualities because of its superior composition. Had Leonardo da Vinci grouped the individual characters in his painting "The Last Supper" in a different fashion or (we beg the reader's indulgence) painted some of them upside down, he might have displayed even greater skill than he did but it is questionable whether he had produced a work of art. On the other hand, if skill is lacking neither self-expression nor the intellective element involved in artistic endeavour will compensate for the lack of craftsmanship. Self-expression, no matter how eloquent (its role has been vastly overrated) and thought, no matter how productive, may be devoid of any esthethic quality. Although the intensity of esthetic pleasure does not necessarily parallel the degree of skill necessary to produce a work of art—even simple designs of lines and colors may please the higher senses—it is fair to say that, other things being equal, esthetic enjoyment grows with the skill involved in the artist's work. The gratification experienced by the artist grows with the skill displayed in creative effort; and the degree of esthetic pleasure involved in the appreciation of a work of art, both by the artist and the recipient, grows with the display of skill that goes into it, or went into it.

THE ROLE OF AFFECTIVITY IN ART

In the life of the creative mind, there may alternate periods of productivity with those of barreness. At the age of 31, Goethe wrote in his diary: "I must make some comment on the wheel which turns within me, in days good and bad. Passions, attachments, the drive to do things, inventing, perfecting and organizing, everything changes and moves in a regular cycle. Hilarity, crispness, strength, elasticity, weakness, apathy, lust,—they come and go. I have yet to find out how long it takes to make me circle around myself." Moebius (*77*) interprets the periods of productivity which, in Goethe's life, would mount to feverish drive and alternate with those of emptiness of the soul as phases of a mild manic-depressive psychosis. Kretschmer (*57*) believes that Albrecht Dürer was a cycloid personality, extremely productive in the hypomanic phase. Tepley (*132*) lists, as frankly manic–depressive individuals, Ludwig van Beethoven, Tolstoy, Tschaikowsky, and Charles Dickens.

It would thus appear, at least from Goethe's introspective experiences, that artistic inspiration is more likely to occur in manic or at least in euphoric states, and that artistic creation is more readily sustained than in states of dysphoria. In the former, both the core-elements and the fringe-elements of concepts, especially, perhaps, the fringes, are apt to produce a wealth of ideas. Because of their potentially palpable character, these elements may produce dissociative states which, owing to the dynamic, organizing rather than passive function of the personal self, differ from true, pathological, states of dissociation of consciousness. It is further to be noted that, although positive affects are conducive to artistic creation, negative affects do not necessarily play an inhibitory role and, although certain works of art express the artist's feelings, emotions and moods at the time of their creation, concordance does not exist throughout, as will be exemplified by some of Beethoven's and Tschaikovsky's compositions. Lastly, the emotions produced by a work of art in the recipient do not necessarily correspond to those expressed by the artist while the work of those artists who compose in a "cold, detached manner" (granted that they are the exception than the rule) may have a tremendous impact on the listener. The relationships between affective states on the one hand and artistic endeavour and realization on the other are very complex and can hardly be understood without further probing into the nature of art.

ARTISTIC BEHAVIOUR

What, ultimately, lies behind the desire to engage in artistic production? As expressed in terms of neuropsychology, *artistic behaviour is basically a system of seeking responses directed toward the realization of patterns having esthetic qualities.* As someone once said: "Art is an excuse to make a design." The realization of forms, be they auditory or visual, produces gratification which, acting as a self-perpetuating stimulus, gives rise to the "closed loop response" (Fig. 10), or maintenance of the productive processes which are carried to the point of saturation. We remind ourselves that gratification, the mode in which there is experienced the consummation of seeking reactions, assumes, for a time at least, the properties of an impelling, positive affect which re-initiates the original seeking reaction. As far as can be gathered from the introspective experiences of many artists, the affect associated with the con-summatory response may be overwhelming, and the saturation potential of the artists almost limitless. Moreover, the awareness on the part of the artist of his own creative ability and the exercise of skill creates a feeling of exhilaration superiority and self-assertiveness. Lastly, because of its affective loading, and the fact that artistic behaviour satisfies an innate need, it is related to instinctive behaviour. (In fact, these needs may erupt at a very early age.) More accurately, instinctive behaviour is primordially related to artistic behaviour and, as we have said, to thinking in general. Artistic endeavour is thinking in configurational terms; artistic realization, its translation into action.

In studying seeking responses at various levels of cognition we remarked that, at the *configurational level, gratification is attained by consummatory responses to certain temporally patterned auditory stimuli or spatially organized visual impressions.* The artist's personality structure is characterized by its predilection for gratification at the configurational level of experience, that is, by a particular type of gratification preference which distinguishes him not only from that of plain man, but also from the scientist. This in no way contradicts the statement made previously,

namely, that the artist converts inner states in objective reality while the scientist transform objective reality into inner states at the conce tual level.

The patterns produced may or may not be sh through with conceptual elements. Althou Goethe made a good case for the opposit namely, the absence of ideational factors, it m be stated that, in poetry, the melody of langua and the meaning of the poem are combined to higher form of artistic expression. The combin tion of configurational and conceptual elemen on the part of the artist is an instance of the "r ciprocal potentiation of level specific resource which plays a crucial part in language functions. similar potentation is produced by the combin tion of the resources of the configurational ar the perceptual level of sensation, as evidenc by the effects of particular colors and lines as e ments of visual gestalten (compare, e.g., Mo drian's work *79*) and particular qualities of sou embodied in harmonies and melodies. It is tr that esthetic qualities of patterns may be intens fied by the admixture of conceptual or (eleme tary) perceptual elements or both but the qua ties under study are essentially attributes of ce tain configurations. *Styles* are variations on bas patterns or variations on basic configuration themes, be they auditory or visual in charact while conceptual and expressive elements as, f example, those which come to the fore in th gothic style, are secondary determinants, as a perceptual factors.

Artistic behaviour, having *productive* (moto and *receptive* (sensory) aspects, is of a twofo nature. Extending the definition given in one the preceding paragraphs, it may be said that t behaviour under study aims at both the *produ tion* and the *appreciation* of visual and auditor patterns having esthetic qualities. The cruci factor in artistic realization is the production gestalten on the part of the artist, be they aud tory, visual, kinetic, or static. There can be fitte into this simple framework of classification, an category of art, be it the art of drawing, of pain ing, of sculpture, of architecture, of composing dance, etc., and similar considerations apply, o the sensory side, to the recipient who enjoys rk of art. In advance of what will be said later, rks of art, both visual and auditory, may be *sentative* or *representative*. (The former are netimes referred to as abstract or non-objec- e.) Irrespective of the prevailing trend, artistic lization must conform to the principles of hetics, commonly defined as the science of the utiful in art and nature.

ESTHETIC EXPERIENCE

At this point the question arises whether es- tic experience depends solely on the apprecia- n of the beautiful. At the same time we are nfronted with the question what constitutes uty. Clearly, it is the quality of an object that kes it appeal to the higher senses. But what the nature of this particular quality?

Freud (*29*) wrote that the science of esthetics mines the conditions under which we exper- ce beauty but that it failed to give an explana- n of its nature and genesis. It is beyond the pe of this work to attempt even a sampling of theories proposed by philosophers, psycholo- ts and artists. Suffice it to refer to the definition Bosanquet (*13*) who discussed the concept of at constitutes beauty as it developed from the y of the pre-Socratics up to the turn of the last tury. "There suggests itself as a comprehen- e definition of the beautiful," he writes, "that ich has characteristic or individual expressive- ss for sense perception or imagination, subject the conditions of general or abstract expressive- ss in the same medium." Yet he hastens to add nat with the birth of the modern world . . . it came impossible that impartial theory should nsider that the beautiful was adequately ex- ined as the regular and harmonious or as the ple expression of unity in variety." Ulti- tely, he defines beauty as "the characteristic far as expressed for sense impression and for agination" yet he tends to eliminate the ele- nt of the characteristic stressing, by contrast, he element of unity or totality as symbolized by rmonious, symmetrical, or coherent disposition lines, surfaces, colors and sounds." One would ree that the element of the characteristic should ve no place in the definition of what is beauti- for, obviously, it applies to caricature or defect harmony, as Bosanquet himself remarks. vertheless, since the emphasis on the harmoni-

ous begs the question, his definition is not entirely free from circularity.

It is perhaps only to be expected that Freud should have sought "the origin of beauty in the field of sexual feelings and considered beauty and charm primarily as qualities of the sexual object itself, particularly of certain secondary sex char- acteristics." But charm and beauty are by no means the only qualities that make the sexual object attractive. It is true that both sexes appre- ciate beauty, but the male is attracted primarily by femininity, while the female appreciates mas- culine qualities which do not necessarily include beauty. Women appreciate beauty in other women, but they do not usually seek it in man. Shall we thus assume that only men are capable of appreciating beauty or, for that matter, feminine qualities in a work of art? And shall we accept the implication that esthetic enjoyment in women, being directed toward the equivalent of a sex object, reveals a basically abnormal attitude? The applicability of Freud's ideas on the subject is limited for still another reason. Even granted that we succumb, say, to some of Michelangelo's paintings and sculptures and to some of Beetho- ven's symphonies because of their masculine spell (as indeed we succumb to the thunderous prose of a great orator) and that we are fascinated by some of Boticelli's and Mozart's work because of its feminine charm, it is common experience that sexual characteristics are wholly inapplicable to the vast majority of works of art.

However, in spite of the objections that may be raised against Freud's philosophy of the beauti- ful, his ideas approach the truth more closely than those of the estheticists with which he dis- agreed. Both feminine and masculine qualities have no existence of their own; they are attributes of life. At least some works of art, apart from the atmosphere of sexual pleasure they admittedly conjure up, give rise to esthetic enjoyment by their compositional unity which, in a way, is akin to that of the organism. Like the organism, the true work of art has an inner life of which we be- come immediately aware and which speaks to us. The artist is a creator of organisms that live their lives and work their spell in the sphere of the sense to which they appeal. Most assuredly, there is no true work of art that does not have the quali- ties of life, which, if this were possible, would materialize within the configurational dimensions offered by the senses of hearing and vision. In art, styles are the organizational themes or modes in which the life qualities of artistic creation come to the fore, just as in nature organizational plans reveal themselves in the variety of forms she has produced.

However, acceptance of the idea that esthetic qualities have their roots in a unity akin to that of the organism, is only a further step toward approximation to the truth. Granted that there can be no work of art without organizational unity, the awareness of such unity alone does not necessarily impart esthetic qualities to the creation of man, for an organism displays unity no matter how ugly it may be.

The only conclusion to be drawn appears to be that the quality of beauty is linked to the unity of the organism only to the extent that the unity of a manifold of sensory data is an attribute of certain configurations or gestalten. More specifically, beauty is an attribute of gestalten inasmuch as they embody the principle of organization at a certain level of sensuous experience. And yet, the quality of beauty can hardly depend on a physiological factor alone; neither can changes in taste in various cultural settings be readily reconciled with the presumed constancy and uniformity of cerebral organization. Perhaps, the impression of what is beautiful is, to a degree at least, dependent on the qualities of a work of art that can be expressed in mathematical terms. Sir Thomas Browne's dictum that "there is music where there is harmony and proportion" (he obviously followed the Pythagoreans) may thus apply to beauty in general, but there may be as many different standards of beauty as there are different geometries. We shall return later to the problem of esthetic taste.

Spheres of art

THE AUDITORY ARTS

The nature of auditory art

Music as the language of emotion

Long ago, Herbert Spencer (123) believed that all music was originally produced by the agency of certain muscles which were excited by pleasurable and painful feelings and that their stimulation accounts for the fact that affective states express themselves in sounds as well as in movements. In a word, that music has its roots in the tones, intervals, and cadences of speech which express affects. Variations of voice are the physiologic result of variations of feeling; hence, Spencer taught, each inflection or modulation is the natural outcome of some passing sensation or emotion. The explanation of all kinds of vocal expression may be found in this general reaction between mental and muscular excitement. These vocal peculiarities indicating excited feeling, namely, loudness, quality of timbre, pitch intervals and rate and variation are those which especially distinguish song from ordinary speech. The distinctive traits of sound are simply the traits of emotional speech intensified and systematized. Vocal music and, by consequence, all music is an idealization of the natural language of passion. The variations of timbre and the other modifications of voice produced by feelings are the means of exciting like feelings in others. To prove his point, Spencer refers to various composers as "men of extremely acute sensibilities" and he considers an emotional nature as characteristic of musical composers; the musician regards with emotion events, scenes, conducts and characters which upon most men produce no appreciable effect.

Spencer's theory can be readily integrated with certain physiologic discoveries previously mentioned, and made long after his day. This, as far as we can see, can hardly be said about other ideas on the nature of music the number of which is legion. To mention only two representative works, Moos' (80) opus, covering the relatively short period from Kant to E. v. Hartmann, comprises almost 700 pages. Gatz (43) produced a volume, largely in the nature of an annotated bibliography, of equally impressive dimensions. Clearly, it is impossible (and beyond us) to discuss the various theories. Put in a nutshell, the trend of theorizing appears to be the following: Original thinkers conceived the basic concepts. Second-line writers interpreted the original ideas differently; they either agreed or accused the originators of having erred on basic points or of having made inconsistent statements—if not, indeed, of having failed to understand the products of their own mind. A third set of writers accused the former to have misapprehended the original authors or to have distorted their ideas in one way or the other. Exegesis replaced originality. As the perusal of the current literature indicates, the disagreement among the authorities continues unabated (58).

In the writings of the theorists, one frequently encounters the term *representative*, or *heteronomous* and *presentative*, or *autonomous* music. *Representative* music is said to express the composer's inner states including emotional reactions to various experiences; while *presentative* music, being pure, or absolute, expresses "merely" itself. Should it be possible to reconcile the two conflicting views? And should music be a composite entity rather than the unitary phenomenon as represented by Spencer?

We shall discuss representative music first. Schumann said to be affected by everything that went on in the world, including politics, literature and people, to think it all over in his own way and then to express his feelings and find an outlet for them in music. He was well aware of the fact that his compositions, being "connected with distant interests," were sometimes difficult to understand. As already noted, Spencer thought that all composers are highly sensitive individuals. "Mozart," he wrote, "was of an intensely active affection and of a highly impressionable temperament. Beethoven was full of fine feeling, and Chopin incredibly sensitive." Cowell (16) wrote that the musical ideas as they run through his mind seem to be an exact mirror of his emotions at the moment, or of moments which he recalled through memory." It may well be that the spectrum of the composer's emotions is immeasurably rich as compared to that of average man and that the urge to express them overwhelming. In line with Spencer's ideas, one may assume representative music to have its origin in the songs of love, joy and mourning. Moreover, from the composer's viewpoint at least, instrumental music may be a more natural and also a more adequate way than speech to objectify inner states. For this reason, they tend to express their feelings in "non-propositional" language. Van Beethoven, improvising at the piano, said to a mother mourning the loss of her child: "This is much more than I could ever have said in words." "People usually complain," Mendelsohn wrote in one of his letters, "about the ambiguity and the indefiniteness of music; while everyone understands words, they do not know what to think when listening to it. I myself made exactly the opposite experience; in contrast to music, whole sentences and words appear hazy and indefinite to me. Music fills the soul with a thousand things which are better than words. What the kind of music I love expresses, rather than vague thoughts, are thoughts which are too definite. You are asking what I was thinking while writing my 'Songs without Words.' I thought exactly the song as you hear it." Franz Liszt said that feeling lives and shines in music without pictorial representation and without being mediated by either deed or thought.

As far as the composer is concerned, the potentialities of expressive music are unlimited; as to the listener, they may or may not evoke feelings similar to those which gave rise to the tonal expressions on the part of the composer, neither may they evoke the imaginal experiences which produced the emotional states demanding expression. For example, Schumann, in composing his song "In der Nacht", thought of Hero and Leander while I. D. Rodgers, perhaps influenced by its title, thought of "the moon struggling through the clouds in a wild night."

Although music may express the composer's emotions, it lacks the properties of propositional language. The same may be said about program music which attempts to propositionalize in spite of the lack of concepts with which to operate. Program music is the composer's private idiom, a language whose appreciation is based on its sensuous appeal rather than the meaning it conveys, or the ideas it conjures up. However, the most uncompromising theorist who condemns tonal mimicry will forgive Respighi for copying the sweet sounds to which he listened in the pine woods of Rome; and no one in his right mind will reject the beauty of Wagnerian leit-motifs, the breathtaking passages of the Pastoral Symphony and Richard Strauss' painting of people's minds, moods and fates. No matter what has been said about program music by its various interpreters (take for example Berlioz' and Wagner's different concept of the "Eroica"), the effect of representative music lies in its appeal to the ear rather than in the communication of emotionally colored ideas.

The foregoing statement would seem to demand a re-examination and, possibly, a revision of the thesis that music invariably expresses feelings and moods or, at most, emotionalized thoughts. Were music truly expressive of moods, a composer, who happens to be in a sombre mood, should compose sombrely; one being in a good mood, gay music. This however, does not hold true for some of Weber's, Schubert's and Beethoven's compositions, which proves that experiences do not necessarily give rise to analogous expressions; in other words, that the productive stimulus may be unspecific. Beethoven's "Waldstein-Sonata," composed during a period of great mental depression shows no traces of his sadness. C. M. v. Weber remarked that a "joyous sunrise may create a melancholy adagio" and Tschaikovsky once wrote that "a work composed under the happiest of surroundings may be touched with dark and gloomy colors."

The fact that the first proposition, namely, that music is the language of emotion, cannot claim general validity suggests that, as was only to be expected, insight into the nature of auditory art may have to be gained by the synthesis of two opposing arguments.

Mathematical aspects of music

Why do certain tonal structures appeal to the ear? That harmonies can be mathematically defined was known already to the Pythagoreans who, some 2500 years ago, determined the relations between sounds and the tension of vibrating strings. It has been known ever since that the sounds of the tonal scale expressed in terms of vibrations conform to certain mathematical relationships. Similar relationships underly, likewise, the musical factors of timbre, overtone, dissonance, rhythm, etc. Leibniz (62) defined music as "exertitium arithmeticae occultum nescientis se numerare animi," or, in Bosanquet's translation, "a felt relation of number." Scarletti referred to his music as the "daughter of mathematics," similar views having been held by Bach's pupil Mizler and the Leipzig Society of Musical Science

early in the 18th century. More recently, t mathematical approach to the phenomenon music was expounded by Schillinger (111, 11 who transformed musical quantities into time a space structures, i.e., into the geometrical re tions of their components, and who projecte musical notions into spatial configurations. promulgated the idea that music is capable of e pressing everything that can be translated in some form of motion, a space-time entity capab of graphic projection, and that musical materi can be analyzed and synthetized by the unifyii principle of mathematical logic. The same math matical laws, he thought, are also realized natural objects and have been intuitively appli by musicians in their work. He believed th Richard Wagner unwittingly projected spiral fo mations into sounds and that other compose utilized similar principles of dimensional transl tion. According to Schillinger, music is part that general process of pattern formation which, commonly, the term "evolution" applied. Schillinger's philosophy of music cu minates in the idea that musical compositio being based on a system of number values, ca be literally computed.

If this were true, music would be a matter drafting board technique and should better studied at M.I.T. than at the Conservatori where it is taught at present. However, because the systematic study of mathematical relatio ships embodied in tonal expression, Schillinger analysis has both merit and dialectic fertilit It is true that all melodies, harmonies, an rhythms have mathematically definable relatio ships but it is equally true that this statemen cannot be reversed. Only certain tonal structure have musical qualities while others lack esthet value altogether. It would seem that, ultimatel the esthetic properties in question depend on subjective element, which is "consonant" as were with auditory organization. Admittedl as demonstrated by the temporal and geograph cal (let alone individual) differences in taste an music appreciation, the organizational framewor is rather liberal and leaves ample room for cor ventionalization. Harmony, dissonance and othe musical elements would be the way certain mathe matical relationships affect the sense of hearing a fashioned by cultural and other trends. To th extent that pure music becomes the realization

laws governing the organization of the audi-
y apparatus (an apparatus which is culturally
iditioned and individually variable), the
lodies of pure music become discoveries of
propriate tonal and, for that matter, mathema-
al relationships. Composers move tones play-
ly before their mental ear; according to Cowell
very conceivable tone quality and beauty of
ance, every harmony and dysharmony, or any
mber of simultaneous melodies can be heard at
ll by the trained composer; he can hear not only
e sounds of every instrument or combination of
struments but an almost unlimited number of
inds which cannot as yet be produced by any
strument." Like musicians manipulate sounds,
ithematicians amuse themselves by turning
gebraic problems over in their minds. Henri
incaré's (92) saying that the mathematician
ooses from among his thoughts and calculations
ose which excel by their beauty briskly illum-
ates the seemingly close relationship between
usic and mathematics. (See p. 492.)

Music as expression vs. music as tonal structure: An attempt at resolution

In the preceding chapter we defined mathema-
s as sceletized logic expressed in a language
10se words are symbols indicating magnitudes,
1ose thoughts and sentences express relation
tween quantities and whose syntax mirrors the
ecificity of these relations. Similarly, music
ould be a language whose "words" are sounds,
hose "thoughts" are motifs and themes and
hose syntax (the rules according to which sounds
e combined to tonal structures) reflects the
ode of organization of the higher auditory pro-
nces of the brain and, at the same time, the
eway of pattern formation. Just as different
ometries employ different concepts of space, so
fferent musical styles, based on different tem-
oral and chromatic coordinates, represent dif-
rent concepts of melody, harmony and rhythm.
The above expressed ideas may be challenged
1 the ground that absolute music, like absolute
ntax is a conceptual artifact; further, that the
ontent of musical language, like the meaning of
ropositional speech, is of necessity representa-
ve and lastly, that there must be content
herever there is form. The truth seems to be that
ure music does exist in the way pure syntax

exists, namely, as an aggregate body of forms that
governs the structure of sentences but that, musical ideas having no propositional value properly
so called, tonal form is the essence of music and
that the framework of form can be filled in with
any "content" that appeals to the ear. Even a
poem, although we may not understand the language in which it was composed, may excel in
musical quality a poem recited in our own
language.

The two opposing propositions, namely, that
music does express the composer's affective states
and, again, that it may not do so, can be resolved
in the following fashion. Music has expressive and
architectonic aspects. In its pure form, the expressive component represents a language of emotions
while the architectonic, or constructive component is a play with sounds. Pure forms of music
however are limiting cases for, generally, the expressive and the constructive component are integrated and, to some extent, reciprocal; musical,
like propositional language is put together according to certain rules of construction while tonal
material organized according to its own laws expresses and gives rise to esthetic experiences
which are by their very nature emotionally
colored. In spite of the basic constancy of the
sensuous material and the perceiving brain
mechanism, the "rules" of the play illustrating
the ways artists think in terms of tonality, in
terms of musical styles that is, vary from composer to composer, from culture to culture and
from period to period. Evidently, sensuous brain
mechanisms admit of variation, as does living
matter, and styles grow as naturally as the "artforms" of nature. Music is representative inasmuch as it expresses and evokes (even though it
does not necessarily mirror) affective states; it is
presentative as the unfolding of its own laws, or,
in inexhaustible variations, the application of formal principles to the grouping of sounds. In this
sense, autonomous and heteronomous music are
not mutually exclusive; they are supplementary
aspects of a unitary entity.

Psychophysiological aspects of musical aptitude

Preparatory to the discussion of the dissolution
patterns of musical aptitude caused by organic
brain lesions, it will be necessary to deal with the

psychophysiological background of musical ability. The highly technical character of the subject precludes however a detailed study. For an extensive coverage of the subject, the interested reader may be referred to the works of Helmholtz (39), Stumpf (131), Redfield (101), Schoen (114–117), Seashore (120), Hanson (36) and other psychologists and teachers of music, the studies of Knoblauch (55), Doellken (22), Henschen (56), and especially to Billroth's (10) posthumous work. Although lacking formal psychological training, Billroth, a friend of Johannes Brahms and a highly gifted musician himself, produced an incisive analysis of musical ability. Henmeter (40), in an appreciation of Billroth's book, states that the feeling for rhythm, the memory for rhythmic forms, the power of perceiving differences in tone-pitch, tone-sound, tone-strength and the capacity to differentiate these qualities in rapid change and combination are some of the psychophysiologic correlates of what we call musical. At the same time, he emphasized that the "life and essence of music" does not depend on physical facts only. Henschen thought that musical aptitude is related to a certain degree of development not only of the "cortical cochlea" in Heschl's convolution (level I.s.) but also to the higher central representations of the sense of hearing. However, the relationship between musical aptitude and sound perception is by no means clear cut. Van Beethoven for example, having been deprived of segment I.s. of the auditory system during the later years of his life, nevertheless was able to make use of the resources of the higher auditory levels. On the other hand, as pointed out by Edgren (25), other musicians were severely handicapped by the secondary effects of deafness, involving, perhaps, the loss of perceptual control and stimulation. Henschen distinguishes between the following musical faculties: (a) the sense of rhythm, (b) the capacity to differentiate between tones of various pitch and to produce correct tones either vocally or by means of instruments, (c) the capacity to appreciate and produce melodies, (d) to appreciate and reproduce timbre, (e) to appreciate nuances and (f) to express them by means of changes in intensity, intonation, and accentuation. It would appear that the above enumerated abilities depend primarily on the function of the auditory segment of the sensory-motor and the psycho-neural levels. Musical thought on the other hand, (the ability to think in musical phrases or to produce relationships between sounds which have an esthetic value) should depend on a high degree of development of the acoustic system at the intellectual level. The composer Cowell (16), to whose writings we had repeatedly occasion to refer, describes his experiences as follows: "By an almost superhuman effort I could bring these musical visitations about. I practiced doing this until I became able to produce them at ease. . . . At first able to control only a note or two during a musical flow lasting perhaps half an hour, I became able, by constant attempt to produce more and more readily whatever melodies and harmonies and tone qualities I desired without altering the nature of the flow of sounds. I practiced directing the flow into the channels of the sounds of a few instruments at a time until I could conjure them up at will." Sessions (122) depicts the way he develops musical ideas into phrases and periods, how the musical train of thought may sharpen and clarify them and how he throws musical ideas into relief by appropriate contrasts.

The foregoing analysis suggests a classification of the musical talent somewhat analogous to the categories of mathematical aptitude dealt with in the concluding pages of Chapter IV. At the *lowest* level, we find merely the ability to appreciate the diverse qualities of sounds; an *intermediate* group of talented persons would show some measure of artistic ability which, however would hardly exceed the bounds of pure artisanship while the *highest category* of musicians excels in either field and, moreover, is endowed with the gift of discovering tonal relationships of esthetic value—just as the mathematical genius brings to light significant relationships between magnitudes. It is this group which experiences musical inspirations, many of them in the form of delusional hallucinatory, dream-like and kindred states. Lastly, as in the field of mathematics, precocity, heredity, memory, etc., play a major role.

Stanton (127) found that musical parents from musical stock tend to have musical children, while the opposite holds true for non-musical parents from non-musical stock and that parents one of whom is musical while the other is non-musical from non-musical stock tend to have both musical and non-musical children; lastly, that the inheritance of musical aptitude would seem to follow Mendelian principles. According to Mjoen (75) untalented parents never have talented children while very talented parents never have untalented children. It is curious to note that the lower forms of musical ability like the more primitive forms of mathematical aptitude are independent of general intelligence. Minogue (73) reported the case of a 27 year old man who, as a result of menigeal infection contracted at the age of three, became mentally retarded but who nevertheless played the most difficult music by sight and ear. He was, however, unable to produce any original composition. The patient, at the time of the publication of Minogue's paper the inmate of an institution, had been a musical prodigy at a very early age. It is worthy of note that his father's mother was a pianist of exceptional ability and his sister's daughter an unusually gifted player. Donath (21) reported the case of a four-year-old mental defective who had a repertoire of some 50 melodies and who learned new melodies quite easily. Evidently, there exist not only idiots savants and idiots mathématiques as, for example, Tom Fuller, but also idiots musicales.

Dissolution of musical aptitude

There are various patterns of dissolution of musical aptitude, or *amusia*. Amusia may be isolated or it may develop within the framework of generalized mental deterioration. In other cases, amusia is combined with aphasia. A peculiar disorder of lack of musical appreciation is "*musical anhedonia*" (27) in which, however, the perceptual and gnostic musical functions are spared.

DISTURBANCES OF THE TEMPORAL DIMENSIONS OF MELODIES

Disturbances of rhythm were studied especially by Würthen (140) and Agadschanianz (1) who observed, in one of his patients, the inability to imitate specific sequences of sounds, while another patient made different errors depending on whether he used his right or his left hand. Isolated impairment of the sense of rhythm however is uncommon. The patients, although finding it difficult or impossible to appreciate the chromatic dimensions of melodies, may still be able to recog-

nize them by the perception of their temporal sequences.

DISTURBANCES OF THE CHROMATIC DIMENSIONS OF MELODIES

A patient may be unable to recognize melodies although he can distinguish the various instruments by their sounds; or he may be able to recognize the time value of notes but fails to recognize their pitch. Proust (100) reported the case of a patient who had lost his capacity to read notes but who could sing and appreciate melodies. Patients who have lost their capacity to read notes may be able to sing and play by heart. Musical alexia and alexia for words and letters may or may not be combined. (See below.) Instrumental and vocal amusia may occur either singly or in combination. One of Würthen's observations exemplifies unilateral instrumental apraxia in that his patient could play a melody with his left hand only although his right upper extremity was otherwise not apractic.*

SENSORY AMUSIA

Complete sensory amusia is the inability to recognize sounds, melodies, the chromatic and temporal structure of patterned sound sequences and to read notes. The patient's acoustic experiences vary; tones may sound like noises, which may be extremely unpleasant, or they may appear as a jumble of sounds. On testing, perception and discrimination of various pitch intervals, chords, and other musical elements appear to be impaired in most cases. At the same time, the capacity to recognize, appreciate, reproduce, and to recall melodies may be reduced or abolished. The individual disturbances are sometimes referred to as *paramusia* and *amnestic amusia*. The term acoustic agnosia and sensory amusia are for all practical purposes identical. The disorder is not necessarily associated with ideo-motor apraxia.

MOTOR AMUSIA

It is difficult to determine whether motor amusia (109) is a disturbance of a higher motor

---

* However, he would hear the melody he intended to play with his inner ear, while using, or attempting to use, either hand for playing (110).

function, comparable to Broca's aphasia (with which it may be combined), or an ideo-motor function, i.e., a disturbance of ideo-motor integration. Mozart for example, a master at the keyboard, lacked general manual dexterity. Motor amusia may or may not be combined with ideo-motor apraxia. Botez and Wertheim (12a) reported the case of a right handed patient with a glioma involving the posterior portion of the first and second frontal convolution on the right side of the brain. The patient could play the piano with either hand separately but failed in bimanual playing. Moreover, his "accordion production to singing was absolutely wrong." Accordingly, there was a "deep degree of dissociation between the vocal and the instrumental parts" and the patient, who had full insight into his condition, complained that "his fingers could not carry out the order." There was no agnostic or other receptive difficulty.

DISSOCIATION BETWEEN MUSICAL APTITUDE AND LANGUAGE FUNCTIONS

Musical aptitude may be preserved in the presence of the most severe language disturbances, as first observed by Béhier, and later by Meige (68), Falret (26), Bouillaud (14) and Grasset (34), whose patients could sing but were otherwise speechless. In the cases described by Behier and Meige the patients were able to sing the tune but unable to form the words even after the aphasia had completely subsided. In the case of a professional musician reported by Walthard (137) amusia was still present even after complete restitution of the sensory aphasia. Agraphia may or may not be combined with the ability to copy notes, and musical alexia and musical agraphia are not necessarily associated. Disturbances of the inner language of music and of musical thought in persons in which they were previously present were first reported by Dupré and Nathan (24) and, later, by Alajouanine (2) in the composer Maurice Ravel.

BRAIN LESIONS CAUSING AMUSIA

Receptive amusia and disturbances of musical thought were observed by Dupré and Nathan, Bernard (8), Bianchi (9), Edgren (25), Pick (89),

Oppenheim (85), Probst (99) and Henschen (. in lesions involving the anterior portion of eit the left or the right (or of both) temporal c volutions T¹ and T². *Expressive amusia* on other hand, as described by Kleist (53), Opp heim (185), and Henschen (41) is caused lesions in the lower motor area and the adjace portions of the frontal lobe. As already point out, the lesions involved a similar locality in t case of the patient reported by Botez and W theim. Mendel (69), Mann (66), Rohard (10 H. Foerster (28) and Jossman (49) found inabil to sing in frontal lobe lesions. The "whole-fu tion" theorists and gestaltpsychologists asse that the manifestions of higher cerebral dysfu tions are artifacts produced by the particu. technique of examination employed. However, is difficult to understand how in all cases in wh the examiner "happened to concentrate" on wh they prefer to call the sensory aspects of the d turbance, the lesions should have been found the post-rolandic part of the cortex; in those which he chanced to pay attention to the mot aspects, in the pre-rolandic segment. In contra to propositional language, the psycho-neu component of musical ability, more especia the expressive component of musical aptitud seems to be mediated by both hemispheres wh musical thought, as far as known, is intimate linked to the dominant side of the brain.

VISUAL ART

The nature of visual art

It is rewarding to compare visual with audito art. Music is not only a language but at the san time a play with sounds satisfying the criteria esthetics. To evoke esthetic experiences, the pla must conform to certain rules, like language, to comprehensible, must conform to the rules syntax. In a similar fashion, the factors of expre sion and play operate in the visual arts althoug visual building material, which is exquisite suited to represent both the perceptual and th conceptual world, does not lend itself as readi to the expression of affective states as acousti material. Its domain is the realm of things rathe than of feelings. Yet visual art, quite apart fror the selection of themes and motifs, is by no mean inarticulate; to some extent, it arouses and objec es feelings and moods by the combination of ors, lines and shapes to wholes of a higher der.

Non-objective visual art bears comparison to esentative music. In analogy to musical styles, torial styles express the way the artist thinks visual terms and, as we shall attempt to ow later, brings into harmony the properties of e visual world with the principles governing the preciation of lines, surfaces, forms and colors. ere are countless gradations between objec- ity and non-objectivity; and, as any visitor to nodern art gallery knows, countless gradations non-objectivity. In the extreme case, works of presentative visual art are products of slavish pying of an animate or inanimate object or, for at matter, their equivalents in the imagination, ile the factor of composition is minimal. By e same token, works of presentative visual art e abstract designs composed of any form of nsuous building material wherein the shapes oduced may be entirely unrelated to the form any known object, and where the factor of mposition is maximised. As Henri Matisse (67a) marked: "A picture must never show anything at can be described in words, or that exists in r memory. A picture is an organism in its own ;ht. Whenever I see a picture I forget what it presents. The only thing that counts is lines, rms and colors."

Conventional visual art displays both presenta- /e and representative trends. No doubt the numerable styles to be found in both pictorial t and in sculpture (and to a certain extent in chitecture and in other visual arts) owe their fference to the different proportions of repre- ntative and presentative elements. The varie- s of visual art are differential ranges of a uni- ry scale. Presentative visual art comprises ab- ract painting while its opposite aims at the pic- rial or plastic representation of objects. Between e two extremes, namely, slavish copying and e composition, there extends the domain of nventional drawing, painting and sculpture in nich there are blended non-objective and turalistic trends. However, since in the objec- /e visual arts, esthetic effects depend on the uilibrium between naturalistic and abstract inciples, the freedom of objective visual art is nited to the extent that it expresses feelings d ideas through the medium of objects.

The problem of harmonizing presentative and representative (or non-objective and objective) trends has been solved in various ways, which may be epitomized by reference to the paintings of Klimt, Schiele and Gleizes. Klimt (54) who "played" objects against their decorative setting was singularly successful in creating esthetic effects. I am thinking in particular of the painting "The Kiss", of the white, black and gold or- namentation on the coat of the man, and of the composition in green, blue and red, the idealized flower bed on which the couple is kneeling. Against the contrapuntal relationship of the two designs, the artist sets the lover's hands and faces, which are painted naturalistically by comparison and which merge with the non-objective elements of the painting into a sweeping chord of lines and colors. Schiele (110) resolves the conflict between the two philosophies, that is, between presenta- tion and representation, by the blending rather than the segregation of object and ornament; the former undergoes a considerable transformation. Nevertheless, both artists underscore rather than preserve the visual properties of objects. Gleizes' "Harvest Threshing" is a monumental composi- tion in which presentative elements predominate. They become absolute in some of Picasso's paint- ings, the titles of which bear no recognizable re- lationship to their "content," and which are visual designs comparable to musical harmonies and melodies. Other schools of non-objective visual art, which play line-music, color-music, weight-music, mass-music, etc., carry the prin- ciple of abstraction to its very limits; yet the various compositions seem to have a life of their own and they give rise to esthetic experiences. By contrast, to cite only one example, all of Kandin- sky's (50) work with which I am familiar is unin- telligible without digestion of its weird philosophy of colors. Non-objective and objective trends are likewise combined in the art of caricature, or visualizing depth psychology, examples of which are Rodin's incomparable "Balzac," the work of Daumier, George Grosz and other painters, sculptors and cartoonists.

Psychophysiological aspects of pictorial aptitude

While there is no dearth of investigations on the psychophysiological background of musical aptitude, the number of studies devoted to the physiology of pictorial ability appears to be small. Unable to find any literature on the subject, I propose to base the following outline on considerations of a general nature, on introspective data, on experiences with otherwise normal individuals who lack pictorial aptitude, and on experiences with persons with organic brain lesions involving the visual sphere.

Although the data on which the following sketch is based are meagre, it is probably fair to assume that pictorial aptitude depends on a variety of factors which may be readily correlated with the hierarchical organization of higher cerebral functions. They include several partial abilities, namely, a *visuo-perceptual*, a *visuo-mnemonic*, a *visuo-gnostic*, a *visuo-intellectual* and a *visuo-motor*. Applying the above criteria, pictorial aptitude can be graded as was suggested for the mathematical and the musical talent.

Visuo-perceptual competence, setting aside the elementary factors of visual acuity, the appreciation of colors, etc., involves visual attention and the appreciation of spatial organization. As applied to pictorial aptitude, visuo-gnostic ability comprises gestaltperception, more especially the simultaneous surveying and the appreciation of gestalten in their true proportions, the intense awareness of the relationship between figure and background and their synthesis to a higher unit of perception. Because of the dependence of artistic realization on the reproduction of gestalten, visuo-motor integration, or "constructional ability" plays a crucial role not only in the objective, or realistic, but also in the non-objective pictorial arts. In the former, the artist copies objects; in the latter, he reproduces the products of his own imagination which have no counterpart in the external world. Inadequacy of visuo-motor integration, that is, of duplicating the spatial relationships of visual data, may be present in otherwise normal persons or, as will be shown later, may be the result of organic brain lesions. The reproduction of elementary visual patterns requires relatively simple integrative acts. They involve essentially the resources of the visual and the motor sphere, and they materialize without noticable intellectual effort while the reproduction of more complicated patterns requires, in addition, a certain measure of intellectual activity. The psychological analysis of the process of copying, carried out on a previous occasion (*113*), demonstrated that the process of copying more complicated patterns required an operational plan which develops in stages and which is suggested to the draftsman by the special properties of pattern or objects. The individual phases of this plan are made more or less explicit by a process of association. Although the existence of such a plan may appear to be a truism its importance becomes obvious on testing the performance of "physiologically" agnostic persons, of true agnostics and of senile persons. If the individual steps of the plan of operation were to be put into words, the idea underlying the reproduction of patterns, for example, the "grid" (Fig. 42) would have to be formulated somewhat as follows: The vertical lines must be counted; it is not sufficient to note that vertical lines exist. The exact number of horizontal lines must be determined, and both their mutual distance and the relation of their distance to the distance between the horizontal lines appreciated. The reproduced pattern must be constantly compared with the original. It is necessary to note the relationship between the oblique lines to the horizontal and vertical lines; it is not sufficient to be aware of the fact that oblique lines are present "somewhere." While the sequence of phases in which the plan develops is not rigid, certain sequences are preferable to others and the omission of any of the above phases is bound to produce errors. The adequate reproduction of the pattern depends on the alternation of the individual more or less specific "statements" with the appropriate visuo-motor acts and, needless to say, in the absence of the original, on an almost photographic memory.

Thus far, we have concerned ourselves essentially with those partial aptitudes which are necessary to reproduce objects and patterns. Although the original may to a certain extent be transformed by a process of analysis and interpretation, the degree of pictorial aptitude involved may be regarded as rather low because of the relative absence of a creative element in the process concerned. At a higher level of artistic realization, patterns are not only produced; they are composed in conformity with the principles of esthetics. Lastly, it is important to appreciate the significance of a general intellectual factor in addition to the specific visuo-intellectual element involved in artistic realization. That drawing disturbances may be the result of general mental impairment was already pointed out by Head (*38*). General intelligence plays an important part not only in overcoming the technical difficulty involved in drawing, painting, sculpturing, etc., but particularly in the choice of motifs and in the process of composition, which depends on both creativity and judgment. Admittedly, a clear cut distinction between visuo-intellectual and general intellectual ability may be difficult.

Dissociation of pictorial aptitude

In the field of pictorial art, the *sensory* variety of dissociation which corresponding to sensory amusia may be regarded as a subcategory of the agnosias. The *motor* disturbances, on the other hand, corresponding to motor amusia, belong to the group of apraxias.

DISSOCIATION OF PICTORIAL ABILITY AND VISUAL AGNOSIA

Visual agnosia and difficulty in revisualization is not necessarily associated with complete inability to draw spontaneously or on command, as observed by Stauffenberg (*128*), Lissauer (*65*), Wilbrand (*139*) and Leroy (*63*); and the ability to copy may be preserved as in the cases of Kleist (*53*), v. Monakow (*78*), Lissauer (*65*), Stauffenberg (*128*) and H. Strauss (*129*).

DISSOCIATION OF PICTORIAL ABILITY AND APRAXIA

The ability to draw and to paint may or may not be part of constructional, apraxia, which is a subcategory of *ideomotor apraxia*. That this particular disability is not caused by optic agnosia (with which however it may be combined) may be readily demonstrated whenever the patient is aware of the faulty structure of patterns he tried to duplicate but which he is unable to correct, unless, as could be demonstrated in a case of my observation (*113*), the disturbance was virtually unilateral. Like a teacher corrects the errors of his pupil, the patient corrected the errors made by her apractic hand with her eupractic hand; in fact, on several occasions, when she used both hands, they seemed to fight each other.

According to Kleist (*53*) and H. Strauss (*129*) constructional apraxia is caused by lack of visuo-kinaesthetic integration. However, it appears more likely that the disturbance is due to the faulty coordination of optic and motor functions and that there is at fault the guidance, by visual data, of imitative or reduplicative movements, or visuo-motor integration. Although coordinated motor function depends on proprioceptive feedbacks, kinaesthetic control is only an auxiliary factor as control observations on patients suffering from cervical tabes have demonstrated (*113*). The role of proprioception in skilled movements, pictorio-graphic or otherwise, is undisputed. However since, in spite of adequate gnosis, movements that cannot be imitated can be carried out on command (that is, in a setting in which kinaesthetic control because of the absence of visual guidance is of even greater importance) it is difficult to accept the notion that dys-kinaesthesia is responsible for the inability to copy figures, to build with blocks, and to imitate movements.

The following demonstrates the futility of stipulating "ground functions," or "fundamental functions", loss of which, supposedly, accounts for deterioriation in a variety of performance fields. Disturbances of drawing may or may not be associated with sensory aphasia, and pictorial ability may be preserved irrespective of the severity of the speech disturbance. Mirallé (*74*) reported a case of alexia combined with disturbances of both spontaneous drawing and copying, especially the latter while, in a similar case mentioned by Bonvicini (*11*), alexia was accompanied by disturbances of synoptic vision. In a case of alexia reported by v. Monakow (*78*) the patient was unable to copy an object, whereas in some of his other patients the ability to copy was unimpaired. Other writers reported similar experiences. In 1866, Falret (*26*) published the case of a patient suffering from sensory aphasia who was unable to write yet whose ability to copy and to draw from memory was preserved. Crouzon and Valence (*17*) pointed out that spontaneous drawing may be possible in spite of visual agnosia. According to Bonvicini, sensory aphasia is typically associated with disturbances of spontaneous drawing and of drawing on command. The individual parts of the picture display a peculiar disorientation in space and the general composition shows a primitive and rather infantile character. By contrast, copying is relatively uninvolved. Similar defects were observed by Head (38) in patients showing nominal, syntactic and semantic aphasia while those in which the verbal (motor) components of aphasia were involved showed no impairment of drawing ability. As demonstrated by a more recent observation of Alajouanine (2) the dissolution pattern described is however by no means typical. The patient, a professional painter, failed to show disturbances of "plastic figurated realization" in spite of a severe aphasia of the Wernicke type. This observation is of particular interest in view of Bonvicini's statement that sensory aphasia interferes with drawing and painting ability. If this were true, Alajouanine's patient should have been more severely handicapped than the average person. It is of interest that agnosia for pictures may or may not be associated with agnosia for objects and with alexia, in other words, with agnosia for written language; and that, in cases of motor aphasia associated with right-sided hemiparesis, the artist may learn to draw with his left hand, as for example the painter Vierge (134) and Wyllies' (141) patient.

The pathological aspects of visual art refer not only to its dissolution under the impact of organic brain disease which involves the centers of recognition and skill or causes generalized mental deterioration. They refer also to the role of *psychopathologic trends*. Futurism, cubism, etc., which reflect an inordinate preponderance of formal principles, defeat their own purposes by the distortion and, ultimately, the destruction of the very objects they presumably interpret. Some of Picassso's work and, no doubt, the paintings and constructions of many others have esthetic

value, but one wonders whether some discipl of non-objective art might not have been inspir by emancipatory currents that did not necessari originate in the sphere of art and which eventua became frankly negativistic. The more tange tiality and elusive flavor their products displa the less they deserve the name "works of art Eventually, emancipation is achieved at the pri of destruction of what might have been a produ of artistic endeavour and realization. Here, agai is the familiar combination of the devices of co munication and concealment, here again t faulty selection of the goals of thought, the ar trary (or complex determined?) contaminati and condensation of concepts; briefly, the d realization of reality. The esthetic, poetical, a philosophical writings of the emancipators enri the psychiatric literature with interesting case hi tories. In fact, works of pathological art may divided into those of *parathymic, dysphrenic* a *mixed* origin. The underlying factor in par thymic, more especially, perhaps, of dyspho art is inapposite affectivity; in dysphrenic a abnormal concept formation discussed under t heading of schizophrenic illness. More often th not, both trends operate by the very nature things in combination and, apart from the choi of motifs, express themselves at the perceptu and the configurational level of sensation. T role of *periodicity* is likewise unmistakable. Ne ways of expression came to the fore in Van Gogh art whenever his psychosis was about to reach new height (106). For a more detailed discussio of the subject from various angles the intereste reader may be referred to the writings of Anasta and Foley (3), Prinzhorn (98), Naumburg (8 and Weygandt (138).

--------------- ## Concluding remarks

Art is, first and foremost, a reflection of the autonomous activity of the auditory and visual centers at the psychoneural level of integration. The function of these centers is autonomous in spite of the fact that they may be actuated by extraneous factors which operate in the fashion of releasing stimuli in instinctual behaviour. Works of art are products of the pattern forming activity

of the human brain. This activity, in turn, is a to occur in states of dissociation of the self, whic however, differ in important respects from pat ological forms of dissociation.

Yet, the patterns so produced are true works art only if they have *esthetic qualities*, that please the higher senses—the work of art, to r peat a sentence which we have put at the he of this chapter, is "the product of the union of the sense with what it loves." Further, its realization is dependent on *skill*, if not on virtuosity. Other features of artistic activity are, perhaps, secondary by comparison. Works of art may be initiated by *emotions* which, in the process of creative work, may be geared to the highest pitch. They may be shot through with *intellective elements* which play a part in their organization. Lastly, artistic expression may assume the character of a *language*. It is this *multiplicity of factors and their combination which establishes the singularity of art within the framework of higher cerebral functions*. If set apart from the activity of the brain as the creative organ, the phenomenon of art is left suspended in midair. Simple definitions, no matter how attractive, fail to do justice to its complexity. Neither do pompous phrases and mystic terms.

It follows from what has gone before that, in artistic endeavour, the *hierarchy of the sensory levels of the brain is at a crucial point reversed*. The ordinarily dominant conceptual sphere becomes an instrument of the configurational level which utilizes, at the same time, the resources of the subordinate, perceptual grade, that is, which, in the course of pattern formation, makes use of certain qualities of lines, colors, and sounds. No longer is reality-control the main purpose of the brain but, rather, the supplementation of objective reality by the creation of forms. Although the impression of what we call beautiful is thus produced by combinations of lower, perceptual, and higher, gestalt-qualities, attempts at defining this impression in objective terms, more especially in terms of harmony and proportion, have not been entirely successful largely because of the presence of a subjective factor involved in the appreciation of art. To be universally valid criteria, mathematical proportions would have to be more or less fixated, while subjective factors vary in one and the same culture, if not at times in one and the same individual, and, from the start, are likely to be different in different cultures. The nature of the subjective element is not fully understood; somehow, it seems, it is related to gratification, the feeling produced by the consummation of a seeking reaction in the instinctual sphere. (If this is true, instinct may be regarded as the functional primordium not only of thought but of art as well.) We are inclined to regard beauty as a particular auditory or visual gestaltquality productive of gratification. Whatever accepted standards of beauty there may be, depends, ultimately, on apposite affectivity, that is, apposite emotional responses aroused by the work of art. These standards have the same personal latitude as responses, be they seeking or aversive, to any higher stimulus category.

In conclusion, it may be well to keep in mind that, in the enjoyment of the arts, gratification is self-contained, contemplative and alien to the otherwise self-centered character of man. Art, having in a certain sense a life of its own and thought by many to exist for its own sake, lightens man's burden inherent in his very nature.

Epilog

An empirical acquaintance with facts rises to a scientific knowledge of facts as soon as the mind discovers beneath the multiplicity of simple productions the unity of an organic system.

MAX MÜLLER

One of the main points brought out in the present study is the existence of derivative relationships between higher central nervous system functions and those of a lower order, in fact, biological phenomena at large—of events that follow a design-like course, or of integrative acts that operate in concerted, interlocking patterns. I have attempted to show how certain classes of integrative processes are related to specific functional primordiums, from which they developed by a process of differentiation and elaboration as, for example, thought from its matrix, perception. One of my aims was to produce a low power view of the workings of the nervous system, especially its commanding echelons, which would show at a glance what can be seen although not necessarily all there is.

To my knowledge, a comparable attempt to work out a unifying approach to the function of the brain in health and in disease has not been made in recent times. There is, it is true, no dearth of topologically oriented investigations concerned, e.g., with the individual lobes of the brain, the corpus callosum, the rhinencephalon, the hypothalamus, the activating system of the brainstem and, naturally, the cortex of the cerebral hemispheres. Other monographs are devoted primarily to individual functions under normal and abnormal conditions, including language, thought, aphasia, apraxia, agnosia, neurosis and psychosis. In all these publications, valuable as they are as studies in their own right, the over-all function of the brain, let alone the nervous system as a whole, has been given only secondary attention. Yet, since whatever brain functions one may study constitute but a component of the activity of one and the same organ, sooner or later the question is bound to arise how these individual activities are interrelated.

Now, our knowledge of nervous system functions (as, indeed, of the organism in general), although based on empirical data, is in the final analysis interpretive rather than factual, and probably always will be. In my opinion, some attempts at understanding nervous system functions are approximations to the truth, notably Hughlings Jackson's doctrine, which formed the guiding line of the present investigation. Other attempts embody both true and false elements, while still others are worse than useless. I found myself in the position of a cartographer who, on exploring a territory he knows only imperfectly, takes with him several maps, none of which is entirely adequate. To correct them, he will reduce to true proportions what he finds to be oversized, make larger what is too small, indicate how seemingly unrelated regions are connected with one another, fill in blank spots, and lastly, establish a unitary pictorial language, having found that his predecessors indicated identical features by different symbols and, conversely, represented different data by the same signs. To exploit the analogy to the full, he will direct his attention to geological formations, which will enable him to reconstruct the history of the territory, or at least to throw light upon some crucial phases of its origin.

By the same token, the student of higher brain functions will accept certain opinions and views although, in the interest of consistency, not without modification. In line with the re-interpretation of existing views, or concurrently with the introduction of new concepts (which I do not need to enumerate) I had to replace several unassimilable terms with new expressions. I regard these new terms—each of which has been defined and related, step by step, to other terms as soon as their significance became clear—as one of the salient features of this investigation.

The question naturally arises whether or not these new terms explain anything. Now, there is one point that we should bear in mind, namely, that, in the final analysis, many explanations become verbal, that is, translate words into other words. Yet since these "other words" stand for concepts or ordering devices that categorize the data of reality, it is imperative that appropriate terms be used in what are bound to become descriptive generalizations. Let us keep in mind that the term "explain" has more than one meaning. For example, physiology will in the course of time discover more and more cause-effect relationships between events that constitute the phenomena of life; and pathology will elucidate more and more combinations of events that cause disease. In this respect, both physiology and pathology are explanatory sciences. Yet, from a different angle, explanation is merely the discovery of conformity of certain classes of events with known patterns of being and behaviour, nothing more. To explain may thus mean to find a law, of which the law to be explained is a particular instance, and which can thereby be fitted into a more general, more comprehensive or incorporative law. And while it may sound presumptuous to refer here to some of the greatest accomplishments in the history of science, we mention that there is (as the physicists tell us) no explanation for the laws of planetary motion other than that they conform to the law of general gravitational attraction; and that, the term attraction being an anthropism, there is no explanation for gravitational forces other than that the planets follow geodesic lines, which are the shortest possible routes in the curved space of non-Euclidian geometry. Yet even this relatively recent version of celestial mechanics is non-explanatory. It does not line up events in terms of causes and effects. Rather, it specifies what the physicist calls the structure of a process, that is, the irreducible whole of its formal properties.

It is disappointing that we cannot define, in terms of molecular events, some of which are causes while others are effects, what goes on in the brain of a person who experiences an emotion, thinks a thought, performs a skilled movement or composes a symphony. Nevertheless, we can say that the individual events have the same relation-structure as more primitive functions and that both sets of phenomena can be described in unifying neuropsychological language.

Just as in physics events are "explained," that is to say, their structure described in terms of mathematical formalism, so, biological events, as a whole at least, can be explained only in terms of the phenomenalism of evolution or, for that matter, of growth and differentiation, the progress from the general to the special in function and from the simple to the involved in structure. Ultimately, even the most complex biological phenomena are manifestations of a unitary process although, it is true, one unfolding in numberless themes and dimensions. In this sense one may understand Goethe's remark that Nature has made things more complicated than one can possibly imagine—and simpler than one might ever dream.

Bibliography

I. BASIC CONCEPTS

1. Ashby, W. R.: Adaptiveness and equilibrium, J. Ment. Sc., 1940, 86: 487.

2. Bargman, W.: Neurosekretion und Hypothalamus-Hypophysenystem, Dtsch. Med. Wchnschr., 1953, 78: 1335; *3*. Bastian, H. Ch.: On the "muscular sense", and on the physiology of thinking, Brit. Med. J., 1869/I., pp. 394, 437, 461, 509; *4*. ——: The human brain, Mac Millan Magazine, Nov. 1865, p. 71; *5*. ——: A treatise on aphasia and other speech defects, London, H. K. Lewis, 1898, VIII., 366 p.; *6*. Betz, W.: Über die feinere Struktur der Grosshirnrinde des Menschen, Zbl. f. med. Wissensch., 1881; pp. 193, 209, 231; *7*. Bichat, M. F. X.: Recherches physiologiques sur la vie et la mort., Paris, Brosson, Gabon & Cie, 1800, 449 p.; *8*. Binet, A.: Psychology of reasoning, Open Court, Chicago, 1899, 191 p.; *9*. Beuler, E.: Mechanismus, vitalismus, mnemismus, Berlin, J. Springer, 1931; *10*. Bonin, E. von: On encephalometry, J. comparat. Neurology, 1941, 57: 286; *11*. Bok, S. T.: Gibt es einen gemeinsamen Blauplan in den Kernen und Bahnensystemen der verschiedenen Querschnitte des Neuralrohres? Zeitschr. f. d. ges. Neurol. u. Psychiat., 1925/26, 100: 678; *12*. Boycott, B. B., and Young, J. Z.: The comparative study of learning. (In "Symp. of the Soc. f. experim. Biol., Physiological Mechanism in animal behaviour.), Acad. Press, Inc., New York, 1950. See also J. Neurophysiol., 1941, 4: 483; *13*. Broadbent, H. W.: On the central mechanism of speech and thought, Medico-chirurg. transact., 1872, 55: 145.

14. Cannon, W. B.: Organization for physiological homeostasis, Physiol. Rev., 1931, 38: 281; *15*. Cassirer, E.: The problem of knowledge. (Transl. W. H. Wogblom), New Haven, Yale Univ. Press, 1950, XV., 334 p.; *16*. Cohen, M. R.: A Preface to Logic, H. Holt and Co., XI., 209 p.

17. Darwin, Ch.: Autobiography, London, Watts & Co., 6th Ed., 1949, 164 p.; *18*. Driesch, H. A. E.: Die Maschine und der Organismus, Leipzig, 1935, viii + 76 p. (See also Bios, vol. 4.); *19*. Dunning, S., and Wolff, H. E.: Relation between function and vascularity in the nervous system, Transact. Amer. Neurol. Ass., 1936, 62: 150; *20*. Durig, A.: Ueber Automatik und deren Grenzen, J. Mount Sin. Hosp., 1952, 19: 38.

21. Eberstaller, O.: Zur Anatomie und Morphologie der Insula Reili, Anat. Anz., 1887, 2: 659; *22*. Eddington, quoted by Durig; *23*. Economo, C. von: Der Zellaufbau der Grosshirnrinde und die progressive Zerebration, Erg. d. Physiol., 1929, 29: 83; *24*. —— and Koskimas, C. N.: Die Cytoarchitektonik der Grosshirnrinde des erwachsenen Menschen, J. Springer, Berlin, 1925.

25. Finley, K. H.: Angioarchitecture of the hypothalamus and its peculiarities, Ass. Res. Nerv. ment. Dis. Monogr., 1940, 20: 268; *26*. Flechsig, P.: Die Lokalisation der geistigen Vorgänge, Leipzig, Veit and Co., 1969, 88 p.; *27*. Flourens, P.: Recherches physiques sur les propriétés et les fonctions du système nerveux dans les animaux vertèbres, Arch. gen. de Med., 1823, 2: 321, 160; *28*. Frédérique, L.: Quoted by Cannon (Ref. *14*) and Needham (Ref. *50a*).

29. Goldstein, K.: The organism. A holistic approach to biology derived from pathological data in man, New York, Amer. Book Co., 1939, XVII, 535 p.; *30*. Guldberg, G. A.: Zur Morphologie der Insula Reili, Anat. Anz., 1887, 2: 659; *31*. Gruenthal, E.: Vergleichend anatomische Untersuchungen über die Zentren des Hypothalamus, Arch. f. Psychiat. 1930, 90: 216.

32. Harlow, H. F.: The nature of learning sets, Psychol. rev., 1939, 56: 320; *33*. Hartmann, E. von: Philosophie des Unbewussten, Leipz., W. Friedrich, 10th Ed., 3 vols, (See Vol. I., p. 26) (1st Ed., Berlin,

C. Duncker, 1870, IV, 742 p.); *34.* Head, H.: Aphasis. A historical review, Brain, 1920, 43: 390; *35.* Heisenberg, W.: Physics and Philosophy, Philosoph. Libr., New York, 1958, 206 p.; *36.* Hess, W. R.: Das Zwischenhirn. Syndrome, Lokalisation, Funktionen, Benno Schwabe, Basel, 1949, VII, 187.

37. Ingram, W. H.: How do genes act? Scient. Amer., 1958, 198: 70.

38. Jackson, J. H.: "Selected writings of Hughlings Jackson," ed. by J. Taylor, Hodder and Staughton Ltd., 1932, vol. 2, p. 29.

39. Kainz, F.: Psychologie der Sprache, Stuttgart, F. Enke, 1941–1954, 3 vols; *40.* Kant, I., quoted by Cassirer; *41.* Kleist, K.: Bericht über die Hirnpathologie und ihre Beziehungen zur Neurologie und Psychiatrie, Zeitschr. f. d. ges. Neurol. u. Psychiat., 1937, 158: 159; *42.* Kuhlenbeck, H.: Brain and consciousness, Basel, New York, S. Karger, 1957, iv + 344 p.

43. Lange, F. A.: The history of materialism (Transl. E. Ch. Thomas), London, Kegan Paul, Trench, Trubner & Cie, 1925, (First German Edition 1865); *44.* Lashley, K. S.: Mass action of cerebral function, Science, 1931, 73: 245; *45.* Laycock, Th.: Mind and Brain, New York, Appleton and Co., 1869, (See esp. chapter VIII); *46.* Lillie, R. U.: The transmission of physiological influence in nerve and other living matter, Scientia, 1920, 94: 429; *47.* Lotzka, A. S.: Elements of mathematical biology, Dover Publishing Co., New York, 1954, XXX, 460 p.

48. Magoun, H. W.: The ascending reticular system, Ass. Res. Nerv. Ment. dis. Monogr., 1952, 30: 480; *49.* Meyerhof, O.: Chemical dynamics of life phenomena, London, J. P. Lippincott and Co., 924, 110 p.; *50.* Mercier, Ch.: Hughlings Jackson on evolution and dissolution of the nervous system, Brain, 1884/85, 7: 283; *51.* Meynert, Th.: Neue Untersuchungen über den Bau der Grosshirnrinde und ihrer örtlichen Verschiedenheiten, Öster. Med. Jahrbücher, 1869; *52.* Mueller, J. H.: The problem of genetic modification, Verh. d. V. Internat. Kongr. f. Vererbung. vol. I., 1928.

53. Nachmansohn, D., Ochea, S., and Lipman, F. A.: Otto Meyerhof: 1884–1951, Science, 1952, 115: 305; *54.* Needham, J.: Man a machine, London, Kegan Paul, Trench, Trubner & Co., Ltd., 1927, 111 p.

55. Oparin, A. I.: The origin of life (Transl. S. Margolis), New York, Dover Public., 2nd Ed. 1953, XXV, 270 p.

56. Pflüger, quoted by Cannon; *57.* Polyak, St. L.: The vertebrate visual system; its origin, structure and function and its manifestations in disease, Chicago, Chicago Univ. Press, 1957, 1390 p.

58. Reichenbach, H.: The rise of scientific philoso-phy, Univ. of California Press, Berkeley and Los Angeles 1951, ix + 333 p.; *59.* Richet, Ch. R.: Physiologie, Paris, Alcan 1893–1909, 6 vols; *60.* Rignano, E.: Man not a machine. A study of the finalistic aspects of life. London, K. Paul, Trench, Trubner & Co., 1926, 77 p.; *61.* Russel, E. S.: The directiveness of organic activities, Cambridge University Press, 1945, VII, 196 p.; *62.* Rose, M.: Die Inselrinde des Menschen und der Tiere, Journ. f. Psychol. u. Neurol., Leipzig, 1929, 37: 467.

63. Scharrer, E., and Scharrer, B.: Secretory cells within the hypothalamus, Ass. Res. nerv. Ment. Dis. Monogr., 1940, 20: 170; *64.* Schlesinger, B.: Mental changes in intracranial tumors and related problems, Conf. Neurol., 1950, 10: 225, 322; *65.* Schopenhauer, A.: Die Welt als Wille und Vorstellung, (J. Frauenstaedt, Ed., vol. II., p. 375—Parerga, vol. II., p. 185; *66.* Sherrington, Ch.: The integrative action of the nervous system, Cambridge University Press, 1947, 433 p.; *67.* ——: Goethe on nature and on science, Ibid., 1942 ,31 p.; *68.* Snyder, R. S.: Recent contributions to the anatomy and the physiology of the cerebellum, Arch. Neurol. and Psychiat., 1950, 64: 196; *69.* —— and Eldred, E.: Cerebral projection to the tactile and auditory areas of the cerebellum, Anat. Rec., 1948, 100: 125; *70.* Spencer, H.: An Autobiography, London, William and Norgate, 1904, 2 vols.; *71.* Stanley, W. M.: On the nature of viruses, Modern Med., July 1, 1958; *72.* Stent, G. S.: The multiplication of viruses, Sc. Amer., 1953, 188: 36; *73.* Sugar, C. Chusid, J. G., and French, J. D.: A second motor area in the monkey, macacca mulatta, J. Neuropathol. and experiment. neurol., 1948, 7: 182.

74. Vogt, M.: Concentration of sympathin in different parts of the nervous system under normal conditions and after the administration of drugs, J. Physiol. 1934, 123: 451.

75. Weaver, W.: Probability, Scient. Amer., 1950, 83: 44; *76.* Wilder, J.: Modern psychophysiology and the law of initial value, Amer. J. Psychotherapy, 1958, XII., 199.

77. Zaunick, R.: Oken, Carus, Goethe. Zur Geschichte des Gedankens der Wirbelmetamorphose, J. Springer, Berlin, 1930.

II. AFFECTIVITY

1. Abse, D. W.: The diagnosis of hysteria, J. Wright and Sons, Bristol, 1950, 112 p.; *2.* Ach, N.: Ueber die Willenstätigkeit und das Denken, Göttingen, Vandenhook und Ruprecht, 1905, 294 p.; *3.* Adley, W. R., and Meyer, M.: Hippocampal and hypothalamic connections of the temporal lobe in monkey, Brain, 1952, 75: 358; *4.* Adrian, E. D.: The basis of sensation, Brit. Med. J., 1954, 1: 287; *5.* Alexander, F.: Fundamental conceptions of psychosomatic research, Psychosom. Med., 195, 13: 205; 6. Allan, W. F.: Effect of ablating frontal lobe, hippocampus and occipital lobe on positive conditioned and olfactory reflexes, J. comp. Neurol., 1948, 8: 424; 7. ——: Formatio reticularis and reticulospinal tracts, their visceral functions and possible relationships to tonicity and tonic contraction, J. Washingt. Acad. of Science, 1932, 22: 490; 8. Allers, R.: The successful error, A critical study of Freudian psychoanalysis, Sheed and Ward, New York, 1940, IX, 266 p.; 9. ——: Über die Begriffe eines archaischen Denkens und der Regression, Wien Zeitschr. f. Nervenheilk., 1948, 1: 39; 10. Alpers, B. J.: Relation of hypothalamus to disorders of personality, Arch. Neurol. and Psychiat., 1927, 38: 291; 11. Alsen, V.: Zur Klinik und Differentialdiagnose zentraler Schmerzen, Dtsch. Zeitschr. f. Nervenheilk., 1955, 173: 214; 12. Altschule, M. D.: Effects of factors that modify cerebral blood flow on hallucinations in schizophrenia, J. clinic. and experiment. Psychopathol., 1951, 12: 123; 13. ——: Physiological data bearing on the problem of anxiety, New York State J. Med., 1956, 56: 864; 14. Alvord, E., and Stevenson, C.: Neuropathological findings in phenylpyruvic oligophrenia. (Phenylketonuria), J. Neuropathol. and experiment. Neurol., 1950, 9: 298; 15. Alzheimer, A.: Beiträge zur pathologischen Anatomie der Dementia Praecox, Zeitschr. f. d. ges. Neurol. u. Psychiat., 1913, 7: 621; 16. Anand, B. K., and Brobeck, J. R.: Food intake and spontaneous activity of rats with lesions in the amygdaloid nuclei, J. Neurophysiol., 1952, 15: 421; 17. —— and Dua, S. T.: Circulatory and respiratory changes induced by electrical stimulation of limbic system (Visceral brain), J. Neurophysiol., 1956, 19: 393; 18. Anderson, C. M.: Organic factors predisposing to schizophrenia, Nerv. Child, 1952, 10: 36; 19. Andler, M.: Focal lesions as cause of coma, Bull. Los Angel. Neurol. Soci., 1948, 13: 123; 20. Angyal, A., Freeman, H., and Hoskins, R. G.: Physiological aspects of schizophrenic withdrawal, Arch. Neurol. and Psychiat., 1940, 44: 421; 21. —— and Sherman, M. A.: Postural reactions to vestibular stimulation in schizophrenic and normal subjects, Amer. J. Psychiat., 1942, 98: 857; 22. Anton, G.: Theodor Meynert, J. f. Psychol. u. Neurol., 1929/30, 40: 256; 23. —— see Zingerle, Ref. 920; 24. Anton-Stephens, D.: Preliminary observations on the psychiatric use of chlorpromazine (Largactil), J. ment. Sc., 1954, 100: 543; 25. Arduini, A., and Moruzzi, G.: Sensory and thalamic synchrony in the olfactory bulb, EEG and Clin. Neurophysiol., 1953, 5: 234; 26. ——: Olfactory arousal reaction in the "cerveau isolé" of cat, Ibid., p. 243; 27. Arieti, S.: Interpretation of schizophrenia, R. Brunner, New York, 1955, XVI, 522 p.; 28. ——: The possibility of psychosomatic involvement of the central nervous system in schizophrenia, J. nerv. ment. dis., 1956, 123: 324; 29. Arnold, M.: The status of emotion in contemporary psychology, See Roback, (Ref 719a), p. 135; 30. Arnold, O., and Hoff, H.: Die Bedeutung der experimentellen Pharmakologie für die Neurologic u. Psychiatric, J. Mount Sin. Hosp., 1952, 19: 191; 31. Ashby, W. R.: Design for a brain, New York, Wiley and Sons, 1952, IX, 259 p.; 32. ——: A report on the current status of an attempt to correlate abnormality of distribution of an enzyme with mental dysfunction, J. nerv. ment. dis., 1950, 112: 425; 33. Axel, M.: Ten borderline cases. A report on the question of pseudoneurotic schizophrenia, Psychiat. Quarterly, 1955, 29: 558; 34. Azima, H., and Ogle, W.: Effects of Largactil in mental syndromes, Canad. Med. Ass. J., 1954, 71: 116.

35. Babinski, J. F. F.: Ma conception de l'hystérie et de l'hypnotism. (Pythiatism), Chartres, Impr. Durant, 1906, 31 p.; 36. Baeumer, H.: Veränderungen am Thalamus bei Schizophrenen, Zeitschr. f. Hirnforschung, 1954, 1: 156; 37. Bailey, P.: Janet and Freud, A. M. A. Arch. Neurol. and Psychiat., 1956, 76: 76; 38. —— and Bremer, F.: A sensory cortical representation of the vagus nerve, J. Neurophysiol., 1938, 1: 405; 39. —— and Davis, E. W.: Effect of lesions in the periaqueductal gray matter in the cat, Proc. Soc. exper. Biol. and Medicine, 1942, 51: 305; 40. Baird, H. W., Guidelti, B., Reyes, V., Wycis, H. T., and Spiegel, E. A.: Stimulation and elimination of the anterior thalamic nucleus in man and cat, Pflüger's Arch., 1952; 255: 58; 41. Baldwin, M., Frost, L. L., and Wood, Ch. D.: Investigation of the primate amygdala. 2. Effect of selective ablation, Neurology, 1956, 6: 288; 42. Bangs, W. J.: Bilateral lesions in the anterior cingulate gyrus, Bull. Los Ang. Neurol. Soc., 1956, 21: 149; 43. Bard, P. A., and Mountcastle, V. B.: A diencephalic mechanism for the expression of rage, with special reference to the sympathetic nervous system, Assoc. res. nerv. ment. dis. monogr., 1948, 27: 362; 44. Barker, R. G.: An experimental study of the resolution of conflict in children. In "Studies in Personality". Ed. Q. McNemer and M. A. Merrill, New York, McGraw Hill Co., 1942; 45. Barris, R. W., and Schuman, H. R.: Bilateral anterior cingular gyrus lesions, Neurology, 1953, 3: 44; 46. Baruk, H.: Volonté et personalité morale, Presse medic., 1947, 55: 498; 47. Barza, J. A., and Kline, N. S.: A comparative study of reserpine, chlorpromazine and combined therapy, A. M. A. Arch. Neurol. and psychiat., 1956, 76: 90; 48. Bauer, J.: Constitution and disease. Applied constitutional pathology, New York, Grune and Stratton, 1945, XIII, 245 p.; 49. Bayerthal, quoted by K. Kleist, Ref. 468; 50. Beach, F. A.: Review of physiological and psychological studies of

sexual behaviour in mammals, Psychol. Rev., 1947, 27: 240; *51.* Bechterew, W. R.: Über Störungen des Zeitgefühles bei Geisteskranken, Zbl. f. Nervenkr. 1903, 26: 620; *52.* Beckett, P. G. S., Robinson, D. B., Frazier, Sh. H. a. ass.: Studies in schizophrenia at the Mayo Clinic. I. The significance of exogenous traumata in the genesis of schizophrenia, Psychiatry, 1956, 19: 137; *53.* Beethoven L. v.: Beethoven's letters, (Transl. J. S. Shadlock) London, J. M. Dent & Sons, 1909, 2 vols.; *54.* Bein, H. J.: Significance of selected central mechanism for the analysis of the action of reserpine, Ann. N. Y. Acad. Sc., 1955, 61: 4; *55.* Bellak, L.: A multiple factor psycho-somatic theory of schizophrenia, Psychiat. Quart., 1949, 23: 738; *56.* ——: Manic-depressive psychosis and allied conditions, New York, Grune and Stratton, 1952, 306 p.; *57.* Bellak, L.: Toward a united concept of schizophrenia, J. nerv. ment. dis., 1955, 121: 60; *58.* Bender, L.: Childhood schizophrenia, Amer. J. Orthopsychiat., 1947, 17: 40; *59.* Benedek, L. and Juba, A.: Weitere Beiträge zur Frage des anatomischen Substrates des Korsakoffschen Symptomenkomplexes, Arch. f. Psychiat. u. Nervenkrankh., 1941, 112: 505; *60.* Benedetti, G., Kind, H., and Mielke, F.: Forschungen zur Schizophrenielehre Fortschr. d. Neurol. u. Psychiat., 1957, 25: 101; *61.* Bennet, D. H., and Robertson, J. P. S.: The effect of habit training on chronic schizophrenia, J. ment. sc., 1955, 101: 664; *62.* Bente, D., and Klages, W.: Zur Psychopathologie des affektiv-dysaesthetischen Halbseitensyndroms, Monatschr. f. Psychiat. u. Neurol., 1955, 130: 257; *63.* —— and Kluge, E.: Sexuelle Reizzustände im Rahmen des Uncussyndromes, Arch f. Psychiat. u. Z. Neur., 1953, 190: 357; *64.* Bercel, N. A., Travis, L. E., Olinger, L. B., and Dreikurs, E.: Model-psychoses induced by LSD-25 in normals. (I.), A. M. A. Arch. Neurol. and Psychiat., 1956, 75: 588; *65.* Bergmann, G. von: Die vegetative Stigmatisierten, Med. Klin., 1928, 24: 814; *66.* Bergson, H.: Durée et spontaneité, 5th Ed., p. 60 ff.; *67.* Beringer, K.: Beitrag zur Analyse der schizophrenen Denkstörung, Zeitschr. f. d. ges. Neurol. u. Psychiat., 1924, 93: 55; *68.* ——: Der Meskalinrausch. Seine Geschichte und Erscheinungsweise, Berlin, J. Springer, 1927, IV, 315 p.; *69.* ——: Ueber Störungen des Antriebes bei einem von der unteren Mantelkante ausgehendem Meningiom, Zeitschr. f. d. ges. Neurol. u. Psychiat., 1941, 171: 451; *70.* ——: Rhythmischer Wechsel von Gehemmtheit and Enthemmtheit als dienzephale Antriebsstörung, Nervenarzt, 1942, 15: 225; *71.* Bernard, Cl.: Leçons sur les propriétés des tissues vivants, Paris, Baillière 1866, 490 p.; *72.* ——: Leçons sur les phenomènes de la vie commune aux animaux et aux végétaux, Paris, Baillière et Fils, 1878/79. 2 vols.; *73.* Bernfeld, S.: Freud's earliest theories and the school of Helm-

holtz, Psychanalyt. Quart., 1944, 13: 349; *74.* Bernhaut, M., Gellhorn, E., and Rasmussen, A. T.: Experimental contribution to the problem of consciousness, J. Neurophysiol., 1953, 16: 21; *75.* Bernheim, H.: Suggestive therapeutics (Transl. C. A. Harter), G. T. Putnam and Sons, 1895; *76.* Berze, J.: Die primäre Insuffizienz der psychischen Aktivität, Leipzig und Wien, F. Deuticke, 1914, VIII, 404 p.; *77.* ——: Störungen des psychischen Antriebes, Zeitschr. f. d. ges. Neurol. u. Psychiat., 1932, 142: 720; *78.* ——: Grundsätzliches und kritisches zur Frage der Schizophrenie, Ibid., 1942, 175: 256; *79.* Bethe, A.: Rhythmus und Periodizität in der belebten Natur, Stud. gen., 1949, 2: 67; *80.* Bianchi, L.: The mechanism of the brain and the function of the frontal lobes (Transl. J. H. McDonald), W. Woods and Co., 1922, 348 p.; *81.* Bickensdorfer, E.: Zur ätiologischen Problem der Psychosen vom akuten exogenen Reaktionstypus, Arch. f. Psychiat. u. Z. Neur., 1952, 188/89: 226; *82.* Bierens de Haan, J. A.: Animal Psychology. Its nature and problems, Hutchinson's University Library, London, VI, 160 p.; *83.* Billings, E. G.: Handbook of experimental psychobiology, New York, McMillan, 1939, XV, 271 p.; *84.* Birkmayer, W., Frühmann, E., and Strotzka, H.: Motorische Schablonen im Erwachen nach dem Eelektroschock, Arch. f. Psychiat. u. Z. Neur., 1955, 193: 513; *85.* —— and Palisa, Ch.: Bewegungsautomatosen im Insulinshock, Archiv f. Psychiat. u. Nervenkrankh., 1939, 109: 87; *86.* Blau, A.: A unitary hypothesis of emotion. I. Anxiety, emotions of displeasure and affective disorders, Psychanal. Quart., 1955, 24: 75; *87.* Bleuler, E.: Das Unbewusste, J. f. Psychol. u. Neurol., 1913, 20: 89; *88.* ——: The physiogenic and psychogenic in schizophrenia, Amer. J. Psychiat., 1930, 10: 203; *89.* ——: Dementia Praecox or the group of schizophrenias (Transl. J. Ziskin), Internat. Univers. Press, 1950, New York, 548 p.; *90.* ——: quoted by Loewenfeld (Ref. *547*); *91.* —— M.: Forschungen und Begriffswandlungen in der Schizophrenielehre (1941–1950), Fortschr. a. d. Geb. d. Neurol. u. Psychiat., 1951, 19: 385; *92.* ——: Eugen Bleuler's conception of schizophrenia—a historical sketch, Bull. Isaac Ray Med. Libr., 1953, 1: 47; *93.* ——: Gedanken zur heutigen Schizophrenielehre, Wien. Zeitschr. f. Nervenheilk., 1953/54, 7/8: 255; *94.* Blum, R. H.: Alpha-Rhythm responsiveness in normal, schizophrenic and brain damaged persons, Science, 1957, 126: 794; *95.* Bochnik, H. J.: Tagesrhythmen nach halbseitiger präfrontaler Leukotomie, Dtsch. Zeitschr. f. Nervenheilk., 168: 95; *96.* Böök, J. A.: Schizophrenia as a gene mutation, Acta Psychiat. et neurol. Scand., 1953, 4: 133; *97.* Bonheoffer: Die exogenen Raektionstypen, Arch. f. Psychiat., 1917, 58; *98.* ——: Quoted by Bumcke, (Ref. *131*); *99.* Borenstein, P., Dabbati, M., and

Metzger, J.: L'encephalographie fractionnée dans les syndromes schizophréniques, Ann. de Med. Psychol., 1957, 2: 385; *100*. Bosselman, B. Ch.: Neurosis and psychosis, Ch. C. Thomas, Springfield, Ill., 2nd Ed. 1955, X, 186 p.; *101*. Bostroem, A.: Der amyostatische Symptomenkomplex, J. Springer, Berlin, 1922, 205 p.; *102*. ——: Ueber organisch provozierte endogene Psychosen, Zeitschr. f. d. ges. Neurol. u. Psychiat., 1930, 131: 1; *103*. Bower, W. H.: Chlorpromazine in psychiatric illness, New Engl. J. of Med., 1954, 251: 689; *104*. Bowlby, J.: Maternal care and mental health, World Health Organ. Monogr., Series No. 2, Col. Univ. Press, New York, 1952; *105*. Boycott, B. B., and Young, J. Z.: See Chapter I., Ref. *12*; *106*. Bradley, Ch. and Bowen, M.: Behaviour characteristics of schizophrenic children, Psychiat. Quarterly, 1941, 15: 296; *107*. Braitenberg, V.: Zur Frage der Anatomie des Gehirns bei der Schizophrenie, Münchn. Med. Wochenschr., 1954, 96: 365; *108*. Bramwell, J. M.: Hypnotism, 2nd Ed., Rider and Son, London, 1913; *109*. Braun, L.: Herz und Psyche in ihren Wirkungen aufeinander, F. Deuticke, Wien und Leipzig, 1920, III, 153 p.; *109a*. Bremer, F.: Analyse oscillographique des reponses sensorielles des écorces cérébrales et cérébelleuses, Rev. neur., 1952, 87: 65; *110*. Breslauer: Zur Frage des Hirndruckes, Arch. f. klin. Chir., 1914, 103: 478; *111*. Breuer, J., and Freud, S.: Studien über Hysterie, 2nd Ed., Leipzig und Wien, F. Deuticke, 1909, VI, 269 p.; *112*. Briand, quoted by Jeliffe, (Ref. *419*); *113*. Brickner, R. M.: The intellectual functions of the frontal lobes, New York, McMillan Co., 1936, XVI, 354 p.; *114*. Brickner, R. M.: Bilateral frontal lobectomy. Follow-up of a case, Arch. of Neurol. and Psychiat., 1939, 41: 580; *115*. ——: Conscious inability to synthetize thought in a case of right frontal lobe tumor and lobectomy, Arch. Neurol. and Psychiat., 1939, 41: 1116; *116*. —— and Stein, A.: Intellectual symptoms in temporal lobe lesions, including "déja pensée", J. Mount Sinai Hosp., 1942, 9: 334; *117*. Broadbent, W. H.: See Chapter I., Ref. *13*; *118*. Broca, P.: Anatomie comparée des circonvolutions cérébrales. Le grand lobe limbique et la scissure limbique dans la série des mammères, Dev. anthropol., 1878, Sér. 2. 1:285; *119*. Brodal, A.: Neurological anatomy in relation to clinical medicine, Oxford, Clarendon Press, X, 496 p.; *120*. ——: The hipoocampus and the sense of smell, Brain, 1947, 70: 179; *121*. Brodie, B.: Psychological inquiries, 3rd Ed., Longman, Brown, Green and Longmans, London, 1865; *122*. Brodie, B. B.: Interaction of psychotripic drugs with physiological and biochemical mechanisms in the brain, Modern Medicine, August 1, 1958; *123*. Brodie, B. P., Bogdanski, D. F. and Shore, P. A.: The action of psychotropic drugs. A biochemical and physiological

interpretation. In "Chemical concepts of Psychosis." See Ref. 187; *124*. Bromberg, W.: The effects of marihuana, Ass. res. nerv. ment. dis. monogr., 1939, 19: 180; *125*. Brown, S. and Schaeffer, E. A.: An investigation into the functions of the occipital and temporal lobes, Phil. Transactions, 1888, 179: 203; *126*. Bruecke, E. W. von: Vorlesungen über Physiologie, W. Braumeuller, Wien, 1873–1875, 2 vols.; *127*. Bruetch, W. L.: Mental disorders arising from organic disease, In "Biol. of ment. health and dis." Paul Hoeber, Inc., New York, 1952, XXV, 654 p.; *128*. Brun, R.: General theory of neurosis, Internat. Univers. Press, 1951, VII, 468; *129*. Bucy, C. P. and Kluever, H.: Anatomical changes secondary to temporal lobectomy, Arch. Neurol. a. Psychiat., 1940, 44: 1142; *130*. Bull, N., and Strongin, E.: The complex of frustration. A new interpretation, J. Nerv. a. Ment. Dis., 1956, 123: 531; *131*. Bumcke, O.: Lehrbuch der Geisteskrankheiten, 3rd Ed., München, J. F. Bergmann, 1929, XVI, 806 p.; *132*. Buessow, H.: Ueber paranoid halluzinatorische Psychosen bei der perniziösen Anämie, Nervenarzt 1940, 13: 49; *133*. Buscaino, V. M.: Le cause anatomico-patologiche delle manifestazioni nella demenze precoce, Riv. path. nerv., 1920, 25: 197; *134*. Busemann, A.: Einfallsarmut nach Hirnverletzung, Arch, f. Psychiat. u. Z. Neur., 1947/48, 179: (118): 538, and Dtsch. Med. Wochenschr. 1947, 72: 60; *135*. Buttlar-Brentano, K. von: Pathologische Feststellungen am Basalkern von Schizophrenen, J. nerv. ment. dis., 1952, 116: 646.

136. Cabanis, P. J. G.: Ouevres complètes de Cabanis, Paris, Bossange Frères, 1823–1825. (See also Ref. *409*); *137*. Cairns, H., Oldfield, R. C., Pennybacker, J. B., and Whitteridge, D.: Akinetic mutism with an epidermoid cyst of the third ventricle, Brain, 1941, 64: 273; *138*. Cameron, D. E.: Early schizophrenia, Amer. J. Psychiat., 1938, 95: 567; *139*. Cameron, N.: The functional psychoses, In J. Mc. V. Hunt, Ed., "Personality and Behaviour disorders", 1944, The Ronald Press; *140*. —— and Margaret, A.: Behaviour pathology, Ed. L. Carmichael, Boston, Houghton Mifflin Co., 1951, 645 p.; *141*. Campbell, R. J. and Harlow, H. F.: Problem solution by monkeys following bilateral removal of the prefrontal association areas. Spatial delayed reactions, J. experim. Psychol., 1945, 35: 110; *142*. Camus, J.: Centres psychoregulatoires et centres psychiques extracocorticales, La Médecine, 1922/25, 4: 351; *143*. Cannon, W. B.: The James-Lange theory of emotions; a critical examination and an alternative theory, Amer. J. Psychol., 1927, 39: 106; *144*. Cannon, W. B.: Bodily changes in pain, hunger, fear and rage. An account of recent researches into the functions of emotional excitement, New York, D. Appleton and Co., 1929, XVIII, 404 p.; *145*. ——:

See Chapter I., Ref. *14; 146.* ——: Again the James-Lange theory and the thalamic theory of emotion, Psychol. Rev., 1931, 38: 281; *147.* ——: The wisdom of the body, W. N. Norton and Co. Publ., New York, 1932, IX, 312 p.; *148.* Cantril, H.: The roles of the situation and adrenaline in the production of emotions, Amer. J. Psychol., 1934, 46: 568; *149.* —— and Hunt, W. J.: Emotional effects produced by the injection of adrenaline, Amer. J. Psychol., 1932, 44: 300; *150.* Carmichael, E. A., and Stern, R. O.: Korsakoff's syndrome. Its histopathology, Brain, 1931, 54: 89; *151.* Carpenter, J. A.: Anticipative behaviour in the rat following frontal lobe lesions, J. compar. Psychol., 1952, 45: 413; *152.* Carpenter, M. B.: The influence of frontal topectomy upon gastric secretion, J. nerv. ment. dis., 1951, 113: 52; *153.* Carpenter, W. B.: Principles of human physiology, 5th Ed., Blanchard and Lea, Philadelphia, 1853; *154.* Carr; quoted by Pick, A.; *155.* Cassirer, E.: See Chapter 1, Ref. *15; 156.* Chamberlain, G. H. A., and Russel, J. G.: The electroencephalograms of relatives of schizophrenics, J. ment. sc., 1952, 98: 654; *157.* Chapman, W. P., Livingston, K. E., and Poppen, J. L.: Effect upon bloodpressure of electrical stimulation of tips of temporal lobes in man, J. Neurophysiol., 1950, 13: 65; *158.* ——, Rose, A. J., and Salomon, H.: Measurement of heat stimulus producing motor withdrawal reactions in patients following frontal lobotomy, Ass. Res. nerv. ment. dis. monogr., 1948, 27: 754; *159.* Charaban, F. B. E.: An evaluation of Chlorpromazine, ("Largactil") in psychiatry, J. ment. sc., 1954, 100: 882; *160.* Charcot, J. B. A. E.: Oeuvres complètes, Paris, Bureaux de Progrès médicale, 1994, 1894. (See esp. vol. XI. Metallotherapie et hypnotism); *161.* Clardy, E. R.: A study of the development and course of schizophrenia in childhood, Psychiat. Quarterly, 1951, 25: 81; *162.* Clark, W. E. Le Gros: The connections of the frontal lobes of the brain, Lancet I, 1948, p. 353; *163.* Clark, W. E., Le Gros, Beattie, J., Riddoch, G., and Dott, N. M.: The hypothalamus. Morphological, functional, clinical and surgical aspects, Oliver and Boyd, Edinburgh, 1938, (see esp. p. 212); *164.* —— and Boggon, H. R.: On the connections of the anterior nucleus of of the thalamus, J. of Anatomy, 1933, 67: 216; *165.* —— and Meyer, A.: Anatomical relationships between cerebral cortex and hypothalamus, Brit. Medic. J., 1950, 6: 341; *166.* Clarke, quoted by Jastrow, Ref. *418a; 167.* Coghill, G. J.: The structural basis of the integration of behaviour, Proc. Nat. Academy of Science, 1930, 16: 673; *168.* Cooper, I. S.: Disorders of the electrolyte metabolism in diseases of the nervous system, Neurology, 1953, 3: 119; *169.* Cooper, L. F., and Erickson, M. H.: Time distortion in hypnosis, Bull. Georgetown Univ. Med. Center, 1950, 4: 3; *170.* Cossack, H.: Kriminogene

Persönlichkeitsveränderungen nach Stirnhirnschaden, Arch. f. Psychiat. u. Nervenkrankh., 1936, 105: 291; *171.* Cox, L. B.: Tumors of the base of the brain. Relation to pathological sleep and other changes in consciousness, Med. J. of Austr., 1929, 1: 742; *172.* Craig, W.: Appetites and aversions as constituents of instincts, Biol. Bull., 1918, 34: 91; *173.* Craik, K. J. W.: The nature of explanation, Cambridge Univ. Press, 1943, VIII, 121 p.; *174.* Crane, G. E.: Further studies on iproniazid phosphate, J. nerv. ment. dis., 1956, 124: 322; *175.* Creutzfeld, H. G.: Hirnveränderungen bei Gewohnheitstrinkern, Zbl. f. d. ges. Neurol. u. Psychiat., 1928, 50: 321; *176.* Cushing, H.: Papers relating to the pituitary body, hypothalamus and parasympathetic system, Ch. Thomas, Springfield, 1932, VII, 234 p.

177. Dana, Ch. L.: The anatomic seat of the emotions; a discussion of the James-Lange theory, Arch. Neurol. and Psychiat., 1921, 6: 634; *178.* Darwin, Ch.: The expression of emotions in man and animals, New York, Appleton and Co., 1873, 374 p.; *179.* ——: See Chapter I, Ref. *17; 180.* Davey, L., Kaada, B. R. and Fulton, J. F.: Effects of gastric secretion of frontal lobe stimulation, Ass. Res. Nerv. ment. dis. monogr., 1950, 29: 617; *181.* David, G. B.: The pathological anatomy of schizophrenia, In "Schizophrenia. Somatic aspects." Ed. D. Richter, The McMillan Co., New York, 1957, VII, 181 p. (See p. 93); *182.* Deboor, W.: Zur Frage der Kombination von genuiner Epilepsie unf Schizophremie, Nervenarzt, 1948, 19: 279; *183.* De Crinis, M.: Verfall der Gesittung bei Hirngeschwülsten, Ztschr. f. d. ges. Neurol. u. Psychiat., 1937, 160: 426; *184.* Dejerine, J., and Roussy, G.: Le syndrome thalamique, Rev. neurol., 1906, 14: 521; *185.* De Jong, H. H.: Experimental catatonia. A general reaction form in the central nervous system and its implications for human pathology, Williams and Wilkins, Baltimore, 1945, XII, 225 p.; *186.* Delay, J. J.: États hysteroides d'origine medicamenteuse, Canad. psychiat. ass. J., 1958, 3: 132; *187.* Delay, J. J. and Deniker, P.: Hysteria and drug-induced hysteria-like states, In "Chemical concepts of psychosis", Ed. M. Rinkel and H. C. B. Denber, McDowell Obolensky, New York, 1958, XX, 485; *188.* Delgado, J. M. R.: Report on respiratory centers of frontal lobes, Ass. Res. nerv. ment. dis. monogr., 1948, p. 433; *189.* Dempsey, E. W. and Morison, R. S.: Production rhythmically recurrent cortical potentials after localized thalamic stimulation, Amer. J. Psychiat., 1942, 135: 293; *190.* Denber, H. C. B., and Merlis, S.: Studies on mescaline, I. Action in schizophrenic patients, Psychiat. Quarterly, 1955, 29: 421; *191.* Denny-Brown, D.: The frontal lobes and their function, In "Modern trends in Neurology." Ed. A. Feiling, Butterworth and Co., London, 1951, 717 p.

(See p. 13); *192.* De Shon, H. J. Rinkel, M., and Salomon, H. C.: Mental changes experimentally produced by LSD-25, Psychiat. Quarterly, 1952, 26: 33; *193.* Despert, J. L.: The early recognition of childhood schizophrenia, Med. Clin. of North America, 1947, 31: 680; *194.* Deussen, P. Lecture notes on Schopenhauer's philosophy; *195.* Dide, Guiraud and Lafage: Syndromes parkinsonien dans la démence précoce, Rev. neurol., 1921, 37: 692; A study of the effects of LSD. Physiologic and psychologic changes and their interrelations, Amer. J. Psychiat., 1957, 114: 309; *196.* Di Mascio, A., Greenblatt, M., and Hyde, R. W.: A study of the effects of LSD; physiological and psychological changes and their interrelations, Amer. J. Psychiat., 1957, 114: 309; *197.* Dimitz, L., and Schilder, P.: Ueber die psychischen Störungen bei der Encephalitis epidemica des Jahres 1920, Zeitschr. f. d. ges. Neurol. u. Psychiat., 1921, 68: 299; *198.* Dockeray, F.: Psychology, New York, Prentice-Hall, 1942, XIV, 504 p.; *199.* Dollard, J., Miller, N. E., Dobb, L. W., Mowrer, O. H., and Sears, R.: Frustration and aggression, Published by the Institute of Human relations by Yale Univ. Press, New Haven, Conn., 1943, VIII, 209 p.; *200.* Dorer, M.: Historische Grundlagen der Psychoanalyse, Leipzig, F. Meiner, 1932, III, 184 p.; *201.* Dott, N. M.: See Ref. *163*; *202.* Duffy, E.: Leeper's "motivational theory of emotion," Psychol. Rev., 1948, 55: 324; *203.* Dunning, H. S., and Wolf, H. E.: See Chapter I., Ref. 19; *204.* Durham-Seitz, Ph. F.: Symbolism in conversion, Psychosomatic Med., 1957, 13: 254; *205.* Dynes, J. B.: An objective method of distinguishing sleep from hypnotic trance, Arch. Neurol. and Psychiat., 1947, 57: 84.

206. Economo, C. von: See Chapter I, Ref. *22;* *207.* ———: Encephalitis lethargica; its sequelae and its treatment, (Transl. K. O. Neuman) London, H. Milford, 1931, XIV, 200 p.; *208.* ——— and Koskinas: Die Zytoarchitektonik der Grosshirnrinde des erwachsenen Menschen, Berlin, J. Springer, 1925; *209.* Edinger, E. F.: Archetypal patterns in schizophrenia, Amer. J. Psychiat., 1955, 112: 255; *210.* Edinger, L.: Vorlesungen über den Bau der nervösen Zentralorgane, Leipzig, Thomas, 1911, XII, 386 p.; *211.* Edwards, E., Landau, W., Freygang, W., and Marshall, W.: Some effects of lysergic acid diethylamide and bufotenin on electrical activity in the cat's visual system, Amer. J. Physiol., 1955, 182: 594; *212.* Elmadjan, F., Hope, J. M., and Freeman, H.: Metacholine test and epinephrine and arterenol excretion, A. M. A. Neurol. and Psychiat., 1957, 77: 399; *213.* Elsässer, G., and Grünewald, H. W.: Schizophrene oder schizophrenieähnliche Psychosen bei Hirntraumatikern, Arch. f. Psychiat. and Z. Neur., 1953, 190: 134; *214.* Erickson, M. M.: An experimental investigation of the hypnotic subject's apparent ability to become unaware of stimuli, J. of Gen. Psychol., 1944, 31: 191; *214a.* Emery, J. C., and McMillan, M.: Observations on the female sex chromatin and on the value of skin biopsy in determining sex, J. Path. and Bact., 1954, 68: 17; *215.* Ethelberg, S.: On "cataplexy" in a case of frontal lobe tumor, Acta Psychiat. et neurol., Scand., 1949, 24: 420; *216.* Evarts, E., Landau, W., Freygang, W., and Marshall, W.: Some effects of lysergic acid diethylamide and of bufotenin of the electrical activity of the cat's visual cortex, Amer. J. Physiol., 1955, 182: 594; *217.* Ewald, G.: Vegetatives Nervensystem und Psychiatrie, Fortschr. a. d. Geb. d. Neurol. u. Psychiat., 1950, 18: 577; *218.* ———: Zur Theorie der Schizophrenie, Dtsch. Med. Wochenschr., 1954, 79: 1813; *219.* Eysenck, H. L.: Suggestibility and Hypnosis, J. Neurol., Neurosurg. a. Psychiat., 1943, 6: 22; *220.* ———: Uses and abuses of Psychology, Penguin Books, 1954, 318 p.

221. Fabing, H. D.: Frenquel, a blocking agent against experimental LSD-25 and mescaline psychosis, Neurology, 1955, 5: 319; *222.* Fairbanks: quoted by Guntrip (Ref. *312*); *223.* Faust, Cl.: Zur Symptomatologie der frischen und der alten Stirnhirnverletzungen, Arch. f. Psychiat. u. Neurol., 1955, 193: 78; *224.* Felsinger, J. M., von, Lasagna, L. and Beecher, H. K.: Drug-induced mood changes in man. 2. Personality and reaction to drugs, J. Amer. Med. Ass., 1955, 157: 1006; *225.* Fenichel, O.: The psychoanalytic theory of neurosis, Norton, New York, 1955; *226.* Féré, quoted by Froebes, (Ref. *256*); *227.* Ferraro, A.: Nosologic position of neurasthenia in psychiatry, J. nerv. ment. dis., 1954, 119: 299; *228.* ———: Pathological changes in the brain of a case clinically diagnosed as dementia praecox, J. Neuropath. and experiment. Neurol., 1943, 2: 84; *229.* Feuchtinger, S.: Konträre und paradoxe Reaktionen als Folge hypophysärer Stoerungen, Nervenarzt, 1943, 16: 428; *230.* Feuchtwanger, L. E.: Die Funktionen des Stirnhirns, J. Springer, Berlin, 1928; *231.* ——— and Mayer-Gross, W.; Hirnverletzung und Schizophrenie, Schw. Arch. Neurol. u. Psychiat., 1938, 41: 17; *232.* Fields, W. S. (Ed.): Brain mechanism and Drug action, Springfield, C. C. Thomas, 1957, 147 p.; *233.* Finan, L. S.: Delayed responses with pre-delay reinforcement in monkeys after removal of the frontal lobes, J. Neurophysiol., 1938, 2: 208, and J. Psychol., 1942, 55: 202; *234.* Finkh, O.: Psychogene Initialsymptome bei Schizophrenie, Arch. f. Psychiat. un. Nervenkrankh., 1927, 81: 152; *235.* Finley, K. H.: See Chapter I, Ref. *25;* *236.* Finley, K. H., and Campbell, M. C.: The electroencephalogram in schizophrenia, Amer. J. Psychiat., 1941, 98: 374; *237.* Fish, F. J.: The classification of schizophrenia. The view of Kleist and his coworkers, J.

Ment. Sc., 1957, 103: 443; *237a*. ——: Leonhard's classification of schizophrenia, J. Ment. Sc., 1958, 104: 943; *238*. Fischer, F.: Zeitstruktur und Schizophrenie, Zeitschr. f. d. ges. Neurol. u. Psychiat., 1929, 121: 544; *239*. Fisher, R.: Schizophrenie. Ein regressiver Adaptationsprozess, Monatschr. f. Psychiat. u. Neurol., 1953, 12: 313; *239a*. Fitt, A. B.: Seasonal influence on growth, function and inheritance, Wellington Council for Educational Research, 1941, XI, 182; *240*. Fitzherbert, J.: Increase in intelligence quotient at onset of schizophrenia. Three adolescent cases, Br. J. Educat. Psychol., 1955, 28: 191; *241*. Flechsig, P.: Die Leitungsbahnen im Gehirn und Rückenmark, Leipzig, W. Engelmann, 1905; *242*. Foerster, O.: Zur Pathogenese des epileptischen Krampfanfalles, Dtsch. Zeitschr. f. Nervenheilk., 1926, 94: 15 (See p. 47); *243*. ——: Die Leitungsbahnen des Schmerzgefühles und die chirurgische Behandlung der Schmerzzustände, Berlin and Wien, Urban and Schwarzenberg, 1927, VII, 360; *244*. —— and Gagel, O.: Ein Fall von Ependymzyste des dritten Ventrikels. Ein Beitrag zur Frage der Beziehungen zwischen psychischen Störungen und Hirnstamm, Zeitschr. f. d. ges. Neurol. u. Psychiat., 1933, 149: 312; *245*. Ford, W. R., and Yaeger, C.: Changes in the EEG in subjects under hypnosis, Dis. nerv. system., 1948, 9: 190; *246*. Fordham, F.: An introduction to Jung's psychology, Penguin Books, Baltimore, 1954, 128 p.; *247*. Forel, A.: Einige Bemerkungen über Hypnotismus, Münchn. Med. Wochenschr., 1888, No. 13; *248*. Fox, H. M., Gifford, S., and Murawski, J.: Psychological effects of ACTH and cortisone, Conn. State J. Med., 1955, 19: 453; *249*. Fränkel, F.: Über die psychiatrische Bedeutung der subkortikalen Ganglien und ihre Beziehungen zur Katatonie, Zeitschr. f. d. ges. Neurol. u. Psychiat., 1921, 70: 312; *250*. Fraenkel and Joel: quoted by Jaspers, K., (Ref. *418*); *251*. Frankl, L. and Meyer-Gross, V.: Personality changes after prefrontal lobotomy, Lancet II, 1947, p. 820; *252*. Frankl, V. E., and Pötzl, O.: Über die seelischen Zustände während des Absturzes, Monatsschr. f. Psychiat. u. Neurol., 1951, 123: 363; *253*. Frantze, A., Vestergaard, P., Kobbennagel, F., and Nielsen, A.: Adrenal cortical function in chronic schizophrenia, Acta endocrin., 1951, 8: 244; *254*. Franz, S. J.: On the function of the cerebrum, Psychol. Monogr., No. 2, New York, Science Press, 1907; *255*. Frédérique: (See Chap. I, Ref. *27*); *256*. Freeman, W.: Mass action versus mosaic function of the frontal lobe, Bull. Los Ang. Neurol. Soc., 1950, 15: 220; *257*. ——: Frontal lobotomy 1936-1956. A follow up study of 3000 patients from one to twenty years, Amer. J. Psychiat., 1957, 113: 877; *258*. —— and Carmichael, H. T.: A pharmacodynamic investigation of the nervous system in schizophrenia, Arch.

Neurol. a. Psychiat., 1935, 33: 342; *259*. —— and Watts, M. J.: The interpretation of the function of the frontal lobe, Yale J. of Biol. and Med., 1939, 11: 527; *260*. —— and ——: Physiological psychology, Ann. rev. of Physiol., 1944, 6: 577; *261*. —— and Watts, J. W.: Psychosurgery. Intelligence, emotions and social behaviour following prefrontal lobotomy for mental disease, Ch. Thomas, Springfield, Ill., 1951, XXVIII, 589 p.; *262*. French, J. D.: The reticular formation, J. Neurosurg., 1958, 15: 97; *263*. ——, Amerongen, F. K., and Magoun, H. W.: An activating system in the brainstem of the monkey, A. M. A. Arch. Neurol. a. Psychiat., 1952, 68: 577; *264*. ——, Hernandez Peon, R., and Livingston: Projection from the cortex to cephalic brainstem (reticular formation) in monkey, J. Neurophysiol., 1955, 18: 74; *265*. —— and Magoun, H. W.: Effects of chronic lesions in the central cephalic brainstem of the monkey, J. Neurophysiol., 1952, 68: 591; *266*. ——, Verzeano, M., and Magoun, H. W.: An extralemniscal system in the brain, Ibid., 1953, 69: 505; *267*. Freud, A.: Psychoanalysis for parents and teachers, New York, Emerson Books, 1935, 117 p.; *268*. —— S.: Analyse eines Falle von chronischer Paranoia, Neurol. Zentralbl., 1896, 15: 442; *268a*. ——: Introductory Lectures to Psychoanalysis; *269*. ——: Formulations regarding the two principles of mental functioning (1911), In "Collected papers", vol. 4. Hogarth, London, 1925; *270*. ——: Gesammelte Schriften, Internat. Psychoanlyt. Verlag, 1924–1934, 12 vol.; *271*. ——: An outline of psychoanalysis, (Transl. J. Strachey), New York, Norton and Co., 127 p.; *272*. Freyhan, F. A.: Study of a schizophrenic family, Delaw. Med. J., 1951, 23: 213; *273*. Froebes, J.: Lehrbuch der experimentellen Psychologie, Freiberg, Hèrder, 1922/23, 2 vols.; *274*. Froeschels, E.: A peculiar intermediary state between waking and sleeping, Amer. J. of Psychotherapy, 1949, 3: 19; *275*. Fromm-Reichmann, F.: Psychiatric aspects of anxiety, In "An Outline of Psychoanalysis." Ed. Milton Mazer and Earl Witenberg. The Modern Library, New York, p. 113; *276*. ——: Notes on the development of treatment of schizophrenics by psychoanalytic therapy, Psychiatry, 1948, 11: 262; *277*. Frost, L. L., Baldwin, M., and Woods, Ch. D.: Investigation of the primate amygdala; movements of the face and jaw, Neurology, 1958, 8: 543; *278*. Frowein, R., and Kruecke, W.: Klinisch-anatomische Untersuchungen bei diffuser Sklerose mit schizophrenieartigen Symptomen, Dtsch. Zeistchr. f. Nervenheilk., 1951, 166: 103; *279*. Fünfgeld, E. W.: Der nucleus anterior thalami bei Schizophrenie, Journ. f. Hirnforschung, 1954, 1: 46; *280*. Fulcher, J. H., Gallagher, W. J., and Pfeiffer, C. C.: Comparative lucid intervals after amobarbital, CO_2 and are-

coline in the chronic schizophrenic, A. M. A. Arch. Neurol. and Psychiat., 1957, 78: 392; *281.* Fulton, J. F.: Physiology of the nervous system, New York, Oxford Univ. Press, 3rd Ed., VIII, 667 p.; *282.* ——— and Bailey, P.: Tumors in the region of the third ventricle; their diagnosis and relationship to pathological sleep, J. Nerv. ment. dis., 1929, 69: I, 145, 261; *283.* Furneaux, W. D.: Hypnotic suggestibility as a function of waking suggestibility, In Le Cron, L. M., "Experimental Hypnosis", New York, MacMillan, Co., XVIII, 583 p.
284. Gagel, O.: Die Dienzephalosen, Klin. Wochenschr., 1947, 24/25, 389; *285.* Gall, F. J.: Dr. F. J. Gall's neue Entdeckungen in der Gehirn-Schädel und Organlehre, Carlsruhe, 1807; *286.* Gamper, E.: Schlaf, Delirium tremens, Korsakoff'-sche Psychoses, Zbl. f. d. ges. Neurol. u. Psychiat., 1928, 51: 236; *287.* ———: Zur Frage der Polioencephalitis haemorrhagica der chronischen Alkoholiker, Dtsch. Zeistchr. f. Nervenheilk., 1928, 102: 122; *288.* Gannt, W. H.: Experimental basis for neurotic behaviour, Psychosom. Med. Monograph 3, Nos. 3 and 4, 1944; *289.* Garattini, S. and Ghetti, V. (Eds.): International symposium on psychotropic drugs, Amsterdam, Elsevier Publishing Co., 1957, 606 p.; *290.* Gastaut, H.: The epilepsies. Electroclinical considerations, Ch. C. Thomas, Springfield, Ill., 1954, XVI, 149 p.; *291.* Gates, R.: Human genetics, New York, McMillan, 1948, 2 vols.; *292.* Gauthier, C., Mollica, A., and Moruzzi: Physiological evidence of localized cerebellar projections to bulbar reticular formation, J. Neurophysiol., 1956, 19: 468; *293.* Gebhard and Siegel: quoted by Nielsen, C. K.; *294.* Gellhorn, E.: Physiological foundations of neurology and psychiatry, Univers. of Minnesota Press, 1953, 556 p.; *295.* ———: Physiological processes related to consciousness and perception, Brain, 1954, 77: 401; *296.* ———, Koella, W. B., and Ballin, H. M.: Interaction on cerebral cortex of acoustic and optic with nociceptive impulses. The problem of consciousness, J. Neurophysiol., 1954, 17: 14; *297.* German, G., May, A. R., and Folkson, A.: The use and action of chloropromazin in psychoneurosis, Br. Med. J., 1954, II, p. 439; *298.* Gerstmann, J.: Zur Frage der Einwirkung psychischer Faktoren auf zerebrale Mechanismen und über den Begriff der physiogenen Neurosen, Wien. klin. Wochenschr., 1920, 33: 557; *299.* ———: Grundsätzliches zur Frage der Akinese und Hyperkinese bei Erkrankungen des striären Systems, Monatschr. f. Psychiat. u. Neurologie, 1923, 55: 35; *300.* Gerstmann, J. and Kauders, O.: Über den Mechanismus der postenzephalischen "psychopathieähnlichen" Zustandsbilder bei Jugendlichen, Arch. f. Psychiat., 1924, 71: 165; *301.* ——— and Schilder, P.: Studien über Bewegungsstörungen, Zeitschr. f. d. ges. Neurol. u. Psychiat., 1920, 58:

266, 276; *302.* Gibbs, C. E.: Sexual development and behaviour in male patients with dementia praecox, Arch. Neurol. a. Psychiat., 1923, 9: 73; *303.* ———: Sexual behaviour and development in female patients with dementia praecox, Ibid., 1924, 11: 179; *304.* Gibbs, I. A.: Abnormal electrical activity in the temporal region and its relationship to abnormalities of behaviour, Ass. res. nerv. ment. dis. monogr., 1956; *305.* Gjessing, R.: Beiträge zur Symptomatologie der periodischen Katatonie, Arch. f. Psychiat. u. Z. Neur., 1954, 191: 191, 220, 247, 297; *306.* Glauss, A.: Bedeuting exogener Faktoren bei der Entstehung und dem Verlauf der Schizophrenien, Schw. Arch. Neurol. u. Psychiat., 1929, 43: 32; *307.* Glees, P.: The interaction of the thalamus and the sensory motor cortex, Monatschr. f. Psychiat. u. Neurol., 1953, 125: 129; *308.* Cole, J., Whitty, C. W. M. and Cairns, H.: The effects of lesions in the cingulate gyrus and adjacent areas in the monkey, J. Neurol., Neurosurg., and Psychiat., 1950, 13: 178; *309.* Gloor, P.: Autonomic functions in the diencephalon. A summary of the experimental work of Prof. W. R. Hess, A. M. A. Arch. Neurol. a. Psychiat., 1954, 71: 773; *310.* Goethe, J. W. von: quoted by Cassirer, (see Chap. I, Ref. *15*); *311.* Goldstein, K.: The mental changes due to frontal lobe damage, J. Psychol., 1944, 17: 187; *312.* ———: Frontal lobectomy and abstract attitude, J. nerv. and ment. dis., 1949, 101: 93; *313.* ——— and Scheerer, M.: Abstract an concrete behaviour, Psychol. Monogr., 1941, 53: 1; *314.* Golla, F. L.: Prefrontal leucotomy with reference to indications and result, Proc. Royal Soc. Med., 1946, 39: 443; *315.* Gornall, A. G., Eglitis, B., Miller, A., Stokes, A. B., and Dewan, J. G.: Long term clinical and metabolic observations in periodic catatonia, Amer. J. Psychiat., 1952, 10: 584; *316.* Gowers, W. R.: The borderland of epilepsy, London, Ph. P. Blakiston's Son Co., VI, 121 p.; *316a.* Grahman, H.: Periodische Ausnahmszustände in der Reifezeit als dienzephale Regulationsstörungens, Psychiat. et Neurol., 1958, 135: 361; *317.* Granit, R. A.: Receptors and sensory perception, New Haven, Yale Univ. Press, 1955, 369 p.; *318.* Grewel, F.: Das Syndrom von Klein-Lewin: Schlafperioden und Hunger, Ned. Tijdschr. f. Genesk.; *319.* Grosch, H.: Krankheitsbilder mit pathologischen Rhythmus des Zwischenhirns, 1948, 73: 560; *320.* ———: Umdämmerungen von 4-wöchentlichem Rhythmus in der Pubertät, Dtsch. Zeitschr. f. Nervenheilk., 1949, 160: 105; *321.* Grossman, Ch.: Electro-ontogenesis of cerebral activating system, A. M. A. Arch. Neurol. u. Psychiat., 1955, 74: 186; *322.* Grünthal, E.: Über die Pick'sche umschriebenen Atrophie der Grosshirnrinde, Münchn. Med. Wochenschr., 1927, 14: 614; *323.* ———: See Chapter I, Ref. *30;* *324.* ———: Über ein Brüderpaar mit Pick'scher Krankheit, Zeitschr.

f. d. ges. Neurol. u. Psychiat., 1930, 29: 530; *325*.
——: Über den Korsakoff'schen Symptomenkomplex, Conf. Neurol., 1939, 2: 64; *326*. Grünthal, E.,
and Störring, G. E.: Über das Verhalten bei um-
schriebener, völliger Merkunfähiskeit, Monatsschr.
f. Psychiat. u. Neurol., 1930, 74: 354; *327*. Gruhle,
H. W.: Theorie der Schizophrenie, In "Handbuch d.
Geisteskrankheiten", Ed. O. Bumcke a.o., vol. 9:
705, Berlin, J. Springer, 1935; *328*. ——: C. Schneider's "Schizophrene Symptomenverbände," Nervenarzt, 1942, 15: 353; *329*. ——: Wernicke's psy-
chopathologische und klinische Lehren, Nervenarzt,
1955, 26: 505; *330*. Gudden, H. W.: Klinische und
anatomische Beiträge zur Kenntnis der multiplen
Alkoholneuritis, Arch. f. Psychiat., 1896, 28: 696;
331. Guntrip. H.: A study of Fairbank's theory of
schizophrenia reaction, Brit. J. med. psychol., 1952,
25: 86; *332*. Gurewitsch, M.: Postenzephalitische
Geistesstörungen und vergleichende Topistik der
psychischen Mechanismen, Zeitschr. f. d. ges. Neurol. u. Psychiat., 1924, 92: 283; *333*. Guttmann, E.
and Herrmann, K.: Über psychische Störungen bei
Hirnstammerkrankungen und das Automatosesyn-
drom, Zeitschr. f. d. ges. Neurol. u. Psychiat., 1932,
140: 439.

334. Habel, quoted by Nonenbruch and Feuchtinger; *335*. Hall, C. S.: A primer of Freudian psychology, A Mentor Book, New York, 1955, 127 p.;
336. Häffner, H.: Störung des Plan- und Ent-
wurfsvermögens bei Stirnhirn läsionen, Arch. f. Psychiat. and Z. Neur., 1955, 193: 569; *337*. ——: Psychopathologie des Stirnhirns, Fortschr. a. d. Geb. d.
Neurol. u. Psychiat., 1957, 25: 205; *338*. Halstead,
W. C.: Brain and intelligence, A quantitative study
of the frontal lobe patient, Univ. of Chicago Press,
1947, XIII, 206 p.; *339*. ——: Frontal lobe function
and intelligence, Bull. Los Angel. Neurol. Soc., 1950,
15: 205; *340*. Hamilton, W.: Lectures on metaphysics
and logic, Edinburgh, W. Blackwood, 1877, 4 vols.;
341. Hampshire, St.: Spinoza, Penguin Book, Baltimore, 1953, 237 p.; *342*. Hanberra, J., Ajmone Marsan and Dilsworth, G.: Pathways of non-specific
thalamo-cortical projection systems, EEG and Clin.
Neurophysiol., 1954, 6: 103; *343*. Harlow, H. F.:
Functional organization of the brain in relation to
mentation and behaviour, In "Biology of Mental
Health and Disease", p. 244; *344*. Harlow, H. F.,
Davis, R. T., and Settlage, P. H.: Analysis of frontal
and posterior association systems in brain injured
monkeys, J. compar. physiol. psychol., 1952, 45: 419;
345. —— and Johnson, T.: Problem solution by monkeys following bilateral removal of the prefrontal
areas. III. Test of initiation of behaviour, J. experiment. Psychol., 1943, 32: 459; *346*. Harlow, J. M.:
Passage of an iron rod through the head, Bost. Med.
a Surg. J., 1848, 39: 383; *347*. ——: Recovery from

the passage of an iron rod through the head, Mass.
Med. Publ., 1868, 2: 327; *348*. Harris, A., and Lubin,
A.: The prognosis of the functional psychoses,
Monatschr. f. Psychiat. u. Neurol., 1952, 124: 126;
349. Harrowes, W. M.: The significance of a neurotic
reaction as a precursor of schizophrenia, J. Ment.
Sc., 1931, 77: 375; *350*. Hart, B.: Psychopathology;
its place and development in medicine, Cambridge
Univ. Press, 1929, 178 p.; *351*. Hart, E. R., Langfit,
T. W., and Marazzi, A. S.: Some cerebral synaptic
aspects of the pharmacology of toxic psychises, tranquilizers and antidotes, J. Pharmacol. and exper.
Ther., 1956, 116: 27; *352*. Hartmann, E. von (See
Chapter I, Ref. *32*); *353*. Hartmann, H., Kris, E.,
and Loewenstein, R.: Some comments on the
formation of psychic structure, The psychoanalyt.
study of the child, 1947, 2: 1; *354*. Haskoveč, L.: Le
psychism sous-cortical, Encéphale, 1929, 24: 846;
355. ——: A propos de la question de la localization
de la conscience, Rev. neurol., 1942, 31: 276; *356*.
Hauptmann, A.: Der Mangel an Antrieb von innen
gesehen, Arch. f. Psychiat., 1922, 66: 615; *357*. Head,
H.: Aphasia. A historical review, Brain, 1920, 43:
390; *358*. Head, H. and Holmes, G.: Sensory disturbances from cerebral lesions, Brain, 1911, 34:
102; *359*. Heath, R.: Effect on behaviour in humans
with the administration of taraxein, Amer. J. Psychiat., 1957, 114: 14; *360*. ——, Martens, St., Leach,
B. E., Cohen, M., and Feigley, A.: Behavioural
changes in nonpsychotic volunteers following the
administration of taraxein, the substance obtained
from serum of schizophrenic patients, Ibid., 1958,
114: 917; *361*. Hebb, D. O.: Man's frontal lobes. A
critical review, Arch. Neurol. a. Psychiat., 1945, 54:
10; *362*. Hebb, D. O., and Penfield, W.: Human behaviour after extensive bilateral removal from the
frontal lobes, Ibid., 1940, 44: 421; *363*. Heilig, R.,
and Hoff, H.: Über psychische Entstehung des
Herpes labialis, Med. Klin., 1928, 24: 1472; *364*.
Heimann, A., and Heimann, H.: Nachuntersuchung
eines Falles von "Umschr'ebener, völliger Merkun-
fähigkeit," Monatschr. f. Psychiat. u. Neurol., 1952,
74: 272; *365*. Heimann, H.: Hypnose und Schlaf,
Monatschr. f. Psychiat. u. Neurol., 1953, 125: 488;
366. Helmholtz, H. L. F. von: Popular lectures on
scientific subjects, New York, Appleton and Cie,
1888, 397 p.; *367*. Hench, P. S., Kendall, E. C.,
Slocum, C. H., and Poley, H. F.: The effect of a
hormone of the adrenal cortex (compound E) and a
pituitary adrenocorticotropic hormone on rheumatoid arthritis; preliminary report, Proc. Staff Meet.
Mayo Clinic, 1949, 24: 181; *368*. Henderson, D. K.,
and Gillespie, R. D.: A textbook of psychiatry, New
York, Oxford Univ. Press, 5th Ed., 1941, XII, 660 p.;
369. Hendrickson, W. S.: Etiology in childhood
schizophrenia. An evolution of current views, Nerv.

Child, 1952, 10: 36; *370*. Henschen, S. E.: Klinische und anatomische Beiträge zur Pathologie des Gehirns, Upsala, Almquist Wicksell, 1890–1930, 8 vols.; *371*. Henson, R. A.: On thalamic dysasthesias and their supression by bilateral stimulation, Brain, 1949, 72: 576; *372*. Herbart, J. F.: A textbook of psychology, London, R. Appleton & Co., 1916, XIV, 206 p.; *373*. Herrick, Ch. J.: The brain of the tiger salamander, Univ. of Chicago Press, 1948, VIII, 407 p.; *374*. ———: Localization of functions in the nervous system, Proc. Nat. Acad. of Science, 1930, 16: 643; *375*. Herrick, Ch. J.: The function of the olfactory part of the cerebral cortex, Proc. Nat. Acad. of Science, Washington, 1933, 19: 7; *376*. ———: The evolution of cerebral localization patterns, Science, 1933, 78: 439; *377*. Hertz, D. G., Fellner, K. H., and Rosenblum, M.: Psychosomatic approach to frontal lobe lesions, A. M. A. Arch. Neurol. and Psychiat., 1956, 75: 78; *378*. Hess, W. R.: Die funktionelle Organization des vegetativen Systems, Basel, 1948, Benno Schwabel, 226 p.; *379*. ———: Das Zwischenhirn; Syndrome. Localization, Funktionen, Ibid., 1949, 187 p.; *380*. ———: Die formatio reticularis im verhaltensphysiologischen Aspekt, Arch. f. Psychiat. u. Z. Neur., 1957, 196: 329; *381*. ——— and Bruegge, M.: Das subkortikale Zentrum der affektiven Abwehrreaktion, Helv. physiol. et pharmacol. Acta, 1943, 1: 33; *382*. Heyk, H.: Kritischer Beitrag. zur Frage anatomischer Veränderungen in Thalamus der Schizophrenen, Monatschr. f. Psychiat. u. Neurol. 1954, 128: 106; *383*. Hill, D.: E ectroencephalogram in schizophrenia, In "Schizophrenia. Somatic aspects." See ref. 755, p. 33; *384*. Hill, Spencer and Horseley, V.: Quoted by Breslauer, Ref. *110; 385*. Hines, N., and Boyton, E. P.: The maturation of excitability in the precentral gyrus of the young, Carnegie Inst. of Washington Publ., 1940, 309: 193; *386*. Hoagland, H.: Some biochemical considerations of psychotic behaviour, J. c'in. and experim. Psychopathol., 1951, 12: 111; *387*. ———: Metabolic and physiologic disturbances in the psychoses, In "The biology of mental health and disease", p. 434, New York, Paul Hoeber, 1952, XVII, 654 p.; *388*. Hoch, A.: Precipitating mental causes in dementia praecox, Amer. J. of Insanity, 1914, 70: 637; *389*. Hoch, P. H.: Traumatic neurosis, In "Workman's compensation and the physician." Ed. H. H. Jordan, New York, Oxford Univ. Pr., 1941, 180 p.; *390*. ———, Cattell, J. P., and Pennes, H. H.: Effects of Mescalin and Lysergic acid (LSD-25), Amer. J. Psychiat., 1952, 108: 579; *391*. ———, ——— and ———: Effect of drugs, Amer. J. Psychiat., 1952, 108: 5858; *392*. ——— and Polatin, P.: Pseudoneurotic forms of schizophrenia, Psychiat. Quarterly, 1949, 23: 248; *393*. Hoche, A.: Die Bedeutung der Symptomenkomplexe in der Psychiatrie, Zeitschr. f. d. ges. Neurol. u. Psychiat.,

1912, 12: 540; *394*. ———, quoted by Gruhle, Ref. *309; 395*. Hoffer, A.: Induction of sleep by autonomic drugs, J. nerv. ment. dis., 1954, 119: 421; *396*. ———: Toxicity of schizophrenic fluids for L-strain fibroblasts, Read at Soc. f. Biol., Psychiat. Meeting, Chicago, April 1956; *397*. ———: Epinephrine derivatives of potential schizophrenic factors, J. clin. and experiment. Psychopathol., 1957, 18: 27; *397a*. Hoffer, A., and Osmond, H.: The adrenochrome model of Schizophrenia, J. nerv. ment. dis., 1959, 128: 18; *398*. ———, Osmond, A., and Smythies, J.: Schizophrenia: a new approach. II. Results of a years' research, J. ment. sc., 1954, 100: 29; *399*. Hoheisl, H. P., and Walsh, R.: Über manisch-depressive und verwandte Verstimmungszustände nach Hirnverletzung, Arch. f. Psychiat. and Z. Neur., 1952, 188: 1; *400*. Holt, E. K., and Tedeschi, C.: Cerebral patchy demyelinat'on, J. Neuropath. and experiment. Neurol., 1943, 2: 306; *401*. Hollingsworth, H. F. L.: Abnormal psychology. Its concepts and theories, New York, Ronald Press, 1930, XI, 590 p.; *402*. Homburger, A.: Über die menschliche Motorik und ihre Beziehungen zu dem Bewegungsstörungen der Schizophrenie, Zeitchr. d. d. ges. Neurol. u. Psychiat., 1922, 78: 562; *403*. Hopf, A.: Orientierende Untersuchung zur Frage pathoanatomischer Veränderungen im Pallidum und Stratum bei Schizophrenie, Journ. f. Hirnforschg., 1954, 1: 96; *404*. Hoskins, R. G.: The Biology of Sch'zophrenia, New York, Norton, 1946; *405*. ———: The thyroid pituitary apparatus as a servo (feedback) mechanism, J. clinic. Endocrinol., 1949, 9: 429; *406*. Hotchkiss, G. D., Carmen, L., Ogleby, A., and Eisenfeld, S.: Mothers of young male schizophrenics as visitors in a mental hospital, J. nerv. ment. dis., 1955, 121: 452; *407*. Howland, C. I., and Sears, R. R.: Experiments on motor conflict. I. Types of conflict and their resolution, J. experiment. Psychol., 1938, 23: 477; *408*. Huber, G.: Das Pneumoenzephalogramm am Beginne schizophrener Erkrankungen, Arch. f. Psychiat. u. Z. Neur., 1955, 193: 406; *409*. ———: Endogene Psychosen und hirnatrophischer Befund, Fortschr. d. Neurol. u. Psychiat., 1958, 26: 354; *410*. Hume, D.: An enquiry concerning the human understanding, Chicago, Open Court Publishing Co., 1912, XXV, 267 p.; *411*. ———, quoted by Margetts; *412*. Humphrey, G.: Thinking. An introduction to its psychology, Melhuen & Co., Ltd., London, 1951, 331 p.; *413*. Hunt, J. Mc V.: The effects of feeding frustration upon adult hoarding in the albino rat, J. abnorm. a. soc. Psychol., 1941, 36: 338; *414*. ———, Schlossberg, H. J., Salomon, R. L., and Stellar, E.: Studies of the effect of infantile experience on adult behaviour in rats, I. Effect of infantile feeding frustration on adult hoarding, J. comp. physiol. Psychol., 1947, 40: 291; *415*. Hunt,

T.: Psychological testing of psychiatric patients undergoing prefrontal lobotomy, Psychol. Bull., 1940, 37: 566; *417*. Hutton, E. L., and Basset, M.: Effects of leucotomy on creative personality, J. ment. science, 1948, 94: 332; *416*. Huszak, I.: Über den heutigen Stand und die Probleme der Schizophrenieforschung, Arch. f. Psychiat. u. Zeitschr. f. d. ges. Neurol. u. Psychiat., 1958, 197: 32. *418*. Ingram, W. R., Barris, R. W., and Ranson, S. W.: Catalepsy, Arch. Neurol. a. Psychiat., 1936, 35: 1175; *419*. Isserlin, M.: Über Jung's Psychopathologie der Dementia Praecox, Zbl. f. Nervenheilk. u. Psychiat., 1907, 30: 329; *420*. ——: Die psychologische Methode Freud's, Zeitschr. f. Psychiat. und Neurol., 1910, 1: 52.

421. Jackson, J. H., see Chapter I, Ref. *37; 422*. Jackson, S. L. O.: Psychosis due to Isoniazid, Brit. Med. J., 1957, II: 743; *423*. Jacob, H.: Über Todesfälle während der Insulinbehandlung nach Sakel, Nervenarzt, 1939, 12: 302; *424*. Jacobi, W.: Über die Bedeutung des psychischen Traumas für die Entstehung und den Verlauf der Schizophrenie, Allg. Zeitschr. f. Psychiat., 1923, 79; *425*. Jacobi, W., and Winkler: Enzephalographische Studien an Schizophrenen, Arch. f. Psychiat., 1927, 81: 299; *426*. Jacobsen, C. F.: Studies of cerebral functions in primates I. The function of the frontal association areas in monkeys, Arch. Neurol. a. Psychiat., 1935, 33: 564; *427*. Jacorzynski, G. K., and Davis, L.: An experimental study of the function of the frontal lobes in man, Psychosomat. Med., 1945, 7: 97; *428*. Jahn, D., and Greving, H.: Untersuchungen über die körperlichen Störungen bei katatonen Stuporen und der tödlichen Katatonie, Arch. f. Psychiat., 1936, 105: 105; *429*. James, W.: What is an emotion? Mind, 1884, 9: 189; *430*. ——: The principles of psychology, Dover Publications, 2 vols.; *431*. Jancke, H.: Vom Sinn und Unsinn des psychisch Unbewussten, Monatschr. f. Psychiat. u. Neurol., 1953, 125: 494; *432*. Janet, Paul: Schopenhauer et la physiologie française; Cabanis et Bichat; Rev. de deux monds, 1880, 39: 35; *433*. Janet, Pierre: The major symptoms of hysteria, New York, Macmillan Co., 1920, XIII, 345 p. (2nd Ed.); *434*. ——: Les automatismes psychologiques, Paris, F. Alcan, 1930, 496 p.; *435*. Jarvie, H. F.: Frontal lobe wounds causing disinhibition, J. Neurol. Neurosurger., and Psychiat., 1954, 17: 14; *436*. Jarvie, H. F.: The frontal lobes and human behaviour, Lancet 12, 1958, p. 356; *437*. Jasper, H.: Diffuse projection systems; the integrative action of the thalamo-reticular system, EEG. and clin. Neurophysiol., 1949, 1: 405; *438*. Jasper, H. H., and Ajmone-Marsan, C.: Thalamo-cortical integrating mechanisms, Ass. Res. Nerv. ment. dis. monogr., 1952, 30: 493 (Chapter 23); *439*. ——, —— and Stoll, J.: Cortico-fugal projections to the brain

stem, A. M. A. Arch. Neurol. and Psychiat., 1952, 67: 155; *440*. —— and Droogleever–Fortuyn, J.: Experimental studies on the origin of petit mal, Ass. Res. nerv. ment. dis. monogr., 1947, 2: 272; *441*. Jaspers, K.: Allgemeine Psychopathologie, Berlin, J. Springer, 6th ed., 1953, 748 p.; *442*. Jastrow: The unconscious, Boston, Houghton Mittlin Co., 1906, IX, 549 p.; *443*. Jeliffe, G. E.: The mental changes in schizophrenia and epidemic encephalitis, Amer. J. Psychiat., 1927, 6: 413; *444*. Jenkins, R. L.: The schizophrenic sequence. Withdrawal, disorganization, psychotic reorganization, Amer. J. Orthopsychiat., 1952, 22: 738; *445*. Jerusalem, W.: Lehrbuch der Psychologie, Wien und Leipzig, W. Braumüller, 7th Ed., 1922, 219 p.; *446*. Jones, E.: Why is the "Unconscious" unconscious?, Br. J. Psychopathol., 1918, 9: 247; *447*. ——: Psychoanalysis and the instincts, Ibid., 1936, 26: 273; *448*. ——: The life and work of Sigmund Freud, Basic Books, 3 vols., 1953–1957; *449*. Jones, E. G.: The waning of consciousness, Psychol. Rev., 1909, 16: 51; *450*. Jung, C. G.: The psychology of the unconscious. A study of the transformations and symbolisms of the libido. A contribution to the history of the evolution of thought, New York, Dodd, Mead and Co., 1927, CV, 566 p.; *451*. ——: The psychology of dementia praecox, Nerv. a. ment. dis. monogr., Mo. 3, 1936; *452*. ——: On the psychogenesis of schizophrenia, J. ment. science, 1939, 85: 999; *453*. ——: Modern man in search of a soul, (Transl. W. S. Dell and C. F. Bayes), Harcourt, Brace & Co., 1933, 244 p.; *454*. ——: Die Schizophrenie, Schweiz. Arch. Neurol. u. Psychiat., 1958, 81: 163.

455. Kaada, B. R.: Somatomotor, autonomic and electroencephalographic responses to stimulation of the rhinencephalon and other structures in primates, cat and dog, Acta physiol. Scand., 1951, Suppl. 83, 285 p.; *456*. ——, Anderson, P., and Jansen, J.: Stimulation of the amygdaloid nucleus complex in unanaesthetized cats, Neurology, 1954, 4: 48; *457*. ——, Jansen, J., and Anderson, P.: Stimulation of the hippocampus and medial cortical areas in unanaesthetized cats, Ibid., 1953, 3: 844; *458*. —— and Jasper, H.: Respiratory responses to stimulation of temporal lobe, insula, hippocampus and limbic gyri in man, Arch. Neurol. a Psychiat., 1952, 68: 609; *459*. ——, Pribram, H. K., and Epstein, J. A.: Respiratory and vascular responses in monkeys from temporal pole, insula, orbital surface and cingulate gyrus, J. Neurophysiol., 1949, 12: 347; *460*. Kahn, E.: Die psychopathischen Persönlichkeiten, In "Handb. der Geisteskrankheiten", Ed. O. Bumcke, a.o., Berlin, J. Springer, 1928, vol. V, p. 227; *461*. Kahn, R. L., and Schlesinger, B.: Preoperative and postoperative personality changes accompanying frontal lobe meningioma, J. nerv. a. ment. dis., 1951,

114: 492; *462*. Kallmann, F. J.: The genetics of schizophrenia, New York, J. J. Angerstein, 1938; *463*. ——: The genetic theory of schizophrenia. An analysys of 691 schizophrenic twin index families, Amer. J. Psychiat., 1946/47, 103: 309; *464*. ——: Genetics in relation to mental disorders, J. ment. science, 1948, 94: 250; *465*. ——: The role of genetics in schizophrenia, Amer. J. Psychother., 1957, 11: 885; *466*. —— and Barrera, S. E.: The heredo-constitutional mechanism of predisposition and resistance to schizophrenia, Amer. J. Psychiat., 1942/1843, 98: 544; *467*. Kant, I.: Critique of pure reason (Transl. M. Müller), New York, McMillan and Co., 1896, 2nd Ed.; *468*. Kant, O.: Problem of psychogenic precipitation in schizophrenia, Psychiat. Qu., 1942, 16: 341; *469*. Kantor, R. E., Wallner, J. M., and Winder, C. L.: Process-and reactive schizophrenia, J. consultat. Psychol., 1954, 17: 157; *470*. Kanzer, M.: Personality changes with brain tumors, Amer. J. Psychiat., 1941, 97: 812; *471*. Kaplan, L.: Grundzüge der Psychoanalyse, Leipzig und Wien, F. Deuticke, 1914, 306 p.; *472*. Kardiner, A.: The traumatic neuroses of war, New York, Paul Hoeber, 1941; *473*. Kappers, C. U., Ariens, Huber, G. C., and Crosby, E. C.: The evolution of the nervous system in invertebrates, vertebrates and man, New York. The McMillan Co., 1926, 2 vols.; *474*. Karliner, W., and Savitzky, N.: Pseudonneurotic manic-depressive psychosis, J. Hillside Hosp., 1954, 3: 131; *475*. Karnosh, L. J., and Quinn, T. W.: Clinical aspects of anxiety states and hysteria, Cleveland clin. Quarterly, 1952, 19: 57; *476*. Karpman, B.: Passive parasitic psychopathy, Psychoanal. Rev., 1947, 34: 103; *477*. ——: Lying; a minor inquiry into the ethics of neurotic and psychopathic behaviour, Psychiat. Qu., 1949, 23: 1; *478*. Katzenelbogen, S.: Formulation of dementia praecox by Kraepelin, Bleuler and Meyer, Psychiat. Quarterly, 1942, 16: 439; *479*. Kauders, O.: Zur Klinik und Analyse der psychomotorischen Störungen, Berlin, J. Springer, 1931; *480*. Kekulé von Strachonitz, A.: Berichte der Dtsch. chem. Gesellschaft, (No title), 1861, 13: 1306; *481*. Kennard, M. A.: Alterations in response to visual stimuli following lesions of frontal lobe in monkeys, Arch. Neurol. and Psychiat., 1939, 41: 1153; *482*. —— and Levy, S.: The meaning of the abnormal electroencephalogram in schizophrenics, J. nerv. ment. dis., 1952, 116: 413; *483*. Kennedy, F.: The neuroses related to the manic-depressive constitution, Med. Clin. North Amer., 1944, 28: 452; *484*. Keupp, W.: Die Biochemie der Schizophrenie. Eine kritische Stellungnahme, Monatschr. f. Psychiat. u. Neurol., 1954, 128: 56; *485*. Kirschbaum, W.: Excessive hunger as a symptom of cerebral origin, J. nerv. a. ment. dis., 1951, 113: 115; *486*. Klaesi, J.: Über den Ursprung und die Bedeutung der Stereotypien, Ber-lin, S. Karger, 1929, 111 p.; *487*. Klages, W.: Körpermissempfindungen bei Thalamuskranken und bei der Schizophrenie, Arch. f. Psychiat. u. Z. Neur., 1954; *488*. Klein, R.: Clinical and biochemical investigations in a manic-depressive with short cycles, J. ment. Science, 1950, 96: 293; *489*. Kleist, K.: Die Influenzapsychosen und die Anlage zu Infektionskrankheiten, Monogr. a. d. Gesamtgeb. d. Neurol. u. Psychiat., 1921, Heft 21; *490*. ——: Die psychomotorischen Störungen und ihr Verhältnis zu den Motilitätsstörungen bei den Erkrankungen der Stammganglien, Monatschr. f. Psychiat. u. Neurol., 1922, 52: 253; *491*. ——: Die Auffassung der Schizophrenien als psychische Systemerkrankungen, Klin. Woschenschr., 1923, 21: 962; *492*. ——: Die Störungen der Ich-Leistungen und ihre Lokalisation in Orbital-Innen-and Zwischenhirn, Monatschr. f. Psychiat. u. Neurol., 1930, 71: 338; *493*. ——: Hirnpathologie, Leipzig, J. A. Barth, 1934; *494*.——: Bericht über die Hirnpathologie und ihre Beziehungen zur Neurologie und Psychiatrie, Zeitschr. f. d. ges. Neurol. u. Psychiat., 1937, 158: 159; *495*. ——: Störungen des Denkens und ihre hirnpathologischen Grundlagen. (Paralogische und alogische Denkstörung), In "Gegenwartsprobleme der psychiatrischen und neurologischen Forschung", Ed. Roggenhan, Berlin, 1939; *496*. ——: Die Katatonien, Nervenarzt, 1943, 16: 1; *497*. Kleitman, N.: Biological rhythms and cycles, Physiol. Rev., 1949, 29: 1; *498*. Klemperer, E.: Hypnosis and hypnoanalysis, Med. Circle Bull., 1958, 5: 1; *499*. Klien, H.: Beiträge zur Psychopathologie u. Psychologie des Zeitsinnes, Ztschr. f. Psychopathol., 1914/19, 3: 307; *500*. Knepel, A.: Ueber psychische Stöungen bei Stirnhirntumoren, Arch. f. Psychiat. u. Nervenkrankh., 1933, 100: 377; *501*. Knoll, H.: Klinisch generalogischer Beitrag zur Frage der perniziöen Katatonie, Arch. f. Psychiat. u. Z. Neur., 1954, 192: 1; *502*. Koernyey, St., and Saethre, H.: Die hypothalamische Lokalization der histologischen Befunde in Korsakoff-Fällen, Act. Psychiat, and neurol. Scand., 1937, 12: 491; *503*. Kolb, L. C.: Clinical evaluation of prefrontal lobotomy, J. Amer. Med. Ass., 1953, 152: 1085; *504*. Koller, S.: Ueber den Erbgang der Schizophrenie, Zeitschr. f. d. ges. Neurol. u. Psychiat., 1939, 164: 199; *505*. Korchin, Sh. J., Grinker, R., Persky, H., Heath, H.: Experience of perceptual distortion as a source of anxiety, A. M. A. Arch. Neurol. a. Psychiat., 1958, 180: 98; *506*. Korsakoff, S. S.: Ueber eine besondere Form psychischer Störungen verbunden mit multipler Neuritis, Arch. f. Psychiat., 1890, 21: 669; *507*. Koskoff, W. D., Denin, W., Lazovik, D., and Wheeler, E. T.: The psychological effect of frontal lobotomy for the alleviation of pain, Ass. Res. nerv. ment. dis. monogr., 1948, 27: 723; *508*. Kraepelin, E.: Über die Beeinflussung einfacher psychischer Vorgänge durch einige Arzneimittel, Jena, G. Fischer, 1892, 259 p.; *509.* ——: Traumstudien, Psychol. Arb., 1895,5: 79; *510.* ——: Über Hysterie, Zeitschr. f. d. ges. Neurol. u. Psychiat., 1913, 18: 261; *511.* ——: Dementia Praecox, (Transl. E. Bacley, Ed. M. Robertson), Edinburgh, 1919, E. & S. Livingstone, 1919, X, 331 p.; *512.* Kral, V. A., and Durost, H. B.: A comparative study of the amnestic syndrome in various organic conditions, Amer. J. Psychiat., 1953, 110: 41; *513.* Kremer, W. F.: Autonomic and somatic responses induced by stimulation of the cingulate gyrus in dogs, J. Neurophysiol., 1947, 10: 371; *514.* Kretschmer, E.: Die Neurose als Reifungsproblem, Leipzig, Thieme, 1922, 92 p.; *515.* ——: Die typischen psychologischen Komplexe als Wirkung juveniler Entwicklungshemmungen, Zeitschr. f. d. ges. Neurol. u. Psychiat., 1930, 127: 660; *516.* ——: Hysterie, Reflex und Instinkt, Leipzig, Thieme, 5th Ed., 1948; *517.* ——: Medizinische Psychologie, Ibid., 5th Ed., 1950, V, 304 p.; *518.* ——: Körperbau und Charakter, Heidelberg und Berlin, J. Springer, 1951, 20th Ed.; *519.* Kris, E.: The significance of Freud's earliest discoveries, Internat. J. Psychoanal., 1950, 31: 100; *520.* ——: The contributions and limitations of psychoanalysis, In "Art and psychoanalysis", Ed. W. Phillips, Criterion Books, New York, 1957, See esp. p. 211; *521.* Kroll, M. B.: Die neuropathologischen Syndrome, Berlin, J. Springer, 1929, X, 554 p.; *522.* Kronfeld, A.: Das Erleben in einem Falle von katatoner Erregung, Monatschr. f. Psychiat. u. Neurol., 1914, 35: 275; *523.* Kueppers, E.: Ueber den Ursprung und die Bahnen der Willensimpulse, Arch. f. Psychiat., 1923, 68; *524.* Kuhlenbeck, H.: See Chapter I, Ref. *40a,* *525.* ——: The derivatives of the hypothalamus in the human brain; their relation to the extrapyramidel and autonomic systems, Mil. Surg., 1949, 105: 26; *526.* Kuntz, A.: Visceral innervation and its relation to personality, Springfield, C. C. Thomas, 1951, 160 p.

527. Lacey, J. I., Bateman, D. E., and van Lehn, R.: Autonomic response specificity; experimental study, Psychosomat Med., 1953, 15: 8; *528.* Laignel-Lavastine et Logre: Hebephrenocatatonie et encephalite léthargique, Encéphale, 1920, 00: 473; *529.* Laignel-Lavastine, M. and Perel, L.: Gall, fondateur de la physiologie moderne de l'encéphale, Hippocrates, Verlag, Paris, 1938, 6: 259; *530.* Lamark, J. B. de: Philosophie zoologique (1809), (Transl. H. Elliot), London, McMillan Co., VIII–XCII; *531.* Landis, C., Zubin, J., and Mettler, F. A.: The functions of the human frontal lobe, J. of Psychol., 1950, 30: 123; *532.* Landis, C.: Remarks on psychological findings attendant on psychosurgery, In "The Biology of mental health and disease", p. 262; *533.*

Lange, C. G., and James, F.: The emotions, Baltimore, Williams and Wilkins, 1922, 135 p.; *534.* Lange, C. G.: Ueber Gemütsbewegungen. Eine psycho-physiologische Studie, (Transl. Kinella) Leipzig, Thomas, 1887, VI, 92 p.; *535.* Lange, J.: Katatone Erscheinungen im Rahmen striärer Erkrankungen, Monogr. a. d. Gesamtgeb. d. Neurol. a. Psychiat., Heft 31, 1922, IV, 170 p.; *536.* ——: Ueber Encephalitis lethargica and dementia praecox, Zeitschr. f. d. ges. Neurol. u. Psychiat., 1923, 84: 266; *537.* ——: Die endogenen reaktiven Gemütserkrankungen, In "Handb. d. Geistskrankh.", Ed. K. Beringer a.o., J. Springer, Berlin, 1928; *538.* Lange, J. F. E. A.: Crime and destiny, (Transl. Ch. Haldane), New York, Boni, 1930, 250 p.; *539.* Langworthy, O. L.: Newer concepts of the central control of emotions, Amer. J. Psychiat., 1955, 111: 481; *540.* Lasagna, L. S., Felsinger, J. M. von and Breecher, H. K.: Drug induced mood changes in man, J. Amer. Med. Ass., 1955, 159: 1006; *541.* Lashley, K. S.: Studies on cerebral function in learning. V. The retention of motor habits after destruction of the so called motor areas in primates, Arch. Neurol. a. Psychiat., 1924, 12: 249; *542.* ——: The thalamus and emotion, Psychol. Rev., 1938, 45: 42; *543.* ——: Discussion to Penfield, Arch. Neurol. a. Psychiat., 1952, 67: 196; *543a.* Lashley, K. S., and Colby, K. M.: An exchange of views on psychic energy, Behaviour. Sc., 1957, 2: 234; *544.* Lassek, A. M.: The pyramidal tract. Basic considerations on cortico-spinal mechanisms, Ass. Res. Nerv. a. ment. dis. monogr., 1948, 27: 106; *545.* Laughlin, H. D.: The dissociative reactions, Med. Ann. Distr. Col., 1953, 22: 541, 578; *546.* ——: The conversion reactions, Ibid., 1953, 22: 581; *547.* Leary, R. W., Harlow, H. F., Settlage, Ph., and Greenwood, D. D.: Performance on double alternation problems by normal and brain-injured monkeys, J. compar. physiol. Psychol., 1952, 54: 576; *548.* Le Cron, L. M.: Experimental hypnosis, New York, McMillan, 1952, 483 p.; *549.* Leeper, R. W.: A motivational theory of emotion to replace "Emotion and disorganized response," Psychol. Rv., 1948, 55: 5; *550.* Lehman, H. E.: Therapeutic results with chlorpromazine (Largactil) in psychiatric conditions, Canad. Med. Ass. J., 1955, 72: 91; *551.* Lehrman, D. S.: A critique of Konrad Lorenz' theory of instinctive behaviour, Quart. rev. of Biol., 1953, 28: 337; *552.* Leibniz, G. W., quoted by Froebes, Ref. *256; 553.* ——: De arte combinatoria, quoted by Stevens, (Ref. *829*); *554.* ——: The monadology and other philosophical writings, (Transl. R. Latta), Clarendon Press, Oxford, 1898; *555.* Lemke, R.: Ueber schizophrene Psychosen nach Encephalitis, Zentralbl. f. Neurol., 1950, 108: 315; *556.* ——: Über doppelseitige Stirnhirntumoren, Arch. f. Psychiat. u. Nervenkrank., 1936/

1937, 106: 54; *557*. Lenz, H.: Mord nach Leukotomie, Wiener Ztschr. f. Nervenheilk., 1957, 13: 248; *558*. ———: Neuere biologische Gesichtspunkte zum Problem der Schuldhaftigkeit, Jurist. Blätter, 1952, 73: 79; *559*. Leonhard, K.: Enzephalitische und katatone Motilitätsstörungen, Zeitschr. f. d. ges. Neurol. u. Psychiat., 1922, 78: 553; *560*. ———: Die defektschizophrenenen Krankheitsbilder, Leipzig, Thieme, 1936, 134 p.; *561*. ———: Zur Unterteilung und Erbbiologie der Schizophrenie, Allg. Zeitschr. f. Psychiat., 1942, 121: 1 (See also Ibid., 1943, 122: 39, 149, 1944, 123: 9 and 1944, 123: 177, and Zentralbl. f. Neurol. u. Psychiat., 1950, 108: 309; *562*. ———: Formen und Verläufe der Schizophrenie, Monatschr. Psychiat, u. Neurol. 1952, 124: 169; *563*. Leupp, R.: Katatone Symptome bei Enzephalitis, Arch. f. Psychiat. u. Z. Neur., 1956, 195: 193; *564*. Levine, A., and Schilder, P.: The catatonic pupil, J. nerv. ment. dis., 1926, 96: 1; *564a*. Levy, J.: Postencephalitic behaviour disorder—a forgotten entity: A report of 100 cases, Amer. J. Psychiat., 1959, 115: 1062; *565*. Levine, I.: The unconscious; an introduction to Freudian psychology, (Transl. A. Freud) New York, McMillan, 1923, 215 p.; *566*. Lévy-Bruehl, L.: Primitive mentality, (Transl. L. A. Clare) London, Allan and Unwin, 1923, 458 p.; *567*. Lidell, H. S.: A comparative approach to the dynamics of conditioned neurosis, Ann. of the New York Academy of Sciences, 1953, 56: 164; *568*. Lidz, Th.: Analysis of frontal lobe syndrome and its theoretical implications, Arch. Neurol. and Psychiat., 1949, 62: 1; *569*. Liébeault, A. A.: Le sommeil provoqué et les états analogues, Paris, W. Masson & fils, 1866, 335 p.; *570*. Lillie, R. U.: See Chapter I, Ref. *44*; *571*. Lindemann, E., and Finesinger, J. E.: The subjective response of psychoneurotic patients to adrenaline and mecholyl, Psychosom. Med., 1940, 3: 231; *572*. Lindner, G. A.: Manual of empirical psychology, Boston, D. C. Heath and Co., 1890, XIII, 274 p.; *573*. Lindsley, D. B., Bowden, J. W., and Magoun, H. W.: Effect on the EEG of acute injury to the brainstem activating system, EEG and clin. Neurophysiol., 1949, 1: 475; *574*. ———, Schreiner, L. H., Knowles, W. B., and Magoun, H. W.: Behavioural and EEG changes following chronic brainstem lesions in the cat, Ibid., 1950, 2: 483; *575*. Linn, L.: Psychological implications of the activating system, Amer. J. Psychiat., 1953, 110: 61; *576*. Lipps, Th.: Leitfaden der Psychologie, Leipzig und Wien, W. Engelmann, 1909, 3rd Ed., 369 p.; *577*. Loevenhart, A. S., Lorenz, W. F., and Waters, R. M.: Cerebral stimulation, J. Amer. Med. Ass., 1929, 92: 880; *578*. Löwenfeld, L.: Hypnotismus und Medizin, München und Wiesbaden, J. F. Bergmann, 1922, 130 p.; *579*. Loewenstein, O., and Westphal, A.: Kimematographische Untersuchungen über die Störungen der Pupillenbewegungen mit besonderem Hinblick auf den Spasmus mobilis, Arch. f. Psychiat. u. Nervenkrank., 1928, 82; *580*. Loewi, M.: Aus dem differential-diagnostichem Grenzgebiet zwischen hysterischen und schizophrenen Symptomen, Monatschr. f. Psychiat. u. Neurol., 1921, 49: 272; *581*. Logre: Deux cas de l'encéphalite léthargique avec syndrome psychique resemblant un syndrome hébéphrenocatatonique, Soc. de Psychol., June 1920; *582*. Lorente de Nò, R.: Studies on the structure of the cerebral cortex, J. f. Psychol. u. Neurol., 1934, 45: 381, and 46: 113; *583*. Lorenz, K.: Zur Geschichte des Instinktbegriffes, Naturwissensch., 1927, 25: 289, 307, 324; *584*. Lotmar, F.: Allgemeine Symptomatologie der Stammganglien, In Handb. d. Neurol., Ed. O. Bumcke and O. Foerster, J. Springer, Berlin, 1936, vol. 5, p. 404. *585*. McCulloch, W. S.: Some connections of the frontal lobes established by physiological neuronography, Ass. Res. Nerv. ment. dis. monogr., 1948, 27: 94; *580*. Graf, C., and Magoun, H. W.: A corticobulbar reticular pathway from area 4s, J. Neurophysiol., 1946, 9: 127; *587*. ——— and Henneman, E.: The projection of area 19 to the reticular formation, Fed. Proc., 1950, 30: 495; *588*. McDougall: Man or robot?, Ped. Sem. and J. of genet. psychol., 1926, 33: 71; *589*. ———: The energies of man, New York, Charles Scribner's Sons, 1933; *590*. ———: An introduction to social psychology, 23th Ed., 1936; *591*. McFarland, R. A., and Goldstein, H.: The biochemistry of dementia praecox, Amer. J. Psychiat., 1939, 95: 509; *592*. McLardy, T.: Thalamic projection to frontal cortex in man, J. Neurol., Neurosurg., and Psychiat., 1950, 13: 198; *593*. ———: Uremia and trophic death following leucotomy. Neuroanatomical findings, Ibid., 1950, 13: 106; *594*. ———: Diffuse thalamic projection systems; an anatomical critique, EEG and clinic. Neurophysiol., 1951, 3: 187; *595*. McLean, P. D.: Some psychiatric implications of physiological studies on fronto-thalamic portion of limbic system. (Visceral brain), EEG and clinic. neurophysiol., 1952, 4: 407; *596*. ———: The limbic system ("visceral brain") and emotional behaviour, Arch. Neurol. a. Psychiat., 1955, 73: 130; *597*. ——— and Delgado, J. M. R.: Electrical and chemical stimulation of fronto-temporal portion of limbic system in the waking animal, EEG and clinic. Neurophysiol., 1953, 5: 91; *598*. McLeary, quoted by Carpenter, W. B.; *599*. Macrae, D.: Isolated fear, a temporal lobe aura, Neurology, 1954, 4: 497; *600*. Mabille, quoted by Löwenfeld; *601*. ——— and Pitres, A.: Sur un cas d'amnesie de fixation postapoplectique ayant persisteé pendant vingt-trois ans, Rev. de Med., 1917, 23: 257; *602*. Mach, E.: The analysis of the sensations and the relation of the physical to the psychic (Transl. C. M. Williams), Chicago & London, Open Court Publ., 1914, XV, 380 p.; *603*.

Macht, L. I.: Phytotoxic properties of normal, pathological and irradiated blood sera and their usefulness in medial research, Cincinnati, J. of Med., 1948, 29: 616; *604*. Magoun, H. W.: Coma following midbrain lesions in the monkey, Anat. Rec., 1948, 100: 720; *605*. ——: Caudal and cephalic influences of brain stem reticular formation, Physiol. Rev., 1950, 30: 459; *606*. ——: The ascending reticular system, Ass. res. nerv. ment. dis. monogr., 1952, 30: 480; *607*. Mahler, M. S.: On child psychosis and schizophrenia, Psychoanalyt. study of the child, 1946, 2:; *608*. Maier, N. R. F.: Reasoning in humans, I. On direction, J. compar. Psychol., 1931, 12: 181; *609*. ——: Mechanism in frustration, In "Brain and Behaviour", Ed. W. C. Halstead, (Comp. Psychol. Monogr., vol. 20, No. 1); *610*. —— and Schneirla, T. C.: Principles of animal psychology, McGraw Hill Comp. Inc., New York and London, 1935, XIII, 529 p.; *611*. Maine de Biran, F. P. G, quoted by Margetts, Ref. *586; 612*. Malamud, W.: Developments in research in dementia praecox, Ment. Hyg., 1953, 37: 14; *613*. Malmo, R. B.: Psychological aspects of frontal gyrectomy and frontal lobotomy in mental patients, Ass. Res. nerv. ment. dis. monogr., 1948, 27: 537; *614*. Malmo, R. B., and Shergass, C.: Physiological studied of reaction to stress in early schizophrenia, Psychosomat. Med., 1949, 11: 9; *615*. Maranon, G.: Contribution a l'étude de l'action émotive de l'adrenaline, Rev. franc. d'endocrinol., 1924, 301; *616*. Marazzi, A. S.: Ganglionic and central transmission, Pharmac. rev., 1954, 6: 105; *617*. Marazzi, A. S.: The effect of drugs on neuron and synapses, See Ref. *713a; 618*. —— and Hart, E. R.: Some indication of cerebral humoral mechanism, Science, 1953, 118: 367; *619*. Marbe, K.: Experimentelle psychologische Untersuchungen über das Denken, 1901; *620*. Margetts, E. L.: The concept of the unconscious in the history of medical psychiatry, Psychiat. Qu., 1953, 27: 115; *621*. Marquardt, J. I.: The pattern of punishment and its relation to abnormal fixation in adult human subjects, J. genet. Psychol., 1948, 39: 107; *622*. Marshall, unverifiable reference; *623*. Masserman, J.: Diagnosis and prognosis in psychiatry, J. ment. sc., 1938, 84: 893; *624*. ——: Principles of dynamic psychiatry, Philadelphia, W. B. Saunders, 1946, 323 p.; *625*. —— and Pechtel, C.: Neuroses in monkeys; a preliminary report of experimental observations, Ann. New York Acad. of Science, 1953, 56: 253; *626*. Maudsley, H.: The physiology and the pathology of the mind, London, McMillan & Co., 1895, XI, 571 p.; *627*. May, Rollo: The meaning of anxiety, New York, Ronald Press, 1950, XV, 376 p.; *628*. Mayer-Gross, W.: Self description from confusional states. The oneroid experience, Berlin, 1924; *629*. ——: Early diagnosis of schizophrenia, Brit. Med. J., 1938, 2: 936; *630*. —— and

Slater, E. T. O.: Clinical psychiatry, Baltimore, Willians and Wilkins, 1955, 652 p.; *631*. Meadow, A., Greenblatt, M., and Salomon, H. C.: Looseness of association and impairment of abstraction in schizophrenia, J. nerv. ment. dis., 1953, 11: 27; *632*. Menninger, U. A.: The schizophrenic syndrome as a product of acute infectious disease, Ass. Res. nerv. ment. dis. monogr., 1928, 5: 182; *633*. Menninger, W., and Chidesh, L.: The role of financial loss in the precipitation of mental illness, J. Amer. Med. Ass., 1933, 100: 1398; *634*. Mettlach, M.: Stirnhirnerkrankungen mit typischem Stirnhirnsyndrom, Allg. Zeitschr. f. Psychiat., 1942, 119: 199; *635*. Mettler, F. A.: Physiological effects of bilateral simultaneous lesions in the frontal cortex, J. compar. Neurol., 1944, 81: 105; *636*. ——: Perceptual capacity, functions of the corpus striatum and schizophrenia, Psychiat. Qu., 1955, 29: 89; *637*. Meyer, Adolf: Dementia praecox, Boston, Badger, 1911; *638*. ——: Constructive formulation of dementia praecox, Amer. J. Psychiat., 1922, 1: 355; *639*. ——: Fundamental concepts of dementia praecox, In "Collected papers of Adolf Meyer", Ed. E. E. Winters, Johns Hopkins University Press, vol. II, 1951; *640*. Meyer, Alfred: Zur pathologischen Anatomie der epidemischen Metenzephalitis im Kindesalter, Arch. f. Psychiat., 1927, 80: 634; *641*. ——: The Wernicke Syndrome, with special reference to manic syndromes associated with hypothalamic lesions, J. Neurol., Neurcsurg., and Psychiat., 1944, 7: 66; *642*. —— and McLardy, T.: Leucotomy as an instrument of medical research, Proc. Royal soc. of Med., 1946/1947, 4: 141; *643*. Meyer, B. C.: Report of a family exhibiting hereditary mirror movements and schizophrenia, J. nerv. ment. dis., 1942, 96: 138; *644*. Meyer, J. S., and Hunter, J.: Behavioural deficit following diencephalic lesions, Neurology, 1952, 2: 112; *645*. Meyerhof, O.: Zur Energetik der Zellvorgänge, Vandenhoek und Ruprecht, Göttingen, 1913; *646*. ——, see Chapter I, Ref. *49; 647*. Meynert, Th., see Chapter I, Ref. *51; 647a*. Mickle, F., and Ades, H. W.: A composite sensory projection area in the cerebral cortex of the cat, Amer. J. Psychol., 1952, 170: 682; *648*. Milici, P.: Postemotive schizophrenia, Psychiat. Qu., 1939, 13: 278; *649*. —— and Salzen, Ch.: Situational schizophrenia, Ibid., 1938, 12: 650; *650*. Mill, J. St.: An examination of Sir William Hamilton's philosophy, New York, Henry Holt, 1874, 2 vols.; *651*. Millar, W. M.: Hysteria—a re-evaluation, J. Ment. Sc., 1958, 104: 813; *652*. Miller, J. G.: Discrimination without awareness, Amer. J. Psychiat., 1939, 52: 562; *653*. Miller, N. E., Sears, R. R., Mowrer, O. H., Doab, L. W., and Dollard, J.: The frustration aggression hypothesis of neurosis, Psychol. Rev., 1941, 48: 337; *654*. Miller, W. R.: Relationship between early schizophrenia and neurosis, Amer. J.

Psychiat., 1940, 96: 889; *655*. Mills, Ch. K.: Some theoretical and some practical aspects of psychoanalysis, Arch. Neurol. a. Psychiat., 1921, 6: 595; *655*. Mill, J. St., quoted by Froebes; *656*. Minkowski, M.: Anatomische Untersuchungen zur Frage der extrapyramidalen Motorik und ihrer Bahnen im Zusammenhang mit den physiologischen Versuchen von W. R. Hess, Praxis, 1942, 31: 804; *657*. Moll, A.: Hypnotismus, New York, Scribner and Welford, 1890, XII, 410 p.; *658*. Moniz, E.: How I succeeded in performing the prefrontal leucotomy, J. clin. and experim., Psychopathol., 1954, 15: 373; *659*. Moniz, E., and Lima, A.: Syndrome lobe préfrontal, Rev. neurol., 1936, 43: 582; *659a*. Monroe, R. R.: Episodic behavioural disorders—schizophrenia or epilepsy, A. M. A. Arch. gen. Psychiat., 1959, 1: 205; *660*. Moore, T. M., Nathan, D., Elliot, A. R., and Laubach, C.: Encephalographic studies in schizophrenia, Amer. J. Psychiat., 1933, 89: 801; *661*. Morgan, C. H.: Instinct, behaviour and enjoyment, Brit. J. Psychol., 1921, 12: 1; *662*. Morgan, C. L., and Woods, W. M.: Cortical localization of symbolic processes in the rat. II. Effect of cortical lesions upon delayed alternation in the rat, J. Neurophysiol., 1943, 6: 173; *663*. Morison, R. S., Dempsey, E. W., and Morison, B. R.: On the propagation of certain cortical potentials, Amer. J. Physiol., 1941, 131: 744; *664*. Moruzzi, G.: The physiological properties of the brain-stem reticular formation, In "Brainstem mechanisms and consciousness." Eds. E. D. Adrian, F. Bremer, and H. H. Jasper, Charles C. Thomas, Springfield, 1954, XV, 566 p.; *665*. Moruzzi, G., and Magoun, H. W.: Brainstem reticular formation and activation of the EEG, EEG and clin. Neurophysiol., 1949, 1: 455; *666*. Mozart, W. A.: Mozart's Briefe, (Ed. L. Nobel), Salzburg, 1865, Verlag der Mayr'schen Buchhandlung, XV, 498 p.; *667*. Muehlig, W. A.: Schizophrenia. Neurological signs, J. Mich. Med. Ass., 1940, 39: 116; *668*. Mueller, C.: Der Übergang zwischen Zwangeneurose und Schizophrenie, Schw. Arch. Neurol. u. Psychiat., 1954, 22: 218; *669*. Mueller, J.: The physiology of the senses, (Transl. W. Baldy-Taylor), Walton and Maberly, London, 1848; *670*. Mueller-Suur, H.: Die Wirksamkeit allgemeiner Sinnhorizonte im schizophrenen Wahnerleben, Fortschr. d. Neurol. u. Psychiat., 1954, 22: 38; *671*. Muensterberg, H., Ribot, a.o.: Subconscious phenomena, Boston, R. G. Badger, 1910, 141 p.; *672*. Mullahy, P.: Oedipus myth and complex. A review of psychoanalytic theory, New York, Grove Press, 1955, XII, 370 p.; *673*. Mulvany, B.: Depressive mental illness, Med. J. Aust., 1952, 2: 761; *674*. Murphy, J. P., and Gellhorn, E.: Further investigations on diencephalo-cortical relations and their significance for the problem of emotion, J. Neurophysiol., 1945, 8: 431; *675*. —— and Newman,

M. A.: A fatal cerebro-vascular accident with catatonic schizophrenia, Arch. Neurol. a. Psychiat., 1943, 49: 724; *676*. Murray, E. G. D.: A surmise on some trends in bacteriology, Lancet, 1954, 1: 221; *677*. Myers, L. H.: Human personality, Longman, Green and Co., 1907, XVIII, 470 p.; *678*. Myerson, A.: Social anxiety in relation to schizophrenia, Amer. J. Psychiat., 1948, 105: 401.

679. Nachmansohn, M.: Die wissenschaftlichen Grundlagen der Psychoanalyse, Abh. a. d. Gesamtgeb. d. Neurol., Psychiat. etc., Berlin, S. Karger, 1928, 106 p.; *680*. Nauta, W. J. H.: Hypothalamic regulation of sleep in rats, J. Neurophysiol., 1946, 9: 285; *681*. Netzky, M., and Starr, H.: Autonomic functions of the frontal lobes. Studies in patients with head trauma, Ass. Res. nerv. ment. dis. monogr., 1948, 27: 610; *682*. Neubauer, P. B., and Steinert, J.: Schizophrenia in adolescents, Nerv. child, 1952, 10: 129; *683*. Nicoll, M.: Why is the "Unconscious" unconscious?, Brit. J. Psychol., 1917/1919, 9: 230; *684*. Nielsen, C. K.: The childhood of schizophrenics, Act. psychiat. et. neurol., Scand., 1954, 29: 281; *685*. Nielsen, J. M.: Basic pathology in schizophrenia, J. Nerv. a. Ment. Dis., 1948, 107: 340; *686*. Nielsen, J. M.: Anterior cingulate gyrus and corpus callosum, Bull. Los Ang. Neurol. Soc., 1949, 14: 459; *687*. ——: The cortical components of akinetic mutism, J. nerv. ment. dis., 1949, 14: 459; *688*. ——, and Jacobi, L. J.: Bilateral lesions of the anterior cingulate gyrus, Ibid., 1951, 16: 230; *689*. Noble, D.: A study of dreams in schizophrenia and allied conditions, Amer. J. Psychiat., 1951, 107: 612; *690*. Nonenbruch, W., and Feuchtinger, O.: Ueber den Wechsel von Fett- und Magersucht als Ausdruck dienzephal-hypophysärer Regulationsstörungen, Schweiz. Mediz. Wochenschr., 1942, 43: 1045; *691*. Norman, R. M.: Thalamic degeneration following bilateral frontal atrophy of the Struempell type, J. Neurol., Neurosurg. and Psychiat., 1945, 8: 52; *692*. Noyes, A. P.: Modern clinical psychiatry, Philadelphia, Saunders and Co., 4th Ed., 1953, 609 p.; *693*. Nyham, A.: Ueber das Unbewusste, Kantstudien, 1929, 34: 151.

694. O'Neal, P., and Rubins, L. N.: Childhood patterns predictive at adult schizophrenia, Am. J. Psychiat., 1958, 115: 385; *695*. Obrador, S. A.: Temporal lobotomy, J. Neuropathol. a. experiment. Neurol., 1947, 6: 185; *696*. O'Kelly, L. I., and Muckler, F. A.: Introduction to psychopathology, Engelwood, Prentice Hall, Inc., 1955, 2nd Ed., XI, 704 p.; *696a*. Olds, J.: Self-stimulation of the brain. Its use to study local effects on hunger, sex and drugs, Science, 1958, 127: 315; *697*. ——, quoted by Weisskrantz and Wilson, Ref. *887*; *698*. Oltman, J. E., McCarry, J. J., and Friedman, S.: Parental deprivation and the "broken home" in dementia praecox and other mental disorders, Amer. J. Psychiat., 1952, 108: 685; *699*. Orne, M. T.: The mechanism of hypnotic age regression, J. abnorm. soc. Psychol., 1954, 46: 213; *700*. Osborn, L. A.: Five psychotic sisters, J. nerv. ment. dis., 1945, 101: 158; *701*. Osmond, H., and Smythies, J.: Schizophrenia: A new approach, J. ment. science, 1952, 98: 309; *701a*. Ostfeld, A. M., Abood, L., and Lebowitz, B. B.: Studies with a new hallucinogen. Some dosage response data for JB 318, A. M. A. Journ. Neurol. a. Psychiat., 1959; *702*. Ossipow, V. P.: Das Zeichen der trockenen Zunge bei Cyklophrenikern, Zeitschr. f. d. ges. Neurol. u. Psychiat., 1933, 146: 413; *703*. Ostow, M.: A psychoanalytic contribution to the study of brain function, Psychanalyt. Qu., 1954, 23: 317.

704. Palmer, H.: The Klein-Lewin syndrome, narcolepsy and akinetic epilepsy as related to disorders of the hypothalamus, New Zealand Med. J., 1950, 49: 28; *705*. Papez, J. W.: Comparative neurology. A manual and text for the study of the nervous system of vertebrates, New York, T. C. Crowell Co., 1929, XXV, 518 p. (See esp. p. 371); *706*. ——: A proposed mechanism of emotion, Arch. of Neurol. a. Psychiat., 1937, 38: 725; *707*. ——: Central nuclear path to intralaminar and reticular nucleus of thalamus for activating EEG related to consciousness, EEG and clinic. neurophysiol., 1956, 8: 117; *707a*. Papanek, H.: Diagnosis and treatment of borderline psychosis, Med. Circle Bull., 1959, 6: 6; *708*. Papez, J. W.: Visceral brain, its component parts and their correlations, J. nerv. ment. dis., 1958, 126: 40; *709*. Parkind, H. A., and Brown, M.: Psychoses resembling schizophrenia with emotional stress and ending in recovery, Amer. J. Psychiat., 1940, 96: 1379; *710*. Partiff, D. N.: The neurology of schizophrenia, J. ment. science, 1956, 102: 671; *711*. Patrick, J. B.: Studies on rational behaviour and emotional excitement. II. The effect of emotional excitement on rational behaviour in human beings, J. compar. psychol., 1934, 18: 153; *712*. Partridge, M. A.: Prefrontal leucotomy, a survey of 300 cases personally followed over 1½ to 3 years, Oxford, Blackwell, 1950, 469 p.; *712a*. Paulins: Molecular key to mental illness, Mod. Med., Feb. 15, 1959, p. 226; *713*. Pattie, F. A.: The production of blisters by hypnotic suggestion, A. abn. soc. Psychol., 1941, 36: 62; *714*. Pavlow, I. P.: Lectures on conditioned reflexes. Conditioned reflexes and psychiatry, New York, Internat. Publ. Co., 1941, 199 p.; *715*. Penfield, W.: Psychical hallucinations and illusions produced by temporal lobe stimulation, EEG and clin. neurophysiol., 1950, 2: 362; *716*. ——: Observations on the anatomy of memory, Fol. Neurol., Psychiat. and neurochirurg., 1950, 53: 777; *717*. ——: Symposion on the brain and mind, A. M. A. Arch. Neurol. a. Psychiat., 1952, 67: 178; *718*. ——: Mechanism of

voluntary movement, Brain, 1954, 77: 1; *719*. —— and Evans, J.: The frontal lobe in man; a clinical study of maximal removals, Ibid., 1935, 58: 115; *720*. —— and Jasper, H. H.: Highest level seizures, Ass. res. nerv. a. ment. dis. monog., 1948, 27: 257; *721*. ——: Epilepsy and the functional anatomy of the human brain, Little, Brown and Co., Boston, 1954, XV, 896 p.; *722*. —— and Kristiansen, K.: Epileptic seizure patterns, Springfield, Ill., Ch. C. Thomas Publ., 1951, VIII, 104 p.; *723*. —— and Welch, K.: A supplementary motor area in the cerebral cortex, A. M. A. Arch. Neurol. and Psychiat., 1951, 66: 289; *724*. Peters, G.: Dementia praecox, In "Handbd. d. spez. pathol. Anat. u. Hist.", Berlin, Springer, 1954; *725*. Pflueger, E. F. W., quoted by Cannon, (See Chapter I, Ref. *14*); *726*. Piaget, L.: Le development de la notion de temps chez l'enfant., Paris, Librarie Alcan, 1946, 298 p.; *727*. Pick, A.: Beiträge zur Pathologie des Denkverlaufes bei Korsakoff'scher Psychose, Ztschr. f. d. ges. Neurol. u. Psychiat., 1915, 28: 344; *728*. ——: Psychopathologie des Zeitsinnes, Ztschr. f. Psychopathol., 1919, 3: 346; *729*. Pincus, G., and Hoagland, H.: Adrenal cortical response to stress in normal men and in those with personality disorders, Amer. J. Psychiat., 1950, 106: 641, 651; *730*. Pinel, Ph.: A treatise on insanity, (Transl. D. A. Davis-Shefflield), W. Todd, 1806, IV, 288 p.; *731*. Polyak, St., (See Chapter I, Ref. *53*); *732*. Planck, M.: Scientific autobiography (Transl. F. Gaynor), Philosph. Libr., New York, 1949, 192 p.; *733*. Pool, J. L. B.: Verbal communication to the author (March, 1958); *734*. Pope, A.: Enzymatic changes in mental disease, In "Biology of Mental Health and Disease", New York, Paul Hoeber, 1952, Ch. 27; *735*. Porteus, S. D., and Kepner, R. de M.: Mental changes after bilateral frontal leucotomy, Genet. Psychol. Monogr., 1944, 29: 4; *736*. Powell, E. W., Haggart, J., Goodfellow, E., and Niemer, W. T.: Hypothalamic seizures from stimulation of rhinencephalon and Isocortex in cat, Neurology, 1951, 7: 689; *737*. Pribram, H., and Barry, J.: Further behavioural analysis of parieto-temporo-occipital cortex, J. Neurophysiol., 1956, 19: 98; *738*. ——, Lennox, H., and Dunsmore, R. H.: Some connections of the orbito-fronto-temporal, limbic and hippocampal areas of macacca mulatta, Ibid., 1950, 13: 127; *739*. Prince, M.: Critique of psychoanalysis, Arch. Neurol. a. Psychiat., 1921, 6: 610; *740*. ——: The dissociation of a personality. A biographical study of abnormal psychology, Longman, Green and Co., 1910, X, 575 p.; *741*. Prout, C. T., and White, M. A.: The schizophrenic sibling, J. nerv. a ment. dis., 1956, 123: 162; *742*. Polatin, P., Eisenstein, V. W., and Barrera, G. E.: Organic psychoses simulating dementia praecox, Psychiat. Qu., 1944, 18: 391; *743*. Poley, H. F., and Mason, H. L.: Rheumatoid arthritis; effects of certain steroids other than cortisone and of some adrenal extracts, J. Amer. Med. Ass., 1950, 143: 1474; *744*. Puner, H. W.: Freud, his life and mind, Grosset and Dunlap, New York, 1947, 265 p.

745. Quensel, F. Traumatische Störungen des Stirnhirns und der Stammganglien, Zentrbl. f. d. ges. Neurol. u. Psychiat., 1929, 94: 539.

746. Rainey, H. G., and Carson, W. R.: Paranoid reactions in three generations, Psychiat. Qu., 1941, 15: 23; *747*. Ramon y Cajal, S.: Einige Hypothesen über den anatomischen Mechanismus der Ideenbildung und der Aufmerksamkeit, Arch. f. Anat. u. Entwicklgsgesch., 1895, p. 367; *748*. Ranson, S. W.: Somnolence produced by hypothalamic lesions in the monkey, Arch. Neurol. a. Psychiat., 1939, 41: 1; *749*. Ranstroem, S.: The hypothalamus and sleep regulation, Act. path. a. microbiol. Scand., Suppl. 70, 90 p.; *750*. Rapaport, D.: On the psychoanalytic theory of thinking, Internat J. Psychoanal., 1950, 31: 161; *750a*. Reeth, P. Ch., Dierkens, J., and Luminer, D.: L'hypersexualité dans l'epilepsie et les tumeurs de lobe temporale, Acta neur. a. psychiat. Belg., 1958, 58: 194; *751*. Reichardt, M.: Oblongataverletzung nach Zysternenpunktion, Monatschr. f. Psychiat. u. Neurol., 1928, 68: 506; *752*. ——: Hirnstamm und Seelisches, Forstchr. a. d. Geb. d. Neurol. u. Psychiat., 1944, 16: 81; *753*. Reiss, M., and Stitch, S. R., The fractionation of urinary neutral 17-ketosteoid from chronic male schizophrenics, J. ment. Sc., 1954, 100: 704; *754*. Reitman, F.: Orbital cortex syndrome following leucotomy, Amer. J. Psychiat., 1946/1957, 103: 238; *755*. Rey, J. H.: Metabolism in recurrent schizophrenia, In "Schizophrenia. Somatic aspects." Ed. D. Richter, p. 147, MacMillan, New York, 1957; *756*. Richards, E. R.: Introduction to Psychobiology and Psychiatry, St. Louis, C. V. Mosby & Co., 1946, 419 p.; *757*. Richet, Ch. R.: Physiologie, Paris, F. Alcan, 1893–1909, 6 vols; *758*. Richman, A., and Tyhurst, J. W.: An extrapyramidal syndrome with reserpine, Canad. Med. Ass. J., 1955, 72: 457; *758a*. Richter, D.: Biochemical aspects of schizophrenia, Congress report of the IInd Internat. Congr. of Psychiatry, Zurich, Switzerland, Sept. 1957, p. 285; *759*. Rinaldi, F., and Himwich, H. E.: A comparison of reserpine and some barbiturates on the electrical activity of cortical and subcortical structures of the brain of rabbits, Ann. New York Academ. of Med., 1955, 61: 27; *760*. Rinkel, M., and Denber, H. C. B., (Eds.): Chemical Concepts in Psychosis, (Zurich Symposium 1957), McDowell, Obolensky, 1958, XV, 485 p.; *761*. Rinkel, M., Greenblatt, M., Coon, G. P., and Salomon, H. C.: Relation of frontal lobes to autonomic functions in man, Arch. Neurol. a. Psychiat., 1947, 58: 570; *762*. ——: Jackson, H., De Shon, R., Hyde, W., and

Salomon, H. C.: Experimental schizophrenia-like symptoms, Amer. J. Psychiat., 1952, 108: 572; *763*. ——: and Salomon, H. C.: Chemical theories of psychosis, J. clin. and experim. Psychopathol., 1957, 4: 323; *764*. ——: Hyde, R. W., Salomon, H. C., and Hoagland: Experimental psychiatry. II. Clinical and physicochemical observations in experimental psychosis, Amer. J. Psychiat., 1955, 111: 881; *765*. Rivers, W. H. R.: Why is the "Unconscious" unconscious? Brit. J. Med. Psychol., 1917/19, 9: 236; *766*. ——: Instinct and the unconscous, Cambridge University Press, 1920; *767*. Roback, A. A. (Ed.): Present day Psychology, New York, Philosoph. Libr., XIV, 995 p.; *768*. Robinson, F., and Lennox, M.: A sensory mechanism in hippocampus, cingulate gyrus and cerebellum in the cat, Fed. Proc., 1951, 10: 110; *769*. Roeder-Kutsch, Th., and Scholz-Wölfling: Schizophrenes Siechtum auf der Grundlage ausgedehnter Hirnveränderungen nach CO-Vergiftung, Arch. f. Psychiat., 1941, 173: 702; *770*. Roizin, D., Moriarty, J. D., and Weil, A. A.: Schizophrenic reaction syndrome in the course of acute demyelination of the central nervous system, Arch. Neurol. a. Psychiat., 1945, 54: 202; *771*. Romanes, G.: Mental evolution in man, London, Kegan Paul, Trench and Co., 1888, VIII, 452 p.; *772*. Rome, H. P., and Braceland, F. J.: The affect of ACTH, cortisone, hydrocortisone and the related steroids on moods, J. clin. and experim. Psychopathol., 1951, 12: 184; *773*. Rosen, I.: The clinical significance of obsessions in schizophrenia, J. ment. sc., 1957, 103: 773; *774*. Rossett, M.: Intercortical systems of the human cerebrum, New York, Columbia University Press, 1933, XVI, 135 p.; *775*. Rosvold, H. E., quoted by McLean; *776*. Roth, M.: Interaction of genetic and environmental factors in the causation of schizophrenia, In "Schizophrenia. Somatic aspects." Ed. D. Richter, see Ref. 755; *777*. Ruch, T. C., and Shenkin, H. A.: The relation of area 13 of the orbital surface of the frontal lobe to hyperactivity and hyperphagia in the monkey, J. Neurophysiol., 1943, 6: 349; *778*. Rudolf, G. de M.: Treatment of depression with sympathicomimetic preparations, Practitioner, 1955, 174: 180; *779*. Ruedin, E.: Erblichkeit und Psychiatrie, Zeitschr. f. d. ges. Neurol. u. Psychiat., 1924, 93: 502; *780*. Ruffin, H.: Stirnhirnsymptome und Stirnhirnsyndrome, Fortschr. a. d. Geb. d. Neurol. u. Psychiat., 1939, 11: 34; *781*. Runeberg, J.: Die Neurologie der Schizophrenie, Act. neurol. a. Psychiat. Scand., 136/137, 11: 523; *782*. Runge, W.: Psychische Störungen bei Encephalitis lethargica, In "Handbuch der Geisteskrankheiten", Ed. Beringer a.o., Berlin, J. Springer, 1928, vol. VII, Spez. Teil III, p. 537; *783*. Russel, E. S.: Perception and sensory signs in instinctual behaviour, Proc. Linn. Soc. of London, 1943, 154: 195; *784*. Russel, E. U.: The behaviour of animals, London, 1943; *785*. Russel, R. W.: Experimentelle Neurose, Fortschr. a. d. Geb. d. Neurol. u. Psychiat., 1953, 21: 78; *786*. Russel, W. R.: Function of the frontal lobes, Lancet, 1948, 254: 356; *787*. Rylander, G.: Mental changes after excision of cerebral tissue, Copenhagen, E. Munksgaard, 1943, 80 p.; *788*. ——: Personality analysis before and after frontal lobotomy, Ass. Res. Nerv. ment. dis. monogr., 1948, 27: 691.

789. Sadger, J.: Sleepwalking and moonwalking, (Transl. L. Brink), Washington, Nerv. ment. dis. public., 1920, Mongr. No. 31; *790*. Salmon, A.: Il somno patologico nei tumori cerebrali, Il cervello, 1928, 7: 159; *791*. Sands, D. E.: The psychoses of adolescence, J. ment. Sc., 1956, 102: 308; *792*. Savage, Ch.: Variations in Ego feeling induced by D-Lysergic acid diethylamide, Psychoanalyt. Rev., 1955, 42: 1; *793*. Scarff, J. E.: Unilateral prefrontal lobotomy with relief of ipsilateral, contralateral and bilateral pain, J. Neurosurg., 1948, 5: 288; *794*. Schilder, P.: Ueber Gedankenentstehung, Zeitschr. f. d. ges. Neurol. u. Psychiat., 1920, 59: 250; *795*. ——: Mind, perception and thought, Col. Univ. Press, 1942; *796*. ——: Medical Psychology, (Transl. and Ed. David Rapaport.) Internat. Universit. Press, New York, 1953, 428 p.; *797*. Schlesinger, B.: Zwangshandlungen und Religionsübung, Jahrb. f. Neurol. u. Psychiat., 1926, 45: 63; *798*. ——: Grasp-reflex and disturbances of attention, J. ment. science, 1940, 63: 178; *799*. ——, See Chapter I, Ref. *64*; *800*. ——: A proposed rationale for topectomy, Dis. nerv. Syst., 1950, 11: 1; *801*. ——: Gliomas of the corpus callosum, Neurology, 1951, 1: 419; *802*. ——: Time, neurologically considered, Monatschr. f. Psychiat. u. Neur., 1955; *803*. ——: Unpublished data; *804*. Schneider, C.: Die Psychologie der Schizophrenie und ihre Beziehungen zur Klinik der Schizophrenie, Leipzig, Thieme, 1930, XI, 301 p.; *805*. ——: Die schizophrenen Symptomenverbände, Abh. a. d. Gesamtgeb. d. Neurol. u. Psychiat., 1942, Heft 71, v, 252 p.; *806*. Schneider, F. W.: Klinisch katamnestische Untersuchungen an Schizophrenen eines Nervenlazarettes des zweiten Weltkrieges, Schw. Arch. f. Neurol. u. Psychiat., 1955, 75: 227; *807*. Schneider, J., Worringer, E., Brogly, G., and Gloor, P.: Le role des systèmes d'integration et du projection diffuse dans le mecanisme de l'anésthesie générale, Rev. neurol., 1951, 58: 178; *808*. Schneider, J. A., and Earl, A. E.: Effects of Serpasil on behaviour and autonomic regulating mechanisms, Neurology, 1954, 4: 657; *809*. ——, Plummer, A. J., Earl, A. E., and Gannt, R.: Neuropathological aspects of Reserpine, Ann. New York Ac. of Sciences, 1955, 61: 17; *810*. Schneider, K.: Zur Frage der Psychotherapie endogener Psychosen, Deutsch. Med. Wochenschr., 1954, 21: 873; *811*. Schneider, R. C., and Crosby, E.

C.: Stimulation of "second" motor areas in the macaque temporal lobe, Neurology, 1954, 4: 612; *812*. Schnyder, P.: Katatonie und striärer Symptomenkomplex, Schw. Arch. Neur. u. Psychiat., 1947, 60: 386; *813*. Schoenwald, R. L.: Freud, the man and his mind, 1856–1956, New York, Alfr. A. Knopf, 1956, 250 p.; *814*. Scholz, W.: Case report, Klin. Verlauf u. Path. Befund. (Ed. F. Plaut u. W. Spielmeyer), 1923, 2: 101; *815*. Schopenhauer, A.: Die Welt als Wille und Vorstellung, (Ed. J. Frauenstaedt), Leipzig, F. A. Brockhaus, 1916, 10th Ed., 2 vols., (See esp. Vol. I, Par. 36, and Vol. II, Chapter 32); *816*. ——: Ueber den Willen in der Natur., In "Arthur Schopenhauer's Sämmtliche Werke", Leipzig, Brockhaus, 1908, vol. 4); *817*. Schulze, quoted by Kraepelin, Ref. *483;* *818*. Schuster, P.: Beiträge zur Pathologie des Thalamus opticus, Arch. f. Psychiat. u. Nervenkrankh., 1936, 105: 358, 550; *819*. ——: Ibid., 1937, 106: 201; *820*. Schwab, H.: Die Schizophrenien, Arch. f. Psychiat., 1949, 182; *821*. ——: Zur Frage der echten zirkulär-schizophrenen Mischpsychose, Allg. Zeitschr. f. Psychiat., 1949, 125: 101; *822*. Schwarz, B. E., Bickford, R. G., and Rome, H. P.: Reversibility of induced psychosis with chlorpromazine, Proc. Staff Meet. Mayo Clinic, 1955, 30: 407; *823*. ——: Watkins, B. E., Wakim, K. G., Bickford, R. G., and Lichtenstein, F. R.: Behavioral and electroencephalographic effect of hallucinogenic drug, A. M. A. Arch. Neurol. a. Psychiat., 1956, 75: 83; *824*. Sears, R. R.: Non aggressive reactions to frustration, Psychol. Rev., 1941, 48: 343; *825*. Selye, H.: The story of the adaptation syndrome, Acta Inc., Medical Publishers, Montreal, 1952, 225 p.; *826*. Semon, R. W.: Mnemic psychology, (Transl. B. Duffy), London, G. Allen and Unwin, 1923, 344 p.; *827*. Shagass, Ch., Naiman, J., and Mihalik, J.: An objective test which differentiates between neurotic and psychotic depression, A. M. A. Arch. Neurol. a. Psychiat., 1956, 75: 461; *828*. Shapiro, L. B.: Schizophrenia-like psychosis following head injury, Ill. Med. J., 1939, 76: 250; *828a*. Shannon, J.: Neuromuscular symptoms simulating conversion hysteria caused by perpherazine, Dis. Nerv. Syst., 1959, 20: 24; *828b*. Sharpley, S., and Jasper, H.: Habituation of the arousal reaction, Brain, 1956, 79: 655; *829*. Shealy, C. N., and Peele, T. L.: Studies on amygdaloid nucleus in cat, J. Neurophysiol., 1957, 20: 125; *830*. Shenan, D.: The effect of cortical stimulation on gastric movements in the monkey, J. Physiol., 1934, 83: 177; *831*. Sherrington, Ch.: The integrative action of the nervous system, Cambridge Univ. Press, 1947, 433 p. (See esp. p. 259); *832*. Sidis, B.: The psychology of suggestion. A research into the subconscious nature of man, New York, Appleton and Co., 1901, IV, 386; *833*. ——: Studies in Psychopathology, Boston Med. a. Surg.

J., 1908, nov. 11; *834*. Sigwald, J., and Bouttier, D.: Le chlorhydrate de chloro-3 (dimethylamine-3' propyl)-phenothiazine en practique neuropsychiatrique courante, Anales de Med., 1953, 54: 150; *835*. Silver, A. B.: Management of children with childhood schizophrenia, Amer. J. of Psychother., 1955, 9: 196; *836*. Silverstein, A., and Kline, N. S.: Autonomic pharmacology of schizophrenia, A. M. A. Arch. Neurol. and Psychiat., 1956, 75: 388; *837*. Slater, E. T. O.: Genetics in psychiatry, J. ment. Sc., 1944, 90: 17; *838*. ——: Genetic causes of schizophrenic symptoms, Monatschr. f. Psychiat. u. Neurol., 1947, 50: 113; *839*. ——: Psychopathological personality as a genetic concept, J. ment. sc., 1948, 94: 227; *840*. ——: Psychotic and neurotic illness in twins, Great Britain Med. Res. Council Spec. Rep. Series, London, 1953, 385 p.; *841*. Sloan, N., and Kaada, B. R.: Effects of anterior limbic stimulation on somato-motor and electrocortical activity, J. Neurophysiol., 1945, 8: 241; *842*. Smith, G. E.: Notes on the natural subdivision of the cerebral hemispheres, J. Anat. and Physiol., 1901, 35L431; *843*. ——: The morphology of the true limbic lobe, corpus callosum, septum pellucidum and fornix, Ibid., 196, 30: 157; *844*. Smith, W. K.: The representation of respiratory movements in the cerebral cortex, J. Neurophysiol., 1938, 1: 55; *845*. Smith, W. K.: Functional significance of the rostral cingulate gyrus by its response to electrical stimulation, J. neurophysiol., 1945, 8: 241; *846*. ——: Non-olfactory functions of the pyriform-amygdaloid hippocampal complex Fed. Proc., 1950, 9: 118; *847*. Snyder, R. S., See Chapter I, Ref. 68; *848*. Solms, H.: Relationship between chemical structure and psychosis with the use of psychotoxic substances, J. clin. a. experim. Psychopathol., 1956, 17: 429; *849*. Spencer, H.: The principles of psychology, New York, Appleton and Co., 1899, 3rd Ed., 2 vols.; *850*. Spiegel, E. A.: Bemerkungen zur Theorie des Bewusstseins und zum Schlafproblem, Ztschr. f. d. ges. exp. Med., 1927, 55: 83; *851*. ——: Neurological aspects of body mind problem, J. nerv. ment. dis., 1957, 125: 615; *852*. ——, Kletzky, M. S., Szekely, D. V. M., and Wycis, H. T.: The role of hypothalamic mechanisms in thalamic pain, Neurology, 1954, 4: 739; *853*. ——, Miller, H. R., and Oppenheimer, M. J.: Forebrain and rage reaction, J. Neurophysiol., 1940, 3: 538; *854*. —— and Wycis, H. T.: EEG studies following thalamic lesions in human, Fed. Proc., 1948, 7: 119; *855*. ——, Wycis, H. T., Freed, H., and Lee, M. S.: Stereoencephalotomy, Proc. Soc. exp. Med. a. Biol., 1948, 69: 175; *856*. ——, Wycis, H. T., Shay, H., Conger, K. B., and Fischer, H. K.: Effects of lesions of human thalamus in region of dorsomedial nucleus, Fed. Proc., 1950, 9: 119; *857*. ——, Wycis, H. T., Freed, H., and Orchinik, M. A.: The central mechanism of emotions, Amer. J. Psychiat., 1951, 108: 426; *858*. ——, Wycis, H. T., Freed, H., and Orchinik, C. W.: A follow up study of patients treated by thalamotomy and by combined frontal and thalamic lesions, J. nerv. ment. dis., 1956, 124: 399; *859*. Spielmeyer, W.: Problem of anatomy in schizophrenia, J. nerv. ment. dis., 1930, 72: 241; *860*. Spitz, R.: Anaclitic depression, Psychoanalyt. study of the child, 1946, 2: 313; *861*. Staehelin, J. E.: Über präschizophrene Somatose, Schweiz, Med. Wochenschr., 1943, 23: 1213; *862*. ——: Ueber die Beeinflussung der Periodizität bei psychischen Störungen, Acta Med. Scand., Suppl. 307, 1955; *864*. Stalnaker, J. M., and Richardson, M. V.: The effect of hypnosis on long delayed recall, J. genet. Psychol., 1932, 6: 429; *863*. Stafford-Clark, D.: Drug action in relationship to schizophrenia, In "Somatic aspects of schizophrenia" (Ed. D. Richter), London, New York, Paris, Persgamon Prell., 1957, see p. 162; *865*. Starzl, T. E., and Magoun, H. W.: Organization of the diffuse thalamic projection system, J. Neurophysiol., 1951, 14: 133; *866*. ——, Taylor, C. W., and Magoun, H. W.: Ascending conduction in reticular activating system with special reference to the diencephalon, J. Neurophysiol., 1951, 14: 361; *867*. ——, Taylor, C. W., and Magoun, H. W.: Collateral afferent excitation of reticular formation of brainstem, J. Ibid., 1951, 14: 479; *868*. —— and Whitlock, D. S.: Diffuse thalamic projection systems in the monkey, Ibid., 1952, 15: 449; *869*. Stauder, K. H.: Die tödliche Katatonie, Arch. f. Psychiat., 1934, 102: 614; *869a*. Steinbrecher, W.: Akinetonpsychosen, Dtsch. Med. Wochenschr., 1958, p. 1399; *870*. Stek, H.: Zur psychopathologischen und lokalisatorischen Bedeutung des Parallelismus der psychischen und motorischen Aktivität, Schw. Arch. f. Neurol. u. Psychiat., 1922, 11: 208; *871*. ——: Neurologische Untersuchungen an Schizophrenen, Zeitschr. f. d. ges. Neurol. u. Psychiat., 1923, 82: 2929; *872*. ——: Contributions a l'étude des séquelles psychiques de l'encéphalite epidémique, Schw. Arch. f. Neurol. u. Psychiat., 1924, 15: 27; *873*. Stenstedt, A.: A study of manic-depressive psychosis. Clinical, social and genetic investigations, Acta psychiat. et neurol. Scand., 1952, Suppl. 79, 111 p.; *874*. Stern, F.: Die epidemische Encephalitis, J. Springer, Berlin, 1928, IV, 541 p.; *875*. Stern, K.: Thalamo-frontal projection systems in man, J. Anat., 1942, 76: 302; *876*. ——: Severe dementia associated with bilateral symmetrical degeneration of the thalamus, Brain, 1939, 62: 157; *877*. —— and Dancey, T. E.: Glioma of the diencephalon in a manic patient, Amer. J. Psychiat., 1942, 89: 716; *878*. Stern, W.: General psychology (Transl. H. D. Spoerl), New York, Macmillan Co., 1938, XII, 589 p.; *879*. Stevens, S. S.: Psychology and the science of science, Psychol. Bull., 1939, 36:

221; *880*. Stevenson, I., and Sanchez, A. J.: The antidotal action of sodium succinate in the mescaline psychoses, Amer. J. Psychiat., 1957, 114: 328; *881*. Stevenson, R. L.: The strange case of Dr. Jekyll and Mr. Hyde, In "The great short stories of R. L. Stevenson." New York, Pocket Books, Inc., 1952, 370 p.; *882*. Stoll, W. A.: Lysergsäure-Diamid, ein Phantastikum der Mutterkorngruppe, Schw. Arch. f. Neurol. u. Psychiat., 1947, 60: 279; *883*. ——: Leukotomieerfahrungen der psychiatrischen Nervenklinik Zürich, Nervenarzt, 1954, 25: 195; *884*. —— and Hoffmann, A.: Partial synthesis von Alkaloiden vom Typus des Ergobasins, Helvet. chim. acta, 1943, 26: 944; *885*. Storch, A.: The primitive archaic forms of inner experience and thought in schizophrenia, Nerv. ment. dis. monogr., Publ. Co., New York, 1924; *886*. Stransky, E.: Lehrbuch der allgemeinen und speziellen Psychiatrie, Leipzig, F. C. W. Vogel, 1914–1919, 2 vols.; *887*. Strauss, E. V.: Das Zeiterleben in der endogenen Depression und in der psychopathischen Verstimmung, Monatschr. f. Psychiat. u. Neurol., 1928, 68: 1; *888*. Strauss, E. V., and Griffith: Pseudoreversibility of catatonic stupor, Amer. J. Psychiat., 1955, 111: 680; *889*. Strauss, H.: Karl Kleist. His methods of research and its results, J. nerv. ment. dis., 1928, 67: 1; *890*. Strecker, E. A., and Ebaugh, F. G.: Practical Clinical Psychiatry, Philadelphia, Blakiston & Co., XVIII, 1957, 728 p.; *891*. Strong, O. S., and Elwyn, A.: Human neuroanatomy, Baltimore, The Williams and Wilkins Co., 1943, X, 417 p.; *892*. Sturt, M.: The psychology of time, New York, Harcourt, Brace and Co., 1925, VI, 152 p.; *893*. Sugar, O., Chusid, J. G., and French, J. D. A.: A second motor area in the monkey, J. Neuropath. and exper. Neurol., 1948, 7: 182; *894*. Sullivan, H. S.: Pecularity of thought in schizophrenia, Amer. J. Psychiat., 1925, 5: 21, and 1927, 7: 105; *895*. ——: Affective experiences in early schizophrenia, Amer. J. Psychiat., 1927, 6: 467; *896*. ——: Conceptions of modern psychiatry, Psychiatry, 1940, 3: 1, 117; *896a*. ——, quoted by Arieti, Ref. *26*; *897*. Sweet, W. H., Cotzias, G. C., Seed, J., and Yakovlow, P.: Gastrointestinal hemorrhages, hypoglycemia, azotemia, hyperchloemia, and hypernatremia following lesions of the frontal lobe in man, Ass. res. nev. ment. dis. monogr., 1948, 27: 795; *897a*. Swift, E. G., and McGeoch, J. A.: An experimental study on the perception of filled and empty time, J. exp. Psychol., 1925, 8: 240.

898. Taylor, W. S., and Martin, M. F.: Multiple personality, J. abn. soc. Psychol., 1944, 39: 281; *899*. Terzien, H., and Dalle Ore, G.: Syndrome of Kluever and Bucy reproduced in man by bilateral removal of temporal lobe, Neurology, 1955, 5: 373; *900*. Thiele, R.: Symptomatische Psychose schizophrenen Gepräges im Gefolge der Urämie, Nervenarzt, 1947, 18:

313; *901*. ——: Zur Kenntnis der psychischen Residuäererscheinungen nach Encephalitis epidemica bei Kindern und Jugendlichen, Berlin, S. Karger, 1926, 100 p.; *902*. Thigben, C. H., and Cleckly, H.: A case of multiple personality, J. abn. soc. Psychol., 1954, 49: 141; *903*. Thorpe, L. P.: Learning and instinct in animals, Cambridge, Harvard Univ. Press; *904*. ——: Some concepts of ethology, Nature, 1954, 174: 101; *905*. —— and Katz, L. P.: The psychology of abnormal behaviour, Ronald Press, 1948, XVI, 877 p.; *906*. Thulhier, J. E.: Psychosis and autonomic drugs, See Ref. *713a; 907*. Tietze, quoted by Nielsen; *908*. Tinbergen, N.: A study of instincts, Oxford, The Clarendon Press, 1951, XII, 228 p.; *990*. Toman, U.: Zum Problem der psychoanalytischen Theorie, Stud. gen., 1954, 7: 473; *910*. Trizard, B.: The psychological effects of frontal lobe lesions, Acta. Psychiat. et Neurol. Scand., 1958, 33: 232; *911*. Trömmer: Das Problem des Schlafes, München, J. F. Bergmann, 1912; *912*. Tuckey, L. C.: Treatment by hypnotism and suggestion, London, Baillière, Tindall and Co., 4th Ed., 1921; *913*. Turner, W. S., Merlin, S., and Carl, A.: Concerning theories of Indole in schizophrenogenesis, Amer. J. Psychiat., 1955, 112: 466.

914. Ullmann, M.: Herpes simplex and second degree burn under hypnosis, Amer. J. Psychiat., 1947, 103: 828; *915*. Urstein, M.: Dementia praecox und ihre Beziehungen zum manisch-depressiven Irresein, Urban and Schwarzenberg, Berlin und Wien, 1909; *916*. ——: Katatonie unter dem Bilde der Hysterie und Psychopathie, Berlin, S. Karger, 1922, VIII, 456 p.

917. Victor, M., and Yakowlev, P. I.: S. S. Korsakoff's psychic disorder in conjunction with peripheral neuritis. A translation of Korsakoff's original article, Neurology, 1955, 5: 394; *918*. Vigotzky, L.: Thought in schizophrenia, Arch. Neurol. and Psychiat., 1934, 31: 1063; *919*. Vives, quoted by Margetts; *920*. Vogt, C. and O.: Ueber anatomische Substrate, Bemerkungen zum patho-anatomischen Befund bei Schizophrenie, Ärztl. Forschung, 1948, 2: 101; *921*. ——: Resultats de l'étude anatomique de la schizophrenie, Congrès Internat. d'histologie du système nerveux 1952.

922. Wachholder, K.: Die allgemeinen Grundlagen der Lebensrhythmen, Acta Med. Scand., 1955, Suppl. 307; *923*. van Wagenen, W., and Herren, R. Y.: Surgical division of commissural pathways in the corpus callosum. Relation to spread of epileptic attack, Arch. Neurol. a. Psychiat., 1940, 44: 740; *924*. Wagner, W.: Anosognosie, Zeitrafferscheinungen und Uhrzeitsagnosie, Nervenarzt, 1943, 16: 49; *925*. Walberg, A. E., and Brodal, A.: Pyramidal tract fibers from temporal and occipital lobes, Brain, 1953, 76: 491; *926*. Wall, P. D., and Davis, G. D.: Effect of electrical stimulation of the temporal pole in the Rhesus monkey, Fed. Proc., 1950, 9: 132; *927*. ——, Glees, P., and Fulton, J. E.: Corticofugal projections of posterior orbital surface in Rhesus monkey, Brain, 1950, 74: 66; *928*. Wallenberg, A.: Anatomische Beiträge zum Problem der Empfindung, Wahrnehmung und Aufmerksamkeit, Monatschr. f. Psychiat. u. Neurol., 1949, 117: 380; *929*. Walshe, F.: The brainstem conceived as the "highest level" of function of the nervous system, etc., Brain, 1957, 80: 510; *930*. Ward, A. A.: The anterior cingulate gyrus and personality, Ass. Res. Nerv. ment. dis. monogr., 1948, 27: 438; *931*. Ward, A. A., Jr., and McCulloch, W. S.: The projection of the frontal lobe on the hypothalamus, J. Neurophysiol., 1947, 10: 39; *932*. Warren, H. C.: Human Psychology, Boston, Houghton Mifflin Co., 1919, XX, 460 p.; *933*. Watkins, J. G.: Antisocial compulsions induced under hypnotic trance, J. abnorm. soc. Psychol., 1947, 42: 256; *934*. ——: A case of trance induced in a resistance subject in spite of active opposition, Br. J. Med. Hypn., 1951, 2: 26; *935*. Wechsler, I. S.: Sigmund Freud: A critical appreciation, In "The neurologist's point of view", New York, A. A. Wyn, Inc., 1950, p. 188; *936*. ——: The neurotic conflict between the individual and the society, Ibid., p. 94; *937*. Weil, A. A.: Ictal depression and anxiety in temporal lobe disorders, Amer. J. of Psychiat., 1956, 133: 149; *938*. Weininger, O.: Sex and character, New York, G. P. Putnam's Sons, 1906, XXII, 356 p.; *939*. Weinstein, M. R.: Histopathological changes of the brain in schizophrenia. A critical review, A. M. A. Arch. neurol. and Psychiat., 1954, 71: 539; *940*. Weiss, P.: Selfdifferentiation of the basic patterns of coordination, Comp. Psychol. Monogr., 1941, 17: 1; *941*. Weisskrantz, L., and Wilson, W. A.: The effects of reserpine on emotional behaviour of normal and operated monkeys, Ann. New York Acaed. of Med., 1955, 61: 36; *942*. ——: Behavioural changes associated with ablation of the amygdaloid complex in monkeys, J. compar. psychol. Psychol., 1956, 49: 381; *943*. Welch, L., and Diethelm, D.: Effects of pathological anxiety on inductive reasoning, Arch. Neurol. and Psychiat., 1950, 63: 87; *944*. Wehner, J. S., and Stroengren, E.: Clinical and genetic studies on benign schizophreniform psychoses based on a follow-up study, Acta Psychiat. et neurol., scand., 1958, 33: 377; *945*. Welt, E.: Über Characterveränderungen des Menschen infolge Läsionen des Stirnhirns, Dtsch. Arch. f. Klin. Chir., 1888, 42: 339; *946*. Wenger, M. A.: The measurement of individual differences in autonomic balance, Psychosom. Med., 1941, 3: 427; *947*. ——: Preliminary study of the significance of measures of autonomic imbalance, Ibid., 1947, 11: 301; *948*. Werner, M.: Was wird aus den Enzephalitis-Kindern? Zeitschr. f. d. ges. Neurol. u. Psychiat., 1926, 1927, 107: 231; *949*. Wernicke,

C., quoted by Gruhle, H., Ref. *310; 950*. ——: Grundriss der medizinischen Psychiatrie in klinischen Vorlesungen Leipzig, Thieme, 1894, 3 vols.; *951*. Westphal: Ueber Pupillenphänomene bei Katatonie, Hysterie und myotonischen Symptomenkomplexen, Monatschr. f. Psychiat. u. Neurol., 1920, 47: 187; *952*. Wheatley, M. D.: The hypothalamus and affective behaviour in cats, Arch. Neurol. a. Psychiat., 1944, 52: 289; *953*. Whitehorn, J. C.: Concerning emotions as impulses and instincts as mentation, Amer. J. Psychiat., 1932, 88: 1093; *954*. Whitty, C. W. M., Duffield, J. E., Tow, P. M., and Cairns, H.: Anterior cingulectomy in the treatment of mental disease, Lancet I., 1952, p. 475; *955*. Wiedorn, W. S., and Ervin, F.: Schizophrenic-like psychotic reactions with administration of isoniazid, A. M. A. Arch. Neurol. and Psychiat., 1954, 72: 321; *956*. Wiener, N.: Cybernetics, or control and communication in the animal and the machine, New York, John Wiley and Sons, Inc., 1948, 194 p.; *957*. Wilckens, H. A.: Zur pathologischen Anatomie der Metencephalitis chronica mit psychischen Störungen, Arch. f. Psychiat., 1925, 99: 139; *958*. Wilbrandt, H.: Die Seelenlähmung als Herderscheinung und ihre Beziehungen zur homonymen Hemianopsie, zur Alexie und Agraphie, Wiesbaden, 1887, Bergmann, 192 p.; *959*. Wilder, J.: Cholesterol metabolism in melancholic and reactive depression, Amer. J. Psychother., 1947, 1: 495; *960*. ——: The law of initial value in neurology and psychiatry, J. nerv. a. ment. dis., 1957, 125: 73; *961*. ——: Modern Psychophysiology and the law of initial value, Amer. J. Psychother., 1958, XII, 199; *962*. Williams, M.: The structure of emotions reflected n epileptic experiences, Brain, 1956, 79: 29; *963*. ——: Psychophysiological responsiveness to psychological stress in early chronic schizoid reactions, Psychosom. Med., 1953, 115: 456; *964*. —— and Pennybacker, J.: Memory disturbances in third ventricle tumors, J. Neurol., Neurosurg. and Psychiat., 1954, 11: 115; *965*. Wilmans, K.: Die Schizophrenie, Zeitschr. f. d. ges. Neurol. u. Psychiat., 1922, 78: 232; *966*. Wilson, S. A. K., and Bruce, A. N.: Neurology, Baltimore, Williams and Wilkins, 1940, 2 vols.; *967*. Wimmer, A.: Ueber Charackter und Temperaments. veränderungen bei Stirnhirnverletzungen, Allg-Zeitschr. f. Psychiat., 1926, 84: 451; *968*. Winkelman, N. W.: Histopathology of mental disease, *969*. Wolf, A., and Cowen, D.: Histopathology of schizophrenia and other psychoses of unknown origin, New York, H. Holt, 4th Ed., XIII, 639 p.; *971*. Wooley, D. W., and Shaw, E.: A. biochemical and pharmacological suggestion about certain mental disorders, Science, 1954, 119: 587; *972*. Wundt, W.: An introd. to psychology, Transl. from the 2nd German Edition. New York, MacMillan, 1912, XI, 198 p.

973. Yacorzhinsky, G. K., and Davis, L.: Experimental studies of functions of the frontal lobes in man, Psychosom. Med., 1945, 7: 97; *974*. Young, I. Z.: The structure of the synaptic junction. In "Nerve Impulse", Ed. H. H. Merritt, Josiah Macy Foundation Symposia, 1952, 176 p.

975. Zacher: Ueber einen Fall von doppelseitiger Erweichung im Stirnhirn, Neurol. Zentralbl., 1901, 20: 1047; *976*. Zehnder, M.: Ueber Krankheitsbild und Krankheitsverlauf bei schizophrenen Geschwistern, Monatschr. f. Psychiat. u. Neurol., 1941, 103: 231; *977*. Zendig: Beiträge zur Differentialdiagnose der Dementia Praecox und des mansich depressiven Irresein auf Grund katamnesticehr Forsschungen, Zentralbl. f. Nervenheilk., 1909, 32: 689; *977a*. Ziehen, Th., see Chapter III, Ref. *366*; *978*. Zingerle, H.: Ueber subkortikale Anfälle, Dtsch. Ztschr. f. Nervenheilk., 1936, 140: 113; *929*. Zondek, H.: Diseases of the endocrine glands (Transl. C. Prausnitz), Baltimore, Williams and Wilkins, 1944, (See esp. p. 301); *980*. Zucker, K., and Hubert, R.: A study of the changes in function found in schizophrenic thought disorder, J. ment. sc., 1935, 88: 1.

III. THOUGHT

1. Ach, N., see Chapter II, ref. *3*; *2*. Adrian, E. D.: Sensory discrimination, with some evidence from the olfactory system, Brit. Med. Bull., 1950, 6: 1534; *3*. Anonymous: Mathematical machines, Newsweek, 1945, 26: 93; *4*. ——: The great electromechanical brain, Life, 1945, 20: 73; *5*. ——: The thinking machine, New York Times Magazine, Jan. 23, 1950; *6*. Aristotle; see Butcher, S. H.; *7*. Ashby, W. R.: see Chapter I, Ref. *1*; *8*. ——: Design for a brain, New York, Wiley and Son, 1952, IX, 259 p.; *9*. Automatic Flight: Paper 151-56/DO-74. August 14, 1956. Radio Technical Commission for Aeronautics, Washington, D. C.;

10. Babbage, see Manebrea (Ref. *210*); *11*. Balta, E. J.: Leonardo da Vinci, ein genialer Vorläufer unseres wissenschaftlichen Zeitalters, Stud. Gen., 1955, 8: 616; *12*. Bartlett, F. C.: Remembering, Cambridge Univers. Press, 1932, X, 307 p.; *13*. Bax, Cl.: Leonardo da Vinci, Edinburgh, P. Davis, 168 p., 1932; *14*. Bell, E. T.: Mathematics, the Queen and Servant Of Science, McGraw Hill Books Co., New York, XX, 437 p.; *15*. Beringer, K., see Chapt. II, Ref. *67*; *16*. Berkeley, E. C.: Giant Brains and Machines that Think, New York, Wiley and Sons; *17*. ——: 2150 A.D.—A preview of the robot age, New York Times Magazine, Nov. 19, 1950; *17a*. ——: Machine intelligence, Science Fiction, 1949, p. 82; *18*. Baron, B. J., and Unold, R. W.: Multipurpose automatic navigator, Aerospace Engineering, May 1958, p. 55; *19*. Berkeley, E. C., and Jensen, R. A.:

Constructing Electronic Brains, Radio Electron., Oct. 1951; *20*. Berry, R. J. A.: Brain Size and Mentality, Brit. Med. J., 1936/II: 62; *21*. Binet, A., see Chapt. I, Ref. *8*; *22*. Birch, H. G.: The Relation of Experience to Insightful Problem Solving, J. Compar. Neurol., 1945, 38: 367; *23*. Black, M.: The nature of mathematics, A critical survey, New York, Harcourt, Brace and Co., 1933, XIV, 219 p.; *24*. Blanshard, B.: The nature of thought, Allen and Unwin, London, 1940, 2 vols.; *25*. Bleuler, E., see Chapter I, Ref. *89*; *26*. ——: see Chapt. II, Ref. *88*; *27*. Blossfeld, K. von: Artforms in Nature, New York, E. Weyhe 1929–1932, 2 vols.; *28*. Bonhoeffer, K.: Modelle der Nervenerregung, Die Naturwiss., 1953, 40: 301; *29*. Bowerman, W. S.: The One Hundred Most Eminent People of all Times, Soc. Sc., 1945, 20: 159; *30*. Brazier, M. A. B.: Neural Nets and Behaviour, In "Perspectives in Neuropsychiatry", Ed. D. Richter, London, H. K. Lewis and Co. Ltd., 1950 (p. 35); *31*. Bremer, F.: Nerve and synaptic conduction, Ann. Rev. Physiol , 1947, 9: 457; *32*. Brindley, G. V.: Surgery forty years ago; today and tomorrow, Curr. Med. Dig., 1951, 18: 32; *33*. Brooks, C. McC., and Eccles, J. G.: An electrical hypothesis of central inhibition, Nature, 1947, 159: 760; *34*. Brown, H. Ch.: The work of Henri Poincaré, J. Phil., Psychol. and Scient. Meth., 1914, 11: 225; *35*. Bumcke, O., see Chapt. II, Ref. *124*; *36*. Burke, H. C.: A survey of analog to digital converters, Proc. Inst. Electric. Engin., 1953, 41: 1455; *37*. Busemann, A., see Chapt. II, Ref. *134*; *38*. Butcher, S. H.: Aristotle's Theory of Poetry and Fine Art, London, McPrice and Co., Sec. Ed. 1898, XXXII, 409 p.; *39*. Bruner, J. S., Goodnow, J. J., and Austin, G. B.: A study of thinking. With an appendix on language by R. W. Brown, New York, Wiley and Sons, 1957, XI, 330 p.

40. Cajori, F.: A History of Elementary Mathematics, New York, McMillan, 1917, VIII, 324 p.; *41*. Cameron, N. A.: Reasoning, regression and communication in schizophrenia, Psychol. Monogr., 1938, 50; *42*. ——: Schizophrenic thinking in a problem solving situation, J. Ment. Sc., 1838, 85: 1012; *43*. Carey, E. J.: Studies in the dynamics of histogenesis, Anat. Rec., 1920, 19, No. 4; *44*. Carmichael, R. D.: The Logic of Discovery, Chicago, London, The Open Court Publ. Co., 1930, IX, 280 p.; *45*. Cassirer, E., see Chapter I, Ref. *15*; *46*. Castle, C. S.: A statistical study of eminent women, New York, Science Press, 1913. (See also Arch. Psychol., 1913, Nov. 27); *47*. Cattell, C. S.: Man of Science. A statistical study of eminent men, New York, Science Press 1947. (See esp. vol. II, p. 165); *48*. Cippico, A.: Leonardo da Vinci, The nineteenth Cent. and after 1919, 86: 1053; *49*. Claparède, E.: Génèse de l'hypothèse, Arch. de Psychol., 1934, 24: 1; *50*. ——:

L'association des idées, Paris, Octave Doin, 1903 v426 p.; *51.* Cleveland, A. A.: The psychology of Chess, Amer. J. Psychol., 1905, 18: 2269; *52.* Cohen, M. R., see Chapter I, Ref. *16; 52a.* Coleman, J. A.: Relativity for the Layman, New York, Mentor Books, 1958, XI, 127 pp. (See esp. p. 32); *53.* Colerus, E.: Mathematics for Everyman, Emerson Books Vom Einmaleins zum Integral, Berlin, Wien. London, P. Szolnay, 1934, 404 p.; *54.* Conally, C. J.: External Morphology of the Primate Brain, Springfield, Ill., Ch. Thomas, 1950, 378 p.; *55.* Conklin, E. G.: Heredity and Environment in the Development of Man, Princeton Univ. Press, 5th Ed., 1922, XVII, 379 p.; *56.* Cooley, H. R.: College Algebra, New York, London, McGraw Hill Co., 1942, XIII, 384 p.; *57.* Cox, C. M.: Genetic Study of Genius. Vol. II. The early mental traits of 300 geniuses, Stanford Univ. Press, Stanford, Calif., IX, 842 p.; *58.* Craik, K. J. W., see Chapt. II, Ref. *163* and this Chapt., Ref. *300.*

59. Dam, J. A., and Wangeman, Ch. H.: The practical and technical encyclopedia, New York, H. W. Wise and Sons, Inc., 1948; *60.* Dampier, W. C.: A History of Science, Cambridge University Press, 1949, XVII, 527 p.; *61.* Dantzig, T.: Number, the language of science, Garden City, N. Y., A. Doubleday and Co., 4th ed., 1954, XII, 345 p.; *62.* Darwin, Ch., see Chapter I, Ref. *17; 63.* Descartes, R., see Sullivan, J. W. N., (Ref. *305*) and Haldane, E. S., (Ref. *99*); *64.* Deutsch, J. A.: A new type of behaviour theory, Brit. J. Psychol., 1954, 44: 304; *65.* ———: A machine with insight, Quart. J. experim. Psychol., 1954, 6: 6; *66.* Dewey, Th.: How we think, Boston, D. C. Heath and Co., 1933, VI, 301 p.; *67.* Draper, Ch. St.: CBS Broadcast, March 1958; *68* Du Bois, Raymond E.: Erfinder und Erfindungen, J. Springer, Berlin, 1906, 284 p.; *68a.* ———: Die Grenzen des Naturerkennens, In "Reden", Leipzig, Veit and Co., 1886, 2 vols.; *69.* Duncker, K.: A qualitative (experimental and technical) study on productive thinking, Paed. Sem. and J. experim. Psychol., 1926, 33: 642; *70.* ———: On problem solving, Psychol. Monogr., 1945, 58, No. 270, IX, 133 p.; *71.* Durkin, H. E.: Trial and error, gradual analysis and sudden reorganization, Arch. of Psychol , 1937, No. 210, v. 30.

72. Eccles, J. C.: Conduction and synaptic transmission in the nervous system, Ann. Rev. Physiol., 1948, 19: 93; *73.* ——— and McIntyre: Plasticity of monosynpatic mammalian reflexes, Nature, 1951, 157: 466; *74.* Eckert, J. P.: A survey of digital computer memory systems, Proc. Inst. Rad. Engin., 1953, 41: 1393; *75.* Edison, Th. A., see Porterfield; *76.* Eddington, A. S.: New Pathways in Science, Cambridge Univ. Press, 1935; *77.* Einstein, A., see Lenzen; *77a.* ———: Out of my later years, New York,

Philosophical Library, 1950; *78.* Eisenhart, Ch.: Cybernetics, a new science, Science, 1949, 109: 397; *79.* Ellis, H : Impressions and Comments, Boston, Haughton Mifflin Co., VII, 262 p.

80. Fernel, see Sherrington; *81.* Fischer: Napoleon and Goethe, Inaugur. Diss., Huber and Co., 1899, II, 160 p.; *82.* Fontenelle, B. le: Life of Sir Isaac Newton, with an account of his writings, London, 1728; *83.* Forbes, A.: The interpretation of spinal reflexes in terms of present knowledge of nerve conduction, Physiol. Rev., 1922, 2: 361; *84.* Fra Luca Paccioli, see Morrison; *85.* Freud, S., see Chapter II, Ref. *270.*

86. Galton, F.: Thought without words, Nature, 1887, 3: 28; *87.* ———: Hereditary Genius. An inquiry into its laws and consequences, London, MacMillan and Co., 1914, XXVII, 379 p.; *89.* Gauss, K. F. and H. C. Schumacher: Briefwechsel, Ed. C. A. F. Peters, Altona, G. Esch., 1860–1865, 6 vols.; *88.* ———, see Bell (Ref. *14*), Kramer (Ref. *167*) and Porterfield (Ref. *260*); *90.* Giddings, J. L.: Laplace, Scient. Amer., 1954, 190: 76; *91.* Goethe, J. W.: The autobiography of J. W. Goethe. Truth and Poetry; from my life, London, H. G. Bohn, 1848, 2 vols.; *91a.* Goethe, J. W.: Faust, (Transl. R. B. Taylor), Modern Library, New York, 1912, XX, 258 p. (see p. 65); *92.* Goldscheider, H. H.: Über materielle Veränderungen bei Associationsbildung, Neurol. Zentralbl., 1906, 25: 146; *93.* Gomlucki, B. L.: The development and the present status of the trace theory of memory, Brit. J. Psychol. Monogr., Suppl. XXIX, 1953, VI, 94 pp.; *94.* Goddard, H. H.: The Kalikak Family, New York, McMillan, 1916, XV, 121 p.; *95.* Graves, R. P.: The life of Sir W. R. Hamilton, Dublin, 1882, 2 vols. (See esp. II, p. 434–436); *97.* Gray, J. and Lissman, H. W.: Further observations on the effects of de-afferentiation on the locomotor activity of amphibian limbs, J. exp. Biol., 1946, 23: 121; *96.* Gray, H. J., Levonian, P. V., and Rubinoff, M.: An analog to digital converter for serial computing machines, Proc. Inst. Rad. Eng., 1953, 41: 426; *98.* Grewel, F.: Aphasia and linguistics, Folia phoniatrica, 1951, 3: 100; *99.* Grillparzer, F.: Selbstbiographie und Reisetagebücher, Wien, A. J. Walker, 1946, 404 p.

100. Hadamard, J.: An Essay on the theory of invention in the mathematical field, Princeton Univ. Press, 1939, XIII, 145 p.; *101.* Haeff, A. V.: A memory tube, Electr., 1947, 20: 80; *102.* Hagelbarger, quoted by Shannon, Cl., (Ref. *285*); *103.* Haldane,, E. S.: Descartes. His Life and Times, London, J. Murray, 1905, VII–XXVIII, 398 p.; *104.* Hall, R. A., see Leitch; *105.* Hamilton, W. S., see Graves, R. P.; *106.* Hanfman, E. and Kasanin, J.: Conceptual thought in schizophrenia, Nerv. Ment. Dis. Monogr., VIII, 115 p.; *107.* Hardy, G. H., Aiyar, S. and Wislon, B.: Collected papers of Srinivana Ramanujan, Cambridge Univ. Press., 1927, XXXVI, 535 p.;

109. Harlow, H. F.: Studies in discrimination. III. Factors influencing the facility of solution of discrimination problems by the rhesus monkey, J. Genet. Psychol., 1945, 32: 213; *110*. ——: Studies in discrimination. IV. Relative difficulty in discrimination between stimulus objects and between comparing patterns with homogenous and heterogenous grounds, Ibid., 1945, 32: 317; *108*. ——: The nature of learning sets, Psychol. Rev., 1939, 56: 320; *111*. ——: Thinking, In "Theoretical Foundations of Psychology." Ed. H. Helson, Van Norstrand, New York, 1951, XIX, 787 p.; *112*. ——: The effects of large cortical lesions in the solution of oddity problems of monkeys, J. Comp. Physiol. Psychol., 1951, 44: 320; *113*. ——: The Brain and learned behaviour, Computers and Automation, 1955, 4: 6; *114*. Hartree, D. R.: The differential analyser, Nature, 1935, 135: 40; *115*. ——: The Eniac, an electronic computing machine, Ibid., 1946, 158: 500; *116*. ——: Letter, London Times, Nov. 7, 1946; *117*. ——: Calculating instruments and machines, The University of Illinois Press, 1949, IX, 138 p.; *118*. Hearnshaw, L. S.: The psychological study of conceptual thinking, Brit. J. Psychol., 1954, 45: 1; *119*. Heaton, Ch. W.: The Life of Leonardo da Vinci, McMillan Comp., London and New York, 1874, VII, 111 p.; *120*. Heaviside, O., see Lee, G.; *121*. Heidbreder, E.: The attainment of concepts. VIII. The conceptualization of verbally indicated instances. Psychol. Rev., 1945, 52: 1. *121a*. ——: Toward a dynamic psychology of cognition, Journ. of Psychol., 1929, 27: 263; *122*. Heisenberg, W., see Cassirer, E. (Chapter I, Ref. *15*); *123*. Helmholtz, H., see Du Bois Raymond, E.; *124*. Helson, H. and Helson: Some common features of concrete and abstract thinking, Amer. J. Psychol., 1946, 69: 468; *125*. Hemmeter, J. C.: Leonardo da Vinci as scientist, Ann. Med. History, 1921, 3: 26; *126*. ——: Leonardo da Vinci. Personality and psychography, Ann. Soc. Med. Hist., New York, 1924; *127*. Herschel, J., see Pledge, (Ref. *245*); *128*. Hertz, H. R.: The principles of mechanics, presented in a new form, Pres. by H. von Helmholtz, (Transl. D. E. Jones, A. J. T. Wells), New York, Dover Publications, 1956, (46) 271 p.; *129*. Hilgard, E. L.: Theories of Learning, New York, Appleton Century Crofts, 2nd Ed., VI, 400 pp., 1956; *130*. Himwich, H. E.: Thought processes as related to brain metabolism in certain abnormal conditions, J. Nerv. Ment. Dis., 1951, 114: 450; *131*. Hodgkin, A. L.: Conduction of nerve impulses. Some recent experiments, Brit. Med. Bull., 1950, 6: 1352; *132*. Hollingworth, E. L.: General laws of redintegration, J. Genet. Psychol., 1928, 1: 79; *133*. Hooke, R., see Jourdain, Ref. *145*; *134*. Hull, C. L.: The mechanism of the assembly of behavioural segments in novel combinations suitable for problem solutions, Psychol Rev., 1935, 42: 219;

135. Hull, C. L.: Mind, mechanism and adaptive behaviour, Ibid., 1927, 44: 1; *136*. Hume, D., see Chapter II, Ref. *389*; *137*. Humphrey, G.: Directed thought, Brit. J. Psychol., 1940, 30: 183; *138*. Husserl, E.: Die Philosophie Eduard Husserls, Kantstudien, 1930, 35: 119; *139*. Hutchison, E. D.: Material for the study of creative thinking, Psychol. Bull., 1931, 28: 392; *140*. ——: The nature of insight, Psychiatry, 1941, 4: 31.

141. Inaudi, see Scripture, E. W.; *142*. Ittelson, W. H., and Kilpatrick, E. P.: Experiments in perception, Scientif. Amer., 1951, 185: 50.

143. Jefferson, Sir G.: The mind of mechanical man, Brit. Med. J., 1949/I, p. 1105; *144*. Jekels, L.: The turning point in the life of Napoleon L., Imago, 1914, 3: 4; *145*. Jevons, W. S.: The principles of science, London, McMillan and Co., 1924, 786 p. (See esp. p. 283); *146*. Johnson, C. L.: Analog computer techniques, McGraw Hill Book Co., New York, 1956, XI, 264 p.; *147*. Johnson, D. M.: The psychology of Thought and Judgement, Harper and Brothers Publ., New York, 1955, VII, 515 p.; *148*. Jones, E., Chapter II, Ref. *440*; *149*. Jordans, P.: Die Quanteumechanik und die Grundprobleme der biologie und Psychologie, Naturwissenschaften 1932, 20: 815; *150*. Jourdain, Ph.: Robert Hooke as precursor of Newton, Monist, Chic., 1913, 23: 353; *151*. Jung, G. C., Chapt. II, p. 451.

151a. Kainz, see Ch. IV, Ref. *248*; *152*. Kant, Imm., see Jevons, W. S. (Ref. *142*); *152a*. ——: Kritik der reinen Vernunft, Kehrbachsche Ausgabe, p. 320; *153*. Kasanin, J. S.: Language and thought in schizophrenia, University of Chicago Press, Berkeley and Los Angeles, 1946; *154*. Katz, B.: The nerve impulse, Scient. Amer., 1952, 187: 55; *155*. Katz, B. and Halstead, W. C.: Protein organization and mental function, Comp. Psychol. Monogr., 1950, 20: 1; *156*. Keels, D.: Leonardo da Vinci on the movement of the heart and blood, London, 1952, XVIII, 142 p. Harvey and Blythe; *157*. Keister, W.: The logic of relay circuits, Transact. Inst. Electr. Engin., 1949, 67: 720; *158*. Kettner, F.: Leonardo da Vinci, the biosopher, The biosocial Series, No. V, The Biosophical Inst., New York, 1940; *159*. Keyser, C. J.: Mathematical Philosophy, E. P. Dutton and Co., 1922, XIV, 466 p.; *160*. ——: Thinking about thinking, Spec. Edit. by E. P. Dutton Incorp. for Scripta Mathematic., 1942; *161*. Kekulé von Strachonitz, see Chapter II, Ref. *455*; *162*. Kingsley, H. L., and Garry, R.: The nature of conditioning and learning, Prentice Hall Inc., 1957, 2nd Ed., IX, 565 p.; *163*. Kircheisen, F.: Bibliographie du temps de Napoléon, Berlin, E. S. Miller u. Sohn, 1909–1912; *164*. Kleist, K.: Zur hirnpathologischen Auffassung der schizophrenen Grundstörung. Die alogische Denkstörung, Schweiz. Arch. f. Neurol. a. Psychiat., 1930, 26: 99;

165. ——, see Chapter II, Ref. *441a; 165a.* ——: Gehirn und Seele, Dtsch. Med. Wochenschr., 1951, 76: 1197; *166.* —— and Schwab, H.: Die verworrene Schizophrenie auf Grund katamnestischer Untersuchungen, Arch. f. Psychiat. u. Neurol., 1950, 184: 63; *167.* Kline, M.: Mathematics and plausible reasoning, by Polya, G. (Book review), Scientif. Amer., 1955, 192: 107; *168.* Klose, R.: Das Gehirn eines Wunderkindes (Des Pianisten Soekeland), Monatschr. f. Psychiat. u. Neurol., 1920, 48: 63; *169.* Kluever, W.: Behaviour mechanisms in monkeys, Chicago, Univ. Press of Chicago, XVII, 387 p.; *170.* Koehler, W.: Gestaltpsychology, Liveright Publ. Corp., New York, 1947, 369 p.; *171.* Kraepelin, E., see Chapter II, Ref. *509; 172.* Koehler, W. and Held, C.: The cortical correlate of pattern vision, Science, 1949, 109: 442; *173.* Kramer, E. E.: The main stream of mathematics, New York, Oxford University Press, 1952, XII, 321 p.; *174.* Kris, E.: On preconscious mental processes, Psychoanalyt. Quarterly, 1950, 19: 540; *175.* Kubie, L. L. S.: Theoretical applications to some neural problems of the properties of excitational waves which move in closed circuits, Brain, 1930, 53: 166; *176.* Külpe, O.: Vorlesungen über Psychologie, Ed. K. Buehler, 1922; *177.* Kuhlenbeck, H., see Chapter II, Ref. *296; 177a.* ——: The meaning of "postulational psycho-physical parallelism," Brain, 1958, 81: 588.

178. Lanza, C. H.: Napoleon on modern war, Edited by the U. S. War Department, XIV, 158 p.; *179.* Laplace, see Giddings, J. C.; *179a.* Laplace, P. S. de: Essai philosophique sur les probabilités, Paris, 1814, vol. I, (p. 2); *180.* Lashley, K. S.: Brain mechanism and intelligence, Univ. of Chicago Press, 1929, XIV, 186 p.; *181.* ——: An examination of the continuity theory as applied to discriminative learning, J. genet. Psychol., 1942, 26: 241; *182.* ——: Visual mechanisms, Biolog. Symp., 1942, 7: 30; *183.* ——: The problem of serial order in behaviour, The Hixon Symposion. L. Jeffers, Ed., John Wiley and Sons, New York, 1951; *183a.* ——, see Chapt. I, Ref. *44; 184.* Lee, G.: Oliver Heaviside, London and New York, Longmans, Green, 1947, 32 p.; *185.* Leibniz, G. W., see Locke, L. L., (Ref. *185); 186.* Leitch, D.: Geology in the life of man, Thinker's Library, No. 108, London, Watts, 1948, V. 118 p.; *187.* Lenard, Ph.: Great men of science, (Transl. H. Stafford-Hatfield), London, Bull. and Sons Co., Ltd., 1954, XIX, 389 p.; *188.* Lenzen, V. F.: Einstein's theory of knowledge, In "Schilpp, P. A., Albert Einstein." Library of living philosophers, 1940, Vol. V, XVI, 781 p. (See p. 355); *189.* Liepmann, H.: Ueber Ideenflucht, Samml. zwangl. Arb. a. d. Geb. d. Nerven- und Geisteskrankh., 1904, 84: No. 8; *190.* Lindworsky, J.: Das schlussfolgernde Denken, Freiburg i. Breisgau Herder, 1916, XVI, 454 p.; *191.* Lindley,

E. H.: A study of games and puzzles, Amer. J. Psychol., 1897, 8: 431; *192.* Lindley, S. B.: Maze Learning ability of anosmic and blind rats, J. Gen. Psychol., 1930, 37: 245; *193.* Locke, L. L.: Pure mathematics, New York, Current Lit. Publ., 1909, XXII, 324 p.; *194.* Loewi, O.: Personal communication to the author; *195.* ——: Aspects of the transmission of the nerve impulse, J. Mount Sinai Hosp., 1945, 12: 803; *196.* Lorente de Nò. R., see Chapt. II, Ref.*550; 197.* Lovelac, Countess, see Manebrea, Ref. *219; 198.* Luce, R. D., and Raiffa, H.: Games and Decisions, John Wiley and Sons, New York, 1957, 509 p.; *199.* Ludwig, O.: Leonardo da Vinci. (In "Genie und Character", New York, 1927, Berlin, E. Rowohlt, 1922, 285 p.

200. Mach, E.: Erkenntnis und Irrtum, J. A. Barth, Leipzig, 1905; *200a.* ——, quoted by Cassirer, E. (See Chapter I, Ref. *15); 201.* McCulloch, W.: The brain as a computing machine, Electr. Eng., 1944, 68: 492; *202.* ——: A recapitulation of the theory, with a forecast of several extensions, Ann. New York Academy of Medicine, 1948, 50: 259; *203.* ——: Why the mind is in the head, In: "Cerebral mechanisms in behaviour" (The Hixon Sympsion) Ed. L. A. Jeffers, New York, J. Wiley and Sons, 1951, XI, 311 p.; *204.* McCulloch and Pitts, W.: Machines that think and want, Comp. Psychol. Monogr., 1950, 20: 39; *205.* McCurdy, E.: The life of Leonardo da Vinci, Dood, Mead and Co., New York, 1948, 360 p.; *206.* McDouglas, N.: What is a computer? Comput. and Automat., 1954, 3: 14; *207.* McGeoch, J. A.: The psychology of human learning, Longmans, Green and Co., New York, 1942, VII, 633 p.; *208.* McKay, D. M.: Mindlike behaviour in artifacts, Brit. J. Med. Psychol., 1951, II, 105; *209.* ——: Ashby's design for a brain. (Review), Amer. J. Psychiat., Febr. 1954; *210.* McKellar, P.: Imagination and thinking. A psychological analysis, Basic Books, Inc., New York, 1957, VII, 219 p.; *211.* McMurrich, J. P.: Leonardo da Vinci, the man and the scientist, Carnegie Inst. of Washigt. Publ., Williams and Wilkins, Balt. 1930, XX, 265 p.; *212.* Maier, N. R. F.: Reasoning in the white rat, Comp. Psychol. Monogr., 1929; *213.* ——: Reasoning in the human, I. On direction, J. Comp. Psychol., 1930, 10: 115; *214.* ——: Reasoning in humans. II. The solution of a problem and its appearance in consciousness, Ibid., 1931, 12: 181; *215.* ——: Reasoning in humans. III. The mechanism of equivalent stimuli and of reasoning, J. exp. Psychol., 1945, 35: 349; *216.* ——: Reasoning and learning, Psychol. Rev., 1931, 38: 332; *217.* ——: Cortical destruction of the posterior part of the brain and its effect on reasoning, J. comp. Psychol., 1932, 4: 179; *218.* ——: An aspect of human reasoning, Brit. J. Psychol., 1935, 19: 97; *219.* ——: In defense of reasoning in rats. A reply. J.

comp. Psychol., 1935, 19: 97; *220*. ——: Reasoning in children, Ibid., 1936, 21: 357; *221*. ——: Reasoning in rats and human beings, Psychol. Rev., 1937, 44: 365; *222*. ——: A further analysis of reasoning in rats, Comp. Psychol. Monogr., 1939, 46: 241; *223*. ——: The specific processes constituting the learning functions, Psychol. Rev., 1939, 46: 241; *224*. ——, see Chapt. II, Ref. *609; 224a* Magnus, R.: Goethe as a scientist, (Transl. H. Norden.), H. Schuman, New York, XIX, 259 p.; *225*. Marmont, see Sloane, Ref. *289; 226*. Marbe, E., see Chapter II, Ref. *585; 227*. Marx, K. F. H.: Marc' Antonio della Torre und Leonardo da Vinci, die Begründer der bildlichen Anatomie, Goettingen, Dieterich, 1894, 20 p.; *228*. Manebrea: Sketch of the analytical engine invented by Charles Babbage, Scient. Memoirs, 1843, 3: 636 and 669; *229*. Masson, F.: Napoleon, London, Lipponcot and Co., 1894, 2 vols.; *230*. Maurer, F.: Das Gehirn Ernst Haeckels, Jena, 1924; *231*. Mayo, Ch., see Brindley, Ref. *32; 232*. Messer, A.: Experimentelle psychologische Untersuchungen über das Denken, Arch. f. d. ges. Psychol. 1906, 8: 1; *233*. Metternich, Cl. von: Mémoirs. Documents et écrits divers laissés par le Prince de Metternich, Ed. Prince Richard Metternich (Transl. A. Napier), Charles Savier, New York, 1773–1815, 8 vols.; *234*. Michelson, A. A., see Whitehead, Ref. *336a; 235*. Montmasson, J. M.: Invention and the unconscious, (Transl. H. Stafford-Hartfield), London, K. Paul, Trubner, Trench & Co., Ltd., 1931, XXIV, 338 p.; *236*. Morison, St.: Fra Luca Paccioli, New York, The Grolier Club, 1933; *237*. Moskiewitz, G.: Zur Psychologie des Denkens, Arch. f. d. ges. Psychol., 1918, 304: 328; *238*. Mueller, G. E.: Zur Analyse der Gedächtnistätigkeit und des Vorstellungsablaufes, III. Teil Zeitschr. f. Psychol., 1918, 304, 328; *239*. Müller, J.: The physiology of the senses, etc., Taylor, Walton and Maberly, London, 1948; *240*. Myers, G. G. C.: A study in incidental memory, Arch. Psychol., 1913, No. 26, 108 p.

241. Nachmansohn, D. (Ed.): Nerve impulse. Transact. of the First Confer., March 2, 3, 1950, New York, J. Macy Jun. Foundation, 159 p.; *242*. Nagel, E.: A study of thinking, by Bruner J. S. and ass., Scientific Amer., 957, 196: 153 (Book Review); *243*. Neumann, H. von: The general and logical theory of mathematical machines, The Hixon Symposion. (See Ref. *183*); *244*. Newman: Reason and Chance in scientific discovery, by R. Taton, Scientific. Amer., Book Review, 1958, 198: 141; *245*. Newton, Sir I., see Fontenelle.

246. Oettinger, A. G.: Programming of digital computers to learn, Phil. Mag., 1952, 7: 1243; *247*. O'Malley, Ch. de and de Saunders, J. B.: Leonardo da Vinci and the human body, Henry Schuman, New York, 1952, 506 p.; *248*. Ornstein, J.: Mechanical translation. New challenge to communication, Scient. Amer., 1955, 122: 745.

249. Papez, W.: The brain of Helen H. Gardner, Amer. J. Physiol. and Anthropol., 1927, 11: 29; *250*. ——: The brain of Sutherland Simpson, J. comp. Psychol., 1930, 51: 165; *251*. Pascal, Bl., see Locke, Ref. *185; 252*. Pasteur, L.: The attenuation of the virus of foul cholera, Compt. rend. acad. d. scienc. 1880, vol. 9; *253*. Pierce, see Keyser, Ref. *155; 254*. Pitts and McCulloch, W.: Machines that think and want, Comp. Psychol. Mon., 1950, 20: 39; *255*. Platt, W. and Baker, R. A.: The relation of scientific hunch to research, J. chemic. Educ., 1931, 8: 1969; *256*. Planck, M.: Scientific Autobiography, (Transl. F. Gaynor), Philosophical Library, New York, 1948, 192 p.; *257*. Pledge, H. T.: Science since 1500, London, His Majesty's Stationery Office, 1947, 357 p.; *258*. Poincaré, H.: The foundation of science, Garrison, New York, Science Press, 1931, 2 vols. (See also ref. *34*); *259*. Polya, G.: Mathematics and plausible reasoning, Princeton University Press, 1954, 2 vols.; *260*. Porterfield, A. L.: Creative factors in scientific research, Duke University Press, 1941, XI, 282 p.

261. Rademaker, G. G. J.: Réactions labyrinthiques et équilibre. L'ataxie labyrinthique, Paris, Masson & fils, 1935, VIII, 262 p.; *262*. Ramon Y Cajal, see Chapt. II, Ref. *702; 263*. Ranson, see Chapt. II, Ref. *703; 264*. Reibmayr, A.: Die Entwicklungsgeschichte des Talents und des Genies, München, Lehmann, 1910, 2 vols.; *265*. Read, C.: The functions of relations in thought, Brit. J. Psychol., 1911, 4: 342; *266*. Rees, M.: Digital Computers. Their nature and use, Amer. Scientist, 1952, 40: 328; *267* Reid, L. St.: The development of non-continuity from continuity learning in the albino rat, Ohio State Univ. abstr. of dissert., 1949/50, No. 62; *268*. Reifler, E.: The mechanical determination of meaning, In Locke, NN and Booth, M.D. (Ed.) Machine translation of languages. M.I.T. Public. and Wiley and Sons, New York, 1955; *269*. Rémusat, Cl. de: Mémoirs, 1802–1808, 3 vols., Paris, 1880 (Third Edition); *270*. Ribot, Th. A.: Essai sur l'imagination créatrice, Paris, Alcan, 1900, VII, 304 p.; *271*. Richter, J. P.: Leonardo da Vinci, Marston, Low and Livingston, London, 1884, XII, 136 p.; *272*. Riese, W. and Goldstein, K.: The brain of Ludwig Edinger, J. Comp. Neurol., 1950, 92: 133; *273*. Rignano, E.: The psychology of reasoning, (Transl. W. A. Stoll), Harcourt, Brace and Co., London, 1932, VIII, 395 p.; *274*. Roederer, P. L. Comte de: Autour de Bonaparte, Journal de Comte P. L. Roederer, Paris, Daragon, 1909, XIII, 356 p.; *275*. Roemer, O., see Dampier, Ref. *59; 275a*. Rohrbacher, H.: Die Arbeitsweise des Gehirns und die psychischen Vörgange, München, J. A. Barth, 1953; *276*. Rose, H. H.: The life of Napoleon, 11th Ed., G Bell and Sons, London,

1934, XV, 512, 620 p.; *277.* Rossman, J.: The psychology of the inventor. A study of the patentee, Washington, D. C., The Inventor's Publ. Co., 1931, X, 252 p.; *278.* Rushton, W. A. H.: Conduction of nerve impulses, In Feiling, Chapt. II, Ref. *177; 279.* Russell, B. R.: The principles of mathematics, New York, McMillan & Co. Inc., 1938, XXXIX, 534 p.; *280.* Russel, E. S., see Chapter I, Ref. *55.*

281. Samuel A. L.: Computing bit by bit—or digital computers made easy, Proced. Inst. Rad. Engin., 1953, 41: 1223; *282.* Schaffer, K.: Ueber das hirnanatomische Substrat der menschlichen Begabung, Arch. f. Psychiat., 1932, 96: 683; *283.* Schlesinger, B., see Chapt. II, Ref. *752; 284.* Schneider, A.: Sprachstörungen bei Schizophrenen, Zeitschr. f. d. ges. Neurol. u. Psychiat., 1927, 108: 491; *284a.* Schneider, E.: Von der Null zur Unendlichkeit, Gebr. Weiss Verl. Berlin-München, 322 p.; *285.* Schopenhauer, A., see Chapt. II, Ref. *815; 286.* Schroedinger, E.: What is matter?, Scient. Amer., 1953, 189: 52; *287.* Scripture, E. W.: Arithmetical prodigies, Amer. J. Psychol., 1891, 4: 1; *288.* Secheheye, M.: Autobiography of a schizophrenic girl, Transl. O. Rubin, Grune and Stratton, New York, 1951, XI, 159 p.; *289.* Sells, S. B.: The atmosphere effect. An experimental study of reasoning, Arch. of Psychol., 1936, No. 200; *290.* Selz, O.: Die Gesetze der produktiven Tätigkeit, Arch. f. Psychol., 1913, 27: 377; *291.* Selz, O.: Über die Gesetze des geordneten Denkverlautes, Teil 1–2, Bonn, F. Cohen, 1931–1922, 2 vols.; *292.* Senden, M. von: Raum-und Gestaltauffassung bei Blindgeborenen nach der Operation, Leipzig, J. A. Barth, 1932, IX, 303 p.; *293.* Shannon, Cl.: A symbolic analysis of relay and switching circuits, Transact. Amer. Inst. Electr. Engin., 1938, 57: 713; *294.* ——: The mathematical theory of communication, Urbana, 1949; *296.* ——: Programming a computer for playing chess, Phil. Mag., 1950, 41: 256; *297.* ——: Presentation of a maze solving machine, Transact. of the 8th Cybernetical conference, New York, 1952, p. 173; *298.* ——: Computers and automata, Proc. of the Inst. of Rad. Eng., 1953, 42: 1234; *298a.* ——: Automata studies. [by] W. R. Ashby and others. Ed. Cl. Shannon and J. McCarthy, Princeton, Princeton Univ. Press, 1956, VIII, 285 p.; *299.* —— and Moore, E. F.: Ibid., 1952, 41: 1348; *300.* Shepherd, J. F. and Foglsong, H. M.: Studies in association and inhibition, Psychol. Rev., 1913, 20: 290; *301.* Sherrington, Sir Ch.: The endeavour of Jean Fernel, with a list and edition of his writings, Cambridge University Press, Cambridge, 1946, 273 p.; *302.* Slaugh, M. E.: Romance of mathematics, Math. Teacher, 1927, XX: 303; *303.* Sloane, W. M.: Life of Napoleon Bonaparte, New York, The Century Library Co., 1896, 4 vols.; *304.* Smith, A.

B.: Telephony, including automatic switching equipment, Chicago, Frederik J. Drake and Co., 1924, 450 p.; *305.* Smith, D. E. The poetry of mathematics, The Scripta Mathem. Libr., No. 1, 1934; *306.* Somerset de Chair, Ed.: Napoleon I., Emperor of the French, New York, Harper Brothers, 1950, 605 p.; *307.* Soroka, W. W.: Analog computers in computation and simulation, McGraw Hill Book Co., 1954, VIII, 385 p.; *308.* Spearman, Ch. E.: Creative mind, London, Nisbet and Co., 1930, XII, 153 p.; *309.* ——, see Chapter III, Ref. *454; 310.* Spence, K. W.: Gradual vs. sudden solution of discrimination problems by chimpanzees, J. Comp. Psychol., 1938, 25: 213; *311.* ——: Solution of multiple choice problems by chimpanzee, Comp. Psychol. Monogr., 1939, 15: No. 3, Ser. No. 75; *312.* ——: An experimental test of the continuity and non-continuity theory of discrimination learning, J. exper. Psychol., 1945, 35: 283; *313.* Spencer, H., see Chapter I, Ref. *70; 313a.* ——: Principles of psychology, (see esp. part VI, Par. 299), Ed. 1899; *314.* Sperry, R. W.: In "The central nervous system and behaviour," M. A. B. Brazier, Ed., Josiah Macy Found. etc., 1959, see Discussion, p. 421; *315.* Spiegel, E. A., see Chapt. II, Ref. *801; 316.* Spilsbury: (Review, Phil. of Science, Baltimore 1943, 10); *317.* Spitzka, E. A.: Study of brain of six eminent scientists, Transact, Amer. Philos. Soc., 1907, 21: 175; *318.* Stent, G. S., see Chapter I, Ref. *65a; 319.* Stöhr, A.: Psychologie, Braumüller, Vienna, 1918; *320.* Strachey, C. S.: Logical or nonmathematical programming, Proc. Ass. of Comput. machin., Toronto, 1952, p. 46; *321.* Sullivan, J. W. N.: The history of mathematics in Europe, Oxford University Press, 1925, 109 p.

322. Taine, H.: Napoleon, Pan Verlag, Berlin, 1912, VIII, 100 p.; *323.* Taton, R.: Reason and chance in scientific discovery, Philosophical Library, New York, 1957, 171 p.; *324.* Taylor, R. L., and Straube, H. M: "Nerve type" transmission lines, Bell. Lab. Rec., 1954, 32: 21; *325.* Terman, L. M.: Psychological approach to the biography of genius, London, 1947; *326.* Thorndyke, E. L.: The psychology of arithmetic, McMillan, New York, 1922, XVI, 314 p.; *327.* ——: Adult learning, McMillan, New York, 1928, X, 314 p.; *328.* Tredgold, A. F.: A textbook of mental deficiency, Baltimore, Williams and Wilkins, 1947, XVI, 534 p.; *329.* Turing, G.: Computation machinery and intelligence, Mind, 1950, 50: 433; *330.* Tustin, G.: Do modern machines help us to understand the mind?, Br. J. Psychol., 1955, 44: 24.

330a. Valentin, A.: Leonardo da Vinci. The tragic pursuit of perfection, New York, Grosset and Dunlap, 1938, 561 p.; *331.* Vasari, G.: Leonardo da Vinci, Phaidon Press, 1943; *332.* Vigotzky, L.: Thought in schizophrenia, Arch. Neurol. and Psychiat., 1934,

31: 1063; *333*. Vinacke, W. E.: The psychology of thinking, New York, McGraw Hill Co., 1952, XIII, 392 p.; *334*. Vietor, C.: Goethe, the thinker, (Transl. B. Q. Morgan), Harvard Univ. Press, 1950, 212 p.

334a. Wahle, R., see Ziehen, Th., Ref. *349; 335*. Waismann, F.: Introduction to mathematical thinking. The formation of concepts in modern mathematics (Transl. J. Benac), Fred. Ungar Publishing Co., New York, 1951, IX, 260 p.; *336*. Walter, Grey: A machine that learns, Scient. Amer., 1951, 185: 60; *337*. Walter, W. Grey: The living brain, New York, Grune & Stratton, 583 p.; *337a*. Walter, W. Grey: An imitation of life, Scient. Amer., 1950, 182: 42; *338*. Wallace, A. R.: On the Law which has regulated the introduction of new species, Ann. Mag. Nat. Hist. 1855, 16: 148; *339*. Wallas, G.: The art of thought, New York, Harcourt, Brace & Co., 1926, 314 p.; *340*. Warren, J. M. and Harlow, H. F.: Learned discriminatory performances by monkeys after prolonged postoperative recovery from large cortical lesions, J. comp. physiol. Psychol., 1952, 45: 119; *341*. ——: Discriminatory learning by normal and brain operated monkeys, J. genet. Psychol., 1952, 81: 45; *342*. Watt, H. J.: Beiträge zur Psychologie des Denkens, Arch. f. d. ges. Psychol., 1904, 4: 289; *343*. Wegrocky, H.: Generalizing ability in schizophrenia, Arch. of Psychol., 1940, 36, No. 254; *345*. Weierstrass, K. Th. W., see Smith (Ref. *291*) and Slaugh (Ref. *288*); *344*. Weidenreich, F.: The human brain in the light of human development, Scient. Monthly, 1948, 67: 103; *346*. Weininger, O.: Geschlecht und Charakter, Wien, Braumüller, 1920, 19th Ed., XIII, 599 p.; *347*. Weinschenk, C.: Uber Pawlows Lehre von der Physiologie der Grosshirnhemisphaeren und ihrer Beziehung zur Neurologie und Psychiatrie, Nervenarzt, 1957, 28: 488; *348*. Weaver, W.: The scientist speaks, New York, Boni and Gaer, 1947, XIII, 369 p.; *349*. Welty, C.: Birds as flying machines, Scientif. Amer., 1955, 192; *350*. Weyl, H.: Philosophy of mathematical and natural science, Princeton Univ. Press, 1943; *351*. Wertheimer, H.: Productive thinking, Harper Brothers Publ., New York, London, 1943, XI, 224 p.; *352*. Whitehead, A. N.: An introduction to mathematics, Cambridge University Press, 256 p.; *353*. ——: Science and the modern world, The New Amsterdam Library, 1952, X, 212 p.; *354*. Whithacker, E.: Eddington's principles in the philosophy of science, Amer. Scientist, 1952, 40: 45; *355*. Wilder, J., see Chapter II, Ref. *904; 356*. Wiener, N.: Cybernetics, Wiley and Sons, New York, 1948; *357*. ——: Time, communication and the nervous system, Ann, New York Acaed. of science, 1948, 50: 197 (see also Wisdom, Ref. *359*); *358*. Wilkes, J. O.: Can machines think?, Proced. Inst. Rad. Engin., 1953, 41: 1230; *359*. Wisdom, J. O.: Collective review. (Craik,

Wiener, Asby), Internat. J. Psychoanal., 1949, 30: 133; *360*. Woodsworth, R. S.: Psychological Issues. Selected papers (See esp. "Imageless thought"), New York, Columbia University Press, 1939, VIII, 421 p.; *361*. ——: Heredity and environment. A critical survey, New York Social Science research Council Bull., No. 47, 1941, X, 95 p.; *362*. Woodsworth, R. S., and Sells, S. B.: An atmosphere effect of formal syllogistic reasoning, J. exp. Psychol., 1953, 18: 451; *363*. Wykoff, L. B.: A mathematical model and an electronic model for learning, Psychol. Rev., 1954, 60: 89.

364. Young, J. Z.: Doubt and certainty in science, Oxford, Clarendon Press, 1951, 168 p.

365. Zaslow, R. W.: A new approach to the problem of conceptual thinking in schizophrenia, J. consult. Psychol., 1950, 14: 335; *366*. Ziehen, Th.: Leitfaden der physiologischen Psychologie, 12. Auflage, Jena, S. Fischer, 1924, 653 p. (See esp. p. 415.)

IV. SKILL

1. Ach, N., see Chapter II; ref. *2; 2*. Ades, H. W., and Raab, D. L.: Studies on the corpus callosum and the anterior commissure in monkeys, Fed. Proc., 1946, 5: 1; *3*. Aird, R. B., and Garoutte, B.; Studies on the cerebral pacemaker, Paper, read at the 10th Meeting of the Amer. Ac. Neurol., 1958; *4*. De Ajuriaguerra, J., and Hecaen, H.: The cortex cérébrale; étude neuro-psycho-pathologique, Paris, Masson, 1949, viii, 413 p.; *5*. Akelaitis, A. J.: Psychobiological studies following section of the corpus callosum, Amer. J. Psychiat., 1941, 97: 1147; *6*. Akelaitis, A. J., Risteen, W. A., Herren, R. Y. and van Wagenen, W. P.: Studies on the corpus callosum. III. A contribution to the study of dyspraxia following partial and complete section of the corpus callosum, Arch. Neurol., and Psychiat., 1942, 47: 971; *7*. Alajouanine, A., and Moziconazzi, P.: L'aphasie, Sem. des Hop., 1947, 29: 1221; *8*. Alford, L. B.: Cerebral localization. Outline of a revision, Nerv. Ment. Dis. Monogr., Series No. 77, 1948, 77p.; *8a*. Anastasopoulos, G. K.: Linksseitige Hemiplegie mit Alexie, Agraphie bei einem polyglotten Rechtshänder, Dtsch. Zeitschr. f. Nervenheilk., 1959, 179: 120; *9*. Anton, G.: Blindheit nach beiderseitiger Hirnerkrankung mit Verlust der Orientierung im Raume, Mitt. der Vereinig. d. Ärzte in Steiermark. 1996, 33: 41; *10*. ——: Beiderseitige Erkrankung der Scheitelgegend des Grosshirns, Wien. Klin. Wochenschr., 1899, No. 48; *11*. Arbuse, D. J.: The Gerstmann syndrome. Case report and review of the literature, J. nerv. ment. dis., 1947, 105: 359; *12*. Arens, H.: Sprachwissenschaft., Karl Alber, Freiburg/München, X, 568 p.;

13. Arnold, O., and Hoff, H.: Die Bedeutung der experimentellen Pharmakologie für die Neurologie und Psychiatrie, J. Mount Sin. Hosp., 1952, 19: 191; *15.* Ashby, W. R., see Chapter III; ref. *8.*
14. Babinski, J.: Contribution a l'étude des troubles mentaux dans l'hemiplegie organique cérbérale (anosognosie), Rev. neurol., 1914, 22: 845; *15.* Babkin, B. D.: Pavlow. A Biography, Univers. of Chicago Comm. Publ., in Biol. and Med., 1949, 364 p.; *16.* Baer, E. K. von, quoted by Holmes (ref. *226*); *17.* Baginski: Aphasie infolge schwerer Nierenerkrankung, Klin. Woschenschr., 1871, 8: 439; *18.* Baldy, R.: Le syndrome de l'artère cérébrale antérieure, Thèse de Paris, 1927, Jouve et Cie, 120 p.; *19.* Bailey, P., see chapter II. ref. *37; 20.* ——: Le cortex cérébrale, Rev. neurol., 1950, 82: 3; *21.* —— and von Bonin: Concerning cytoarchitectonics, Transact. Amer. Neurol. Ass., 1946, 0: 89; *22.* ——: The isocortex of man, Urbana, Univ. of Illinois Press. 1951, 301 p.; *23.* Balint, R.: Seelenlähmung des Schauens, optische Ataxie, räumliche Störungen der Aufmerksamkeit, Monatsschr. f. Psychiat. u. Neurol., 1909, 25: 51; *24.* Bartlett, J. E. A.: A gestaltapproach to the symptomatology of temporo-parietal lesions, Brit. J. Psychol., Febr. 1953; *25.* Bastian, H. C.: A treatise on aphasia and other speech defects, London, H. K. Lewis, 1898, VIII., 366 p.; *26.* Bay, E.: Disturbances of visual perception and their examination, Brain, 1953, 76: 515; *27.* Bawkin, H.: Lateral dominance, J. Ped., 1950, 36: 385; *28.* Bay, E., and Lauenstein, O: Zum Problem der optischen Agnosie, Deutsch. Zeitschr. f. Nervenheilk., 1953, 168: 1; *29.* Bechterew W. v.: Die Funktionen der Nervenzentra, Transl. R. Weinberg, 3 vols, G. Fischer, Jena; *30.* Beck, E.: Typologie des Gehirns am Beispiel des dorsalen menschlichen Schläfelappens, Deutsch. Zeitschr. f. Nervenheilk., 1955, 173: 267; *31.* Behrtn-Pinnow, C. v.: Die mathematische Begabung in der Familie Bernouilli, Arch. f. Rassen-und Gesellschaftsbiol., 1934, 27: 395; *32.* Bell, E. T., see Chapter 111; ref. *14; 33.* Bell, E., and Karnosh, L. J.: Cerebral hemispherectomy. Report of a case ten years after operation, J. Neurosurgery, 1949, 6: 85; *34.* Bender, L., and Jung, R.: Abweichungen der subjektiven optischen Vertikalen und Horizontalen bei Gesunden und Hirnverletzten, Arch. f. Psychiat. Etc. 1948, 181: 193; *35.* Benton, A. L., Hutcheon, J. F., and Seymour, E.: Arithmetic ability, finger localization and right left discrimination in normal and defective children, Amer. J. Orthopsychiat., 1951, 21: 765; *36.* Berger, H.: Akalkulia, Arch. Psychiat. u. Nervenkrankh., 1926, 7: 238; *37.* Bergson, H.: Creative evolution, Transl. A. Mitchell, the Modern Library, New York; Random House, XXV., 435 p.; *37a.* ——, see

Chapter II, ref. *19; 38.* Beringer, K. und Stein, J.: Analyse eines Falles von reiner Alexie, Ztschr. f. d. ges. Neurol. u. Psychiat. 1930, 123: 472; *39.* Bertalanffy, L. v.: Kritische Theorie der Formbildung, Abhandl. z. Theoret. Biol., 1928, Heft 27, Bornträger, Berlin, 243 p.; *40.* ——: The theory of open systems and physics and biology, Science, 1950, 11: 23; *41.* Best, F.: Zur Frage der Seelenblindheit, Arch. f. Psychiat. u. Z. Neur., 1952, 188: 511; *42.* ——: Hemianposie und Seelenblindheit bei Hirnverletzten. Graefe's Arch. 1917, 93: 49; *43.* Bidder, see Scripture, Ref. *441a; 44.* Bielschowsky, quoted by Lange; *45.* Bierens de Haan, see Chapter II Ref. *76; 46.* Binet, A.: La psychologie des grands calculateurs et jouers d'échec, Paris, Librarie Hachet et Cie, VIII., 364 p.; *47.* Binswanger, L.: Ueber Sprache und Denken, Stud. phil., Basel, 1946, 6: 30; *48.* Blackwell, A. M.: A comprehensive investigation into the factors involved in mathematical ability of boys and girls, Brit. J. Educ. Psychol., 1940, 10: 143, 2121; *49.* Blau, A.: The masterhand; a study of the origin and meaning of right and left-handedness and its relation to personality and language, New York, Amer. Orthopsychiat. Assoc., 260 p.; *50.* Bleuler, E., see Chapt. II, Ref. *81; 51.* Bliss, G. A.: Mathematical interpretation of geometrical and physical phenomena, Amer. mathem. Monthly, 1933, 40: 472; *52.* Bloomfield, L.: Language, New York, Henry Holt and Co., 1933. IX, 564 p.; *53.* Blum, J. S.: Cortical organization in somesthesis. Effects of lesions in posterior associative cortex on somato-sensory functions in macacca mulatta, Comp. Psychol. Monographs, 1951, 20/3; 219; *54.* Blum, J. S., Chow, K. L., and Pribram, K. H.: A behaviour analysis of the temporo-parieto-occipital cortex, J. comp. Neurol., 1950, 93: 53; *55.* Boas, Fr.: Handbook of American Indian Languages, Washington, 1911; *56.* Boehlke, U.: Störungen im Umgang mit Zahlen, ihre Art und Lokalisation, Arch. f. Psychiat. u. Z. Neurol., 1947/1948, 179: 599; *57.* Bonin, G. von: Essay on the cerebral cortex, Ch. Th. Thomas, Springfield, Ill., 1950, 168 p.; *58.* Bonvicini, G.: Die Störungen der Lautsprache bei Temporallappenläsionen, In: "Handbuch d. Neurologie des Ohres," Ed. G. Alexander and O. Marburg, vol. II., part II. 1929, p. 1571, Vienna. 1929; Urban and Schwarzenberg; *59.* Bornstein, B.: Ueber Mitbewegungen, Schw. Arch. f. Neurol. u. Psychiat., 1952, 86: 242; *60.* Bostroem, see Chapter II, Ref. *101; 61.* Bouillaud, J.: Recherches cliniques, Arch. gén. de la medicine, 1825, 8: 25; *62.* Brain, R. W.: Visual object agnosia related to gestalt-theory, Brain, 1941, 64: 244; *63.* ——: Visual object agnosia, Brain, 1951, 73: 465; *64.* Bramwell, B.: On crossed aphasia, Lancet/II, 1899, p. 1473;

65. Branford, B.: A study on arithmetical education, Oxford, Clarendon Press, 1908, 292 p. (See Bidder, Chapter VII); 67. Brill, A. A.: Some peculiar manifestations of memory, with special reference to lightening calculators, J. Nerv. a. ment. dis., 1940, 92: 704; 68. Brissaud, E.: Sur l'aphasie d'articulation et l'aphasie d'intention, Sem. med. 1894, 14: 341; 69. Broadbent, W. H., see Chapter I., ref. 13; 70. Brobeil, A. and Stallwitz, G.: Beiträge zur Aphasielehre, I. Rückbildungserscheinungen bei totaler Aphasie, Arch. f. Psychiat. u. Z. Neur., 1953, 190: 166; 71. Broca, P.: Remarques sur le siège de la faculté de langage articulé, etc., Bull. Soc. Anat. Paris, 1861, 36: 330; 72. Brown, J. R., and Simonson, M. A.: A clinical study of 100 aphasic patients. I. Observations on the lateralization and the localization of the lesions, Neurology, 1957, 7: 777; 73. Brown, T. G., and Sherrington, C. S.: On the instability of a motor point, Proc. Royal Soc. Med., 1912, 85: 250; 74. Brun, R.: Klinische und anatomische Beiträge zur Apraxie, Schw. Arch. f. Neurol. u. Psychiat., 1921, 10: 48, 185, and 1922, 9: 29; 75. Bruns, L.: Ueber Seelenlähumng, Neurol. Zentralbl. 1898, 17: 604; 76. Buck, D.: Les para-kinesies, J. de Neurol., 1899, 4: 361; 77. Bucy, P.: Is there a pyramidal tract? Brain, 1957, 70: 376; 78. Bucy, P. and Kluever, see Chapter 11; Ref. 122; 79. Buehler, K.: Sprachtheorie. Die Darstellungs-tätigkeit der Sprache, Jena, 1934, xvi, 434 p.; 80. Buehler, K.: The mental development of the child. (Transl. O. Olser), London, 1930, K. Paul, Trubner and Co. XI, 170 p.; 81. Bunts, A. T., and Chaffee, J. S.: Agenesis of the corpus callosum, Arch. Neurol. and Psychiat., 1944, 51: 35; 82. Burt, C.: The backward child, London, Univ. of London Prell, 3rd. Ed. 1950, 704 p.; 83. Buyssens, E.: Speaking and thinking from the linguistic stand-point, In "Thinking and Speaking." (Ed. G. Révérz) Amsterdam, 1954, North Holland Publ. Co., 206 p.

84. Cairns, H., and Davison, M. A.: Hemi-spherectomy in the treatment of infantile hemiplegia, The Lancet, 1951, II. 411; 85. Carpenter, M. B.: Agenesis of the corpus callosum, Neurology, 1954, 4: 200; 86. Carr: Quoted by Pick, A., J. of abnormal Psychology, II. p. 265; 87. Charcot, J. B. A. E., see Chart I, Ref. 152; 88. Chesher, B. N.: Some observations concerning the relation of handedness to language mechanisms, Bull. Neur. Inst. of New York, 1936, 4: 556; 89. Chow, K. L.: Effects of partial extirpation of posterior associative cortex on visually mediated behaviour in monkeys, Comp. Psychol. Monogr., 1951, 20/.3/.Ser/. No. 105; 90. Christian, P.: Neue Ergebnisse der Funktions-analyse auf dem Gebiete der Wahrnehumg and Motorik, Deutsche Ztchr. f. Nervenheilk., 1950,

164: 54; 91. Christian, P. and Schmitz, W.: Unter-suchungen von Sehhirnverletzten mit optischen Periodenreizen, Ibid., 1942, 154: 81; 92. Chusid, J. G., de Gutierrez Mahoney, W., and Chaffee, U.: Agenesis of the corpus callosum, Arch. Neurol. and Psychiat., 1939, 62: 840; 93. Cibis, P. and Bay, E.: Funktionswandel und Gesichtsfeld bei Sehhirn-verletzten, Dtch. Zeitschr. f. Nervenheilk., 1950, 163: 577; 94. Clark, G.: The mode of representation in the cerebral cortex, Brain, 1948, 71: 320; 95. Cog-hill, G. J., see Chapter II; ref. 167; 96. Cohen: Stereognostische Störungen, Deutsch. Zeitschr. f. Nervenheilk., 1926, 93: 228; 97. Conrad, K.: New problems of aphasia. (With 14 references to Conrad's writings on aphasia and related problems.), Brain, 1954, 77: 491; 98. Cooper, L. P. and Erickson, M. D., see Chapter II, Ref. 169; 99. Critchley, McDonald: Mirror writing, K. Paul, Trench, Trubner, London, 1928, 80 p.; 99a. Cordeau, J. P. and Marcia, M.: Evidence for the existence of an electroencephalographic synchronization mechanism originating in the lower brainstem; EEG. and Clin. Neurophysiol., 1959, 11: 551; 100. ———: The anterior cerebral artery and its syndromes, Brain, 1930, 53: 120; 101. ———: The language of gestures, London, Edw. Arnold and Co., VII., 128 p.; 102. Critchley, McDonald: Aphasic signalling (constitutional and acquired) occurring in naval signal men, J. Mount Sinai Hosp., 1942, 9: 363; 103. ———: Tactile thought, with special reference to the blind, Brain, 1953, 76: 19; 104. ———: The parietal lobes, London, E. Arnold and Co., 1953, 480 p.; 105. ———: Parietal syndromes in ambidextrous and left-handed patients, Zentralbl. f. Neurochir., 1955, 14: 4; 106. Cronholm, B.: Phantom limbs in ampu-tees, Acta psychiat. et neurol. Scand., Suppl. 72, 1951; 107. Curschmann, H.: Beiträge zur Physiologie und Pathologie der kontralateralen Mitbewegungen, Dtsch. Zeitschr. f. Nervenheilk., 1906, 31: 1; 108. Curtis, H. J.: An analysis of the cortical potentials mediated by the corpus callosum, J. Neurophysiol., 1940, 3: 4141;

109. Dandy, W. E.: The location of the conscious-ness center in the brain. The corpus striatum, Bull. Johns Hopkins Hospital, 1946, 79: 34; 110. Déjérine, J.: Étude sur l'aphasie, Rev. de Med., 1885, 5: 174; 111. ———: Semiologie des affections nerveux, Paris, Massen et Cie, 1926, XXV, 1219 p.; 112. Dejerine J., et Vialet, N.: Contribution a l'étude anatomo-pathologique des differents variétés de cécité verbale, Compt. rend. de la soc. de Biol. 1893, 11: 983; 113. Delacroix, H.: Le langage et la pensée, Paris, Librarie Alcan, 1924, 602 p.; 114. ———: L'analyse psychologique de la fonction lin-guistique, Oxford, Clarendon Press, 1926, 28 p.; 115. Denny Brown, D.: The nature of apraxia, J.

Nerv. ment. dis., 1958, 126: 9; *116*. Derwort, A.: Formen des Leistungsabbaues bei der Motorik, Dtsch. Zeitschr. f. Nervenheilk., 1950, 164: 80; *117*. ——: Ueber Leistungswandel der Sprachhandlung bei den Aphasien, Ibidem, 1954, 171: 202; *118*. Driesch, H.: The history and theory of vitalism, (Transl. C. G. Ogden), London, MacMillan and Co, 1914, VIII, 239 p.; *119*. Duensing, F.: Zur Frage der optisch räumlichen, Agnosie, Arch. f. Psychiat. u. Z. Neur., 1954, 192: 185; *120*. Dufour, R.: Hemianopsie relative et alexie, Conf. neurol., 1929, 9: 413; *121*. Durost, W. N.: The development of a battery of objective group tests of manual laterality with the result of their application to 1300 children, Genet. Psychol. Monographs. 1934, 16: 225.

122. Economo, C. von, see Chapter I; ref. *22*; *123*. Ehrenfels, Ch. von: Ueber Gestaltqualitäten, Vierteljschr. f. Wissenschaftl. Philosophie., 1890, 14: 249; *124*. Ehrenwald, H.: Verändertes Erleben des Körperbildes mit konsekutiver Wahnbildung bei linksseitiger Hemiplegie, Monatschr. f. Psychiat. u. Neurol., 1950, 75: 89; *125*. Ehrenwald, H.: Störungen der Zeitauffassung, der räumlichen Orientierung, des Zeichnens und des Rechnens bei einem Hirnverletzten, Zeitschr. f. d. ges. Neurol. u. Psychiat., 1931, 132: 518; *126*. Einstein, A. and Infeld, L.: The evolution of physics. The growth of ideas from early concepts to relativity and quanta, Simon and Schuster, New York, 1952, 316 p.; *127*. Ekehorn, J. E. G.: Sherrington's "Endeavour of Jean Fernel" and "Man on his Nature," Stockholm, P. A. Norstand and Soner, 1947. (Acta Med. Sc. and Suppl., 187); *128*. Ellis, W. D.: A sourcebook of Gestaltpsychology. Prepared by W. D. Ellis, with an introduction by Prof. K. Koffka, New York, Harcourt Brace & Co., 1938, xii–xiv, 403 p.; *129*. Erdmann, B.: Die psychologischen Grundlagen der Beziehungen zwischen Sprechen und Denken, Arch. f. system. Philosphie, 1896, 2: 355, 1897, 13: 31 and 1901, 7: 147; *130*. Ethelberg, S.: On changes in circulation through the anterior cerebral artery. A clinico-pathological study, Acta psychiat. et neurol. Scand., Suppl. No 75, 1951, 211 p.; *131*. Ettlinger, G.: Sensory deficits in visual agnosia, J. Neurol. Neurosurg. am Psychiat., 1956, 19: 297; *132*. Ettlinger, G., Jackson, C. V., and Zangwill, O. L.: Dysphasia following right temporal lobectomy in man, J. Neurol., Neurosurgery and Psychiat., 1955, 18: 214; *133*. Ettlinger, G., Warrington, E., and Zangwill, O. L.: A further study of visual spatial agnosia, Brain, 1957, 80: 335; *134*. Eustin, R. S.: Specific reading disability, New Engl. J. Med., 1947, 237: 242; *135*. Ewing, A. W.: Aphasia in children, London, H. Milford, 1930, XI., 152 p.; *136*. Exner, S.: Untersuchungen über

die Lokalisation der Funktionen in der Grosshirnrinde des Menschen, Wien, W. Braumüller, 1881, VII, 180 p.

137. Falkenberg, K.: Ueber isolierte Apraxie des linken Beines. Ein Beitrag zur lokalisatorischen Bedeutung des Balkens, Arch. f. Psychiat. und Nervenkran heiten, 1941, 141: 58; *138*. Faust, Cl.: Entwicklung und Abbau optisch-agnostischer Störungen nach traumatischer Hirnschädigung, Ibid., 1951, 22: 176; *139*. Feuchtwanger, E.: Amusie. Studien zur pathologischen Psychologie der akustischen Wahrnehmung and Vorstellung und ihrer Strukturgebiete, besonders der Musik und Sprache, J. Springer, Berlin, 1930, V, 295 p.; *140*. Faust, Cl.: Hirnpathologische Studien zur kongenitalen Schreib Leseschwäche, Nervenarzt, 1954, 25: 137; *141*. Ferrier, D.: Functions of the brain 2nd Ed., London, Smith Elder and Co, 1886; *142*. Flechsig, P.: Die Lokalization geistiger Vorgänge, Leipzig, Veit und Co, 1896, 88; *143*. Foerster, O.: Motor Cortex in man in light of Hughlings Jackson's doctrine, Brain, 1936, 59: 135; *144*. Foix, Ch. et Hillémand, P.: Contribution a l'étude d'agraphie ideo-motrice, Revue neurologique, 1916, I., 283; *145*. Forbes, A., see Chapter III, Ref. *81*; *146*. Forster: Ein diagnosticher Fall von Balkentumor, Neurol. Zentralbl., 1908, 27: 540, and 1929, 28: 1290; *147*. Franz, Sh. I.: On certain fluctuations in cerebral function in aphasics, J. exper. Fsychol., 1916, 1: 355; *148*. Freiman, I. S., Michels, L. S., and Kahn, R. L.: A hereditary syndrome characterized by mirror movements, left handedness and organic mental defect, Transact. Amer. Neurol. Ass., 1949, 74: 224; *149*. Freud, S.: On aphasia. A critical review, Transl. Stengel, E., Intern. Univers. Press, 1953, 105 p.; *150*. Frisch, G.: Chimpanzee handedness, Science, 1941, 54: 19; *151*. Fuchs, W.: Eine Pseudofovea bei Hemianopikern, Psychol. Forsch., 1922, 1: 151; *152*. Fulton, J., see Chapter II, Ref. *264*.

153. Galambos, R., and Rosenl lueth, W. A.: Brainstem response to acoustic stimuli, EEG and Clinic. Neurophysiol., 1940, 1: 254; *154*. Galton, F., see Chapter III Ref. *86*; *155*. Gamper, E.: Bau und Leistungen eines menschlichen Mittelhirnwesens, Zeitschr. f. d. ges. Neurol. u. Psychiat., 1926, 102: 154 and 104: 49; *155a*. ——, see Chapter II, Ref. *286*; *156*. Gans, E.: Uber Tastblindheit und über die Störungen der räumlichen Wahrnehmung der Sensibilität, Ibid., 1916, 31: 303; *157*. Gardner, W. J., Karnosh, L. J., McClure, C. C. and Gardner, A. K.: Residual function following hemispherectomy for tumor and for infantile hemiplegia, Brain, 1955, 78: 487; *158*. Gauss, K. F., see Chapter III, Ref. *88*; *159*. Gelb, A. and Goldstein, K.: Psychologische Analysen hirnpathologischer Falle, Zeitschr. f. Psychol. u. Physiol. d. Sinnesorgane, 1920, 183: 1;

160. Geller, W.: Ueber Lokalisationsfragen bei Rechenstörungen, Fortschr. d. Neurol. u. Psychiat. 1952, 20: 173; 161. Gerstmann, J.: Syndrome of fingeragnosia; disorder for right and left disorientation agraphia and akalkulia, Arch. Neurol. and Psychiat., 1940, 44: 44; 162. ――: Problem of imperception of disease and impaired body territories with organic lesions, Ibid., 1942, 48: 890; 163. Gerstmann, J. and Schilder, P.: Uber eine besondere Gangstörung bei Stirnhirnerkrankung, Wiener Medizinische Wochenschrift, 1926, 76: 97; 164. Gerstmann, J.: Some notes on the Gerstmann syndrome, Neurology, 1957, 7: 866; 165. Glees, P. and Cole, J.: Recovery of skilled motor functions after small lesions of neocortex in the macaque, J. Neurophysiol., 1950, 13: 137; 165a. Goethe, J. W., see Chapt. III, Ref. 91; 166. Goddard, H. H.: The Kalikak family, New York, McMillan Co., 1916, xv, 121 p.; 167. Goldstein, K.: Zur Lehre von der motorischen Apraxie, J. f. Psychol. und Neurol., 1908, 11: 196, 270; 168. ――: Der mikroskopische Hirnbefund bei meinem Fall von linksseitiger motorischer Apraxie, Neurol. Zentralbl., 1909, 28: 898; 169. ――: Über eine amnestische Form der apraktischen Agraphie, Ibid., 1910, 29: 252; 170. ――: Über transkortikale Aphasien, G. Fischer, Jena, 1915; 171. ――: Die zwei Formen der Störungsmöglichkeit der Sprache durch Hirnschädigung, Arch. f. Psychiat., 1931, 95: 738; 172. ――: The organism. A holistic approach to biology derived from pathological data in man, New York, American Book Co., 1939, XVII, 535 p.; 173. ――: Some remarks on Russel Brain's article concerning object agnosia, J. nerv. ment. dis., 1943, 98: 148; 174. ――: Language and language disturbances, New York, Grune and Stratton, 1948, 374 p.; 175. ――: Remarks on localization, Conf. neurol., 1946, 7: 25; 176. ――: Physiological aspects of convalescence and rehabilitation following central nervous system injuries, In "Symposium on physiological aspects of convalescence and rehabilitation." Ed. A. Keys, 1944; 177. Goodglass, H. and Quadfasel, F. A.: Language laterality in left handed aphasics, Brain, 1954, 77: 521; 178. Gooddy: Cerebral representation, Brain, 1956, 79: 167; 179. Gordiner, H. C.: A case of brain tumor of the base of the second left frontal convolution, Amer. J. Med. Science, 1899, 117: 526; 180. ――: Arguments in favour of the existence of a separate center for writing, Ibid., 1903, 126: 490; 181. Grasset, H.: Localization des maladies cérébrales, C. Coulet Montpellier, 1880, VIII, 387 p.; 182. ――: Le fonction du language et la localization des centres psychiques dans le cerveau, Rev. de Philosoph., 1907, 7: No. 1; 183. Greenblatt: Verbal communication; 184. Grewel, K.: Akalkulia, Ned. Tijdschr.

Psychol., 1950, 5: 167; 185. Griesinger, W.: Die Pathologie und Therapie psychischer Krankheiten, Berlin, 1892 (See also Hecaen, De Ajuriaguerra, p. 227); 186. Griffin, D. R.: Sensory physiology and the orientation in animals, Amer. Scientist, 1953, 41: 209; 187. Gutmann, E.: Aphasia in children, Brain, 1942, 65: 205.

188. Hadamard, J., see Chapter III; ref. 100; 189. Haecker, V. and Ziehen, Th.: Beitrag zur Lehre von der Vererbung und Analyse der mathematischen und zeichnerischen Begabung, Zeitschr. f. Psychol. u. Physiol. d. Sinnesorgane, Abt. f. Psychol., 1931; 190. Haidenhain, A.: Beiträge zur Kenntnis von der Seelenblindheit, Monatschr. f. Psychiat. u. Neurol., 1927, 66: 1; 191. Hallgren, B.: Specific dyslexia. Congenital word blindness, Act. Psychiat. a. Neurol. Scand., Suppl. 65, XIII, 287 p.; 192. Harlow, H., see Chapter II; ref. 324; 193. Harlow, H., Davis, R. T., Settlage, P. H. and Meyer, D. R.: Analysis of frontal and posterior associational systems in brain damaged monkeys, J. compar. physiol. psychol., 1952, 45: 419; 194. Hartmann, E. von, see Chapter II; ref. 333; 195. Hartmann, F.: Beitrag zur Apraxielehre, Monatschr. f. Psychiat. u. Neurol., 1907, 2L; 196. ――: Aphasie, Asymbolie, Apraxie, Neurol. Zentralbl., 1907, 26: 935; 197. Hauptmann, A.: Ist die amnestische Aphasie Teilerscheinung einer Beeinträchtigung des kategorialen Verhaltens? Monatschr. f. Psychiat. u. Neurol., 1931, 79: 302; 198. Head, H.: Studies in Neurology, Cambridge University Press, 1926, 2 vols; 199. ――: Aphasia and kindred disorders of speech, Cambridge, 1926, 2 vols; 200. ――: Aphasia. A historical review, Proc. Royal Soc. Med., 1920/21, 14: 1; 201. Head, H. and Holmes, G.: Sensory disturbances from cerebral lesions, Brain, 1911, 34; 202. Hécaen, H., and Ajuriaguerra, J. de: Balint's syndrome (psychic paralysis of visual fixation) and its minor forms, Brain, 1954: 77: 373; 203. Hécaen, H., Penfield, W., Bertrand, C., and Malmo, R.: The syndrome of apractagnosia due to lesions of the minor cerebral hemisphere, A.M.A. Arch. Neurol. and Psychiat., 1956, 75: 400; 204. Heidbreder, E.: The attainment of concepts. VIII. The conceptualization of verbally indicated instances, J. of Psychol, 1949, 27: 263; 205. Heilbronner, K.: Die aphasischen, apraktischen und agnostischen Störungen Handb. d. Neurol., I. Teil 2., p. 982 (Ed. Lewandowsky), J. Springer, Berlin, 1910; 206. Heine, H.: Hirnelektrische Befunde bei Balkenagenesie, Deutsch. Zeitschr. f. Nervenheilk, 1952, 169: 225; 207. Heisenberg, W.: Die Einheit des wissenschaftlichen Weltbildes, Leipzig, J. A. Barth, 1942, 32 p.; 208. Heisenberg, W.: Physics and Philosophy. (See Chapter I; ref. 35); 209. Helmholtz, H.: Treatise on physiological

optics (Transl. from the German Edition), 1924, p. 1925, 3 vols. Optical Society of America; *210*. Hemphill, E. and Stengel, E.: A study of pure word deafness, J. Neurol. and Psychol., 1940, 3: 251; *211*. Henneberg, R.: Reine Worttaubheit, Neurol. Zentralbl, 1926, 43: 251 and 1918, 37: 458; *212*. Henschen, S. E.: Acalculia, Zeitschr. f. d. ges. Neurol. u. Psychiat., 1919, 52: 284; *213*. Henschen, S. E.: Bemerkungen zu Pick's "Lokalisatorische Tendenzen in der Aphasielehre," Zeitschr. f. d. ges. Neurol. u. Psychiat., 1925, 99: 518; *214*. ——: Aphasiesysteme, Monatschr. f. Psychiat. u. Neurol., 1927, 65: 86; *215*. ——, see Chapter II; ref. *370; 216*. Herrick, C. J., see Chapter II; ref. *374; 217*. Hildreth, G.: The development of training and hand dominance, Ped. Sem. a. J. genet. Psychol., 1949, 75: 221 and 76: 39; *218*. Hoenigswald, R.: Philosophie und Sprache. Problemstellung und System, Basel, 1937, Haus zum Falken Verlag, X, 461 p.; *219*. Holmes, G.: Disturbances of visual orientation, Brit. J. Ophthalm., 1918, 349: 506; *220*. ——: A contribution to the cortical representation of vision, Brain, 1931, 51: 470; *221*. ——: Disturbances of vision in cerebral lesions, 1918, 2: 353; *222*. ——: Disturbances of visual space perception, Brit. Med. J., 1919, 2: 230; *223*. ——: Cerebral integration of ocular movements, Ibid., 1938, 2: 107; *224*. ——: Hoch, P., see ref. 388; *225*. Holmes, G. and Horrax, G.: Disturbances of spatial orientation and visual attention with loss of stereoscopic vision, Arch. Neurol. and Psychiat., 1919, 1: 385; *226*. Holmes, S. I.: K. E. von Baer's perplexities of evolution, Isis, 1947: 37: 7; *227*. Humboldt, W. von: Gesammelte Werke, Berlin, G. Riemer, 1841–1852, 7 vols. in three; *228*. Humphrey, M. E., and Zangwill, O.: Dysphasia in left handed persons with missile wounds, J. Neurol., Neurosurg., and Psychiat., 1952, 15: 104; *229*. Hunter, W. S. A.: A consideration of Lashley's theory of equipotentiality of cerebral action, J. genet. Psychol., 1930, 3: 455.

230. Isserlin, M.: Hugo Liepmann zum Gedächtnis, Zeitschr. f. d. ges. Neurol. u. Psychiat., 1925, 99: 636; *231*. ——: Aphasie, In "Handb. d. Neurologie und Psychiatrie, Ed. O. Bumke and O. Foerster, vol VI., p. 262. Berlin, J. Springer, 1936. (See esp. p. 734); *232*. Isserlin, M., Gräfin Kuenberg, von, and Hofbauer: Zur Pathologie der Beziehungen zwischen Denken und Sprechen, Zentralbl. f. Neurol., 1927, 47: 252.

233. Jackson, J. H.: Papers on aphasia and kindred disorders of speech, Brain, 1915, 38: 1; *234*. Jacob, H.: Ueber die Stufung des optischen Wahrnehmungswandels bei organischen Bewegungsstörungen, Deutsch. Zeitschr. f. Nervenheilk., 1949, 164: 71; *235*. Jaensch, E. and Grünhut, L.:

Ueber Gestaltpsychologie and Gestalttheorie, Paed. Magaz. Heft 262, 1929, 167 p.; *236*. Jasper, H. H., and Raney, E. T.: The physiology of lateral cerebral dominance, Psychol. Bull., 1937, 34: 151; *237*. Jastrow, J.: The subconscious, Boston, New York, Houghton Mifflin Co., 1906, ix, 549 p; *238*. Jeliffe, G. E.: The mneme. The engram and the subconscious. Richard Semon. His life and work, J. Nerv. ment. dis., 1932, 57: 329; *239*. Jendrassik, E.: Über den Mechanismus und die Lokalisation geistiger Vorgänge, Neurol. Zentralbl., 1907, 26: 194, 254; *240*. Jesperson, O.: Language. Its nature, development and origin, London, Allen and Unwin, 1934, 444 p.; *241*. Joel, A. E.: Relay preference. Lockout circuits in telephone switching, Transact. Amer. Inst. of Electric Engineering, 1949, 67/68: 720; *242*. Johnston, P. W.: Hereditary mirror movements, Bull. Los Ang. Neurol. Soc., 1948, 13: 120; *243*. Jossman, P.: Dyslexia, J. nerv. ment. dis., 1947, 106: 93; *244*. Jung, R.: Neurophysiologische Grundlagen der Hirnpathologie, Nervenarzt, 1948, 19: 521; *245*. ——: Bemerkungen zu Bay's Agnosiearbeiten, Ibid., 1951, 22: 192; *246*. Joy, H. H.: Agnostic and alexia, without agraphia, Transact. Amer. Ophth. Soc., 1947, 1; *247*. Kainz, F.: Psychologie der Sprache, 3 vols, F. Enke, Stutgart, 1941–1954. (Ist vol. 2nd Ed., 1954); *247a*. Kant, Imm.: Critique of Pure Reason, London, N. Kemp-Smith, 1929; *248*. Kainz, F.: Vorformen des Denkens. In "Thinking and Speaking." (Ed. G. Révesz.), Amsterdam, 1954, North Holland Publ. Co.; *249*. Karnosh, L. J., and Gardner, W. J.: The physical and mental capacity after removal of the right hemisphere, Dis. nerv. syst., 1940, 1: 343; *250*. Katz, D.: Gestaltpsychologie, 2nd Ed., B. Schwalbe, Basel, 1948, 157 p.; *251*. Kauders, O. Ueber polyglotte Reaktionen bei sensorischer Aphasie, Zeitschr. f. d. ges. Neurol. u. Psychiat., 1929, 122: 651; *252*. Kennard, M. A.: Reorganization of motor function in the cerebral cortex of monkeys deprived of motor areas in infancy, J. Neurophysiol., 1938, 1: 477; *253*. Kennard, M. A., and Fulton, J. F.: The syndrome of the premotor cortex in man etc., Brain, 1934, 57: 69; *254*. Kennard, M. A. and Fulton, J. F.: Age and reorganization of central nervous system, J. Mount Sinai Hospit., 1942, 9: 594; *255*. Kennedy, F.: Stock-brainedness, the causative factor in the so called "crossed aphasia," J. Amer. Med. Ass., 1916, 152: 894; *256*. Kerr, J.: Left-handedness and mirror writing, Amer. J. Sch. Hyg., 1920, 4: 1; *257*. Klein, R.: Ueber frontale Störungen des Gehens, Monatschr. f. Psychiat. u. Neurol., 1928, 69: 12; *258*. ——: Denkinhalt und Aphasie, Zeitschr. f. d. ges. Neurol. u. Psychiat., 1929, 121: 36; *259*. Kleist, K., see Chapter II; ref. *468; 260*. ——: Der Gang und der gegenwärtige Stand der Apraxiefrage Erg. d. ges. Neurol. u. Psychiat., 1911, 1: 343; *261.* ——: Über sensorische Aphasie, J. für Psychol. u. Neurol., 1928, 37: 146; *262.* ——, see Chapter II; ref. *468; 263.* ——: Jubilarehrung Oskar and Cécile Vogt, Arch. f. Psychiat., 1950, 185: 619; *264.* Klimes, K. and Mezaros, A.: Zur Frage der Simultanagnosie, Arch. f. Psychiat., 1942, 11: 661; *265.* Koehler, W.: Gestaltpsychologie. An introduction to new concepts in modern psychology, New York, Liveright Publ., 1947, 639 p.; *266.* ——: New facts in visual perception, Transact., New York Academy of Sc., 1944, 7: 39; *267.* ——, and Held, R.: The cortical correlate of pattern vision, Science, 1949, 109: 442; *268.* Koffka, K.: Principles of gestaltpsychology, New York, Harcourt, Brace and Co., 1935, XI, 72 p.; *269.* Kornmueller, K.: Erregbarkeitssteuernde Elemente und Systeme des Nervensystems, Fortschr. a. d. Geb. d. Neurol. u. Psychiat., 1950, 18: 437; *270.* Külpe, O.: Vorlesungen über Psychologie. (Ed. K. Bühler), Leipzig, S. Hirzel, 2nd Ed., 1922, viii, 340 p.; *271.* Kussmaul, A.: Disturbances of speech. An attempt in the pathology of speech, In "Cycloped. pract. med.," New York, 1887, 14: 379.

272. Lange, J.: Fingeragnosie und Agraphie, Monatschr. f. Psychiat. u. Neurol., 1930, 76: 129; *273.* ——: Agnosie und Apraxie, In "Handbuch der Neurologie, Ed. O. Bumke and O. Foerster, Vol. 0; *274.* Lashley, K. S.: Studies of cerebral functions in learning. V. The retention of motor habits after destruction of the so-called motor areas in primates, Arch. Neurol. a. Psychiat., 1924, 12: 249; *275.* ——: Brain mechanism and intelligence; a quantitative study of injury to the brain, University of Chicago Press, 1929, XIV, 186 p.; *276.* ——: Mass action in cerebral function, Science, 1931, 73: 245; *277.* ——: The mechanism of vision. XII. Nervous structures concerned with the acquisition and retention of habits based on relation to light, Comp. Psychol. Monogr., 1925, vol. 11, No. 2, p. 43; *278.* ——: Studies on cerebral function in learning. XII. Loss of the maze habit after occipital lesions in the blind rat, J. compar. Neurol., 1943, 79: 431; *279.* ——: Apparent absence of transcortical association in maze learning, Ibid., 1944, 80: 257; *280.* ——: Structural variations in the nervous system in relation to behaviour, Psychol. Rev., 1947, 54: 325; *281.* ——: The problem of interaction of cerebral areas, Transact. Amer. Neurol. Ass., 1949, 74: 187; *282.* ——: In search of the engram, Sympos. of the Soc. for experiment. Biol., 1950, 10: 454; *283.* Lashley, K. S., Chow, K. L., and Semmes: Examination of the electrical field theory of cerebral integration, Psychol. Rev., 1951, 58: 123; *284.* Lashley, K. S. and Clark, G.: The cytoarchitectonics of the cerebral cortex in Ateles. A critical examination of architectonic studies, J. Comp. Neurol., 1946, 85: 223; *285.* Lassek, A. M., Woolsey, C. N., Walker, A. E., and Boshes, B.: The pyramidal tract, Neurology, 1957, 7: 496; *286.* Leary, R. W., Harlow, H. F., Settlage, P. H. and Greenwood, D. O., see Chapt. II; ref. *578; 287.* Leibniz, G. W., quoted by Arens, Ref. *12; 288.* Leischner, A.: Ueber die Aphasie der Mehrsprachigen, Arch. f. Psychiat., 1948, 180: 731; *289.* ——: Über Störungen des Stenographierens. Ein Beitrag zur Agraphie, Arch. f. Psychiat. and Neur., 1950, 185: 271; *290.* Lenz, H.: Veränderungen der Körperfühlsphäre als Teilerscheinung einer Raumstörung bei Hirnverletzten, Ibid., 1944, 117: 68; *291.* Leonhardt, K. and Wiehler, H.: Zwei Fälle von angeborener Schreibleseschwäche bei Jugendlichen; *292.* ——: Ibid., 1954, 25: 447; *293.* Leyton, A. S. F., and Sherrington, C. S.: Observations on the excitable cortex of the chimpanzee, Orangutan and Gorilla, Quart. J. exper. Physiol., 1917, 11: 135; *294.* Lewin, K.: Principles of topological psychology (Transl. F. Herfer), McGraw Hill Co., 1936, XV, 231 p.; *295.* Lichtheim; Ueber Aphasie, Arch. klin. Med., 1885, 3: 204; *296* Lidell, E. G. T., and Phillips, C. G.: Thresholds of cortical representation, Brain, 1950, 73: 125; *297.* Liebers, M.: Ueber kongenitale Wortblindheit, Psychiat., Neurol. u. Mediz. Psychol., 1953, 5: 83; *298.* Liepmann, H.: Das Krankheitsbild der Apraxie, ("Motorische Asymbolie") auf Grund eines Falles von einseitiger Apraxie, Monatschr. f. Psychiat. und Neurol., 1900, 102: 182; *299.* ——: Der weitere Krankheitsverlauf bei einem einseitigen apraktischen und der Gehirnbefund auf Grund von Serienschnitten, Ibid., 1905, 17: 289, and 1906, 19: 217; *300.* ——: Drei Aufsätze aus dem Apraxiegebiet, Berlin, S. Karger, 1908, 80 p.; *301.* ——: Zum Studium der Aphasiefrage, Neurol. Zentralbl., 1909, 28: 449; *302.* ——: Motorische Aphasie und Apraxie, Neurol. Zentralbl., 1915, 33: 289; *303.* ——: Bemerkungen zu von Monakow's Kapitel "Die Lokalisation der Apraxie" in seinem Buch die "Lokalisation im Grosshirn," Monatschr. f. Psychiat. u. Neurol., 1914, 35: 490; *304.* ——: Apraxie, Ergebn. der Med., 1920, 1: 516; *305.* ——: Liepmann, H. und Maas, O.: Linksseitige Apraxie und Agraphie, Berl. Klin. Wochenschr., 1907, I, 757; *306.* Liessens, P.: L'alexie chez les enfants arrières, Act. psychiat. et neurol. Belg., 1949, 49: 102; *307.* Lindley, D.: Physiological growth of the brain, Thirty-third Annual Meeting of the Ass. f. Res. in Nerv. a. Ment. Dis., New York, Dec. 11, 1959; *307a.* Lindsley, D. B.: Bilateral differences in brain potentials from the two cerebral hemispheres in relation to bilaterality and stuttering, J. exper.

Psychol., 1940, 26: 211; *308*. Lissauer, H.: Ein Fall von Seelenblindheit nebst einem Beitrag zur Theorie derselben, Arch. f. Psychiat., 1890, 21: 222; *309*. Lordat, J.: Analyse de la parole, pur servir a la theorie de divers cas d'alalie, Montpellier, L. Cartel, 1843 (See also ref. *415*); *310*. ——, see Chapter II, ref. *550*; *311*. Lotmar, F.: Ueber zentrale Störungen der Sprache und über das Problem der Lokalisation höherer psychischer Leistungen im Gehirn, Schw. Zeitschr. f. Psychol., 1949, 8: 133, 253, 235; *312*. ——: Zur Lehre von der erschwerten Wortfindung und ihrer Rückwirkung auf das Denken der Aphasichen, Ibid., 1940, 45: 341; *313*. Lourié, O.: La langage et la verbomanie. Essay de psychologie morbide, Paris, F. Alcan 1912, 275 p.; *314*. Lüers, Th.: Ueber den Verfall der Sprache bei Pickscher Krankheit, Arch. f. Psychiat., 1947, 179: 94;

315. McFie, J., Piercy, M. F. and Zangwill, A.: Visuo-spatial agnosia associated with lesions of the right hemisphere, Brain, 1950, 73: 167; *316*. McDougall, M.: Men or Robots? Ped. Sem. a. J. genet. Psychol., 1926, 71: 112; *317*. Mahoudeau, D.: Considérations sur l'agraphie, a propos d'un case observé sur un traumatims du crâne, porteur d'une lésion de la deuxième et troisième frontale, La Sem. des Hop., 1950, 62: 1598; *318*. ——: Un cas d'agraphie chez un traumatism du crâne porteur d'une lésion du pied du deuxième et trosième de la circonvolution frontale gauches, Rev. neurol., 1951, 84: 159; *319*. Marbe, K., see Chapter Il, ref. *385*; *320*. Marie, P.: Revision de la question de l'aphasie, Sem. ned., 1906, (Oct. 17); *321*. Marcuse: Apraktische Symptome bei einem Fall von seniler Demenz, Zentralbl. f. Neurol. u. Psychiat., 1904; *322*. Martin, L. P.: Zur Lehre von den Bewegungsvorstellungen, Zeitschr. f. Psycholog., 1910, 56: 441; *323*. Maspes, P. S.: Le syndrome experimental chez l'homme de la section du splenium du corps calleux, Rev. neurol., 1948, 80: 100; *324*. Mayer Gross, W.: The question of visual impairment in constructional apraxia, Proc. Royal Soc. Med., 1936, 29: 1396; *325*. Messer, A., see Chapter II, Ref. *223*; *326*. Meyer, S.: Die Lehre von den Bewegungsvorstellungen, Zeitschr. f. Psychol., 1913, 65; *327*. Meyers, R.: Relation of 'thinking" to language. Arch. of Neurol. and Psychiat., 1948, 60: 119; *328*. ——: The extrapyramidal system. An inquiry into the validity of the concept, Neurology, 1953, 3: 627; *329*. Meynert, Th.: Anatomische Begründung gewisser Arten von Sprachstörungen, Österr. Zeitschr. f. Heilk., 1866, 12: 199; *330*. Mindus, E.: "Reine" Astereognose an zwei Fällen erläutert, Act. Med. Scand., 1943, 113: 58; *331*. Minkowski, M.: Constantin von Economo, Schw. Arch. f. Neurol. u. Psychiat., 1931, 27: 1; *331a*. Meyer, A., see Chapter

II; Ref. *00*; *332*. Misch, W. and Frankl, K.: Beitrag zur Alexielehre, Monatschr. f. Psychiat. u. Neurol., 1927, 71: 1; *333*. Mitchell, F. D.: Mathematical prodigies, Amer. J. Psychol., 1907, 18: 61; *334*. Moebius, P.: Über die Anlage zur Mathematik, Leipzig, J. A. Barth, 1900, vi, 331 p.; *335*. Moleen, G. A.: Frontal lobe phenomena, Arch. Neurol. a. Psychiat., 1921, 6: 640; *336*. Monakow, Const. von: Aufbau und Lokalisation der Bewegungen beim Menschen, Arb. a. d. hirnanatom. Instit. Zürich, 1911, 5: 1; *337*. ——: Lokalisation der Grosshirnfunktionen, J. f. Psychol. und Neurol., Leipzig, 1911, 17: 185; *338*. ——: Die Lokalisation im Grosshirn und der Abbau der Funktionen durch lokale Herde, J. F. Bergmann, Wiesbaden, 1919, 1033 p.; *339*. ——: Gehirnpathologie, Sec. Ed., Vienna, Hölder, 1915, XIV, 1319 p.; *340*. ——: Theoretische Betrachtungen über die Lokalisation im Zentralnervensystem, insbesondere im Grosshirn, Erg. d. Physiol., 1913, 13: 206; *341*. —— and Mourgue, R.: Biologische Einführung in das Studium der Neurologie und Psychiatrie (Transl. Katzenstein, E.), Stuttgart and Leipzig, Hippocrates Verlag 1930, XIX, 400 p.; *341a*. Morgan and Woods, see Chapt. 1, Ref. *662*; *342*. Mourgue, R.: La conception de neurologie dans l'oeuvre de Kurt Goldstein, Encéphale, 1937, 32: 32; *343*. Morlääs, J.: Contribution a l'étude de l'apraxie, Paris, A. Legrand, 1928, 231 p.; *344*. Munk, H.: Ueber die Funktionen der Grosshirnrinde, Berlin, Hirschwald, 1881, X, 133 p.; *345*. Moruzzi, G. and Magoun, H. W., see Chapter II, Ref. *629*; *346*. Muskens: Das supravestibuläre System, Noord Hollandische Uitsgewertsmaatschippy, 1934, XVIII, 557 p.; *347*. Mutschler, D.: Der Abbau der Wahrnehmungsgestalt und der taktilen Bewegungsgestalt, Deutsch. Ztschr. f. Nervenheilk., 1948, 159: 427; *348*. Myers, R. E.: Interocular transfer of pattern discrimination in cats following section of crossed optic fibers, J. compar. physiol. Psychol., 1955, 48: 470; *349*. Myers, R. E.: Function of corpus callosum in intraocular transfer, Brain, 1956, 79: 358; *350*. —— and Sperry, R. W.: Interhemispheric communication through the corpus callosum, A.M.A. Arch. Neurol. a. Psychiat., 1958, 80: 298.

351. Nathan, W.: Facial apraxia and apractic dysarthria, Brain, 1947, 70: 449; *352*. Needles, W.: Concerning transfer of cerebral dominance to the function of speech, J. nerv. ment. dis., 1942, 95: 270; *353*. Nielsen, J. M.: Unilateral cerebral dominance as related to mindblindness, Arch. Neurol. and Psychiat., 1937, 38: 108; *354*. ——: The unsolved problems of aphasia. I. Alexia in "motor aphasia," Bull. Los Ang. Neurol. Soc., 1938, 4: 114; *355*. ——: Fundamental principles in aphasia based on autopsy

material in crucial cases, Ibid., 1942, 7: 77; *356.*
——: Agnosia, apraxia, aphasia; their value in cerebral localization. With the association of J. P. Fitzgibbon, Sec. Ed., New York, P. Hoeber, 1946, 292 p.; *357.* ——: The cortical motor pattern apraxias, Ass. Res. Nerv. Ment. dis. Monogra., 1948, 27: 565; *358.* —— and Carnes, W. M.: Visual agnosia for inanimate objects, Ibid., 1956, 21: 95; *359.* —— and Friedman, A. P.: Fundamental principles in aphasia based on autopsy material in crucial cases, Ibid., 1942, 7: 77; *360.* —— and Sult, C. W.: Agnosia and the body scheme, Ibid., 1939, 4: 69.

361. Oates, O. A.: Left-handedness in relation to speech defects, intelligence and achievement, For. Educ., 1929, 7: 91; *362.* O'Brien, J. D.: Removal of the right cerebral hemisphere. A case report, Ohio State Med. J., 1932, 28: 645; *363.* Odham, H. W.: A psychological study of mathematical ability, Br. J. Educ. Psychol., 1927/38, 7: 269 and 8: 16; *364.* Odom, G. L. and Lyman, R. S.: Speech disorders following excision of postcentral gyrus, Transact. Amer. Neurol. Ass., 1946, 71: 67; *365.* Oeser, O. A.: Critical notes on gestaltpsychology and gestalttheory, Br. J. Psychol., 1930/31, 21: 73; *365a.* Ohrbach, J.: Disturbances of maze habit following occipital cortex removals in blind monkeys, A.M.A. J. Neurol. a. Psychiat., 1959, 81: 49; *366.* Ombredane, A.: L'aphasie et l'élaboration de la pensée explicite, Presses Universitaires de Paris, 1951, 440 p.; *367.* Oppenheim, H.: Lehrbuch der Nervenkrankheiten, Störungen der Sprache, 3rd Ed., Berlin, S. Karger, 1902, XII, 1220 p.; *368.* Orton, S. T.: Reading, writing and speech problems in children, New York, Morton and Co., 1927, 215 p.; *369.* Osborn, quoted by Bonvicini.

370. Pallis, C. A.: Impaired identification of faces and places with agnosia for colors, J. Neurol., Neurosurg. and Psychiat., 1955, 18: 218; *371.* Pappenheim, E.: Beiträge zum Problem der Entfremdungserlebnisse bei Hirnkranken, Ztschr. f. d. ges. Neurol. u. Psychiat., 1927, 107: 599; *372.* Pascal, Bl.; quoted by Bell, E. T. (Ref. *14*); *373.* Paterson, A., and Zangwill, O. L.: Recovery of spatial orientation in the postraumatic confusional state, Brain, 1944, 67: 54; *374.* ——: A case of topographical disorientation with a unilateral cerebral lesion, Brain, 1945, 68: 188; *375.* Pavlow, I. P., see Chapter II, Ref. *672; 376.* Penfield, W., see Chapter II, Ref. 716; *377.* ——: Centrencephalic integrating system, Brain, 81: 231; *378.* —— and Jasper, see Chapter II, Ref. *720; 379.* —— and Keasley, W.: Instability of motor points in the cerebral cortex, Fed. Proc., 1948, 7: 91; *380.* Peritz: Zur Pathophysiologie des Rechnens, Dtsch. Ztschr. f. Nervenheilk., 1952, 67: 178; *381.* Pfeifer, R. A.:

Pathologie der Hörstrahlung und der kortikalen Hörsphaere, In "Handbuch der Neurol. und Psychiat., vol. VI, p. 533. (Ed. O. Bumcke and O. Förster, J. Springer, Berlin, 1936); *382.* Pick, A.: Beiträge zur Pathologie und pathologischen Anatomie des Zentralnervensystems mit Bemerkungen zur normalen Anatomie desselben, S. Karger, Berlin, 1898; *383.* ——: Studien über motorische Apraxie und ihre nahestehende Erkrankungen, Deuticke, Wien, 1905, 129 p.; *384.* ——: Zur Symptomatologie des atrophischen Hinterhauptlappens, Arb. a. d. Deutsch. Psychiat. Universitätsklinik, Prag, 1908, 42 p.; *385.* ——: Ueber das Sprachverständnis. Drei Vorträge, J. A. Barth, Leipzig, 1909; *386.* ——: Reduplicative paramnesia; Brain, 1903, 26: 26; *387.* ——: Die agrammatischen Sprachstörungen. Studien zur psychopathologischen Grundlegung der Aphasielehre, Berlin. J. Springer, 1913, 291 p.; *388.* ——: Die neurologische Forschungsrichtung in der Psychiatrie, Abh. a. d. Grenzgeb., d. Neurol. u. Psychiat., 1921, 13: 247; *389.* ——: Aphasie, In "Handb. d. norm. u. path. Physiol.," (Ed. Bethe., v. Bergmann a.o.) 1931, 15/II, p. 1436; *390.* Piëron, H.: Thought and the brain (Transl. Odgen), New York, Harcourt, Brace and Co., 1927, XIV, 2626 p.; *391.* Pillsbury, W. B. and Meadow, C. L.: The psychology of language, Appleton and Co., London, 1928, vii, 306 p.; *392.* Pineas, H.: Ein Fall von linksseitiger motorischer Apraxie nach Balkenerweichung, Monatschr. f. Psychiat. u. Nervenkrankh., 1924, 56: 43; *393.* ——: Der Mangel an Krankheitsbewusstsein, Verh. d. Ges. Dtsch. Nervenärzte, 1926, 16: 283; *394.* Pitres, A.: Etude sur l'aphasie chez les polyglottes, Rev. de med., 1895, 15: 873; *394a.* Polyak, St., see Chapter II, Ref. *731; 395.* Planck, M.: Scientific autobiography and other papers (Transl. Frank Gaynor), Philosophical Library, New York, 192 p.; *396.* Poppelreuter, W.: Die psychischen Störungen durch Kopfschuss im Kriege 1914–1918, Die Störungen der niederen und höheren Sehleistungen durch Verletzungen des Occipitalhirns, Leipzig, L. Voss, 1917, vol. 1; *397.* Pribram, H. B. and Barry, J.: Further behaviour analysis of parieto-temporo-occipital cortex, J. Neurophysiol., 1956, 19: 99; *398.* Puusepp, L. and Levin: Zur Frage der Störungen des Schluckens von apraktischem Charackter, Zeitschr. f. d. ges. Neurol. u. Psychiat., 1923, 87: 441.

399. Ranson, S. W., and Hinsey, J. C.: Reflexes in the hindlimbs of cats after transsection of the spinal cord at various levels, Amer. J. Physiol., 1930, 94: 472; *400.* Raney, E. T.: Brain potentials and lateral dominance in identical twins, J. exper. Psychol., 1938, 23: 302 and 1939, 24: 21; *401.* Rees, H. E.: The psychology of artistic creation, Bureau of

Publishers, Teacher's college, Columbia University, New York, 1942, X, 209 p.; *402.* Reichardt, M.: see Chapter II, Ref. *707; 403.* Reinhold, M.: A case of auditory agnosia, Brain, 1950, 73: 203; *404.* Reitan, R. M.: Intellectual functions in aphasic and non-aphasic brain injured subjects, Ibid., 1953, 3: 202; *405.* Revesz, G.: The origin and prehistory of language (Transl. J. Butler), Philosophical Library, New York, 1956, VIII, 240 p.; *406.* Revesz, G. (Ed.): Thinking and Speaking. A symposium, Amsterdam, 1954, North Holland Publ. Co., 205 p.; *407.* Riddoch, G.: Visual disorientation in visual half fields, Brain, 1935, 58: 376; *408.* ———: Phantom limb and body scheme, Ibid., 1941, 64: 197; *409.* Rieger: Ueber Apparate in dem Hirn, Arb. a. d. psychiat. Klinik Würzburg, 1909, vol. V; *410.* ——— and Wolff, quoted by Gerstmann, J. Ref. *165; 411.* Riese, W.: Die Überwertigkeit der einen Hemisphäre auf Grund hirnmorphologischer Untersuchungen, Monatschr. f. Psychiat. u. Neurol., 1927, 46: 185; *412.* ———: Kurt Goldstein's Stellung in der Geschichte d. Neurologie, Schw. Arch. f. Neurol. u. Psychiat., 1927, 64: 185; *413.* ———: Auto-observation of aphasia. Reported by an eminent nineteenth century scientist, Bull. of the hist. of medicine, 1954, 28: 237; *414.* Riese, W.: Hughlings Jackson's doctrine of aphasia and its significance today, J. nerv. ment. dis., 1955, 122: 1; *415.* Rosset, see Chapter II; Ref. *726; 416.* Roth, M.: Disorders of the body image caused by lesions of the right parietal lobe, Brain, 1949, 72: 89; *417.* Rubin, E.: Visuell wahrgenommene Figuren, quoted by Ellis, W. D. (Ref. *130*) See esp. p. 131; *418.* Russel, B.: Human knowledge. Its scope and limitations, London, 1948, Simon and Schuster, 538 p.

419. Sandifer, P. H.: Anosognosia and disorders of the body scheme, Brain, 1946, 69: 122; *420.* Sapir, E.: Language. An introduction to the study of Speech, Harcourt, Brace, and Co., New York, 1949, VI, 242 p.; *421.* Schafer, K.: Ueber das Verhalten der amnestischen Aphasie zu Kurt Goldstein's kategorialem Verhalten, Arch. f. psychiat., 1933, 100: 427; *422.* Scheller, H.: Ueber das Wesen und die Abgrenzung agnostischer Störungen, Nervenarzt, 1951, 22: 187; *423.* ——— and Seidemann, H.: Zur Frage der optisch räumlichen Agnosie, Monatschr. f. Psychiat. u. Neurol., 1931/32, 81: 178; *424.* ——— Scheincker, I. M. und Kuhr, B. M.: Motor aphasia and agraphia caused by small vascular lesions confined to the second and third convolution of left frontal lobe, Ass. Res. nerv. ment. dis. monograp., 1948, 27: 582; *425.* Scheerer, M., Rothmann, E., and Goldstein, K.: A case of "idiot savant." An experimental study on personality organization, Psychol. Monogr., 1945, No. 269.

Vol. 58, No. 4, 63 p.; *426.* Schilder, P.: The image and appearance of the human body, London, Kegan Paul, Truebner, Trench and Co., Ltd., 1935; *427.* Schilder: Congenital alexia and its relation to optic perception, J. genet. Psychol., 1944, 65: 67; *428.* Schiller, B.: Aphasia studied in patients with missile wounds, J. Neurol., Neurosurg., and Psychiat., 1947, 10: 182; *428a.* Schlesinger, B.: Zur Auffassung der optischen und konstruktiven Apraxie, Ztschr. f. d. ges. Neurol. u. Psychiat., 1928; *429.* Schlesinger, B., see Chapter II, Refs. *801* and *802; 430.* ———: Delayed effects of seemingly minor head injuries, Dis. nerv. system, 1950, 11: 259; *431.* ———: Einige Bemerkungen zur Arbeit von Zutt: Rechts-Links-Störung, konstruktive Apraxie und reine Agraphie, Monatschr. f. Psychiat. u. Neurol., 1932/33: 382; *432.* ———: A study of dissociation and reorganization of cerebral function, Confin. neurol., 1940, 4: 14; *433.* ———: Über irreführende Lokalzeichen bei Hirntumoren und einige Bemerkungen über die Technik der Lokaldiagnose, München. med. Wochenschr., 41: 1666; *434.* Schmid, J., Quoted by Bonvicini; *435.* Schopenhauer, A.: Parerga, II., p. 599; *436.* ———: Essays, Walter J. Black, Inc., New York, 1931. (See esp. p. 140); *437.* Schuell, H.: Aphasic difficulties in understanding spoken language, Neurology, 1953, 3: 176; *438.* ———: Auditory impairment in aphasia, J. Speech and Hearing Disorders, 1953, 18: 14; *439.* ———: Clinical observations on aphasia, Ibid., 1954, 4: 179; *440.* Scripture: Arithmetical prodigies, Amer. J. Psychol., 1891, 4: 1; *441.* Sedgwick, R. P.: Pure visual verbal agnosia with spatial disorientation, Bull. Los Ang. Neurol. Soc., 1948, 13: 64; *442.* Semmes, J.: Agnosia in animals and man, Psychol. Rev., 1953, 60: 140; *443.* Semon, R. W.: Mnemic psychology. (Transl. B. Duffy), London, G. Allan and Unwin, 1923, 344 p.; *444.* Shannon, J. S. and Sperry, R. W.: Function of corpus callosum in cortical transfer of somesthetic discrimination in cats, J. compar. physiol. psychol., 1957, 50: 138; *445.* Sherrington, Ch., see Chapter I, Ref. *60; 446.* Siemerling: Ein Fall von sogenannter Seelenblindheit nebst anderen zerebralen Symptomen, Arch. f. Psychiat., 1890, 21: 284; *447.* Sinclair, A. H. H.: Developmental aphasia, Br. J. Ophthalmol., 1948, 32: 522; *448.* Sittig, O.: Ueber Apraxie. Eine klinische Studie, Berlin, S. Karger, 1931, vii, 248 p.; *449.* Smith, K. U.: The role of the commissural systems of the cerebral cortex in the determination of handedness, eyedness, and footedness in man, J. genet. Psychol., 1945, 32: 39; *450.* ———: Bilateral integrative action of the cerebral cortex in man in verbal and associational sensory-motor coordination, J. exper. Psychol., 1947, 37: 367; *451.* ———: The function of the intercortical neurons in sensory-motor integration and thinking in man, Science, 1947, 105: 117; *452*. ——: Learning and the association pathways in the human brain, Ibid., 1951, 114: 117; *453*. Spalding, J. M. K., and Zangwill, O. L.: Disturbances of number form in cases of head injuries, J. Neurol., Neurosurg., and Psychiat., 1950, 13: 24; *453a*. Spamer, R.: Über Aphasie und Asymbolie nebst einer Theorie der Sprachbildung. Arch. f. Psychiat., 1876, 6: 496; *454*. Spearman, C. E.: The confusion that is gestaltpsychology, Amer. J. Psychol., 1927, 50: 369; *454a*. Sperry, R. W.: Preservation of high-order functions in isolated somatic cortex in callosum sectioned cat, J. Neurophysiol., 1959, 22: 86; *455*. Stamm, J. S., and Sperry, R. W.: Function of the corpus callosum in contralateral transfer of somesthetic discrimination in cats, J. compar. physiol. Psychol., 1957, 50: 138; *456*. Stauffenberg, W.: Ueber Seelenblindheit, Arb. a. d. Hirnanatom. Inst. Zürich, 1907, 64: 203; *457*. Stein, H.: Die Labilität der Drucksinnschwelle bei Sensibilitätsstörungen, Deutsch. Zeitschr. f. Nervenheilk., 1923, 80: 57; *458*. ——: Die Nachempfindung bei Sensibilitätsstörungen als Folge gestörter Umstimmung, Ibid., 1924, 80: 219; *459*. —— und Weizsaecker, V. von: Der Abbau der sensiblen Funktionen, Ibid., 1927, 99: 1; *460*. —— und Weizsaecker, V. von: Zur Pathologie der Sensibilität, Erg. d. Physiol., 1928, 27: 657; *461*. Steinthal, H.: Einleitung in die Psychologie der Sprache 1871; *462*. Stein, J. and Buerger–Prinz: Funktionswandel im Bereiche des optischen Systems, Dtsch. Ztschr. f. Nervenheilk., 1932, 124: 189; *463*. Stellar, S., Morgan, C. T., and Yarisch, M.: Cortical localization of symbolic processes in the rat, J. compar. Neurol., 1942, 34: 107; *464*. Stoehr, A.: Psychologie, Braumüller, Vienna, 1918; *465*. Stern, C. and W.: Die Kindersprache, Third Edit., 1921, J. A. Barth, Leipzig, VII, 434 p. (See esp. p. 273 ff.); *466*. Strauss, E.: Der Sinn der Sinne, J. Springer, Berlin, 1936; *467*. Strauss. H.: Ueber konstruktive Apraxie, Monatschr. f. Psychiat. u. Neurol., 1924, 56: 65; *468*. Strauss, A., and Werner, H.: Deficiencies in the fingerscheme and relation to arithmetic disabilities (Fingeragnosia and acalculia), Amer. J. Orthopsychiat., 1938, 8: 719; *469*. Strohmeyer, W.: Zur Kasusitik der transkortikalen motorischen Aphasie, Deutch. Zeitschr., f. Nervenheilk., 1903, 24: 381; *470*. ——: Ueber subcortikale Alexie und Agraphie, Ibid., 1903, 24: 372; *471*. Sugar, O., Chusid., and French, J. D.: A second motor area in the monkey, macacca mulatta, J. Neuropathol. and experiment. Neurol., 1948, 7: 182; *472*. Stumpf, quoted by Froebes, (See Chapter II; Ref. 256) page 276, vol. II; *473*. Sunderland, J. G.: The distribution of commissural fibers in the corpus callosum, J. Neurol. and Psychiat., 1940, 3: 6;

474. Sweet, W. H.: Seeping intracranial aneurysm, simulating neoplasm. Syndrome of the corpus callosum, Arch. Neurol. and Psychiat., 1941, 45: 86. *475*. Taylor, J. H. (Editor) see Chapt. I, Ref. *37*; *476*. Thiele, R.: Der gegenwärtige Stand in der Gehirnpathologie, Zeitschrift. f. d. ges. Neurol. u. Psychiat., 1937, 118: 251; *477*. Tilney, F.: In a discussion of a presentation by F. Kennedy, Arch. Neurol. a. Psychiat., 1936, 36: 897; *478*. Trescher, J. H. and Ford, F. R.: Colloid cyst in the third ventricle, Arch. Neurol. a. Psychiat., 1937, 37: 959; *479*. Trotter, W. B., and Davies, H. M.: Experimental studies on the innervation of the skin, J. Physiol., 1907, 38: 134; *480*. Tureen, L. L., Smolik, E. A., and Tritt, J. H.: Aphasia in the deaf mute, Neurology, 1953, 3: 237; *481*. Turlow, W. R., Gross, N. B., Kemp, E. H., and Loewy, K.: Microelectric studies of neural activity of the cat. I. Inferior colliculus, J. Neurophysiol., 1951, 14: 280.

482. Valkenburg, E. T. van: Experimental and pathological anatomical researches on the corpus callosum, Brain, 1913, 37: 119; *482a*. Vasari: Life of the artists, (Transl. Ed. B. Burrough), Simon and Schuster, New York, 1946. See esp. p. 192; *483*. Vernon, M. D.: Visual perception, Cambridge University Press, 1937, X, 247 p.; *484*. van Vleuten, C. F.: Linksseitige motorische Apraxie, Allg. Zeitschr. f. Psychiat., 1907, 64: 203; *485*. Victoria, M.: Un cas de lésion de la troisième frontale gauche sans aphasie, Encéphale, 1937, 32: 85; *486*. Vogel, P.: Diskussion zum Thema Agnosie, Nervenarzt, 1951, 22: 191; *487*. Vogt, O.: Ueber frontale und parietale Storungen der Motilität, Neurol. Zentralbl., 1912, 31: 135, 175; *488*. Vogt, C.a.O.: Der heutige Stand der zerebralen Organologie und die zukünftige Hirnforschung. Eine Huldigung für Theodor Meynert anlässlich der 50. Wiederkehr seines Todestages, Anat. Anz., 1943, 51: 222; *489*. Vold, J. M.: Ueber den Traum. Experimentell psychologische Untersuchingen (Ed. O. Klemm), J. A. Barth, Leipzig, 1912. (See esp. vol. II).

490. van Wagenen, H. W., and Herren: Surgical division of the commissural pathways of the corpus callosum, Arch. Neurol. a. Psychiat., 1940, 44: 740; *491*. Walshe, F. R. M.: On the physiological analysis of some clinically observed disorders of movement, Lancet, 1929, p. 963, 1024; *492*. ——: The anatomy and physiology of cutaneous sensibility, Brain, 1943, 65: 48; *493*. ——: The brainstem conceived as the highest level, Ibid., 1957, 80: 510; *494*. Walter, K.: Beitrage zum Problem der angeborenen Schreib-Leseschwäche, Nervenarzt, 1954, 25: 146; *495*. Warrington, R., and Zangwill, O. L.: A study of alexia, J. Neurol., Neurosurg. and Psychiat., 1957, 201: 208; *496*. Watson, J. B.: Psychology as the behaviourist sees it, Psychol. Rev., 1913, 20: 158;

497. Weber, A. O.: Estimation of time, Psychol. Bull., 1933, 30: 223; *498.* Wechsler, I. S.: On the difficulties of localizing aphasic symptoms in the localization of brain tumors. A report of four cases with necropsy, J. nerv. ment. dis., 1924, 59: 31; *499.* ——: Excision of speech area without aphasia, Ibid., 1939, 86: 54; *500.* Weinstein, E. A., and Kahn, R.: The syndrome of anosognosia, A.M.A. Arch. Neurol. and Psychiat., 1950, 64: 772; *501.* Weinstein, E. A., Kahn, R. and Sugerman, L.: Phenomenon of reduplication, Ibid., 1952, 67; *502.* Weisenburg, Th. H.: A study of aphasia, Arch. Neurol. and Psychiat., 1934, 31: 1; *503.* Weisenburg, Th. H. and McBride, E.: Aphasia. A clinical and psychological study, New York, The Commonwealth Fund, 1935, 634 p.; *503a.* Weizsaecker, F. V.: Die Geschichte der Natur, Zürich, S. Hirzel, 1948; *504.* Weizsaecker, V. von: Leistung, Form und Menge in der Lehre von den nervösen Funktionen, Nervenarzt, 1931, 4: 433, 526; *505.* ——: Untersuchung der Sensibilität, In "Handbuch der Neurologie," Ed. O. Bumcke and O. Foerster, Vol. III, p. 701. J. Springer, Berlin, 1937; *506.* ——: Der Gestaltkreis, 3. Auflage, Stuttgart, G. Thieme, 1947, 208 p.; *507.* ——: Funktionswandel und Gestaltkreis, Dtsch. Zeitschr. f. Nervenheilk., 1950, 164: 43; *508.* Wernicke, C.: Aphasie und Anarthrie, Deutsch. Med. Wochenschr., 1882; *509.* ——: Der aphasische Symptomenkomplex. Eine psychologische Studie auf anatomischer Grundlage, Breslau, M. Cohn and Weigert, 1873, 72 p.; *510.* ——: Über Herderkrankungen des unteren Scheitellappens, Arch. f. Psychiat., 1889, 20: 243; *511.* ——: Outlines of Psychiatry in clinical lectures, (Transl. W. A. Corn), St. Louis, 1902–1903, 3 vols.; *512.* Wernicke, C.: Zwei Fälle von Rindenläsion, Arb. a. d. psychiat. Klinik Breslau, 1895, 2: 35; *513.* ——: Ueber Halluzination, Ratlosigkeit and Desorientierung und ihre wechselseitigen Beziehungen, Monatschr. f. Psychiat. u. Neurol., 1901, 9; *514.* Wertheimer, M.: Über das Sehen von Bewegungen, Zeitschr. f. Psychol., 1912, 61: 161; *515.* Wertheimer, M.: Drei Abhandlungen zur Gestaltheorie, Erlangen, Phil. Akad., 1925, 184 p.; *516.* ——, see Chapter III; Ref. *351;* *517.* Whatley, quoted by Mitchell, Ref. *339;* *518.* Wilbrandt, H.: Die Seelenblindheit als Herderscheinung und ihre Beziehungen zur homonymen Hemianopsie, zur Alexie und Agraphie, Wiesbaden, Bergmann, 1887, 192 p.; *519.* Wilson, K.: A study of apraxia, Brain, 1908, 31: 164; *520.* Wizel, D. A.: Ein Fall von phänomenalem Rechentalent bei einem Imbezillen, Arch. f. Psychiat., 1904, 38: 122; *521.* Woerkom, V.: Ueber das Denken der Aphasiepatienten, Monatschr. für Psychiatr. u. Neurol., 1925, 59: 256; *522.* Wolpert, I.: Die Simultanagnosie. (Störungen der Gesamtauffassung), Zeitschr. f. d. ges. Neurol. u. Psychiat., 1924, 93: 397; *523.* Woodworth, F. R.: Recovery from aphasia, Bull. Los Ang. Neurol. Soc., 1945, 10: 73; *524.* Woodworth, R. S.: Contemporary schools of psychology, The Ronald Press, Inc., IX, 279 p.; *525.* Woolard, H. H., Wedell, G., and Harpman, J. A.: Observations on neurohistological basis of cutaneous pain, J. Anat., 1940, 74: 413; *526.* Worster-Drought, C. and Allen, J. M.: Congenital auditory imperception (congenital word deafness) and its relation to idioglossia and other speech defects, J. Neurol. and Psychopathol., 1930, 10: 193.

527. Zangwill, O. L.: Agraphia due to left parietal glioma, Brain, 1954, 177: 540; *528.* Zollinger, R.: Removal of the left cerebral hemisphere, Arch. Neurol. and Psychiat., 1935, 34: 1054; *529.* Zutt, J.: Rechts-Linksstörung, konstruktive Apraxie und reine Agraphie, Monatschr. f. Psychiat. u. Neurol., 1932, 82: 253.

V ART

1. Agadschanianz, N.: Amusie, Zentralbl. f. Neurol., 1914, 33: 247; *2.* Alajouanine, Th.: Aphasia and artistic realization, Brain, 1948, 71: 229; *3.* Anastasi, A. and Foley, J.: An experimental study of the drawings behaviour of adult psychotics in comparison with that of an adult control group, J. exper. Psychol., 1944, 34: 160.

4. Bahle, J.: Der musikalische Schaffensprozess. Psychologie der schöpferischen Erlebnisse und Antriebsformen, Leipzig, S. Hirzel, 1936, XV, 253 p.; *5.* ——: Einfälle und Inspiration im musikalischem Schaffen, Arch. f. d. ges. Psychol., 1934, 90: 495; *6.* Ballet: Le Langage intérieur; *7.* Behier, quoted by Ballet; *8.* Bernard, D.: De l'aphasie, Le Crosinier et Babe, Paris, 1889; *9.* Bianchi, L.: La fonction musicale du cerveau et sa localization, Scientia, 1922; *10.* Billroth, Th.: Wer ist musikalisch? Ed. Hanslick, Berlin, Paetel Verlag, XII, 245 p.; *11.* Bonvicini, G., see Chapter IV; ref. *58;* *12.* ——: Die Aphasie des Malers Vierge, Wiener Med. Wochenschr., 1924, vol. 1.; *12a.* Botez, M. I., and Wertheim, N.: Expressive aphasia following right frontal lesion in right-handed man, Brain, 1959, 82: 186; *13.* Bosanquet, B.: A history of aesthetics from the Greeks to the 20th century, Meridian Library, 1957, XXIII, 502 p.; *14.* Bouillaud, quoted by Polyak; *15.* Brissaud, E.: Sur l'aphasie d'articulation etc., Sem. méd., 1894, 14: 341.

16. Cowell, H.: The process of musical creation, Amer. J. Psychol., 1926, 37: 233; *17.* Crouzon et Valence: Un cas d'alexie, Bull. et memoirs de la Soc. Med. d. Paris, 1923, Series III, 38 ann.

18. Darwin, Ch., See Chapter I; ref. *17; 19.* Dejerine. See Chap. IV; ref. *110; 20.* Delacroix, H.: Psychologie de l'art. Essai sur l'activité artistique, Paris, F. Alcan, 1927, 483 p.; *21.* Donath, J.: Beitrag zur Lehre von der Amusie, nebst einem Falle von instrumenteller Amusie bei beginnender progressiver Paralyze, Wien. Klin. Woschenschr., 1901, 14: 935; *22.* Doellken, N.: Zentren und Sammelstellen der Hirnrinde, Dtsch. Med. Wochenschr., 1926, 62: 757; *23.* Downey, J.: Creative imagination, New York, Harcourt, Brace and Co., 1929, VIII, 238 p.; *24.* Dupré, E., and Nathan, M.: Le langage musicale, Paris, F. Alcan, 1911.

25. Edgren, J. G.: Amusie, (musikalische Aphasie), Dtsch. Zeitschr. f. Nervenheilk., 1894, 6: 1.

26. Falret, J.: Sur l'aphasie, Gazette Hebd., 1865, 2nd series, vol. II, p. 227, 241, 273; *27.* Feuchtwanger, E., see Chapter IV; ref. *143; 28.* Foerster, H.: Ein Fall von motorischer Amusie, Zentrbl. f. wanger, E., see Chapter IV; ref. *00; 28.* Foerster, H.: Ein Fall von motorischer amusie, Zentrbl. f. Neurol., 1918, p. 437; *29.* Freud, S.: Civilization and its discontents, New York, J. Cape and H. Smith, 1930, 144 p. (See esp. p. 39).

31. Gatz, F. M.: Musik-Ästhetik in ihren Hauptrichtungen, Stuttgart, F. Enke, 1929, XX, 544 p.; *30.* Galton, F.: Enquiries into the human faculty and development, London, J. M. Dent and Sons, 1928; *32.* Goethe, J. W. von, see Chapter III; ref. *91; 33.* Goodman, H.: Creating the short story, New York, Harcourt Brace 1929, XIII, 508 p.; *34.* Grasset: La fonction du langage articulé et la localization des centres psychiques dans le cerveau, Rev. de Philosph., 1907, ann. 7. Nov. 1; *35.* Griswold, F. H.: The phenomena of inspiration and creative power, Philadelphia, David McKay Co., 1939, 176.

36. Hanson, see Schullian; *37.* Harding, R. E. M.: The anatomy of inspiration and an essay on creative mood, Cambridge, W. Hoffer and Sons Ltd., 1948, XVI, 190 p.; *38.* Head, H., see Chapter IV; ref. *199; 39.* Helmholtz, H., see Chapter II; ref. *366; 40.* Hemmeter: Theodor Billroth, musical and surgical philosopher. A biography and a review of his work on psychophysiological aptitude in music, Johns Hopkins Hosp. Bull., 1900, 11: 297; *41.* Henschen, S. E.: Uber Sprache-, Musik- and Rechenmechanismen und ihre Lokalisation im Grosshirn, Ztschr. f. d. ges. Neurol. u. Psychiat., 1919, 52: 273; *42.* Hertzmann, E.: Mozart's creative process, Musical Quart., 1957., 43: 187; *43.* Hindemith, P.: Craft of musical composition. I. Theory, (Transl. A. Mendel) Ass. Music Publ., 1942, VI, 223 p.; *44.* Hoffmann, H. F.: Erbpsychologie der Höchstbegabungen, Handb. d. Erbbiologie, 1939, vol. 5. Teil 1, p. 669; *45.* Houseman, A. E.: The

name and nature of poetry, New York, McMillan, 1933.

46. Jamblichus, P.: Life of Pythagoras, (Trans. Th. Taylor, A. S. Valpy, 1818; *47.* Jaspers, K.: Strindbergh and van Gogh, Berlin, J. Springer, 1926, 151 p.; *48.* Jellinek, A.: Zur Phaenomenologie der Amusie, Jb. f. Psychiat. u. Neurol.—1933, 50 115; *49.* Jossman, P.: Die Beziehungen der motorischen Amusie zu den apraktischen Störungen, Monatschr. f. Psychiat. u. Neurol., 1927, 53; *50.* Juda, A.: The relationship between highest mental capacity and psychic abnormalities, Amer. J. Psychol., 1949, 106: 296; *51.* ——: Höchstbegabungen, ihre Erbverhältnisse sowie ihre Beziehungen zu psychischen Anomalien, München, Urban und Schwarzenberg, 1953, 114 p.

52. Kandinsky, W.: On the spiritual in art, New York, published by the S. R. Guggenheim Foundation for the Museum of non-objective painting, 1946; *53.* Kleist, J., see Chapter II; ref. *493; 54.* Klimt, G., see Pirchan; *55.* Knoblauch, N.: Störungen der musikalischen Leistungsfähigkeit durch Hirnläsion, Arch. klin. Med., 1888, 43: 331. (See also Brain, 1890, 13: 312); *56.* Knowlson, Th. S. Originality, Lipincott, 1918, XVI, 303 p.; *57.* Kretschmer, E.: The psychology of the man of genius, London. 1931, Transl. R. B. Cattell, K. Paul, Trench, Truebner and Co., XX, 256 p.

58. Laaf, E. Atonalität; Melos, 1950, 17: 161; *59.* Lancereau: Valeur semiologique de l'aphasie, Gaz. Med. de Paris, 1865; *60.* Lange-Eichbaum, W.: Das Genieproblem, München, 1931; *61.* —— Genie, Irrsinn und Ruhm, München, 1928; *62.* Leibniz, G. W.: Philosophischer Briefwechsel, Ed. Preuss. Akad. d. Wissenschaften, I. (1663–1658) Darmstadt, O. Reichl, 1926; *63.* Leroy, E. B.: Le langage, Paris, Alcan 1905; *64.* Levey, H. B.: A theory concerning free creation in the inventive arts, Psychiatry, 1940, 3: 229; *65.* Lissauer, see Chapter III; ref. *308.*

66. Mann, M.: Ein Fall von motorischer Amusie, Zentralbl. f. Neurol., 1917, p. 149; *67.* Marcus, H.: Sensorische Paramusie, Zeitschr. f. d. ges. Neurol. u. Psychiat., 1923, 81: 625; *68.* Meige, quoted by Bonvicini; *67a.* Matisse, H., quoted by Zahn; *69.* Mendel, K.: Motorische Amusie, Neurol. Zentralbl., 1916, p. 345; *70.* Meyer, M.: How we hear. How tones make music, Boston, C. T. Bardford & Co., 1950, 117 p.; *71.* Meyers, R. H.: Music in the modern world, London, E. Arnold, 2nd Ed., 1948, 211 p.; *72.* Michelangelo Buonarotti: Michelangelo, (Transl. and Ed. R. W. Carden) Houghton Mifflin Co., Boston, 1913; *73.* Minogue, B. M. A case of secondary mental deficiency with musical talent, J. appl. Psychol. 1923, 7: 349; *74.* Miraillié, Ch.: De l'aphasie sensorielle, Thèse de Paris, 1896;

75. Mjoen, J. A.: Zur psychologiscieh Bestimmung der Musikalität, Ztschr. f. angew. Psychol., 1926, 27: 217; 76. Möbius, P.: Ueber Kunst und Künstler, Leipzig, J. A. Barth 1910, VIII, 296 p.; 77. ——: Goethe, Leipzig, J. A. Barth, 1913; 78. Monakow, C. von, see Chapter III; ref. 340; 79. Mondrian, P.: Neue Gestaltung, Bauhausbücher, Müchen, 1914; 80. Moos, P.: Die Philosophie der Musik von Kant bis E. v. Hartmann, Stuttgart Deutsch Verlagsanstalt, 2nd Ed. 1922, 666 p..

81. Naumburg, M.: Schizophrenic art, New York, Grune & Stratton 1950, 247 p.; 82. Newman, H. H.: Identical twins, American Naturalist, 1933, 67; 83. —— Freeman, F. N., and Holzinger, K. J.: Twins. A study of heredity and environment, Chicago, 1937; 84. Nirenstein, O.: Egon Schiele. Persönlichkeit und Werk, Paul Zsolnay Verlag, Wien, 1940.

85. Oppenheim, H.: Lehrbuch der Nervenkrankheiten, Berlin, S. Karger, 1913 2 vols.

86. Patrick, C.: Creative thought in artists, J. Psychol., 1937, 4: 35; 87. ——: Creative thought in poets, Arch. Psychol., 1935, no. 178, 74 p.; 88. ——: Whole and part relationship in creative thought, Amer. J. Psychol., 1941, 54: 128; 89. Pick, A.: Zur Analyse der Elemente der Amusie und deren Vorkommen bei aphasischen Störungen, Monatschr. f. Psychiat. u. Neurol., 1906, 8: 87 (See also Bethe, Handbuch der Physiol., vol. 15, part 2, J. Springer, Berlin); 90. Pirchan, E.: Gustav Klimt, Bergland Verlag, Wien, 1956; 91. Plaut, P.: Zur Psychologie der produktiven Persönlichkeit, Stuttgart, Enke, 1929, 324 p.; 92. Poincaré, H., see Chapter III; ref. 258; 93. Porterfield, see Chapter III; ref. 260; 94. Pratt, C. C.: The meaning of music; a study in psychological esthetics, New York and London, McGraw Hill Book Co., Inc., 1931, 253 p.; 95. ——: Structural versus expressive forms of music, The Department of Psychology, Rutgers University, Provincetown, Mass. 1937, p. 149–156; 96. ——: Music as a language of emotions, Washington, 1952, 26 p.; 97. Prescott, F. C.: The poetic mind, New York, McMillan Co., 1922, 308 p.; 98. Prinzhorn, H.: Bildnerei der Geisteskranken, J. Springer, Berlin, 1922, VIII, 361 p.; 99. Probst: Ueber die Lokalisation des Tonvermögens, Arch. f. Psychiat., 1891, 32: 410; 100. Proust: De l'aphasie, Ann. de Med. 1872.

101. Redfield, J.: Music. A science and an art, Tudor Publishing Co., New York, 1949, 307 p.; 102. Rees, H. E.: A psychology of artistic creation as evidenced by autobiographical statements of artists, Bureau of Publications, Teacher's College, Columbia Univ., 1942, 209 p.; 103. Reibmeyr, see Chapter III; ref. 264; 104. Reinoehl, F.: Die Vererbung geistiger Begabung, München und Berlin, J. F. Lehmann, 1927, 380 p.; 105. Reznizek, quoted by Plaut; 106. Riese, W.: Ueber den Stilwandel bei Vinzent van Gogh, Zeitschr. f. d. ges. Neurol. u. Psychiat., 1925, 98: 1; 107. ——: Vinzent van Gogh in der Krankheit. Ein Beitrag zurm Problem der Beziehungen zwischen Kunstwerk und Krankheit, München, Bergmann, 1926; 108. Rodin, A.: Art, New York, Dodd, Mead and Co., 1928; 109. Rohardt: Ein Fall von motorischer Amusie, Zentralbl. f. neurol., 1919, vol. 6.

110. Schiele, E., see Nirenberg; 111. Schillinger, J.: The mathematical basis of arts, Philosophical Libr., New York; 112. ——: The Schillinger system of composition, New York, C. Fischer, Inc. 1946, 2 vols.; 113. Schlesinger, B., see Chapter III; ref. 428a; 114. Schoen, M.: The effects of music, London, K. Paul, Trench, Truebner and Co., 1927, IX, 273 p.; 115. ——: The psychology of music, Ronald Press, 1940; 116. ——: The understanding of music, 1945; 117. Schoen, M.: The enjoyments of the arts, New York, Philosophical Library, 1944; 118. Schopenhauer, A.: Parerga I, p. 245 Frauenstaedt Edition 1908 (Brockhaus); 119. Schullian, D.M.: Music and medicine, New York, Schumann, 1948, X, 499 p.; 120. Seashore, C. E.: Psychology of music, New York, McGraw Hill 1938; 121. ——: Why we love music, Philadelphia, Oliver Ditson and Co., 1941, VI, 82 p.; 122. Sessions, R.: The musical experience of composer, performer and listener, Princeton Univ. Press, 1950, 127 p.; 123. Spencer, H.: The origin and function of music, Fraser's Magazine for Town and Country, 1857, 56: 396; 124. ——: See also Essays: Scientific, Political and Speculative, 1885; 125. Spoerri, Th.: Genie und Krankheit. Eine psychologische Untersuchung der Familie Feuerbach, Bibl. Psychiat. und Neurol. Fasc. 92, 1952, 136 p.; 126. Squires, P. L.: The creative psychology of C. M. von Weber, Charact. und Persönlichkeit, 1938, 6: 203; 127. Stanton, H. M.: The inheritance of specific musical capabilities, Eugenics, Genetics, and the Family, I, 1923; 128. Stauffenberg, W. von: Ueber die Seelenblindheit, Arb. a. d. hirnanatom. Inst. Zürich, Wiesbaden Bergmann, 1914; 129. Strauss, H.: Ueber konstruktive Apraxie, Monatschr. f. Psychiat. u. Neurol., 1924, 65: 65; 130. Strauss, R., Quoted by Bahle; 131. Stumpf: Tonpsychologie, Zeitschr. f. Psychol., 1916, 75: 39.

132. Tepley, L. V.: Mania-depression of famous man, In "Miksell, W. H., Modern abnormal psychology," New York, Philosophical Library, 1950, IX, 880 p.

133. Ustvedt, H. J.: Über die Untersuchung der Musik. Funktionen bei Patienten mit Gehirnleiden besonders bei Patienten mit Aphasie, Acta Med. Scand., 1937, Suppl. 86, 737 p.

134. Vierge, see Bonvicini; *135*. Vinci, Leonard da, See Chapter O, ref. 00.

136. Wallatschek, R.: Ueber die Bedeutung derc Aphasie fuer den musikalischen Ausdruck, Leipzig, Breitkopf and Haertl, 1891; *137*. Walthard, K. M.: Bemerkungen zum Amusieproblem, Schw. Arch. f. Neurol. u. Psychiat., 1927, 20: Heft 2; *138*. Weygandt, W.: Zur Frage der pathologischen Kunst, Ztschr. f. d. ges. Neurol. u. Psychiat., 1925, 94:

421; *139*. Wilbrandt, see Chapter IV; ref. *958*; *140*. Wuerthen: Einzelne Formen der Amusie, an Beispielen erläutert, Dtsch. Ztschr. f. Nervenheilk., 1903, 24: 465; *141*. Wyllie, J.: The disorders of speech, Edinburgh, Oliver and Boyd, 1894, VIII, 495 p.

142. Zahn, L.: Kleine Geschichte der modernen Kunst, Ullstein Bücher, Frankfurt a M. 1958, 183 p.

INDEX

Explanation of symbols: (c) denotes *Critical Comments*, (d) *Definition* and (s) *Summary*, and vs, *"as opposed to."* Depending on the particular aspect discussed, polymorphous terms, e.g., the terms center, concept, and instinct require several, supplementary definitions.